D1412500

Course 2

GLENCOE
Macmillan/McGraw-Hill

New York, New York Columbus, Ohio Mission Hills, California Peoria, Illinois

Science Interactions

Student Edition
Teacher Wraparound Edition
Teacher Classroom Resource Package
Laboratory Manual: SE
Laboratory Manual: TE
Study Guide: SE
Study Guide: TE
Transparency Package
Computer Test Bank
Spanish Resources
Science and Technology Videodisc Series
Science and Technology Videodisc Teacher Guide

Send all inquiries to:

GLENCOE DIVISION
Macmillan/McGraw-Hill
936 Eastwind Drive
Westerville, OH 43081

ISBN 0-02-826098-8

Printed in the United States of America

6 7 8 9 10 11 12 13 14 15 VH/LP 00 99 98 97 96 95 94

Authors

Bill Aldridge, M.S.
Executive Director
National Science Teachers Association
Washington, DC

Russell Aiuto, Ph.D.
Director of Research and Development
Scope, Sequence, and Coordination
National Science Teachers Association
Washington, DC

Jack Ballinger, Ed.D.
Professor of Chemistry
St. Louis Community College at Florissant Valley
St. Louis, MO

Anne Barefoot, A.G.C.
Physics and Chemistry Teacher
Whiteville High School
Hallsboro, NC

Linda Crow, Ed.D.
Assistant Professor
Baylor College of Medicine
Houston, TX

Ralph M. Feather, Jr., M.Ed.
Science Department Chairperson
Derry Area School District
Derry, PA

Albert Kaskel, M.Ed.
Biology Teacher
Evanston Township High School
Evanston, IL

Craig Kramer, M.A.
Physics Teacher
Bexley High School
Bexley, OH

Edward Ortleb, A.G.C.
Science Lead Supervisor
St. Louis Board of Education
St. Louis, MO

Susan Snyder, M.S.
Earth Science Teacher
Jones Middle School
Upper Arlington, OH

Paul W. Zitzewitz, Ph.D.
Professor of Physics
University of Michigan-Dearborn
Dearborn, MI

Consultants

CHEMISTRY

Richard J. Merrill
Director, Project Physical Science
Associate Director, Institute for Chemical Education
University of California
Berkeley, California

Robert Walter Parry, Ph.D.
Dist. Professor of Chemistry
University of Utah
Salt Lake City, Utah

EARTH SCIENCE

Allan A. Ekdale
Professor of Geology
University of Utah
Salt Lake City, Utah

James B. Phipps, Ph.D.
Professor of Geology and Oceanography
Gray's Harbor College
Aberdeen, Washington

LIFE SCIENCE

Mary D. Coyne, Ph.D.
Professor of Biological Sciences
Wellesley College
Wellesley, Massachusetts

Joe Wiliam Crim, Ph.D.
Associate Professor of Zoology
University of Georgia
Athens, Georgia

John J. Just, Ph.D.
Associate Professor of Biology
University of Kentucky
Lexington, Kentucky

Richard D. Storey, Ph.D.
Associate Professor of Biology
Colorado College
Colorado Springs, Colorado

PHYSICS

Karen L. Johnston, Ph.D.
Professor of Physics
North Carolina State University
Raleigh, North Carolina

MIDDLE SCHOOL SCIENCE

Thomas Custer
Coordinator of Science
Anne Arundel County
Ellicot City, Maryland

Gerald Garner
LA Unified
Van Nuys, California

Garland E. Johnson
Science and Education Consultant
Fresno, California

READING

Barbara Pettegrew, Ph.D.
Director of Reading/Study Center
Assistant Professor of Education
Otterbein College
Westerville, Ohio

SAFETY

Robert Tatz, Ph.D.
Instructional Lab Supervisor
Department of Chemistry
The Ohio State University
Columbus, Ohio

MULTICULTURAL

Carol Mitchell
Science Supervisor
Omaha Public Schools
Omaha, Nebraska

Karen L. Muir, Ph.D.
Department of Social and Behavioral Sciences
Columbus State Community College
Columbus, Ohio

LEP

Harold Frederick Robertson, Jr.
Science Resource Teacher
LAUSD Science Materials Center
Van Nuys, California

Ross M. Arnold
Magnet School Coordinator
Van Nuys Junior High
Van Nuys, California

Linda E. Heckenberg
Director, Eisenhower Program
Van Nuys, California

Barbara Sitzman
Chatsworth High School
Tarzana, California

COOPERATIVE LEARNING

Linda Lundgren
Bear Creek High School
Lakewood, Colorado

SPECIAL FEATURES

Timothy Heron, Ph.D.
Professor
Department of Educational Services & Research
The Ohio State University
Columbus, Ohio

Reviewers

Assunta Black
Life Science Teacher
Lindenhurst Junior High
Lindenhurst, New York

Jayne Brown
7th Grade Science Teacher
Valley Springs Middle School
Arden, North Carolina

Mitchell Kyle Carver, Sr.
Science Department Chairperson
Reynolds Middle School
Asheville, North Carolina

James Cowden
Science Teacher Specialist
Chicago Public Schools
Chicago, Illinois

Gloria M. Dobry
Departmental Science Teacher
Gunsaulus Academy
Chicago, Illinois

Daniel H. Domenigoni
Science Department Chairperson
Milwaukie Junior High
Milwaukie, Oregon

Cheryl B. Domineau
Science Department Chairperson
Vero Beach Junior High
Vero Beach, Florida

Alex Domkowski
Physics Teacher
Saint Mary's Hall
San Antonio, Texas

Nancy Ann Drain
Teacher
Bell Junior High School
San Diego, California

Nancy Prevatte Dunlap
7th Grade Science Teacher
Central Middle School
Whiteville, North Carolina

Laraine O. Franze
Life Science Teacher
Greenwood Lakes Middle School
Lake Mary, Florida

John A. George
Science Department Chairperson
Rivera Middle School
Miami, Florida

Corless Horne Goode
Teacher
New Hope School
Rutherfordton, North Carolina

Raymond Pat Hadd
Science Department Chairperson
Richbourg Middle School
Crestview, Florida

Karen Sue Hewitt
Teacher
Coldspring High School
Coldspring, Texas

Gordon N. Hopp
Environmental Science Teacher
Carmel Junior High School
Carmel, Indiana

Barbara D. Johnson
Life Science Teacher
Deep Creek Junior High School
Chesapeake, Virginia

Thomas E. Johnson
Life Science Teacher
Western Branch Junior High School
Chesapeake, Virginia

Lonnie L. Lewis
Science Department Chairperson
Ramona Junior High School
Chino, California

William T. Martin
8th Grade General Science Teacher
Atkins Middle School
Winston-Salem, North Carolina

Vito Charles Mazzini, Jr.
Science Department Chairperson
H. D. McMillan Middle School
Miami, Florida

George Graham Ohmer
Teacher
Clay Junior High School
Carmel, Indiana

Thomas J. Pedersen
Graduate Research Assistant
North Carolina State University
Raleigh, North Carolina

Chuck Porrazzo
Science Department Chairperson
CJHS 145
New York City, New York

Allan G. Reisberg
6th Grade Teacher
Abraham Lincoln
Chicago, Illinois

Steven F. Rinck
Supervisor of Science
Pasco County School Board
Land O'Lakes, Florida

Ouida E. Thomas
Life Science Teacher
B. F. Terry High School
Rosenberg, Texas

Mary Coggins White
Science Department Chairperson
Sequoia Intermediate School
Newbury Park, California

Nedra A. Williams
Science Department Chairperson
Los Cerritos Intermediate School
Thousand Oaks, California

CONTENTS

An Overview

UNIT 1 Forces In Action 1

The expression "May the force be with you" is used by one of the characters in the movie "Star Wars." In the movies, we're not sure what "the force" really is. But in real life, there are forces all around us, under us, and inside us.

Chapter 1 Forces and Pressure 2

You may have seen what happens to the dummies in car crash tests. What causes them to go forward when the car hits something? Should air bags be safety features in new cars? This is all a part of how force and motion affect us.

Chapter 2 Forces Inside Earth 34

Earthquakes and volcanoes happen all around the world—maybe even where you live. Or maybe you've seen pictures of cars sliding off a bridge that was split during an earthquake. What causes this force, and how does it work?

Chapter 3 Circulation in Animals 64

What does blood moving through veins have to do with forces and earthquakes? Some of the things that happen in our own bodies are caused by the same physical principles that cause earthquakes. After all, our system of circulation is more than just plumbing.

UNIT 2 Energy At Work 97

Have you seen any examples of energy in action today? Even if you stayed in bed all day with the covers over your head, the answer would be "yes." Everything you see or do, from reading the words on this page to coming to school today, involves energy. You can't touch it or smell it. In many cases, you can't see it. But we are surrounded by energy and its effects every day.

Chapter 4 Work and Energy 98

If we whistle while we work, are we using energy? This chapter helps you to understand when work is going on, and the forms of energy necessary for work to happen.

Chapter 5 Machines 130

What do a doorstop and a pencil sharpener have in common? They are both simple machines. We tend to think of machines as complicated things like cars and lawn mowers, but there is an advantage to using a machine, complicated, or not.

Chapter 6 Thermal Energy 162

Why does black pavement get hot in the summer? This chapter is hot stuff. It will tell you that answer, and also let you figure out what heat, cold, and temperature really are.

Chapter 7 Moving the Body Machine 192

With amazing power and grace, a basketball player leaps from the surface of the court, defying gravity and reaching over ten feet in the air to make a slam-dunk. The human body must be quite a machine to do that!

Chapter 8 Controlling the Body Machine 220

Now that we know about the moving parts of the human machine, let's take a look at the wiring. There must be some kind of switchboard in there controlling everything.

UNIT 3 Earth Materials and Resources 251

What are airplanes, ships, and cars made of? What are these materials and why do we use them for these things?

Chapter 9 Discovering Elements 252

"Good as gold!" "Get the lead out!" "Bright as a penny!" We sure talk a lot about metals. We should be able to tell the difference between metals and nonmetals.

Chapter 10 Minerals and Their Uses 284

We have minerals in our bodies, on our bodies, and around our bodies. In this chapter, we explore how some of them are formed, and why some of them are prized.

Chapter 11 The Rock Cycle 314

Many buildings are made of different kinds of rocks. This makes us think that rocks are very stable and they never change. You'll see that this is not true at all.

Chapter 12 The Ocean Floor and Shore Zone 346

Not everyone lives near a shore, but almost everyone knows about them. Besides making nice vacation spots, they are constantly changing because of the interaction of waves and sand or rock.

Chapter 13 Energy Resources 376

Think about how life must have been when the horsepower only came from horses! Coal, oil, and natural gas have changed our lives. But what is the cost to Earth, and what about the future?

UNIT 4 Air: Molecules In Motion 409

Airplanes fly through it; when it's moving fast enough, it can knock over a tree; and we breathe it. It's air, of course. In this unit you'll find out what's so important about this stuff you can't even see.

Chapter 14 Gases, Atoms, and Molecules 410

How can a tire that has only air in it support a car that weighs thousands of pounds? There must be a lot more to air than we think.

Chapter 15 The Air Around You 440

We hear about our atmosphere all the time. Here, you'll discover what causes a smog report, how high up outer space is, and how the sun interacts with our atmosphere to affect the weather.

Chapter 16 Breathing 468

What do you have in common with a goldfish and a grasshopper? You all three need air to live. But you each take in air and process it a little differently.

UNIT 5 Life At the Cellular Level 497

In this unit we'll look at the basic unit of life—the cell. But just studying cells is not enough. We need to know how to study them—what kinds there are, how they work, and how some can exist by themselves.

Chapter 17 Mirrors and Lenses 498

Did you know that you could use a bathroom mirror to see things invisible to the eye? Learn the basics of mirrors and lenses to better understand microscopes and telescopes.

Chapter 18 Basic Units of Life 530

In this chapter you'll find out more about cells, including how they increase in number.

Chapter 19 Chemical Reactions 564

To your brain, pizza means great taste. But to your body overall, pizza means energy. In this chapter, find out how pizza helps you to play soccer.

Chapter 20 How Cells Do Their Jobs 596

For such little things, cells sure are busy! Stuff going in and out, energy being converted, respiration going on! This chapter gives you a chance to see how these processes keep you on the move.

Chapter 21 Simple Organisms 626

If cells can move materials in and out, convert energy, and respire, they must be able to "go it alone". You're right! Some cells *can* exist as simple organisms, and a lot of them are pretty important to us.

CONTENTS

In Depth

Introducing **Science Interactions** **xxiv**

UNIT 1 Forces In Action **1**

LESSONS		ACTIVITIES	
Chapter 1 Forces and Pressure			**2**
		EXPLORE! Why doesn't the penny move?	3
1–1 Force and Motion	4	FIND OUT! What factors affect the acceleration of objects?	6
		INVESTIGATE! Measuring Inertial Mass	8
		FIND OUT! Is friction a force?	10
1–2 Newton's Second Law of Motion	12	INVESTIGATE! Acceleration and Mass	13
		EXPLORE! How can forces be measured?	15
1–3 Newton's Third Law of Motion	17		
1–4 Pressure and Buoyancy	19	EXPLORE! How are weight and pressure related?	19
		FIND OUT! What is the relationship of fluid depth to pressure?	21
		FIND OUT! How much water does an object displace?	23

EXPANDING YOUR VIEW

A CLOSER LOOK **Centripetal Force 25**

LIFE SCIENCE CONNECTION **How Does a Fish Use Its Swim Bladder? 26**

SCIENCE AND SOCIETY **Deep-Sea Submersibles 27**

HISTORY CONNECTION **A Royal Solution 29**

TECHNOLOGY CONNECTION **Transducers in Your Life 30**

LESSONS		ACTIVITIES	
Chapter 2 Forces Inside Earth			**34**
		EXPLORE! How do forces inside Earth affect rock layers?	35
2–1 Movements That Cause Earthquakes	36	FIND OUT! How do different objects react when they are bent or stretched?	36
		EXPLORE! How do rocks at a strike-slip fault move past each other?	40
2–2 Learning About Earthquakes	42	EXPLORE! How can a coiled spring be used to demonstrate two types of earthquake waves?	42
		FIND OUT! Which is faster—a compression wave or a transverse wave?	43
		INVESTIGATE! Locating an Epicenter	46
2–3 Volcanic Eruptions	48	EXPLORE! How does magma move?	48
		INVESTIGATE! Analyzing Volcanoes	53

EXPANDING YOUR VIEW

A CLOSER LOOK Different Kinds of Force 55

PHYSICS CONNECTION Passing the Limit 56

SCIENCE AND SOCIETY Preparing Buildings for Earthquakes 57

TECHNOLOGY CONNECTION Seismic Waves and the Search for Oil 59

GEOGRAPHY CONNECTION The Many Climates of the Himalayas 60

LESSONS		ACTIVITIES	
Chapter 3 Circulation in Animals			**64**
		EXPLORE! How can you make a model of circulation?	65
3–1 Circulatory Systems	66	FIND OUT! What are the parts of the heart?	68
		FIND OUT! Can you hear your heart?	70
3–2 A System Under Pressure	73	EXPLORE! How can you find out about the pumping activity of your heart?	73
		INVESTIGATE! Pulse Rate	75
		FIND OUT! Can you make a liquid move?	76
		INVESTIGATE! Blood Pressure	77

LESSONS		ACTIVITIES	
3–3 Disorders in Circulation	82	FIND OUT! What happens to liquid flow in a clogged tube?	83

EXPANDING YOUR VIEW

A CLOSER LOOK Optical Fibers Invade Circulatory System 87

PHYSICS CONNECTION The Physics of Blood Pressure Measurement 88

SCIENCE AND SOCIETY Changing a Nation's Lifestyle 89

TECHNOLOGY CONNECTION Ball in the Cage 90

HISTORY CONNECTION "Sewed Up His Heart" 91

TEENS IN SCIENCE Chill Out—It's Good for You 92

UNIT 2 Energy at Work....97

LESSONS		ACTIVITIES	
Chapter 4 Work and Energy			**98**
		EXPLORE! What is work?	99
4–1 Energy and Fuel	100		
4–2 Work	103	EXPLORE! Is it work?	103
4–3 Forms of Energy	106	EXPLORE! Does a softball have energy?	108
		INVESTIGATE! Potential and Kinetic Energy	111
		EXPLORE! How is the work stored?	112
		FIND OUT! Where did this energy go?	114
4–4 Conservation of Energy	116	FIND OUT! How far will it go?	116
		INVESTIGATE! The Motion of a Pendulum	118

EXPANDING YOUR VIEW

A CLOSER LOOK Energetic Toy 121

EARTH SCIENCE CONNECTION Voyage of the Century 122

TECHNOLOGY CONNECTION The Search for Perpetual Motion 123

MUSIC CONNECTION Musical Motion 124

HOW IT WORKS Vacuum Cleaner 125

HISTORY CONNECTION What's in a Name? 126

LESSONS		ACTIVITIES	
Chapter 5 Machines			**130**
		EXPLORE! How can a machine make it easier to move an object?	**131**
5–1 Simple Machines	**132**	EXPLORE! How does a lever work?	133
		FIND OUT! Can a pulley reduce the force you have to exert to get a job done?	136
		FIND OUT! Are screwdrivers and screws simple machines?	139
5–2 Mechanical Advantage	**142**	FIND OUT! Can the length of a lever affect the amount of force needed to do work?	143
		INVESTIGATE! Measuring Mass with Levers	146
5–3 Using Machines	**148**	EXPLORE! What kind of machine is a can opener?	148
		FIND OUT! Can you measure the power of a toy car?	150
		INVESTIGATE! Calculating Power	151

EXPANDING YOUR VIEW

A CLOSER LOOK **Efficiency 153**

LIFE SCIENCE CONNECTION **One Step at a Time 154**

SCIENCE AND SOCIETY **Pedal Power 155**

LEISURE CONNECTION **Spills, Chills, Waves, and Dunks 157**

TEENS IN SCIENCE **Hard Work—The Easy Way to Have Fun 158**

LESSONS		ACTIVITIES	
Chapter 6 Thermal Energy			**162**
		EXPLORE! How do we feel heat?	**163**
6–1 Thermal Equilibrium	**164**	EXPLORE! Is your sense of touch accurate for judging temperature?	164
		INVESTIGATE! How Cold Is It?	166
		FIND OUT! How do you make a temperature scale?	168

LESSONS		ACTIVITIES	
6–2 Heat and Temperature	170	EXPLORE! How does heat do work in a thermometer?	171
		EXPLORE! How does thermal energy transfer from one object to another?	172
		INVESTIGATE! Watching Ice Melt	175
6–3 Making Heat Work	179	EXPLORE! Why is a heat engine inefficient?	179
		EXPLORE! How does refrigeration work?	181

EXPANDING YOUR VIEW

A CLOSER LOOK Latent Heat 183

LIFE SCIENCE CONNECTION How We Use Calories 184

SCIENCE AND SOCIETY Thermal Pollution 185

HISTORY CONNECTION Keeping Cool 187

CONSUMER CONNECTION Solar Energy for Solar Homes 188

LESSONS		ACTIVITIES	
Chapter 7 Moving the Body Machine			**192**
		EXPLORE! Is your body like a marionette?	**193**
7–1 Living Bones	194	EXPLORE! How does your skeletal system support your body?	194
		FIND OUT! Why are bones hard?	196
		INVESTIGATE! Structure of Bone	199
7–2 Your Body in Motion	201	EXPLORE! Do you need joints?	201
		EXPLORE! What movements do joints allow?	202
7–3 Muscles	205	FIND OUT! What are the levers in your body?	205
		INVESTIGATE! Muscles and Bones	208
		FIND OUT! How do muscles work together?	209

EXPANDING YOUR VIEW

A CLOSER LOOK Bone Density 211

PHYSICS CONNECTION Strong Bones 212

SCIENCE AND SOCIETY Spud Dud 212

HOW IT WORKS Robot Arms 214

HEALTH CONNECTION Athletic Epidemic 215

TEENS IN SCIENCE Lending a Helping Hand 216

LESSONS		ACTIVITIES	
Chapter 8 Controlling the Body Machine			**220**
		EXPLORE! Why does your dog bark?	221
8–1 The Nervous System: Master Control	222	EXPLORE! How do you keep your balance?	222
		FIND OUT! How does information move through your nervous system?	224
8–2 The Parts of Your Nervous System	226	EXPLORE! What does a central information computer do for you?	226
		INVESTIGATE! Reaction Time	230
8–3 Senses and Reflexes	234	EXPLORE! How important are your senses?	234
		INVESTIGATE! Testing for Skin Sensitivity	237
		FIND OUT! How are you protected from light?	238

EXPANDING YOUR VIEW

A CLOSER LOOK **Teach Your Old Pet a New Trick 241**

PHYSICS CONNECTION **Voice-Activated Computers 242**

SCIENCE AND SOCIETY **Alzheimer's Disease 243**

TECHNOLOGY CONNECTION **Watching the Brain 245**

PSYCHOLOGY CONNECTION **Infant Learning 246**

UNIT 3 Earth Materials and Resources.......................251

LESSONS		ACTIVITIES	
Chapter 9 Discovering Elements			**252**
		EXPLORE! What elements are in your environment?	253
9–1 Discovering Metals	254	EXPLORE! What element is it?	254
		EXPLORE! How can you identify a metal?	255
		INVESTIGATE! Identifying Metals	257
		FIND OUT! What are the current prices of silver and gold?	262

LESSONS		ACTIVITIES	
9–2 Discovering Nonmetals	264	EXPLORE! How can you identify nonmetals?	264
		EXPLORE! What are some properties of hydrogen?	265
		INVESTIGATE! Preparing and Observing Oxygen	268
9–3 Understanding Metalloids	272	EXPLORE! What elements are in your mineral supplements?	274

EXPANDING YOUR VIEW

A CLOSER LOOK **Thermostats 275**

EARTH SCIENCE CONNECTION **Diamonds and Pencils 276**

SCIENCE AND SOCIETY **Recycling Aluminum 277**

CONSUMER CONNECTION **The Prices of Precious Metals 278**

HOW IT WORKS **Metalworking in Jewelry 279**

TECHNOLOGY CONNECTION **Neon Lights 280**

LESSONS		ACTIVITIES	
Chapter 10 Minerals and Their Uses			**284**
		EXPLORE! What makes jewels valuable?	**285**
10–1 Minerals and Their Value	286	FIND OUT! What shapes do halite and quartz crystals take?	288
		EXPLORE! How are metallic and nonmetallic minerals used?	290
10–2 Characteristics of Minerals	291	FIND OUT! How does a scratch test help identify minerals?	291
		EXPLORE! How does looking at minerals help identify them?	293
		FIND OUT! What is a streak test?	295
		EXPLORE! How do clear minerals compare?	296
		INVESTIGATE! How Are Minerals Identified?	298

LESSONS		ACTIVITIES	
10-3 Mineral Formation	300	INVESTIGATE! How Do Crystals Form?	301

EXPANDING YOUR VIEW

A CLOSER LOOK Evolution of Iron 305
LIFE SCIENCE CONNECTION Minerals in the Body 306
SCIENCE AND SOCIETY Asbestos Debate 307
TECHNOLOGY CONNECTION Quartz and Computers 309
HISTORY CONNECTION Rewriting Prehistory 310

LESSONS		ACTIVITIES	
Chapter 11 The Rock Cycle			**314**
		EXPLORE! How are rocks different?	315
11–1 Igneous Rocks	316	EXPLORE! What makes a rock unique?	316
		FIND OUT! What happens as a mineral cools?	318
		INVESTIGATE! Classifying Igneous Rocks	322
11–2 Metamorphic Rocks	324	FIND OUT! What can happen to a rock when it is exposed to pressure?	324
		EXPLORE! From what do metamorphic rocks form?	325
11–3 Sedimentary Rocks	328	FIND OUT! How can sediments become cemented together?	329
		FIND OUT! What can happen to dissolved minerals?	331
		INVESTIGATE! Sedimentary Rocks	334

EXPANDING YOUR VIEW

A CLOSER LOOK Natural Glass 337
LIFE SCIENCE CONNECTION Animals Eat Rocks 338
SCIENCE AND SOCIETY Who Owns the Rocks? 339
LEISURE CONNECTION Collecting Rocks 341
TEENS IN SCIENCE Caving Clan 342

LESSONS		ACTIVITIES	
Chapter 12 The Ocean Floor and Shore Zones			**346**
		EXPLORE! From rock to sand—how can it happen?	**347**
12–1 Shore Zones	348	EXPLORE! How do waves affect the shoreline?	349
		INVESTIGATE! Beach Sand	353
12–2 Humans Affect Shore Zones	355	FIND OUT! How do you clean up an oil spill?	357
12–3 The Ocean Floor	361	FIND OUT! How can you determine the shape of something you can't see?	361
		INVESTIGATE! Ocean-Floor Profile	364

EXPANDING YOUR VIEW

A CLOSER LOOK Mining Minerals at the Rift Zones 367

LIFE SCIENCE CONNECTION Adaptations of Marine Life in the Rift Zones 368

SCIENCE AND SOCIETY Beach Erosion 369

TECHNOLOGY CONNECTION Offshore Oil 371

TEENS IN SCIENCE Rescue Team Is All Wet 372

LITERATURE CONNECTION A Real Find 372

LESSONS		ACTIVITIES	
Chapter 13 Energy Resources			**376**
		EXPLORE! How much does electricity mean to you?	**377**
13–1 The Electricity You Use	378	FIND OUT! How can thermal energy be converted to mechanical energy?	379
13–2 Fossil Fuels	382	EXPLORE! What does a piece of coal look like?	382
		EXPLORE! How do water and oil react?	385
		INVESTIGATE! Retrieving Oil	386

LESSONS		ACTIVITIES	
13–3 Resources and Pollution	388	INVESTIGATE! Predicting Natural Gas Reserves	390
13–4 Alternative Energy Resources	393	EXPLORE! How many different methods can you use to make your pinwheel spin?	393

EXPANDING YOUR VIEW

A CLOSER LOOK Electric Expense 399

PHYSICS CONNECTION Promises and Problems 400

SCIENCE AND SOCIETY Using Coal Resources 401

HOW IT WORKS Solar Panels 402

TECHNOLOGY CONNECTION Clean, Cheap, Fast! 403

HISTORY CONNECTION Lights Out! 404

HEALTH CONNECTION Bicycle Fuel 404

UNIT 4 Air: Molecules In Motion....................................409

LESSONS		ACTIVITIES	
Chapter 14 Gases, Atoms, and Molecules			**410**
		EXPLORE! Does air exert pressure?	411
14-1 How Do Gases Behave?	412	EXPLORE! Do gases move?	413
		INVESTIGATE! Pressure and Volume	415
		FIND OUT! How does the volume of gas depend on its temperature?	417
14-2 What Are Gases Made Of?	420	EXPLORE! Can you see air?	420
		EXPLORE! How do gas particles move?	421

LESSONS		ACTIVITIES	
14–3 What Is the Atomic Theory of Matter?	424	FIND OUT! How do hydrogen and oxygen make up water?	424
		INVESTIGATE! Definite and Multiple Proportions	428

EXPANDING YOUR VIEW

A CLOSER LOOK The Density of a Gas 431
EARTH SCIENCE CONNECTION Research Giants 432
TECHNOLOGY CONNECTION What Is a Vacuum? 433
HEALTH CONNECTION Breathing Underwater 434
LEISURE CONNECTION Cooking Under Pressure 435
HISTORY CONNECTION The Gas Laws 436

LESSONS		ACTIVITIES	
Chapter 15 The Air Around You			**440**
		EXPLORE! Does air have mass?	441
15-1 So This Is the Atmosphere	442	INVESTIGATE! How Much Oxygen Is in the Air?	443
		FIND OUT! What solids are in the air around you?	445
15-2 Structure of the Atmosphere	446	EXPLORE! Is atmospheric pressure the same in all layers of the atmosphere?	448
		INVESTIGATE! Atmospheric Pressure	449
15-3 Air and the Sun	451	FIND OUT! How does a greenhouse trap heat?	453
		EXPLORE! Why does hot air move?	454

EXPANDING YOUR VIEW

A CLOSER LOOK Global Warming and the Greenhouse Effect 459
LIFE SCIENCE CONNECTION City Smog and Our Health 460
SCIENCE AND SOCIETY The Disappearing Ozone Layer 461
HEALTH CONNECTION Cigarette Smoke and the Air We Breathe 463
LITERATURE CONNECTION What Happened to the Animals? 463
TEENS IN SCIENCE Flying High and Loving It 464

LESSONS		ACTIVITIES	
Chapter 16 Breathing			**468**
		EXPLORE! What happens when you breathe?	469
16-1 How Do You Breathe?	470	EXPLORE! What can you learn by watching a goldfish?	471
		EXPLORE! What is your trachea like?	473
		EXPLORE! How does your chest size change when you breathe?	475
		INVESTIGATE! How Can Your Lung Capacity Be Measured?	476
16-2 The Air You Breathe	478	FIND OUT! What other gas do you exhale?	479
		INVESTIGATE! What Effect Does Exercise Have on Respiration?	481
16-3 Disorders of the Respiratory System	483	EXPLORE! What is percussing?	484

EXPANDING YOUR VIEW

A CLOSER LOOK **Unusual Breathers 487**

PHYSICS CONNECTION **Your Larynx 488**

SCIENCE AND SOCIETY **Lifesaving Techniques 489**

TECHNOLOGY CONNECTION **Garrett A. Morgan: Gas Mask Inventor 490**

HEALTH CONNECTION **Plants—Natural Air Purifiers 491**

HISTORY CONNECTION **Keeping a Nation Healthy 492**

UNIT 5 Life at the Cellular Level..................................497

LESSONS		ACTIVITIES	
Chapter 17 Mirrors and Lenses			**498**
		EXPLORE! How do mirrors change your reflection?	**499**
17-1 Reflection of Light	500	EXPLORE! How do you look in a mirror?	500
		FIND OUT! How does light behave?	501
		INVESTIGATE! Angles of Reflection	503
17-2 Curved Mirrors	505	FIND OUT! What happens as light strikes a mirror that curves inward?	505
		EXPLORE! How can you bring a building indoors?	508
		EXPLORE! Can you capture every image?	509

LESSONS		ACTIVITIES	
17-3 Refraction and the Optics of Lenses	**511**	EXPLORE! What do lenses do to light?	511
		FIND OUT! What shape of lens makes light bend more?	514
		EXPLORE! Is a concave lens' image real?	517
17-4 Optical Instruments	**518**	INVESTIGATE! Making a Refracting Telescope	519

EXPANDING YOUR VIEW

A CLOSER LOOK **Cameras 521**

EARTH SCIENCE CONNECTION **Mirrors for Radio Waves 522**

SCIENCE AND SOCIETY **Telescopes in Space 523**

HEALTH CONNECTION **Lenses and Vision 525**

HOW IT WORKS **The Periscope 526**

LESSONS		ACTIVITIES	
Chapter 18 Basic Units of Life			**530**
		EXPLORE! What are living things made of?	**531**
18-1 The World of Cells	**532**	FIND OUT! What is everything made of?	532
		FIND OUT! Do all cells look the same?	533
		FIND OUT! Does the size of a living thing tell you anything about the size of its cells?	535
		FIND OUT! What is the relationship between the size of an object and the distance to its center?	536
		INVESTIGATE! Exploring Cell Size	538
18-2 The Inside Story of Cells	**540**	EXPLORE! What holds a cell together?	540
		FIND OUT! What's inside cells?	543
		FIND OUT! Where is the cell's command center located?	544
		EXPLORE! How do plant and animal cells differ?	546
		FIND OUT! What structures are unique to green plant cells?	548

LESSONS		ACTIVITIES	
18-3 When One Cell Becomes Two	549	FIND OUT! How do you grow taller?	550
		FIND OUT! When are chromosomes visible?	551
		INVESTIGATE! 24-Hour Cell Reproduction	553

EXPANDING YOUR VIEW

A CLOSER LOOK How Temperature Affects Cells 555

PHYSICS CONNECTION Light Microscope 556

HOW IT WORKS Using a Microscope 557

HEALTH CONNECTION Skin Cell Mitosis and Cancer 558

SCIENCE AND SOCIETY Our Aging Population 559

LESSONS		ACTIVITIES	
Chapter 19 Chemical Reactions			**564**
		EXPLORE! What kinds of things rust?	565
19-1 How Does Matter Change Chemically?	566	FIND OUT! Are all chemical changes alike?	566
19-2 Word Equations	569	FIND OUT! Is oxygen changed inside your body?	569
		EXPLORE! Do substances change partners in chemical reactions?	574
		INVESTIGATE! Single Displacement	575
19-3 Chemical Reactions and Energy	577	EXPLORE! Does a rubber band have energy?	577
		INVESTIGATE! Energy Changes	581
19-4 Speeding Up and Slowing Down Reactions	583	FIND OUT! Can a chemical reaction be made to go faster without adding energy?	583

EXPANDING YOUR VIEW

A CLOSER LOOK Steely Recipes 587

LIFE SCIENCE CONNECTION Edible Fuel 588

SCIENCE AND SOCIETY What's in Your Food Besides Food? 589

HEALTH CONNECTION Are You Too Awake? 590

TECHNOLOGY CONNECTION What We Breathe Can Eat Bridges! 591

TEENS IN SCIENCE Cellular Fun 592

LESSONS		ACTIVITIES	
Chapter 20 How Cells Do Their Jobs			**596**
		EXPLORE! How does salt affect living things?	**597**
20-1 Traffic in and out of Cells	598	FIND OUT! What substances can pass through a barrier?	598
		EXPLORE! How do tea bags work?	601
		FIND OUT! How does diffusion occur?	603
		INVESTIGATE! Eggs As Model Cells	605
20-2 Why Cells Need Food	607	FIND OUT! Does respiration release energy?	609
		INVESTIGATE! Respiration and Temperature	611
20-3 Special Cells with Special Jobs	613	FIND OUT! How do cells vary in size and shape?	613

EXPANDING YOUR VIEW

A CLOSER LOOK **The Cell Membrane 617**

CHEMISTRY CONNECTION **Does Mother Nature's Math Add Up? 618**

SCIENCE AND SOCIETY **End Stage Renal Disease: Costly in Different Ways 619**

HEALTH CONNECTION **Shaping Up: You Can't Do It Overnight 620**

HOW IT WORKS **The Artificial Kidney Machine 622**

LESSONS		ACTIVITIES	
Chapter 21 Simple Organisms			**626**
		EXPLORE! What does yeast look like?	**627**
21-1 Living Organisms	628	FIND OUT! How do two organisms compare to each other?	628
		INVESTIGATE! Shapes of Viruses	631
21-2 Classifying Simple Organisms	634	EXPLORE! In what ways can you classify organisms?	634

LESSONS

21-3 Simple Organisms Doing Their Jobs 637

ACTIVITIES

FIND OUT! What causes milk to spoil? 637
EXPLORE! What organisms live in pond water? 641
EXPLORE! What can you learn from a diatom? 642
FIND OUT! What characteristics do different protozoans have? 643
EXPLORE! What can you learn about fungi by observing them? 645
INVESTIGATE! What Is Needed for Molds to Grow? 647
EXPLORE! How do fungi reproduce? 648

EXPANDING YOUR VIEW

A CLOSER LOOK The Versatile Molds 649
EARTH SCIENCE CONNECTION Bacteria That Solve Pollution Problems 650
SCIENCE AND SOCIETY Using Viruses to Fight Disease 651
HISTORY CONNECTION The Countess's Powder 653
TEENS IN SCIENCE When Are Gibberellins Too Much of a Good Thing? 654

Appendices 659

Appendix A International System of Units 660
Appendix B SI/Metric to English Conversions 661
Appendix C Safety in the Science Classroom 662
Appendix D Safety Symbols 663
Appendix E Care and Use of a Microscope 664
Appendix F The Cell 665
Appendix G Classification of Monera and Protista 666
Appendix H United States Map 668
Appendix I World Map 670
Appendix J Periodic Table 672
Appendix K Minerals with Nonmetallic Luster 674
Appendix L Minerals with Metallic Luster 676

Skill Handbook 677

Organizing Information 678
Thinking Critically 682
Practicing Scientific Methods 686
Representing and Applying Data 689

Glossary 692

Index 696

Introducing Science Interactions

In 1991, in a desert in Arizona, a complicated experiment called Biosphere II began. A very large, enclosed dome containing plants, animals, microbes, rocks, soil, water, and people were sealed from the outside world. All organisms and objects within this dome were to remain within it for two years.

What might it be like to be sealed within a dome for two years? It doesn't sound so bad—you could eat whatever you wanted and sit around watching TV without having to go to school. There has to be a catch to all this—it sounds too good to be true. First of all, you can't order in food. Instead, you'll have to grow your own, and raise chickens for meat and eggs. You'll catch fish from ponds, and get milk from the few goats that are also sealed inside.

Now it doesn't sound so easy and relaxing anymore, does it? Seven days a week you would be busy taking care of the chickens, milking the goats, and farming the crops just so you'd have enough to eat.

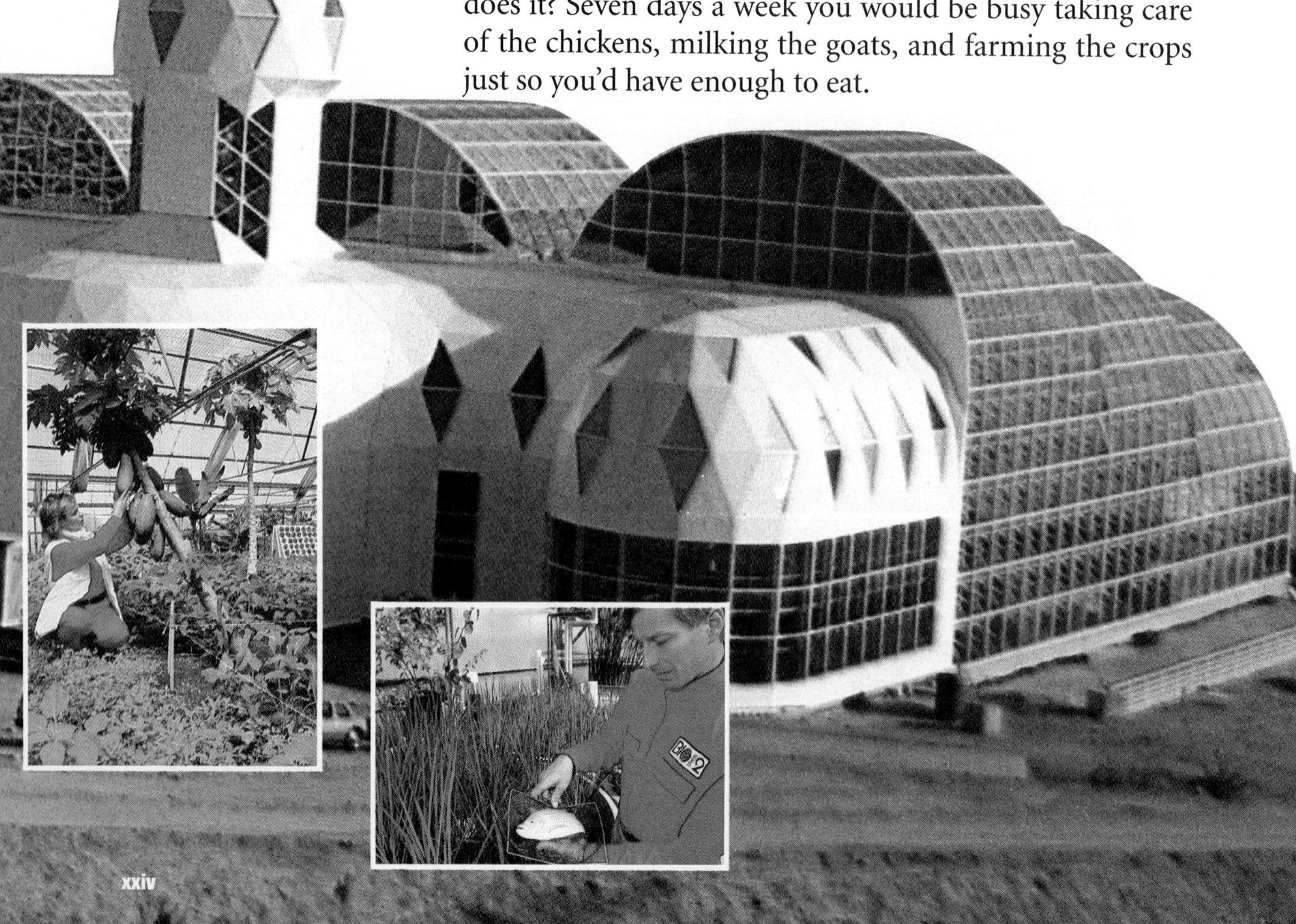

The Challenge of Biosphere II

Why are the people in Biosphere II sealing themselves from the outside world and providing for all of their own needs? Why do they have **to reuse or recycle all waste-**water instead of bringing in fresh water? Why can't they exchange air inside the dome for fresh air outside the dome? What can we learn from this gigantic living laboratory? If scientists in Biosphere II remain healthy, similar closed ecosystems may be built in the future to house people living in orbiting space stations or on other planets. Also, scientists will make careful observations and do experiments that may help us better manage Earth's natural resources.

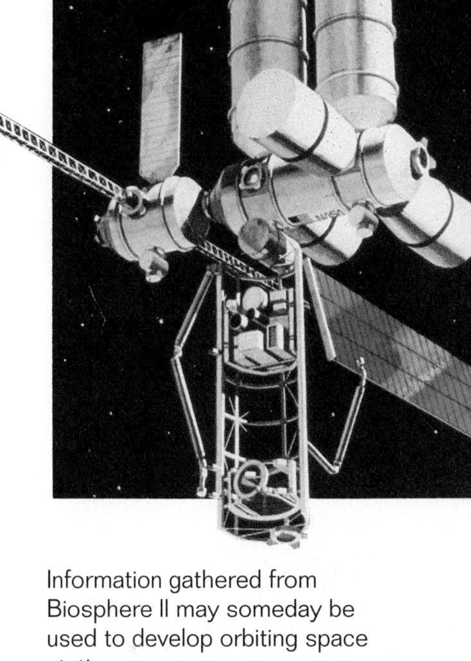

Information gathered from Biosphere II may someday be used to develop orbiting space stations.

For example, Biosphere II scientists will experiment with new methods for growing bigger and better crops. They will observe how the energy generated from the interactions between heat and light affects plant growth. Too much heat and light will cause the plants to die; so will too little.

How will the balance be maintained in this closed system between the carbon dioxide gas expelled each time the scientists exhale and the oxygen produced by the plants? And how will changes in this balance affect the plants, humans, and other animals within this closed system? To find out, Biosphere II scientists will monitor air gases and their effect on respiration and photosynthesis, topics you will learn about in Chapters 15 and 20.

Earthrise from the moon

Mushrooms on a fallen log

Discovering Science Interactions

Scientists can observe interactions and energy relationships in a closed system like Biosphere II; these same interactions and relationships occur around you every day on Earth. As you explore science this year, you'll see many examples of interactions, such as the interaction between water and heat inside Earth (Chapter 2). Another interaction you'll study is that between fungi and fallen trees on the forest floor.

The scientists will also use scientific methods to seek answers to hundreds of other questions. Will some animal species become "extinct" in Biosphere II's environment? If so, why? Which plants will thrive without commercial pesticides? Will the people and other living things inside this sealed environment thrive-or will the interactions between the various plants, animals and bacteria make them sick?

The methods used by Biosphere II scientists to observe the environment, propose hypotheses, conduct experiments, and gather data are the same methods you will use throughout this text to find out more about your world, Biosphere I.

Geysers in Yellowstone National Park

FIND OUT!

How can you create a miniature biosphere?

Design your own biosphere using a clear two-liter soft drink container. Whether you create a land or water biosphere, you'll need to think carefully about what and how much you could put in it. How much water or soil will you put in it? How many and what kinds of plants or small animals will you put in your biosphere? Plan your biosphere carefully. Check the design for your biosphere with your teacher. When you've finished your biosphere, seal the container. Once you seal it, you cannot add or take anything out. Place your biosphere on a window ledge in indirect sunlight for several weeks. As you observe your biosphere, think about and answer the following.

1. Write down your predictions of how your biosphere will change after one week, after two weeks, after three weeks, and so on.
2. Observe your biosphere every few days and record any changes you see. Compare your observations with your predictions.
3. Try to explain the changes you observe.
4. Was your biosphere a success (did it remain balanced)? How well did the plants and animals interact and survive?
5. How would you change the design of your biosphere if you could start over?

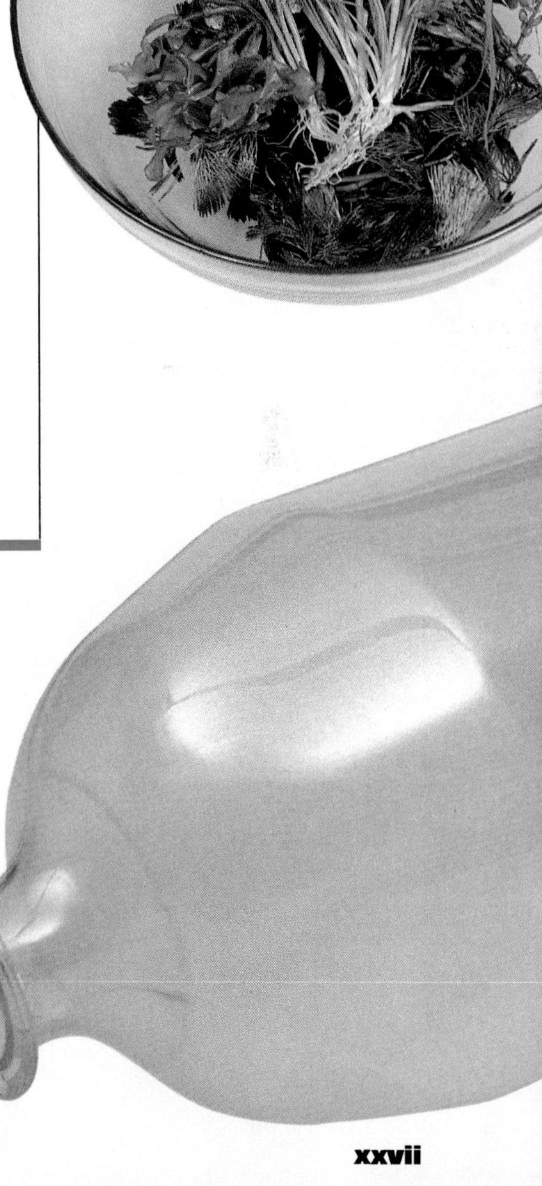

EXPERIENCE SCIENCE

HAVE FUN
WHILE YOU
LEARN SCIENCE

IN THE "EXPANDING YOUR VIEW" FEATURES, YOU'LL EXPLORE HOW SCIENCE CONNECTS TO ALL PARTS OF YOUR EVERYDAY WORLD

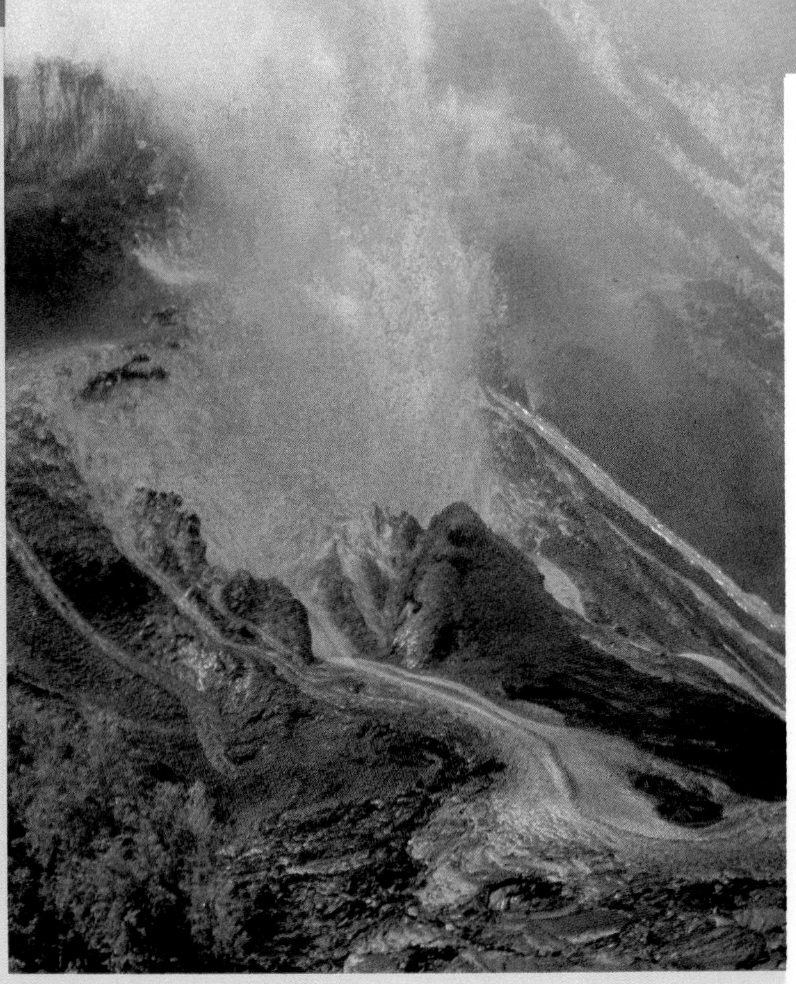

UNIT 1 FORCES IN ACTION

CONTENTS

Chapter 1 Forces and Pressure
Chapter 2 Forces Inside Earth
Chapter 3 Circulation in Animals

UNIT FOCUS

In Unit 1, you will learn about forces. As you travel in a car or school bus there are forces that act on your body, forces within your body, and other forces in the world around you. You have felt how forces cause objects to move when the car or bus you are riding in stops suddenly and your body still moves forward. Forces inside your body cause the blood to flow continuously through your blood vessels and forces inside Earth cause earthquakes and volcanoes.

TRY IT

The weight of air in our atmosphere produces a pressure on all things on the surface of Earth. How can you observe this pressure? Lay a meterstick on a table with 45 cm extending over the edge. Place a large sheet of newspaper over the part of the meterstick on the table. Now quickly push down the free end of the meterstick extending over the edge of the table. What do you feel? After you've learned more about forces, try this activity again and explain your observation.

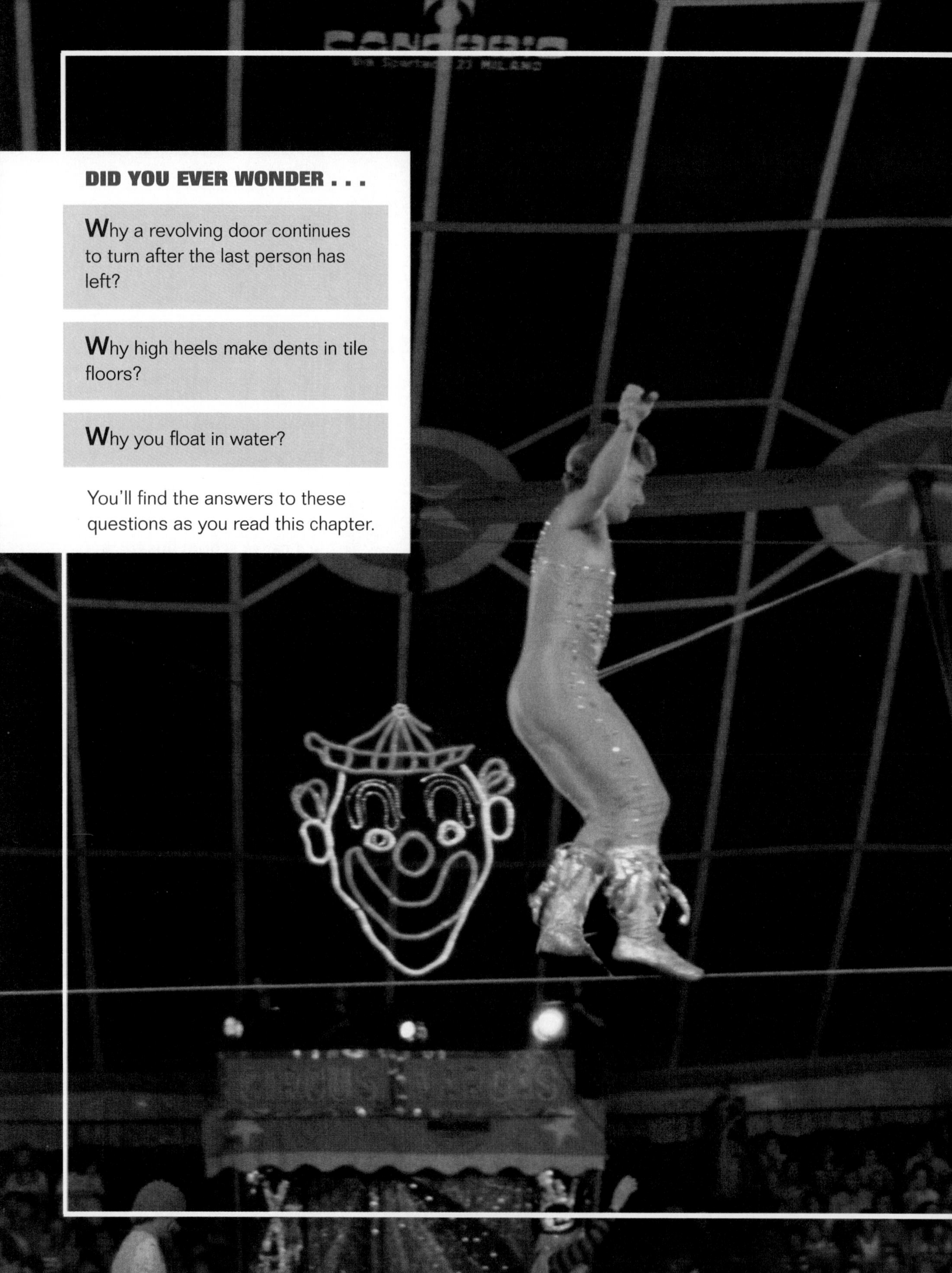

DID YOU EVER WONDER . . .

Why a revolving door continues to turn after the last person has left?

Why high heels make dents in tile floors?

Why you float in water?

You'll find the answers to these questions as you read this chapter.

Chapter 1

Forces and Pressure

A tightrope walker balances high overhead. Dogs stand on trotting horses while elephants perform amazing feats of balance. Jugglers spin their rings, and the clowns keep everyone laughing. You can't decide where to look first. You're afraid you'll miss something if you look away for a second.

As amazing and complicated as these circus acts are, they are all based on a few simple principles of motion. These same principles apply to activities that go on around you every day. For example, the grocery cart you push continues to roll down the aisle by itself. You slam your locker door, and it flies back at you.

In this chapter, you'll learn the most important laws of motion. You'll also see what makes objects move as they do, and what it takes to change their motion. In fact, when you understand these principles, you might surprise your friends with your own tricks.

EXPLORE!

Why doesn't the penny move?
Lay an index card over the top of a glass or beaker. Place a penny on the card, centered over the glass. With a flick of your finger, give the card a quick horizontal push. What happens? Wad up a small piece of paper to about the size of a marble. Place it on the card and flick the card away. What happens?

1-1 Force and Motion

OBJECTIVES

In this section, you will

- relate inertia to mass;
- identify the forces acting when objects interact;
- describe and use Newton's First Law of Motion.

KEY SCIENCE TERMS

inertia
inertial balance

KEEP ON MOVING

Picture yourself in the car in Figure 1-1 on your way to the grocery store. You're waiting at a stoplight. When the light turns green, the car moves forward. You feel like you're being pushed back into the seat. When the car slows to a stop, you feel pushed forward. And when the car turns a corner, you feel as if you're being pushed outward. What's happening to make you feel as if something is pushing you?

Recall what you've learned about velocity and acceleration. Velocity is speed in a given direction. When either the speed or the direction changes, that is described as acceleration. What happens in the car? When you are either stopped at the light or moving at a steady speed, your velocity is constant and you feel no sense of being pushed. But when you change velocity by either speeding up, slowing down, or changing direction, you do feel a push. In each case, the car has accelerated. As the car speeds up, or accelerates forward, you feel pushed back. As the car slows down, you move forward in your seat, as if you are pushed from behind. When the car turns left, your body leans toward the right.

FIGURE 1-1. What forces act on you as a car accelerates?

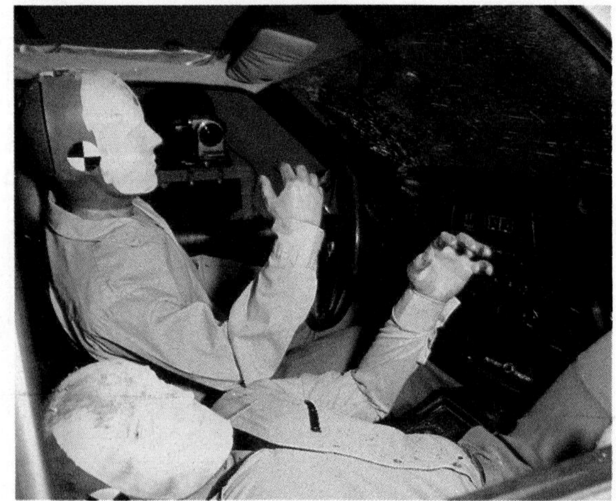

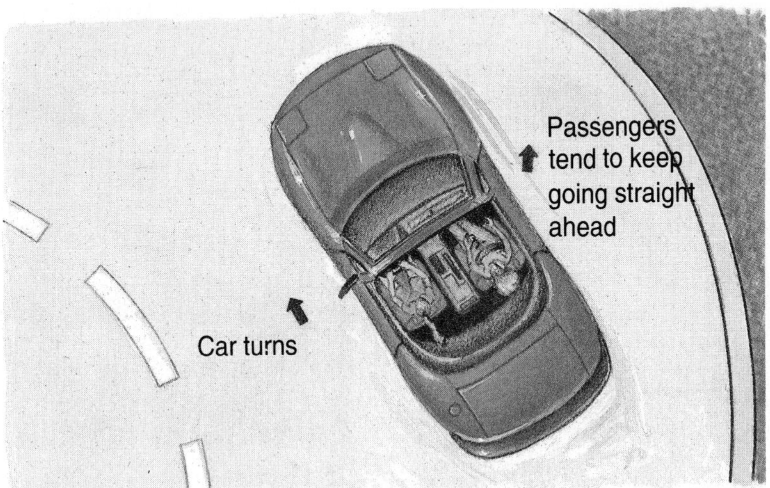

FIGURE 1-2. When a car turns, the passengers continue moving straight ahead.

Are you actually being pushed? If there were no push or pull on you, what would happen? You'd continue to move as you had been moving, right? When you and the car were stopped at the stoplight, you were both at rest. As the car accelerates forward, your body tends to remain at rest. It's as if the car is moving out from under you. Wouldn't that give you the feeling of being pushed backward? You experience a similar kind of push, but in different directions, when the car slows or goes around a corner.

Whenever you experience pushes and pulls associated with changes in velocity, something very simple is happening. You tend to continue the motion, or lack of motion, that you had before the acceleration began.

This tendency to resist changes in motion is called **inertia**. In the Explore at the beginning of the chapter, you saw a very good example of inertia in action. Both the card and coin were at rest until your flick of the card caused it to accelerate horizontally. Why didn't the coin accelerate with the card? Imagine that you were riding in a car with smooth plastic seatcovers and there was no back on the seat. What would happen when the car accelerated forward? Right! You'd slide backward right off the seat. But what really happens? You remain at rest and the car drives out from under you! The same thing happens to the coin. It tends to remain at rest, so when the card accelerates horizontally, the coin falls into the glass.

FIGURE 1-3. What physics principle makes this magician's trick possible?

FIGURE 1-4. A full shopping cart has more inertia than an empty one.

MASS AND INERTIA

Think about food shopping, and look at Figure 1-4. It's easy to start your shopping cart rolling when it's empty. As you add more to your cart, you find that it takes more effort to accelerate it and to get your cart to stop. As you add food, your cart is gaining inertia because there is more matter and therefore more mass. You may have noticed from this example that mass is more than how much matter is in an object. Mass is also a measure of an object's inertia—how much it resists changes in motion. Let's find out about the inertia of objects as they interact.

FIND OUT!

What factors affect the acceleration of objects?

Team up with another student who is either much lighter or much heavier than you are. Find two rolling chairs. You sit in one and have your partner sit in the other. Bring the two chairs close together with the palms of your hands against those of your partner. Then push each other away. Which chair moves away with the greatest final velocity? Which chair is given the greater acceleration? How does the direction of your acceleration compare with that of your partner?

Repeat this activity while both of you are pushing and then when only one of you is pushing.

Conclude and Apply

1. Are there any differences in the resulting accelerations for these different ways of pushing each other?
2. How does the rate of acceleration of each chair compare with how heavy each of you is?
3. Turn your chair around and let your partner push on the back of your chair, rather than pushing against your hands. How is what you experience different from when you pushed hand to hand?
4. What causes you to accelerate in this case?

DID YOU KNOW?

The word *inertia* comes from a Latin word that means idle or lazy. Objects seem lazy because they don't want to change the way they move.

Recall that mass is a measure of the amount of matter in an object. In this activity, you found that the person with the greater mass did not accelerate as much as the person with less mass. Apparently, the greater the mass, the greater the tendency to resist acceleration. That is, as mass increases, so does inertia.

In the Find Out, you and your partner interacted and that interaction produced acceleration. If your partner had pushed your chair on an icy pond instead of the floor, what would have happened once you started moving? In imagining the icy pond instead of the floor, what interaction are we getting rid of? If no such interaction existed, once you began moving, your inertia would make you continue to move until something stopped you. This tendency to remain at rest or in uniform motion is called Newton's First Law of Motion. It's the result of observations and calculations made by Sir Isaac Newton. An object remains at rest or in uniform motion unless it interacts with another object.

You know that on Earth, you can use a balance to find the mass of an object. But you've probably seen pictures that show objects in a spacecraft floating. Would a laboratory balance work there? We said that the mass you find on a balance and the mass that is a measure of an object's inertia are the same. Is there a way to measure inertia directly? Let's investigate.

FIGURE 1-5. Sir Isaac Newton discovered more than falling apples.

INVESTIGATE!

1-1 MEASURING INERTIAL MASS

We can measure the way an object speeds up or slows down, and we can compare that with the way known masses speed up or slow down to find the mass of the object.

PROBLEM

How can you find the mass of an object without a laboratory balance?

MATERIALS

inertial balance
pan balance
clamp
assorted marked masses
second timer
heavy rubber bands
object of unknown mass
graph paper

PROCEDURE

1. Copy the data table.
2. Clamp one end of the inertial balance to the table as shown in the diagram.
3. Place enough masses on the outer platform to make a total of 1 kg, including the platform itself. Secure these with heavy rubber bands.

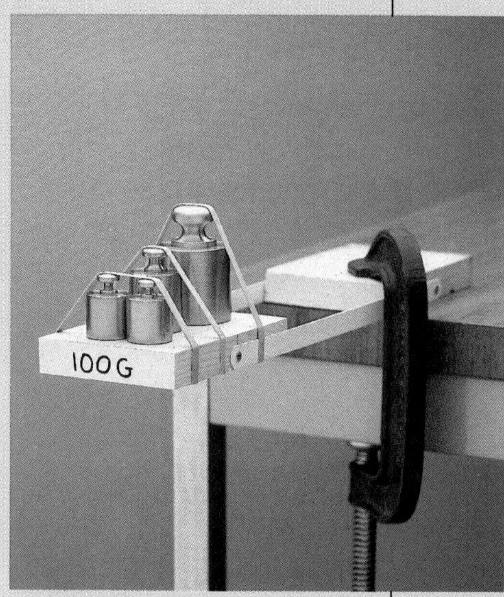

4. Pull the outer platform sideways and let go. What happens? Measure the time for 10 complete back-and-forth cycles. Record your data.
5. Repeat Steps 3 and 4 two more times, with total masses of 2 kg and 3 kg.
6. Attach the unknown mass to the platform and measure the time for 10 complete cycles. Record.

DATA AND OBSERVATIONS

MASS	PERIOD
1 kg	
2 kg	
3 kg	

ANALYZE

1. The period of a cycle is the time it takes for one complete back-and-forth motion. **Calculate** the period for each of your four masses.
2. **Plot a graph** of the three known masses. Plot period on the horizontal axis and mass on the vertical axis. Connect the points with a smooth curve.
3. Find the period of the unknown mass on the graph. **Predict** what the mass should be.
4. Subtract the mass of the platform from the mass you predicted. This will give you the mass of the unknown object.
5. Check your results by **measuring** the unknown mass on a pan balance.

CONCLUDE AND APPLY

6. What is the relationship between the mass and the period?
7. How did your prediction compare with the actual measured mass?
8. A period of .75 seconds on this inertial balance would indicate how much mass?
9. **Going Further:** What would be the period of an object with a mass of 5 kg?

The device you used in the Investigate is called an inertial balance. An **inertial balance** measures an object's mass by measuring its resistance to a change in motion. You've seen that an inertial balance measures mass just as well as a regular balance. The way that the inertial balance moves back and forth doesn't depend on any interaction with Earth. Therefore, it could be used anywhere, whether or not gravity was present.

FIGURE 1-6. The pushes were equal, but the acceleration depended on mass.

INTERACTIONS THAT PUSH OR PULL

When you sat in that rolling chair and pushed on your partner's hands, each of you pushed the other. Your pushes were equal but opposite in direction, and you were both accelerated in opposite directions. In each case the person with less mass (less inertia) experienced the greater acceleration. A push or pull is commonly referred to as a force. Let's see how forces are involved in motion.

When you pushed on your fellow student in the rolling chair, what caused you to accelerate—the force you used to push on her, or the force she was exerting on you? Can you push on yourself and make your body speed up? No, something else must push on you. When you put your feet on the floor, it is the floor pushing back on your feet that gives you the motion. You must have a force pushing on you, and then you will accelerate in the direction of that force.

Earlier in the chapter, we talked about what would happen if you were on a slippery plastic seat and there were no seat back. Let's take that one step further. Imagine a block of ice on a flatbed truck.

The truck is at rest and the block of ice is right behind the driver. What will happen when the truck starts up? What force is needed for the ice to accelerate with the truck? There must be an interaction between the ice and the truck bed. That interaction is friction. Friction is necessary when we want one object to accelerate with another one, as with the ice on the flatbed truck. At

FIGURE 1-7. How does the block behind the runner's foot help the runner start the race?

FIGURE 1-8. Why can't these students move forward?

other times, when we want something to keep moving, friction slows it down. But is friction a force—a push or a pull? Let's find out.

FIND OUT!

Is friction a force?

Place a sheet of plain white paper on a flat surface. Set a 20-g mass on the paper about 7 cm from one end. Grip the other end of the paper and give it a smooth, quick pull. Now repeat the procedure replacing the white paper with a sheet of coarse sandpaper, rough side up.

Conclude and Apply

1. Compare and contrast what happens to the 20-g mass with each piece of paper.
2. Use Newton's First Law of Motion to explain your observations.

Since the 20-gram mass had the same inertia in both cases, it would require a horizontal force to make it move in the direction of the paper. You exerted a horizontal force on the paper when you pulled it, but you didn't exert a force directly on the mass. Therefore, the paper must have exerted the horizontal force on the mass.

What if there were no friction? Your feet couldn't grip the ground. You couldn't accelerate unless something bumped into you and started you going. Once you were moving, you'd keep moving at a constant speed in the same direction until you interacted with something else.

DID YOU KNOW?

In the English system, the pound is the unit of force and the unit of acceleration is feet/second^2. What is the unit of mass? Believe it or not, it's called a slug! One slug = 14.6 kg.

Like friction, gravitational interaction is so common that we usually ignore it. You know that free-falling objects accelerate downward at about 9.8 meters per second per second (9.8 m/s^2). This acceleration is due to gravitational force, which pulls you toward Earth's center.

When a ball is dropped, Earth is exerting a force that accelerates the ball downward. Is the ball causing Earth to accelerate upward, too? What if you sat in a chair with rollers and pushed your hands against the back of a 2-ton automobile? Which of you would accelerate the most?

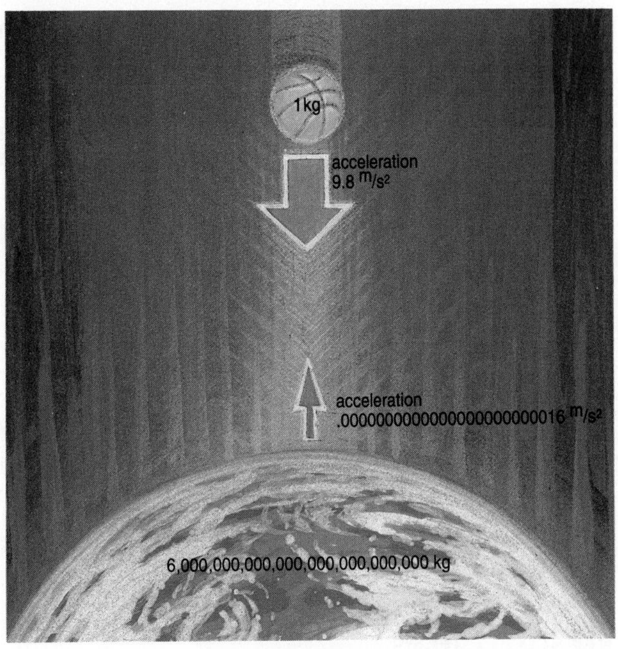

FIGURE 1-9. As Earth's gravitational force accelerates the ball, the ball's gravitational force accelerates Earth.

You can see that if the mass of the object you are interacting with is very large the object's acceleration would be so small you couldn't even measure it. In the same way, the gravitational interaction between the ball and Earth, shown in Figure 1-9, is such that only the ball appears to accelerate.

As objects fall, more massive objects are more strongly attracted to Earth, and for that reason you would expect them to fall more quickly. On the other hand, they are also harder to accelerate. Their inertia reduces their acceleration by exactly as much as their greater attraction increases it.

In the next section, we'll discover how the three factors of mass, force, and acceleration all work together. They are a part of everything you do and everything that happens around you.

Check Your Understanding

1. What determines an object's inertia?
2. Describe two forces that don't depend upon physical contact.
3. Briefly state and give an example of Newton's First Law of Motion.
4. **APPLY:** Describe two activities where you need frictional forces and two where you would like smaller frictional forces.

1-2 Newton's Second Law of Motion

OBJECTIVES

In this section, you will

- describe the relationships between force, mass, and acceleration;
- use Newton's second law to predict acceleration.

KEY SCIENCE TERMS

force

newton

balanced forces

weight

ACCELERATION, MASS, AND FORCE

Two objects may interact by contact, electrical force, frictional force, gravitational force, or magnetic force. No matter what the force, the interaction will always have an interesting result. You know that if you push a cart harder it moves faster. From your experience, you also know that a car is more difficult to push than a bicycle. How is the force you use related to the object's motion? Suppose each object could move, like the carts in Figure 1-10. What kind of relationship might exist between the motion and forces of the two carts?

Isaac Newton was one of the first to notice it. His observations led him to develop his second law of motion. You can discover this law for yourself in the Investigate. Figure 1-10 shows two carts held together by a thread. The compressed spring between the carts is trying to push them apart. What do you think will happen when the spring is cut? Will the carts accelerate at the same rate? What is the relationship between the mass of the carts and their acceleration?

FIGURE 1-10. These spring-connected carts can help you observe the second law of motion.

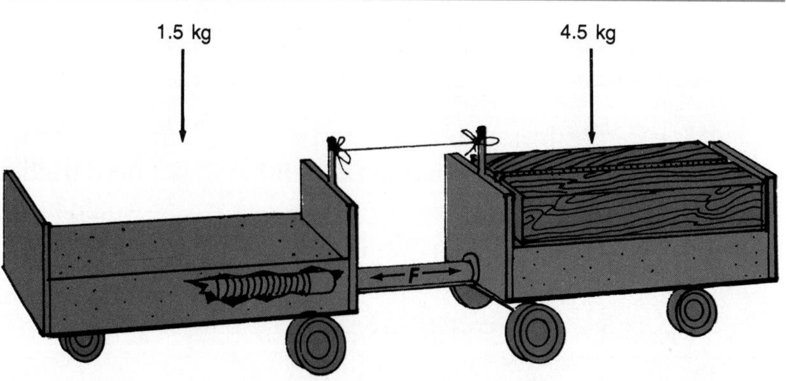

INVESTIGATE!

1-2 ACCELERATION AND MASS

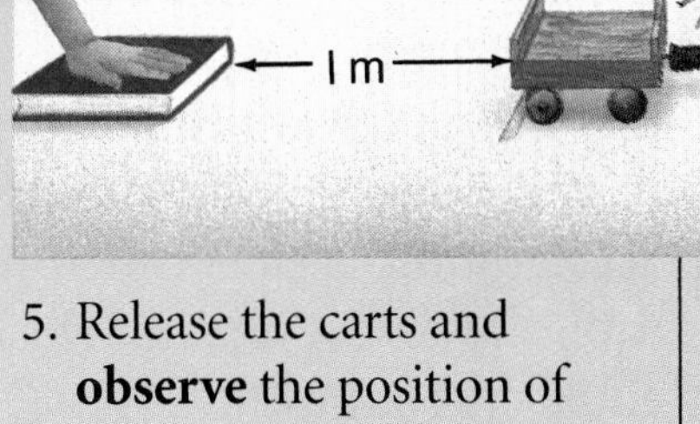

You know that velocity is the rate of change of position and that acceleration is the rate of change in velocity.

PROBLEM

What is the relationship between the mass and acceleration of an object?

MATERIALS

balance with 5 kg capacity
masses of 1 kg and less
masking tape
2 books
spring carts
meterstick

PROCEDURE

1. Copy the data table.
2. Measure and record the mass of Cart 1.
3. Place masses on Cart 2 until its total mass is double that of Cart 1. Tape the masses to the cart.
4. Attach the two carts and place them on the floor. Place a piece of tape even with the front wheels of each cart. Place a book one meter away from each cart.
5. Release the carts and **observe** the position of Cart 2 when Cart 1 hits the book. Be sure to hold the books in place.
6. **Predict** what starting position will allow the carts to hit the books at the same time.
7. Move the carts to the predicted position and repeat Steps 4 and 5. Remember to move the tapes. Repeat Step 7, until the two carts stop at the same time. **Measure** and record the distance that each cart traveled.
8. Add more masses to Cart 2 so that it has three times the mass of Cart 1. Repeat Steps 4–7.

ANALYZE

1. Complete the table by calculating the ratio of the distance traveled by Cart 2 to the distance traveled by Cart 1 for each set of masses.
2. How do these distance ratios **compare** to the ratio of the masses?
3. What happened to the acceleration of Cart 2 as the mass increased?

CONCLUDE AND APPLY

4. What force produces acceleration? Is it the same for both carts?
5. **Going Further:** If you added more masses to Cart 2, until it had four times the mass of Cart 1, what would you **predict** would happen to the distance traveled by Cart 2? How would it have compared to the distance traveled by Cart 1?

DATA AND OBSERVATIONS

	MASS OF CART 1, kg	MASS OF CART 2 + MASSES, kg	DISTANCE, m	RATIO OF MASSES	RATIO OF DISTANCES
Trial 1					
Trial 2					

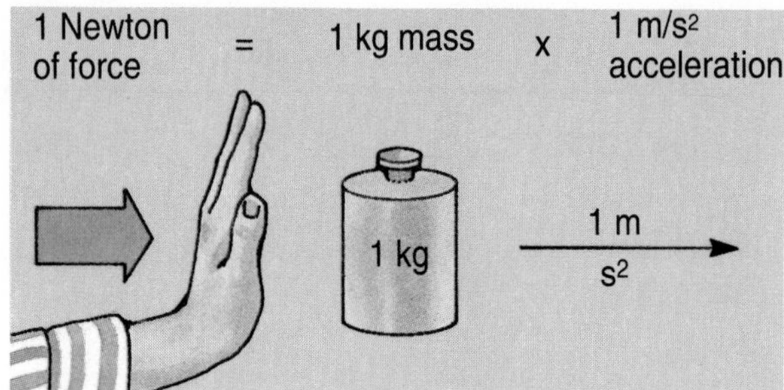

FIGURE 1-11. One newton is the force needed to accelerate one kilogram at the rate of one meter per second squared.

If you had measured acceleration in the Investigate, you would have found that the first cart's acceleration multiplied by its mass equals the second cart's acceleration multiplied by its mass. This relationship has been found in many interactions and leads to Newton's Second Law of Motion: During the interaction of any two objects, the mass times the acceleration of one object always equals the mass times the acceleration of the other object. The product of the mass times the acceleration is called the force of the interaction. Therefore, the forces on the two interacting objects are always equal and opposite.

In most books, you'll find Newton's Second Law of Motion stated more simply by the equation:

$$\text{Force} = \text{Mass} \times \text{Acceleration.}$$

THE MEANING OF FORCE

Defining force in these terms gives us a more useful definition of force. **Force** is mass times acceleration. In other words, a force is what accelerates a mass.

If force = mass × acceleration, in what unit do we measure force? You know that mass is measured in kilograms and acceleration in meters per second squared (m/s^2). The unit of force is therefore,

$$\text{kilogram} \times \frac{\text{meter}}{\text{second}^2}.$$

This not only looks strange, it takes a lot of words to say it. The unit of force is therefore given another name. It is called a **newton**, abbreviated N. In the English system, the unit of force is the pound.

FIGURE 1-12. Gravity pulls down on the book, and the hand pushes up on it.

BALANCED AND UNBALANCED FORCES

When does an object with a given mass accelerate? Hold a book steady on the palm of your hand. What forces are acting? Earth exerts a downward force on the book and your hand exerts an upward force on the book. Both of these forces are acting on the same object, but in opposite directions. Are these forces equal? Balanced? If they weren't, the book would have to be accelerating. It would accelerate upward if the force of your hand were greater than the force pulling the book down, and downward if the force of your hand were less than the pull on the book. But the forces are balanced. **Balanced forces** means that whatever forces act on an object cancel one another. The effect is as if no force is acting. If an object is at rest or moving at a constant velocity, the forces on that object must be balanced.

What happens when forces are not balanced? If you increase your upward force against the book, it moves. Objects only accelerate when they are acted upon by unbalanced forces, that is, when there is a greater force acting on an object in some direction. This force produces a change in motion.

Analyzing the forces acting on an object can help us predict whether that object will accelerate. How are forces measured? Let's explore a way of measuring a force.

DID YOU KNOW?

The pull of gravity differs from place to place. In the United States, gravity is greatest in Minot, North Dakota and smallest in Key West, Florida.

EXPLORE!

How can forces be measured?

Hang a 1-kg mass from the hook of a spring balance that is calibrated in newtons. What causes the spring to stretch? How much force does the mass exert on the spring?

You discovered that a 1-kg mass exerts a downward force of 9.8 N. How does this happen? The force due to gravity accelerates the mass downward at 9.8 m/s^2 and the mass, in turn, pulls the spring downward. If there weren't an equal opposing force, in this case the force exerted by the spring, the mass would continue to accelerate downward.

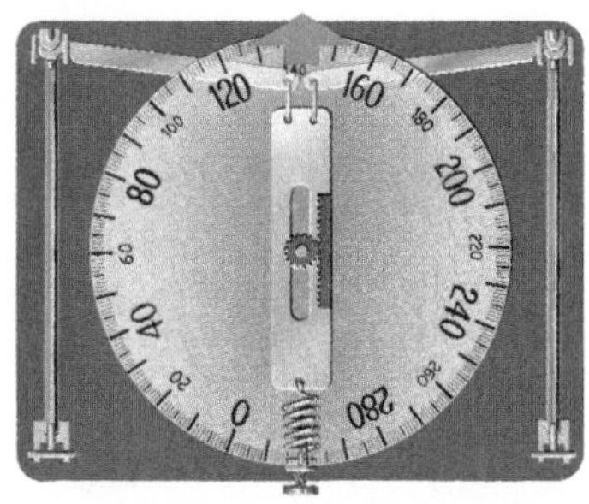

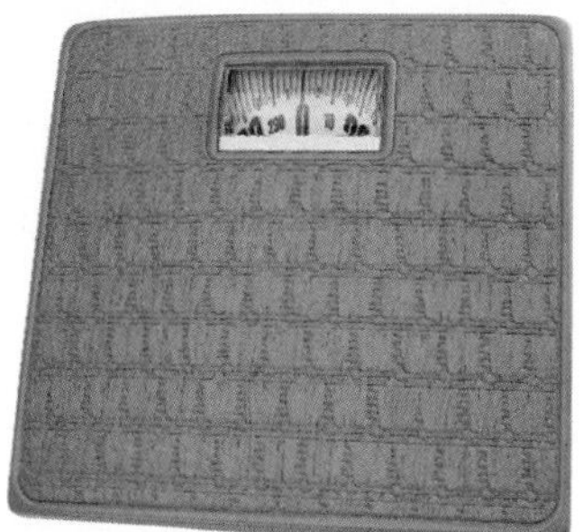

FIGURE 1-13. When you step on a bathroom scale, the downward force of gravity—your weight—is balanced by the upward force exerted by the spring.

WEIGHT AS FORCE

When you jump off a step onto the floor, every part of you is interacting with the entire Earth. You are accelerating downward at the rate of 9.8 m/s^2. When your feet touch the floor, you stop moving. But does the force of gravity stop acting on you? No. The only reason that you stop falling is because the floor is exerting an equal force upward on your feet. Earth is still pulling on you with the same force. The gravitational force on you or any object is called **weight.**

How can Newton's second law be used to measure force even when an object isn't moving? Did you notice that the force acting on a one-kilogram mass was numerically the same as the acceleration produced by the force of gravity? This is no accident.

Force (N) = mass (kg) × acceleration (m/s^2)
9.8 N = 1 kg × 9.8 m/s^2

The force exerted on the 1-kg mass is actually its weight, measured in newtons. When the force being measured is gravitational force, force and weight are equivalent.

If you have a mass of 50 kg, what is your weight?
Force (N) = 50 kg × 9.8 m/s^2
Your weight is 490 N.

Why do you bend your knees when you jump from a height? Although you do it automatically, the laws of motion can explain why it is effective. In the next section, we'll look at forces from a different perspective and discover yet another law of motion.

Check Your Understanding

1. Complete the following:
   a. If the mass is constant, as force increases, acceleration ____.
   b. If the force is constant, as mass increases, acceleration ____.
2. Write a short paragraph explaining how the following words are related: force, weight, newton, pound.
3. A 10-kg object interacts with a 30-kg object. As a result, the 10-kg object accelerates at 60 m/s^2. What would be the acceleration of the 30-kg object?
4. **APPLY:** When a stuntman jumps from a height, he uses a large bag filled with air. What is the purpose of this bag in terms of what you learned in this section?

1-3 Newton's Third Law of Motion

OBJECTIVES

In this section, you will

- identify pairs of forces;
- describe the difference between balanced forces and action-reaction forces.

KEY SCIENCE TERMS

action force
reaction force

INTERACTIONS COME IN PAIRS: ACTION AND REACTION

In all of the interactions we have seen so far, there are always two equal and opposite forces involved. You push on someone and that person pushes back on you. If you push on the wall, the wall pushes back. These forces are always equal in size but opposite in direction. We even defined force as the product of mass times acceleration because when objects interact, these products are the same, except for direction.

Whenever you push on something, that force is called an **action force**. The force that pushes back on you is called the **reaction force**. Action and reaction forces always occur in pairs, but more important, they always act on different objects. Newton's Third Law of Motion states that for every action there is an equal and opposite reaction.

Every day, we see hundreds of examples of the third law in action. When you press lightly on a wall, the wall presses lightly back. A car is set in motion by the push of the ground on the tires as the tires push back on the ground. When a rifle bullet is fired forward, there is a "kick" or recoil backward against the shoulder. As you walk, you push on the ground and the ground pushes back. If the ground didn't push back, could you walk? Can you make yourself move by exerting a force on yourself?

If an object must be acted on by unbalanced forces in order to accelerate, and action-reaction forces are always balanced, how can anything ever move? Look at Figure 1-15, which describes the forces acting when you pick up a bowling ball. When your hand exerts a force on the ball, the ball exerts a force on your hand that is the same size, but in the opposite direction. This is shown by the red and blue arrows

FIGURE 1-14. This woman's jacket is padded to protect her shoulder from the reaction force.

FIGURE 1-15. Each pair of action-reaction forces is equal (a). However, there is a net upward force on the bowling ball, causing it to accelerate upward (b).

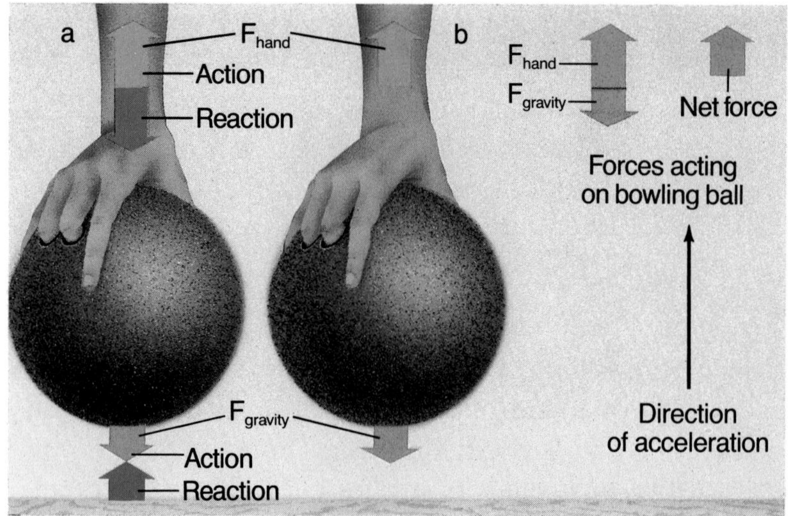

at the top of the ball. A second pair of forces occurs as Earth exerts a downward force on the ball and the ball exerts an upward force on Earth. These forces are shown by the red and blue arrows at the bottom of the ball. Both of these pairs of forces are action-reaction forces. They are balanced. Whether the ball will accelerate is determined by whether the upward force of your hand on the ball is balanced by the downward force of gravity on the ball. These are not action-reaction forces. Each of them comes from a different pair of forces and they are acting on the same object, the ball. This relationship is shown by the two red arrows in the second picture. The upward force is larger than the downward force, so there is an unbalanced force acting on the ball and it will accelerate upward.

Forces always come in pairs. When one object exerts a force on a second, the second exerts an equal and opposite force on the first. This is Newton's Third Law of Motion.

SKILLBUILDER

CAUSE AND EFFECT

When using a high-pressure hose, why is it necessary for firefighters to grip the hose strongly and plant their feet firmly? If you need help, refer to the **Skill Handbook** on page 683.

Check Your Understanding

1. When you push a door closed, you're exerting a force on the door. Where is the equal and opposite force and what is it pushing on?
2. When you lift a suitcase, describe the action-reaction force pairs and explain why the suitcase moves upward.
3. **APPLY:** A piece of fishing line breaks if the force exerted on it is greater than 500 N. Will the line break if two people at opposite ends of the line pull on it, each with a force of 300 N?

1-4 Pressure and Buoyancy

AREA AND FORCE

In a previous section, you measured the force exerted by a 1-kg mass and found that it was 9.8 N. If you set the mass on the table, does it still exert the same force? What if you hammered the mass into a flat plate—would the force change? In this section, we're going to look at the relationship of the force exerted to the area that the force acts on.

OBJECTIVES

In this section, you will

- calculate pressure from a given force and surface area;
- explain how objects can float in a liquid;
- interpret and use Archimedes' Principle.

KEY SCIENCE TERMS

pressure

buoyant force

EXPLORE!

How are weight and pressure related?

Place a sheet of graph paper lined 1 inch by 1 inch on the floor and cover it with a sheet of carbon paper. Put on a pair of women's high-heeled shoes and step onto the paper with your full weight on one heel. This should make an impression showing the surface area of the heel. Find your weight. From the impression, estimate what fraction of a square inch the heel covered. Divide your weight by this surface area to find the force per square inch. Have a much heavier person stand on the heel of a man's shoe with the carbon paper and graph paper underneath. This time the surface impression is larger than before. Use this person's weight and divide it by this area. How does this result compare with the high heel?

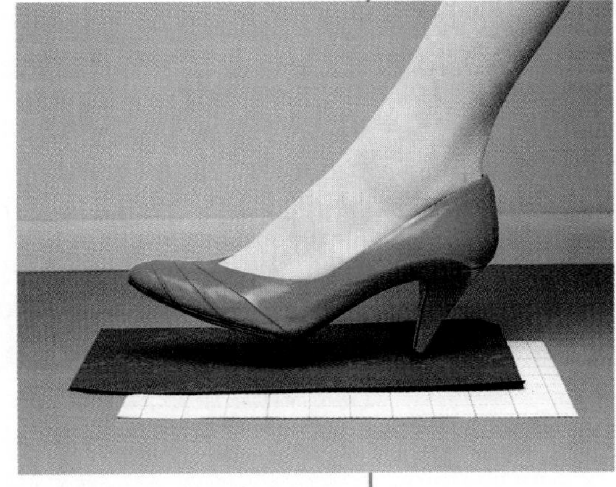

When you divide the weight of a person by the surface area of the heel of a shoe on which he or she is standing, you are finding something called pressure. **Pressure** is defined as the weight or force acting on each unit of area.

FIGURE 1-16. If a woman's high heels are very thin, she may be exerting as much pressure on the floor as an elephant.

Pressure = Force/Area on which it is acting.

A 100-pound person balanced on 1 square inch of floor exerts a pressure of 100 lb/in^2. Imagine the pressure exerted by an elephant in the circus when it stands on one leg! Still, a woman in high heels might exert even more pressure!

By reducing the area on which force acts, you can get a lot of pressure from a little bit of force. Think about a needle. Suppose its point has a surface of 0.001 square inches. How much pressure will that needle exert if you push on it with just 1 pound of pressure? Divide 1 by 0.001 and you get 1000 pounds per square inch. That's a very high pressure, especially considering that you only applied 1 pound of force. You can see, then, why doctors would want very sharp needles for stitching up wounds or giving injections.

IT'S DIFFERENT WITH FLUIDS

What would you think exerts more pressure—10 cm of water on the bottom of a coffee can, or the same depth of water on the bottom of a wading pool? Or would it make any difference?

FIND OUT!

What is the relationship of fluid depth to pressure?
Weigh three or four graduated cylinders of different diameters. If you don't have graduated cylinders, you may use cans or glasses, but they must have vertical sides. Record the weights. Fill each container with water to the same height from the base. Weigh the containers again. Subtract the weights of the empty containers from the weights of the filled containers. This gives you the weight of each column of water.

Measure the inside diameter of each container. Divide each diameter by 2 to get the radius. Multiply the radius by itself, and then multiply that number by 3.14. That gives you the cross-sectional area of each cylinder as shown in the diagram.

Divide the weight of each column of water by its container's cross-sectional area. This tells you how much pressure the water exerts on the bottom of its cylinder.

Conclude and Apply

1. How do the pressures compare?
2. If you had a 30-foot vertical pipe filled with water, how do you think the pressure on the bottom of that pipe would compare with the pressure at the bottom of a 30-foot deep lake?

FIGURE 1-17. The pressure at the bottom of a container is greater than the pressure at the top.

You've just seen that the pressure at the bottom of a container of water depends only on the height of the water. For liquids other than water, the pressures would be different.

But what about pressure other than at the bottom of a column of liquid? A fluid is any substance that does not have a definite shape. Liquids and gases are fluids. Does fluid exert pressure in any direction other than down? Your experience tells you the answer. If you fill a paper cup with water and poke a hole halfway down the cup's side, what happens? Water flows from the hole. So there must be sideways pressure forcing the water out.

Your experience guides you well. If you could move a pressure detector around in any container of fluid, you'd find that the fluid exerts pressure in all directions. This fact was first expressed with precision by the French mathematician Blaise Pascal. In his honor, it's now known as Pascal's Law.

WHY YOU FLOAT

Picture yourself in Figure 1-18. If you've ever gone swimming, you know that there are more forces at work in a pool of water than just the pressure exerted against the pool's bottom and sides. You know that something about the water allows you to float. You know that you can easily lift friends in the water, even if you could barely budge them on land. Why is that?

Let's first examine the question in a somewhat smaller body of water. We'll move from the swimming pool to the bathtub. When you sit in your tub, the water level rises. That's no surprise. After all, you added something to the water: yourself. How much do you think the water rises?

When you float in the pool, the water doesn't rise by an amount equal to the volume of your entire body. Your entire body isn't under the water. How much does it rise, then? What determines just how far your body sinks into the water? Let's find out.

FIGURE 1-18. Find the action-reaction forces in this picture.

FIND OUT!

How much water does an object displace?

Fill a beaker to the brim. Put a pan underneath it so that you can catch any water that overflows. Using a spring scale, weigh an object dense enough to sink in the beaker. Record its weight. Leaving the object attached to the spring scale, suspend the object in the water so that it is completely beneath the surface, but not touching the bottom. Use the figure as a guide. Some water will overflow into the pan below. Use the spring scale to determine the object's weight while in the water.

Weigh a small can with a wire handle. Transfer as much of the water that overflowed from the beaker into the can as possible. Weigh the can again. Subtract to find the weight of the water.

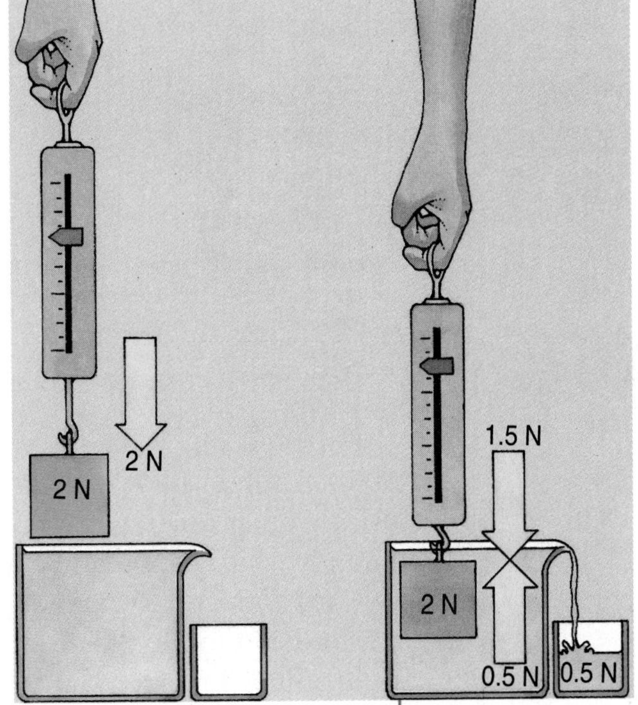

Conclude and Apply

1. How much weight did the object lose when you submerged it in water?
2. What is the relationship between the weight of the water that overflowed and the weight the object lost?

As you saw in the Find Out, when an object is immersed in water, it pushes aside some amount of water. The weight of the object is reduced by the weight of the water that is pushed aside. This relationship was discovered by the Greek mathematician Archimedes in the third century B.C.E. Known as Archimedes' Principle, it says that the weight of water displaced by an object is equal to the amount of weight lost by the object. The greater the weight of water you displace, the more your weight is reduced.

a 

b 

FIGURE 1-19. Compare the pictures of the people floating in fresh water (a) and salt water (b). The man in salt water floats higher because it takes a smaller volume of displaced salt water to equal your weight because salt water is more dense than plain water.

But hold on. What's this about losing weight? Water doesn't get rid of gravity, does it? No, but it can lift you up as much as gravity pulls you down. If you lose 40 pounds while standing in a pool, the water is exerting an upward force of 40 pounds on you. This force is called the **buoyant force**. When something is pushed upward by fluid, that's known as buoyancy. All objects experience buoyancy, whether they're more or less dense than the fluid they're in.

We began this chapter by considering the many different kinds of motion and force present in a variety of circus acts. Can you understand now how, regardless of how amazing these acts seem, they are all based on a few simple laws developed by Isaac Newton several hundred years ago?

Check Your Understanding

1. Describe what happens to the pressure exerted by a force as the area that the force acts on increases.
2. How does the diameter of a column of water affect the pressure at the bottom of the column?
3. Explain why a block of wood can float in water and a block of metal of equal volume cannot.
4. **APPLY:** If you step into a pool and displace 50 pounds of water, how much weight have you lost?

EXPANDING YOUR VIEW

CONTENTS

A Closer Look
Centripetal Force 25

Life Science Connection
How Does a Fish Use Its Swim Bladder? 26

Science and Society
Deep-Sea Submersibles 27

History Connection
A Royal Solution 29

Technology Connection
Transducers in Your Life 30

A CLOSER LOOK

CENTRIPETAL FORCE

Remember how you feel pushed to the side when the car you're riding in turns a corner? We've already seen that there really is no outward force to the side, only the car keeping you from continuing in a straight line while the car changes its direction.

When you swing a mass on the end of a string, the mass is whirling around with uniform circular motion. The speed of the mass may be constant, but the velocity is always changing because the direction is changing. Therefore, we can say that the mass is accelerating.

When the athlete in the picture lets go, the hammer moves away in a straight line. The only thing that keeps it moving in a circle is the force acting toward the center of the circle—the pull that the athlete exerts on the rope.

If a satellite were in orbit and Earth's gravity were suddenly shut off, what would happen to the satellite? Because of its inertia, it would move off in a straight line. The force of gravity keeps pulling it back in. At any point on the circle, you could think of the path of the satellite as a tiny straight line. To change the direction, there must be a force acting toward the center of the circle—in this case, toward Earth. This is centripetal force.

Centripetal force is the force exerted to keep an object moving in a circle. An object traveling in a circle is constantly accelerating toward the center of the circle. Next time you ride a bike, notice how you lean toward the center of the curve. The force that pushes you toward the center of the curve is the force of the road on the tires—the centripetal force.

YOU TRY IT!

While standing in your schoolyard or some other outdoor area, swing a half-full bucket of water over your head. Using what you now know about centripetal force, explain the movement of the bucket and the water.

LIFE SCIENCE CONNECTION

HOW DOES A FISH USE ITS SWIM BLADDER?

It is easy to tell the difference between sharks and bony fish in the water. Sharks constantly thrash their tails and never stop swimming in an effort to stay at a certain level. They sink if they do not keep swimming because they lack buoyancy.

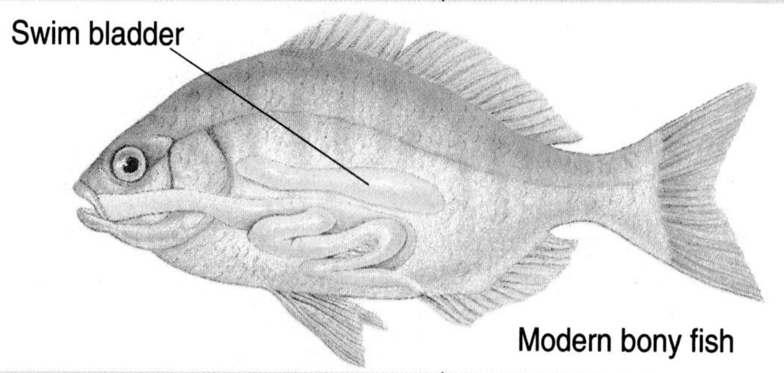

Unlike sharks, bony fish have been freed from this need for constant motion by having a swim bladder—a sac-like structure that holds air. This organ helps a fish adjust its buoyancy by changing the amount of gas in the bladder. More gas in the bladder increases the volume of the fish. The fish then displaces just the amount of water needed to keep it buoyant. The fish does not have to swim in order to keep from sinking.

From what you have learned about buoyancy, you should be aware that a fish in water is buoyed up by a force equal to the weight of the water it displaces.

As a fish swims upward or downward in the water, the pressure on it changes. The swim bladder helps it react to the changes. The bladder is equipped with two separate organs. One organ allows additional gas from the blood to seep into the swim bladder as it is needed. The other organ removes excess gas from the bladder and returns it to the blood. These organs help a fish maintain buoyancy as its depth changes.

For fish that stay more or less at a certain level, the pressure on their bodies is always about the same. Some fish, however, migrate upward or downward in the water. They may, for example, remain on the bottom during the day but swim upward at night to feed. They have to be able to compensate for the change in pressure on their bodies.

When a fish migrates upward, it expels some gas from the swim bladder. When it returns to a deeper level, it takes more gas into the bladder. This is necessary to overcome the effect of pressure on its swim bladder at a greater depth. The ability to swim at different depths allows fish to search for food at any depth.

WHAT DO YOU THINK?

How does the swim bladder help fish to survive? Divers do not have a swim bladder. How are they able to overcome the buoyant force on their body at different depths?

SCIENCE AND SOCIETY

DEEP-SEA SUBMERSIBLES

A plane carrying four hydrogen bombs collides with another plane off the coast of Spain. Three bombs are recovered shortly after the crash, but one bomb sinks offshore to the bottom of the Mediterranean Sea. Does this sound like the plot of a late-night movie? The hero of the story is not your usual Hollywood type. This hero, named Alvin, is a deep-sea submersible that helped operators locate the bomb so it could be brought to the surface. The time was 1966, and the story was not a movie plot at all, but a scary, real-life situation!

Submersibles are lightweight, self-propelled vehicles that travel underwater with a crew of three to five persons. They are not attached by cable to a ship at the surface. Almost all submersibles have a spherical hull made of steel, titanium, or acrylic material to withstand the pressure at the depths of the ocean. Even if a submersible descends to a depth of 4000 meters, the air inside of the cabin is at the same pressure as it is at the surface.

Alvin is lowered into the water, carrying a weight that will help it descend to the bottom. This saves the pilot from turning on the vertical thrusters, which could be used to maneuver the vessel downward. The thrusters run on batteries, and batteries must be conserved for horizontal travel when the vessel is in deep waters near the ocean floor.

To make small changes in buoyancy while underwater, some submersibles have spheres filled with air and oil. The oil can be pumped

into flexible bags on the outside of the vessel. The bags make the vessel as buoyant as the pilot wants, depending on how much oil is pumped into the bags. The more oil in the bags, the greater upward push the vessel receives from the water displaced. When a submersible is ready to ascend, however, using the oil bags is not enough to get it to the top. The pilot must also drop the weight that helped it descend. Then the submersible becomes positively bouyant and rises to the surface.

A submersible may have an echo sounder (sonar) that keeps the pilot informed about the vessel's distance from both the surface of the ocean and the ocean floor. Sonar also guides the submersible away from large objects in its path.

Small submersibles touch the lives of people who have never even seen the ocean. These vehicles allow scientists to observe and photograph at greater depths and for longer periods of time than any deep-sea diver could. The crew can manipulate mechanical

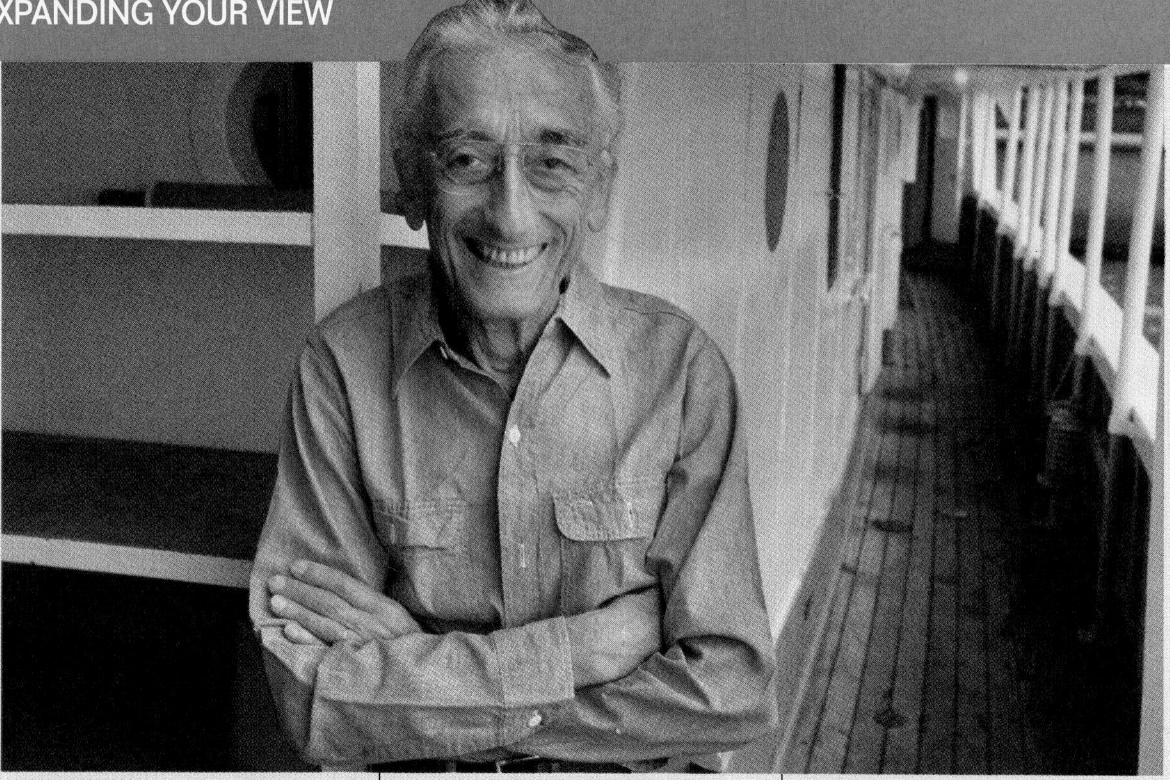

arms to collect marine specimens or break off pieces of rock. People now know more about ocean habitats because scientists traveling in submersibles have visited these places.

In 1977, the crew aboard Alvin descended to the ocean floor at the Galapagos Rift in the Pacific Ocean. They wanted to study the hot springs believed to exist there. Imagine their surprise when they found a complex community of living things, living at two kilometers beneath the surface, where not even the faintest light could reach! They had come across a whole new food web on the ocean floor—one that did not depend on plants that convert energy from the sun into chemical energy! Because of a submersible, we now know that some food chains in the ocean have bacteria, not plants, as their base. These bacteria change hydrogen sulfide, present in the hot springs, into proteins and other nutrients that animals feed on. Submersibles are also helpful after an offshore oil well blows out. The firsthand information troubleshooters gather while traveling in submersibles helps them determine the best way to stop the flow of oil.

Jacques Cousteau, who designed the first submersible, used these vehicles to study deep-sea marine life. Cousteau's studies made people aware that pollution is harming the wildlife in the oceans.

WHAT DO YOU THINK?

Some people like to discuss how submersibles will affect people's lives in the future. They say that at an underwater resort it will be possible to go to a lock-out compartment and hire a submersible that will carry you around to see the underwater sights far from your hotel.

How might such widespread use of submersibles affect wildlife in deep-sea habitats? In what way might people enjoy this experience without harming fragile habitats?

History CONNECTION

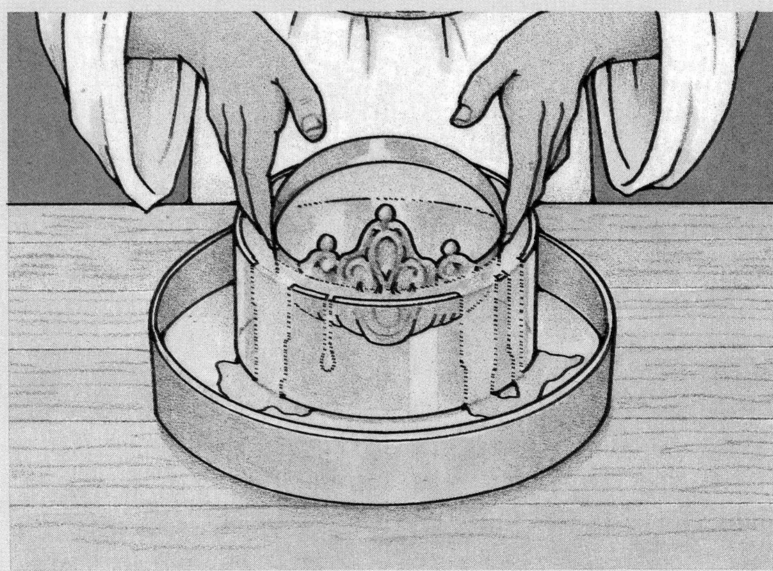

A ROYAL SOLUTION

Have you ever tried to figure out a difficult puzzle? If so, you know how it holds your attention until you think of a solution. That's what happened to Archimedes, the Greek mathematician you read about in connection with buoyancy. Legend has it that King Hiero II of Sicily ordered a gold crown to be made. When the crown was delivered, the king suspected that the gold had been mixed with silver. Archimedes was given the task of finding out whether the crown was made of pure gold.

Archimedes was puzzled about how he could do this. He could weigh the crown and then find a gold piece that weighed the same as the crown. If both the gold piece and the crown had the same volume, he could be certain that the crown was pure gold. If the crown had a larger volume than the gold piece, he could be sure that silver had been mixed with the gold. He based his strategy on the fact that, for equal volumes, silver weighs less than gold. But, there was a problem. Even though Archimedes was a mathematician, he had no idea how to find the volume of the crown. How could he measure such an irregular object?

Then one day, as he sank into his bathtub filled with water, Archimedes noticed that water spilled over the top of the tub. He realized that his body had displaced some of the water in the tub. He reasoned that the volume of the water that spilled over was equal to the space that his body took up in the water.

Archimedes submerged the king's crown in water and collected the water the crown displaced. He measured the volume of the displaced water because he knew it equaled the volume of the crown. Archimedes had the solution to his problem, and he proved to the king that the crown was made of a mixture of gold and silver. He concluded that the man who had made the crown had, indeed, tried to cheat the king.

YOU TRY IT!

Find and compare the volume of five objects of irregular shape by measuring the volume of water each displaces when submerged.

TECHNOLOGY CONNECTION

TRANSDUCERS IN YOUR LIFE

You may not have heard of the word *transducer* before, but you've certainly used gadgets that contain them. A transducer is a device that converts one form of signal into another form. When you speak into a telephone, a transducer converts one kind of information—sound, or variations in air pressure—into another kind of information—electrical signals. The electrical signals are carried over wires to another place, where they are then converted back to sound.

A transducer can convert motion to electrical signals, or vice versa. The fuel gauge in an automobile, like the one in the picture, is an example. The transducer is mounted on the fuel tank. A float moves up and down as the amount of fuel changes. The motion of the float is converted to an electrical signal that is transmitted by a wire to the gauge on the dashboard.

Many of the instruments used in laboratories have transducers. In this chapter, you have measured force, pressure, and acceleration. Some instruments can convert a measurement of a mechanical quantity such as force to an equivalent electrical signal. This happens when you weigh something on an electronic scale.

When machine parts are being cast in metal, it is important that the mold be held together by a large enough force. If the force is less than needed, the part that is cast will be defective. A force transducer is needed to indicate on a gauge how much force is being exerted.

Your blood pressure can be measured using a blood-pressure transducer. Because of the pumping action of the heart, blood pressure pulsates. The transducer keeps track of these pulsations and converts them into an accurate and fast record of the blood pressure.

Another kind of pressure transducer is on board an airplane. It lets the pilot know the air pressure, and hence, the altitude at which the plane is flying.

A transducer that measures acceleration is used in designing safe containers for the shipment of fragile objects. A table to which a delicate instrument is attached is raised or lowered abruptly to determine the amount of acceleration the instrument can tolerate before it malfunctions.

YOU TRY IT!

Keep in mind that transducers work by changing signals from one form to another. How is an electric switch a simple form of transducer? In what ways, other than those mentioned, might transducers be used?

Chapter 1

Reviewing Main Ideas

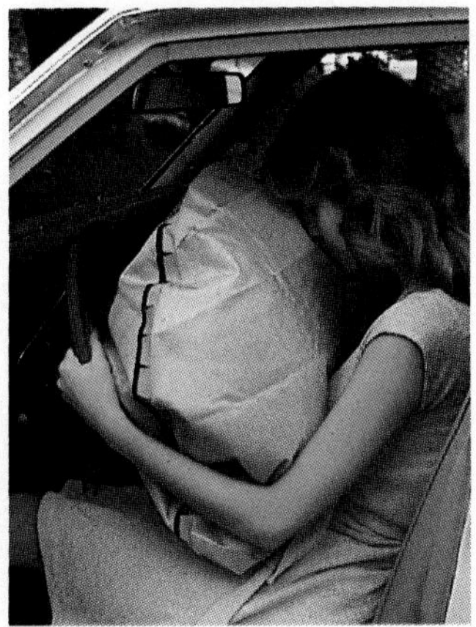

1. Objects in motion tend to continue moving in a straight line and at constant speed unless acted on by an unbalanced force. Objects at rest tend to remain at rest. This tendency is called inertia (Newton's First Law of Motion). When objects interact, the mass times the acceleration is equal to the force of the interaction (Newton's Second Law of Motion).

2. Forces always occur in pairs. When one object exerts a force on a second object, the second exerts an equal and opposite force on the first (Newton's Third Law of Motion).

3. Fluids exert an upward force on all immersed objects. Called the buoyant force, it's equal to the weight of the fluid displaced by an object.

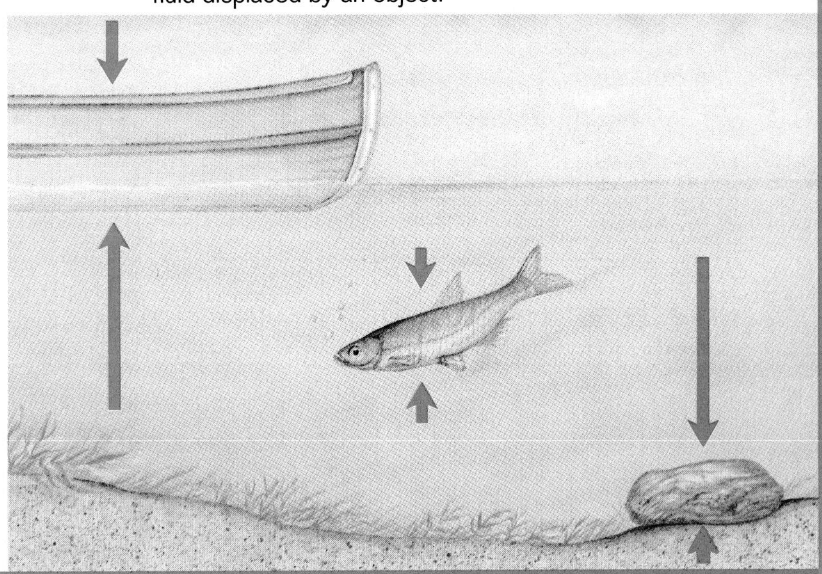

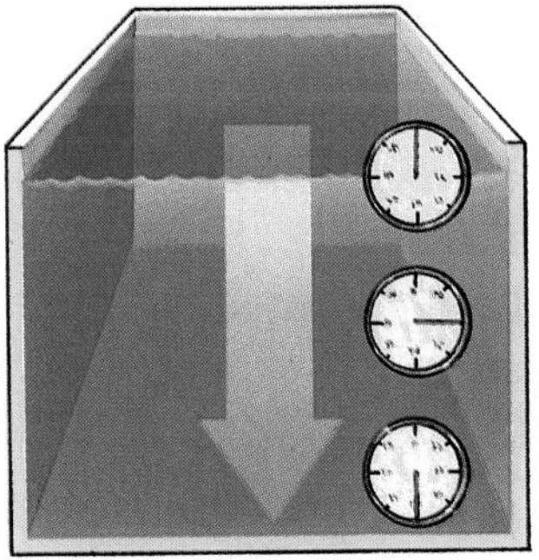

4. Pressure is equal to force divided by the surface area over which it acts. When measuring fluid pressure, the deeper the column of fluid, the greater the pressure.

Chapter Review

USING KEY SCIENCE TERMS

action force	inertial balance
balanced force	newton
buoyant force	pressure
force	reaction force
inertia	weight

Using the list above, replace the underlined words with the correct key science term.

1. The tendency to remain at rest or in motion produces the feeling of being pushed forward when a car stops.
2. The measure of the pull of gravity on an object increases as the mass increases.
3. When an object displaces its weight of water, it is acted upon by a(n) upward push equal to that weight.
4. A balance that determines mass by measuring an object's resistance to motion could be used to measure an object's mass on the moon.
5. An object will continue at rest or at constant velocity when acted upon by forces that are equal.
6. When two objects interact, the push or pull of one object is always balanced by a(n) equal but opposite push or pull of the other object.
7. A person walking on a tightrope exerts a greater force per unit area than that same person walking on a flat surface.

UNDERSTANDING IDEAS

Choose the best answer to complete each sentence.

1. Newton's First Law of Motion could also be called ____.
   a. Archimedes' Principle
   b. the law of buoyancy
   c. the law of inertia
   d. Pascal's Law
2. When an object's mass doubles, its inertia ____
   a. is half as much
   b. stays the same
   c. doubles
   d. is four times as much

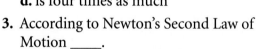

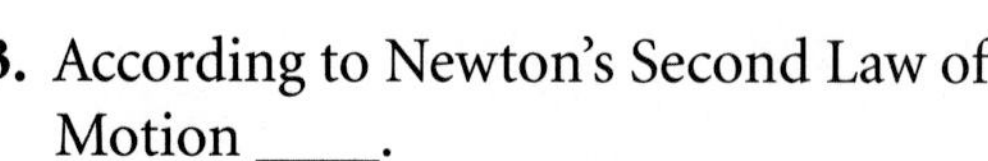

3. According to Newton's Second Law of Motion ____.
   a. force = mass × acceleration
   b. force = mass / acceleration
   c. force = pressure / mass
   d. force = pressure × mass
4. The law or principle that says that the buoyant force on an object is equal to the weight of the fluid it displaces is ____.
   a. Newton's First Law of Motion
   b. Archimedes' Principle
   c. Newton's Third Law of Motion
   d. Pascal's Law
5. If object A is accelerated twice as much as object B by the same force, the mass of object A is ____.
   a. four times the mass of object B
   b. one-fourth the mass of object B
   c. two times the mass of object B
   d. one-half the mass of object B

6. Container A is a cylinder 1 m in diameter and container B is a cylinder 2 m in diameter. Both are filled to the same height with water. The pressure at the bottom of container A will be in what ratio to that at the bottom of container B?
   a. 1:1 **c.** 2:3
   b. 1:2 **d.** 2:1
7. Pressure equals ____.
   a. mass × acceleration
   b. force × area
   c. force / area
   d. mass / area

CRITICAL THINKING

Use your understanding of the concepts developed in the chapter to answer each of the following questions.

1. How can an object be moving if there is no unbalanced force acting on it?
2. How can an object's weight change even though it contains the same mass?
3. The photographs show pictures of two similar oil tankers taken at two different times. What can you tell about the oil tankers from the pictures? Explain your reasoning.

PROBLEM SOLVING

Read the following problem and discuss your answer in a brief paragraph.

"Newton was wrong and I can prove it!" declared Denton McQuarrel. He took two magnets—one big one and one little one, and he pushed their north poles together. "According to Newton," he said, "each magnet experiences equal force. Watch what happens." He held one of the magnets in place on the table as he let go. "All I had to do was hold one magnet in place, and Newton's law doesn't work any more. The magnet I held in place didn't move at all." What's wrong with McQuarrel's argument?

CONNECTING IDEAS

Discuss each of the following in a brief paragraph.

1. Describe the two pairs of forces that are acting when you pick up your books. Why do the books move in an upward direction?

2. People who carry a lot of their weight as fat have an easier time floating than those who are more muscular. What can you conclude about the density of fat compared to muscle?

3. A CLOSER LOOK If a planet were to orbit the sun at a constant speed, would there be a centripetal force acting on it? Explain.

4. HISTORY CONNECTION Describe how you would show that an irregularly shaped piece of metal was pure silver.

5. LIFE SCIENCE CONNECTION Air and water are both fluids. Compare the way a fish uses a swim bladder with the way the pilot of a hot air balloon controls his or her craft.

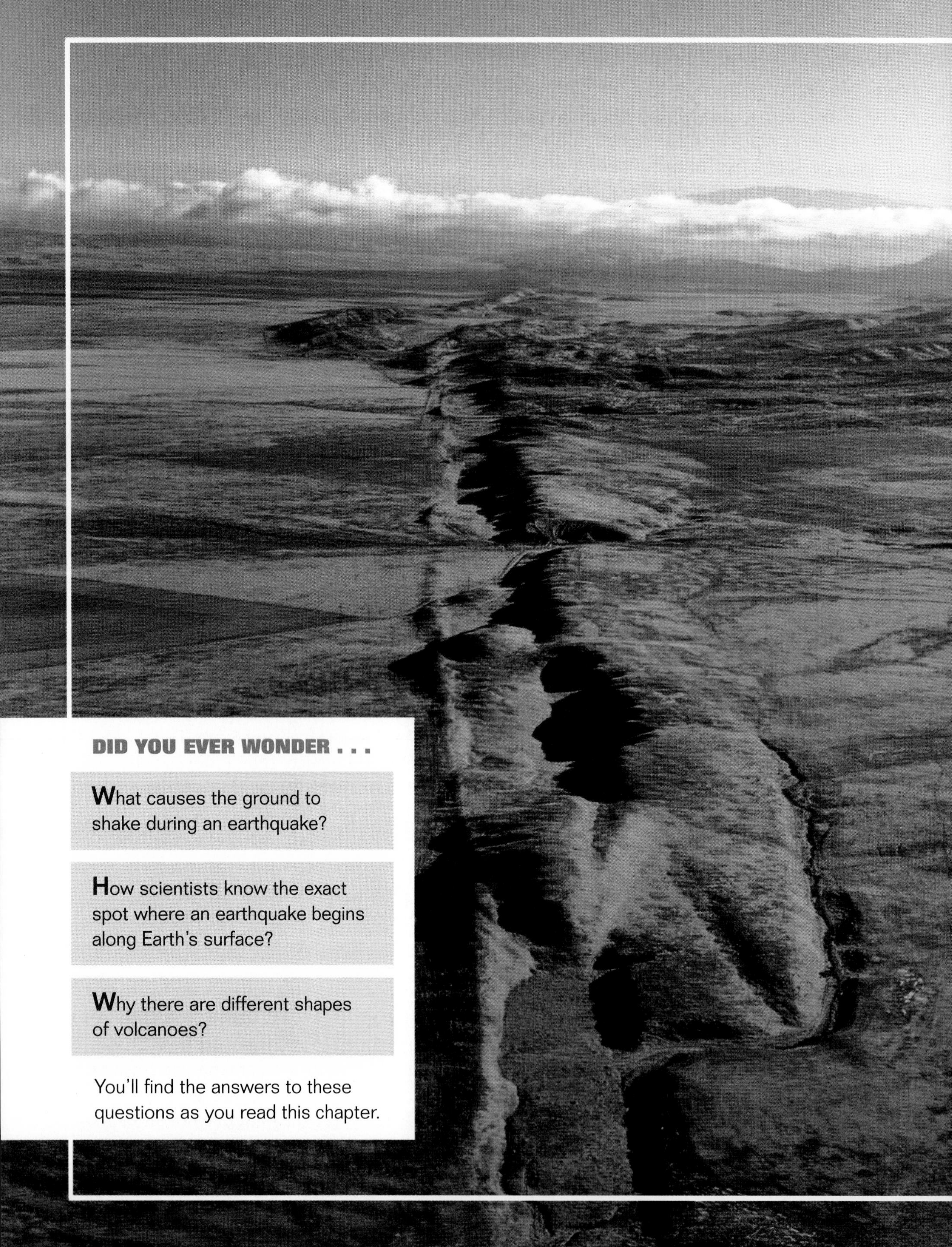

DID YOU EVER WONDER . . .

What causes the ground to shake during an earthquake?

How scientists know the exact spot where an earthquake begins along Earth's surface?

Why there are different shapes of volcanoes?

You'll find the answers to these questions as you read this chapter.

Chapter 2

Forces Inside Earth

You've probably heard about the San Andreas fault, pictured here. The fault has changed California's landscape greatly. Over time, tremendous forces inside Earth exert so much pressure on the rocks along the San Andreas fault that they break and move.

Sometimes this movement is gradual. Rocks on both sides of the fault may slowly move past each other as these forces are exerted on them. But if the rocks aren't free to move, stress builds up. When the rocks finally break free, the movement may be sudden and violent—an earthquake! You can feel the earthquake if you are not too far away from the moving rocks and if the vibrations they produce are strong enough.

Earthquakes are just one example of how forces inside Earth can affect our lives. This chapter will help you understand what these forces can do.

EXPLORE!

How do forces inside Earth affect rock layers?

Place three rectangular layers of different-colored clay on top of one another. Now place your hands on opposite ends of the clay. Slowly push your hands together, compressing the clay. What happens? Draw a picture to show what happened to the clay.

Now place three layers of clay on top of one another as before. With your hands on the opposite ends of the clay, gradually pull the clay apart. What happens? Draw a picture to show what you observed.

2-1 Movements That Cause Earthquakes

OBJECTIVES

In this section, you will

- explain how earthquakes result from the buildup of pressure inside Earth;
- describe the forces inside Earth that result in faults;
- compare and contrast normal, reverse, and strike-slip faults.

KEY SCIENCE TERMS

fault
normal fault
reverse fault
strike-slip fault

PRESSURE IN ROCK LAYERS

Have you ever felt an earthquake? Feeling the ground move and seeing things fall off shelves can be scary. A great deal of pressure inside Earth is released as a result of an earthquake. This pressure built up as a result of force on the rocks underground. You learned in Chapter 1 that pressure is force acting on an area. In the following activity, you'll apply pressure to different objects by bending and stretching them. You'll see what happens when this pressure is released.

FIND OUT!

How do different objects react when they are bent or stretched?

Examine a new large paper clip. Then use the paper clip to hold two sheets of notebook paper together. Remove the paper clip. Has it changed? Repeat this procedure with 5, 20, and 50 sheets of paper. Did the clip change its shape at any point?

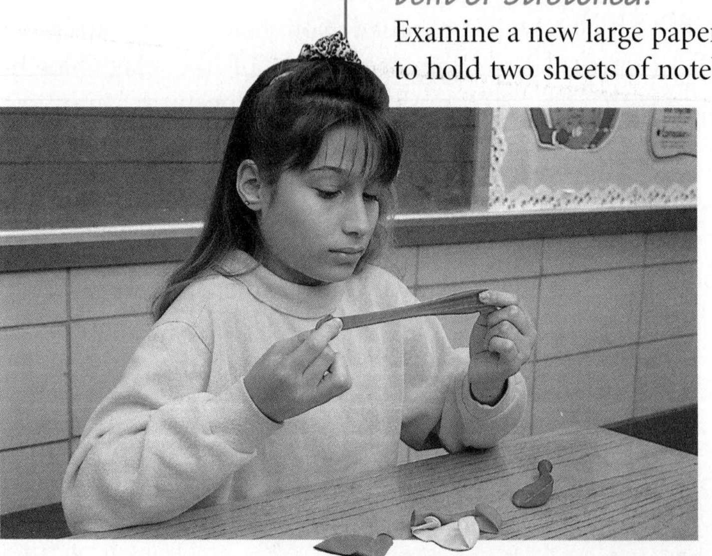

Now measure the length of a new balloon. Stretch the balloon so that it's about $1\frac{1}{2}$ times its original length. For example, if the balloon is 10 cm long, stretch it until it's 15 cm long. Stop stretching and measure it. Did it return to its original length? Now stretch the balloon so that it's twice its original length. After releasing the balloon, measure it again. Did it return to its original length? Now stretch the balloon farther, being careful not to break it, so that after releasing it, it won't return to its original length. Measure the length again. How did the length change?

Hold a pencil with both hands. Without breaking the pencil, can you make it flex by pushing up on it with your thumbs? Did it return to its original shape when you released it?

Conclude and Apply

1. What happened to the paper clip and the balloon when they were bent or stretched too far?
2. What caused these objects to react this way?
3. What would happen if the pencil were bent too far?

As you learned in the Find Out activity, objects will stretch and bend only so much. Bending and stretching are ways to apply pressure to objects. There is a limit to how much pressure a paper clip, a pencil, a balloon, or some other object can withstand and still return to its original shape. This limit is called the elastic limit. Once the elastic limit is passed, a substance will remain bent or stretched out of shape, or it will break.

Layers of rock behave in much the same way when pressure inside Earth bends or stretches them too far. Just as with the paper clip, balloon, and pencil, forces applied to rocks can cause them to fold or stretch without permanent change, but only up to a point. The rocks will remain folded or break once their elastic limit is passed. Rocks that have been folded look like those shown in Figure 2-1. Rocks that break produce the vibrations that are called earthquakes. What tremendous forces must be present inside Earth!

FIGURE 2-1. Folded rock layers are common in some mountainous areas.

SKILLBUILDER

SEQUENCING
Arrange these events that lead up to an earthquake in correct order. If you need help, refer to the **Skill Handbook** on page 678.

rocks undergo pressure
earthquake
elastic limit exceeded
rocks bend and stretch
rocks break and move

FAULTS

When rocks break under pressure, they may move. A fracture within Earth where rock movement occurs is called a **fault**. At the beginning of this chapter, you read about the San Andreas fault. The rocks on one side of this fault move in a different direction from the rocks on the other side of the fault.

Rock layers may experience several different types of forces. In the Explore activity at the beginning of this chapter, you experimented with two of these forces—tension and compression. You used the force of tension to pull the clay apart, and you used the force of compression to push the ends of the clay together. But rocks also may experience a third type of force—shearing. Let's look at these three types of forces inside Earth and the kind of fault that each produces.

Tension and Normal Faults

Remember what happened when you pulled on clay in the opening Explore activity? Think of the clay as a layer of rock that is being subjected to the force of tension. Tension is generated by pulling on a material from opposite directions. Tension can pull rocks apart and create what is called a normal fault. You can see a model of a normal fault in Figure 2-2. Along a **normal fault**, rocks above the fault surface move downward in relation to the rocks below the fault surface.

FIGURE 2-2. The model of a normal fault shows the relative movement of rocks on both sides of the fault line. The Sierra Nevada, a mountain range in California, consists of a series of fault blocks.

Have you heard of the Sierra Nevadas? These California mountains are pictured in Figure 2-2. Millions of years ago, the layers of rocks in this area of the United States began to be pulled apart. As a result, tension broke the rock layers, causing normal faults. As large sections of rock slid downward along these faults, the landscape was transformed into a series of low areas lying beside high mountain peaks.

Compression and Reverse Faults

Remember what happened when you pushed the ends of clay together in the opening Explore activity? This pushing together is compression. The force of compression caused the clay to fold.

The same thing happens to the hard rock layers of Earth when sections of rock push against each other. If the rocks are compressed beyond their elastic limits, they break. Once they break, the rocks continue to move along the fault surface, and a reverse fault is created. You can see a model of a reverse fault in Figure 2-3. At a **reverse fault**, the rocks above the fault surface are forced up and over the rocks that are below the fault surface.

An outstanding example of this rock movement lies along the boundary between India and Asia—the location of the Himalaya Mountains shown in Figure 2-3. The series of reverse faults that make up the Himalayas began forming millions of years ago when India, which

FIGURE 2-3. The relative movement of rocks in a reverse fault results from applied pressure. The Himalaya Mountains of India contain many reverse faults.

FIGURE 2-4. There is very little vertical movement along a strike-slip fault such as the San Andreas fault shown here.

was then a separate landmass, began colliding with the continent of Asia. The colliding is still going on today, and the compression forces continue to push the Himalayas higher and higher.

Shearing and Strike-slip Faults

You've read about normal faults and reverse faults. Now look at the illustration in Figure 2-4. It shows a strike-slip fault. At a **strike-slip fault**, rocks on both sides of the fault surface move past one another without much upward or downward movement. Shearing forces that push on rocks from different, but not opposite directions, cause this kind of movement. In the following Explore activity, you will make a model of a strike-slip fault.

EXPLORE!

How do rocks at a strike-slip fault move past each other?

Place two pieces of 2 × 4 wood side by side on a desk or table. Push the two blocks past each other in different directions so that a side of one block rubs against a side of the other. Now glue sandpaper to one side of each block and push the sandpapered edges past each other. Describe the differences between pushing the smooth surfaces of the blocks past each other and pushing the rough surfaces of the blocks past each other.

Suppose the blocks in the Explore activity were really the rocks on both sides of the San Andreas fault. Do you think the rocks would slide past each other at a constant rate? What would happen if the irregular surfaces of the rocks snagged, but shearing forces inside Earth continued to push them? Pressure would build up, and eventually the elastic limits of the rocks would be reached. Then the rocks along the fault surface would break and move suddenly, and an earthquake may result.

Most earthquakes are the result of faulting in Earth's rocks. Earthquakes occur as a result of all three types of faults—normal, reverse, or strike-slip. In the next section, you will find out how scientists locate earthquakes.

Check Your Understanding

1. Explain how earthquakes can result from the buildup of pressure inside Earth.
2. What happens when compression forces are exerted on rock layers? Tension forces? Shearing forces?
3. How do strike-slip faults differ from reverse and normal faults?
4. **APPLY:** Suppose you were following a young stream through an area where many faults were located. The stream took a sudden sharp turn to the left, flowed for a short distance, and then took a sudden sharp turn to the right. You continued to follow it along its relatively straight path beyond that. How could fault activity be responsible for the stream's sharp turns? What type of fault would most likely be responsible? You may wish to draw diagrams to explain your answers.

2-2 Learning About Earthquakes

OBJECTIVES

In this section, you will

- compare and contrast primary, secondary, and surface waves;
- explain how an earthquake's epicenter is located by using seismic wave information.

KEY SCIENCE TERMS

seismic waves
focus
epicenter

SEISMIC WAVES

Have you ever played with a coiled-spring toy? If so, you probably know how it behaves going down stairs. You may also have used a coiled spring to study how waves travel through matter. Such a coil can help you get an idea of how vibrations travel as waves through Earth after an earthquake has occurred at a fault. Do the following activity to help you understand more about earthquake waves.

EXPLORE!

How can a coiled spring be used to demonstrate two types of earthquake waves?

Stretch a coiled spring between another person and yourself. Squeeze one end of the spring and then release the squeezed portion. What happens?

Now move one end of the spring up and down quickly. How does the wire in the spring move?

When you let go of the squeezed spring, you created a compression wave. Matter that is squeezed and stretched has a compression wave traveling through it.

When you moved the spring up and down, you created a transverse wave. As a transverse wave moves through matter, the matter moves up and down at right angles to the direction that the wave is moving.

Earthquakes generate waves that are similar to the waves you made with the coiled spring. Such waves are called **seismic waves.** The point in Earth's interior where seismic waves originate is the **focus** of the earthquake. The focus can be between 5 and 700 kilometers below the surface. Seismic waves travel outward in all directions from the focus. Scientists use an instrument called a seismograph to detect the waves. Seismographs can detect seismic waves that originated as far away as the other side of the globe. In this Find Out activity, you will graph two seismic waves to compare how fast they travel.

DID YOU KNOW?

About a million earthquakes occur on Earth every year. Most are so minor that only very sensitive seismographs detect them. However, on average, 20 earthquakes that are strong enough to be felt by people occur each day in California.

FIND OUT!

Which is faster—a compression wave or a transverse wave?

The table shows when either a compression wave or a transverse wave arrived at a seismograph station at some distance from an earthquake. Assume that the earthquake occurred at precisely 4:00 P.M. The times given in the table are hour, minutes, and seconds. So a time of 4:06:30 indicates that the wave arrived at a station 6 minutes and 30 seconds after the earthquake occurred.

Make a graph comparing the distance from the earthquake focus and the time it took for the waves to travel there. How many lines will you plot on your graph?

Distance from focus (km)	TIME OF ARRIVAL (HR:MIN:SEC)	
	Compression wave	Transverse wave
250	4:01:00	—
500	—	4:03:00
1000	4:02:30	—
1750	4:04:00	—
2000	—	4:07:30
3000	—	4:10:15
4500	4:08:00	—
5000	—	4:15:00
6000	4:09:30	—
6500	—	4:18:00
7250	4:11:00	—
8000	4:11:45	—
8250	—	4:21:15
9000	4:12:30	—
9500	—	4:22:45

Conclude and Apply

1. Based on your graph, which is faster—a compression wave or a transverse wave?
2. Do the waves remain the same distance apart as they travel?
3. Do they grow closer together or farther apart over time?
4. How could you use your completed graph to fill in the missing arrival times on the table?
5. Based on your observations, why do you think seismologists have named compression waves primary waves and transverse waves secondary waves?

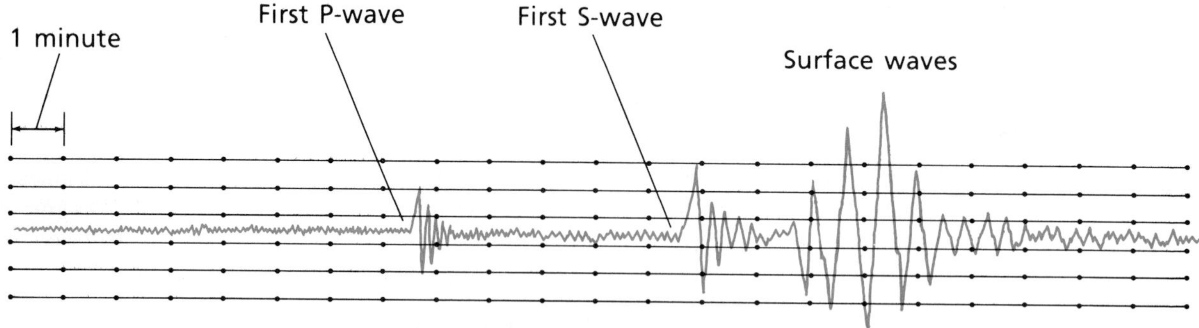

FIGURE 2-5. Seismic waves produced by an earthquake are recorded on a seismogram.

Primary and secondary waves can be detected at Earth's surface by a seismograph. But remember that primary and secondary waves originate from an earthquake's focus and generally travel through Earth's interior. The point on Earth's surface directly above the focus is the **epicenter.** When seismic waves from the focus of an earthquake reach the epicenter, they generate surface waves. These surface waves travel outward from the epicenter the way ripples on a pond's surface travel outward when you throw a stone in. Surface waves travel more slowly than secondary and primary waves. You can see the directions of motion of all three kinds of seismic waves in Figure 2-6.

FIGURE 2-6. Primary and secondary waves travel underground, outward from the focus. Surface waves travel along the surface, outward from the epicenter.

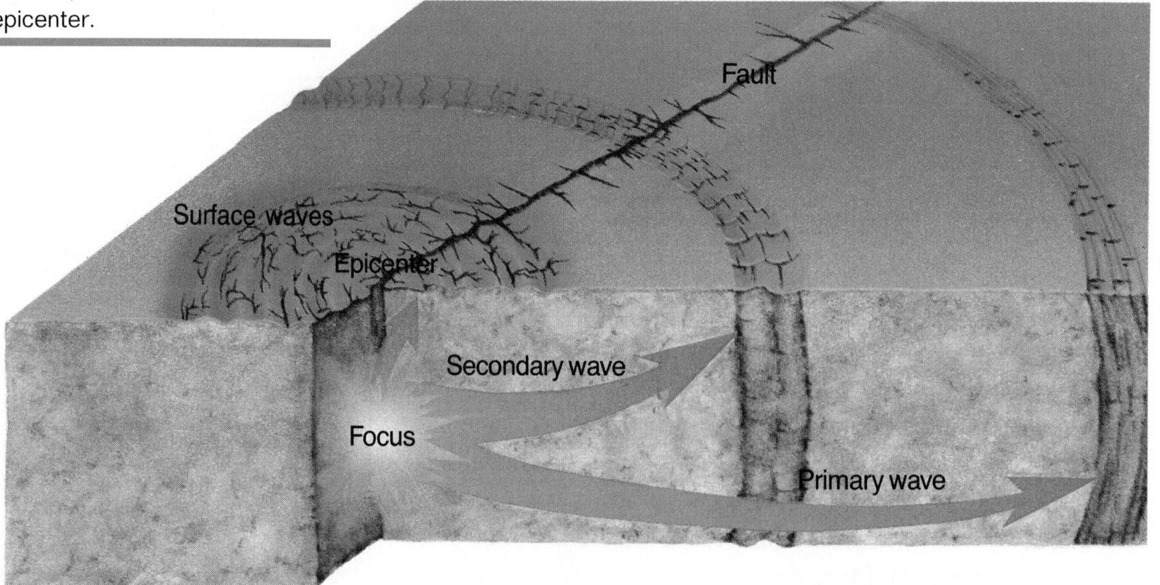

LOCATING AN EPICENTER

As you discovered, seismic waves don't all travel through Earth at the same speed. How can this information be used to determine the location of an epicenter?

Look at Figure 2-7. This graph shows how far primary and secondary waves travel in a certain amount of time. It can be used to determine how far away an epicenter is from a seismograph station. Say, for example, that you are a scientist, and your seismograph detects a primary seismic wave at precisely 3:00 P.M. Then, at 3:06 and 30 seconds, the secondary wave arrives. You look at the time travel graph and find where the two curved lines are separated by 6 minutes and 30 seconds. Where on the graph does this occur? It occurs at the 5000-kilometer mark. What can you conclude from your analysis of the seismograph data and the graph? How far away is your seismograph station from the earthquake epicenter?

Based on your calculations, you can say that an earthquake occurred about 5000 kilometers from your seismograph station. But can you say in which direction? Was it to the north, east, south, or west? So far, you don't have enough information to answer that question. Can you think of a way to determine the exact location of the epicenter? What if more seismograph stations were used? Do the following Investigate activity to see if you are right.

FIGURE 2-7. Primary and secondary waves travel at different speeds. What is the difference in their arrival times at a spot 1500 km away? 2250 km? 4000 km? 7000 km?

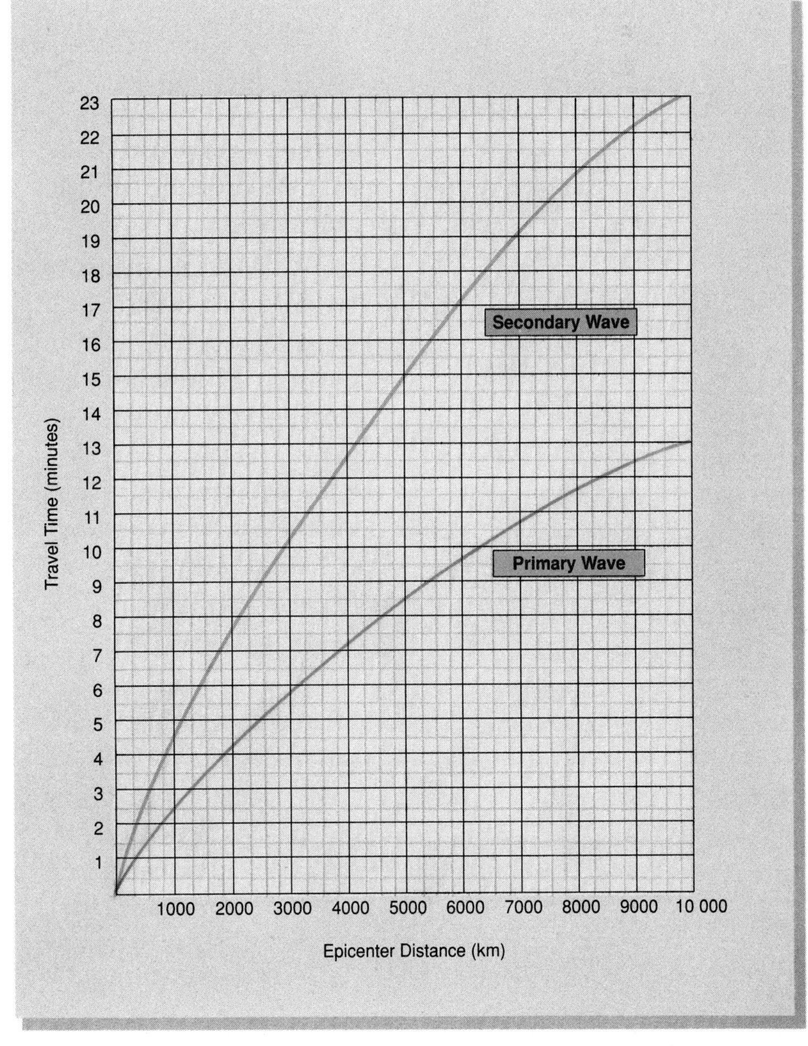

INVESTIGATE!

2-1 LOCATING AN EPICENTER

You know that primary waves travel faster than secondary waves and therefore arrive at a seismograph station first. In the following activity, you will locate epicenters using the arrival times of these waves.

PROBLEM

How are epicenters located?

MATERIALS

paper
Figure 2-7
string
metric ruler
globe
water-soluble marker

PROCEDURE

1. Copy the data table below.
2. Determine the difference in arrival times between the primary and secondary waves at each station for each earthquake in the table above.

LOCATION OF SEISMOGRAPH	WAVE	WAVE ARRIVAL TIMES EARTHQUAKE A	EARTHQUAKE B
(1) New York	P S	2:24:05 PM 2:28:55 PM	1:19:00 PM 1:24:40 PM
(2) Seattle	P S	2:24:40 PM 2:30:00 PM	1:14:37 PM 1:16:52 PM
(3) Rio de Janeiro	P S	2:29:00 PM 2:38:05 PM	——— ———
(4) Paris	P S	2:30:15 PM 2:40:29 PM	1:24:05 PM 1:34:05 PM
(5) Tokyo	P S	——— ———	1:23:30 PM 1:33:05 PM

3. **Interpret the graph** in Figure 2-7 to determine the distance in kilometers of each seismograph from the epicenter of each earthquake. Record these data. An example has been done for you.
4. Using the string, **measure** the circumference of the globe by using the ruler to measure the length of string needed to circle the globe. Determine a scale of centimeters of string to kilometers on the surface of Earth (Earth's circumference = 40,000 km).
5. For each earthquake, A and B, place one end of the string at each seismic station location. Use the marker to draw a circle with a radius equal to the distance to the epicenter of the earthquake.

DATA AND OBSERVATIONS

Earthquake	CALCULATED DISTANCE FROM EPICENTER (KM) FOR EACH SEISMOGRAPH LOCATION (1)	(2)	(3)	(4)	(5)
A					
B				9750	

ANALYZE

1. The epicenter is the point at which all the circles intersect. What is the location of the epicenter of each earthquake?
2. **Compare** the distance of a seismograph from the earthquake with the difference in arrival times of the waves. How are these data related?

CONCLUDE AND APPLY

3. What is the minimum number of seismograph stations needed to locate an epicenter accurately?
4. **Going Further:** What information would only two seismograph stations give you in regard to the location of an epicenter? Make a drawing to show what information two stations would provide about the epicenter.

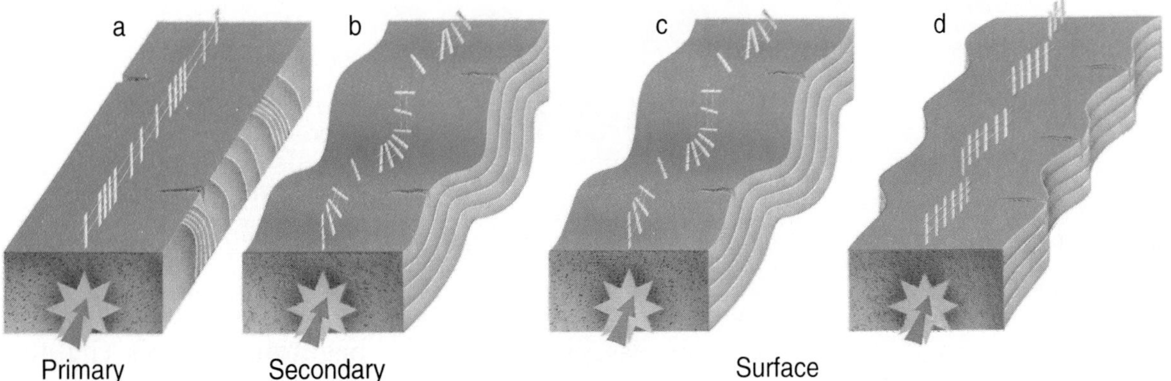

FIGURE 2-8. Primary waves cause the ground to compress and stretch (a). Secondary waves cause the ground to move perpendicular to the direction of the wave (b). Surface waves produce two kinds of movement: vertical movement (c), similar to a secondary wave, along with sideways movement (d).

THE MOST DESTRUCTIVE WAVES

Primary and secondary waves are used to determine an earthquake's epicenter at the surface. However, these waves usually aren't the cause of major damage at the surface. When you think of an earthquake, you probably think of shaking ground and crumbling buildings. It is the surface waves that are responsible for most of this destruction.

Figure 2-8 shows the effects of earthquake waves on the ground. You can see why surface waves cause the most damage. The waves cause one part of a building to move up, while another part moves down. At the same time, the building is moving from side to side. In some areas of the United States and elsewhere in the world, many buildings are constructed so that they are better able to withstand vibrations caused by these surface waves.

Thus far, you have learned how forces inside Earth can send seismic waves through Earth and along its surface, and how seismologists use these waves to locate the epicenter of an earthquake. In the next section, you will find out how forces inside Earth can cause volcanoes to erupt.

Check Your Understanding

1. Compare the origins of the three kinds of seismic waves. Which originate at an earthquake's focus? Which originate at an earthquake's epicenter?
2. What do you think would happen to a row of evenly spaced utility poles as a surface wave travels along the row?
3. **APPLY:** If all seismic waves traveled at the same speed, could the epicenter be located? Explain.

2-3 Volcanic Eruptions

OBJECTIVES

In this section, you will

- explain what causes volcanoes to erupt;
- explain the difference between a quiet and an explosive eruption.

KEY SCIENCE TERMS

vent

WHAT CAUSES VOLCANOES TO ERUPT?

You've learned that earthquakes strike along faults like the San Andreas pictured at the beginning of this chapter. Volcanoes and earthquakes often occur in the same regions. In fact, the movement of magma and volcanic eruptions may trigger some earthquakes.

Although heat and pressure within Earth can cause rocks to melt and form magma, some rocks deep inside Earth are already melted. Others are so hot that only a small rise in temperature or slight change in pressure is needed to melt them and form magma.

What causes magma to rise toward the surface and erupt to form a volcano? You can see how this process takes place if you do the following activity.

EXPLORE!

How does magma move?

Turn a closed bottle of cold syrup upside down. Watch the air bubbles be forced up by the syrup and rise to the surface. What causes the bubbles to rise? Which is less dense—the syrup or the air?

The air bubbles in the syrup rise to the surface for the same reason that magma rises toward Earth's surface. If you remember Archimedes' Principle from Chapter 1, you'll recall that less-dense materials are pushed up by denser materials so that the less-dense materials rise. Magma is less dense than the rocks around it, so it is

FIGURE 2-9. Before the 1980 eruption, magma inside the Mount Saint Helens volcano had solidified, blocking the vent. But magma from below continued to rise, causing pressure to build up in the volcano. In May of 1980, the volcano released its pressure in an explosive eruption.

pushed up by the denser material and slowly rises toward the surface.

When the magma reaches Earth's surface, it flows out through openings called **vents**. At this point, the magma is called lava. Any time volcanic material reaches Earth's surface, we call the event an eruption. As the lava flows out, it cools and becomes solid, forming layers of volcanic rock around each vent. Often the volcanic material piles up around the vent to form a cone. How does the type of magma determine the type of eruption that occurs and the kind of volcanic cone that forms?

TYPES OF ERUPTIONS

Some volcanic eruptions are explosive, like the noisy, violent eruptions of Mount Saint Helens in the state of Washington and Mount Pinatubo in the Philippines. But other eruptions are quiet and nonexplosive, like the fluid lava flows of Kilauea in Hawaii. Compare Figure 2-9 and Figure 2-10. What factors cause the differences in these eruptions?

FIGURE 2-10. Mount Kilauea erupts unexplosively, and the lava runs down the sides of the volcano.

Two factors determine whether an eruption will be

DID YOU KNOW?

Five separate volcanoes rising from the ocean floor (Kohala, Mauna Kea, Mauna Loa, Hualalai, and Kilauea) have merged to form the island of Hawaii.

explosive or quiet. One is the amount of water vapor and other gases that are trapped in the magma. The second is the composition of the magma.

You can get an idea of how the amount of gas in the magma can cause explosive eruptions by recalling what happens when you open a bottle of soft drink. Carbon dioxide gas is dissolved in the soft drink. The gas is held in solution because it is under pressure within the closed bottle. The pressure is suddenly released when you open the bottle, and the gas comes out of solution. In a similar way, gases such as water vapor and carbon dioxide are trapped in magma. Surrounding rock puts pressure on magma when it is deep underground. Under this great pressure, the magma can contain many dissolved gases. But when the magma is pushed toward the surface, the pressure on it decreases. Magma under low pressure cannot hold as much gas, just as soft drink in a newly opened bottle cannot hold as much gas. As a result, the gas begins to escape as the magma nears Earth's surface.

What would happen if the gases were trapped within the magma and not allowed to escape? This is, in fact, what happens when magma is very thick and dense. Recall your last Explore activity and how slowly the air bubbles moved up through the thick syrup. How would they have moved if the syrup were thinner? Similarly, gases move out of magma more easily if the magma is thin and fluid than if it is thick and not very fluid.

Gases trapped in thick magma build up pressure until they finally escape in an explosive blast, similar to the way carbon dioxide sometimes blasts out of a soda-water solution very quickly, carrying the liquid with it. Generally, gases in thin, fluid magma escape in a quiet, nonexplosive way because they are released gradually before a significant amount of pressure builds up.

FIGURE 2-11. Reduced pressure inside an opened container of soft drink causes the carbon dioxide gas to come out of solution.

What determines whether magma is thick or fluid? Magma contains many different elements and compounds. Some magma contains a lot of the compound silica. Magma that is silica-rich tends to be very thick. In fact, it can be so thick that it clogs a volcanic vent. With the vent closed, the magma below becomes trapped, and the gases within it are under even greater pressure than before. Eruptions from silica-rich magma are usually very

FIGURE 2-12. Quiet eruptions with thin, fluid lava form shield volcanoes.

explosive. The magma itself often explodes into dust, ash, and rock fragments. When low-silica magma reaches the surface, it flows from a vent in a much less explosive manner, like a red river.

FORMS OF VOLCANOES

You may remember learning that volcanoes develop in three basic forms: shield, cinder cone, and composite cone. The form of volcano that is produced is determined by the nature of its eruption. If the eruption is quiet, a gently sloping shield volcano is produced, like the one shown in Figure 2-12. If the eruption is explosive, a steep-sloped cinder cone is produced, like the one shown in Figure 2-13. Sometimes, however, eruptions alternate between quiet and explosive. Then a composite cone vol-

FIGURE 2-13. Explosive eruptions of thick magma blown into dust, ash, and rocks form cinder cones.

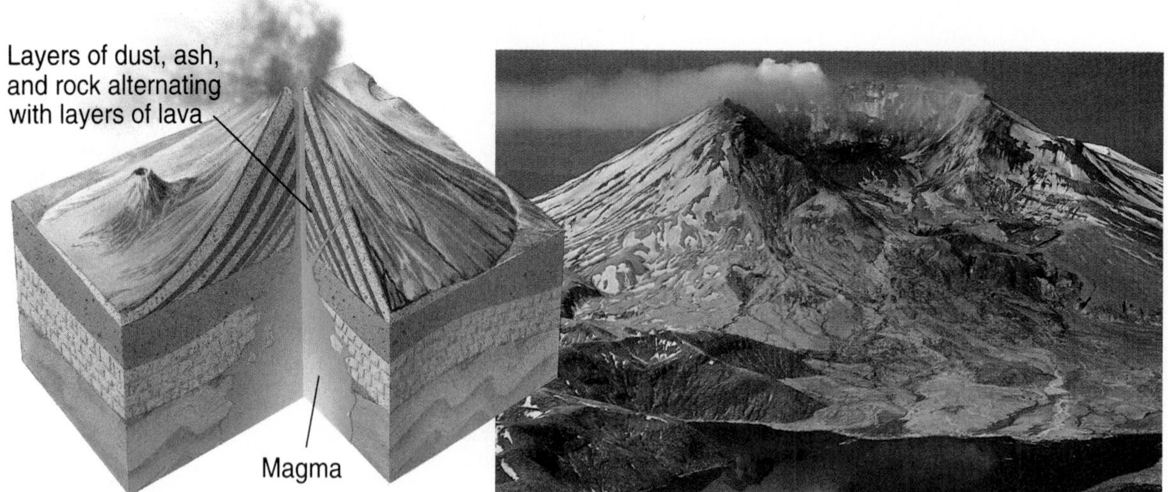

FIGURE 2-14. Alternating quiet and explosive eruptions form composite cones.

cano is produced, like the one shown in Figure 2-14. You can compare some major eruptions of shield, cinder cone, and composite cone volcanoes in Table 2-1. Then use the table to continue your study of volcanoes in Investigate 2-2.

TABLE 2-1. Selected Eruptions

Volcano and Location	Type of Volcano	Eruptive Force	Magma Content		Ability of Magma to Flow
			Silica	Water Vapor	
Etna, Sicily	composite	moderate	high	low	medium
Tamboro, Indonesia	cinder	high	high	high	low
Krakatoa, Indonesia	cinder	high	high	high	low
Pélee, Martinique	cinder	high	high	high	low
Vesuvius, Italy	composite	moderate	high	low	medium
Lassen, California	composite	moderate	high	low	low
Mauna Loa, Hawaii	shield	low	low	low	high
Parícutin, Mexico	cinder	moderate	high	low	medium
Surtsey, Iceland	shield	moderate	low	low	high
Kelut, Indonesia	cinder	high	high	high	low
Arenal, Costa Rica	cinder	high	high	low	low
Helgafell, Iceland	shield	moderate	low	high	medium
Saint Helens, WA	composite	high	high	high	medium
Laki, Iceland	shield	moderate	low	low	medium
Kilauea Iki, Hawaii	shield	low	low	low	high

I N V E S T I G A T E !

2-2 ANALYZING VOLCANOES

You have learned that certain properties of magma are related to the type of eruption and the form of the volcano that will develop. In the following activity, you will **make and interpret a table** that relates the properties of magma to the form of volcano that develops.

PROBLEM

How are the properties of magma related to volcano type?

MATERIALS

Table 2-1
paper
pencil

DATA AND OBSERVATIONS

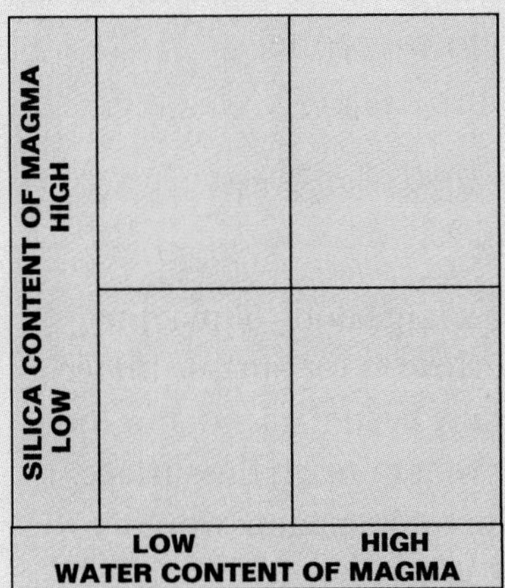

PROCEDURE

1. Copy the data table.
2. Using the information from Table 2-1, indicate the magma content data for each of the volcanoes listed by writing the name of the basic type of volcano in the appropriate spot on the data table. The data for the eruption of Mount Etna has already been listed for you.
3. When you have listed all 15 volcanoes, **compare and contrast** the volcanic types on the diagram to answer the questions.

ANALYZE

1. Which eruptions are the most numerous—eruptions with high silica content or low silica content?
2. Which eruptions are the most numerous—eruptions with high water-vapor content or low water-vapor content?
3. Which eruption contained low silica and a high water-vapor content? Why might this type of eruption be rarer than the others?

CONCLUDE AND APPLY

4. **Determine the effect** the silica content and water-vapor content of magma seem to have on its ability to flow.
5. Which of the two variables (silica or water-vapor content) would you **infer** has the greater effect on the eruptive force of a particular volcano?
6. **Going Further:** What relationship appears to exist between the silica and water-vapor content of the magma and the type of volcano that is produced?

SKILLBUILDER

CLASSIFYING
Mount Fuji is a volcano in Japan. Its steep sides are made of layers of silica-rich lava and ash. Classify Mount Fuji as a shield, composite cone, or cinder cone volcano. If you need help, refer to the **Skill Handbook** on page 678.

FIGURE 2-15. The often-erupting Kilauea volcano in Hawaii destroyed homes with this lava flow.

VOLCANOES AND HUMANS

Like earthquakes, volcanic eruptions can be tragic events in the lives of humans. On November 13, 1985, Nevado del Ruiz erupted explosively, killing over 22,000 people in Armero, Colombia. On May 26, 1991, Mount Unzen in Japan erupted explosively after having been dormant for about 200 years. Soon after, the eruptions of Mount Pinatubo in the Philippines killed over 300 people during the month of June 1991.

In this chapter, you have explored the causes of earthquakes and the different types of volcanoes. You will probably read and hear in the news about earthquakes and volcanoes throughout your life. These naturally occurring events are interesting to everyone!

Check Your Understanding

1. What characteristic of magma causes it to rise to Earth's surface and eventually erupt?
2. Some volcanic eruptions are quiet, yet others are explosive. What causes this difference?
3. **APPLY:** Suppose a large body of magma moves upward close to the surface under what has generally been flat land, but the magma has no vent to reach the surface. How do you think the magma would affect the land? Why?

EXPANDING YOUR VIEW

CONTENTS

A Closer Look
Different Kinds of Force 55

Physics Connection
Passing the Limit 56

Science and Society
Preparing Buildings for Earthquakes 57

Technology Connection
Seismic Waves and the Search for Oil 59

Geography Connection
The Many Climates of the Himalayas 60

A CLOSER LOOK

DIFFERENT KINDS OF FORCE

Try this simple experiment to demonstrate the effects of tension, compression, and shear forces on different materials.

Materials (for each group of three or four students)

- two gum erasers
- two pieces of nylon fabric
- two pieces of construction paper

Procedure

1. Each student selects one of the three materials (erasers, fabric, and paper) to demonstrate compression, shear, and tension in action.
2. The student who has selected the gum eraser places it on a tabletop.
3. While the other group members observe and take notes, the student pushes the ends of the gum eraser toward its center to demonstrate compression.
4. To demonstrate shear, the student holds one eraser on the tabletop while rubbing the second eraser along its top surface.
5. To show the effects of tension, the student grasps the eraser by each end and pulls slowly while others observe and write about what they see. (Leave plenty of elbowroom; you don't want to hit your classmates if the eraser breaks.)
6. The student again demonstrates tension by pulling suddenly on each end of the remaining eraser.
7. Observers compare and summarize their notes. Describe what happened. Tell why.
8. Repeat Steps 1 through 7 for the nylon and paper.
9. Report the observations to the class.

WHAT DO YOU THINK?

How do the observations of other groups differ from your own? Did any of the summaries mention sounds or amount of force exerted? Did anyone note how long forces were applied to the materials? Do you think different kinds of rock might react to the same forces in different ways?

Physics Connection

PASSING THE LIMIT

Elasticity exists in both natural objects and those made by humans. Trees, for example, may look straight and stiff, but what happens when strong winds blow through a forest? Do all the trees snap and fall over? Of course not. Trees change their shape, bending when the force of the wind strikes them, then returning to normal when the wind stops.

But what happens during a hurricane? If the wind is too strong, the force becomes too great for tree trunks and branches, and they pass their elastic limit and break. The same thing happens when you break a stick. If you bend it gently and then let go, it springs back to its original shape. But if you exert too much pressure, you force the stick beyond its elastic limit, and it snaps in two.

What actually happens when objects pass their elastic limit? As you bend a stick, the energy you exert is stored inside. When you let go, that energy is released as the stick springs back into its original shape. Push too hard, and the energy is released as the stick breaks. This release of energy is called elastic rebound.

If you blow into a balloon, you exert a force that pushes the walls of the balloon out. If you continue to inflate the balloon, it will explode when the balloon wall becomes too weak to store the energy. It will reach its elastic limit and release the stored energy, resulting in a pop. The release of energy in the pop is the elastic rebound.

If a car tire were inflated beyond its elastic limit, the resulting explosion would be much greater than that of a balloon bursting. That's because the tire could store much more energy before reaching its elastic limit.

When different forces are exerted on rocks inside Earth, the rocks, like the balloon, can store energy—up to a point. But eventually the forces are too great, and the rocks reach their elastic limit. They break. And what happens next? An earthquake! As the rocks pass their elastic limit, energy is released, causing seismic waves to travel out in all directions from the focus of the earthquake.

WHAT DO YOU THINK?

Can you think of examples of objects around you in which energy is stored? Look for objects in your classroom that have not yet reached their elastic limit.

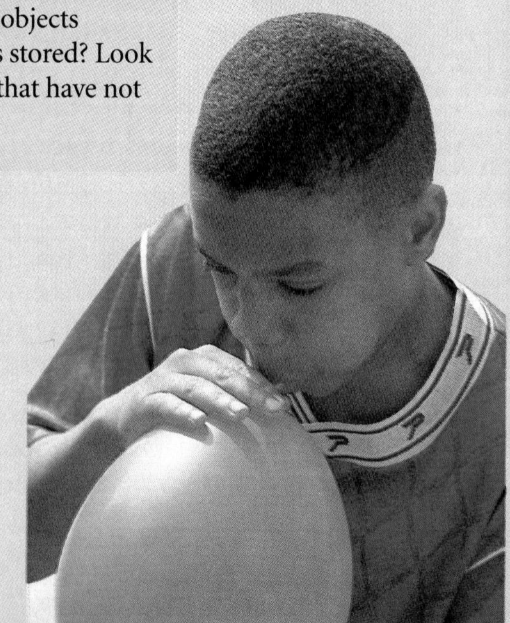

SCIENCE AND SOCIETY

PREPARING BUILDINGS FOR EARTHQUAKES

Experts usually have a pretty good idea where earthquakes are most likely to occur, but they don't know how to predict when the quakes will happen. If they could, buildings could be evacuated and lives saved.

While these experts are trying to better predict the *when* of earthquakes, others are building earthquake-resistant buildings or modifying older buildings to help them survive earthquakes.

For example, an earthquake safety commission in Japan is working closely with construction companies to determine what features help make a building earthquake safe. They have designed and built the small-scale structure you see in the first picture for use in earthquake trials. At each experimental step, the building is fitted with a certain design feature, then vibrated with the force of a powerful earthquake to test its effectiveness, as in the second picture.

A similar project has been undertaken by the National Center for Earthquake Engineering Research (NCEER) in Buffalo, New York, which was established to study techniques to prevent building damage and loss of life during earthquakes. NCEER has also worked with Japanese engineers to build an experimental earthquake-resistant building in Tokyo. The six-story building contains an active system for controlling a building's response to tremors. A computer system in the building tells giant pistons, which move up and down, to shift the level of different areas of the building to counterbalance earthquake waves. This means the computer system must always be prepared for tremors and that the pistons must be able to respond quickly.

This building is considered strong enough to withstand earthquakes common to Tokyo. Researchers study the effectiveness of the computerized active system during the small earthquakes that occur there every year.

A much more common approach to stabilizing buildings during earthquakes is through passive control systems. For example,

WHAT DO YOU THINK?

Does your city have earthquake codes for new buildings? Does it have special requirements for existing buildings? How long have such codes existed in your area?

a building sitting on a huge cushionlike foundation might ride out an earthquake relatively well. This is called a passive system because the cushion is always responding, not waiting like an active system.

"A lot of people feel that a dumb (passive) building that performs well is much preferable to a smart (active) building that may have something go wrong with it," says Professor James D. Jirsa, a structural engineer specializing in earthquake-resistant buildings.

Dr. Jirsa explains that passive and active systems are usually added to already existing buildings to prepare them for future earthquakes. New buildings can be built more earthquake resistant in the first place.

One of the biggest problems in constructing and modifying buildings for earthquake resistance is that each earthquake is different and experts can't always predict the earthquake's strength or its duration. So experts can't be absolutely certain how a building will respond to the next earthquake.

"Every earthquake is a new experience," says Dr. Jirsa. "We can learn from (previous earthquakes), but we never know quite enough to be confident that we've got every angle covered."

Engineers also have to decide whether to construct buildings that only protect people from injuries or that protect people and contents. Buildings designed to protect only people may move during an earthquake, but they won't collapse. The movement of the building, however, might cause the contents of the building to fall or break. Buildings that protect people and contents are more expensive but may be necessary when computers, medical equipment, and communications are involved.

And what about nuclear power plants? Dr. Jirsa says they are usually so durable that active and passive systems aren't necessarily required. Engineers worry more about what will happen to the contents of nuclear plants during an earthquake, he says.

In addition to efforts to prevent human injury and building damage through earthquake-resistant construction, engineers agree there is another extremely important way people can try to protect themselves—education.

"A very important part of this whole thing is education," says Dr. T. T. Soong of NCEER. "People should take precautions so that lives can be saved. One can have earthquake drills, very much like fire drills, so that people can be in safe places when the earthquake strikes."

TECHNOLOGY CONNECTION

SEISMIC WAVES AND THE SEARCH FOR OIL

As you learned in this chapter, earthquakes generate seismic waves, which help determine exactly where an earthquake took place.

With explosive devices, geologists can create their own seismic waves and use them in the difficult search for oil beneath the ocean floor. Oil formed millions of years ago from the remains of marine plants and animals deep inside Earth. Today, much of that oil is contained in reservoir rocks — porous rocks with many tiny holes that trap oil. The reservoir rocks themselves are concealed by faults, folds, and other specific rock formations.

Geologists look beneath the ocean for the right combination of reservoir rocks and protective layers, which point to the possibility of trapped oil. To do this, they cause explosions, which send seismic waves into the rocks beneath the sea. The waves travel down, then bounce back off the different underground rock layers.

Seismic waves travel at different speeds, depending on the kinds of rock through which they're passing. By measuring how long it takes the waves to return to the surface, geologists can map out a cross section of the rock layers.

YOU TRY IT!

Look up the words *seismology* and *geology* in the dictionary. Why do you think the search for oil in the rocks beneath the sea is being done by seismologists and geologists?

Using these maps, as well as their knowledge of the area and other drilling sites, seismologists can then estimate where oil might be found. As you may have guessed, no one can be sure they'll find oil until they actually drill into the rocks and collect samples.

Geography CONNECTION

THE MANY CLIMATES OF THE HIMALAYAS

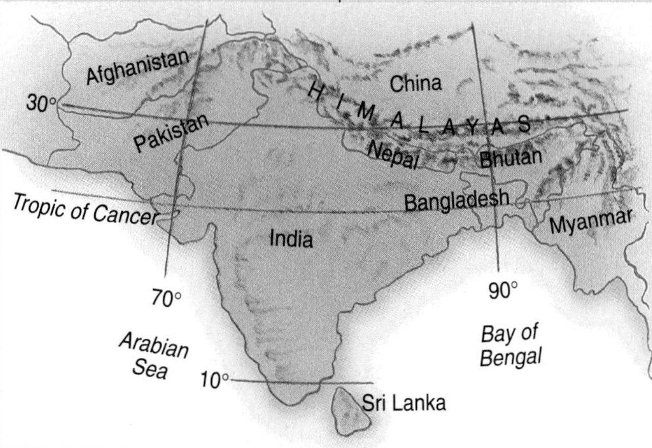

The Himalayas, the world's tallest mountain range, stretch for over 2400 kilometers in Asia. The mountains began forming millions of years ago, when India began colliding with Central Asia. Because these two landmasses continue to slowly crash into one another, the creation of the Himalayas is not yet completed!

Can you guess what kind of weather these mountains might have? Cold and snowy? Right! Warm and wet? Right! Hot and dry? Right again. The Himalayan climate varies greatly from place to place due to altitude and levels of rainfall.

Mt. Everest, the highest mountain in the world, reaches more than 8800 meters above sea level. From that height down to about 4900 meters, the bitterly cold Himalayas are not inhabited by people. The lower Himalayas, from near sea level up to about 2200 meters, have a moist, warm climate that supports dense forests and animal life. A variety of vegetation is able to grow up to about 4900 meters, where the vegetation then becomes scarce. Crops, such as tea and rice, are generally not grown above 3500 meters. Some people and some animals—such as leopards, yaks, and dogs—do, however, manage to live above the crop level.

The people of the Himalayas have adapted to their varied surroundings. Most are farmers, and therefore live below 3500 meters. In fact, they live mainly in fertile valleys, which are the best areas for farming. In areas that receive plenty of rainfall, people cultivate rice. Other regions produce fruit, vegetables, grain, and timber.

Himalayan animal life also varies depending on the altitude. High in the mountains you'll find bears, snow leopards, and eagles. Lower down there are wolves, wild pigs, and goats. On the lower slopes are many of the animals we associate with India, such as tigers, elephants, and rhinos.

YOU TRY IT!

Find a topographic map of the world, the United States, or your state. Locate major cities on the map and look up climatic information about them in an almanac. How does the map help you understand the average annual temperatures and rainfall in the cities you selected?

Chapter 2

Reviewing Main Ideas

1. Forces within Earth cause faults and earthquakes. These forces are tension forces, compression forces, and shearing forces. Each of these forces causes a different type of fault to occur.

2. Primary and secondary seismic waves travel beneath Earth's surface, outward from the focus of an earthquake. Surface waves travel along the surface of Earth, outward from the epicenter of an earthquake.

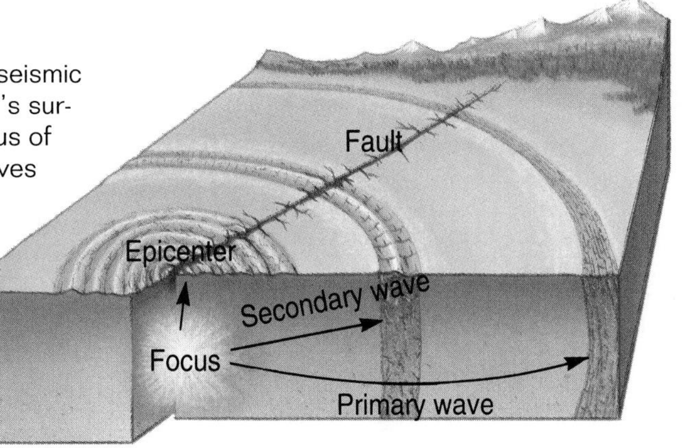

3. Quiet eruptions form shield volcanoes. Explosive eruptions form cinder cones. Alternating quiet and explosive eruptions form composite cones.

Chapter 2

Chapter Review

USING KEY SCIENCE TERMS

epicenter	reverse fault
fault	seismic waves
focus	strike-slip fault
normal fault	vents

Each phrase below describes a science term from the list. Write the term that matches the phrase describing it.

1. waves generated by an earthquake
2. origin of an earthquake inside Earth
3. break in the rock layers of Earth's crust along which movement occurs
4. break in rocks with movement due to tension, or pulling apart
5. place on Earth's surface above where an earthquake originated
6. break in rocks with movement due to compression, or pushing together
7. opening in Earth's surface through which lava flows
8. break in rocks with movement due to shearing forces, or moving past each other

UNDERSTANDING IDEAS

Choose the best answer to complete each sentence.

1. If a substance is compressed and then released before its elastic limit is reached, it will ____.
   a. be permanently stretched
   b. be permanently bent
   c. return to its original shape
   d. break
2. Gases that get trapped under high pressure eventually cause ____.
   a. quiet eruptions
   b. explosive eruptions
   c. very fluid lava
   d. very dense lava
3. Compression waves produced by an earthquake are ____ waves.
   a. primary **c.** surface
   b. secondary **d.** transverse
4. Magma rises toward the surface because it is ____ than the rocks around it.
   a. cooler **c.** less dense
   b. warmer **d.** more dense
5. The Sierra Nevada, a mountain range in California, was formed as a result of tension forces creating ____ faults.
   a. normal **c.** strike-slip
   b. reverse **d.** earthquake
6. The seismic waves that travel the fastest are called ____ waves.
   a. primary **c.** surface
   b. secondary **d.** transverse
7. Seismic waves can be used to determine an earthquake's ____.
   a. fault **c.** vent
   b. magma **d.** epicenter
8. When compression forces push layers of rock together, ____ faults are formed.
   a. normal **c.** strike-slip
   b. reverse **d.** earthquake

CRITICAL THINKING

Use your understanding of the concepts developed in the chapter to answer each of the following questions.

1. Suppose you went for a walk in the area of an active volcano. You discover piles of ash and many rocks lying about that you were told by a geologist were volcanic rocks. What could you infer about the form of the volcano and the kind of eruptions it undergoes?
2. The data table shows some travel times of two waves from an earthquake. Classify each time as belonging to the primary or the secondary wave. How do you know?

Distance From Earthquake (km)	Time (minutes)
1500	5.0
2000	2.5
5000	14.0
5500	7.0
8600	11.0
10,000	23.5

3. Some people have observed animals acting strangely before a major earthquake. Hypothesize about what the animals are detecting that people are not.
4. Do you think it's possible for tension forces and compression forces to be acting on the same rock layers? Explain how this might occur.

PROBLEM SOLVING

Read the following and discuss your answers in a brief paragraph.

Scientists are looking for an approach to predicting earthquakes that will be reliable. Both seismographs and satellites detect movement. Seismographs detect earthquake waves. Satellites emit radio signals that are picked up by radio receivers on Earth's surface. When a radio receiver moves by as little as a few centimeters, it can be detected.

1. Would seismographs be useful for predicting earthquakes? Why or why not?
2. Where could scientists place radio receivers to help detect rock movement that may lead to an earthquake?

CONNECTING IDEAS

Discuss each of the following in a brief paragraph.

1. In what ways do layers of rock behave when forces inside Earth bend or stretch them too far?

2. How do less-dense materials react when they are trapped within denser materials? How is this principle related to volcanic activity?

3. In what ways are earthquakes and volcanoes related?

4. **TECHNOLOGY CONNECTION** Different seismic waves travel at different speeds. What other factor affects the speed at which a wave travels? How do geologists use this information to locate oil?

5. **PHYSICS CONNECTION** What do rocks store and release as forces act upon them?

DID YOU EVER WONDER . . .

How blood keeps moving through your body?

Whether all animals have the same kind of heart and circulation?

Why some people have heart attacks while others don't?

You'll find the answers to these questions as you read this chapter.

Chapter 3

Circulation in Animals

Have you ever helped at school when the annual open house takes place? Maybe someone from the Parent's Association sent you around the cafeteria with a tray full of cheese and crackers and fruit drinks. As you moved through the crowd, you served people. You may have also developed a pattern where you picked up used plates and cups and cleared tables. Then you went back to the kitchen, where someone gave you another tray full of food to take out. In general, you could say that you circulated, or moved about in a path, from the kitchen to the people in the room, and back to the kitchen, doing whatever needed to be done.

In an animal's body, a circulatory system delivers needed materials to all parts of the body and also carries away the wastes that the body produces. The cells in your body have the same needs as the smaller life-forms. In this chapter, you will learn about different kinds of circulatory systems and how they operate.

EXPLORE!

How can you make a model of circulation?

Try the following activity. Place a spoonful of honey on a paper plate. Add a drop of food coloring on one edge of the blob of honey. Tilt the paper plate to make the honey flow in different directions. Observe what happens. What happens to the drop of food coloring as the honey flows in different directions?

3-1 Circulatory Systems

OBJECTIVES

In this section, you will

- explain the role of a circulatory system in animals;
- compare and contrast open and closed circulatory systems;
- describe the path of blood through the heart, lungs, and body;
- compare and contrast arteries, veins, and capillaries.

KEY SCIENCE TERMS

arteries
capillaries
veins

GETTING WHAT YOU NEED TO LIVE

In the living world, there are organisms of all different sizes and shapes. Amazingly enough, whether they are one cell in size or trillions of cells in size, whether they live in a puddle or an apartment building, living organisms all need similar things to stay alive.

Protists, such as the amoeba in Figure 3-1, are one-celled organisms that live in ponds. An amoeba needs nutrients and oxygen to stay alive just as you do. Nutrients are substances needed for the health and growth of the body. The little one-celled protist has only a thin barrier between the inside and outside of its body. In its daily life, nutrients and oxygen move in through this barrier easily. Once inside, they flow through the liquid that makes up most of the protist's body. As the protist uses up these substances, wastes move out through the thin wall of its body just as easily.

Now look at yourself. You and many other organisms are quite a bit larger than the one-celled protist. You are a many-celled organism, meaning that you are made of trillions of cells. Can the nutrients and oxygen you need just pass through your skin to cells deep within your body? No, your body is much more complex. You could swim all day in a pool filled with nutrients and not have your nutritional needs met.

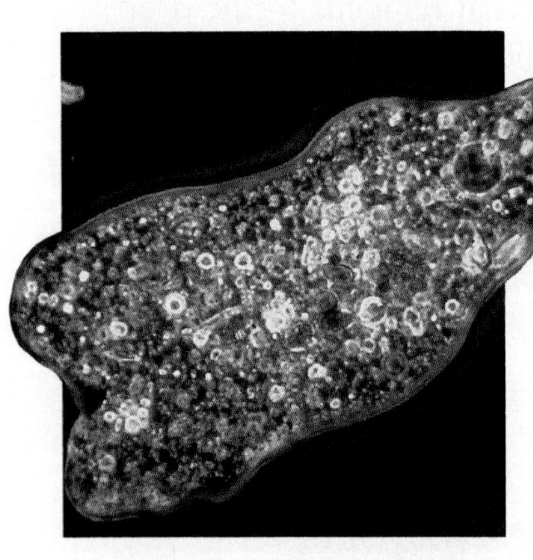

FIGURE 3-1. The one-celled amoeba can easily take in oxygen and nutrients and dispose of wastes.

So how do nutrients and oxygen reach all the body parts of a large organism? Remember in the chapter opening story how you carried trays of snacks through the crowd and picked up used plates and cups? You circulated, or moved around, bringing snacks to people and carrying away used items. Your body has a system that circulates materials for you. This system is called a circulatory system, and it has two jobs. First, it brings nutrients and oxygen to every cell in your body. Its second job is to carry away waste products produced by these cells.

AN OPEN AND CLOSED CASE

Your circulatory system is made up of parts you have heard about all your life, namely a heart and blood vessels. However, not all organisms' circulatory systems have these parts. Materials circulate through the body of the amoeba by a form of motion called streaming. As the liquid inside an amoeba streams about, nutrients and oxygen are mixed with it, much the way the food coloring became mixed with the honey in the Explore activity.

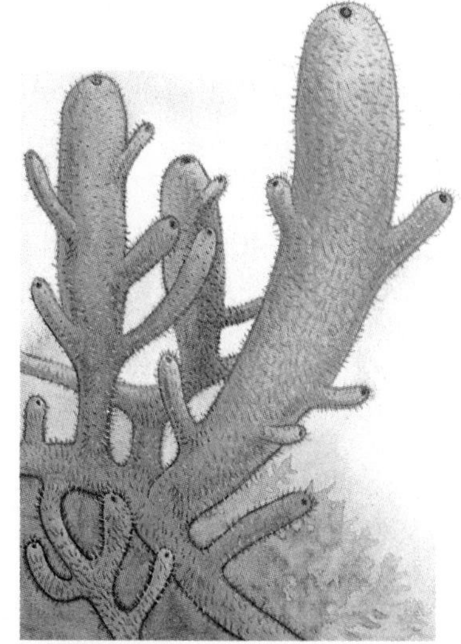

FIGURE 3-2. Water carries oxygen and nutrients to the sponge through its pores.

Once you begin to look at organisms that are made up of many cells, the picture changes. Sponges, like the one shown in Figure 3-2, are larger and more complex than amoebas, with openings or pores all over their bodies. Sponges don't have a circulatory system. Instead, water flows into the pores. Nutrients and oxygen in the water are taken directly into the cells that line the pores. Wastes are washed away as the water leaves the sponge's body through some larger openings.

The larger and more complex an animal is, the more complicated its circulatory system is. This may be because the bodies of complex animals are larger and there are more cells to be nourished. The circulatory systems of complex animals can be one of two types. Animals such as clams have what is called an open circulatory system. An open circulatory system may have a heart and a few simple tubes called blood vessels. Find the heart in the drawing of the clam's circulatory system shown in Figure 3-3. The heart acts like a pump and forces a liquid called blood through vessels. These vessels lead to open spaces, where blood delivers a bath of nutrients and oxygen that washes over the parts inside the body. Then the blood collects into larger blood vessels before it returns to the heart with the help of some contracting

FIGURE 3-3. The clam has an open circulatory system.

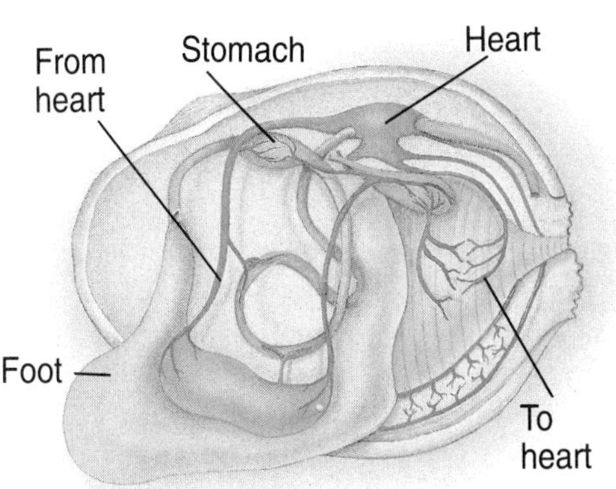

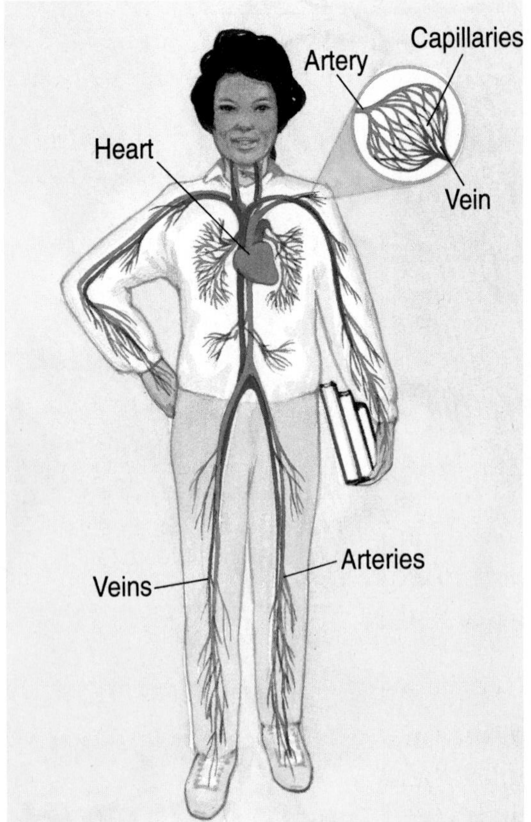

FIGURE 3-4. A closed circulatory system is found in fish, birds, and mammals, including humans.

muscles. Why isn't this a very efficient way to supply an organism with the nutrients and oxygen it needs?

In contrast to the clam, the circulatory system in other animals, including fish, birds, and mammals like yourself, is a closed system. As shown in Figure 3-4, in a closed circulatory system, blood moves throughout the body enclosed in a network of blood vessels, much like a plumbing system in a house. Just like the water in water pipes, blood flows through blood vessels under pressure. The power to push blood through blood vessels is supplied by the heart. Because blood flows in blood vessels under pressure, it can be delivered to cells in the body quickly and efficiently. Can you think of any reasons why animals such as fish, birds, and mammals need such an efficient system? In what way are the activities and lifestyles of these animals affected by the type of circulatory system they have?

YOUR HEART AND BLOOD VESSELS: GOING WITH THE FLOW

Just how important is your heart? Throughout your life, your heart contracts and relaxes continuously. Its job is to push blood through blood vessels to nourish the cells of the body.

FIND OUT!

What are the parts of the heart?

Look at a model of a heart. First, find the two upper chambers called atria. These chambers receive blood that flows back to the heart from the body and lungs. Look for the large blood vessels that bring blood to the atria. Next, locate the two lower chambers called ventricles. These chambers pump blood out of the heart. Look for the large blood vessels that carry this blood from the ventricles. Compare the thickness of the walls of the ventricles to the atria.

Conclude and Apply

What might the structure of each chamber tell you about its function?

As you observed on the model and as you can see in Figure 3-5, your heart has an upper chamber and a lower chamber on each side. Each upper chamber is called an atrium (AY tree uhm). In an office building, an atrium is a large open space that people enter before going off to individual offices. The job of each atrium is to receive blood. Each atrium connects with a lower chamber called a ventricle (VEN trih kul). Ventricles pump blood out of the heart.

In mammals such as yourself, the heart is a two-pump organ. One pump, the right side of the heart, receives oxygen-poor blood after it has moved through the body, and pumps it to the lungs so it can pick up oxygen needed by the body cells. The other pump, the left side, receives this now oxygen-rich blood and sends it out to the body cells.

FIGURE 3-5. The human heart has an upper chamber and a lower chamber on each side.

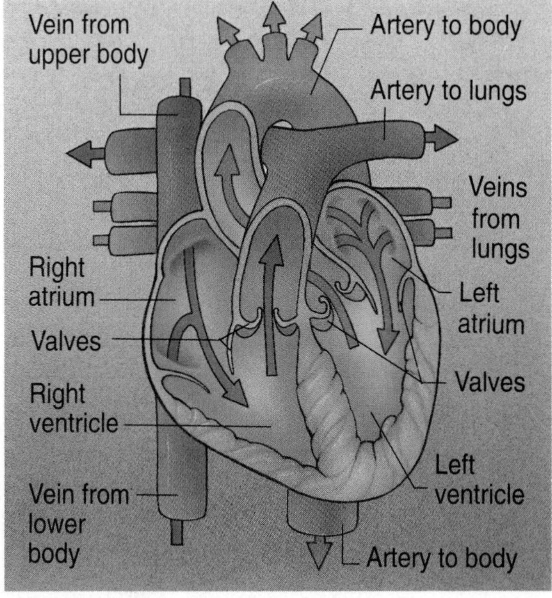

FIND OUT!

Can you hear your heart?

Feel the left side of your chest to find where your heartbeat is strongest. Use a stethoscope to listen to your heart. Listen for about half a minute. You should hear something like a "lub-dup" sound each time your heart beats. Do you hear this pattern in your heartbeat?

Conclude and Apply

Using Figure 3-5, determine what structures make these sounds.

Just as you always enter some buildings through one door and leave by another, blood always enters the heart through an atrium and leaves through a ventricle. There is a one-way flow of blood through the heart. One-way flow is helped by a series of structures called valves. When you listened to your heart in the Find Out, you could hear the sounds of your heart valves closing as blood flowed through and out of the heart.

Find the valves between the atria and ventricles in the model and in Figure 3-5. These valves work like one-way swinging doors, allowing blood to flow in one direction only—from an atrium into a ventricle. If the blood tries to flow back into an atrium, the valves are pushed shut by the pressure of the blood trying to flow back.

Blood also flows through a valve as it leaves each ventricle. These valves stop blood from flowing back into the ventricles as it leaves the heart.

When blood leaves the heart, it begins a journey through three types of blood vessels—first arteries, then capillaries, and finally veins. As shown in Figure 3-6, blood pumped by the left ventricle leaves the heart through a large blood vessel. This blood vessel is an artery known as the aorta. **Arteries** are blood vessels that carry blood away from the heart.

After leaving the left ventricle, the aorta branches into smaller and smaller arteries that carry blood to every part of the body. Eventually, these arteries become smaller and

SKILLBUILDER

SEQUENCING

Trace the sequence of how blood circulates throughout your body, beginning with the blood leaving the left ventricle. If you need help, refer to the **Skill Handbook** on page 678.

smaller as well, until they become microscopic, thin-walled vessels called **capillaries**. Nutrients and oxygen pass easily from your blood to your cells through the thin walls of capillaries. At the same time, your blood is busy picking up waste products such as carbon dioxide from these same cells.

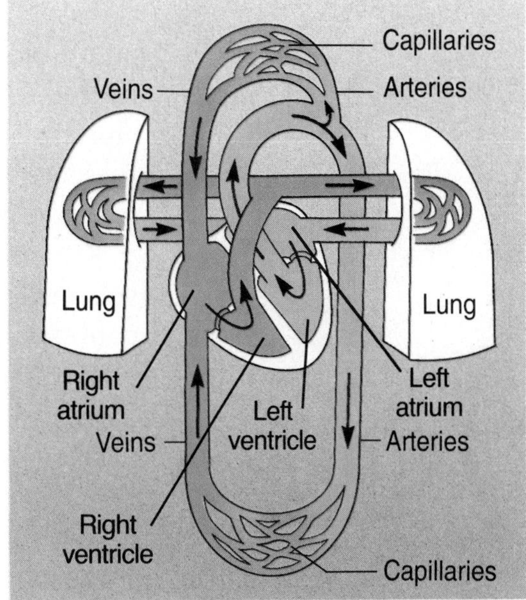

FIGURE 3-6. Blood flows through arteries, capillaries, and veins.

As nutrients and oxygen are delivered to the cells and waste products picked up, your blood has already begun its trip back to the heart. As you can see in Figure 3-6, blood leaving the tissues flows from the capillaries into larger vessels called veins. Blood is carried back to the heart in **veins**. Eventually, veins form larger and larger vessels until the largest veins send blood back into the right atrium of the heart.

Blood that reaches your right atrium contains a lot of carbon dioxide. Just as you clean clothes in a washing machine before you wear them again, your blood isn't sent on another trip through your body until the carbon dioxide is removed in your lungs. As carbon dioxide is removed, new oxygen is put back into your blood. How is this accomplished?

Blood rich with carbon dioxide moves from the right atrium to the right ventricle. From there it is pumped to your lungs, where exchange of carbon dioxide and oxygen occurs.

How do we know?

How blood circulates

In the early 1600s, Dr. William Harvey, shown in the figure, discovered how blood circulates through the body. In one experiment, he placed his finger against a visible vein in a man's arm. While doing this, he always observed that the part of the vein closest to the man's fingers bulged with blood. The part of the vein closest to the man's shoulder never bulged with blood. Through such experiments, Dr. Harvey determined that blood flows in one direction in veins—toward the heart.

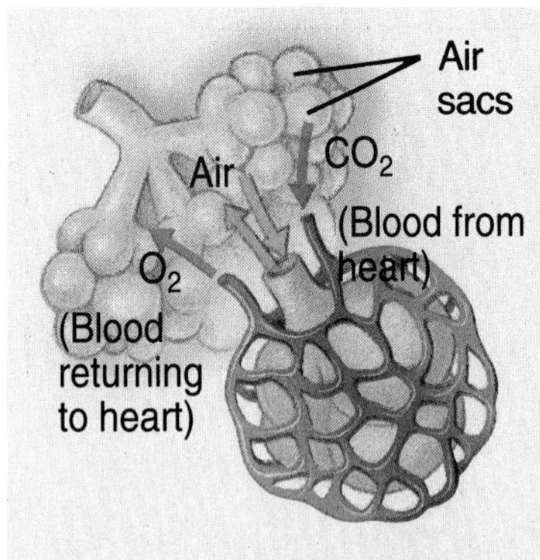

FIGURE 3-7. Your lungs are made up of several hundred million air sacs.

As shown in Figure 3-7, your lungs are made up of several hundred million extremely small air sacs that are arranged in grape-like clusters. Surrounding each of these clusters is a web of capillaries. As blood moves through these capillaries, carbon dioxide is exchanged for oxygen from the air you breathe in.

Replenished with oxygen, the blood returns through veins to the left atrium of the heart. This chamber then contracts and squeezes blood into the left ventricle. Your blood then begins another trip through your body.

In this section, you learned that a circulatory system brings nutrients and oxygen to the cells and removes and exchanges wastes such as carbon dioxide.

Many-celled animals have different methods for delivering oxygen and nutrients to their cells. Some animals have an open circulatory system. In an open circulatory system, a heart pumps blood through a simple network of blood vessels. Oxygen and nutrients are delivered to the cells of the animal as the blood drains from the blood vessels and flows over the parts of the animal.

More complex animals, such as fish, birds, and mammals, have closed circulatory systems. In this system, blood containing oxygen and nutrients is sent throughout the body enclosed in a continuous loop of blood vessels called arteries, capillaries, and veins. The heart supplies the power to push blood through these vessels.

In the next section, you will explore how the heart maintains the pressure necessary to push blood through the circulatory system. You will also learn how blood vessels are designed to handle this pressure.

Check Your Understanding

1. Diagram the pathway of blood through the four chambers of the heart.
2. How are the three types of blood vessels alike? How are they different?
3. Describe the similarities and differences between an open and a closed circulatory system.
4. Discuss the role of circulatory systems in animals.
5. **APPLY:** Describe how a closed circulatory system is more efficient at delivering oxygen and nutrients to cells than an open circulatory system.

3-2 A System Under Pressure

WITH EVERY BEAT OF YOUR HEART

Blood moving throughout your body is pumped by your heart in much the same way a bicycle pump pumps air into a tire. First, pressure is applied to air in the hose, then it is released. Place your hand over your heart. Can you feel your heart beating? With each beat, the muscles of your heart force blood through the blood vessels of your body.

OBJECTIVES

In this section, you will

- explain what causes pulse;
- explain how blood moves through your body under pressure;
- compare the structural adaptations of blood vessels;
- compare the circulatory systems of fish, birds, amphibians, and mammals.

KEY SCIENCE TERMS

pulse
blood pressure

EXPLORE!

How can you find out about the pumping activity of your heart?

Place your fingers just next to your Adam's apple on your neck, as the boy in the picture is doing. Push lightly and move your fingers around until you feel a beat. Count the number of beats you feel for 15 seconds and multiply that number by 4. Next, jog in place for about two minutes and repeat the same procedure.

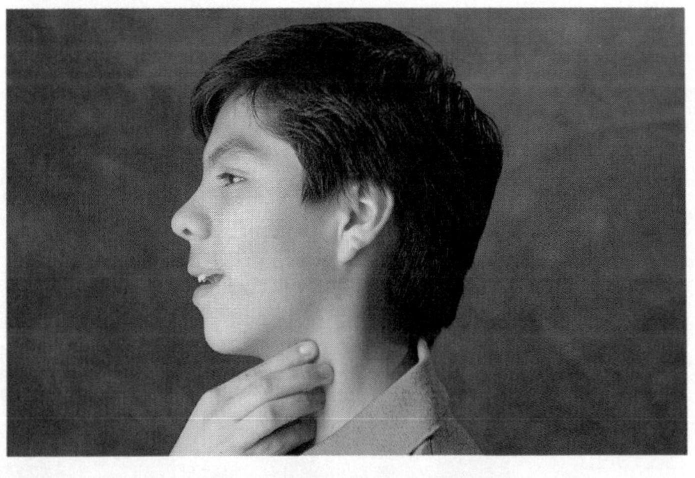

In the last activity, you felt the walls of the carotid artery in your neck expand each time the left ventricle contracted and squeezed blood out. You felt your blood

FIGURE 3-8. Blood is pumped from your heart through the blood vessels in your body in much the same way air is pumped into a tire by a bicycle pump.

rhythmically applying more and then less pressure on the walls of that artery. The rhythmic expanding and contracting of an artery is your **pulse**. Pulse is felt most easily in arteries near the surface of your body wherever they lie over a bone or some kind of firm tissue.

In the Explore, you calculated how many times you felt your artery pulsate in one minute—you calculated your pulse rate. By measuring pulse rate, you can get an idea of how fast the heart is beating. In the next activity, you will investigate how fast an earthworm's heart beats by measuring the pulse rate.

How do we know?

Measuring pulse

In 1731, Stephen Hales made the first accurate measurement of pulse. Hales exposed and tied off an artery in a horse. He then put a brass pipe into the artery and attached the other end to a nine foot-tall-glass tube. Hale's experiment is shown in the figure.

When Hales released the knot restricting the artery, blood gushed into the glass tube, eventually reaching a height of eight feet, three inches. Hales was able to watch the blood in the tube get higher and lower with each beat of the horse's heart.

INVESTIGATE!

3-1 PULSE RATE

Like yourself, an earthworm has a closed circulatory system. In animals with this type of circulatory system, a pulse can be measured. In this activity, you can find out how an earthworm's pulse rate compares with your own.

PROBLEM

How does the pulse rate of an earthworm compare to your own?

MATERIALS

live earthworm
Petri dish with cover
paper towels
water at room temperature
medicine dropper
clock or watch with second hand

PROCEDURE

1. Copy the data table.
2. Place the live earthworm in a Petri dish that has been lined with a moist paper towel. Be sure to keep the earthworm moist by periodically dripping water on it, as shown in the picture.

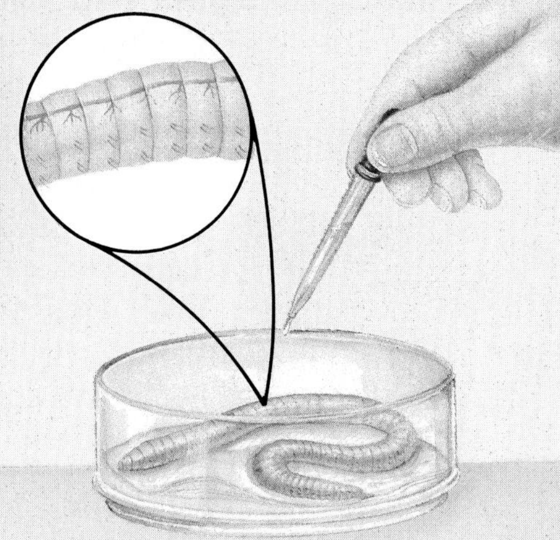

3. Look for the blood vessel along the top surface of the earthworm, as shown. Carefully **observe** the vessel. It will fill and then empty of blood. This filling and emptying indicates pulse.
4. Count the pulse of the earthworm for 15 seconds and record this in the table. Next, multiply this number by 4. This is the earthworm's pulse rate for 1 minute. Record this in the data table.
5. Repeat Steps 3 and 4 three times. Record your observations in the data table.
6. Calculate an average pulse for 1 minute for the earthworm. Record your result.
7. **Predict** how your average pulse rate will compare with that of the earthworm.
8. Find your pulse rate for 1 minute using your carotid artery as in the last Explore.

DATA AND OBSERVATIONS

WORM PULSE RATE

	15 seconds	1 minute
1		
2		
3		
4		
Average Pulse Rate:		

ANALYZE

1. What was the average pulse rate for 1 minute for your earthworm?
2. What was your pulse rate for 1 minute?
3. How does the earthworm's pulse rate compare with your own?

CONCLUDE AND APPLY

4. Was the prediction you made in Step 7 supported by your data? Why or why not?
5. Why was it important to repeat your measurements and determine an average?
6. **Going Further: Hypothesize** about how exercise would affect your pulse rate. Design an experiment to test your hypothesis.

Your pulse rate tells you the rate of your heartbeat. This is called your heart rate. With every beat of your heart, blood pushes through the blood vessels in your circulatory system. How is this accomplished?

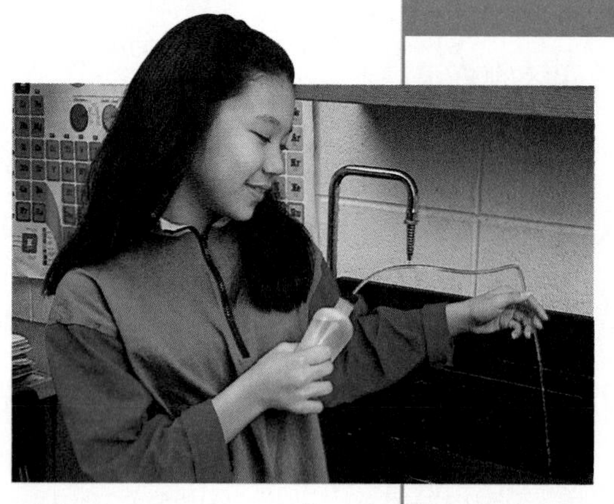

FIND OUT!

Can you make a liquid move?

Take a plastic squeeze bottle filled with water. Fit a plastic or rubber tubing into a stopper. Put the stopper in the water-filled bottle. While holding the bottle and tube over a sink, squeeze the bottle rhythmically.

Conclude and Apply

What happens to the water each time you squeeze the bottle?

When you first squeezed the bottle, you applied a force that pushed the water out of the bottle into the rubber tubing. Each time you squeezed the bottle with your hand, water squirted out. Between squeezes, when you weren't exerting a force, the water didn't move out. Your hand was acting as a pump to move the water.

In a similar way, your heart acts as a pump to move blood through the blood vessels of your body. Like the rhythmic squeezing of the water bottle, each time your heart beats, it exerts a force on your blood to keep it moving.

FIGURE 3-9. When the balloon is filled with water, the water exerts pressure on the walls of the balloon.

BLOOD PRESSURE

Have you ever filled a balloon with water, like the girl in Figure 3-9? If so, you know that when you fill it, you can feel the pressure of the water on the walls of the balloon. The filled balloon helps illustrate Pascal's Law. Pascal's Law states that a fluid, such as water, will exert pressure on the walls of the container it is in.

Blood, too, is a fluid, and it exerts a pressure against the walls of the blood vessels through which it flows. The pressure blood exerts against the inner walls of blood vessels is called **blood pressure**. In the next activity, you will compare blood pressure in arteries and veins.

INVESTIGATE!

3-2 BLOOD PRESSURE

Blood travels throughout the circulatory system under pressure. In this activity, you can use a model to find out how the blood pressure in arteries and veins compares.

PROBLEM

Is blood pressure in arteries and veins the same?

MATERIALS

plastic squeeze bottle
water
rubber stopper and tube assembly
pan or sink
meterstick

PROCEDURE

1. Copy the data table.
2. Fill the plastic squeeze bottle with water.
3. Insert the rubber stopper and tube assembly into the plastic bottle, as shown in the figure.
4. Position the bottle and meterstick over a pan or sink, as shown in the second figure.

5. **Predict** from which tube the water will squirt farther when you squeeze the bottle. One tube is glass, and one tube is plastic.
6. Firmly squeeze the plastic bottle one time. **Measure,** in centimeters, the distance the water squirts from each tube. Record the distance in the data table.
7. Repeat Steps 2 through 4 and Step 6 two more times using the same amount of force each time.
8. Calculate the average distance water squirted from each tube. (Add the three distances and divide the total by 3.) Record this in the data table.

ANALYZE

1. Which tube squirted water further?
2. What body organ does the plastic bottle represent?
3. What body liquid does the water represent?

CONCLUDE AND APPLY

4. The walls of arteries are more muscular but less elastic than veins. Which tube represents an artery, and which represents a vein?
5. **Compare and contrast** blood pressure in arteries and veins.
6. **Going Further:** How would blood pressure in arteries and veins compare if both had the same wall structure?

DATA AND OBSERVATIONS

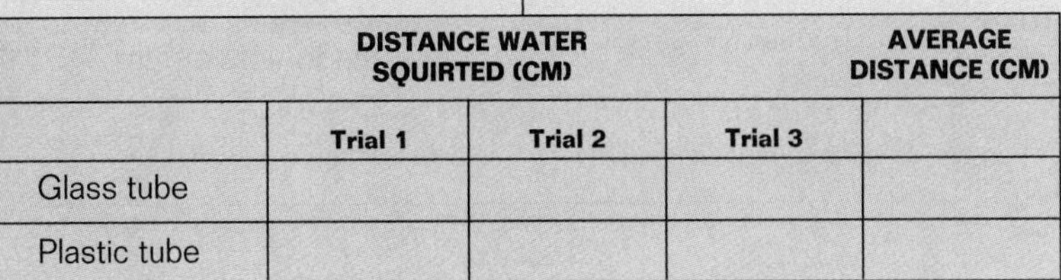

	DISTANCE WATER SQUIRTED (CM)			AVERAGE DISTANCE (CM)
	Trial 1	Trial 2	Trial 3	
Glass tube				
Plastic tube				

DID YOU KNOW?

If you are seriously injured and begin to lose blood rapidly, your blood pressure drops. Your body attempts to adjust by increasing heart rate and narrowing your blood vessels.

While there is pressure in arteries, capillaries, and veins, it is usually measured in arteries. When the left ventricle contracts, it rapidly forces blood under the highest pressure into your aorta. From that point in its trip through your body, your blood pressure becomes less and less.

Look at the graph in Figure 3-10. This graph shows how your blood pressure changes as it travels from the aorta, to smaller arteries, to capillaries, to small veins, and finally to large veins. By the time your blood is ready to enter the right atrium of your heart through the largest veins, the venae cavae, its pressure is almost zero. How does the body handle this difference in blood pressure? With these differences in pressure, would you expect some differences in the structure of arteries and veins?

The walls of arteries and veins have structural differences that tell you something about differences in blood pressure. Arteries have thick, muscular walls that only stretch a little each time your heart pumps blood into them. Arteries exert and withstand great pressure. Veins, on the other hand, have thinner and more elastic walls. Blood in veins does not exert such great pressure.

But because of gravity and because pressure is lower, blood might collect in veins and enlarge them. Without some help, the blood in veins would never make it back to the heart. But we know that it does make it back. Blood in veins receives some help from one-way valves, similar to the valves in your heart. As you can see in Figure 3-11, the one-way valves in your veins stop the blood from flowing backward. If there is a backward movement of

SKILLBUILDER

MAKING AND USING GRAPHS

The graph in Figure 3-10 is a line graph that tells you the blood pressure inside some of your blood vessels. As you see in the graph, the blood pressure is high in some blood vessels and low in others. Think about why this is so. If you need help, refer to the **Skill Handbook** on page 680.

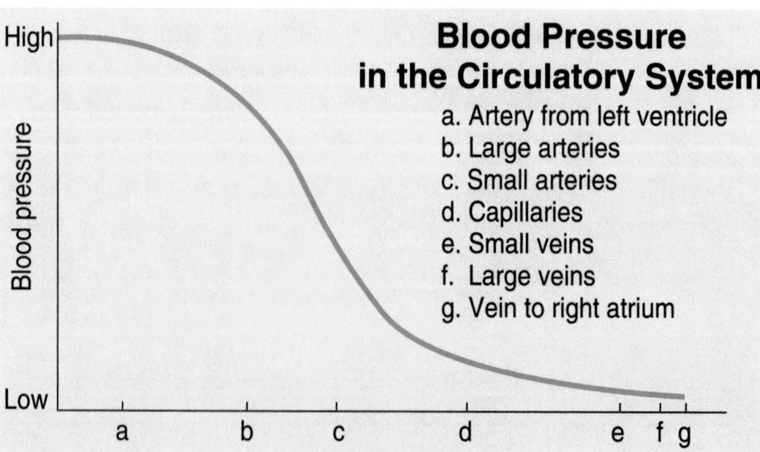

FIGURE 3-10. Blood pressure begins to decrease after it leaves the heart to flow through the blood vessels of the body.

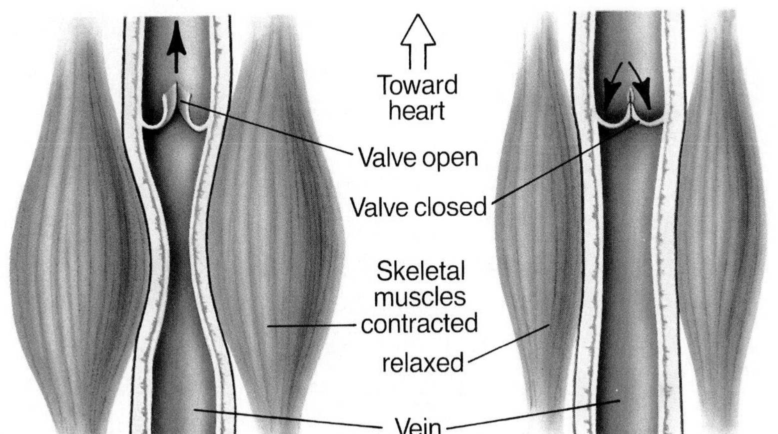

FIGURE 3-11. Valves in veins and muscles help blood flow back toward the heart.

blood, the pressure of the blood itself closes the valves. The veins in your legs contain the greatest number of valves. Why do you think this is so?

Blood in veins also receives a great deal of help in getting back to the heart from the muscles in your body. When the muscles surrounding veins contract, they exert pressure on the veins and help push blood along toward the heart.

BLOOD PRESSURE IN OTHER CLOSED SYSTEMS

As you recall from Section 3-1, reptiles, fish, amphibians, and mammals all have closed circulatory systems where a heart pumps blood through a continuous loop of blood vessels. But not all closed circulatory systems are the same. There are differences in the structure of the heart and blood vessels among these animals. These differences affect blood pressure and the way oxygen and nutrients are moved in the body.

Fish have a very simple closed circulatory system. As you can see from Figure 3-12, the circulatory system of a fish consists of a heart and a single loop of blood vessels. Unlike your heart, a fish's heart has only two chambers, an atrium and a ventricle. When a fish's ventricle contracts, oxygen-poor blood is sent through the loop to the gills, where carbon dioxide is exchanged for oxygen. From the gills, the freshly oxygenated blood flows to the cells of the body through small capillaries. Once nutrients

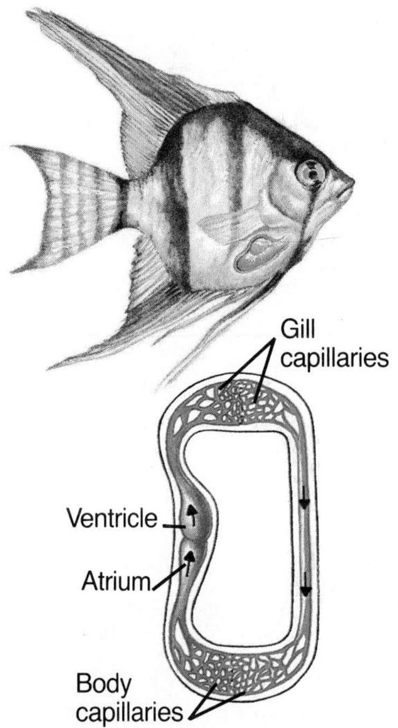

FIGURE 3-12. Fish possess very simple closed circulatory systems.

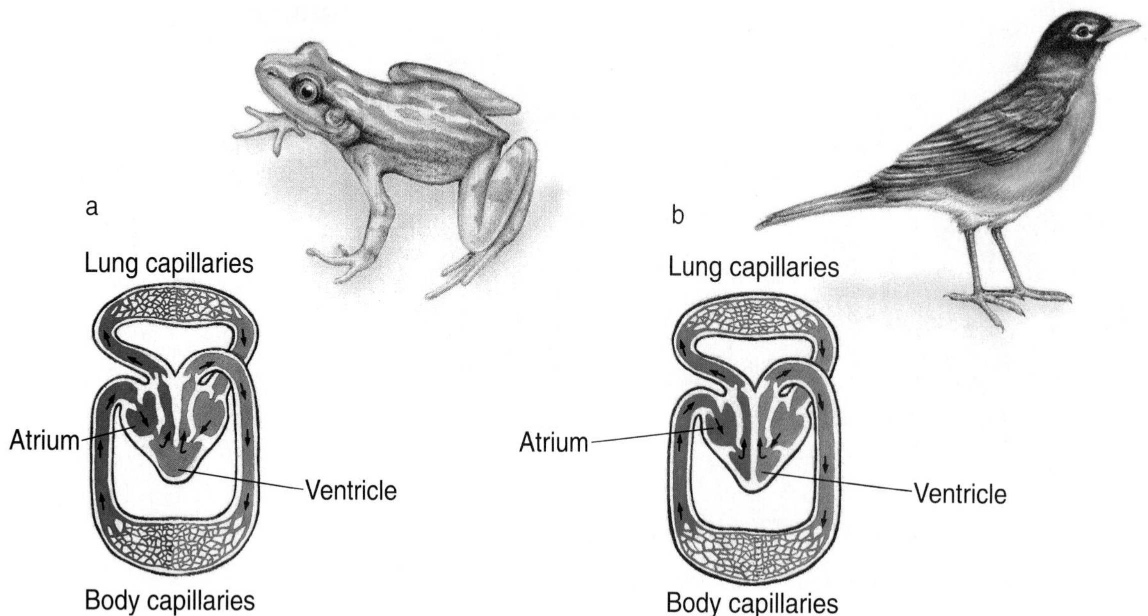

FIGURE 3-13. Amphibians, such as a frog, have three-chambered hearts (a). The bird circulatory system works like your own. Birds have four-chambered hearts (b).

and oxygen are delivered, the carbon dioxide-rich blood returns to the heart, and the cycle begins again.

Blood pumped by a fish's heart has to flow through two networks of capillaries during one cycle through the circulatory system. The first network is in the gills, and the second network is in the rest of the body. How do you think this type of circulatory system affects the pressure of blood as it moves through blood vessels?

Unlike the fish, the circulatory systems of amphibians, reptiles, and birds have two pathways of circulation like your own. One pathway goes to the lungs, and the other goes to the rest of the body. The frog shown in Figure 3-13(a) is a typical amphibian. Its heart has three chambers—two atria and one ventricle. Each atrium in the frog's heart receives blood from one of the pathways. As you can see from the figure, when the atria contract and squeeze blood into the single ventricle, carbon dioxide-rich blood from the body mixes a little with the oxygen-rich blood from the lungs. As a result, oxygen is not brought to the frog's cells as efficiently as in your own circulatory system. However, frogs do absorb oxygen through their skin, and this helps them with their oxygen needs.

Birds, as you can see from Figure 3-13(b), have a four-chambered heart like yours. Unlike the frog, there

DID YOU KNOW?

An average adult human heart pumps about 80 gallons of blood in one hour. This is enough blood to fill the gas tank of a small car every 9 or 10 minutes.

is no mixing of carbon dioxide-rich and oxygen-rich blood. The bird's four-chambered heart works just like your own. The right side of the heart pumps blood only to the lungs, and the left side of the heart pumps blood only to the body.

In this section, you learned that each time your heart beats, blood is pumped through the blood vessels of your circulatory system. Your pulse rate is a measure of how fast your heart is pumping. The pumping of the blood causes it to exert a blood pressure on the walls of the blood vessels.

FIGURE 3-14. Birds possess an efficient circulatory system.

Each type of blood vessel in your body is structured differently. Arteries have thick, muscular walls that withstand the great blood pressure exerted on them. Blood pressure in veins is much lower. Veins have thin, elastic walls. One-way valves and the contraction of skeletal muscles prevent the backward flow of blood.

Finally, not all closed circulatory systems are the same. Fish, birds, and amphibians all have different closed systems. These differences have an effect on the way oxygen and nutrients are brought to the cells of the body.

The structures and arrangement of the circulatory system help blood flow efficiently so the cells of your body receive the oxygen and nutrients they need. Your everyday behavior and lifestyle have been shown to have an effect on how your circulatory system works. In the next section, you will explore what can go wrong in the circulatory system, and how it may be preventable.

Check Your Understanding

1. Explain how the effects of the force of gravity and lower blood pressure are handled in veins.
2. If you receive a serious injury and cut a vein, the blood would flow out smoothly. How would you expect blood to flow out of a cut artery? Explain your answer.
3. Diagram the hearts of fish, amphibians, and birds. Label the following: atria, ventricles, and direction of blood flow.
4. **APPLY:** Hypothesize why animals such as birds and mammals have four-chambered hearts while amphibians and fish do not.

3-3 Disorders in Circulation

OBJECTIVES

In this section, you will

- describe the role of fatty deposits in heart disease;
- relate lifestyles to high blood pressure;
- explain how fainting and shock are related to the circulatory system.

KEY SCIENCE TERMS

atherosclerosis
hypertension

CIRCULATION TO THE HEART

The boy in Figure 3-15(a) is having a physical exam before the start of basketball season. As part of the exam, the doctor uses a stethoscope to listen to the boy's heart. The doctor will also check his blood pressure. These are two ways the doctor checks the health of the boy's circulatory system. Any disease or disorder of the circulatory system can be a serious problem.

Heart disease is a major cause of death in the United States. The term *heart disease* is used to describe any of the health problems that affect the heart. Your heart functions all your life to keep your body supplied with nutrients and oxygen, but what keeps the heart functioning? How do your heart cells get the oxygen and nutrients they need?

Figure 3-15(b) shows that the heart is nourished by two arteries. These arteries are the coronary arteries, and as you can see, they branch out through your heart into smaller vessels and capillaries.

Heart disease can occur when problems arise in the heart's vessels. What can go wrong with these vessels?

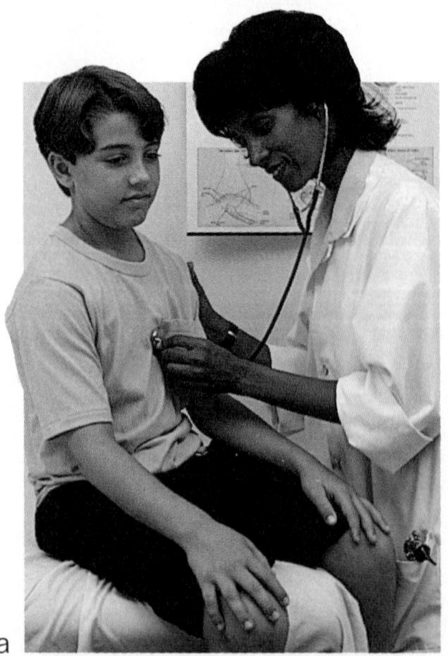
a

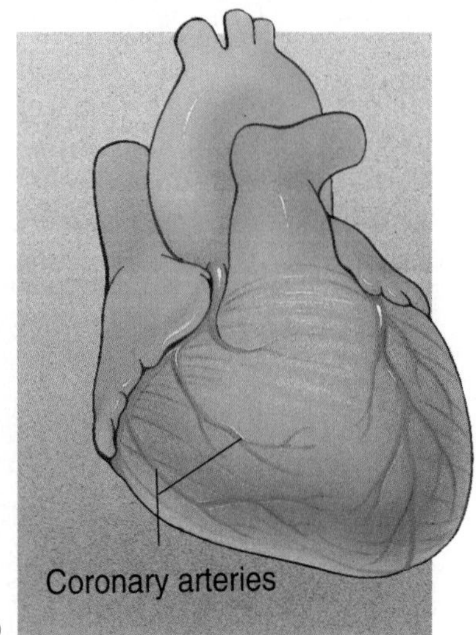

b

FIGURE 3-15. By using a stethoscope to listen to the heart, a doctor can detect any irregularities (a). The heart muscle itself receives its blood supply from the coronary arteries (b).

FIND OUT!

What happens to liquid flow in a clogged tube?

Earlier in the chapter, you used plastic tubing to represent a blood vessel and water to represent blood. Once again, you can make a model using the same equipment. Insert a dropper full of water into a 10-cm piece of plastic tubing, as shown in the picture. Squeeze the dropper to squirt water through the tube. Observe the water that comes out the end of the tube. Next, refill the dropper and squeeze water through a piece of plastic tubing that has been clogged with cotton balls. Again, observe the water coming out the tube.

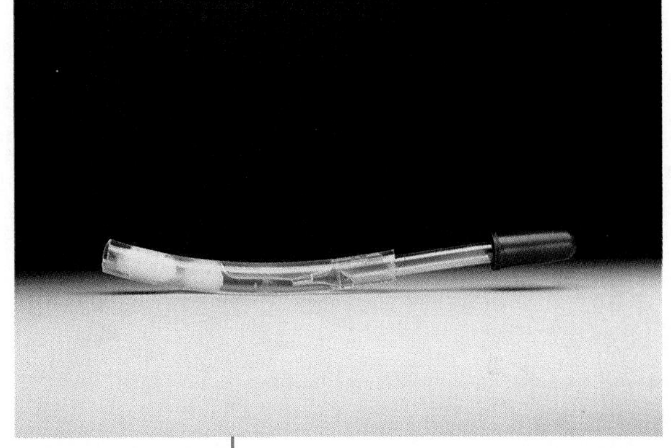

Conclude and Apply

How did the addition of the cotton balls to the tube change the way water flowed through the tube?

One leading cause of heart disease is **atherosclerosis** (a thuh roh skluh ROH suhs), a condition in which fatty deposits build up inside the coronary arteries and clog them. Figure 3-16 shows the stages of atherosclerosis in a coronary artery. As you can see, as fatty deposits build up on the insides of the artery, the pathway for blood becomes smaller and smaller.

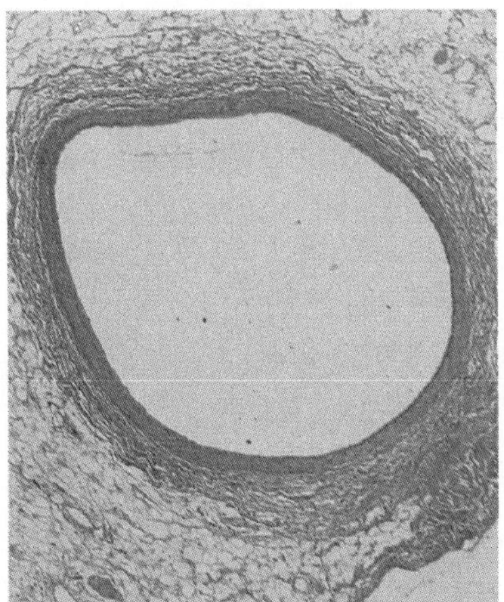

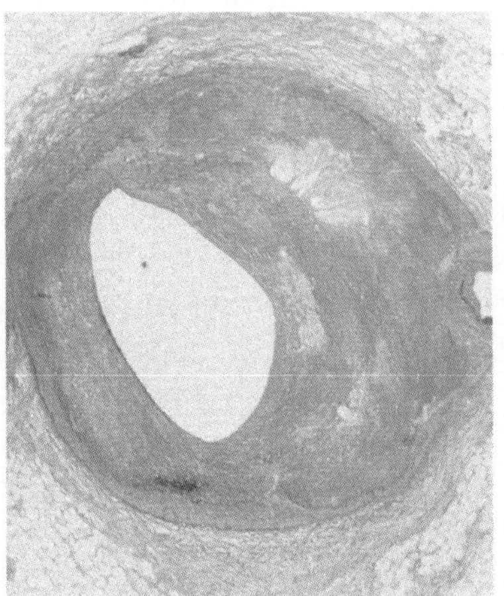

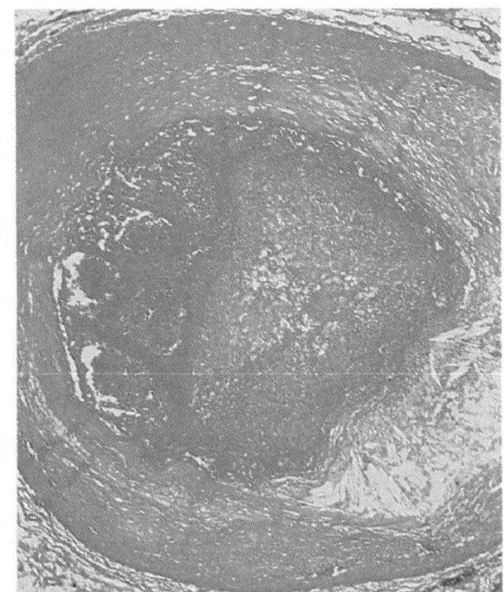

FIGURE 3-16. Fatty deposits build up and clog the coronary arteries, restricting or shutting off the flow of blood to body organs.

FIGURE 3-17. Having your blood pressure taken routinely is one way to see if it lies within a healthy range.

As you observed in the last activity, clogging the plastic tube with cotton severely restricted the flow of water through it. In the same manner, fatty deposits clog a coronary artery so much that blood can be prevented from flowing. When this occurs, the tissues in the heart don't get the oxygen and nutrients they need, and die.

When heart tissue dies, scar tissue forms on the damaged parts. Scar tissue isn't as flexible as normal heart tissue, and the heart's ability to pump blood is affected.

HIGH BLOOD PRESSURE

Blood pressure changes for many reasons. Occasional increases in blood pressure are normal. If you play a hard game of basketball or shovel heavy snow, your heart beats faster, thus increasing oxygen delivery to your body organs. This increase in your blood pressure, is only for a short time. After resting awhile, your heart rate and blood pressure usually return to normal.

In some people, however, blood pressure remains much higher than normal after exercise or even without exercise. A disorder of the circulatory system when blood pressure is higher than is normal is known as **hypertension**.

Although the exact causes of most hypertension are not known, diets high in fat are linked to it. One known cause of hypertension is atherosclerosis. Clogged arteries cause the pressure within a blood vessel to increase by reducing the elasticity of the artery walls and narrowing the pathway of blood flow. This extra pressure puts a strain on the heart, which has to beat faster to keep blood flowing to the rest of the body.

Hypertension can also affect the circulation of blood in other parts of your body. High blood pressure can cause smaller and more delicate arteries, such as the ones in your brain, to rupture. A break or rupture, in a brain blood vessel is known as a stroke. Strokes lead to brain damage by interrupting blood flow to brain cells.

BE GOOD TO YOUR HEART

One of the best things you can do for your circulatory system is to exercise regularly. But not all exercise is the same. To benefit your circulation, you need to regularly participate in aerobic exercises, such as running, swimming, bicycling, or cross-country skiing. Aerobic exercises, or aerobics, promote the efficient use of oxygen by your body. When you exercise, your lungs take in more oxygen, and your heart muscle becomes stronger. It can then pump more blood with each beat. This, in turn, allows your heart rate to decrease while still sending the same amount of oxygen-containing blood into your arteries.

FIGURE 3-18. Exercising regularly is beneficial to your circulatory system, and it can help you stay healthy.

FAINTING AND SHOCK

Fainting and shock are two conditions that result from a drop in blood pressure. Fainting is a temporary loss of consciousness that results from a lessened flow of blood to the brain. This can sometimes occur from lack of food, heavy physical activity in heat, or illness.

When a person faints and falls to the ground, his or her head becomes level with the heart. In this position, blood does not need as much pressure to get to the head, so the person usually regains consciousness fairly quickly.

FIGURE 3-19. Elevating the legs above the head when a person is in shock raises blood pressure in the chest and head.

Shock is a serious condition that can occur when a person has been seriously injured, has lost blood, has had a stroke, or has a severe reaction to an insect bite. Shock is caused by the loss of blood volume, usually from bleeding. When blood volume drops, so does blood pressure. The

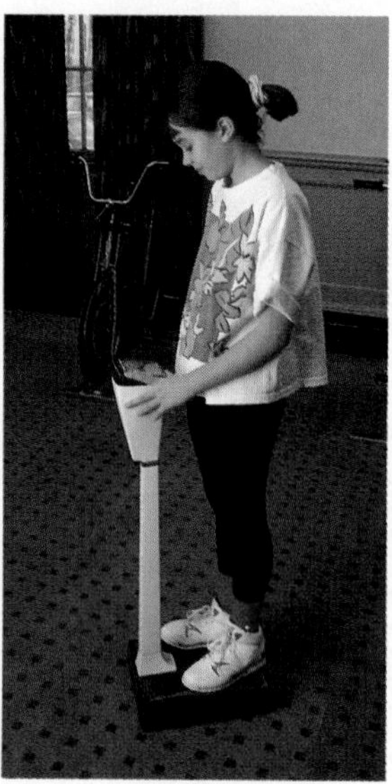

FIGURE 3-20. By eating right, watching your weight, not smoking, and exercising regularly, you have a better chance of reducing the risk of heart disease and hypertension.

body tries to maintain normal conditions by increasing heart rate and by narrowing the blood vessels. Symptoms of shock include pale and clammy skin, weak and rapid pulse, shallow breathing, and lower body temperature.

When a person is in shock, he or she should be kept lying down. It is helpful to elevate the person's legs. Raising the legs above the level of the heart raises blood pressure in the chest and head. Why would you want to increase the blood pressure in the head?

In this section, you have seen that some of the risk factors associated with disorders of circulation are under your control. You can reduce your chances of developing heart disease and hypertension by making good choices while you are young. By doing what the girl in Figure 3-20 is doing, you can protect your important circulatory system.

Check Your Understanding

1. How does a high-fat diet increase the risk of heart disease?
2. Explain how atherosclerosis can lead to hypertension.
3. **APPLY:** Why do some first-aid manuals suggest that if you feel like fainting, you should sit down and put your head between your knees?

EXPANDING YOUR VIEW

CONTENTS

A Closer Look
Optical Fibers Invade Circulatory System 87

Physics Connection
The Physics of Blood Pressure Measurement 88

Science and Society
Changing a Nation's Lifestyle 89

Technology Connection
Ball in the Cage 90

History Connection
"Sewed Up His Heart" 91

Teens in Science
Chill Out—It's Good For You 92

A CLOSER LOOK

OPTICAL FIBERS INVADE CIRCULATORY SYSTEM

When doctors and scientists decide to take a closer look at the circulatory system, they turn to fiberoptic technology. With an instrument called a fiberscope, they can look inside blood vessels and follow the blood as it flows through the body. Long, thin optical fibers transmit light to and from the area to be examined.

A fiberscope has two bundles of optical fibers. One bundle brings light to the area to be examined. The other transmits an image of that area back to the outside world—to an eyepiece, or a camera, or a TV monitor.

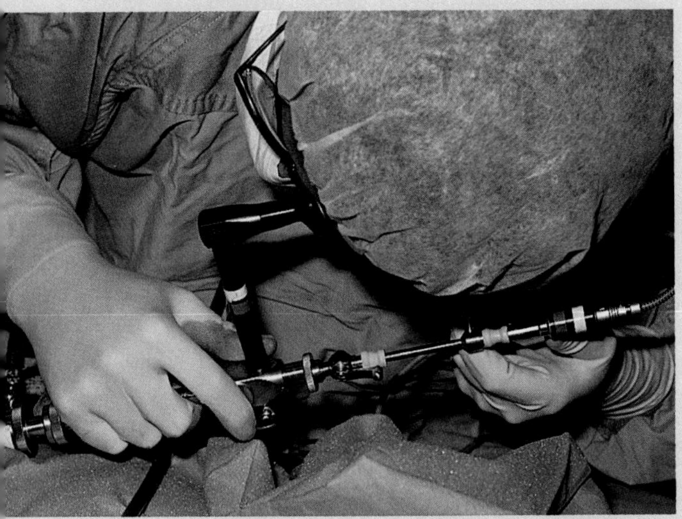

A bundle of optical fibers can contain 10,000 fibers yet be less than a millimeter in diameter! The fiberscope, itself, is so thin it can be inserted into blood vessels to visually examine the circulatory system from the inside. One scientist who is helping develop the fiberoptic technology used in the fiberscope is African-American chemist William R. Northover. Northover's research into increasing the information capacity of fiber light guides is being used in medical procedures such as the fiberscope, computer science, television broadcasting, and telecommunications.

YOU TRY IT!

Form a group to research recent advancements in the use of fiberscopes for surgery. Note both the pros and cons of current methods.

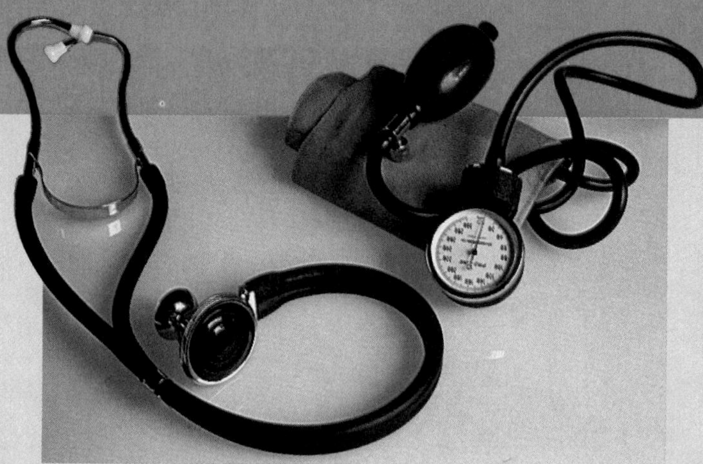

Physics Connection

THE PHYSICS OF BLOOD PRESSURE MEASUREMENT

Have you ever had your blood pressure measured by a doctor? If so, then you've had the cuff of an instrument called a sphygmomanometer (sfig moh muh NAHM uh ter) wrapped around your upper arm. The prefix *sphygmo-* comes from the Greek word *sphygmos,* meaning pulse. A manometer is a U-shaped tube partly filled with a liquid such as mercury. It is used in physics labs to measure gas pressure. How does a sphygmomanometer work?

A sphygmomanometer consists of three parts: an inflatable cuff that is worn around the arm, a hollow rubber bulb that pumps air into the cuff, and a glass tube containing a column of mercury.

To take blood pressure, the rubber bulb is squeezed several times. By pumping air into the cuff, the air pressure inside the cuff can be made to exceed the blood pressure inside the arm artery. As you would guess, when this happens the artery walls collapse, temporarily stopping the flow of blood.

Once blood flow has been cut off, air pressure inside the cuff is slowly reduced by allowing the cuff to deflate. When air pressure becomes less than blood pressure inside the artery, blood begins to surge through the artery again in a pulsating fashion. The pressure at which the flow of blood resumes is called the systolic pressure. It is the pressure exerted when the left ventricle contracts.

As the pressure in the cuff is further reduced, blood moves through the artery freely. The pressure at which blood can move through the artery is the diastolic pressure.

As you can see from this procedure, blood pressure is not really being measured—air pressure inside the cuff is! Blood pressure is measured indirectly.

In a healthy young person, systolic pressure is about 120 mm Hg, and diastolic pressure is about 80 mm Hg. What does this mean? Hg is the symbol for the element mercury. Millimeters of mercury refers to the pressure needed to raise a column of mercury up to a certain level. Therefore, normal systolic blood pressure raises a column of mercury 120 mm, and normal diastolic blood pressure raises a column of mercury 80 mm.

WHAT DO YOU THINK?

Scientists are currently finding out about the health hazards of mercury, yet mercury continues to be used in instruments such as the sphygmomanometer. Can you explain why mercury is used and not water or some other fluid? (Hint: Find out about the physical properties of mercury and other fluids. How is mercury different from most other fluids?)

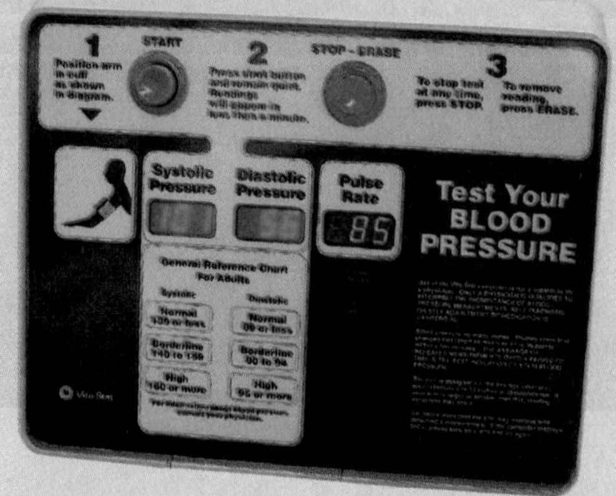

SCIENCE AND SOCIETY

CHANGING A NATION'S LIFESTYLE

In 1980, a United States Department of Health and Human Services report recommended that people in the United States cut back on the fat and fatty foods they consume in order to reduce their cholesterol levels. Scientists had found that high cholesterol levels increase the risk of heart attack, and that cutting back on fatty foods will reduce cholesterol levels and reduce the risk of heart attack. Since that time, many Americans have become more focused on taking care of their bodies and have changed their diets and exercise programs.

According to the United States Department of Agriculture, people are buying more chicken and less red meat than they did in the 1970s and early 1980s. Some fast food restaurants, in their attempts to meet the growing demand for healthier food, have switched from using animal oils to using vegetable oils for deep frying. They have also expanded their menus to include salads, chicken sandwiches, and leaner hamburgers.

Items sold for cooking and eating have changed as well. Foods such as butter substitutes and lower cholesterol snacks are now available.

Because aerobic exercise was found to lower cholesterol levels, some Americans have changed the way they exercise and how much they exercise. Many people participate in programs that involve brisk walking, running, bicycling, and swimming, as well as the familiar dance-type aerobics you see on television. The Bicycling Institute of America, a group which monitors and promotes the sport of bicycling in the United States, estimates that in 1990 there were 25 million adults bicycling regularly (at least once a week) compared to only 10 million in 1983.

CAREER CONNECTION

Dieticians plan menus and supervise food preparation using the principles of good nutrition. They know about diatetics—the relationship between food and health. Dieticians work in hospitals, schools, restaurants, and the food services of businesses. They have a bachelor's degree and have studied nutrition, foods, institution management, biology, and chemistry.

WHAT DO YOU THINK?

Can you think of any scientific announcement that stirred up a similar reaction? Do you think the changes had a major effect on most people? What do you think the next scientific announcement to stir up American society might be?

TECHNOLOGY CONNECTION

BALL IN THE CAGE

Does the above title bring to mind dance or some kind of game? It's actually a description of a heart valve—not a natural valve, but a replacement valve.

There are several diseases that cause heart valve problems. Some damaged valves are replaced by valves from pig hearts. But some damaged valves require more than just surgical repair. Today, a damaged valve is frequently replaced with a mechanical model.

The ball and cage valve is aptly named. Look at the picture. You'll see it consists of a small cage with a small ball inside. When the heart pumps blood, the ball moves forward within the cage. This opens the valve. To prevent backward blood flow when the blood is not being pushed forward, the ball returns to its closed position.

One of the features of this ball valve technique is that the ball easily rotates in the bloodstream. There is, therefore, little wear of moving parts, extending the life of the valve, while the valve is extending the life of its owner!

YOU TRY IT!

The ball and cage valve was the first replacement valve invented. In the library, find out about open heart surgery and different types of replacement valves.

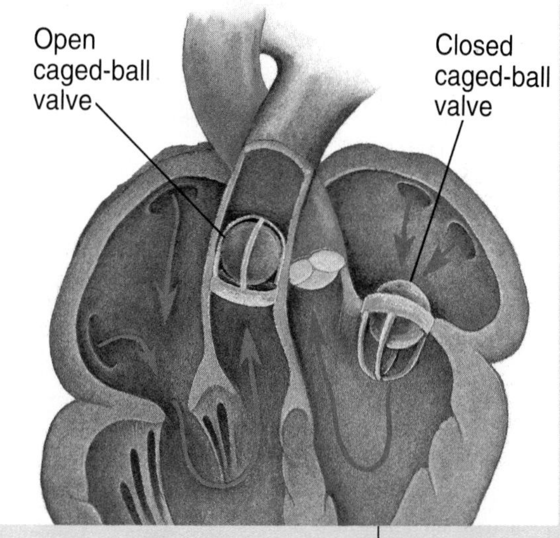

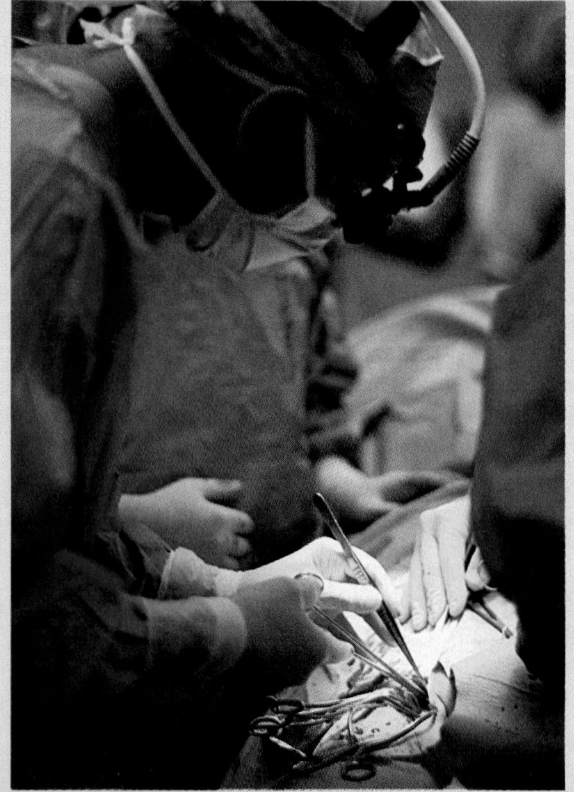

History CONNECTION

"SEWED UP HIS HEART"

"Sewed Up His Heart" was the newspaper headline on the day in 1893 that Dr. Daniel Hale Williams performed the world's first open-heart surgery. Williams (1856-1931) believed he had no other choice but to operate when a man with a severe knife wound to the chest was brought into Chicago's Provident Hospital.

Williams's surgery involved cutting and suturing the pericardium—the sac surrounding the heart. This marked the first time a surgeon had ever entered the chest cavity. At the time of the operation, infection-fighting antibiotics did not exist. The risk of infecting the open chest cavity during surgery was great. Much to the amazement of his colleagues and to the world, Williams's patient recovered completely from surgery.

It would be many years before open-heart surgery became common. Over the next fifty years, fewer than ten of these operations were recorded. The first woman to operate on the heart was Dr. Myra Logan (1908-1977), an African-American physician at Harlem Hospital in New York.

In addition to their surgical achievements, Drs. Williams and Logan made important contributions toward advancing medical practices for African-Americans. Dr. Williams had founded Provident Hospital in 1891. Provident Hospital provided much-needed medical services to African-Americans at a time when most hospitals wouldn't accept them as patients. Provident started one of the first training programs in the country for minority nurses.

When Dr. Logan graduated from New York Medical College in 1933, she served her internship and residency at Harlem Hospital without pay. Later, she became a staff member. Dr. Logan was the first African-American woman elected as a Fellow of the American College of Surgeons. In the course of her medical career, she researched the early detection of breast cancer and pioneered the idea of group practice so that patients could benefit from a variety of services in one place.

WHAT DO YOU THINK?

If you had been the doctor at Provident Hospital, would you have performed the open-heart surgery? Why or why not?

TEENS *in* SCIENCE

CHILL OUT— IT'S GOOD FOR YOU

Your teacher has placed the final exam facedown on your desk. You've studied for weeks and feel confident that you will do well. So why does your heart begin to beat a little faster as you turn the test over?

According to 16-year-old high school junior Tamika Walker, the answer is simple. It's stress.

"Some people think that teenagers don't feel stress as deeply as adults. But that's just not true," Tamika said. To prove her point, Tamika recently conducted a survey to measure the level of stress reported by classmates at her high school in Currie, North Carolina. She wrote and distributed a questionnaire asking the teenagers to rate the stress level of many types of life events.

"The results of the survey showed that there is a lot of stress in most teenagers' lives. Of course, big things like a divorce or a death in the family scored the highest. But I was surprised to discover that even smaller events, like getting a bad grade on a test or losing a textbook, scored high."

Once the survey was complete, Tamika began to research the physical effects of stress. "It's a chain of events," she explained. "Stress affects hormones, which in turn affect the pituitary gland, which eventually begins to wear down a person's immune system. That's why some people get sick when they are under a lot of stress. In fact, my survey showed that kids who had high stress scores also had the highest numbers of sick days. I think that it's time that someone started teaching kids how important it is to learn how to relax."

Tamika has certainly been doing her part to educate teenagers about stress. She entered her report in a regional science fair so that her classmates would have a chance to read the survey results.

Tamika's report was the most widely read exhibit in the fair. "It makes me feel good to know that so many kids took the time to look over the report," Tamika said. "It's time for us to begin learning everything we can about our bodies. After all, the more we know, the better we are likely to feel."

WHAT DO YOU THINK?

Think back to a time in the recent past when you did not feel good. Could stress have played a part in making you ill?

As Tamika has shown, some types of stress are very harmful. There seems to be some evidence, for instance, linking too much stress with high blood pressure. But other types of stress, like excitement about a project, can be very helpful. Make a list of stressful events in your life. For each event, decide whether the stress you feel is helpful or harmful.

Chapter 3

Reviewing Main Ideas

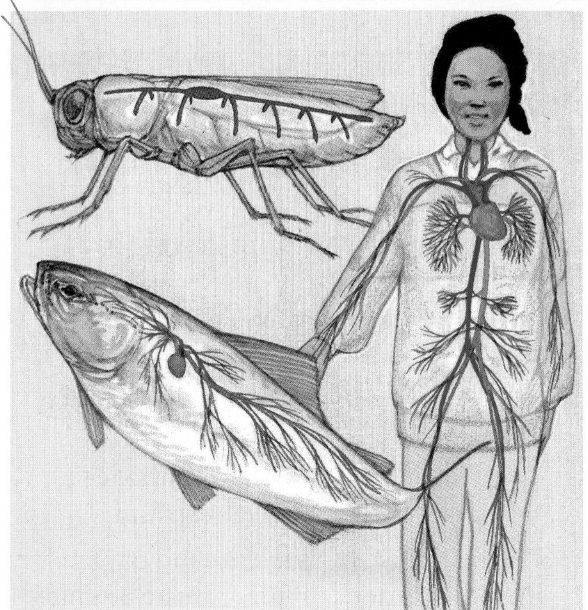

1. Both open and closed circulatory systems exist in animal groups. Circulatory systems deliver nutrients and oxygen to body cells and remove wastes, such as carbon dioxide.

2. In a closed system, blood travels from the left side of the heart through vessels to the body and back to the right side of the heart. In an open system, there are few to no vessels.

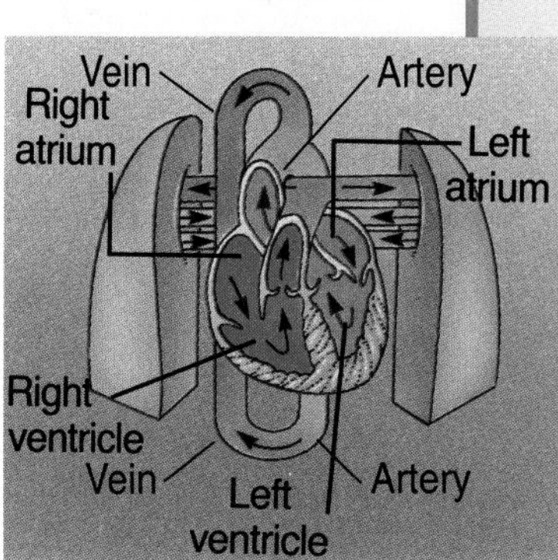

3. Blood is forced under pressure through the circulatory system by the pumping action of the heart.

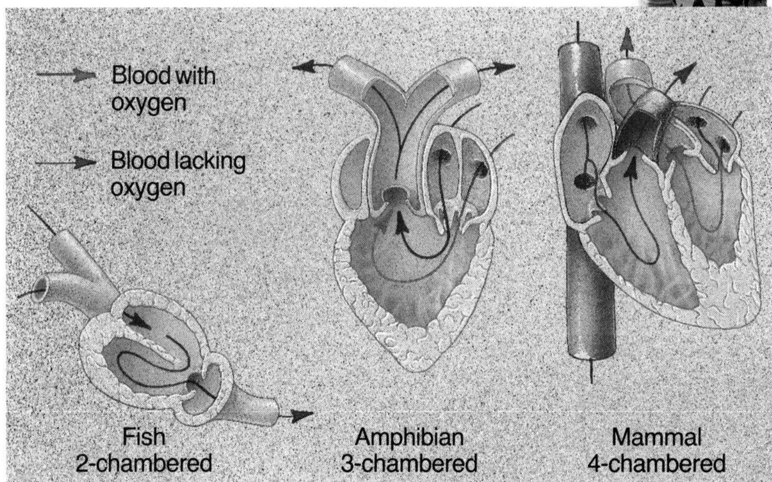

4. Three- and four-chambered hearts, such as the ones in amphibians, reptiles, birds, and mammals, pump blood more efficiently and under greater pressure than does the two-chambered heart of the fish.

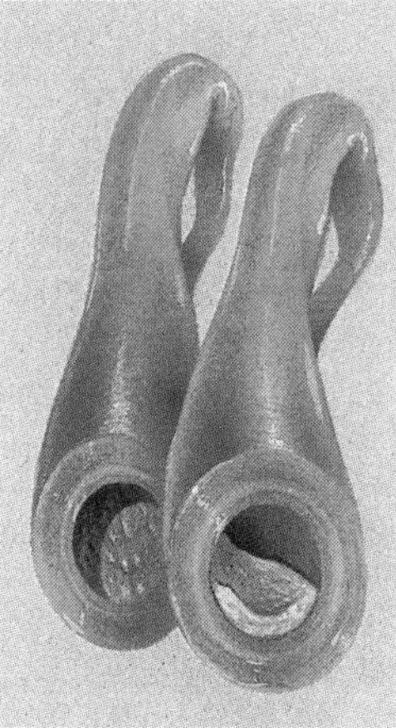

5. Diseases affecting the heart also affect the rest of the circulatory system and body organs. Some reduce or prevent the flow of blood, resulting in heart disease and high blood pressure.

Chapter Review

USING KEY SCIENCE TERMS

arteries
atherosclerosis
blood pressure
capillaries
hypertension
pulse
veins

Using the list above, replace the underlined words with the correct key science term.

1. Oxygen and nutrients pass easily from your blood to your body cells through the walls of <u>extremely small and thin blood vessels</u>.
2. In animals with closed circulatory systems, you can feel a <u>rhythmic expansion and contraction in arteries</u>.
3. As blood moves farther away from your heart, the <u>force per unit area it applies to the inside of your blood vessels decreases</u>.
4. Being overweight, smoking, a high-fat diet, and lack of exercise are factors that can increase your risk of developing <u>a buildup of fatty deposits inside the walls of your arteries</u>.
5. Aerobic exercise, such as bicycling or running, can help many people with <u>abnormally high blood pressure</u>.
6. The atria of your heart are connected to <u>blood vessels that bring blood to the heart</u>, while your ventricles are connected to <u>blood vessels that carry blood away from the heart</u>.

UNDERSTANDING IDEAS

Choose the best answer to complete each sentence.

1. Blood is prevented from flowing backward in veins by ____.
   a. capillaries **c.** valves
   b. atria **d.** the heart
2. Blood is pumped out of the heart to the lungs from the ____.
   a. left atrium **c.** right ventricle
   b. left ventricle **d.** right atrium
3. The exchange of nutrients and oxygen for carbon dioxide and other waste products occurs in the ____.
   a. arteries **c.** heart chambers
   b. air sacs` **d.** capillaries
4. Fatty deposits that build up inside arteries can cause ____.
   a. decreased heart rate
   b. increased blood flow
   c. increased blood pressure
   d. decreased pulse rate
5. Symptoms of shock include ____.
   a. increased blood volume
   b. increased blood pressure
   c. increased body temperature
   d. increased pulse rate

Answer the following questions.

6. How does Pascal's Law apply to the circulatory system?
7. How is your heart like a double pump?
8. Why is hypertension a serious medical problem?

CRITICAL THINKING

Use your understanding of the concepts developed in the chapter to answer each of the following questions.

1. If a person becomes dehydrated, the lack of fluids decreases the volume of blood in the body. How would dehydration affect blood pressure and heart rate?
2. The graph in the figure shows the pulse rate of a boy before, during, and after bicycling. When did the pulse rate increase most rapidly? What was the boy's pulse rate after fifteen minutes of bicycling? How did his pulse rate change when he stopped biking?

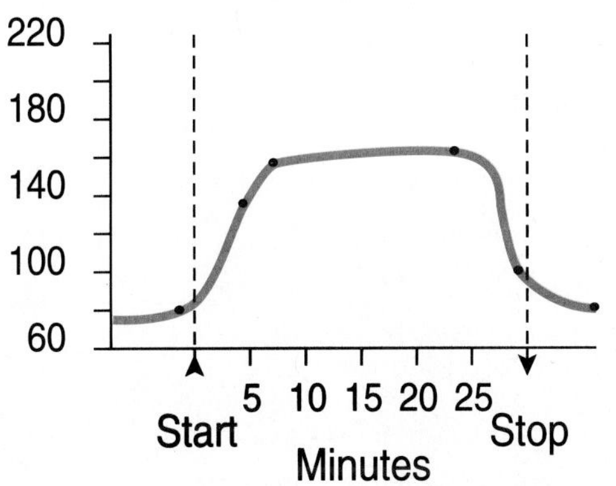

3. Why do you think larger, active animals require an efficient blood delivery system?
4. Imagine that you were designing an artificial heart. List three factors you would have to think about in order to make sure it works well in the body.
5. Doctors often recommend massage of the legs for people who are immobilized due to illness or injury. Why would this be beneficial to circulation?

PROBLEM SOLVING

Read the following problem and discuss your answers in a brief paragraph.

A special device that attaches to your wrist can be used to constantly measure your pulse rate and display the number like a digital clock. If you were to wear one of these devices for 24 hours, when do you think you would find your pulse rate lowest? When would your pulse rate be highest? Why would your pulse rate change during a 24 hour period?

CONNECTING IDEAS

Discuss each of the following in a brief paragraph.

1. Using your knowledge of forces and pressure, explain how a smaller diameter blood vessel affects the pressure of blood within it.

2. Using your knowledge of the force of gravity, explain the operation and importance of the valves in your body.

3. **A CLOSER LOOK** Describe some benefits of using optical fibers to inspect the circulatory system.

4. **PHYSICS CONNECTION** Briefly explain how the three parts of a sphygmomanometer work.

5. **TECHNOLOGY CONNECTION** Using information from this chapter, suggest a reason why it may be better to replace a heart valve with a synthetic one than to repair the original one.

LOOKING BACK

UNIT 1 FORCES IN ACTION

CONTENTS

Chapter 1 Forces and Pressure
Chapter 2 Forces Inside Earth
Chapter 3 Circulation in Animals

UNIT FOCUS

In this unit, you investigated forces producing motions and changes of motion. You learned about Newton's Laws of Motion and how everyday events, such as when you pick up a bowling ball, are affected by them.

You learned how these same kinds of forces within Earth produce earthquakes and volcanic activity. You also learned that forces within your body cause movement of blood and other materials needed for life.

Try the exercises and activity that follow—they will challenge you to use and apply some of the ideas you learned in this unit.

CONNECTING IDEAS

1. Suppose you were in an amusement park ride that was like a large centrifuge. Your head was toward the center. As the ride spun you faster and faster, what would happen to the blood in your body? Explain why you might faint.
2. Why do movements of only two meters along the San Andreas fault cause such great forces to be generated that the ground can vibrate for many miles around?

EXPLORING FURTHER

Draw a longitudinal section diagram of a part of an artery. Add an area with fatty deposits. Use an arrow to show the direction of blood flow. Use the letters "HBP" to indicate where the blood pressure will be the highest.

LOOKING AHEAD

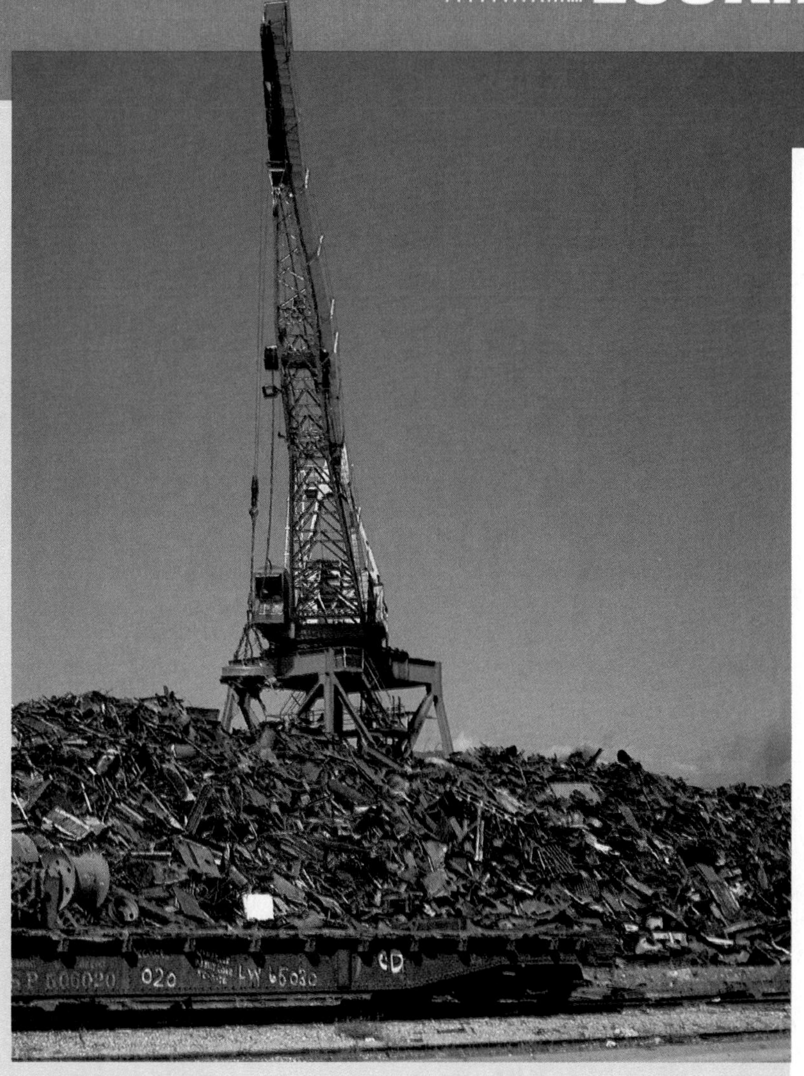

UNIT 2 ENERGY AT WORK

CONTENTS

Chapter 4 Work and Energy
Chapter 5 Machines
Chapter 6 Thermal Energy
Chapter 7 Moving the Body Machine
Chapter 8 Controlling the Body Machine

UNIT FOCUS

In Unit 1, you learned how forces inside your body, inside Earth, and in the world around you are related to changes in motion. As you study Unit 2, you will learn how machines and the human body both use forces to do work. Many machines you see are based on combinations of simple machines, such as the lever and the inclined plane. Bicycles, screwdrivers, and even your bones and muscles all operate on the same basic principles.

TRY IT

Suppose your textbook drops to the floor beside a table. Think of some different ways you could raise the book from the floor to the table. Obviously you could simply reach down and pick it up. Suppose it is too heavy to pick up. Diagram three ways you could raise the book to the table using only your hands. Test one of your ideas. After you've learned more about work, energy, and machines in this unit, identify any simple machines in your diagrams.

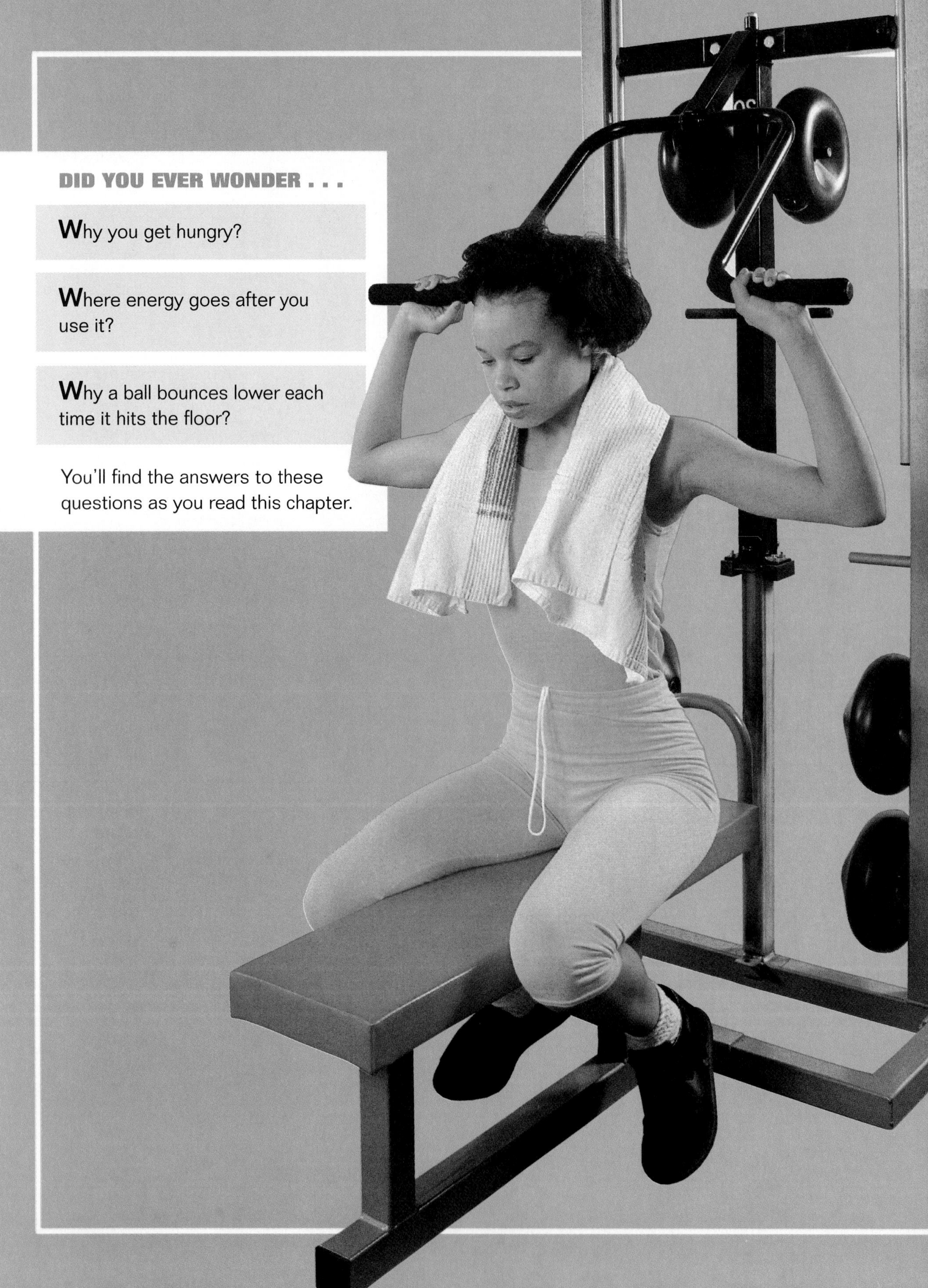

DID YOU EVER WONDER . . .

Why you get hungry?

Where energy goes after you use it?

Why a ball bounces lower each time it hits the floor?

You'll find the answers to these questions as you read this chapter.

Chapter 4

Work and Energy

When you hear the words *work* or *energy*, what do you think of? You probably would say that work is what you do at school or at a job. If you take books home with you, you call it homework. But when do you think that you're not working?

When you're enjoying some sport or activity, it's usually too much fun to be called work. Most of us call work those things we must or need to do. The things that we do for our own pleasure we call recreation or play.

What is energy? You might say that you are full of energy. Television advertisements tell you that a certain food will give you energy. You think of energy as what you have that lets you do different things. It takes energy to do just about anything, whether we call it work or not. What is the relationship between work and energy? Does our ordinary use of these words help or confuse us?

EXPLORE!

What is work?

Stand up and hold your arms out in front of you at waist level, with your hands together, palms up. Have a classmate stack two books on your hands. Raise the books to shoulder level, then lower them. Now try raising them above your head. Is this more work than raising them to shoulder level? Hold the books at shoulder level until you get tired. Are you exerting force? Do you think you are doing work?

4-1 Energy and Fuel

OBJECTIVES

In this section, you will

- explain and use the term energy;
- explain the relationships among fuel, energy, and work.

FUEL, ENERGY, AND JOBS

"I have work to do!" "My father left for work at 7:30." "The dentist worked on my teeth." Do these uses of the word *work* have anything in common? Would you say, "I have to work on my basketball."? You usually think of sports as play, not work. But then why do athletes work out? You buy high-energy cereals. But the cereal certainly doesn't look like it has much energy.

Think about a very simple job, such as lifting books from the floor to place them on bookshelves. Let's use a bookcase with five shelves, spaced one foot apart. If you lift a 1-pound book up 1 foot from the floor and set it on the first shelf, you know that you have used some energy to do this job. If you lift the book from the first shelf to the second shelf, you use some more energy; your body uses some fuel to produce that energy. You could raise the

FIGURE 4-1. Which of these people is doing work?

book two, three, or as many shelves as you could reach. If you lifted the book from the floor to the top shelf, how much more fuel would your body use than if you lifted it only to the first shelf? The job is five times bigger, so you must use five times as much fuel. But the body works in very complicated ways so it would be hard to figure out how much fuel your body actually uses in such situations. Let's use the engine from a model airplane to lift the book onto the shelves.

FIGURE 4-2. Both the rider and the motorcycle require fuel to produce energy.

You can measure the fuel needed to do this job by counting how many drops of fuel are burned in lifting the book to different heights. You could use an eye dropper to measure out the fuel for the engine. A pulley and rope arrangement could be used for the engine to lift the book, as seen in Figure 4-3.

When this experiment is performed, 10 drops of fuel are needed to raise the 1-pound book up 1 foot to the first shelf. Just as the book reached the first shelf, the last of that 10 drops was burned in the engine. The engine sputtered and stopped. How many drops of fuel do you think would be necessary to raise the book from the floor to the second shelf? Right! Twenty drops. If 50 drops of fuel are burned, how high would the book be raised? Five times as much fuel produces five times the energy, and the book would be raised 5 feet to the fifth shelf. Many different experiments like this one convince us that the amount of fuel needed to do jobs is proportional to the job that needs to be done.

FIGURE 4-3. You can measure the fuel this engine uses as it lifts the books.

When matter possesses energy, the energy can change itself or its environment. A bud opens into a flower, a lamp goes on when you plug it into an electrical outlet,

FIGURE 4-4. What fuels are being used in this picture?

> **DID YOU KNOW?**
>
> You use six times as much energy when you run fast as you do when you are standing still.

the tumbler turns and your clothes dry in the dryer. Outside, the sun shines and warms the soil, the lawn mower cuts your grass, and the wind blows the leaves on the trees. Each of these examples is a change, each requires energy, and, in each case, a fuel is necessary to supply that energy. Can you figure out what that fuel might be in each example?

Energy comes from fuel and causes change. Energy allows machines, from steam engines to human bodies, to perform jobs. Is this work? As you've seen, your everyday ideas of work are often tied to your feelings about what you're doing. But in science class, work has a very specific meaning. In the next section, you'll learn how scientists define work and how they measure it.

Check Your Understanding

1. Without using those mentioned in the chapter, give three examples of situations in which energy is being used. How do you know that energy is used?
2. In the three examples from Question 1, what fuel is used to produce the energy? What job is being done in each case? Which one requires the greatest amount of fuel?
3. **APPLY:** Both you and your brother, who weighs one and a half times what you weigh, have the same schedule each day. You eat the same meals and go through all the same actions throughout the day. Which of you is likely to lose weight? Why?

4-2 Work

WORK, FORCE, AND MOTION

Is work done whenever fuel is used? Does energy always produce work? In this section, you'll find out how to sort out the relationship among energy, fuel, and work.

In the Explore at the beginning of the chapter, you lifted books and then held them still. Were both of these actions work? Let's explore again.

OBJECTIVES

In this section, you will

- define work;
- calculate work done on an object, given the force applied and the distance moved in the direction of the force.

KEY SCIENCE TERMS

work

EXPLORE!

Is it work?

Put several books into a backpack and place it on the floor. Now pick it up and put it on the table. Did that action take energy? Did you do work on the backpack? Now hold your hands out in front of you and have another student hand you the backpack. Hold it in place for 10 to 20 seconds. Did you use energy? Did you do work on the backpack?

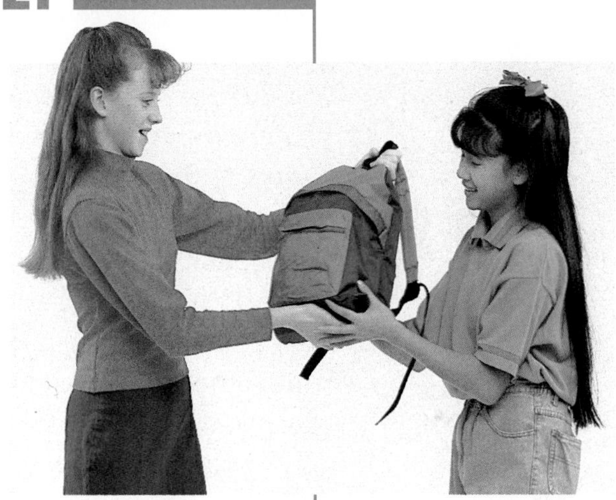

You probably said that in both cases you used energy. This is true. The fuel for this energy was the food you ate earlier. But one action did not involve work on the backpack. Let's find out why.

What was the difference between the two actions in the Explore? In the first, there was motion. You moved the backpack from the floor to the table. In the second, there was no motion. You merely held the bag suspended.

What did the two actions have in common? In both actions you used energy, and you exerted an upward force on the pack.

So, in the first case, there was both force and motion. In the second case, there was force but no motion. In order for an action to be considered work, both force and motion must be present. If there is force but no motion, such as your holding the backpack level, there is no work. If there is motion but no force, there is no work. An example of this might be throwing a ball. As long as your hand is in contact with the ball, both force and motion exist. Once your hand releases the ball, you are no longer doing work on the ball, even though it keeps moving. At this point, something else is doing work on the ball. Can you figure out what it is? What is exerting a force on the ball and changing its direction?

FIGURE 4-5. Work is done on the box only when it moves in the direction of the applied force.

In the Explore, your body used fuel to produce energy, and then you transferred that energy to the backpack as you picked it up from the floor. In scientific terms, **work** is energy transferred through motion. Since there was no motion in holding the backpack steady, no work was done.

But there is one more condition for work to be done. There must be force, there must be motion, and *the force must be in the direction of the motion.* When you picked up the backpack, you exerted an upward force, and the backpack moved in an upward direction. This is work. If you then carry the backpack across the room while holding it level, you are still exerting an upward force, but the movement is at right angles to that force. In scientific terms, no work is done on the backpack as you walk.

Work is done on an object when the object moves while there is a force acting along the direction of motion. The amount of work done is given by multiplying the force times the distance that the object moves.

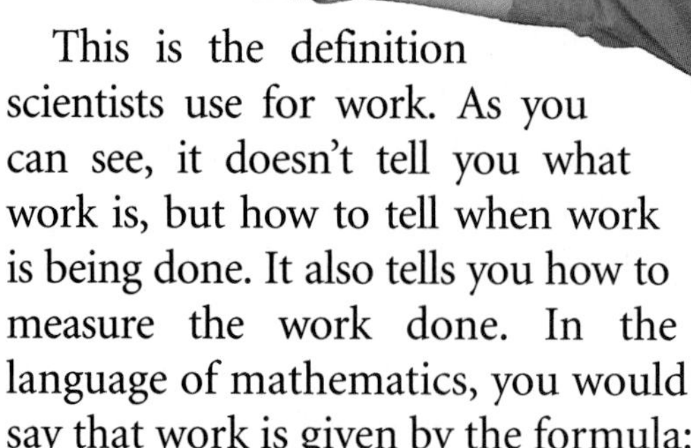

FIGURE 4-6. In this picture, the girl has done work on the Frisbee.

This is the definition scientists use for work. As you can see, it doesn't tell you what work is, but how to tell when work is being done. It also tells you how to measure the work done. In the language of mathematics, you would say that work is given by the formula:

$$W = F \times d$$

W means work done, F means force in the direction of motion, and d means distance moved.

Feet and pounds are common units in the English system. But scientists use SI units for work and energy, and it's important to learn those. When force is expressed in newtons (N) and distance in meters (m), the unit for work is the newton•meter (N•m). This is the work done when a force of one newton acts through a distance of one meter.

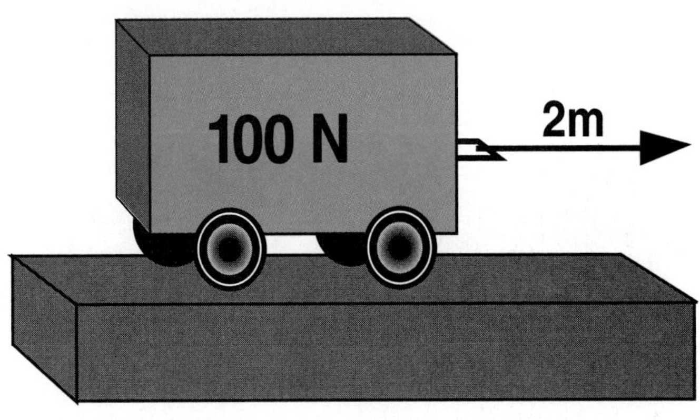

FIGURE 4-7. The work done on this car equals 100 N × 2 m or 200 J.

The N•m has been named the joule (J) to honor James Prescott Joule, who made many important discoveries about energy. Here is an example of a problem in which work is calculated.

A student's backpack weighs 10 N. She lifts it from the floor to a shelf 1.5 m high. How much work is done on the backpack of books?

$$W = F \times d$$
$$W = 10\text{ N} \times 1.5\text{ m}$$
$$W = 15\text{ N•m or } 15\text{ J}$$

Is swimming work? How about tennis or basketball? We've said that work is transferring energy through motion. If a person or machine uses fuel and does work, it loses energy. You know this because after a hard workout, you are tired and hungry. Where does that energy go? What forms does it take? As you can see, there's much more to learn about energy.

SKILLBUILDER

COMPARE AND CONTRAST

Compare and contrast the everyday meaning of *work* and the scientific definition of that term. Give examples of work in the everyday sense that would not be considered work in the scientific sense. If you need help, refer to the **Skill Handbook** on page 683.

Check Your Understanding

1. If you were to go outside and push against the school building as hard as you could for five minutes, how much work would you do? Explain your answer.
2. While performing a chin-up, Carlos raises himself 0.8 m. If Carlos weighs 600 N, how much work does he do? If Carlos holds the chin-up for several seconds before letting himself down, how much more work does he do?
3. **APPLY:** Jill is doing chin-ups on the same bar as Carlos. Jill weighs only 400 N. Compare the amount of fuel Jill uses in doing ten chin-ups to what Carlos uses doing ten chin-ups.

4-3 Forms of Energy

OBJECTIVES

In this section, you will

- describe how work can produce kinetic energy, potential energy, and thermal energy;
- specify how energy is transferred when work is done.

KEY SCIENCE TERMS

kinetic energy
potential energy

ENERGY OF MOTION: KINETIC ENERGY

You've probably seen pictures of sailing ice sleds with steel runners. Imagine that you have a sailing sled and that there is no friction between the runners and the ice. Also imagine that a wind pushes on the sail in one direction with a constant force of 400 N. When a constant, unbalanced force pushes on an object, what happens?

You learned in Chapter 1 that such a force causes the object to move faster and faster, to accelerate. The longer the force acts, the faster the sailing sled will be going. Say that the sled travels 20 m before the wind stops blowing. The wind accelerated the sled by doing (20 m × 400 N)= 8000 joules of work ($F \times d = W$).

What is the difference in the sled after the work is done? Before the work was done, the sled was at rest. Energy is transferred from the wind to the sled. Work resulted in the sled gaining speed. On a perfectly frictionless surface, the work shows itself in the motion of the

FIGURE 4-8. The wind does work on the ice sled and makes it accelerate.

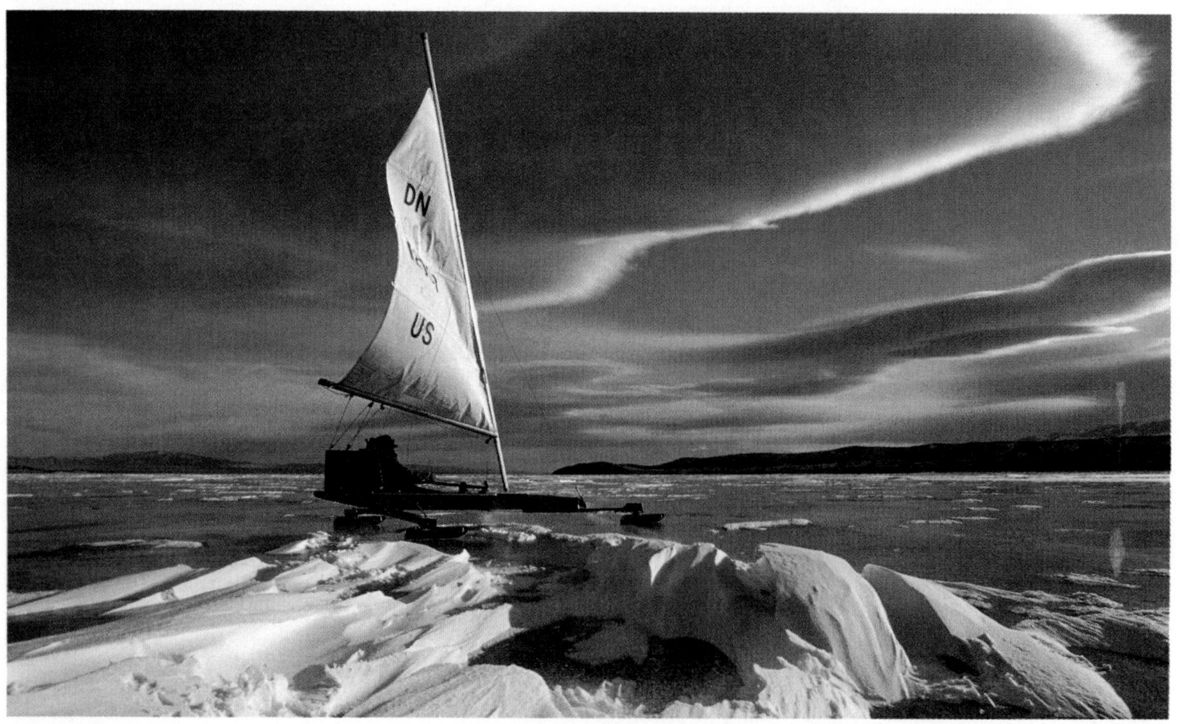

How do we know?

Kinetic Energy Equation

Where does an equation like $E_k = 1/2\,mv^2$ come from? Scientists and mathematicians often use several equations that include information they *do* know to work out new equations for information they don't yet have. This may look complicated but simply involves thinking through a problem step-by-step. First, we know that the wind accelerated the sled by exerting a force of 40 N on it. We know that the sled moved 20 m. From Chapter 1, you know that distance = average velocity × time. Average velocity is the sum of the initial and final velocities divided by two. Since the initial velocity was 0, this equation becomes $d = (v/2 \times t)$ (Equation 1).

You also know by definition that acceleration is the change in velocity divided by time. Again the initial velocity is zero, so this becomes $a = v/t$. If we solve this equation for t, we get $t = v/a$ (Equation 2). In math, you know that equal terms may replace one another. Replace the t in Equation 1 with the v/a from Equation 2-$d = (1/2v) \times (v/a)$ or $d = 1/2v^2a$. This may also be written $ad = 1/2v^2$ (Equation 3).

Finally, we can solve $F = ma$ for a to get $a = F/m$ (Equation 4). Using this value for a in Equation 3, we get $(F/m)d = 1/2v^2$ or $Fd = 1/2mv^2$. What is Fd? That's right. It's work, in this case, the work done by the wind to increase the velocity of the sled. The work has increased the kinetic energy of the sled, so the equation becomes $E_k = 1/2mv^2$.

sled. We would say that the sled is given energy of motion. This energy of motion is called **kinetic energy.**

The kinetic energy of a sled or other moving object may be calculated using a simple formula. It is

$$E_k = 1/2mv^2$$

where E_k is kinetic energy in joules, m is mass in kg, and v is velocity in m/s. Notice that kinetic energy is measured in the same unit as work, namely, joules. The *How do we know* explains how this equation is derived. The amount of kinetic energy an object possesses is equivalent to the amount of work that was done on the object.

EXAMPLE PROBLEM: Calculating Kinetic Energy

Problem Statement: A baseball with a mass of 1.6 kg leaves a bat with a speed of 40.0 m/s. Calculate the kinetic energy of the ball.

Known information: mass = 1.6 kg
velocity = 40 m/s

Equation to Use: $E_k = 1/2mv^2$

Solution: $E_k = 1/2mv^2 = 1.6\text{ kg} \times 1/2 \cdot (40\text{ m/s})^2$
$= 1300\text{ J}$

FIGURE 4-9. The baseball's kinetic energy is 1300 J.

It's fairly easy to tell that a moving object has energy. But how can you tell whether or not an object has energy when it isn't moving?

EXPLORE!

Does a softball have energy?

Hold an ordinary softball in your hand. Does it have any kinetic energy? Does it have any other kind of energy that you can tell? Press a tent stake about halfway into a bucket of dirt. Hold the softball about 1 m above the stake. What kind of energy will the ball have when you drop it? Drop the ball onto the stake. How did the ball transfer its energy? Did the ball's energy perform work? Lift the ball back up to about 1 m. Does the ball have the ability to do work, to produce change now? Does the ball have energy?

ENERGY OF POSITION: POTENTIAL ENERGY

When you held the ball above the tent stake, it looked the same as it did on the ground. There was no obvious change in the ball, and there was nothing to indicate that

FIGURE 4-10. The potential energy of the water above the wheel is converted to kinetic energy as the water falls.

there was any energy in the ball. But as you saw, when you released the ball, it began to move toward Earth. The ball gained kinetic energy. Where did that energy come from if the ball didn't have it in the first place? The only change in the ball was its change in location. Energy was stored in the ball because of its position above the ground. Stored energy is called **potential energy.**

When we say that a person has great potential as a writer or baseball player, we are suggesting that sometime in the future, he or she will demonstrate that writing or baseball ability.

In the same way, the ball had potential energy because at some time, namely when you let go of it, it will demonstrate the ability to do work and drive the tent stake into the dirt.

Where did this energy come from? Originally, the ball was on the ground. Could the ball drive the tent stake into the dirt from its location on the ground? Did the ball have any potential energy when it was there? Then you lifted the ball against the force of gravity. You did work against gravity and transferred some of your energy to the ball. The energy you transferred was stored in the ball as potential energy because of the ball's position above the ground. We call this kind of stored energy *gravitational* potential energy. The force of gravity is able to act on the ball when you release it, increasing its speed until it reaches the ground. As the ball fell, the kinetic energy increased and the potential energy decreased. Just before the ball hit the stake, there was almost total kinetic energy that did the work of driving the stake into the ground.

FIGURE 4-11. Shown here are objects with gravitational potential energy. Which object has the most potential energy? Why?

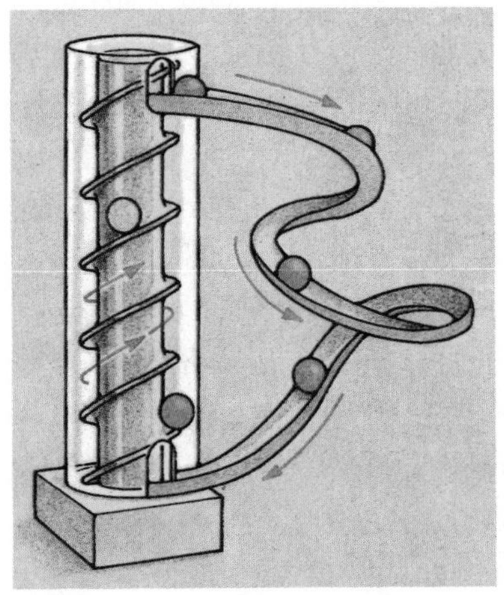

As you may have guessed, the higher you lift the object, the more potential energy it gains. Also, the more an object weighs, the more potential energy it gains. In each case, the ball will be capable of doing more work when it falls. Another way to think of this is that you must do work to lift the object against gravity. The object then possesses the energy you used to do that work and, in turn, can do work as it falls back to Earth.

Gravitational potential energy is the work done in lifting something against the force of gravity. Work equals $F \times d$. When you are lifting something, the force you use, F, must equal the weight of the object. Therefore, gravitational potential energy, E_p, is given by

$$E_p = W \times h,$$

where W is the object's weight and h is the distance lifted. Notice that this is just another version of the equation for work and the units are the same. The potential energy is measured in foot-pounds in the English system and joules in SI units, just as work is. In other words, the gravitational potential energy is equivalent to work, but work done in an up-and-down direction, against gravity.

A car at the top of a hill, like the car shown in Figure 4-12, has potential energy. At some time, work was done on the car to get it to the top of the hill. If the car begins to roll down the hill, the potential energy becomes kinetic energy. Even though the car doesn't fall straight down toward Earth, like the ball, the car is still being affected by gravity. Gravity is pulling it down, not forward. You can measure the gravitational potential energy as long as you know the vertical height of the hill. What is the relationship between the potential energy stored in the car at the top of the hill and the kinetic energy that it has when it reaches the bottom of the hill? Let's investigate this relationship in the following activity.

FIGURE 4-12. How much potential energy does this car have?

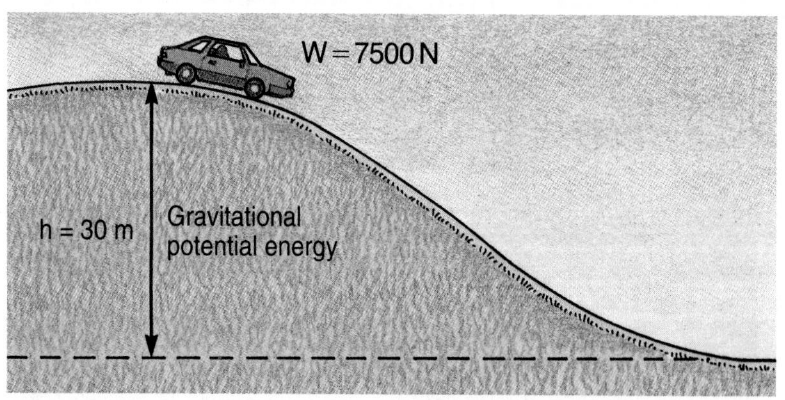

I N V E S T I G A T E !

4-1 POTENTIAL AND KINETIC ENERGY

How can you measure and compare the potential and kinetic energy of a vehicle?

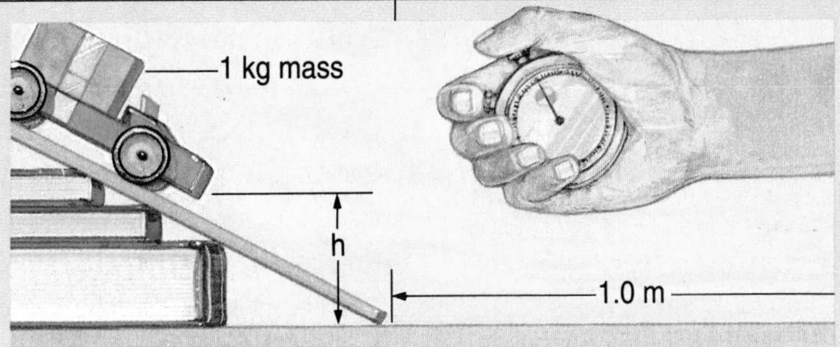

PROBLEM

What is the relationship between kinetic and potential energy?

MATERIALS

20-N spring scale
meterstick
stopwatch
0.5- to 1.0-m ramp
masking tape
1.0-kg mass
cart
several books

PROCEDURE

1. Copy the data table.
2. Use tape to securely attach the 1.0-kg mass to the cart. Find the total weight of the cart and mass with the spring scale.
3. On the floor, set up the ramp as shown in the diagram. Measure the height, *h*, from the front of the cart to the floor.
4. Allow the cart to roll down the ramp. Measure the time needed for the cart to roll 1.0 m along the floor.
5. Repeat Step 4 several times and record the three closest times.
6. Change the angle of the ramp by removing one or two books. Repeat Steps 3 through 5 and record your measurements.

ANALYZE

1. **Compare and contrast** the cart's motion on the ramp and on the floor.
2. **Calculate** the cart's potential energy for each ramp height and record in the table.
3. Average the times for the 1-m run. Then calculate the velocity of the cart during that run using $v = d/t$. Repeat for the other ramp heights.
4. **Calculate** the kinetic energy of the cart for both ramp heights.

CONCLUDE AND APPLY

5. **Compare** the potential and kinetic energy of the cart for each ramp height.
6. What variable do you have in this activity that could **cause** the E_p and E_k to be different?
7. **Going Further:** If you removed the 1.0-kg mass and repeated the activity, what measurements would have changed? In what way?

DATA AND OBSERVATIONS

WEIGHT OF CART AND 1KG MASS (W)	HEIGHT (h)	P.E (K_p=W X h)	TIME (t)	VELOCITY (V=$^d/_t$)	MASS $^W/_{9.8m}$	K.E $E_k=^{mv^2}/_2$

DID YOU KNOW?

The gravitational potential energy stored in a block of stone when it was lifted to the top of a pyramid 2500 years ago is still there, unchanged. Making allowances for erosion or chipping, dropping the stone today could do as much work as when the stone was first put in place.

As you did this Investigate, you may have found that the kinetic energy was a bit less than the potential energy. Is this what you would have predicted? The work you put into the cart to raise it to the top of the ramp is stored in the cart as gravitational potential energy. As the cart rolls down the ramp, gravity accelerates it, turning the potential energy into kinetic energy—motion. When the cart leaves the ramp, does it have any potential energy left? Where is that energy now? If you had been able to do this Investigate on a friction-free surface, what do you think the relationship between the potential energy at the top of the ramp and the kinetic energy at the bottom would have been? You will learn what happened to the energy the cart lost going down the ramp later in this chapter. Simply by looking around, you can see many things in your environment that possess gravitational potential energy. Are there other ways in which work done on an object can be stored? Let's explore.

EXPLORE!

How is the work stored?

Hold a 20-N spring scale flat on the table. Grasp the hook and pull it until the scale reads about 10 N. Have another student measure the distance you moved the hook in centimeters. Now release the hook. What happens? Calculate the work you did on the scale. Don't forget to convert the centimeters to meters. Where was this work after you stopped pulling? Was there an increase in kinetic energy? Potential energy?

Because the scale is not moving after you do the work in the Explore, the work has not produced kinetic energy. However, you didn't lift the scale so it can't be gravitational potential energy. Where is the energy stored? Right! In the spring. You know that when you released the hook, the scale popped back to its original setting. The spring had stored the energy you put in, and that energy showed itself as motion—kinetic energy—when you released it. This kind of stored energy is called *elastic* potential energy. Where else do you see this type of energy storage?

In Figure 4-13, you see the force exerted by the football player's foot on the ball. As his foot follows through, work is done on the ball. The energy given to the ball by the foot is stored in the flattening, or compression, of the ball. As the ball goes back to its normal shape, this energy is released as kinetic energy. The ball moves away from the foot.

Energy is stored as elastic potential energy when work causes an object to be stretched or twisted, or if its shape is changed, as in the objects in Figure 4-13. The object must be capable of going back to its original shape in order to store energy in this way. Rubber bands, trampolines, the spring in a wind-up toy, and diving boards are other examples of objects that can store elastic potential energy. What other ones can you think of?

IS ENERGY USED UP?

What happens when you drop a tennis ball or golf ball from several feet above the floor? Of course, the ball bounces. Actually, it bounces several times, each time a little lower. The potential energy stored in the ball, because of its height, is converted to kinetic energy as it falls. When the ball hits the ground, it is compressed, storing the energy as elastic potential energy.

FIGURE 4-13. How is potential energy stored in these objects?

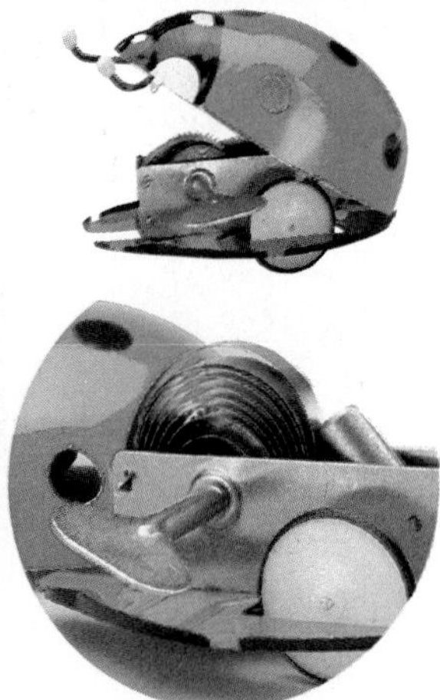

FIGURE 4-14. As the ball bounces, it loses some of its original energy and it becomes slightly warmer.

The energy of motion is stored as elastic potential energy as the ball is flattened. When it regains its shape, that potential energy does work on the ball, increasing its velocity in an upward direction. But why doesn't it bounce as high? Where did that energy go? Does the contact of the ball with the floor have anything to do with it? Let's find out.

FIND OUT!

Where did this energy go?

Attach a 20-N spring scale to the end of a shallow box. Place several books in the box. Pull the box with a steady force 1 m across the table or floor. Record the force needed. Now pull the box with a steady force 1 m across a rug or other rough surface at the same speed you used on the table. Record your measurement.

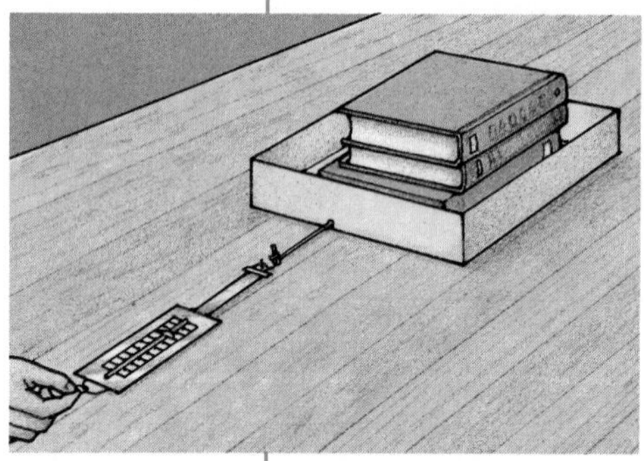

Conclude and Apply

1. Calculate the amount of work done in each case. Compare these values. Why do you think you had to do more work in one case than the other?
2. The work you did transferred energy from you to the box and books. Where is that energy now?

If you put your hand on the bottom of the box right after you finish dragging it, you might notice that the box is a bit warmer than it was before. The surface over which you dragged it would also be a bit warmer. This difference in temperature is so small that you might not be able to feel it, but here's an easy way to demonstrate what happens.

While holding your palms tightly together, move one hand across the other. Do this very fast. What happens to your hands? They get warm, don't they? You are doing work, and the work shows itself in warming your hands. In dragging the box across the table or rug, the work you do shows itself in heating the floor and the bottom of the box. We would say that the work done shows itself as thermal energy.

When you drop a tennis or golf ball, why does the ball bounce a little lower each time? Each time the ball strikes the ground, some of the energy is changed to thermal energy. The floor and the ball get just a little warmer. That energy is no longer available to move the ball.

Think back to the Investigate you did with the cart. Why was the kinetic energy of the rolling cart a little less than the potential energy the cart possessed at the top of the ramp? Where did that energy go? Right! The floor and the wheels of the cart became a little warmer. Some of the kinetic energy was converted to thermal energy.

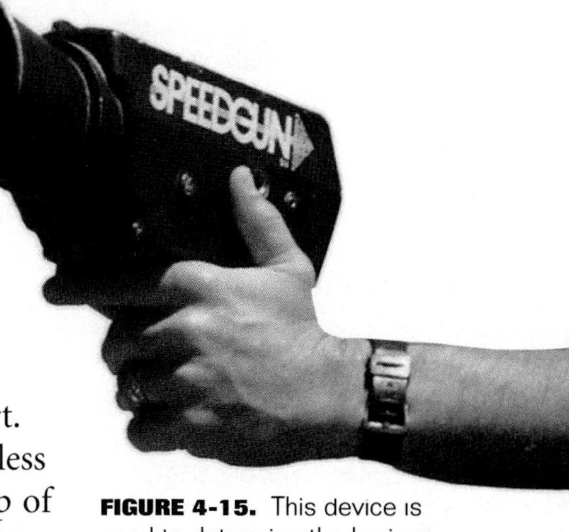

FIGURE 4-15. This device is used to determine the horizontal velocity of such objects as a tennis ball or a baseball.

ENERGY FROM WORK

You've seen that doing work on an object can give different results. If you throw a softball, it gains kinetic energy. If you lift the ball, you increase its gravitational potential energy. If you hit the softball with a bat, it compresses and stores the work as elastic potential energy. And if you roll the softball across the floor, it will eventually stop. The energy isn't used up or lost—it is now present as thermal energy in the ball and floor.

In the next section, we'll track work and energy through several different situations.

Check Your Understanding

1. Give two examples where work done on an object produces kinetic energy.
2. A 15 kg model plane flies horizontally at 2.5 m/s. Calculate its kinetic energy.
3. Which of these three is an example of work producing potential energy?
   a. putting on your hat
   b. carrying a box across the room
   c. hitting a golf ball with a club
4. Why would an arrow shot underwater not go as far as one shot with the same force into the air?
5. **APPLY:** You pick up a bean bag from the table and lift it over your head. Then you drop it to the floor. Discuss the changes in work and energy that take place during these actions. Don't forget to account for the energy after the bean bag has come to a stop.

4-4 Conservation of Energy

OBJECTIVES

In this section, you will

- describe how energy changes from one form to another;
- understand and apply the Law of Conservation of Energy.

KEY SCIENCE TERMS

Law of Conservation of Energy

ENERGY ON THE MOVE

When you do work on an object, such as throwing, hitting, or rolling a ball, you are transferring energy from yourself to that object—the ball. The energy may appear as kinetic energy, such as the movement of the ball, potential energy if you throw the ball into the air or hit it with a bat, or a combination of kinetic and thermal energy if you roll the ball. Let's find out how you can transfer energy to move an object.

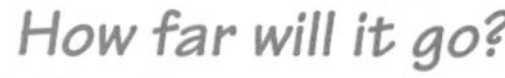

FIND OUT!

How far will it go? 

Obtain a set of materials containing a marble, foam cup, grooved ruler, balloon, tape, and wood splint or tongue depressor. Use these objects to transfer energy in such a way that your marble travels the greatest distance when you release it. You may not throw the marble. You must simply let it go from wherever your starting point is. Try to demonstrate as many different types of energy transfer as you can.

Conclude and Apply

In terms of energy, why did your marble eventually stop moving?

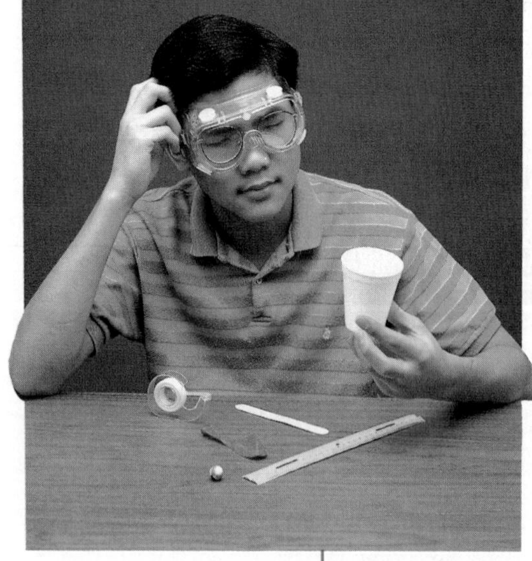

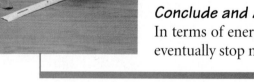

ENERGY IS LIKE MONEY

How is energy transfer, such as the one you just made, like saving and spending money? Let's say that you earn twenty dollars. You put ten dollars in the bank and pocket the other ten. The ten dollars you put into the bank is like potential money. The money in your pocket could be called kinetic money. You pay two dollars for a magazine. That money now belongs to the person who sold you the magazine. She puts it in the bank with the day's receipts and turns your kinetic money into potential money of her own.

FIGURE 4-16. Where did the money come from?

A friend wants to buy a birthday present for his sister so you give him three dollars. Your kinetic money becomes his kinetic money. You get change for the other five dollars and spend two dollars in quarters playing video games. The two dollars of kinetic money changed to another form.

Is there any more or less money than the twenty dollars you began with? No. It has simply moved from place to place and from form to form. When you spend energy on the various jobs you do, you must eventually replace that energy by eating, by consuming fuel. When you do work on an object and produce kinetic energy, that is like spending your kinetic money. When you lift your books, stretch a rubber band, or wind up the spring in a clock, you are putting energy into the bank. That energy can be used later to do work.

THE LAW OF CONSERVATION OF ENERGY

Work is simply the process of transferring energy from one form to another and from one place to another. You learned that doing work transfers energy, and that energy occurs in several forms. We have assumed that when energy disappears in one form, it appears in another, just as you saw happen with money and with your marble invention. We sense that the energy is still around, even if we can't directly observe it. It doesn't seem reasonable that it would just be destroyed. It can't just disappear, any more than it can suddenly appear from nothing. But do we have any proof of this? Let's try another activity to see if we can keep track of energy as it changes.

FIGURE 4-17. Where did the baton get its energy?

I N V E S T I G A T E !

4-2 THE MOTION OF A PENDULUM

What kinds of energy transfers take place in the motion of a pendulum?

PROBLEM

What happens to the energy of a pendulum?

MATERIALS

ring stand and ring
right-angle clamp
support rod and clamp
2 metersticks
2-hole rubber stopper, medium
100 cm of string
masking tape

PROCEDURE

1. Copy the data table. Make room for six trials.
2. Set up the apparatus as shown.
3. Use the masking tape to mark the center of the stopper. Use this line to **measure** heights above the tabletop.
4. Pull the stopper to one side. **Measure** the height of the stopper above the table. Record the measurement.

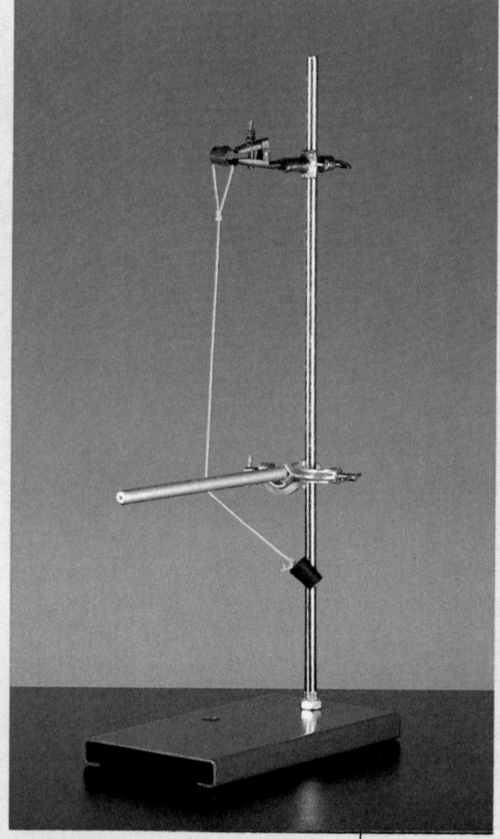

5. Release the stopper and let it swing. **Observe** carefully and measure the greatest height the stopper reaches just before it begins its return swing. Record.
6. Repeat Steps 4 and 5 twice, each time starting the stopper at a greater height.
7. Repeat Steps 4 through 6 with the cross arm in place. Begin the first swing below the cross arm, the second level with the cross arm, and the third above it. Record all data.

DATA AND OBSERVATIONS

TRIAL	STARTING HEIGHT	ENDING HEIGHT
1		
2		

ANALYZE

1. For a single swing without the cross arm, is the ending height of the stopper exactly the same as its starting height? Explain.
2. What is the highest point that the stopper will reach when it hits the cross arm?

CONCLUDE AND APPLY

3. Write or draw a description that **sequences** the changes in kinetic and potential energy of the stopper at various points on its arc.
4. If you could **calculate** the maximum potential energy and kinetic energy of the stopper, what would you **infer** about their relationship?
5. What **caused** the string to wrap completely around the cross arm?
6. **Going Further:** Could a roller coaster be built with its highest point on one of the middle hills? Explain.

Study the diagram in Figure 4-18. Is this similar to the way you answered Question 3 in Investigate? Do you see that this is a good way to describe the continuing energy change that is occurring? If there were no friction where the pendulum is tied and no loss of thermal energy to the air, the pendulum would continue to swing back and forth forever. The potential energy you put in by lifting the stopper would change to kinetic energy and back to potential energy over and over again. When you measure the thermal energy lost to friction, you find that when you add up all the energy at any point during the action, the *total* amount of energy remains the same. It is *conserved* as it transfers from one type to another. This is called the **Law of Conservation of Energy.** In effect, this law says that energy can't be created out of nothing, nor can it be destroyed. Energy may be changed to other forms or transferred to other objects, but the total energy remains unchanged. Energy is conserved.

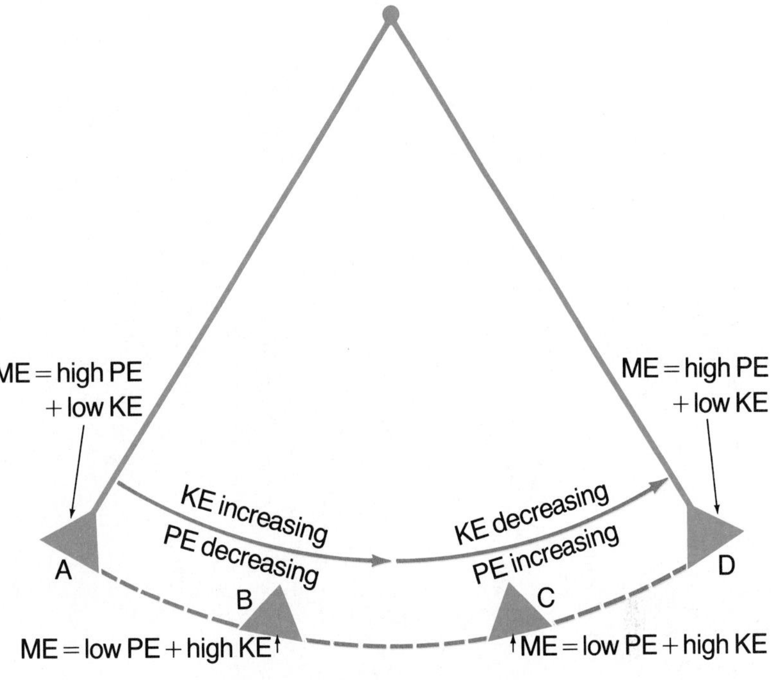

FIGURE 4-18. The total mechanical energy (K. E. + P. E.) of the pendulum is always the same.

Why did your pendulum wrap itself around the cross arm when you started it above the level of the cross arm? Each time, as the kinetic energy at the bottom of the swing was converted back into potential energy, the stopper tried to reach the same height as where it started. But the cross arm blocked it. Because the stopper hadn't completely converted its kinetic energy into potential energy, it still had kinetic energy left. Kinetic energy is moving energy. The stopper moved in the only direction left open to it by the string. It went around the cross arm. Eventually, it stopped when all of its energy had been transferred into thermal energy.

SKILLBUILDER

SEQUENCING

Pick up a tennis ball from the floor, throw it against a wall, and catch it. Sequence the transfers of energy from the food you have eaten for fuel to the time the ball comes to a complete stop. If you need help, refer to the **Skill Handbook** on page 678.

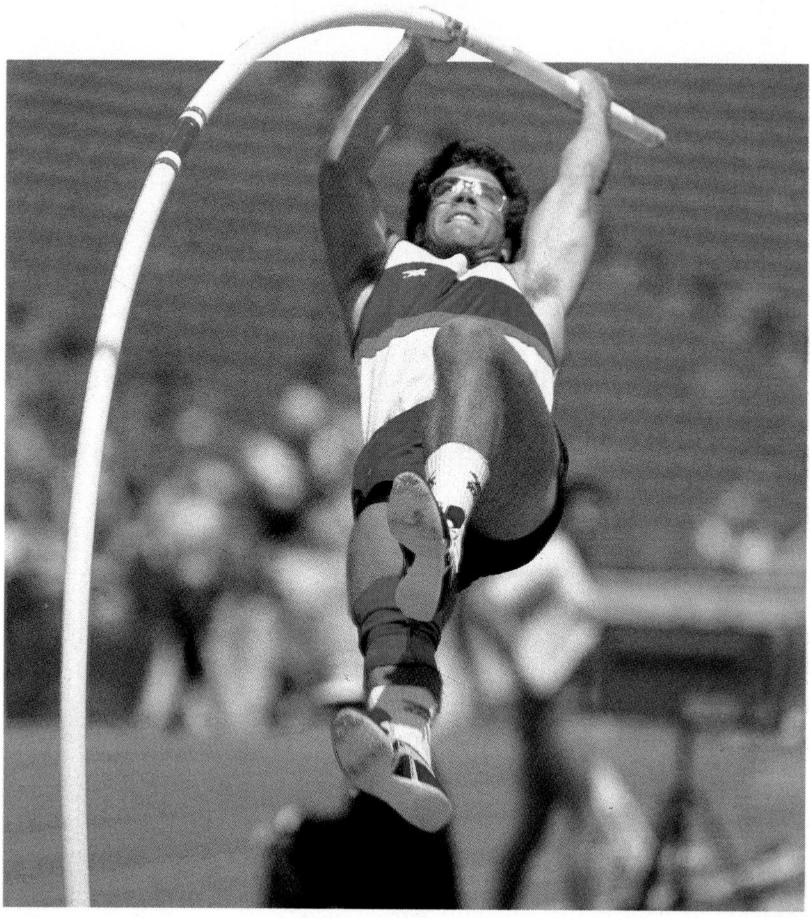

FIGURE 4-19. The kinetic energy of a pole vaulter is first stored in the bending of the pole. As the pole straightens and the vaulter is lifted, it is converted into gravitational potential energy.

Whenever it appears that energy is lost, scientists look for something to explain its disappearance. The Law of Conservation of Energy has always worked. There are no cases in which energy either appears or disappears without coming from or ending up somewhere else.

Whenever energy seems to disappear, scientists have found another form of energy. Some other forms are electrical, electromagnetic, and nuclear energy. Although we still use these terms, scientists now believe that there are only two basic kinds of energy. Regardless of where the energy comes from, it can be described as kinetic or potential. For example, what we have been calling thermal energy is another combination of kinetic and potential energy; you will learn more about this kind of energy in Chapter 6.

Check Your Understanding

1. Give one example for each of the following energy changes:
   a. gravitational potential energy to kinetic energy
   b. kinetic energy to elastic potential energy
2. You are riding your bike on a level surface. Why do you have to keep pedaling to maintain the same speed?
3. Trace the energy changes as a heavy rock rolls down a hill. Is any energy lost?
4. **APPLY:** When a machine burns fuel to do a job only part of the chemical potential energy in the fuel comes out as work on the other end. What can you do to prevent loss of energy to thermal energy?

EXPANDING YOUR VIEW

CONTENTS

A Closer Look
Energetic Toy 121

Earth Science Connection
Voyage of the Century 122

Technology Connection
The Search for Perpetual Motion 123

Music Connection
Musical Motion 124

How It Works
Vacuum Cleaner 125

History Connection
What's In a Name? 126

A CLOSER LOOK

ENERGETIC TOY

Your baby sister is playing with her favorite toy. At first, it seems like an ordinary roll-back toy. But watch closely, and you'll notice that this toy demonstrates how energy can be converted from one form to another. Let's build such a toy so we can take a better look.

Materials

- one pound coffee can
- 2 plastic coffee can lids
- heavy rubber band—folded length about 17 cm
- lead fishing weight, about 2.5 cm long

Procedure

1. Remove both ends from the coffee can.
2. With a skewer or the tip of a scissor, poke two holes in each lid, about 2.5 cm apart. Make the holes just large enough so that the rubber band can pass through them.
3. Cut the rubber band at one end. From the inside of one lid, thread the rubber band up through one hole and back down through the other. Even the ends.
4. Stretching the rubber band slightly, attach the fishing weight to both ends of the rubber band. You may run the rubber band ends through the loop of the weight or tie the weight to both pieces with string.
5. Place the lid and rubber band assembly on the can.
6. Feed each end of the rubber band through the holes on the other lid and tie the ends together. Attach the second lid.

YOU TRY IT!

Place the toy on a smooth surface and push. What happens? How would you explain this motion? Make a list of the energy changes, beginning with your push. Be sure to state whether the energy is kinetic or potential and which type of potential energy is involved. Why does the toy eventually stop?

EARTH SCIENCE CONNECTION

VOYAGE OF THE CENTURY

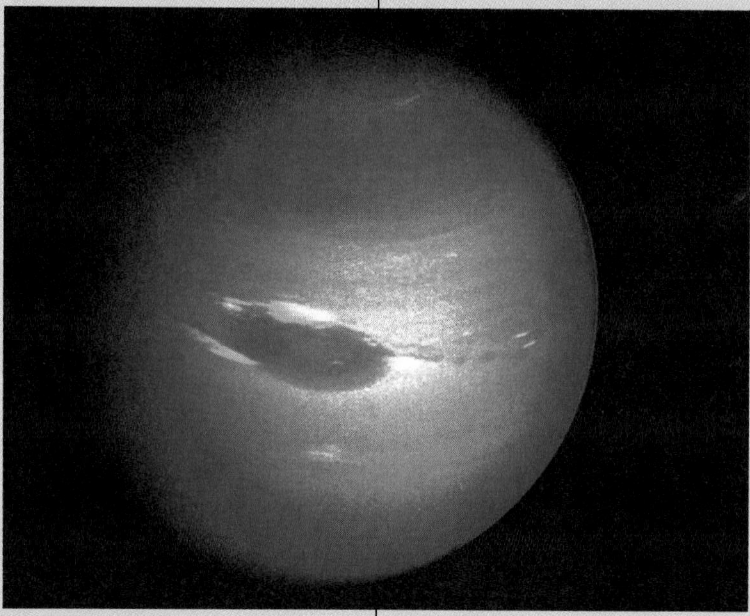

The twin uncrewed space probes *Voyager 1* and *Voyager 2* traveled to Jupiter, Saturn, Uranus, and Neptune. Through the transmissions they beamed to Earth, the world had the incredible experience of riding along and seeing sights never before possible.

By June of 1989, *Voyager 2* had traveled more than 2.8 billion miles to reach Neptune. When the probe gave us our first look at this planet, *Voyager 2* was traveling at a speed greater than when it had left Earth nearly 12 years earlier. A photo of Neptune taken by *Voyager* is shown here. The space probe revealed that Neptune has dark-colored, stormlike features in its atmosphere similar to the Great Red Spot on Jupiter. *Voyager* also discovered that Neptune has a total of eight moons as well as rings that are thin in some places and thick in other places.

How do space probes such as *Voyager* get the energy they need for space travel? Space scientists use a slingshot effect to provide additional kinetic energy to space probes. This effect reduces the amount of fuel the probes must carry. As a probe comes near a planet, it experiences the gravitational pull of the planet. The probe gains potential energy as a result of this gravitational pull. As the probe approaches the planet, this potential energy is converted to kinetic energy. The probe then speeds up and reaches its greatest speed as it moves behind the planet. Behind the planet, the probe's path then takes it away from the surface. The kinetic energy is again changed to potential energy. However, the probe's path leaving the planet is a different shape than the path of the probe approaching the planet. Not all of the kinetic energy it gains is needed to pull it away from the planet's surface. Therefore, the probe has a bit more kinetic energy when it leaves the planet than it had when it approached the planet. This extra energy is used by space probes for their long voyages.

WHAT DO YOU THINK?

What are the advantages of using the slingshot effect? What other source of energy is present in space? How might the probes use this energy instead of providing their own fuel?

TECHNOLOGY CONNECTION

THE SEARCH FOR PERPETUAL MOTION

On July 31, 1790, the first patent in the United States was granted by President George Washington and Secretary of State Thomas Jefferson. Two hundred years later, over five million patents have been issued—a tribute to inventors who don't believe "It can't be done." Just when it seems that everything has been invented that can be invented, someone comes up with a truly revolutionary idea. We say, "Why didn't I think of that? It's so simple!"

One idea that has always fascinated inventors is the idea of a perpetual motion machine. By definition, this is a machine that, once set in motion, will continue with no additional energy required. With the energy shortages being experienced in many parts of the world, this would be a wonderful accomplishment. But scientists believe that this is impossible because the idea violates certain laws.

First, the law of conservation of energy states that energy can neither be created nor destroyed—it can only be transformed into work or heat. In other words, you can't get something from nothing. But what if energy could somehow be recaptured and used over and over? Can the work and heat be converted back into energy to do the work over again? One example of such a machine is a battery that powers a motor that runs a generator that recharges the battery. It sounds good, but why would such a machine not continue forever?

There are moving parts in the device mentioned above. As parts of machines move

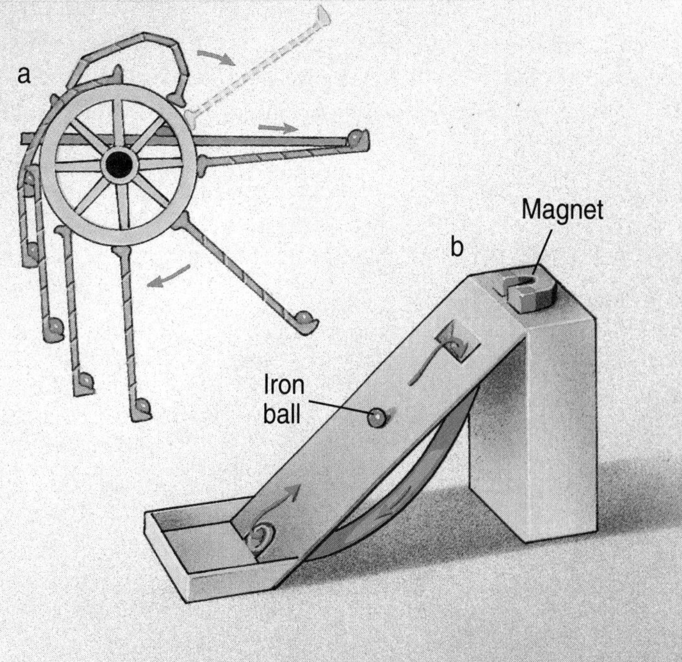

WHAT DO YOU THINK?

Here are two more ideas for perpetual motion machines. Can you find the problem with each of them? Remember that these are ideas for perpetual motion machines. They were not necessarily built!

1. The wheel shown in diagram A is supposed to turn forever because it is always heavier on one side than the other. Steel balls are held in curved spokes that unwind as they reach the top of the wheel. The ball rolls toward the rim, forcing the right side of the wheel down. As the arm moves past horizontal, the ball rolls back to the end. Will the wheel keep turning, once started?
2. In the design shown in diagram B, a magnet at the top of the column is supposed to pull the iron ball up the ramp. As the ball nears the top, gravity will make it fall through the hole, roll back to the start, and be pulled up again. Will it work? If you can't figure out the answer, try it and see for yourself.

against one another, the friction produces thermal energy that ends up distributed through the particles in the air.

Think about allowing a cup of water to boil away on top of a stove. Can you get back the cup of water? Only if you could gather every bit of the water vapor that had escaped into the air. Just as it would require work and energy to gather all the water vapor, it would require work and energy to recapture thermal energy that was distributed in the air and convert it to a form that would do work. Where does that energy come from?

Some would say that people who try to invent perpetual motion machines are foolish and are ignoring the laws of science. Do you think that this is necessarily true? What, if anything, might these people accomplish?

Music CONNECTION

MUSICAL MOTION

While inventors tried and failed to build a working perpetual motion machine, composers have created their own ideas of perpetual motion. Over the years, composers such as Mozart, Bach, Strauss, and Paganini have written musical selections that attempt to give an auditory sense of what perpetual motion would be like.

One approach to this idea was used by the Austro-American composer Arnold Schönberg (1874-1951). Schönberg, pictured here, chose to use the twelve tones in an octave—the black and white keys in a piano octave. The tones were arranged into a pleasing combination, but each tone could be used only once. In this way, Schönberg created a sort of musical closed system that repeated over and over. Variations were allowed, but they all had to be based on the original series. This style reflects the repetitious nature of perpetual motion. How would you represent perpetual motion musically? Would you make your composition fast or slow, loud or soft?

WHAT DO YOU THINK?

Listen to the musical composition *Perpetual Motion* by either Johann Strauss or Paganini. What do you picture when you hear the music? Why do you think the composer chose the particular instruments used? Would the music have had the same effect if it had been played on different instruments or at a different speed? If you had to select a piece of popular music that represents perpetual motion, which one would you choose? Why?

HOW IT WORKS

VACUUM CLEANER

Sometimes "home energy conservation" refers to the use of appliances to conserve human energy. Try telling that to the users of the first vacuum cleaners. One early model, invented around 1908, was made of steel and weighed a hefty 60 pounds. Despite the fact that today's cleaners usually weigh between 6 and 30 pounds, they work on the same principle.

A fan driven by an electric motor blows air through the unit. The moving air creates an area of low pressure. This reduces pressure inside the bag and hose. Since air pressure is now greater than the pressure at the nozzle, dirt and dust are gathered in the air that rushes in to even out the pressure. The fan forces this dirt-filled air into a bag, where the dust is trapped, and the air is blown out.

There are two main types of vacuum cleaners—canisters (or tanks) and uprights. A canister vacuum cleaner has a long, flexible hose that ends in a detachable nozzle. Usually a variety of nozzles come with the vacuum cleaner as attachments. The body of this type of cleaner contains a bag and a powerful fan. Dirt is sucked into the bag through the hose.

An upright vacuum cleaner has a small fan in its base. The base of the machine also contains an agitator—a rotating cylinder covered with bristles that loosens dirt. Dirt is sucked upward into a bag attached to the vacuum cleaner's handle. In addition, there are vacuum cleaners that have both a canister unit for strong suction and an agitator in the nozzle.

WHAT DO YOU THINK?

Make a list of some devices that are considered "labor-savers." If you think of labor as work and work as requiring energy, are these devices really "savers"? Explain your answer.

Some vacuum cleaners could function as leaf blowers. Study the diagrams and suggest what changes might be necessary to do this.

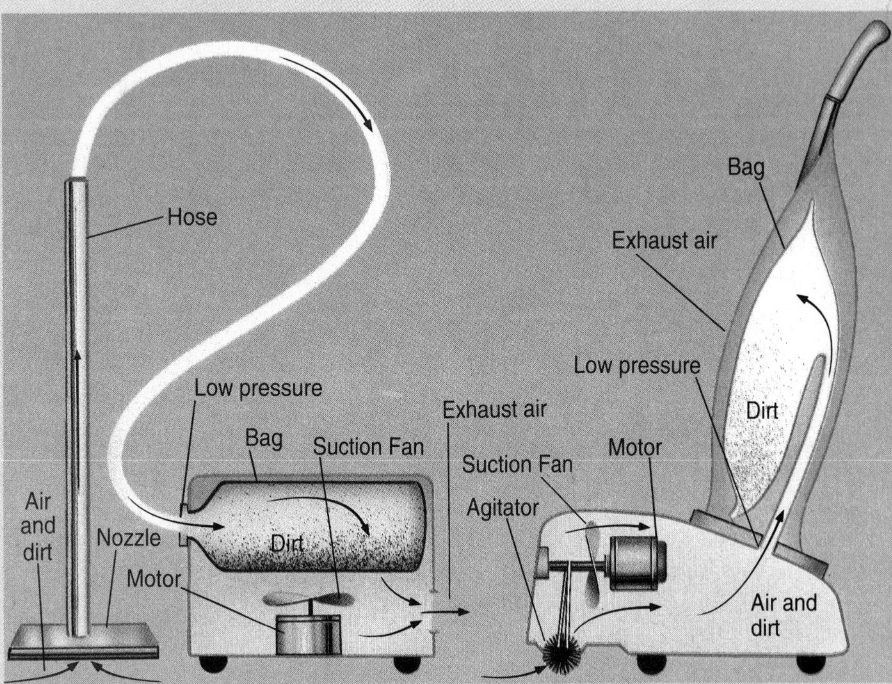

History CONNECTION

WHAT'S IN A NAME?

Can you imagine how a scientist would answer this question? You've learned that in science, names are very important. However, sometimes for convenience, scientists substitute a shorter name for one that is longer. One example is the use of the term *joule* when referring to the newton meter. Who was Joule, and how did he come to have a unit of work named after him?

James Prescott Joule was an English brewer who lived from 1818 to 1889. His hobby was physics. During the 1840s, he put the law of conservation of energy to a thorough test. He believed that if the law applied to all work and all forms of energy, then it had to be shown that one form of energy could be converted into another quantitatively.

In other words, in energy conversions all energy must be accounted for—no energy should be lost in the process, and no energy created. Joule also measured heat produced by an electric current, the friction of water against glass, and so on. He found that a fixed amount of one kind of energy was converted into a fixed amount of another kind. In fact, no energy was either lost or created. It is in his honor that we call a unit of work a *joule.* His ideas were so fundamental to today's understanding of work and energy that most countries use the SI unit *joule* as the unit of energy.

WHAT DO YOU THINK?

It is common to name scientific discoveries after the men and women who make them. In addition to Joule, make a list of other scientists honored in this way.

Imagine that your name is commonly used to describe an important discovery. Describe your discovery.

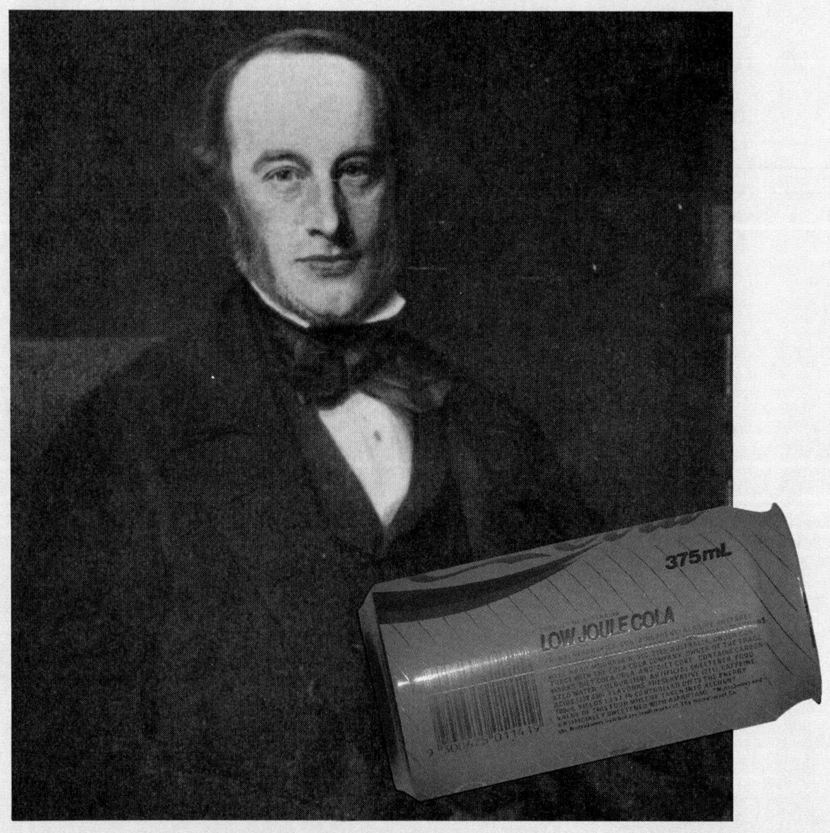

Chapter 4

Reviewing Main Ideas

1. Energy comes from fuel and can be used to do work. The more work is done, the more fuel is needed.

2. Work is energy transferred through motion. When a force acts in the direction of motion, work is done.

3. Kinetic energy is energy of motion. Potential energy is the stored energy of position. Although there are many types of energy, all energy exists in these two forms.

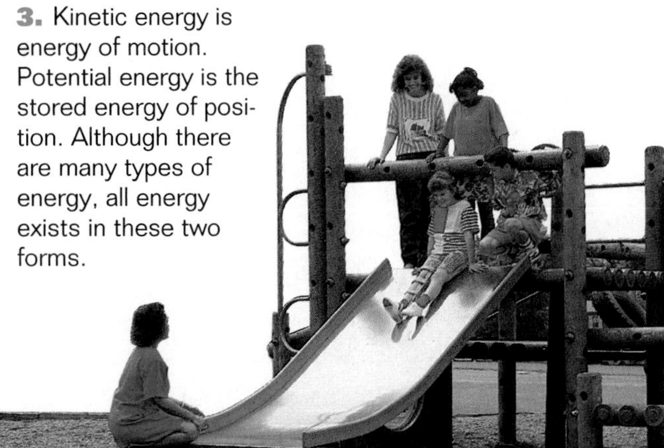

4. Energy can change from one form to another, but it cannot be created or destroyed.

Chapter 4

Chapter Review

USING KEY SCIENCE TERMS

kinetic energy
Law of Conservation of Energy
potential energy
work

Using the list above, replace the underlined words with the correct key science term.

1. Stored energy is available to do work.
2. When you roll a ball across the floor and it stops, you can figure out the amount of thermal energy produced by using the idea that energy cannot be created or destroyed.
3. If you run into a wall, your energy of motion is more likely to do work upon your body than on the wall.
4. When you transfer energy through motion, you must use fuel.

UNDERSTANDING IDEAS

Choose the best answer to complete each sentence.

1. The basic SI unit of energy is the ____.
   a. meter c. newton
   b. joule d. watt
2. If the velocity of an object increases, ____ will also increase.
   a. kinetic energy c. mass
   b. potential energy d. weight
3. Which of these does not represent work done on a rock in a scientific sense?
   a. lifting a rock c. holding a rock
   b. throwing a rock d. pushing a rock
4. The ____of an object depends upon its position.
   a. kinetic energy c. velocity
   b. work d. potential energy
5. When you slide a book across the table and the book stops moving, its kinetic energy has been transformed into ____.
   a. gravitational potential energy
   b. thermal energy
   c. elastic potential energy
   d. chemical potential energy
6. To do twice as much work, how much fuel do you need?
   a. half as much
   b. four times as much
   c. three times as much
   d. twice as much
7. The formula for calculating work is ____.
   a. Work = force × distance
   b. Work = force/distance
   c. Work = mass × velocity
   d. Work = force × velocity

8. Which of these is not a form of potential energy?
   a. kinetic c. gravitational
   b. chemical d. elastic
9. Kinetic energy is directly proportional to _____.
   a. volume c. mass
   b. force d. position

CRITICAL THINKING

Use your understanding of the concepts developed in the chapter to answer each of the following questions.

1. List the examples of kinetic energy, gravitational potential energy, elastic potential energy, chemical potential energy, and thermal energy found in the picture.

2. On Monday morning, you see a small weed growing through a crack in the sidewalk. On Thursday, you notice that the weed has grown bigger. How does this prove that the weed has used energy?
3. Which requires more work: lifting one 100-N weight 3 m off the ground, or lifting each of three 50-N weights 2 m off the ground?

PROBLEM SOLVING

Read the following problem and discuss your answers in a brief paragraph.

Jake loves swimming and wants to be a coach. He doesn't see how science can help swimmers.

1. How could the definition of work help him advise a swimmer how to hold his or her hands as he or she strokes through the water?
2. How could an understanding of potential energy and kinetic energy help a diver know when to flex his or her knees and when to leave the board?

CONNECTING IDEAS

Discuss each of the following in a brief paragraph.

1. A dancer lifts a 400-N ballerina 1.4 m off the ground and holds her there for 5 seconds. How much work did he do?

2. In Chapter 1, you learned that opposing forces can cancel each other. Does this mean that their energies also cancel each other? Explain.

3. **A CLOSER LOOK** Why did the roll-back toy eventually come to a stop?

4. **EARTH SCIENCE CONNECTION** What are the advantages of using the slingshot effect in planning the path of space vehicles such as *Voyager*?

5. **HOW IT WORKS** How can the operation of a vacuum cleaner be compared to drinking through a straw?

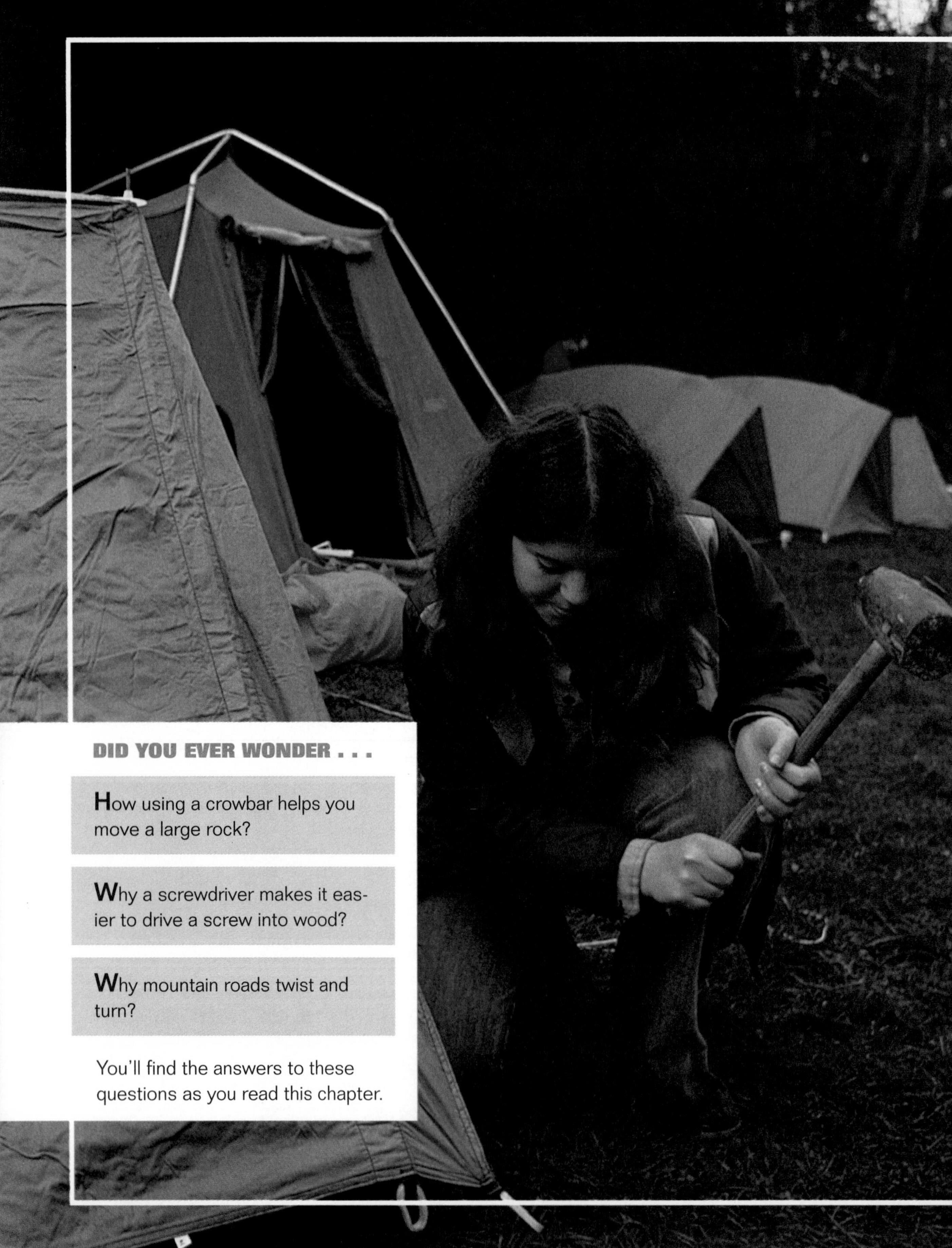

DID YOU EVER WONDER . . .

How using a crowbar helps you move a large rock?

Why a screwdriver makes it easier to drive a screw into wood?

Why mountain roads twist and turn?

You'll find the answers to these questions as you read this chapter.

Chapter 5

Machines

The steep road curves back and forth as it twists up the mountain. A shadowy forest is on one side, a steep drop-off on the other. Three other cars from your group are on the road below. A flag flying above a building tells you that park headquarters is just ahead.

Everyone helps set up camp. You pound tent stakes into the ground with a hammer, while a friend fills water jugs at the outdoor faucet. Two older campers use a crowbar to move a large rock that's in the way of a tent. A counselor is splitting a log with an ax.

It may not seem obvious, but these campers are using several machines. How many can you identify? Certainly, the cars are machines. But there are many more machines at this camp.

We use machines to make jobs easier. Can you imagine trying to pound in a nail without a hammer or chop wood without an axe? What if you had to climb the flagpole to get the flag to the top? What would the world be like if we didn't have machines? In this chapter, you'll use some simple machines, determine how they operate, and find out how much easier they can make the jobs you do.

EXPLORE!

How can a machine make it easier to move an object?

Stack two books on a flat desk or table so the books barely hang over the edge of the desk. Place your fingertips under the bottom book and lift the books with your fingers. Set the books flat on the surface again and slide a ruler under the bottom book. Push up on one end of the ruler to lift the books. Is it easier to lift the books using the ruler?

5-1 Simple Machines

OBJECTIVES

In this section, you will

- identify the six types of simple machines;
- describe how each simple machine makes completing a job easier;
- explain why machines do not reduce the amount of work that must be done.

KEY SCIENCE TERMS

effort force
resistance force
lever
wheel and axle
pulley
inclined plane
screw
wedge

MAKING JOBS EASIER

What do you usually think of when you think of machines? Cars, vacuum cleaners, elevators, bulldozers, and forklifts are machines. But there are also simple machines that don't require motors. In the Explore at the beginning of the chapter, you did work to lift a stack of books. It was not very much work. Even so, you noticed that it took less force to lift the books with the ruler than with just your fingertips. You were using the ruler as a machine.

Machines make work require less of your effort. Think back to the campers at the beginning of the chapter. It's more convenient for a camper to push down on a crowbar to raise a heavy rock than to try to lift something so large and awkward!

When a machine is used to do work, two kinds of force are involved. The force applied *to* the machine (the force you exert) is called the **effort force**. The force applied *by* the machine to act against another force, like gravity or friction, is called the **resistance force.** When campers use a crowbar to move a rock, what is the effort force? What is the resistance force?

Although machines make work easier, they do not actually reduce the amount of work that has to be done. The weight of a rock doesn't change just because you use a crowbar to move it—the same amount of weight has to be moved. How can a machine make work easier if it doesn't reduce the amount of work that has to be done? Let's take a look at the six types of simple machines and find out.

LEVER

FIGURE 5-1. You don't need a can opener to open this package of cocoa. All you need is a lever.

Sitting around the campfire after dark seems like a perfect time for hot chocolate and toasted marshmallows. You dig around in the food boxes for the cocoa and, after a long search, you finally find it. The can has one of those metal lids that fits tightly into the top. You find a spoon and slip the end of the handle under the edge of the lid. One push on the spoon, and the lid comes right off.

Could you have pried off the lid using just your fingers? Let's explore why it is easier with a can opener.

EXPLORE!

How does a lever work?

Watch carefully as your teacher or classmate uses a spoon handle to pry the lid off a can. How far did he or she have to push down on the spoon? How far up does the tip of the spoon handle go to lift the lid? Are these two distances the same or different?

Again, watch as your teacher or a classmate pries the lid off the can. Does the spoon handle rest on a part of the can while the lifting is being done? Look at the length of spoon between his or her hand and the can's edge. How does that length compare to the length of spoon between the can's edge and the lid? What direction is the force he or she exerts on the spoon? In which direction does the lid move?

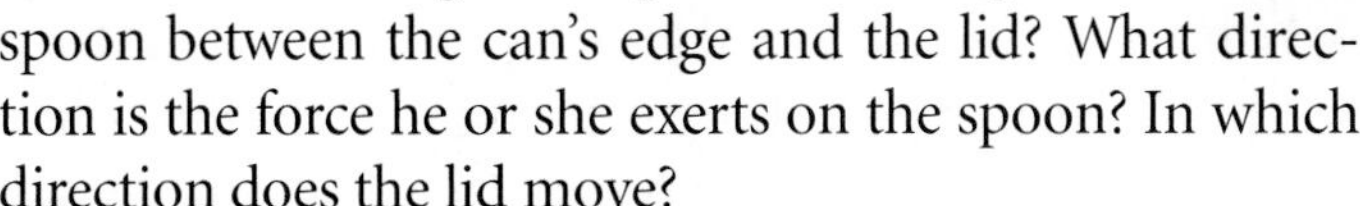

When you use a lever such as the spoon handle, you exert a small force over a long distance. At the same time, the lever exerts a large resistance force over a short distance. Recall the definition of work you learned in Chapter 4:

$$\text{force (N)} \times \text{distance (m)} = \text{work (J)}$$

Think about the Explore activity. Suppose you pushed down on the spoon with a force of 20 N exerted over a distance of 0.1 m:

$$20\text{ N} \times 0.1\text{ m} = 2\text{ J}$$

At the same time, the lever pushed up on the lid with a force of 200 N over a distance of 0.01 m:

$$200\text{ N} \times 0.01\text{ m} = 2\text{ J}$$

In each case, the work done was the same, 2 J. The lever did not reduce the amount of work that had to be done, but it made the job easier because it increased the force

FIGURE 5-2. These are common examples of levers.

you were able to exert on the lid. The lever made the job easier by changing the distance over which the force moved. The smaller effort force (your pushing on the spoon) moved over a longer distance than the resistance force (the lever pushing up the lid). The lever also changed the direction of the force. You pushed *down* on the spoon to pry *up* the lid. The crowbar the campers used to move the rock is a lever. A seesaw is also a lever.

A **lever** is a bar that turns or pivots on a fixed point called a fulcrum. The fulcrum for the spoon handle is the edge of the can. The fulcrum for the campers' crowbar is a small rock or pile of dirt placed under the crowbar. What is the fulcrum for a seesaw?

WHEEL AND AXLE

The water supply at the campground comes from an outdoor faucet. It's your turn to help fill water jugs. You turn the faucet handle to the left (or counterclockwise), and water flows. Turn the handle to the right (or clockwise), and the flow stops.

Locate the handle of the faucet in Figure 5-3. Which would be easier to turn, the faucet handle or the narrower shaft it's attached to?

The handle of the water faucet, like the knob of a doorknob, is a wheel. Each wheel rotates around its center. The shaft attached to the center of the wheel is an axle. You can think of an axle as a small wheel attached to the center of a larger wheel. The wheel and the axle always rotate together.

FIGURE 5-3. A water faucet is an example of a wheel and axle. The round faucet handle is a wheel, and the shaft in the center is an axle.

How does the wheel and axle make it easier to turn a faucet handle or a doorknob? The wheel is larger than the axle, so it's easier for your hand to grasp. Like the lever, the **wheel and axle** also changes the distance over which the effort force moves. Look at the distance moved by the point on the outside edge of the wheels in Figure 5-4. Compare that to the distance moved by a point on the outside edge of each axle. Which point travels farther, the one on the wheel or the one on the axle? When you use a wheel and axle, you exert a smaller effort force over a longer distance. The machine exerts a greater resistance force over a shorter distance. The bigger the wheel, the longer the distance you must move but the smaller the effort force you need to exert.

We have developed many uses for the wheel and axle. You already know this simple machine makes it easier to move cars, carts, wheelchairs, and wagons. But there are also other, less obvious uses for the wheel and axle. Some of these are illustrated in Figure 5-4. They include steering wheels and windmills. All trade force for distance.

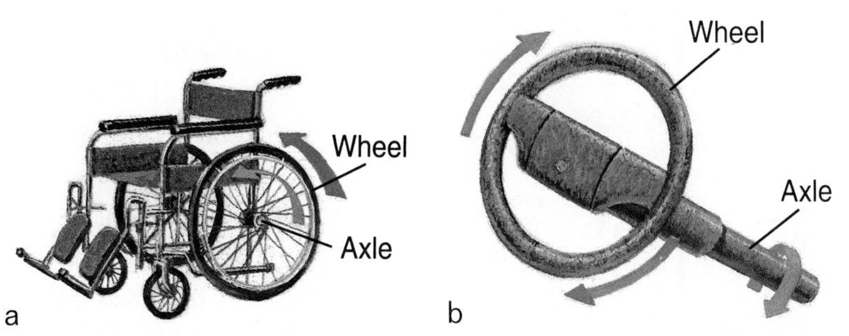

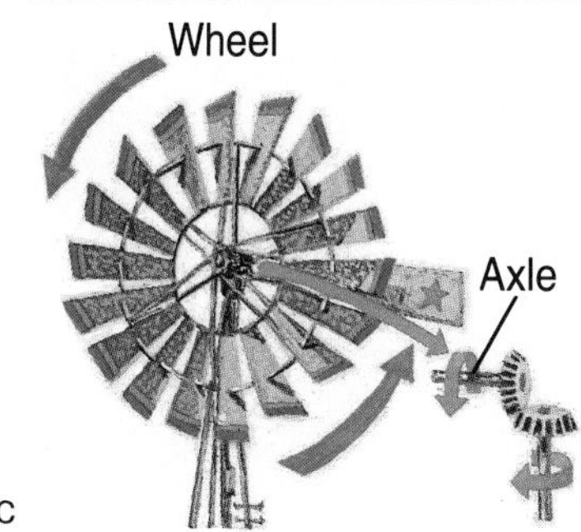

FIGURE 5-4. You know that wheelchairs (a) use the wheel and axle. Did you know that steering wheels (b) and windmills (c) are also examples of the wheel and axle?

PULLEY

It is early on the second morning at camp. You take a walk up to park headquarters. As you go around to the front of the building, you find the ranger is preparing to raise the flag. You help unfold it, and the ranger lets you hook the flag onto the rope and hoist it up the flagpole. You pull down on one strand of rope while the flag goes up with the other strand. Is this easier than having to climb up the flagpole? Have you done any work?

A **pulley** is a wheel that has a rope or chain passing over it. Usually, the wheel of a pulley has a groove around its

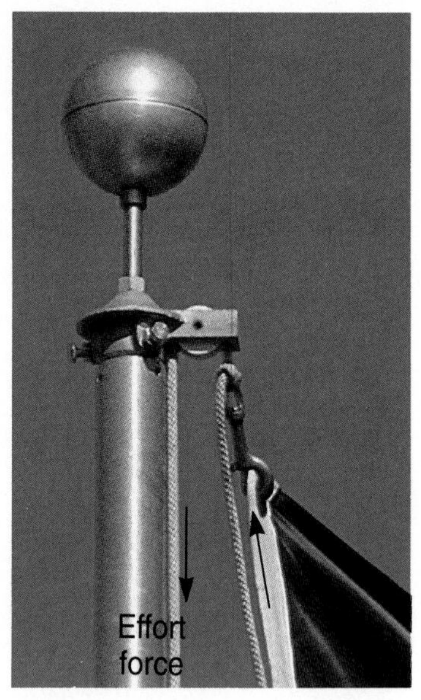

FIGURE 5-5. The single pulley at the top of the flagpole makes it easier to raise and lower the flag because pulling down on one strand of rope causes the other to go up.

edge into which the rope fits. The type of pulley used to raise and lower a flag is attached to the top of the flagpole. This is the simplest type of pulley. It's called a single fixed pulley because it's attached to something that doesn't move.

Name some other uses for fixed pulleys. Clotheslines hung between buildings use fixed pulleys. You pull on one side of the clothesline as you hang the clothes, then pull on the other side when you want to bring the clothes in.

If you have drapes at home, they probably use two fixed pulleys. You pull down the cord on one side of the pulley to open the drapes, and you pull down on the other side to close them. Fixed pulleys change the direction of the force that's applied to an object, but not the amount of force. Can the force exerted to get a job done be reduced when a pulley is used? Let's find out.

FIND OUT!

Can a pulley reduce the force you have to exert to get a job done?

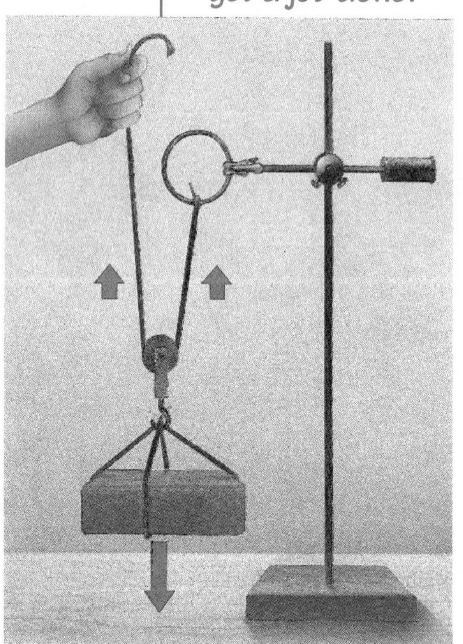

You will need a brick, ring and ring stand, two pieces of string, and a pulley. Tie one end of the first string to the ring stand. Place the pulley in the center of that string, as shown in the figure. Tie the second piece of string around the brick so you can attach the brick to the hook of the pulley.

Now try your assembly. Pull up on the free end of the string. Feel the force you exert when you pick up the brick with the pulley. Compare that force with the force you exert when you pick up the brick with your hands. Which requires more effort from you?

Conclude and Apply

1. How far did you pull up on the free end of the rope?
2. How far did the brick move?
3. Did the pulley reduce the amount of force you had to exert to move the brick?

You've just demonstrated how a single movable pulley works. A single movable pulley increases the effect of the effort force and reduces the amount of effort you must exert to get a job done. But a single movable pulley does not change the direction of the force. A fixed pulley changes the direction of the force, but it does not increase force. A movable pulley increases force but does not change the direction of force.

FIGURE 5-6. This movable pulley does not change the direction of the force and requires less effort.

INCLINED PLANE

A pulley, or a combination of pulleys, can help you lift heavy loads. Is there another simple machine that can help lift heavy objects? Suppose you need to lift a 100-pound box of camping gear a distance of 3 feet, from the ground into the back of a van. Lifting the box straight up and into the van would be difficult. But if you use a board to make a ramp, you could probably push the box up, even though you would have to exert force against the friction between the box and the board.

Look at the diagrams in Figure 5-7. Describe the relationship between the length of the ramp and how much easier the job would be.

If you could lift the box straight up, you would be exerting the largest possible effort force over the smallest possible distance. If you used a ramp, you would reduce your effort by increasing the distance you move the box. An **inclined plane** is a ramp or slope that reduces the force you need to exert to lift something. The inclined plane increases the effort force. Does it change the direction of force?

FIGURE 5-7. An inclined plane makes it easier to move a heavy object from the ground to the van. A longer ramp increases the distance you must push the box, but decreases the effort you must exert.

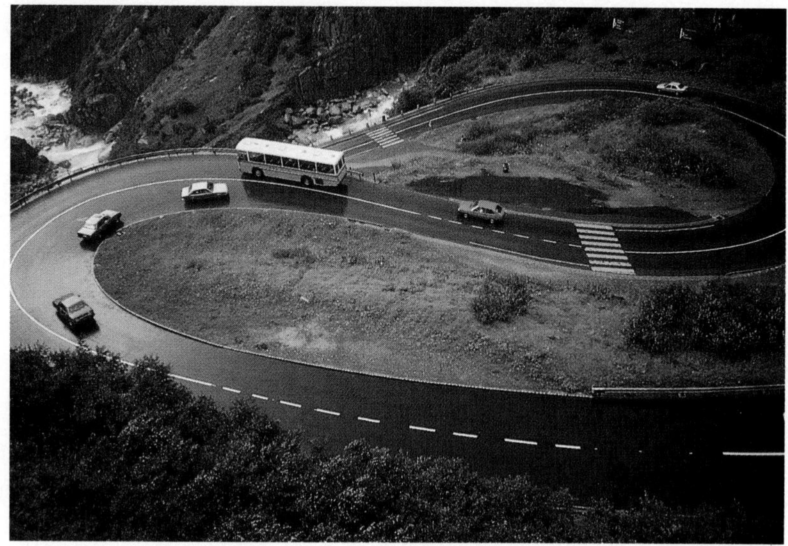

FIGURE 5-8. A winding mountain road is an inclined plane. By increasing the distance traveled, the mountain road decreases the effort force needed to get to the top of the mountain.

DID YOU KNOW?

The lever was one of the first tools used by humans. It was used for thousands of years before anyone described the principles of its operation. About 2200 years ago, a Greek mathematician named Archimedes explained how the lever works.

The campers drove up a winding mountain road to get to their campsite. Can you explain why mountain roads have so many sharp turns? Going straight up a steep mountain is much more difficult than going up a long, gradual slope. A mountain road is a type of inclined plane that allows cars to be raised to the tops of mountains. An inclined plane doesn't have to be straight. The many twists and turns of the mountain road give more length to the ramp, which then reduces the effort force needed.

What are some of the inclined planes you see around you every day? Driveways, ramps in parking garages? Most buildings with entrances that are above or below sidewalk level have a ramp in addition to steps. The ramp makes the building accessible to people in wheelchairs, and makes it easier for people to use carts to move heavy objects into and out of the building.

SCREW

Tomorrow, the counselors are going to drive the campers and their bicycles to the top of the mountain so the campers can ride their bikes back down to camp. This afternoon, you help put together a bicycle rack for one of the cars. You use a screwdriver to turn the screws that hold the rack to the car. Let's find out whether a screwdriver and screws are examples of simple machines.

FIND OUT!

Are screwdrivers and screws simple machines?

You will need materials like those shown in the picture: a board with a hole drilled partially through it, a screwdriver, and a wood screw. Use the screwdriver to drive the screw part of the way into the hole. Now try using your fingers to turn the screw into the hole. Can you do it? Complete the job using the screwdriver. Do you think you could have finished this task if the screwdriver had no handle?

Use the screwdriver to slowly withdraw the screw from the hole.

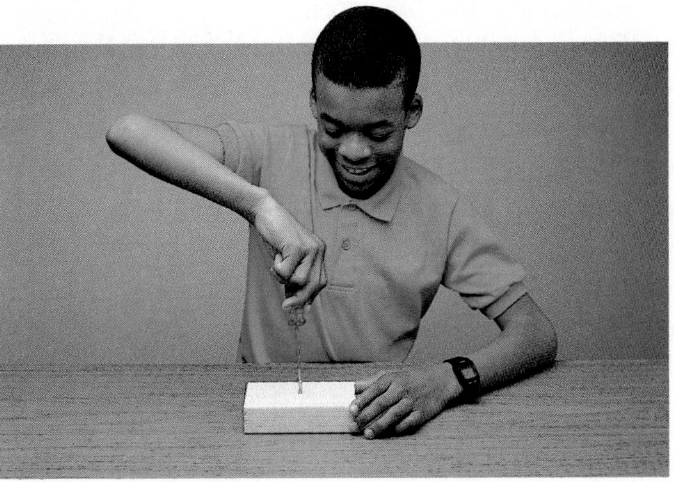

Conclude and Apply

1. Is the screwdriver a simple machine? To decide, you need to compare what it does to what a simple machine can do. Did the screwdriver make the job easier?
2. Did the screwdriver reduce the amount of work that was accomplished?
3. What type of simple machine is the screwdriver? Figure 5-9 may help you decide.
4. What about the screw itself? What type of simple machine is a screw?

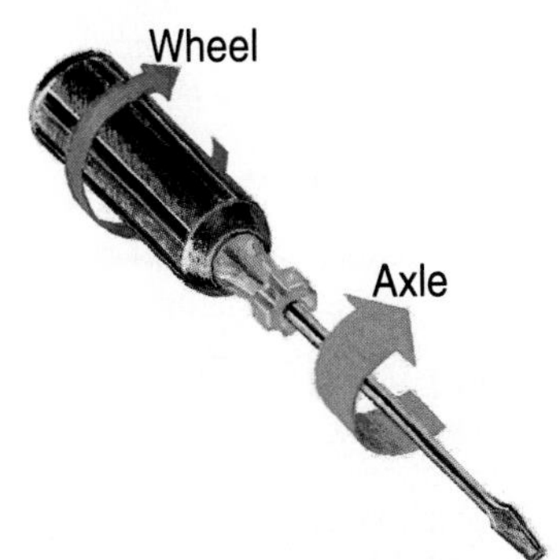

FIGURE 5-9. What kind of simple machine is a screwdriver?

The handle of the screwdriver is the wheel, and the shaft is the axle. It's easier to grip and turn the handle than the smaller metal shaft. What about the screw itself? The ridges spiraling around a screw are called threads. As you drove the screw into the board, the threads seemed

FIGURE 5-10. A screw multiplies force and changes the direction of force.

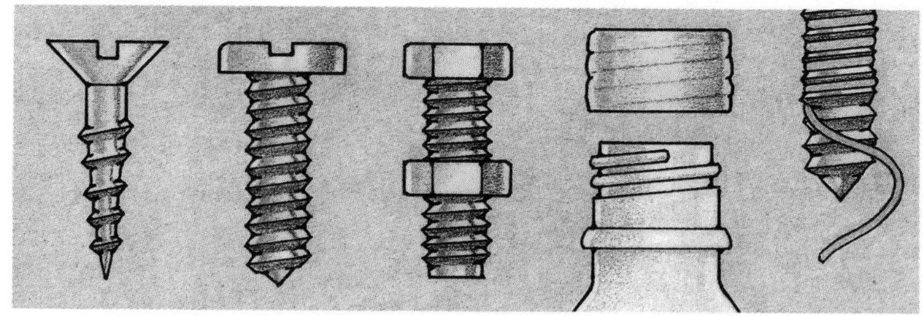

to pull the screw into the wood. Perhaps this leads you to describe a **screw** as an inclined plane wound around a post. In a way, the spiraling inclined plane helped to lift the wood up around the screw.

In Figure 5-10, a piece of thread is wound around the threads of the screw. When the thread is unwound, which will be longer, the length of the thread or the length of the screw? When you apply effort force to a screw, you turn it in a circle, and it moves downward. The screw changes the turning force of the screwdriver to the downward force of the screw. It increases force and changes the direction of force. It also increases the distance.

The wood screw is only one of many types of screws. Nuts and bolts are also screws. But instead of having sharp threads to cut into wood, bolts have rounded threads to match the threads on the inside of the nut. This is shown in Figure 5-10. The tops of bottles and jars work the same way. The threads on the neck of the bottle match the threads on the inside of the lid. Can you think of other devices that use the screw?

SKILLBUILDER

MAKING AND INTERPRETING TABLES

Make three columns on a sheet of paper. Label them *Simple Machines, Changes Direction,* and *Changes Force.* In the first column, list the six simple machines. In the next two columns, write Yes or No. Then answer these questions. If you need more help, refer to the **Skill Handbook** on page 679.

1. Which machines change the direction of force?
2. Which machines multiply the effort force?
3. Which machines both change the direction of the effort force and increase the force?

WEDGE

Once more, think of the campers. In particular, think of the counselor who was splitting logs. Would it be easier to split a log with a round metal club or with a sharp-edged axe? Why?

Figure 5-11 takes a close look at the axe the campers brought along for splitting firewood. Does it remind you of another simple machine? You can see that each side of the axe blade looks like an inclined plane.

A typical inclined plane, such as a ramp or a mountain road, stays in one place while objects move along its surface.

With a wedge, the object remains in one place while the wedge moves through it. A **wedge** is an inclined plane that uses the sharp, narrow end to cut through material.

FIGURE 5-11. A wedge multiplies force and changes the direction of force.

The blade of an axe is a wedge. Driving an axe blade down into a piece of wood exerts a force that pushes the wood away from both sides of the wedge. The blade exerts pressure on both sides of the cut as the wedge widens. The effort force applied by the person using the axe is transferred to the sharp, narrow end of the wedge. The effort force is increased to a larger resistance force capable of cutting through wood. The wedge changes the downward force to an outward force. As the cutting edge moves downward, it forces the wood to move sideways, away from both sides of the axe blade. The axe cuts the wood apart.

Can you think of other types of wedges? Chisels, knives, the teeth of saw blades, and many other sharp-bladed tools use the wedge. Do you think the sharp edges of the threads on a wood screw could be called wedges?

Even though the campers were on vacation, there was much work to do. Recall that work is done when a force is exerted to move an object. Luckily, the campers had some simple machines to help them—levers, wheels and axles, pulleys, inclined planes, screws, and wedges. The campers were probably too busy to think about effort forces or resistance forces. The next time you use a simple machine, however, you should identify these forces. And, in the next section, you'll see a way to compare the resistance force and the effort force. This will allow you to determine how helpful a machine can be.

Check Your Understanding

1. Give one example not given in the text of each kind of simple machine .
2. How do simple machines make it possible for you to exert less force to get a job done?
3. Do any of the simple machines reduce the amount of work that must be done? Explain your answer.
4. **APPLY:** One counselor built a machine. A camper applied a downward effort force to one end of the machine. The force exerted by the other end of the machine was greater, and the direction of the force was up rather than down. What kind of machine did the counselor build? Explain.

5-2 Mechanical Advantage

OBJECTIVES

In this section, you will

- operationally define mechanical advantage;
- calculate the mechanical advantage of several machines.

KEY SCIENCE TERMS

mechanical advantage

HOW MUCH DOES A MACHINE HELP?

The weather on the camping trip has been sunny and warm. But last night a sudden thunderstorm came up. The rain came down in buckets, the lightning was spectacular, and the thunder was so loud you could feel the ground shake. This morning there are puddles everywhere. Two counselors start to take the van into town to get supplies. But as they drive away, one of the tires gets stuck in the mud. Now the counselors are leaning on the crowbar, trying to raise the van enough to slide a board under the stuck tire.

The camp counselors are using the crowbar as a lever. As their muscles exert an effort force on one end of the crowbar, the other end of the crowbar exerts a force on the van. This is shown in Figure 5-12. The crowbar helps the counselors lift the van by increasing the force. How much easier is this machine making the job?

Suppose the portion of the van that has to be raised weighs 2500 N. This is the amount of resistance force the crowbar exerts on the van. The counselors are exerting an effort force of 500 N. You want to know how many times

FIGURE 5-12. Like the crowbar used by the camp counselors, this lever gives the man a mechanical advantage.

greater the resistance force is than the effort force, so you divide 2500 N (the resistance force) by 500 N (the effort force). The result is 5. The force exerted by the crowbar is five times greater than the force exerted by the counselors.

The difference between the resistance force and the effort force is called the mechanical advantage.

The **mechanical advantage** (MA) of a machine tells you how much greater the resistance force is than the effort force. MA tells you how helpful the machine is. You calculate MA by dividing resistance force by effort force. The larger the MA, the more help the machine is providing. In the above example, what is the mechanical advantage of the crowbar?

Don't forget, the crowbar does not change the amount of work that is done. It just increases the force on the object.

Here's another example showing how to calculate MA.

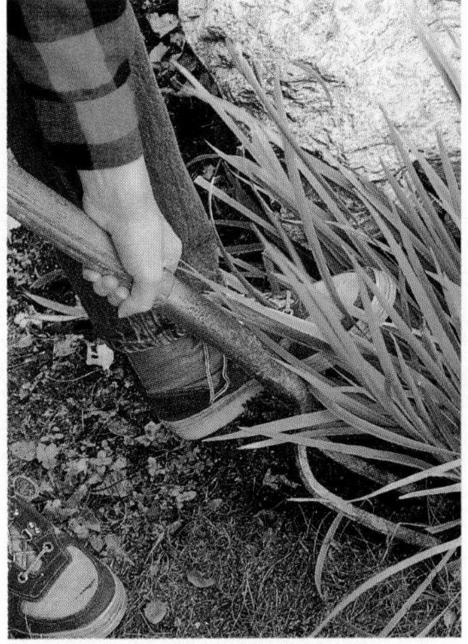

FIGURE 5-13. The gardener is exerting force on the shovel and the dirt. The dirt and plant are exerting a downward force. Which is the larger force?

EXAMPLE PROBLEM: Calculating MA

Problem Statement: Suppose a housepainter applies an effort force of 10 N to a crowbar she's using to pry open a window. The resistance of the window is 500 N.

Known: resistance force, F_r = 500 N
effort force, F_e = 10 N

Strategy Hint: MA has no units; it is a ratio of two quantities with the same units.

Unknown: mechanical advantage, MA

Equation to Use: $MA = F_r/F_e$

Solution: MA = 500 N/10 N = 50

Suppose you don't know the size of the effort force. Or maybe you have no idea how large or how small the resistance force is. Is there another way you can calculate mechanical advantage?

FIND OUT!

Can the length of a lever affect the amount of force needed to do work?

Place a stack of two or three books near the edge of a table. Slide a meterstick under the books so the entire width of the bottom book is resting on the stick, as shown in the figure. Grasp the meterstick at the 30-cm mark. Push up on the stick to lift the books. Try again, this time holding the meterstick at the 90-cm mark.

Conclude and Apply

1. Compare the force you used to lift the books each time. Which time did you need more force to lift the books?
2. How is the distance between the effort force and the fulcrum related to the amount of effort force needed?

The length of a lever arm can affect the amount of force needed to do work. Because of this, you can use the lengths of the effort arm and the resistance arm of the crowbar to calculate MA. In Figure 5-14, the effort arm of the crowbar is between the painter's hands and the fulcrum. The resistance arm is between the fulcrum and the spot where the crowbar meets the window.

EXAMPLE PROBLEM: Calculating MA

Problem Statement:	Suppose the effort arm of the crowbar was 75 cm long and the resistance arm was 1.5 cm long.
Known:	effort length, l_e = 75 cm resistance length, l_r = 1.5 cm
Unknown:	MA
Equation to Use:	$MA = l_e / l_r$
Solution:	MA = 75 cm / 1.5 cm = 50

FIGURE 5-14. This painter would probably not be able to open the window without a tool that gives mechanical advantage.

How does this compare with the MA found using the effort force and resistance force? Use this method to calculate the MA of a wheel and axle. The radius of the wheel is the effort arm, and the radius of the axle is the resistance arm. Here's an example.

EXAMPLE PROBLEM: Calculating MA

Problem Statement: For the ice cream maker shown in Figure 5-15, the wheel has a radius of 20 cm. The axle has a radius of 12 cm. What is the mechanical advantage of this machine?

Known: radius of wheel, $r_w = 20$ cm
radius of axle, $r_a = 12$ cm

Unknown: MA

Equation to Use: $MA = r_w/r_a$

Solution: $MA = 20 \text{ cm}/12 \text{ cm} = 1.66$

Does every machine offer a mechanical advantage? What about a machine that does not increase the force, but only changes the direction of force? Assume you're raising a flag a distance of 10 m to the top of a flagpole. You pull down on 10 m of rope in order to raise the flag 10 m. The effort arm is 10 m long, and the resistance arm is 10 m long. Your effort force moves the same distance as the pulley's resistance force. What is the MA of the pulley? The fixed pulley has a mechanical advantage of one. It just makes raising the flag more convenient.

You have seen that mechanical advantage can be calculated using either the forces or the length of the arms. Let's investigate another way that mechanical advantage can be used.

FIGURE 5-15. The handle acts as the wheel in this ice cream maker.

INVESTIGATE!

5-1 MEASURING MASS WITH LEVERS

This activity will show you another use for mechanical advantage.

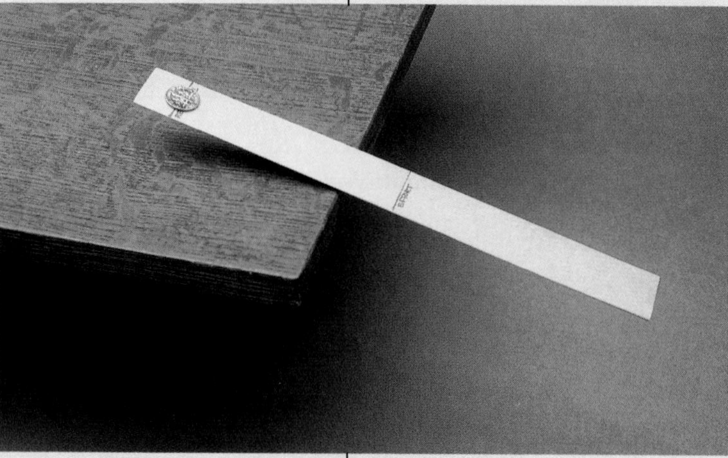

PROBLEM

Can you measure mass with a lever?

MATERIALS

1 sheet of stiff paper, 20 cm *x* 28 cm (8 1/2 *x* 11 in)
3 coins (quarter, dime, and nickel)
balance
metric ruler

PROCEDURE

1. Fold the paper in half lengthwise, then fold it lengthwise again, to make a lever 3 cm wide by 28 cm long.
2. Mark a line 2 cm away from one end of the lever. Label this line *resistance.*
3. Slide the other end of the lever over the edge of a table until the lever begins to teeter but doesn't fall off. Mark a line across the lever at the point where it crosses the table edge. Mark this line *effort.*
4. **Measure** the mass of the lever to the nearest 0.1 g. Write this mass on the effort line.
5. Center a dime on the resistance line.
6. Once again, slide the lever over the edge of the desk until it teeters. Mark a line where the lever crosses the table edge and label it *fulcrum #1.*
7. **Measure** the length of the resistance arm from the center of the dime to the new fulcrum, and the effort arm from the new fulcrum to the effort line. **Measure** to the nearest 0.1 cm.
8. Calculate the MA of the lever.
9. Multiply the MA by the mass of the lever to find the mass of the coin.
10. Repeat Steps 5 through 9 with the nickel and then with the quarter. Mark the fulcrum line *#2* for the nickel and *#3* for the quarter.

ANALYZE

1. Is the total length of the lever a constant or a variable?
2. Describe the length of the effort arm and resistance arm. **Identify** whether the lengths are constant or **variable.**
3. **Infer** what provides the effort force.
4. What does it mean if the MA is less than 1?

CONCLUDE AND APPLY

5. Is it necessary to have the resistance line 2 cm from the end of the lever?
6. **Going Further:** Why can mass units be used in place of force units in this kind of problem?

If you had put two dimes on the resistance point, what would have happened to the fulcrum? What about four dimes? If you had done this Investigate with a number of different masses, you could have plotted a graph of the relationship between the length of the effort arm and the mass. This is an inverse relationship. As one increases, the other decreases, assuming the length of the lever stays constant. Using this relationship, you could find the length of a lever needed to lift different masses. What would happen to the effort force if you moved the fulcrum even closer to the resistance force?

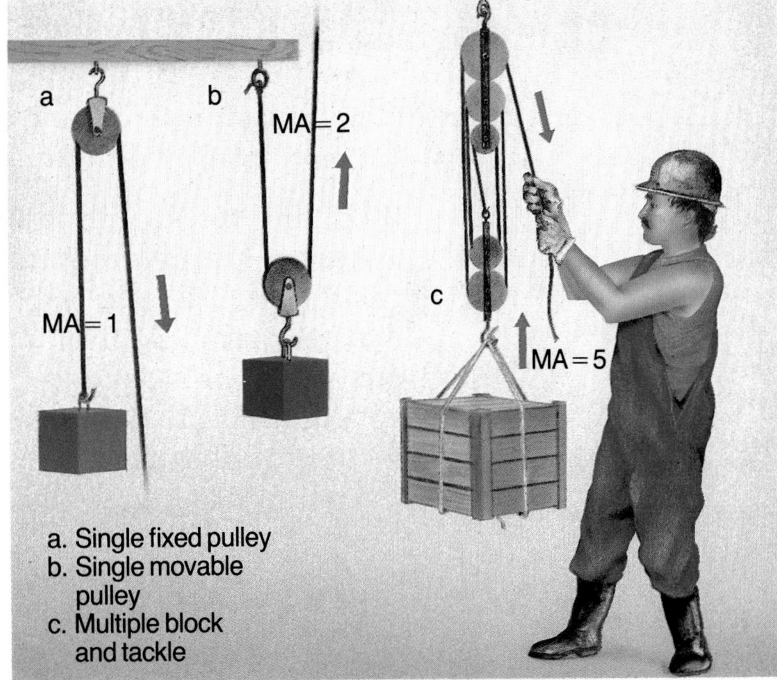

FIGURE 5-16. Combining two or more pulleys into a block and tackle increases mechanical advantage.

Mechanical advantage (MA) tells you the ratio between the resistance force and the effort force. The larger the mechanical advantage, the more help the machine is providing. You calculate MA by dividing resistance force by effort force.

You could use this knowledge to explain to the other campers why they wouldn't necessarily need the biggest, strongest campers to get the van out of the mud. All they would need is a simple machine with a high mechanical advantage.

Check Your Understanding

1. Define mechanical advantage.
2. An automobile steering wheel with a radius of 40 cm is used to turn the steering column, which has a radius of 4 cm. What is the MA of the wheel and axle system?
3. **APPLY:** Each screwdriver in a set has a handle with a radius that is different from every other screwdriver in the set. The radius of each axle is also different. Which screwdriver would you use to get the greatest mechanical advantage?

5-3 Using Machines

OBJECTIVES

In this section, you will

- recognize the simple machines that make up a compound machine;
- describe the relationship between work, power, and time.

KEY SCIENCE TERMS

compound machine

power

watt

COMPOUND MACHINES

It's getting close to dinnertime. You hum a favorite song as you put paper plates, mustard, and potato chips on the picnic table. This is the best possible night to pull cooking duty. The menu says chili dogs, so all you have to do to prepare dinner is put a few things on the table and heat up some canned chili. Everyone will roast his or her own hot dog over the campfire. You pull out the can opener and start working on the chili.

EXPLORE!

What kind of machine is a can opener?

Using what you know about simple machines, examine a can opener and try to describe how it works. What kind of simple machine is it? Is it a combination of simple machines?

As you can see, a can opener is actually composed of several simple machines. The handles are two levers that make it easier to fasten the opener onto the edge of a can. The crank is a wheel and axle that turns a toothed wheel. The toothed wheel is called a gear. The first gear turns another gear that moves a circular wedge along the top of the can. The can opener combines the lever, the wheel and axle, and the wedge into a compound machine that makes it easier to open a can.

A **compound machine** is a combination of simple machines that make it possible to do something one simple machine alone can't do. Can you think of some common compound machines?

DID YOU KNOW?

The tin can was invented early in the 1800s, but the can opener wasn't invented until more than a hundred years later. At first, people had to use a hammer and chisel to open tin cans!

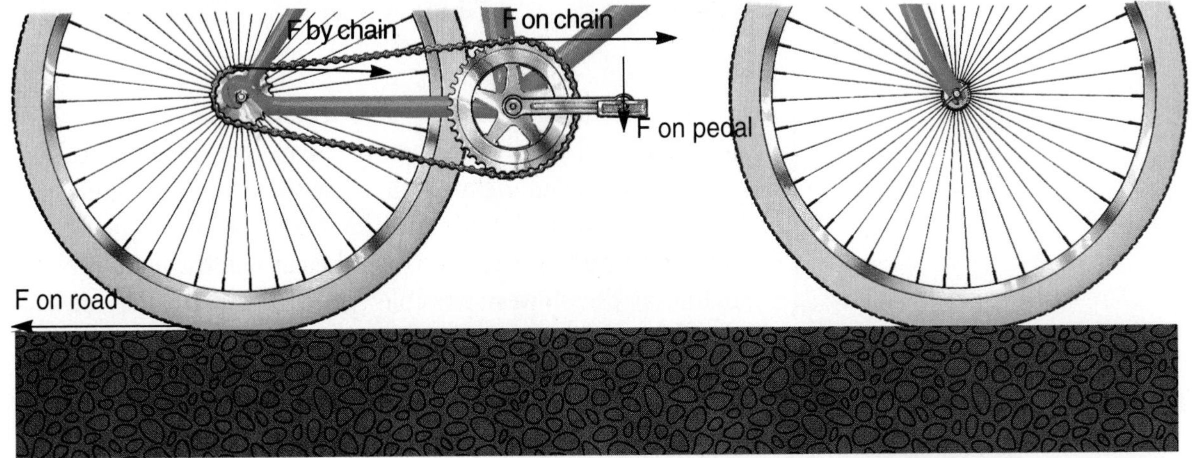

FIGURE 5-17. A bicycle is a compound machine.

A bicycle is a compound machine. Look at the bicycle pictured in Figure 5-17. How many simple machines can you identify?

Suppose you wanted to find the mechanical advantage of the bicycle. Since the bicycle is a compound machine, there are actually several mechanical advantages to be considered. One is the wheel and axle represented by the pedal and pedal gear. As shown in Figure 5-17, a mechanical advantage results when the chain exerts an effort force on the rear wheel gear. Finally, another mechanical advantage results when the wheel exerts a resistance force on the road and the bike moves.

POWER

You and a friend borrow bikes from the park ranger for the afternoon. You and your friend weigh the same, and your bikes are identical. After pedaling several miles you begin getting tired. You round a curve and find you're facing a half-mile of steep hill. You manage to pedal all the way up, while your friend has to get off and push the bike. You get to the top of the hill before your friend. Did you both do the same amount of work? How do you know? Work = force × distance. Since force and distance are equal for both you and your friend, both of you did equal work. The only variable was time. You reached the top of the hill first. That means you did the work at a faster rate.

FIND OUT!

Can you measure the power of a toy car?

You will need a stiff board, a stack of books, and a wind-up toy car. Place one end of the board on the stack of books to create an inclined plane, as shown in the figure. Experiment with the car and the steepness of the plane until you find the angle at which the car will travel up the incline at the slowest possible speed. Wind up the car, place it at the bottom of the plane, and then record the number of seconds (s) it takes to get to the top.

Measure the height of the inclined plane in meters. The height is the distance straight up from the floor or table to the top of the incline. Measure the weight of the car in newtons (N). (A kilogram weighs about 9.8 N on Earth's surface.)

Multiply the weight of the car by the height of the incline to calculate the work done, in joules (J). Now divide J by the number of seconds it took for the car to climb the incline. Your result is the power of the car. It's expressed in a unit called the watt (W).

Conclude and Apply

What was the power of your toy car?

Dividing the amount of work the toy car did by the amount of time to do the work tells you how much power was used. **Power** is the work done divided by the time interval. The formula for calculating power is:

$$\text{power} = \text{work/time}$$

Power is measured in watts. A **watt** is one joule per second. You may already be familiar with the watt because it's used to measure electric power. The power light bulbs use is measured in watts, for example. You probably have a 75-watt or 100-watt bulb in a lamp at home. The watt is a fairly small amount of power. It's about equal to the power required to raise a glass of water from your knees to your mouth in one second. If a machine is using a lot of power, it's often more convenient to use kilowatts instead of watts. A kilowatt (kW) is 1000 watts.

SKILLBUILDER

SEQUENCING

Make an events chain to show the sequence of how some of the simple machines in a bicycle work together to move the bicycle. Start with the feet applying force to the pedals. If you need help, refer to the **Skill Handbook** on page 678.

INVESTIGATE!

5-2 CALCULATING POWER

You can calculate the power used to do a job if you're given the amount of force used, the distance, and the time it took.

PROBLEM

What factors determine the power used in walking up a flight of stairs?

MATERIALS

meterstick
bathroom scale
flight of stairs
watch with second hand or digital chronometer

PROCEDURE

1. Copy the data table.
2. **Measure** the weight, in newtons (N), of a volunteer. Multiply pounds by 4.45 to get newtons. Record the weight in the table.
3. **Measure** the vertical height of one step. Multiply the height of the step by the number of steps. Record the total height of the stairs in the data table.

4. **Measure** the number of seconds it takes the volunteer to walk up the stairs. Record.
5. Calculate the work done, in joules (work = weight x height). Record.
6. Calculate the power (work/time) used in walking up the stairs.
7. Repeat for three more volunteers.

ANALYZE

1. **Compare and contrast** the force exerted by the different people.
2. Which person did the most work? Produced the most power?

CONCLUDE AND APPLY

3. Suppose one volunteer walked up the stairs twice. The first time took 10 seconds. The second time took 15 seconds. When did the volunteer use more power?
4. Suppose the heaviest volunteer walked up the stairs much more quickly than the lightest volunteer. **Predict** the difference in power used by each person.
5. What determines the amount of power used when walking up the steps?
6. **Going Further:** Two volunteers with different weights each increase their speed by two seconds. Which person produces the greater power?

DATA AND OBSERVATIONS

STUDENT'S NAME	FORCE (N)	DISTANCE (M)	WORK (J)	TIME (X)	WORK/TIME (J/S)

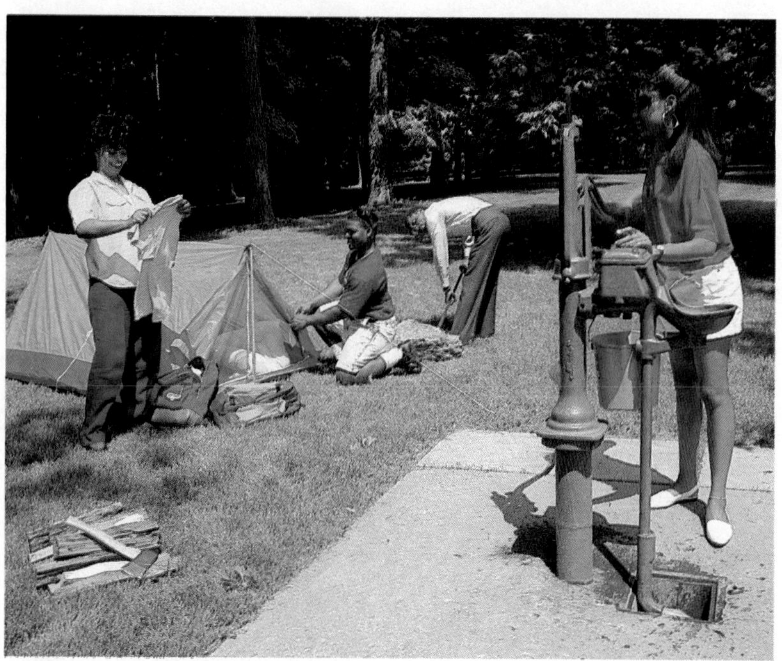

FIGURE 5-18. Machines help make jobs easier.

You've calculated human power, but the same method could be used to calculate the power needed to operate simple and compound machines.

The original campsite scene contained many simple machines. Now, after completing this chapter, you can identify several simple and compound machines. You have determined how much easier these machines can make a task by computing the mechanical advantage. The MA is the ratio of effort force to resistance force.

Finally, you found the power of these machines by dividing the work done by the amount of time it took to do the work. Power = work/time. Now you can compute how much power you use to complete a 3-hour, 5-mile hike up the mountain. What a surprise to find all that work and power at a vacation campsite!

Check Your Understanding

1. Give an example of a compound machine. What are the simple machines that make it up?
2. How are work, power, and time related?
3. **APPLY:** How much power does a person weighing 500 N need to climb a 3-m ladder in 5 seconds?

EXPANDING YOUR VIEW

CONTENTS

A Closer Look
Efficiency 153

Life Science Connection
One Step at a Time 154

Science and Society
Pedal Power! 155

Leisure Connection
Spills, Chills
Waves and Dunks 157

Teens in Science:
Hard Work—
The Easy Way to Have Fun 158

A CLOSER LOOK

EFFICIENCY

When you squeeze the brake handles of the bicycle in the picture, the rubber brake pads clamp down against the rim of the tires, using friction to exert a force on the wheels and slow their speed. Friction occurs whenever two substances rub against each other.

Some of the effort force put into any machine with moving parts is lost to friction. For example, some of the effort force you exert when you pedal a bike is lost to the friction of the pedal gear rubbing against the bicycle chain. The energy used by a machine to work against the force of friction, rather than to do useful work, reduces the efficiency of the machine. Efficiency is the ratio of the useful work done by a machine to the work put into it.

$$\text{efficiency} = \frac{W_{out}}{W_{in}} x100\% = \frac{F_r x\, d_r}{F_e x\, d_e} x100\%$$

Efficiency is usually expressed as a percent. Low-efficiency machines lose much of the work put into them to work against friction—high-efficiency machines do not. A machine that does no work against friction would have

an efficiency of 100 percent. That is, 100 percent of the work put into the machine is used to do useful work. No machine operates at 100 percent efficiency because all machines must work against friction of some kind.

You can increase the efficiency of a machine by adding a lubricant, such as oil or grease, to the surfaces that rub together. Dirt buildup eventually reduces the effectiveness of the lubricant, and it must be replaced. If a bicycle's chain, gears, and other moving parts are cleaned and lubricated periodically, the bicycle will operate more efficiently.

WHAT DO YOU THINK?

The efficiency of an automobile is usually expressed in terms of gas mileage. How can changing the engine oil increase the gas mileage of the automobile?

LIFE SCIENCE CONNECTION

ONE STEP AT A TIME

Have you ever heard anyone refer to the human body as a machine? If so, you may have wondered what happens when a part of the body no longer works correctly. You've probably seen automobile mechanics replacing old or worn-out parts. Can human parts be replaced?

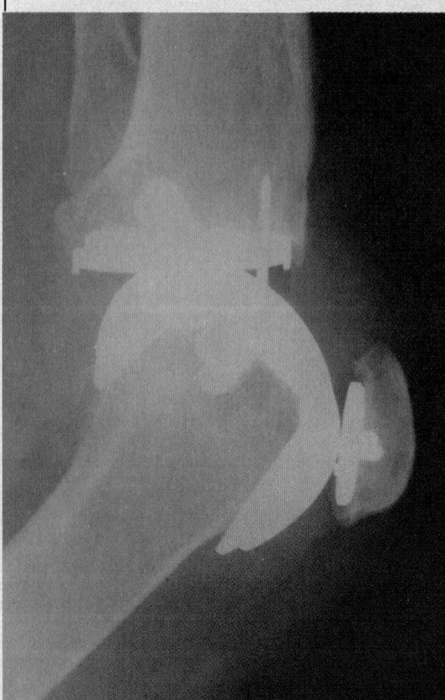

Yes, thanks to bionics—the science of designing artificial replacements for parts of the human body. Today, the knee is one of the most common parts of the human body to be replaced by an artificial device.

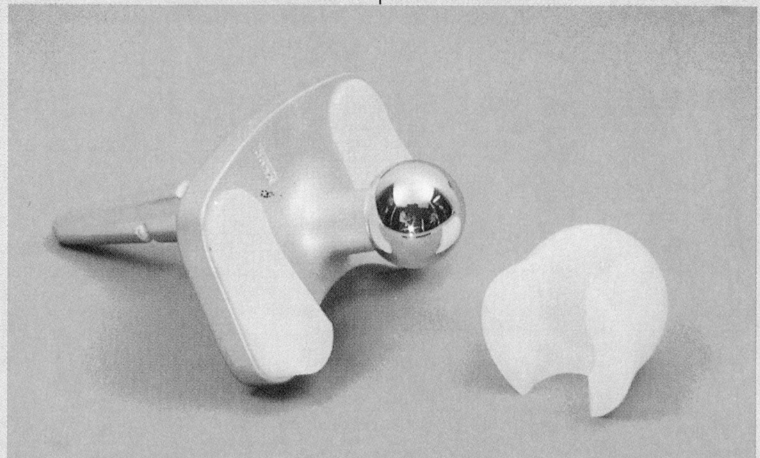

To understand how an artificial knee joint works, you must first understand how a healthy knee joint functions.

The knee joint, as shown in the X ray, connects the bones in your upper and lower leg. With every step you take, these bones rotate, roll, and glide on each other. Connective tissue, called cartilage, forms a smooth weight-bearing surface between the bones that allows for painless movement. However, with injury or aging, the cartilage begins to wear out. Eventually the bones begin to rub together, creating friction and chronic pain.

In the late 1960s, bioengineers developed an artificial joint with a wide enough range of movement to replace the knee. Since that time, many designs and materials have been tested. Today, the most common artificial knee joints, like the one shown above, are made of chrome-cobalt, a hard yet lightweight metal. A plastic material is used to create a durable weight-bearing surface. Once in place, an artificial knee joint works just like the human knee it replaces.

WHAT DO YOU THINK?

Make a list of body parts in each of these categories:

- organs
- limbs
- senses

Some people think that we are tampering with nature when we use artificial body parts. Other people believe that, whenever possible, technology should be used to improve health. What do you think?

SCIENCE AND SOCIETY

PEDAL POWER!

You've spent months fine-tuning your vehicle. You're all set. At the sound of the starting gun, you jump on your pedals.

Jump on your pedals? That's right. How else do you compete in the International Human Powered Vehicle Association's (IHPVA) Annual Speed Championships?

Most people agree that the bicycle is the most efficient means of transportation on Earth. With its annual races, the IHPVA sets out to prove that bicycles can also be fast. Recently, a streamlined bicycle called *Gold Rush* set the IHPVA speed record at 65.5 mph. However, a group of high school students in Saginaw, Michigan, just might give the *Gold Rush* a run for its money.

The Arthur Hill High School Technology Club was founded by drafting teacher and club advisor, Bruce Isotalo. Members of the club use the principles of compound machines to design and build human powered vehicles (HPVs), shown in the picture. In 1988, the club signed up to enter its first IHPVA's Speed Championships.

Mr. Isotalo recalls how the club created that first HPV, the *da Vinci*. "First, we had to decide what we wanted the vehicle to accomplish. We chose speed as our main goal." To meet their goal, the club members paid special attention to the *da Vinci's* body design. As you know, when energy is used to overcome friction, efficiency is reduced. With this in mind, the club chose a streamlined body design to allow air to flow smoothly around the *da Vinci*. To keep the weight of the *da Vinci* low, they selected lightweight aluminum as the building material. Once the design had been finalized, it was time to begin the task of transforming the *da Vinci* from an idea into a road-worthy machine. The students worked for months to perfect the wheel-and-axle system in the vehicle's powerful pedaling mechanism.

The IHPVA's Speed Championships were scheduled for August and would be held in Michigan. During summer vacation, many students worked on the *da Vinci* eight hours a day. "We sent out for a lot of pizza

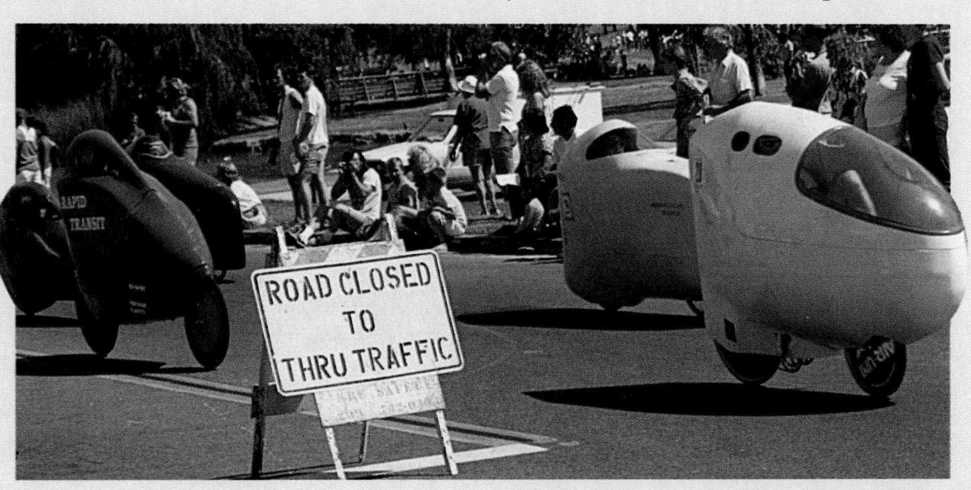

YOU TRY IT!

This experiment shows the effects of streamlining.

Materials

- 1 small candle
- 1 cardboard tube, 5 to 6 inches long
- tape
- paper
- cookie sheet

Putting it together:

1. Carefully light the candle. Drip a small amount of wax on the cookie sheet. Stick the lit candle upright into the melted wax.
2. Tape the tube to the cookie sheet about one inch in front of the candle.
3. Gently slide the cookie sheet from right to left. Note what happens to the candle's flame.
4. Cut and fold the paper into the shape of a cone. Slip the cone over the tube and tape in place.
5. Move the cookie sheet again. Make a note of how the flame reacts now.

Compare your notes and answer this question. How does streamlining affect an HPV's ability to move through wind?

that summer," laughs Mr. Isotalo. "But we stuck with it. I think that was one of the greatest things about this project. We learned that there is nothing that can't be accomplished when you put your mind to it."

On a hot August day in 1989, the *da Vinci* took its place at the starting line of the International Human Powered Vehicle Speed Championships. The club members watched with pride as the *da Vinci* placed among the top 20 in the sprint event.

For those who would return to the Technology Club the following year, the *da Vinci's* debut was a kind of preview. In 1990, they radically altered the design and the *da Vinci 2* placed third in a grueling 24-hour marathon event. Today, the Technology Club is hard at work on the *da Vinci 3*, as they continue to explore the potential of human power.

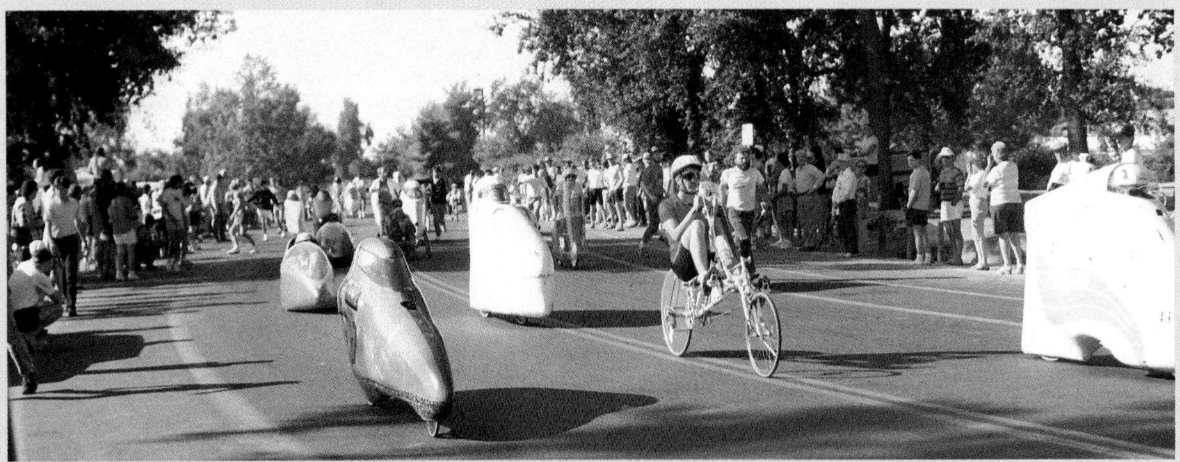

Leisure CONNECTION

SPILLS, CHILLS, WAVES, AND DUNKS

You're zooming down a 60-foot-high water slide at speeds of up to 40 miles per hour. You reach the bottom in as little as 15 seconds, but an engineer may have worked on the design of the slide's inclined plane for years. Every bend and twist has been carefully constructed for both speed and safety. The latest computer technology is used to calculate such factors as the angle of the curves and the lubricating effect of the flowing water. Even the amount of resistance that will be created by your bathing suit is considered.

If your water park has a pool for body surfing and boogie boarding, you can thank a machine for those perfect waves. In the ocean, the wind causes the waves to rise and fall. In a water park, waves are usually created by a computer-operated wave machine. By intermittently pumping air into the pool, the computer generates waves of many sizes and shapes.

You've learned how machines can help to make work easier. The next time you go to a water park, be sure to notice how machines can also work to help you have fun.

YOU TRY IT!

Draw the water slide of your dreams. How tall would your slide stand? How long would it take a person to ride it from top to bottom?

TEENS *in* SCIENCE

YOU TRY IT!

Even though her HPV did not win the IHPVA's Speed Championships, Stephanie is very proud of her work on the *da Vinci.* Which experiences in your life have affected you most? Stephanie Ostler encourages people to try new things. Make a list of some new things you would like to try.

HARD WORK—THE EASY WAY TO HAVE FUN

Have you ever been surprised by how much fun you were having while doing a difficult task? For Stephanie Ostler, an original member of the Technology Club, helping to design and build a human powered vehicle was both a challenge and a thrill.

"For me, working on the *da Vinci* was like putting together a puzzle. Only it was harder, because we had to invent each piece of the puzzle first."

With each stage of the *da Vinci's* production, the club members discovered that a new set of problems developed.

"We all worked together to solve problems. Every decision was made by vote.

"By the time summer came, the *da Vinci* was the only thing any of us thought about."

Stephanie did, however, devote some thought to seeing the world around her in a different way.

"I had just gotten my driver's license when I joined the club. At that time, I thought cars were about the greatest thing on Earth. I never really thought about how they affect the environment. After I drove the *da Vinci,* I was really sold on HPVs as an alternative to cars. Not only do they save energy, but they are good exercise, too!"

As the summer drew to an end, Stephanie realized that the experience of working on the *da Vinci* had an important effect on her. "This may sound weird, but I think one of the best things about the project was completing it. We started out with nothing more than an idea, but we just kept working at it until we had something we could be proud of. I think everybody should explore things they don't know anything about. It really feels good when you figure it out."

The greatest satisfaction, however, was to come on the day of the race.

"I don't think I'll ever forget the race. There we were with inventors and inventions from all over the world. It was awesome. I wonder if Henry Ford had the same feeling when he invented the car."

CAREER CONNECTION

Engineers apply the discoveries of scientists to design, develop, and produce products and systems. Mechanical engineers are unique in the engineering field because they create many of the tools and machines required by other engineers. Mechanical engineers work in industry, business, government service, and universities.

Chapter 5

Reviewing Main Ideas

1. Machines make work easier.

2. There are six simple machines—lever, wheel and axle, pulley, inclined plane, screw, and wedge. They can increase force, change the direction of force, or both.

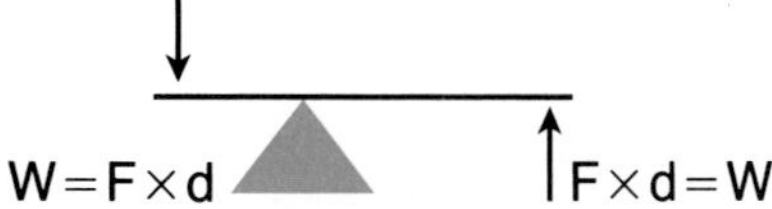

3. Machines do not reduce the amount of work that has to be done.

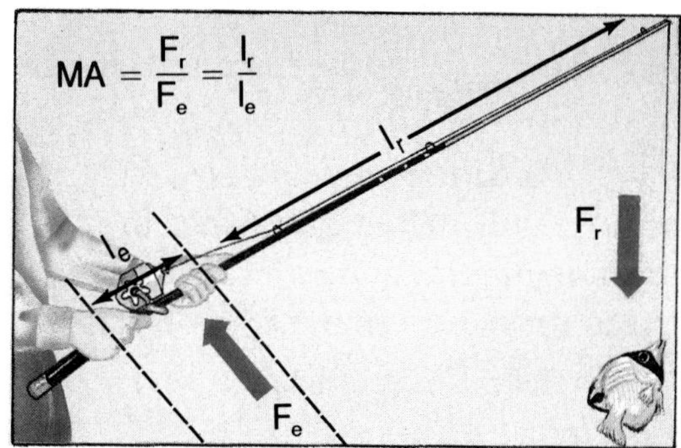

4. Mechanical advantage (MA) tells you how helpful a machine is in doing a job. MA is the ratio between the resistance force and the effort force.

5. Power is the work done divided by the time it took to do the work.

Chapter 5

Chapter Review

USING KEY SCIENCE TERMS

compound machine
effort force
inclined plane
lever
mechanical advantage
power
pulley
resistance force
screw
watt
wedge
wheel and axle

Using the list above, replace the underlined words with the correct key science term.

1. A <u>machine made up of several simple machines</u> is capable of doing jobs that one simple machine alone cannot do.
2. The <u>force you apply</u> to the crowbar is converted into a greater force acting over a smaller distance.
3. A/An <u>inclined plane wound around a post</u> changes the direction of force from a circular motion to a downward motion.
4. A/An <u>inclined plane set on its sharp end</u> changes the direction of force from a downward motion to an outward, or sideways, motion.
5. A <u>grooved wheel with a rope passed around it,</u> when fixed to the top of a flagpole, can change the direction of a force but does not increase the force.

For each set of terms below, choose the one term that does not belong and explain why it does not belong.

6. lever, wheel and axle, power
7. power, watt, mechanical advantage
8. inclined plane, wedge, pulley

UNDERSTANDING IDEAS

Complete each sentence.

1. Machines can never reduce the amount of ____ that has to be done to complete a job, but they can ____ the force a person has to exert to get the job done.
2. ____, ____, and some kinds of ____ and ____ can change the direction of force.
3. ____ and ____ increase force and change the direction of force.
4. A ____ is a combination of fixed and movable pulleys that can change the direction of force and reduce the force a person must exert to move an object.
5. ____ is the ratio of resistance force to effort force.
6. A fixed pulley has an MA of ____ because it does not increase force.
7. Power is the amount of ____ done divided by the ____ required to do a job.
8. The wheel and axle is based on the same principle as the ____.
9. A lever pushes against a closed steel door with a force of 100 N. The amount of work done is ____.

CRITICAL THINKING

Use your understanding of the concepts developed in the chapter to answer each of the following questions.

1. What is the MA of the axe the woodcutter is using to split the log in the figure?
2. To screw a 5-cm screw into a piece of wood requires turning a screwdriver 15 times. For each turn of the screwdriver, your hand moves 15 cm. What is the MA of the screw?
3. A bricklayer is carrying boxes weighing 700 N up a flight of stairs 10 m high. It takes him 90 seconds. A carpenter is hammering in one nail every 30 seconds. He exerts a force of 200 N over a distance of 2 m. How many watts of power does the bricklayer produce in the 90 seconds it takes him to climb the stairs? How much power does the carpenter produce in 90 seconds?

PROBLEM SOLVING

Read the following problem and discuss your answers in a brief paragraph.

Suppose you and a friend are pushing boxes of camping gear up a ramp to load them into a van. All of the boxes weigh the same, but you push faster than your friend. You can move a box up the ramp from the ground to the van in 30 seconds. It takes your friend 45 seconds.

1. Are you both doing the same amount of work? Explain your answer.
2. Assume the boxes weigh 12 N and the ramp is 3 m high. How many watts of power are you each producing?

CONNECTING IDEAS

Discuss each of the following in a brief paragraph.

1. Use the Law of Conservation of Energy to explain why machines cannot reduce the amount of work that must be done to accomplish a task.

2. Using the information from this chapter and Chapter 3, compare your heart to a machine. What work is being done by the heart?

3. **A CLOSER LOOK** Using a ramp 4 meters long, workers apply an effort force of 1250 N to move a 2000-N crate onto a platform 2 meters high. What is the efficiency of the ramp?

4. **SCIENCE AND SOCIETY** What design features did the da Vinci bicycle include that allowed it to conserve energy?

5. **LIFE SCIENCE CONNECTION** Why do you think knee joints are among the most common body joints to be replaced?

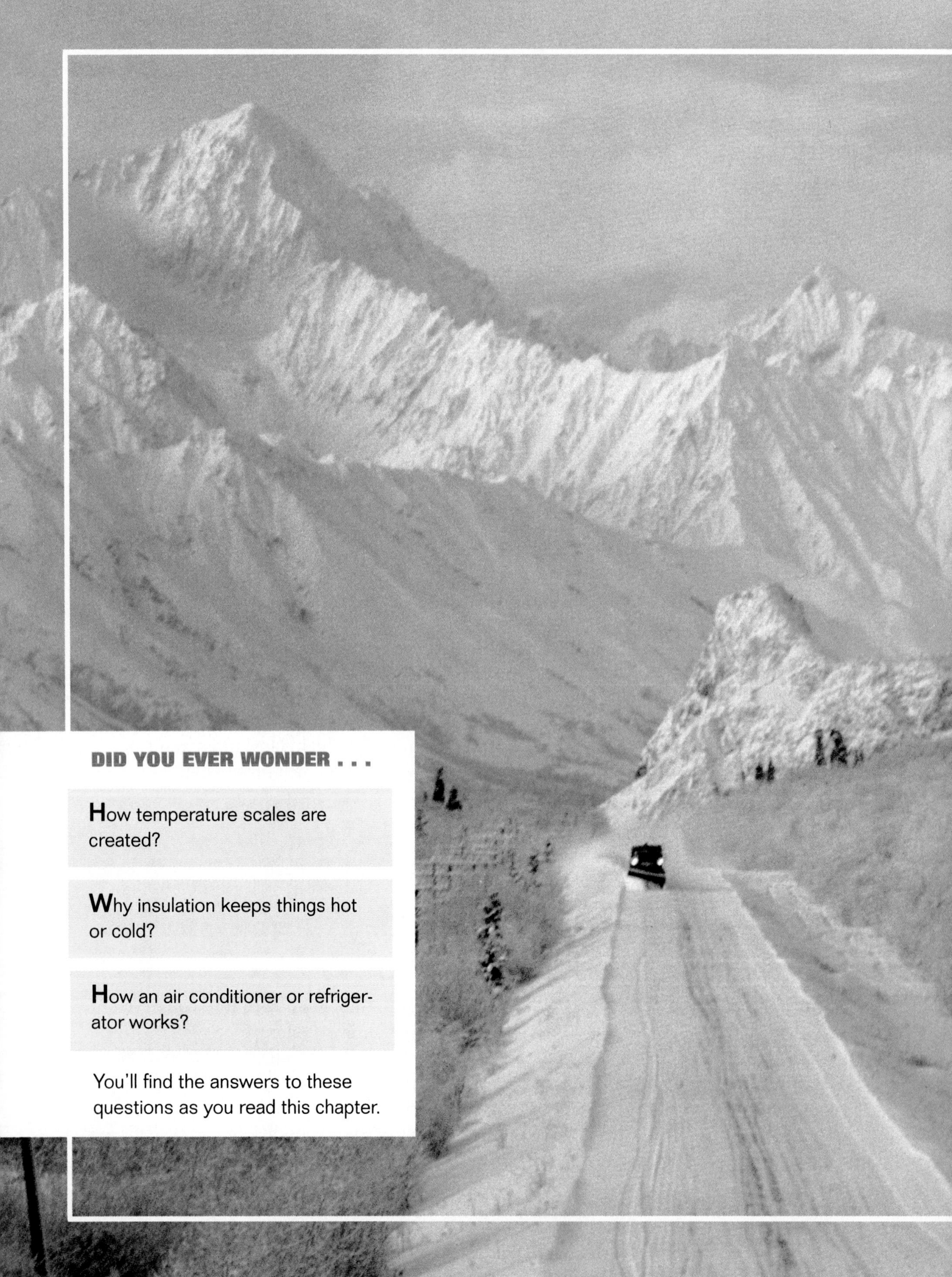

DID YOU EVER WONDER . . .

How temperature scales are created?

Why insulation keeps things hot or cold?

How an air conditioner or refrigerator works?

You'll find the answers to these questions as you read this chapter.

Chapter 6

Thermal Energy

We live on a planet that's both hot and cold. Molten lava from a volcano is very hot. When it flows, it burns nearly everything in its path. And winter in the northern part of Alaska is extremely cold. An unprotected person would rapidly freeze to death on a north Alaskan winter day.

We live our lives in climates that range from hot to cold. For many people on Earth, the seasons bring regular changes. Temperatures will vary from hot to mild to cold and then back again.

Heat and cold are things you feel, things your body reacts to. You sweat under a scorching sun and shiver in freezing wind. Before you even go outside, you'll react to the temperature when you read a thermometer. How you dress might depend on what the thermometer tells you about the outside temperature. A cold day means more clothes and a hot day less. But what actually is heat? What is temperature? Are they the same thing, or are they very different?

EXPLORE!

How do we feel heat?

Place a coin on a piece of carpet. Leave it untouched for several minutes. Use the underside of your wrist to touch the coin, as shown in the figure. This part of your skin is especially sensitive to heat and cold. Make a mental note of how warm or cold it feels. Then touch the carpet with your wrist in the same way. Does the carpet feel warmer than the coin? Do you think that it is?

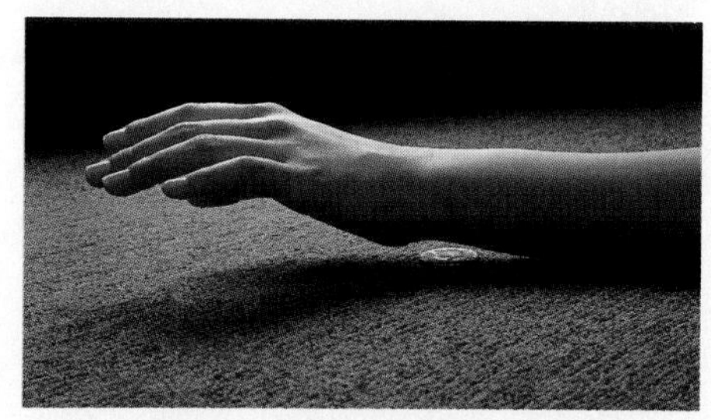

6-1 Thermal Equilibrium

OBJECTIVES

In this section, you will

- describe how two objects achieve thermal equilibrium;
- determine when two objects have the same temperature;
- use the Celsius temperature scale.

KEY SCIENCE TERMS

thermal equilibrium

HOW DO WE KNOW IF SOMETHING IS HOT OR COLD?

You're on the telephone with a friend in another city on a hot summer afternoon. You're both trying to describe how hot it is outside, but neither of you has a thermometer. Can you accurately describe how hot it is?

Like most ideas in science, heat and temperature are connected to our everyday lives. Your sense of touch tells you whether something is hot or cold. It can even tell you when one object is hotter or colder than another object. Or can it?

EXPLORE!

Is your sense of touch accurate for judging temperature?

Fill a pan with lukewarm water. Fill a second pan with cold water and crushed ice. Fill a third with water that's as hot as you can stand. Now put one hand into the cold water and the other into the hot water. Hold them in the water for 15 seconds. Quickly remove both hands from the water and then put both into the pan of lukewarm water. How do they feel now? Do both hands feel the same thing? Can you explain why your hands feel as they do?

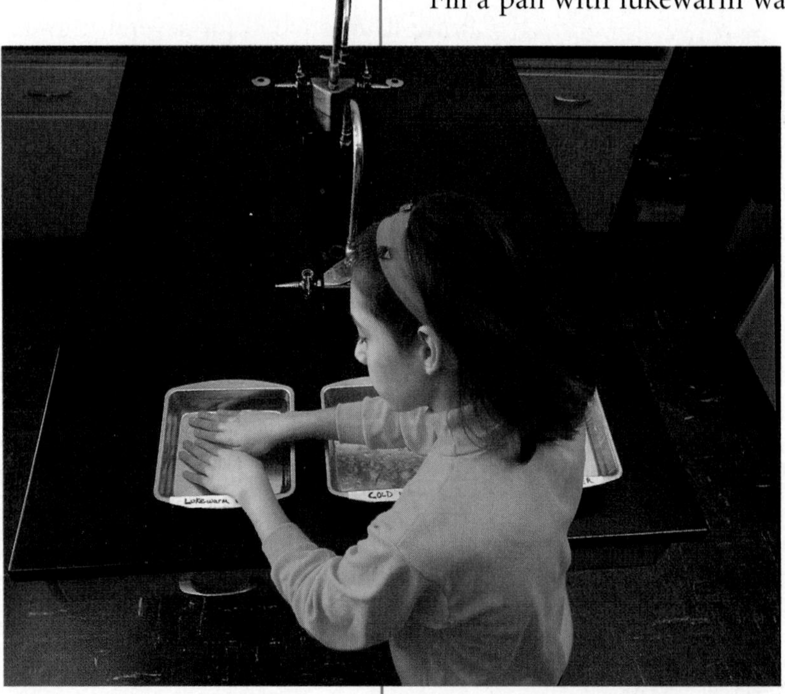

As you've just seen, your sense of touch can be fooled. What does that tell you about your earlier Explore activity with the carpet and the coin? If two items feel different, does that really mean that they're at different temperatures? Relying on our sense of touch doesn't help us tell someone else exactly how hot something is. We need a more precise way to indicate temperature.

Around the year 1600, Galileo Galilei discovered that air takes up more space when it's warm than when it's cold. Galileo used that information in making an instrument called a thermoscope to determine temperature, shown in Figure 6-1. About 100 years later, Dutch scientist G. D. Fahrenheit improved Galileo's design by using alcohol or mercury instead of air. These liquids also take up more space when hot than when cold. But they don't expand as much as air does. Fahrenheit, therefore, had to let the liquids expand in a very narrow tube. Fahrenheit's invention, in Figure 6-2, is the thermometer you've used to find the temperature outside or to check your temperature when you're sick.

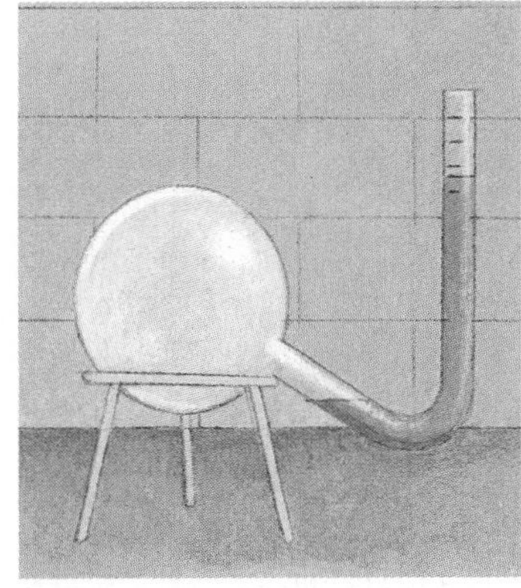

FIGURE 6-1. In Galileo's thermoscope, the air in the bubble would expand as it grew hotter and would push the column of liquid higher up the tube.

THERMAL EQUILIBRIUM

Do you remember the last time your parent or doctor used a thermometer to check your temperature? Did you have to hold it under your tongue for several minutes, or did the thermometer read your temperature instantly? In the next activity, you'll find out why and learn about thermal equilibrium.

FIGURE 6-2. Alcohol and mercury both expand when heated, just as air does. Alcohol and mercury thermometers give more accurate measurements than Galileo's thermoscope.

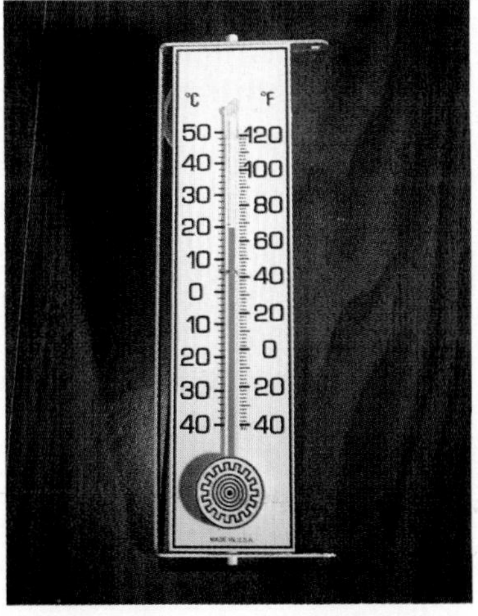

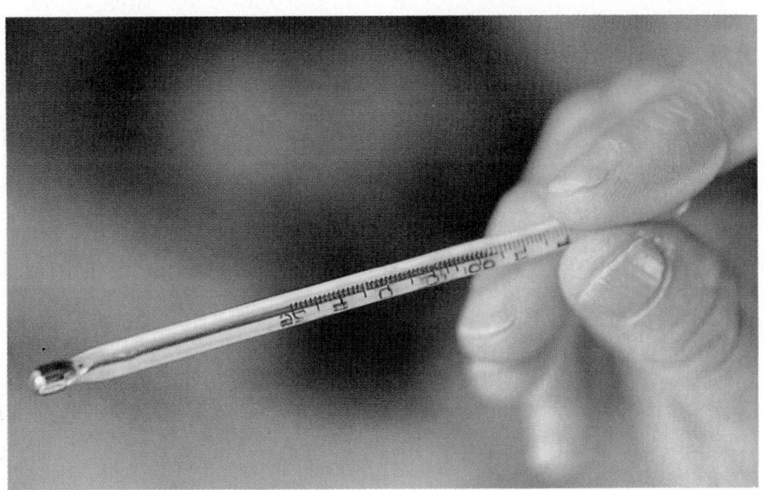

INVESTIGATE!

6-1 HOW COLD IS IT?

In this Investigate, you will **measure** the time needed to change the temperature of a container of water.

PROBLEM

How long does it take to cool a container of water?

MATERIALS  

thermometer
2 400-mL beakers
200 mL of water
hot plate or heating element
crushed ice
stopwatch or clock
graph paper
paper towels

PROCEDURE

1. Copy the data table.
2. Fill one beaker 3/4 full of crushed ice. Add 100 mL of water. Put the thermometer into the ice water and stir gently.

DATA AND OBSERVATIONS

TIME SINCE REMOVAL	FROM COLD WATER	FROM HOT WATER
4 sec.		
8 sec.		
12 sec.		
16 sec.		
20 sec.		
24 sec.		
28 sec.		

temperature in °C: 0 5 10 15 20 25 30 35 40 45 50 55 60 65 70 75 80
time in seconds: 0 2 4 6 8 10 12 14 16 18 20

3. Work in teams of three. Decide who will be timekeeper, who will read the thermometer and stir the mixture, and who will record the readings.
4. The timekeeper signals by counting down, "3, 2, 1, now!" The reader removes the thermometer, wipes it with a paper towel, and reads the temperature. Record the temperature.
5. Stirring between measurements, take a reading every 4 seconds.
6. Heat 100 mL of water in the other beaker until it's between 70°C and 80°C.
7. Stirring between measurements, repeat Steps 4 and 5.
8. **Make a graph** like the one pictured. Be sure the vertical axis runs from your lowest to highest temperatures. The horizontal axis should extend to two minutes.
9. Plot the positions of the time and temperature data from the cold water. Connect the points with a curve. Extend the curve to see what might happen if you took readings for a longer time.
10. Using a different color pencil, repeat Step 9 for the hot water data.
11. Note your thermometer's reading. Draw a horizontal line on your graph corresponding to this final temperature.

ANALYZE

1. What do the two extended temperature curves appear to do?
2. Where does the final temperature line meet the other lines?

CONCLUDE AND APPLY

3. How long would you have predicted it to take for the cold water to reach room temperature? The hot water?
4. **Going Further:** Suppose the water in one beaker started at 80°C and the other started at 30°C. Predict how long it would take for them to reach the same temperature.

In the Investigate activity you just completed, the water's temperature was changing at every data point. You were able to extend your graph, however, to find the temperature at which change would stop. It was the temperature of the air surrounding the water—the temperature of the room. When two items are in contact, as the water and air were, and the temperature of one is the same as the temperature of the other, as in Figure 6-3, they are said to be in **thermal equilibrium.** We call their temperature the equilibrium temperature.

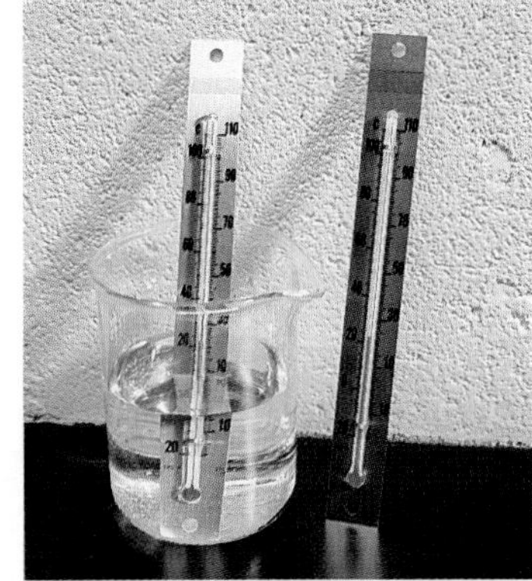

FIGURE 6-3. The water and air both have a temperature of 23°C. They are in thermal equilibrium.

THERMAL EQUILIBRIUM AND ENERGY

When you were studying work and energy, you pulled a heavy box across a surface, doing work on the box. But the box didn't speed up and gain kinetic energy. Nor did it gain potential energy. According to the law of conservation of energy, energy cannot be lost, so you looked elsewhere for some different form of energy. When you felt the bottom of the box, it was warm. One result of doing work was that the box and its surface grew warm.

This experience makes us believe in a form of energy we commonly call thermal energy. If we add thermal energy to some material to make it hot by doing work on it, we can use that energy to make steam to drive a turbine and produce work. Thus, thermal energy can be transferred and can do work.

When your thermometer remained in the ice water, hot water, or air for a long enough time, the thermometer reached thermal equilibrium with its surroundings. Whenever two objects are in thermal equilibrium, they are defined as being at the same temperature. Also, whenever each of two objects is in thermal equilibrium with a third object, all three must be in thermal equilibrium and at the same temperature, as demonstrated by Figure 6-4.

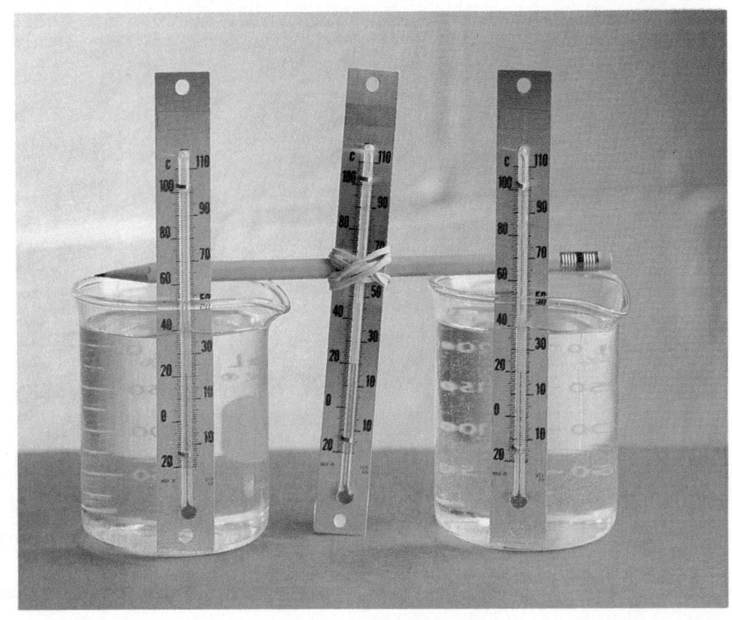

FIGURE 6-4. Each beaker of water is in thermal equilibrium with the air in the room, so they are in thermal equilibrium with each other.

TEMPERATURE SCALES

Think back to you and your friend on the telephone, trying to describe the hot day. You may have no thermometers, but if you can each produce two sets of equal temperatures, you can create your own temperature scale and find out which room is hotter. That's not as hard to do as it might sound.

FIND OUT!

How do you make a temperature scale?

Prepare a beaker of ice water. Use enough crushed ice to get a slushy mixture. Place an unmarked alcohol thermometer in the ice water and put the beaker on a hot plate. Stir the mixture as the ice melts and watch the thermometer. What happens to the thermometer level while the ice is melting? Mark that level on the thermometer. We define this level as the temperature of melting ice.

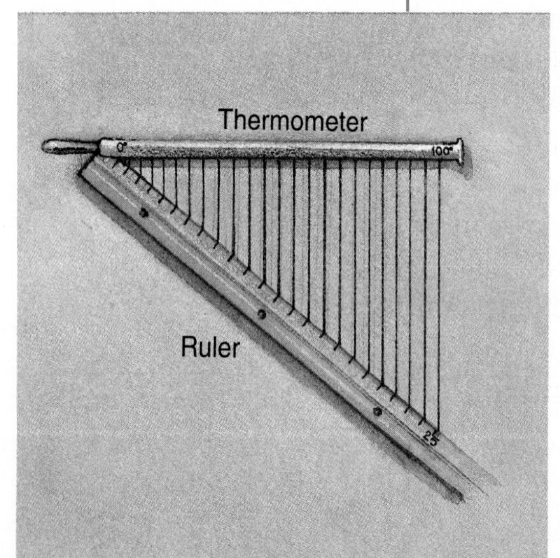

Continue to heat the water until it boils. Keep watching the thermometer level. What happens while the water boils? Mark that level, too.

You now have two points on your thermometer—the temperatures of melting ice and boiling water. Now divide the space between them into units. For this exercise, use the scale derived from one first used by Anders Celsius in the 1740s. Assign 0 to the melting point and 100 to the boiling point.

Now divide the space between 0 and 100 into 25 equal spaces. The figure shows you how to do it with a fine-point marker and a metric ruler. You now have marks 4°C apart. Put marks halfway between the marks you already have to get marks at every 2 degrees. That lets you estimate a temperature within 1 degree.

Conclude and Apply

1. How would your thermometer be different if there were 10 equal spaces between 0 and 100?
2. How would the thermometers change if you used the melting and boiling points of salt water or lemonade?

The scale you just used, known as the Celsius scale, is the one most used throughout the world. But there are others. Weather reports in the United States generally use the scale developed by Fahrenheit in 1715. It uses 32° as the freezing point of water and 212° as water's boiling point. Are the freezing and boiling points of water different in different temperature scales? Does the freezing point of water change from one scale to another?

FIGURE 6-5. The temperature of the ice could be lower than the freezing point of water, depending on the air temperature.

Different temperature scales serve different purposes. The important thing is that two people use the same scale. If you and your friend made your own thermometers and used different scales, you still wouldn't know which city was hotter. But, because you both used the Celsius scale, you know that your cities are about equally hot.

Measuring temperature accurately sets the stage for discussing how your cities got so hot in the first place—and how that heat gets into your homes. You and your friend might also talk about how you could make your homes cool in the hot weather.

Changing things from hot to cold or from cold to hot requires us to look at the concept of transferring thermal energy. You'll do that in the next section.

Check Your Understanding

1. Suppose you remove a spoon from a cup of hot coffee. The coffee has a temperature of 80°C and the room is at 23°C. Sketch a graph of the temperature of the spoon versus time after the spoon is removed from the coffee.
2. Imagine that you could somehow represent the flow of thermal energy. How could you show when the spoon described above was the same temperature as the room?
3. Using the Celsius scale, what temperature would be midway between the freezing point and boiling point of water? What are the temperatures, in degrees Celsius, of the following: ice, boiling water, room temperature, and normal body temperature?
4. **APPLY:** How would the graph you sketched in Question 1 be different if you had measured temperature using the Fahrenheit scale instead of the Celsius scale?

6-2 Heat and Temperature

OBJECTIVES

In this section, you will

- describe heat as the transfer of energy;
- distinguish temperature from heat;
- give examples of heat transfer by conduction, convection, and radiation;
- identify materials that reduce heat transfer most effectively.

KEY SCIENCE TERMS

heat
conduction
convection
radiation

HEAT AS TRANSFER OF ENERGY

You and your friend on the telephone talked about how hot it was outside. Next, you'll learn about heat in relation to energy.

Heat is a transfer of energy. The kind of energy being transferred is commonly called thermal energy. We use that term to indicate that the energy being transferred has something to do with heat.

Think again about dragging a box across a surface. You know you're doing work because there's a force and motion in the direction of the force. Since you're doing work, you transfer energy from yourself to the box. The box gains thermal energy. You can detect the thermal energy when you feel the bottom of the box. It feels warm.

Suppose you place hot water next to cold water, separating the two with a copper sheet, as shown in Figure 6-6. The hot water will grow cooler, and the cold water will grow warmer. Heat moves from the hot water to the cold water. But heat never goes the other way. This transfer of heat will continue until the two samples of water are in thermal equilibrium. When there is thermal equilibrium, the two sides must be at the same temperature.

FIGURE 6-6. Thermal energy moves from the hotter to the colder water until the two are in thermal equilibrium.

WHAT IS THERMAL ENERGY?

You've already seen that heat causes many substances to expand. That's how a mercury or alcohol thermometer works. Next, you'll see how heat does work in a thermometer.

EXPLORE!

How does heat do work in a thermometer?

Place the bulb of a thermometer in crushed ice and water. After it comes to equilibrium with the water and reads 0°C, take the thermometer out of the ice water and place its bulb in boiling water. What happens to the column inside the glass?

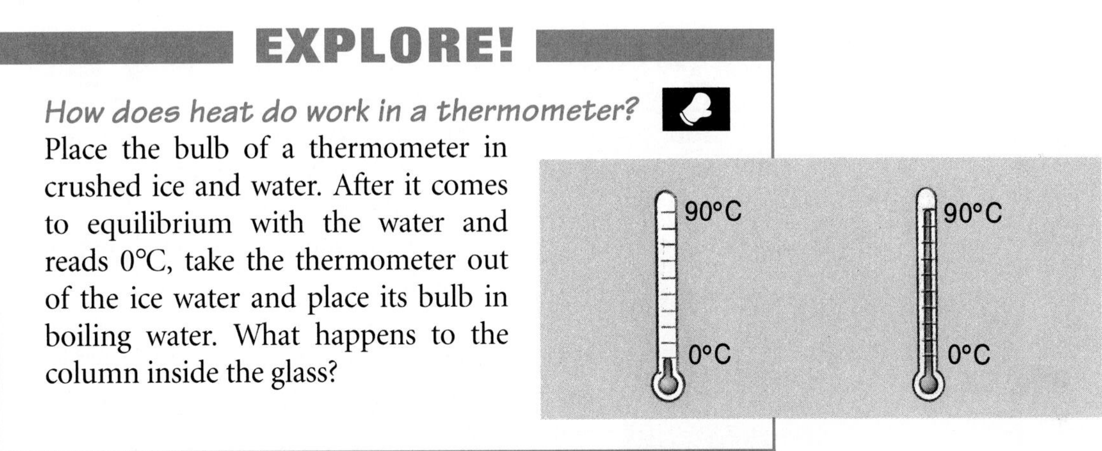

As the thermometer liquid absorbs heat, it expands. The top of the liquid moves upward in the thermometer's stem, as shown in the illustration. Heat transferred from the water to the thermometer bulb did work on the liquid. It lifted some liquid above the bulb. This movement gave the liquid column additional potential energy. What is the source of the energy? Is there work done on the liquid that moves? What do you think does the work? Is the liquid in the bulb warmer when the temperature reads 90°C than when it reads 0°C? What two energy changes happen to the liquid in the thermometer as the bulb is heated?

In the Explore, the heat added to the thermometer made the liquid in the bulb warmer while also doing work on the column of liquid above the bulb. When heat transfers between objects, only some of the energy being transferred warms the object it enters. Part of the energy also goes into doing work. That's why the thermometer in the boiling water reached only 90°C—some energy was used to expand the liquid in the bulb. Heat could be called a transfer of thermal energy. But after it is transferred, the energy is no longer only thermal.

HOW THERMAL ENERGY TRANSFERS

If heat is energy in transit, how does it move? What is it that takes thermal energy from one place to another? Let's find out.

EXPLORE!

How does thermal energy transfer from one object to another?

You've been given three rods of iron, copper, and aluminum, all of the same length and diameter, and two wooden dowels. Tape them together so that the wooden dowels separate the metal rods, as shown in the photograph.

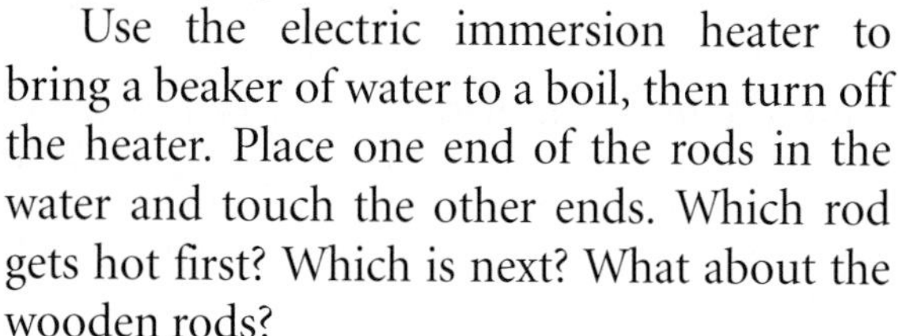

Use the electric immersion heater to bring a beaker of water to a boil, then turn off the heater. Place one end of the rods in the water and touch the other ends. Which rod gets hot first? Which is next? What about the wooden rods?

From the Explore, you could infer that thermal energy traveled from the hot water to the metal rods. Did you see any evidence of energy moving from the water to the rods? If you held the rods about 10 centimeters above the water, do you think they would get warm?

There are many things around your home that move energy from one place to another. Look at a hair dryer. It has a heating element that heats the air around it. It also has a blower that pushes air past the heating element and out into the open. Turn on the hair dryer and aim it at your hand. What do you feel? Turn the heat off but leave the blower on. After a few moments, what does the stream of air feel like? What's carrying the heat when the blower is turned on? Now aim the hair dryer horizontally. Is the hot air moving straight, rising, or falling?

Finally, turn on a light bulb. Be careful not to touch the bulb—it's hot—but bring your hand close to it. What do you feel? How do you think the thermal energy is getting to your hand from the bulb? Hold your hand above and then below the bulb. In which position do you feel more heat?

You already know that hot air rises. Therefore, something else must be letting you feel the heat when you hold your hand below the bulb.

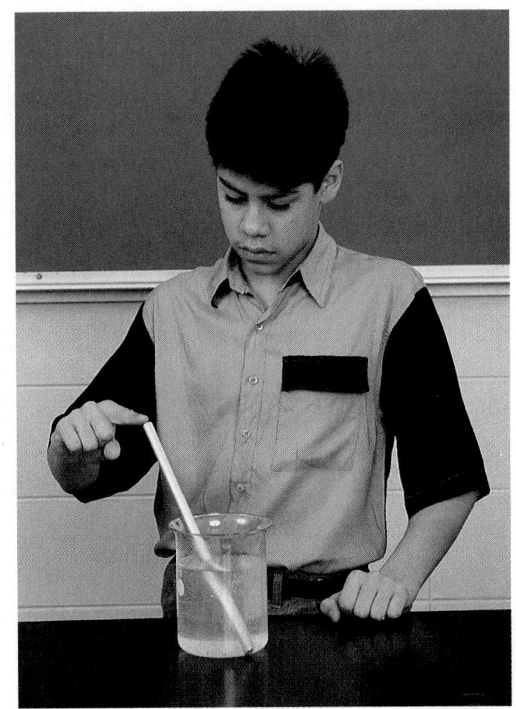

FIGURE 6-7. Conduction is the flow of heat through a substance or from one substance in physical contact with another.

CONDUCTION

In the Explore activity you just completed, you saw that heat was transferred along the metal and wooden rods. This process—heat moving through a material or from one material to another—is known as **conduction.** That's what happened with the metal rods. The heat flowed up the metal to your hand.

In order for thermal energy to transfer by conduction from one object to another, the objects must be in physical contact, as shown in Figure 6-7. Conduction transfers heat from a burner to a pan or from a beaker of boiling water to your hand via the metal rods.

Notice that some substances transfer heat better than others. You saw the difference in the ways aluminum, copper, iron, and wood conducted the heat. Table 6-1 shows how well various substances conduct heat in

TABLE 6-1. Relative Conduction Values

Substance	Conduction Relative to Silver
Air	0.00005
Aluminum	0.51
Brass	0.02
Copper	0.93
Cork	0.00013
Gold	0.71
Ice	0.002
Iron	0.16
Silver	1.00
White oak	0.05
Water	0.00014

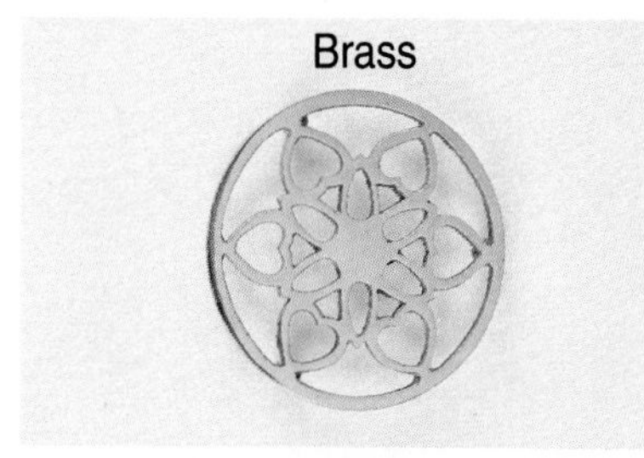

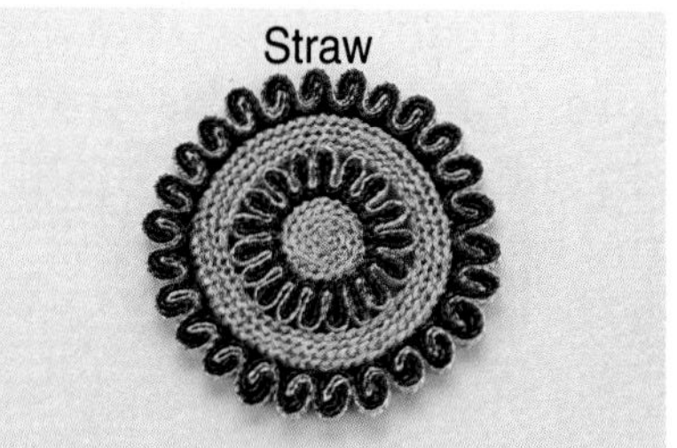

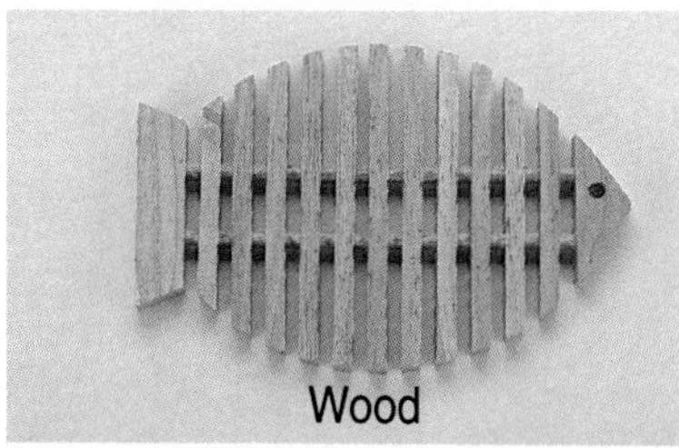

FIGURE 6-8. Which of these stands for hot dishes conducts the most heat away from the hot dish? Which will protect a surface but will not cool the dish as much?

comparison with silver, which conducts heat very well. Notice how poorly air, cork, and water conduct heat.

CONVECTION

Liquids and gases are called fluids because they flow. Fluids conduct thermal energy poorly. Fluids transfer thermal energy quite efficiently, however, by a process called convection. When you felt heat above the hair dryer, the heat was contained in the moving air. Warm winds carry heat from one place to another on Earth. Warm ocean currents carry heat from the tropics to cooler northern climates. Warm air is blown through ducts to heat a home—this is known as forced-air convection. In all of the above examples, a liquid or air carries heat as it moves from one place to another. A material that carries something else is known as a medium, so a fluid can be a medium for carrying heat. **Convection** is heat transfer by motion of a heat-carrying medium.

You know that the air near the ceiling of a room is generally warmer than the air near the floor. You've probably observed that boiling water in a pan appears to move in a circular pattern. Convection is the process in which hot fluids rise and cold fluids sink. You can observe convection in a container of warm water using a colored ice cube.

INVESTIGATE!

6-2 WATCHING ICE MELT

As a colored ice cube melts in warm water, you can **observe** where the cold water from the ice cube goes and how it is affected by the warm water in the glass.

PROBLEM

Where does ice go when it melts?

MATERIALS

colored ice cubes
tongs
thermometers
250-mL beaker
salt
stirring rod

PROCEDURE

1. Copy the data table.
2. Fill the beaker with warm water.
3. Obtain an ice cube that has been strongly dyed with food coloring. Using tongs, gently place the ice cube in the warm water. Do not stir or mix. Keep the beaker and water as still as possible.

DATA AND OBSERVATIONS

FRESH WATER		SALT WATER	
DEPTH	TEMP (°C)	DEPTH	TEMP (°C)
Surface		Surface	
2 cm		2 cm	
4 cm		4 cm	
6 cm		6 cm	
Bottom		Bottom	

4. **Observe** the ice-water mixture for several minutes. Then **measure** the temperature at the surface and at the bottom of the mixture, and at three levels in between. Record the temperatures in your data table.
5. Empty the beaker and refill it with warm water. Add as much salt as will dissolve in the water, stirring vigorously as you pour.
6. Repeat Steps 3 and 4 with the saltwater solution.

ANALYZE

1. As the ice melts, what happens to the meltwater in the fresh water? In the salt water?
2. Does the meltwater blend readily with the warm water, or does it tend to remain separate from it?
3. Describe the changes in temperature within the meltwater–warm-water mixtures.

CONCLUDE AND APPLY

4. **Infer** why convection occurs between fresh water and meltwater but not between salt water and meltwater.
5. Of the three fluids involved in this activity—fresh water, salt water, and meltwater—how can you **infer** which is the most dense? Explain your answer.
6. **Going Further**: What would happen if you were to add warm water to the bottom of a beaker of cold water?

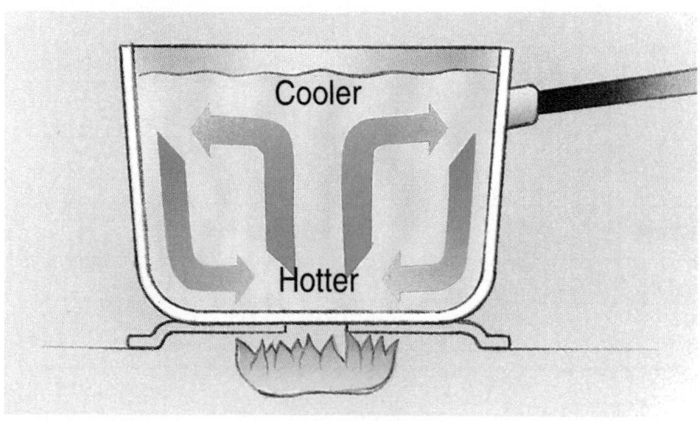

FIGURE 6-9. The water at the bottom of the pot is originally heated by conduction. The cooler water at the top sinks and pushes the less dense heated water to the top. A convection current occurs.

You could see the same process that you saw in the Investigate in a pan of boiling water. When you boil water, the heat from the stove makes the water at the bottom of the pan hot. If you put some food dye into the pan, you can see it being carried upward from the bottom of the pan. Hot water rises because cold, more dense water flows under it and pushes it up. When the hot water rises to the surface, thermal energy then flows into the air. The water cools and moves down toward the bottom, pushing other hot water to the surface and a convection current results. Figure 6-9 shows how convection works in a boiling pot.

RADIATION

If you've ever held your hand near a lighted bulb, you have felt heat. You know the heat from the bulb didn't come from conduction, because air is too poor a conductor. You also know that it didn't come from convection, because hot air would rise, not fall. How then, did the heat get from the bulb to your hand?

You could ask the same question about heat from the sun. Look at Figure 6-10. How does heat from the sun get to Earth? There's no matter in outer space to conduct the heat. This also means there is no air or liquid available to carry heat by convection.

FIGURE 6-10. Everything with thermal energy emits some of that thermal energy as radiation.

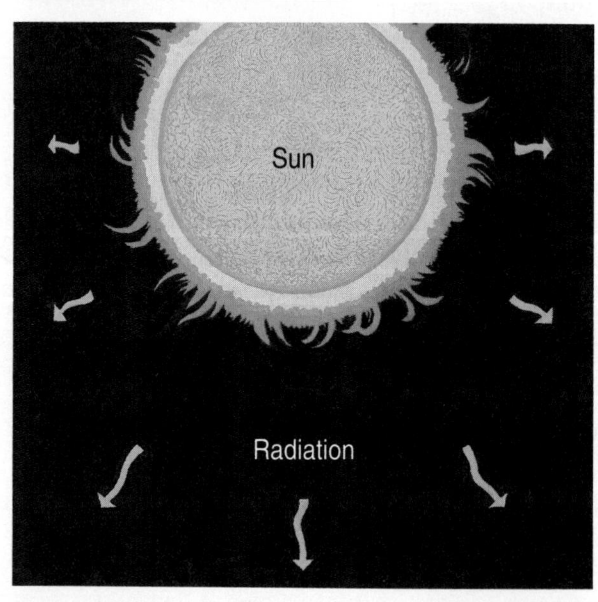

Radiation is the transfer of thermal energy across space. Any object with thermal energy emits radiation. If you've traveled down roads on a very hot day, you may have even seen evidence of this radiation. The air just above the hot pavement shimmers and shakes as heat radiates from the surface. This radiation is very much like radio or television waves. The thermal energy transfers in the same way that radio and television signals travel from the broadcasting station to your home.

MINIMIZING HEAT TRANSFER

Sometimes, you'd rather stop thermal energy from being transferred as it normally would. When it's hot outside, it would be nice to keep the heat out of your room. When you're packing a cold or hot drink to take on an outing, you want to keep it from becoming lukewarm. When you heat your home in winter, you want to keep the energy inside. To do all these things, you need to prevent all three types of thermal energy transfer as much as possible.

You can reduce conduction loss from an object by surrounding it with insulating materials. Because insulators conduct heat very poorly, little heat is conducted in or out of an insulated object or room. Many homes use fiberglass insulation, which contains many pockets of air. Air, as you saw, is a very poor conductor. Containers that keep food hot or cold also use air as a barrier to heat transfer, as shown in Figure 6-11.

Heat can't escape from a home by convection unless the air carrying the heat leaves the house. To keep heat inside in winter and outside in summer, doors and windows need to be well sealed. In Figure 6-12, warm temperatures look orange or red. Cooler temperatures are blue or green.

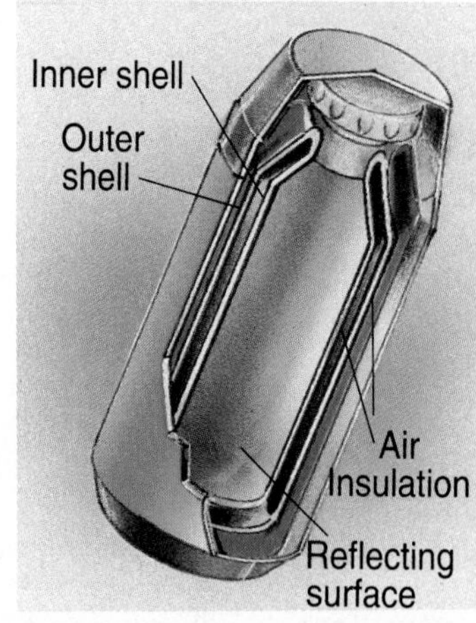

FIGURE 6-11. Insulated food containers often have double walls. The air between the walls insulates because it doesn't conduct much heat.

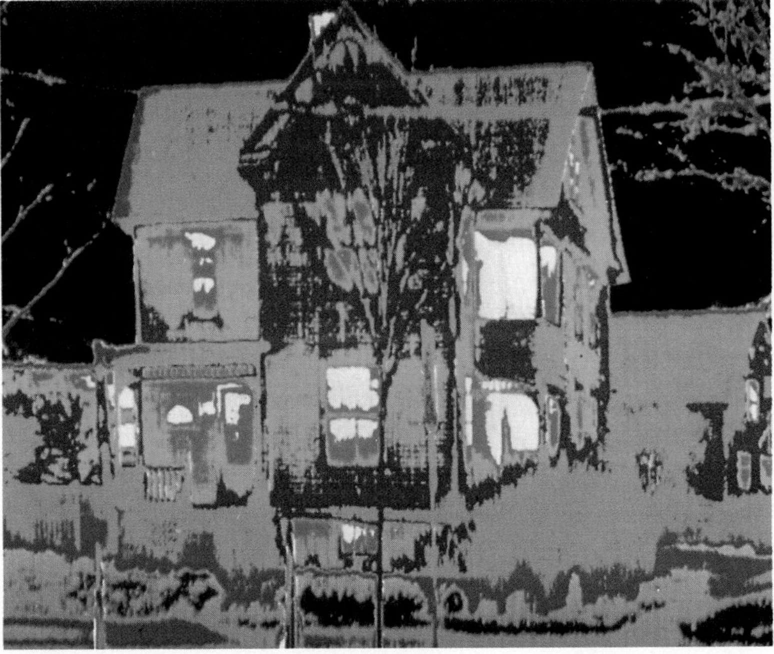

FIGURE 6-12. The film used in a thermogram records the radiation from thermal energy instead of light.

FIGURE 6-13. Fiberglass is an insulator that keeps energy from moving in or out through the walls.

Have you noticed that many home insulation materials have a shiny foil backing, as pictured in Figure 6-13? Shiny surfaces reflect radiation. Much of the thermal energy that radiates toward this material will be reflected back. So thermal energy that would normally radiate out of a building is reflected back inside to keep the building warmer in the winter. Similarly, when energy radiated from the sun strikes the building, much of it will be reflected away to keep the building cooler during the summer.

This brings us back to the discussion about heat that you and your friend were having on the phone. You should now know where all the thermal energy has come from. Some comes from the sun in the form of radiation. Some comes from any light bulbs that may be on. Conduction and convection play a role, too. Hot air can be blown into your room by the wind. Heat can be conducted into your house through the walls. But you may start to wonder: If all this heat you feel is a form of energy, and energy can do work, how much work could the thermal energy in your room do? You'll find out about that in the next section.

Check Your Understanding

1. Describe the transfer of energy as a pan of water is heated to boiling on a gas stove.
2. How can two objects have the same temperature but different amounts of heat?
3. Suppose you needed to keep water hot inside a metal container. Which metal would keep the water hottest for the longest time: aluminum, brass, or gold? Why?
4. Table 6-1 shows that water has a very low thermal conductivity. Yet, when you heat water in a pan, the surface gets hot very fast—even though you're applying the heat to the bottom of the water. Why?
5. **APPLY:** Which of these materials would best protect against loss of thermal energy by radiation: iron, wood, or silver? Why?

6-3 Making Heat Work

WORK FROM HEAT

You've seen heat do work as you performed the various activities in this chapter. Every time you used a thermometer, the transfer of heat did some work on the column of liquid. The energy made the liquid expand or contract, as well as warming it.

Imagine doing the same thing with a column of air, but taking it a step further. We'll put a piston on top of the column of air, as shown in Figure 6-14. When the air heats up, it will expand. What will then happen to the piston?

The piston will rise. Then, when the air cools, it will contract again, and the piston will sink down. The piston will keep going up and down as long and as frequently as we make the air expand and contract. If we hook a shaft to the piston, we can make the shaft turn and use it to drive a motor. That's what a car engine does.

A car engine is an example of a **heat engine.** That's an engine that uses fuel to make thermal energy do work. Heat engines aren't very efficient because most of the heat they produce never does work.

OBJECTIVES

In this section, you will

- describe how heat can produce work;
- explain why a heat engine can't be 100 percent efficient;
- describe how an air conditioner or refrigerator works.

KEY SCIENCE TERMS

heat engine

EXPLORE!

Why is a heat engine inefficient?

You'll need some help from a teacher or parent for this exercise. Feel the hood of a car. Have the car's driver start the engine and let it run for 5 minutes. Then feel the hood again. What's different?

The heat you felt when you touched the car's hood after the engine ran for awhile was heat that was not used to power the engine. The engine itself was far hotter. That heat, too, is wasted thermal energy. Where do you think it came from?

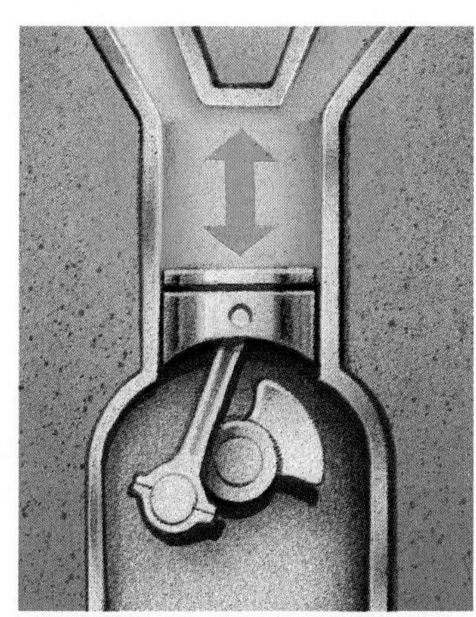

FIGURE 6-14. Work is done on the piston as the air is heated.

How do we know?

What makes heat engines inefficient?

In 1824, the French scientist/engineer Sadi Carnot investigated the amount of work a heat engine produces. He found that even a perfect engine with no friction at all could only use a certain fraction of thermal energy from the fuel. The exact fraction depends upon how much heat the fuel creates and how much the hot exhaust gases can cool in the engine while it runs. But even if the exhaust gases cooled until they were in thermal equilibrium with the surrounding air, there would still be thermal energy left in them. That thermal energy cannot do work because, to make it do so, heat would have to move from a place of lower temperature to a place of higher temperature.

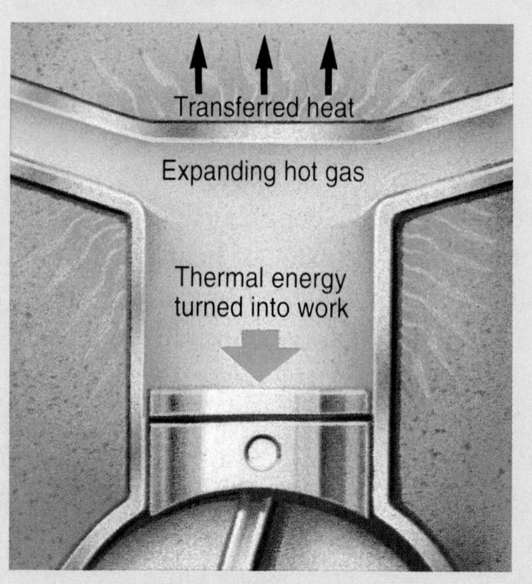

If your first answer was friction, you're only partially right. Some energy is indeed lost to doing work against friction. But a heat engine could be friction free, and it would still be very inefficient. As we saw earlier, heat flows from objects with higher temperatures to objects with lower temperatures. So when gasoline burns in an auto engine, hot air moves the piston, but much of the heat flows away into the surrounding metal.

Loss of heat to the surroundings makes it impossible for an engine operating in cycles to use all the energy from its fuel. Even if you have no friction, most of the energy is wasted. Where does this wasted thermal energy go? The energy moves from the area of higher temperature to an area of lower temperature. That is, rather than doing work, some thermal energy raises the temperature of the surrounding materials.

Not all heat engines are gasoline engines. Other kinds of heat engines include diesel engines and airplane jet turbine engines.

Another kind of heat engine is one that makes air cold, such as a refrigerator or air conditioner. Instead of using fuel to produce heat to do work, a refrigerator uses fuel to do work to transfer energy as heat from a lower temperature to a higher temperature.

DID YOU KNOW?

Laboratory measurements have shown that the maximum efficiency of gasoline engines is less than 30 percent.

REFRIGERATORS: USING WORK TO TRANSFER HEAT

A refrigerator keeps food cool because it can transfer heat from one place to another. The same is true of an air conditioner. The most common refrigeration as well as air conditioning systems use evaporation of a liquid and expansion of a gas to cool something. You can examine the basic principles involved in refrigeration by doing the next activity.

EXPLORE!

How does refrigeration work?

Fill an eyedropper with alcohol and allow a few drops to drip onto the inside of your wrist. How does it feel?

Next, inflate an inner tube with an air pump. After the tube is well filled, feel the outside of the tube. Is it warm or cool? Let it stand for 5 to 10 minutes. Open the valve and let the air out of the inner tube. Feel the valve. Is it warm or cool?

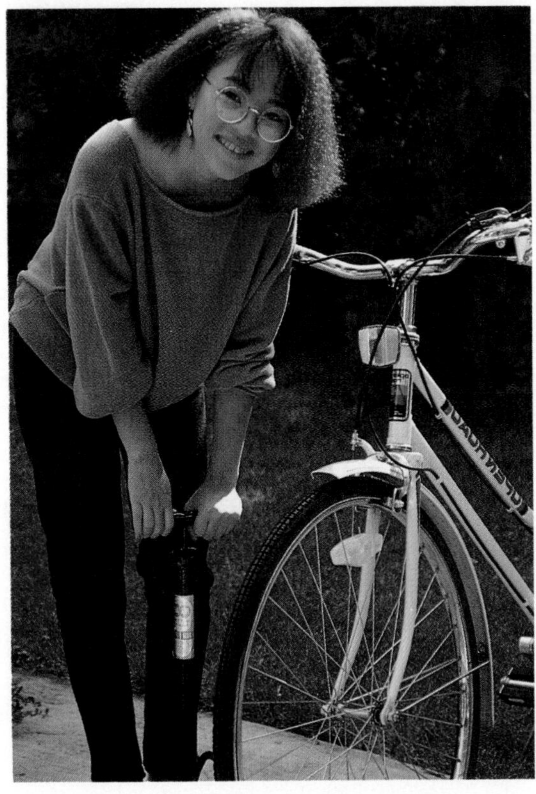

FIGURE 6-15. After inflating the tire, the pump feels warm. What does this tell you about the thermal energy of the air?

Think about what happened in the Explore. When the alcohol hit your wrist, it immediately started to evaporate. As it evaporated, it carried thermal energy from your wrist.

When you inflated the inner tube, you used the pump to do work on air. What you actually did was compress the air into the inner tube. The work increased the thermal energy of the air. You could tell that the thermal energy was increasing because the pump felt hot when you touched it. But when you let the air escape from the inner tube and expand, the nozzle felt cold.

You can infer, then, that air cools as it is allowed to expand. Compressing the air in the inner tube and then allowing the air to expand, is very similar to what a refrigerator or air conditioner does.

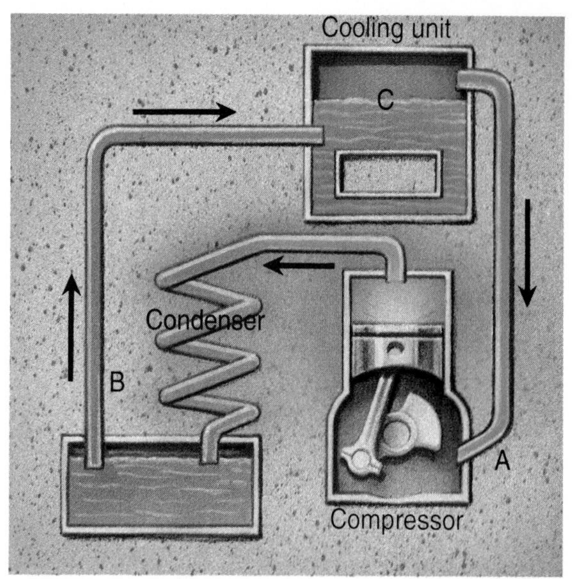

FIGURE 6-16. Manufacturers suggest that there be three inches of space behind and above the refrigerator to avoid overheating. What part of the refrigerator gets hot?

A liquid grows warmer as it evaporates. But the energy a liquid gains as it evaporates has to come from somewhere. It comes from the liquid's surroundings. In other words, when a liquid evaporates to become a vapor, it grows warmer. But it cools its surroundings by absorbing some of its surroundings' energy.

A refrigerator is a machine that works in cycles to take advantage of this means of cooling. But for the refrigerator to work in cycles, the liquid and vapor must be confined. The vapor must be compressed and changed back to a liquid. Then the liquid can evaporate once more.

Follow the cycle in Figure 6-16. We have vapor of some kind at A. It's compressed by the compressor and grows hot—just as air grew hot when you pumped it into the inner tube. At B, the hot vapor is allowed to cool so that it condenses into a liquid. All this takes place on the outside of the refrigerator. But now the liquid is pumped into C, inside the refrigerator. Here, the liquid evaporates, turning back to vapor and absorbing heat from inside the refrigerator. The vapor then flows back to the compressor and the cycle starts again.

By the time you and your friend have finished your discussion of heat, the sun has begun to set. You open a window to let cooler air in and the warmer air out. Thermal energy is leaving your room by convection through the open window and—very slowly—by conduction and radiation through the walls and glass. Tomorrow that energy might be almost anywhere. But the sun will return to provide a new supply.

Check Your Understanding

1. Why can heat do work on a piston?
2. What prevents heat engines from being perfectly efficient?
3. In an air conditioner or refrigerator, what is the process that actually removes heat from inside the room or refrigerator?
4. **APPLY:** Could a refrigerator also be used as a heater? Explain.

EXPANDING YOUR VIEW

CONTENTS

A Closer Look
Latent Heat 183

Life Science Connection
How We Use Calories 184

Science and Society
Thermal Pollution 185

History Connection
Keeping Cool 187

Consumer Connection
Solar Energy for Solar Homes 188

A CLOSER LOOK

LATENT HEAT

In the first Investigate in this chapter you saw that the temperature of ice water didn't change as the ice was melting. Nor did the temperature of boiling water change as the water turned to steam. But you know that thermal energy was being added to the water in each case. Where did the energy go if it didn't result in higher temperatures?

Another similar experiment shows that it takes about 2260 joules to turn water at 100°C to steam at 100°C. The amount of energy required to change the state of a material is known as latent heat. The word latent means hidden. Latent energy got that name because it's not easily seen as a temperature change. Water at 0°C seems as though it has the same amount of thermal energy as ice at 0°C because they both have the same temperature. But water actually has more energy. That extra thermal energy is hidden, or latent. In the same way, 100°C steam has more energy than 100°C water.

Latent energies are the same for freezing or melting and for boiling or condensing. You need to add 334 J to 1 gram of ice at 0°C to make it melt, or remove 334 J from 1 gram of water to make it freeze. You must add 2260 J to 1 gram of water at 100°C to make it boil, or remove 2260 J from 1 gram of steam at 100°C to turn it back to water.

YOU TRY IT!

Put 100 mL of water into a plastic foam cup. Gradually add crushed ice and stir until the ice is all melted and the water is at 0°C. Pour 100 mL of the 0°C water into a second foam cup. Place an electric immersion heater in the cup and turn it on. Record the temperature of the water every 10 seconds until the temperature reaches 80°C.

Water has a density of $1 g/cm^3$. That is, 1 g of water occupies $1 cm^3$, or 1 mL of volume. Use this information to calculate how many grams of water you heated. It takes 4.18 J of energy to raise the temperature of 1 gram of water by 1°C. Find the amount of energy you added to the water.

LIFE SCIENCE CONNECTION

HOW WE USE CALORIES

We use the Calorie to measure how much energy our bodies get from foods and how much energy our bodies use for different activities. One Calorie is equal to 4180 joules. The number of Calories a person needs daily depends on various factors, such as height, weight, age, sex, and level of daily activity. The body of a person who exercises frequently or does hard physical work needs more Calories than does the body of an individual who leads a less active life.

In the United States, people generally get more Calories than they need. The energy or Calories a person eats in excess of what their body needs is stored in the body's fat cells or storage center. When humans lived with alternate periods of scarcity and abundance of food, having excess Calories for later need made sense.

Fat is a productive, efficient way to store Calories. Every gram of fat a person consumes gives the body nine Calories of energy. A pound of fat on a person equals about 3500 Calories. When you use more Calories than you are eating, the body uses the stored fat. To lose a pound of fat, an individual would have to use, or expend, 3500 Calories. Most of us use only 1500 to 3000 Calories a day.

It takes very little to add more Calories to a diet. Twenty-five extra Calories a day consumed in a graham cracker or in a tablespoon of

ice cream equals 175 Calories a week, or 9100 Calories a year. That's 2.6 pounds added to the body a year, or 26 pounds in ten years.

To maintain your proper weight, it is useful to know your ideal weight. Ideal weight is the weight and body composition recommended for your age, sex, height, and body build. Life insurance companies devised tables to find your ideal weights based on sex, height, and body frame. Doctors and nutritionists advise that ideal body for a man should have no more than 15 percent body fat, and for a woman, no more than 18 percent body fat.

CALORIES USED IN 1 HOUR

Type of Activity	Body Frames		
	Small	Medium	Large
Sleeping	48	56	64
Sitting	72	84	96
Eating	84	98	112
Standing	96	112	123
Walking	180	210	240
Playing tennis	380	420	460
Bicycling fast	500	600	700
Running	700	850	1000

YOU TRY IT!

The table to the left shows Calories used by different body frame sizes in one hour during different activities. Analyze the data in the table. Make up questions, such as: How many hours does a small framed person have to walk to make up for one hour of running? Is it the same for medium and large framed persons?

SCIENCE AND SOCIETY

THERMAL POLLUTION

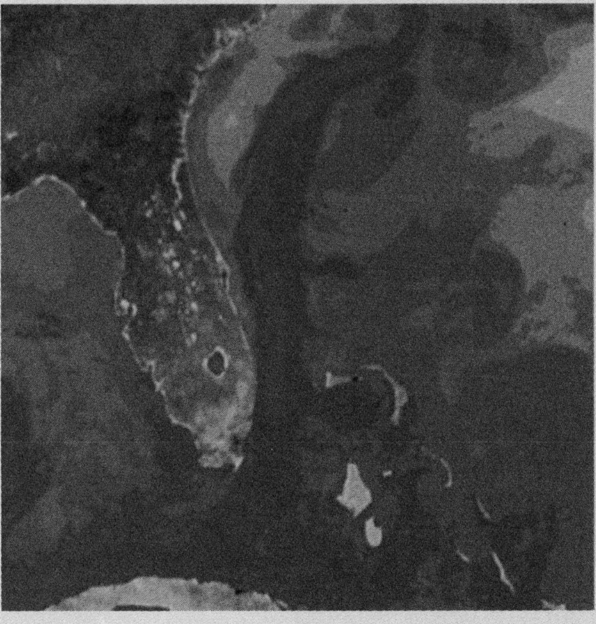

Electric power plants use tremendous amounts of water to cool their machines and equipment. Some plants take water from natural bodies of water and return the water once it is used. When used or excess heated water is returned to natural rivers, lakes, or oceans, the excess heat may damage the ecology of that water. This dumping of heated water is called thermal pollution.

Power plants are not the only facilities responsible for thermal pollution. Manufacturing plants often use water from a nearby river or lake to cool equipment during the manufacturing process. The warm water is often returned to the river or lake. Researchers have several ways to tell if thermal pollution is occurring. One way relies on satellite photographs taken with temperature-sensitive film. In the photo shown here, red areas are cold. This photograph shows warm water along the shore as a result of industry. Hot, or even warm, water drained into a lake or river, or a section of ocean, may raise the temperature of that body of water by as much as 5° to 11°C. This increased temperature may make it difficult for fish to breathe or to incubate their eggs. Also, over time, this increased temperature can disrupt the total ecosystem of a body of water.

You may remember that an ecosystem is a community of organisms interacting with one another and with the environment. A self-contained area shared by various animal and plant species is an ecosystem. Microorganisms, plants, and animals found in any body of water occur in groups. Some of these groups are dependent on each other. For example, certain kinds of fish may need to be present to preserve certain species of microorganisms that feed in the water. Heated water can allow

YOU TRY IT!

Contact a nearby nuclear or fossil fuel power plant. Ask a representative how the plant cools its used water.

Call your local Environmental Protection Agency. Ask to speak to a specialist in water pollution. Ask the specialist how they test water for eutrophication.

the introduction of new organisms, such as species of fish and snails normally associated with areas of warmer water.

In essence, the community changes, the balance of life of various species is disrupted, and the original ecosystem is changed.

Thermal pollution also leads to eutrophication in a body of water. Eutrophication occurs when an excessive amount of nutrients, such as nitrates and phosphates, enter the water and cause an overgrowth of weeds, algae, and other plant life. The nutrient-rich water overfeeds the fast-growing weeds. If too many weeds and algae develop, they use a large percentage of the oxygen in the water.

Eventually fish and other marine life die from suffocation. The body of water becomes overgrown with unwanted plants, and soon the lake or river changes to a dark murky color. The hydrogen in the water combines with other elements and forms foul-smelling gases. When there is no more oxygen in the water, the remaining algae and unwanted weeds decay and die.

Today, most nuclear and fossil fuel power plants have cooling towers like those in the photograph. Heated water is stored in these towers until its temperature is similar to the body of water it is to be returned to. Some facilities send the heated water through sectioned-off rivers or down slow-moving winding creeks, whose angles slow the water and give it time to cool. Other facilities have built their own cooling lakes so that they don't have to rely on natural sources of water for cooling.

CAREER CONNECTION

Water quality engineers, such as the one shown below, are trained in biology, chemistry, and engineering. They study the composition of lakes, streams, rivers, and oceans. They observe effects of pollution and seek ways to protect the available water on the planet.

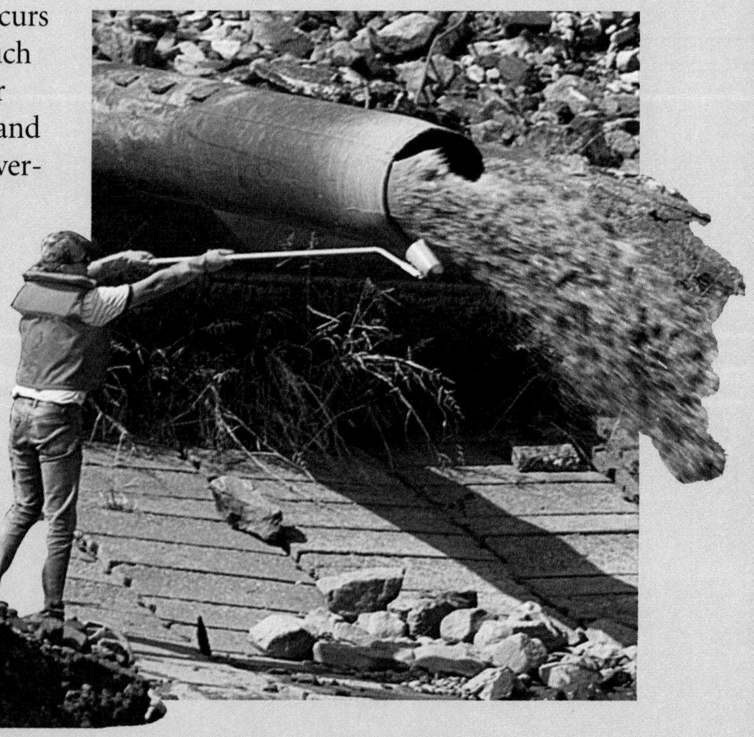

History CONNECTION

KEEPING COOL

The earliest refrigerators, built 4000 years ago, were little more than pits filled with collected ice. People placed the foods they wished to preserve in the pits with the ice. As long as the ice lasted, the foods were preserved.

In 1851, John Gorrie received the first patent for a machine designed to keep objects cold—he had designed the first refrigerator. The refrigerator relies on the principle that as liquid grows warmer and evaporates, it absorbs some energy from its surroundings. The surroundings, in turn, become cooler. In a household refrigerator, the liquid and vapor are confined. The liquid is recycled. It is compressed and changed back into a liquid.

Freon and ammonia are the fluids commonly used in refrigerators. The fluid is pumped into a compressor where it grows hot as it is compressed. Then, the hot vapor is allowed to cool and condense into a liquid. This liquid is pumped through pipes along the cabinet of the refrigerator, where the liquid absorbs heat from inside the refrigerator, and changes back into a vapor.

In the 1900s, German scientist Karl von Linde combined the workings of a refrigerator with the concept of a heat exchanger. In a heat exchanger, two tubes of fluid—one warm, the other cool—pass next to one another. As they pass, the warmer fluid transfers some energy to the cooler fluid. Using a series of heat exchangers combined with refrigeration, von Linde was able to produce liquid oxygen and liquid nitrogen from ordinary air.

Another great stride in refrigeration was made by African-American Frederick McKinley Jones, shown in the photo. In the 1940s, Jones redesigned refrigeration units by transforming them from large, cumbersome equipment into portable units. His efforts made it possible for refrigerators of a smaller size to be used by trains, trucks, airplanes, and ships. Now foods such as milk, meat, eggs, and butter—even ice cream—could be shipped thousands of miles, in any season, without spoiling. Jones's invention even made it possible to transport blood on the battlefields during World War II.

YOU TRY IT!

Make a list of the frozen foods you eat in a week. Also list other foods you eat that might spoil on the way to market if they were not refrigerated. How important do you think refrigerated trucks are to your everyday life?

Consumer CONNECTION

SOLAR ENERGY FOR SOLAR HOMES

Our supplies of fossil fuels, such as coal, oil, and gas, are dwindling. Our use of fossil fuels contributes to air and water pollution. Nuclear energy, while less messy and less polluting, produces radioactive substances that may prove more lethal and difficult to dispose of than any energy waste product known to humans.

Using solar energy, that is, heat from the sun, to cool and heat our homes could be a valuable alternative to some of our present energy sources.

But the sun's energy can't be mined. Sunlight spreads over Earth, making it difficult to harness the sun's energy for our needs.

In 1939, the Massachusetts Institute of Technology built a solar house. Scientists placed solar collectors, devices used to collect the sun's energy, on the roof of the house. By the 1960s, over a dozen homes in the United States used solar energy as a source of thermal energy. And in the 1970s, thousands more solar homes were built, a response to increasing oil prices. The house shown in the photograph has an array of solar panels on its roof.

Perfecting a way to collect the sun's energy remains a concern. The most common kind of solar collector is the flat plate usually installed on roof tops. The solar collector is much like a parked car that sits in the sun on a hot day. The sun's rays pass through the car window and are absorbed by the car's seat. The thermal energy from the sun's rays is trapped inside the car and cannot pass through the glass window. The solar collector works in a similar way. A shallow black box with a lid made of glass or see-through material, such as plastic, sits facing south, on the roof of a house. The sun passes through the collector and hits the plate. The plate, usually made of metal, absorbs energy which then stays trapped in the collector.

There are basically two kinds of solar heating systems: active and passive. In an active system, water or air is used to absorb and transport energy to its destination. An active solar heating system uses pipes and pumps or fans to transport the energy throughout the house. Excess energy is stored in water or a reservoir and used when needed. An active system almost always works with a conventional system like a furnace or forced air heating system that switches on in periods of cold or overcast weather.

In a passive solar system, the sun's energy is collected and absorbed by energy-absorbing masses like walls or water-filled drums and then released at night. Warm air will rise to the ceiling, heating a particular space. Cool air will drop to the hot floor, become heated, and rise again.

YOU TRY IT!

Visit a solar heated home or building in your area. Ask to see the collector. Is the system an active or passive solar heating system?

Chapter 6

Reviewing Main Ideas

1. All objects contain some amount of thermal energy. Energy transferred as the result of temperature difference is heat.

2. Heat always flows from the area of higher temperature to areas of lower temperature.

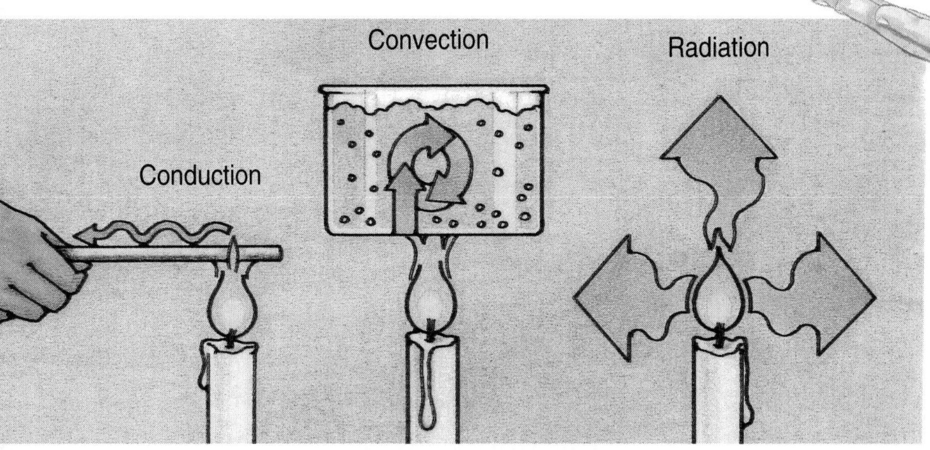

3. Thermal energy transfers in three ways. Heat flowing through an object is conduction. Heat carried by a moving fluid is convection, and heat traveling across space is radiation.

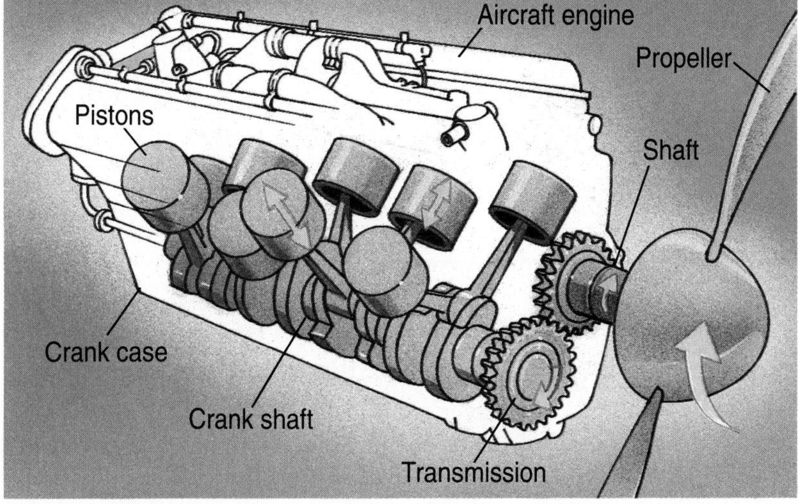

4. Engines may be used to convert thermal energy to work.

Chapter 6

Chapter Review

USING KEY SCIENCE TERMS

conduction	heat engine
convection	radiation
heat	thermal equilibrium

Each phrase below describes a science term from the list. Write the term that matches the phrase describing it.

1. the thermal energy that flows from 95°C water to the 68°C air surrounding it
2. a glass of milk that has been sitting on the table long enough to be at room temperature
3. energy you receive from the sun
4. train locomotive or jet engine
5. heat felt above the burning coals of a barbecue grill
6. heat felt through a metal door

UNDERSTANDING IDEAS

Choose the best answer to complete each sentence.

1. The temperatures of two objects are equal when ____.
   - **a.** they have the same total amount of thermal energy
   - **b.** they are in thermal equilibrium
   - **c.** they can do work on each other
   - **d.** they can transfer heat between them
2. If two objects are in thermal equilibrium with a third object, they____.
   - **a.** are at the same temperature, but not in thermal equilibrium with each other
   - **b.** are in thermal equilibrium, but not at the same temperature
   - **c.** are all three in thermal equilibrium and are at the same temperature
   - **d.** must all have the same volume
3. The Celsius temperature scale uses ____.
   - **a.** 32° as the freezing point of water and 212° as the boiling point of water
   - **b.** 0° as the freezing point of water and 212° as the boiling point of water
   - **c.** 32° as the freezing point of water and 100° as the boiling point of water
   - **d.** 0° as the freezing point of water and 100° as the boiling point of water
4. Heat naturally flows only ____.
   - **a.** from the area of higher temperature to the area of lower temperature
   - **b.** from the area of more total energy to the area of less total energy
   - **c.** toward an area that has both a lower temperature and lower total thermal energy
   - **d.** toward an area that has either a lower temperature or lower total energy
5. During convection, heat is transferred because ____.
   - **a.** liquids get cold and rise
   - **b.** fluids warm and sink
   - **c.** a heat-carrying medium moves
   - **d.** objects are in contact with one another

6. A refrigerator cools down by ____.
   a. solids liquefying
   b. liquid evaporating
   c. liquid solidifying
   d. gas condensing to liquid

CRITICAL THINKING

Use your understanding of the concepts developed in the chapter to answer each of the following questions.

1. Examine the figure. Name at least one place where heat is traveling by conduction, convection, and radiation.

2. Explain this statement: Unless a thermometer is already in thermal equilibrium with the fluid being tested, the act of measuring the temperature either adds or removes thermal energy from the fluid.

3. Before refrigerators were common, many kitchens had an icebox where food was kept cool. The box had one or two shelves in it and a large block of ice was placed at the top of the icebox. The ice block usually weighed 20–30 pounds, and it was often a struggle to place it on top of the box. Why didn't people take it easy and put the ice at the bottom of the icebox?

PROBLEM SOLVING

Read the following problem and discuss your answers in a brief paragraph.

Raphael and his father are planning to add a new room onto their home. They plan to use a forced-air furnace to heat the new room. Raphael thinks the room will look nicer if the heating vents are near the ceiling, out of sight. His dad says the heating bills will be lower if the vents are in the floor.

1. How does Raphael's dad know the heating bill will be less if the hot–air vents are near the floor?
2. How could Raphael use a ceiling fan to make his plan, with vents at the ceiling, more energy efficient?

CONNECTING IDEAS

Discuss each of the following in a brief paragraph.

1. Anyone who has used ropes much for any purpose has heard of rope burn. Explain rope burn in terms of thermal energy.

2. How does heat do work on a hot air balloon?

3. **A CLOSER LOOK** To make yourself a mug of tea, you'll need to heat 250 mL of water from 20°C to boiling. How many joules of energy will you need to add to the water?

4. **SCIENCE AND SOCIETY** What is thermal pollution doing to plant and animal life in rivers and lakes? Are there any ways to keep this from happening?

5. **CONSUMER CONNECTION** Explain how solar energy can be a valuable alternative to some of our present energy sources.

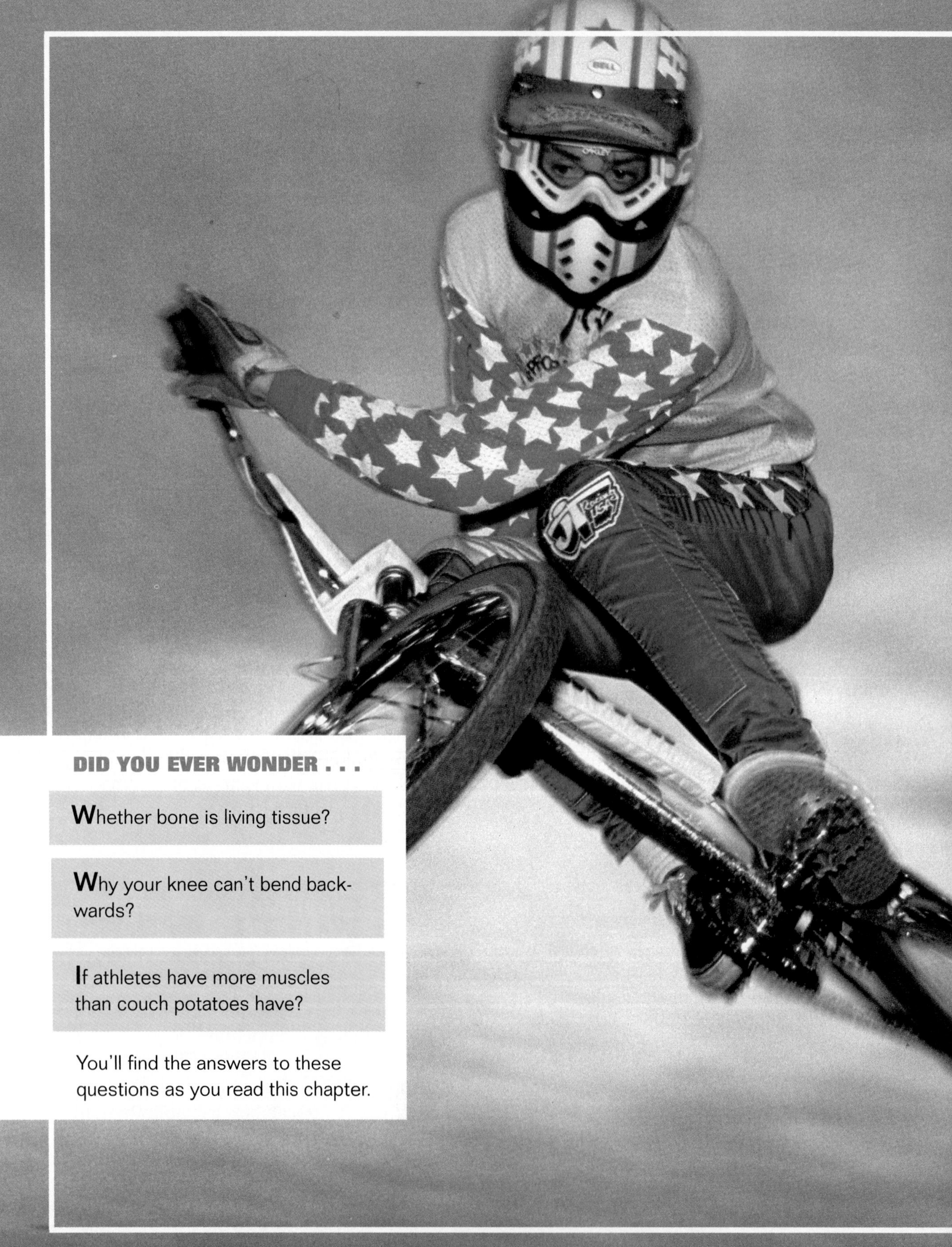

DID YOU EVER WONDER . . .

Whether bone is living tissue?

Why your knee can't bend backwards?

If athletes have more muscles than couch potatoes have?

You'll find the answers to these questions as you read this chapter.

Chapter 7

Moving the Body Machine

This is Felípe's first bicycle motocross. His gloved hands clasp the upturned handlebars. His body jets forward, eyes straight ahead. Then, with legs pumping like pistons, Felípe speeds into the turn, leaving his fellow racers in a dusty dirt cloud.

You may not race, or even cycle, but if you're healthy, you move. You walk and run, sit and stand, twist and turn. You may have even changed positions while reading this paragraph.

That's what motion is—the process of changing place or position. The kind of movements your body makes depends on the structure of your body, which has more than 200 bones and more than 600 muscles. Muscles move bones. In this chapter, you'll explore the structures that support your body, move it, and give it shape—your body's shapers and movers—bones and muscles.

EXPLORE!

Is your body like a marionette?

A marionette is a puppet moved by strings. Its arms and legs are usually made of wood. Make your own marionette using heavy pieces of cardboard. Cut out a head, torso, and arms and legs. Punch holes in each piece for attachments. Use metal fasteners to attach the pieces together. Attach pieces of string to the arms and legs. Pull the strings to make your puppet dance. How would you compare your movements with those of the marionette?

7-1 Living Bones

OBJECTIVES

In this section, you will

- identify the major functions of bone;
- describe bone and its features.

KEY SCIENCE TERMS

compact bone
spongy bone
bone marrow
cartilage

YOUR BODY'S FRAMEWORK

Just as your heart and blood vessels make up your circulatory system, your bones, ligaments, and cartilage make up your skeletal system. If you look at Figure 7-1, you can see that your skeleton is made up of many different shapes of bones which together help the body to stand and move in a coordinated manner. Motion of your body would be impossible without your skeletal system and your muscles. Even as you read this page, the bones in your neck are being moved so that you can turn your head from side to side. The bones in your neck also perform another important job. They are holding up your head.

EXPLORE!

How does your skeletal system support your body? Does your body have anything in common with a building? Using glue and small wooden sticks, build a small model of a house. When it is completed, cover your house with construction paper or fabric. How much of the frame of the model can you see? What is the job of the wooden sticks? What would happen to your little house if you removed the sticks? How is your body like the model?

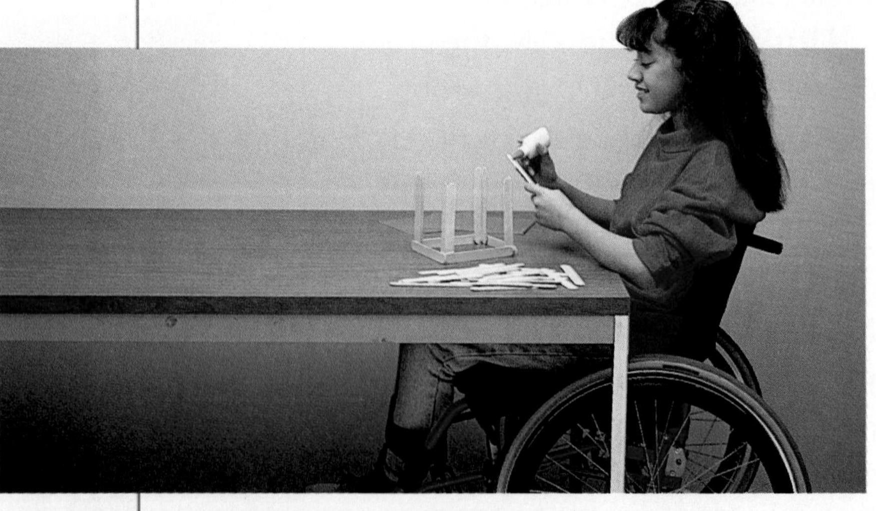

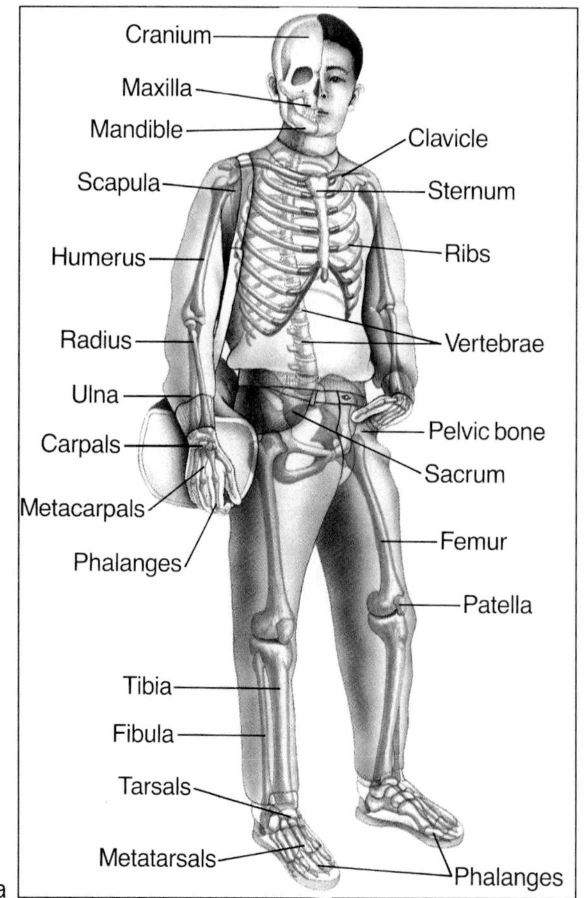

FIGURE 7-1. The human skeleton supports the body (a) in a manner similar to the way the framework of a building supports the entire structure (b).

A skeletal system is an amazing structure with many functions. Blood is formed in bone and the body's supply of calcium and phosphorus is warehoused throughout your body. But the most obvious job of your skeleton is to enable you to have a particular shape that doesn't change. Your skeletal system can be compared to the steel beam framework of a building. Can you see the beams when you look at a building? What would happen if the beams were removed? The building would collapse, wouldn't it? Your skeletal system works in a similar way for your body. It helps to support your body and give it shape. One reason your body doesn't sag is because, like a large building, you have an internal support system. But in your body, bones provide the structure rather than steel beams.

In addition to shape and support, bones also perform a vital job for your internal organs. Look at Figure 7-1 again. What do you notice about the relationship

FIGURE 7-2. Bones are the major structures of the skeletal system.

between the skeleton and the location of the young man's heart and lungs? What about his brain? These organs are protected by bone, aren't they? In Section 7-3, you'll learn that bones also function as the place of attachment for many of the body's muscles.

PARTS OF A BONE

You've seen bones at one time or another. Maybe they were in last night's fried chicken, or you may have watched (and heard) your dog as she chewed on one. You probably know that bones are hard, but did you ever wonder what bones are made of?

FIND OUT!

Why are bones hard?

Take a look at clean chicken bones. How do they feel? Get two pint jars that have lids. Fill one with vinegar and the other with water. Label each one. Put one bone in the jar of vinegar and put another bone in the jar of water. Cover the jars and store them for four days. After four days, remove the bones from their containers and wash them thoroughly. How do the bones feel now? Try bending both bones.

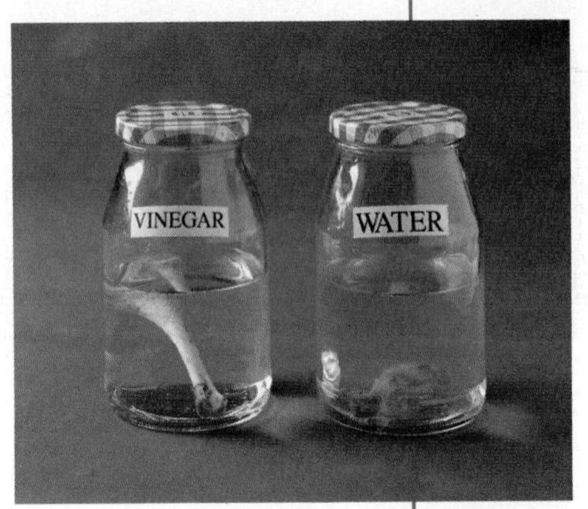

Conclude and Apply

1. Is the bone that was in vinegar different from the bone that was in water?
2. Can you suggest a reason for any changes that took place?

Your bones, like the chicken bones you examined, are unusual because they are made up of both living and nonliving material. Look at Figure 7-3 to see the inside and outside parts of a bone. On the outside, a bone is covered by a thin, living membrane called the periosteum (per ee AHS tee um). This membrane has many blood vessels in it. The blood vessels carry food and oxygen to the living parts of bone.

Minerals make bone hard. Not all parts of a bone are as dense looking as the outer layer of bone. Do you know what a sponge looks like? Sponges have many little openings in them that hold liquids. One part of a bone looks like a sponge. It's called spongy bone. As you see in Figure 7-3, **spongy bone** contains many openings and is found toward the ends of many bones. Unlike a sponge, however, spongy bone is not soft. Like compact bone, the tiny spikes of bone you see in the spongy bone are made of minerals and are hard.

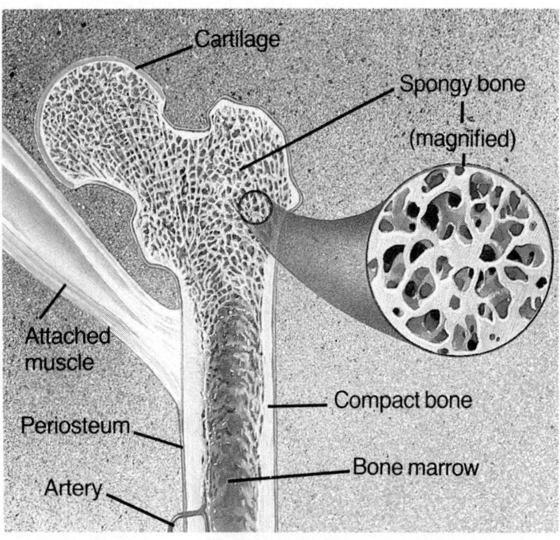

FIGURE 7-3. Spongy bone is hard like compact bone, but lighter weight because it is filled with holes.

Calcium and phosphorus are the nonliving parts of bone that make it hard. Compounds of calcium and phosphorus are concentrated in the thick outer layer called **compact bone**. Besides minerals, compact bone also contains living bone material and elastic fibers. Elastic fibers keep bone from being too rigid.

In the Find Out activity, you learned that by soaking a chicken bone in vinegar, it became flexible. You dissolved something that had made the bone very hard. You were left with a soft, bendable bone. The minerals calcium and phosphorus dissolved in the vinegar. Once the minerals of your chicken bone had been dissolved, the bone was no longer hard, was it? What would happen if you were to lose the minerals from your bones? Rickets and osteoporosis are two diseases that result from lack of minerals in bone. Rickets occurs in children and prevents normal bone growth. Their bones become bent during development. Osteoporosis occurs mainly in older people. Bone material in people with this disease becomes fragile and breaks easily because the bones lack minerals.

FIGURE 7-4. Rickets is a disease that results from mineral loss in bones.

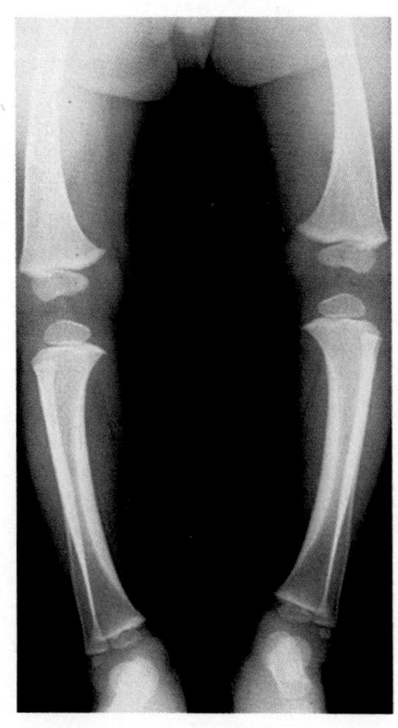

Healthy bones are hard and flexible, and the arrangement of minerals and fibers in bones gives them great strength. Your bones must be strong to withstand the forces that constantly act on them. Recall that a force is a push or a pull. When you stand on the ground, you exert force on the ground, and the ground exerts force on you. Forces that are directed toward an object, such as your body, cause materials in the object to be pressed together, or compressed. Now think of how much force is exerted on your bones when you jump up and down or run. Forces acting on the body are concentrated at contacts between

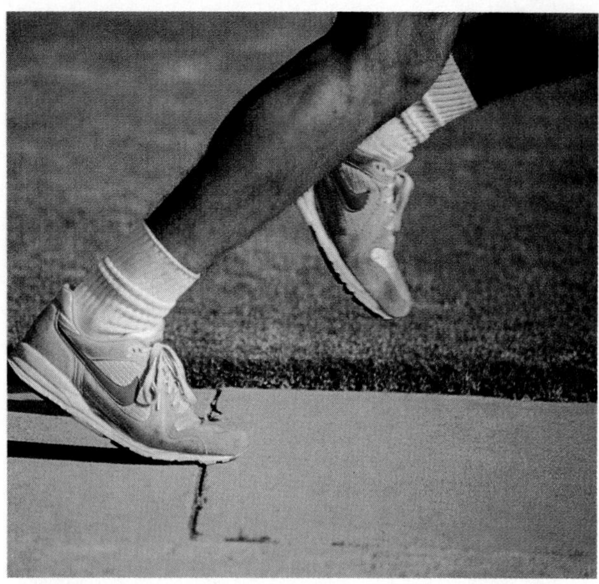

FIGURE 7-5. During strenuous exercise, tremendous force is exerted on your skeleton.

bones. This action places a lot of pressure on these contact points. Because external forces and pressures cause internal stresses, it's a good thing your bones are strong and able to resist most forces without breaking.

But just how strong is bone? Do you think you could exert enough force to crush compact bone? Compact bone has a strength of about 19,000–30,000 lb/in^2. It would take you and about 200 of your classmates all standing on a single one-inch cube of compact bone to crush it! It might seem that bones can withstand greater forces than they will ever encounter, but during strenuous activity, forces exerted on your skeleton may reach several hundred pounds per square inch.

Although bones must be strong, they must also be lightweight enough for you to move. The arrangement of materials in spongy bone helps keep your skeleton lightweight because it has many spaces. The spongy nature of the ends of bone also helps you in another way. The ends of bone function as shock absorbers. A shock absorber is anything that absorbs a force and spreads it out over a large area. You may know that many running shoes have cushioned soles and some have air or a soft gel in their soles. These soles are designed to absorb shock. They work in a similar way to spongy bone.

Making blood cells is another function of bone. Have you ever broken a chicken bone? If you have, you may have been surprised to find that the bone was not solid. Many bones have a hollow area or cavity. This space, as well as the spaces in spongy bone, are filled with a gel-like substance called **bone marrow**. Bone marrow is red or yellow in color. Yellow marrow is found in the long part of bone and is made mostly of fat. Red marrow is found in spongy bone. New blood cells are made in red marrow.

In the next activity, you will be able to see spongy bone. You will also observe the other parts of bone and their features.

SKILLBUILDER

PREDICTING

People suffering from certain blood disorders, such as leukemia—cancer of the blood—sometimes undergo a bone marrow transplant. This involves killing the cells in their own bone marrow and replacing it with the bone marrow from a donor. Predict how a bone marrow transplant might help a person with a blood disorder. If you need help, refer to the **Skill Handbook** on page 691.

I N V E S T I G A T E !

7-1 STRUCTURE OF BONE

Bones may be different in size and shape, but they all have a similar structure. In the following activity, you will examine a bone.

PROBLEM

What are the features of bones?

MATERIALS  

beef bone
eyedropper
microscope
magnifying glass
scalpel
coverslip
spoon
slide

PROCEDURE

1. Copy the data table.
2. Obtain a beef bone cut lengthwise and crosswise.
3. Look at the outside. Is it smooth? List its features in the table. Pull away the outside covering. If the bone is very fresh, you will see small red dots.
4. Examine the inside of the bone with a magnifying glass. Identify the compact bone, spongy bone, and the bone marrow. Describe each feature in the table. Include their colors, textures, and locations.
5. Draw a diagram of the bone and label the parts.
6. Place a single drop of water on a microscope slide. Using a scalpel, remove a very small bit of red marrow from the bone. Place it in the drop of water. Put a coverslip on the slide, and examine it under the microscope, under low and then under high power. Draw, label, and describe what you see.
7. Scoop the marrow out of the center of the bone and then wash the inside.
8. Examine the inside of the bone.

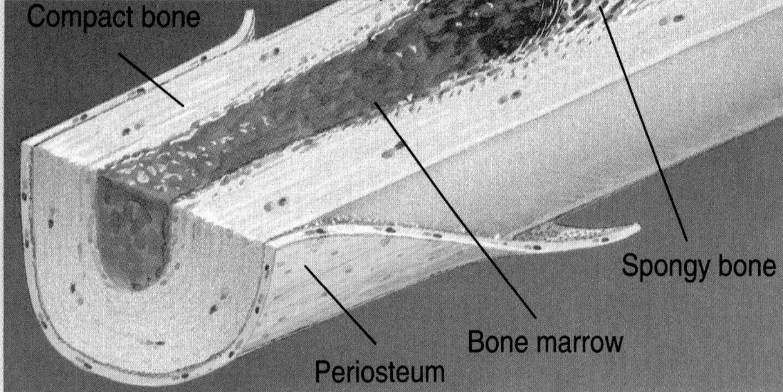

DATA AND OBSERVATIONS

BONE FEATURES	DESCRIPTION
External features	
Compact bone	
Spongy bone	
Marrow	

ANALYZE

1. **Compare and contrast** the middle of the bone with its ends. How is the shape different?
2. **Observe** and describe the portions of the bone that contain marrow.

CONCLUDE AND APPLY

3. **Identify** the covering you pulled away in Step 3. What were the small red dots you may have observed?
4. **Going Further**: What would happen to a bone if the periosteum were to die?

YOUR BONE DEVELOPMENT

The bone you studied in the last activity was hard. But not all parts of your skeletal system are hard. Wiggle the end of your nose with your fingers and feel the external part of your ear. What do they feel like? They feel soft and flexible, don't they? These parts of your body are part of your skeleton, but they are not bone. They are made of **cartilage**, a soft, flexible material. Before you were born, your entire skeleton was made up of cartilage. During development, most of your cartilage was replaced by hard bone.

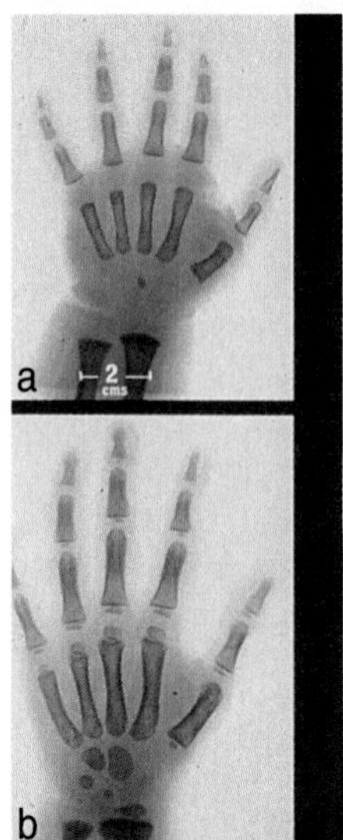

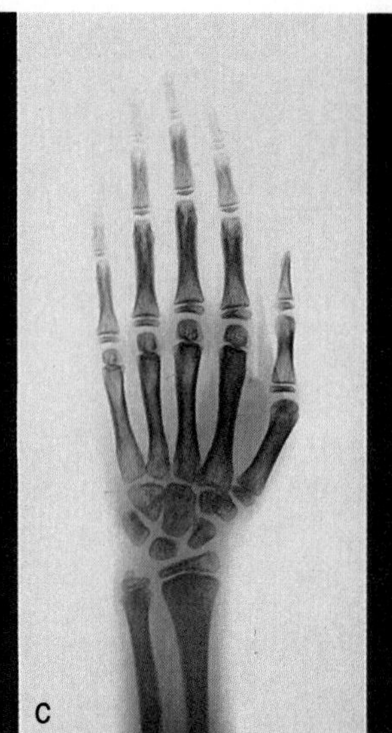

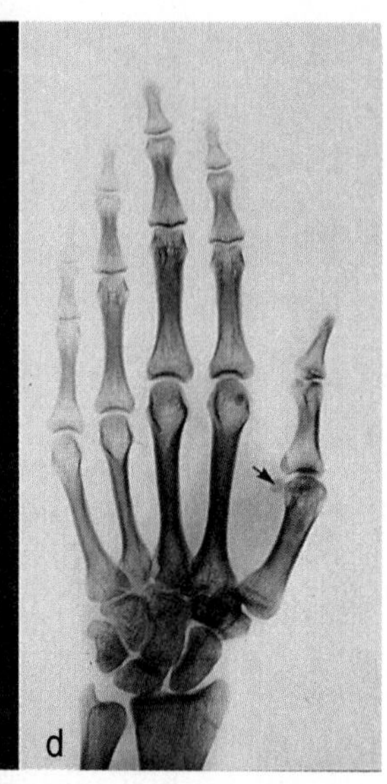

FIGURE 7-6. Large amounts of cartilage are present in the child's hands (a, b); some cartilage is still present in the young adult's hand (c); cartilage in an adult's hand has been replaced by bone (d).

Look at the X-ray pictures of an adult hand and the hand of a two-year-old in Figure 7-6. Are they different? The child's skeleton has a lot more cartilage, which doesn't show up in X rays the way hard bone does. The replacement of cartilage with bone is not complete until a person is about twenty years old. But even then, parts of your skeleton will remain cartilage. You'll learn more about cartilage when you study about joints in Section 7-2.

Without your skeleton, you would have no body support. Your shape might constantly change, and your internal organs wouldn't be protected against injury. Moving would be a challenge. In the next section, you will explore how your body is able to move.

Check Your Understanding

1. What are three functions of the skeletal system? Why is bone important to your circulatory system?
2. How does compact bone differ from spongy bone?
3. **APPLY:** Why do you think certain bones break more easily in an older adult than in a small child?

7-2 Your Body in Motion

THE BODY IN ACTION

Think of the movements your skeletal system goes through when you turn a page in a book, walk, or throw a ball. When you walk, your leg moves in and out at your hip. Your legs bend at the knee. Your foot bends at the ankle, and your toes bend, too. When you throw a ball, your shoulder twists around. Your arm bends and then straightens as the ball is released. Your wrist also bends, and your fingers straighten. Would any of these actions be possible if your skeleton couldn't move?

OBJECTIVES

In this section, you will

- compare and contrast types of joints and their movements;
- describe the functions of ligaments and cartilage in joints.

KEY SCIENCE TERMS

joints
ligaments

EXPLORE!

Do you need joints?

On the hand you write with, use masking tape to tape your thumb and fingers together so that your fingers can't bend and your thumb can't move. Now pick up a pencil. How easy was it? Try some other activities. Button your shirt. Tie your shoelaces. Try to write your name. These are simple things that you probably do every day. Why is it difficult to do them when your fingers are taped? How important is it for you to be able to bend your fingers?

It's very inconvenient to do everyday things without being able to move parts of your skeleton. Your skeleton moves at certain points because it has joints. **Joints** are places in your skeleton where two or more bones meet or are joined together. Where are your joints? You probably know where most are, but look back at Figure 7-1 to see if there are some you didn't know about. Now think about a marionette again. Its "bones" are held together at certain points with small nails. You used metal fasteners for joints in your marionette. Your bones are attached to each other, too. Bones are held together with very strong

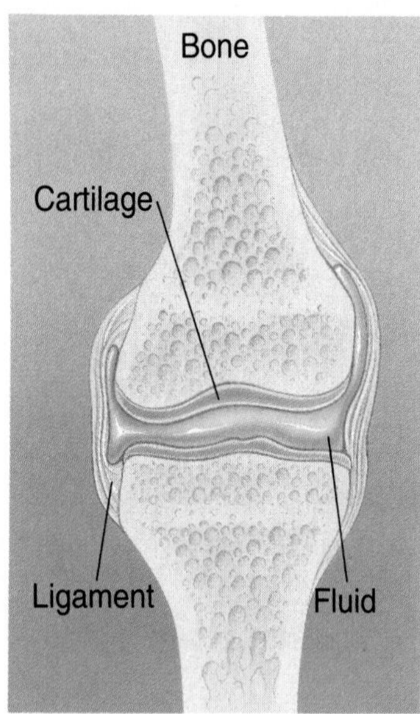

FIGURE 7-7. Fluid and cartilage separate the bones of a joint and reduce friction. Ligaments hold the joint together.

bands of tissue called **ligaments**. In a joint, such as your knee joint, bones are held close together by ligaments. A fluid, also found in the joint, keeps the joint lubricated. This fluid reduces friction, the force that slows down the motion of surfaces that touch. As in machines, parts that move against each other produce friction. Why would it be important to reduce friction on a joint?

Whether in a machine or the human body, friction can make the parts that rub together wear out. A thin layer of cartilage over the ends of the bones reduces friction. Cartilage in healthy joints is like firm, soft plastic, so the bones move smoothly against each other. Because cartilage is flexible, it also acts as a built-in shock absorber in a joint. That helps reduce the effect of forces on the joint by spreading the forces out. Some joints have more cartilage than others. These joints usually bear more forces and pressure. What joints can you think of that might have more cartilage than others?

Because your body makes a variety of movements, your skeleton has different kinds of joints for these different movements. There are even joints that do not allow any movement. But most joints in your body are movable.

EXPLORE!

What movements do joints allow?

In this activity, you will explore the motions at some of your joints. Stand up and make a circular motion with your arm. Now bend your elbow, your wrist, and your fingers, as you carefully observe the motions they go through. Can your elbow, wrist, and fingers do the same things as your shoulder? Try the same movements with your hip, knee, ankle, and toes. Are the movements similar to your arm movements? Finally, nod your head up and down and then back and forth. Are these movements similar to any of the other joints you moved?

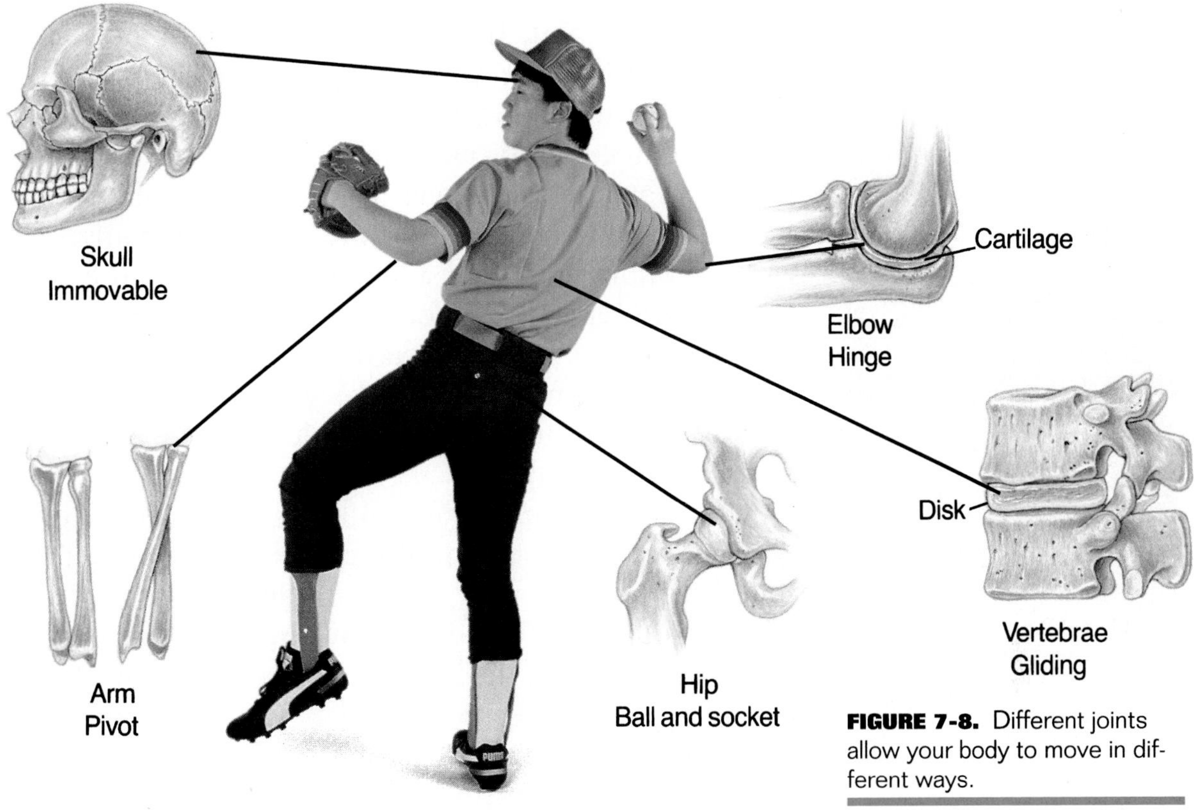

FIGURE 7-8. Different joints allow your body to move in different ways.

Not all your joints make the same motions, do they? You can make a complete circle with your shoulder, but you can't do that with your elbow or fingers. The same is true for your legs. You can make your hip joint move in a circle, but you can't do that same movement with your knee. Movements of your body are allowed by basic kinds of movable joints. Shaking your head to say "no" uses a pivot joint. Pivot joints allow bones to move side to side and up and down. Moving your shoulders or hips in a circle makes use of ball-and-socket joints. These joints allow bones to move in all directions. Ball-and-socket joints allow the greatest range of motion. Unlike your shoulders, movement of your fingers, toes, elbows, and knees is very limited because they have hinge joints. Like the door hinge in Figure 7-9, hinge joints can only move back and forth.

FIGURE 7-9. Where in your body do you have hinge joints?

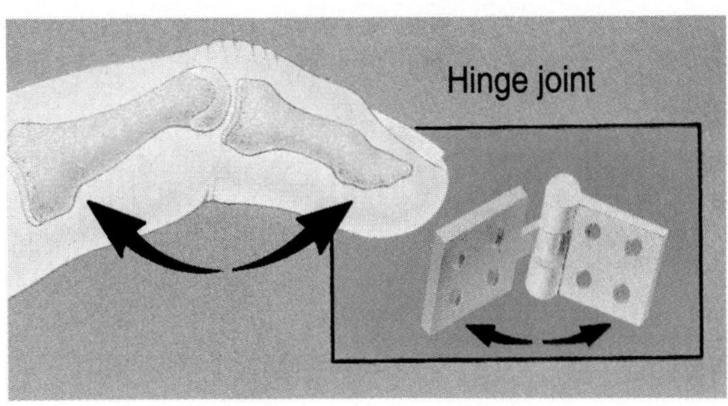

You might think you spend most of your day hinging and pivoting, but actually the most common joint in your body

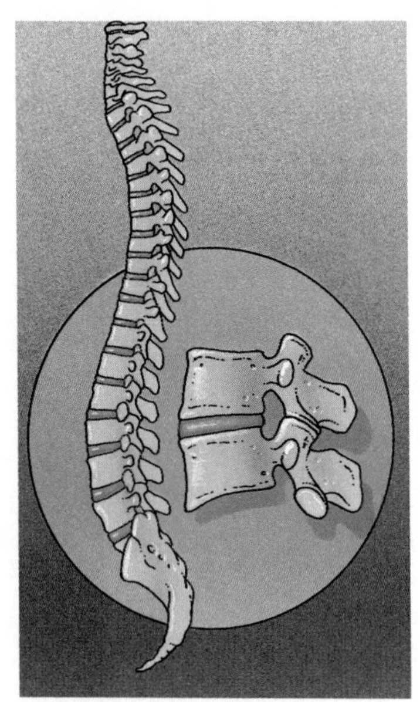

FIGURE 7-10. How many bones make up your backbone?

is the gliding joint. In a gliding joint, one bone glides over another. When you move your wrist back and forth, you use gliding joints. Your backbone also has gliding joints. As you can see in Figure 7-10, your backbone is not one long bone. It is actually made up of many stacked bones, or vertebrae, separated by discs of cartilage. Run your hand along your spine. Each bump you feel is a separate vertebra. The gliding joints in your backbone allow you to make many movements. What are some movements you make with your backbone? How would your movement be limited if your backbone were just one long bone?

As you can see in Figure 7-11, your skull isn't just one bone either. It is made up of many different bones. But, unlike the bones in your back, you can't move the bones in your skull. Joints that don't move are called immovable joints. Look back at the illustration of the skeleton at the beginning of this chapter to see if you can find some other immovable joints. What benefit is there to having some immovable joints?

Think about what would happen if you couldn't move your bones? You wouldn't be able to eat, run, pick up things, bend, throw, or do any number of things you probably don't even think about. In this section, you learned how the structure of joints allows for the different movements of your skeleton. In the next section, you will investigate what moves the joints in your body.

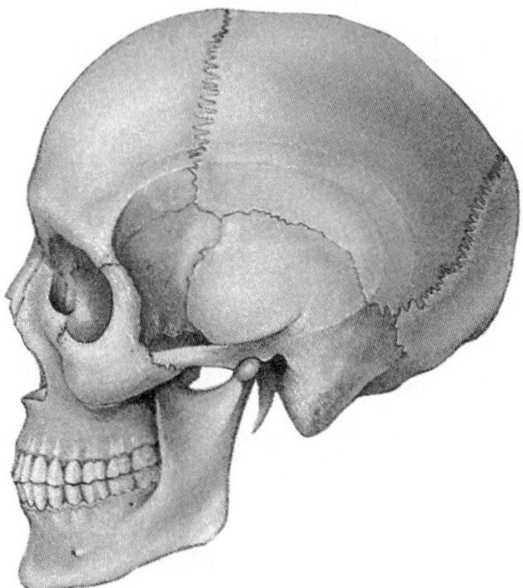

FIGURE 7-11. Separate bones fuse together after birth to form a skull.

Check Your Understanding

1. What makes it possible for you to play the piano? To do sit-ups? Identify the different joints in your body that make these motions possible and the types of joints they are.
2. Compare ligaments and cartilage.
3. **APPLY:** If a football player tears cartilage in the knee, how might this affect the bones at the knee joint?

7-3 Muscles

SKELETAL MOTION

Your bones and joints are designed and assembled to fit together like the parts of a motion machine. Your bones and joints have no power to move by themselves. Where does their power come from? Your muscles move your bones and joints and that enables you to slam-dunk a ball, back flip off a diving board, or even run a marathon, if you want to. Together, all your bone-muscle systems are like machines. In Chapter 5, you learned that machines make work easier by changing the size, direction, or speed of a force. In your body, your bones and muscles are arranged to form levers. Recall that a lever is a rigid structure that transmits forces by turning at a point called the fulcrum. In the next activity, you will learn about levers in your body.

OBJECTIVES

In this section, you will

- describe the three kinds of muscle;
- explain muscle action and how it results in movement of body parts.

KEY SCIENCE TERMS

skeletal muscles
tendons
cardiac muscle
smooth muscle

FIND OUT!

What are the levers in your body?

Rest your elbow, forearm, and hand, palm up, flat on your desk. Lay a heavy book, such as a dictionary, on your hand. Raise your hand, keeping your elbow on the table. You are now using a lever in your body. The book exerts a resistance force that acts downward. Your elbow is the fulcrum. The muscles in your forearm provide the effort force that acts against the resistance force.

Can you imagine trying to lift a heavy book with just your fingers? Try it in the same way you used your elbow and forearm. Do longer bones, such as your arm bones, have better leverage than shorter bones, such as your finger bones?

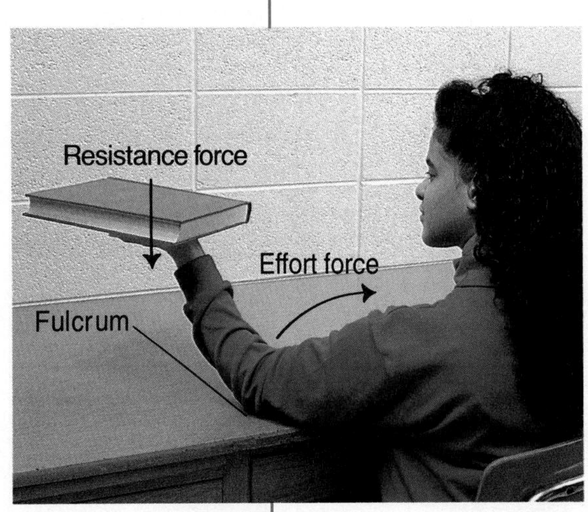

Conclude and Apply

Why is it more difficult to lift the book with your fingers?

DID YOU KNOW?

Tendons are so strong that bones will usually break before tendons will tear. You can see tendons in the skin on top of your hand when you wiggle your fingers. These tendons connect muscles in your palm and wrist to your fingers.

Like all machines, the levers formed by your bones and muscles have mechanical advantage. A mechanical advantage is the number of times the machine multiplies the effort force. You may recall that in certain cases, the machine does not increase the effort force. In fact, the mechanical advantage may be less than one. In these cases, speed is gained. When a baseball pitcher throws a ball, the mechanical advantage of his or her body lever is less than one. But the pitcher gains speed of movement. That's what's important when trying to strike out a batter.

TYPES OF MUSCLE

Different types of muscle in your body perform different functions. The muscles that move bones are **skeletal muscles.** At movable joints, skeletal muscles are attached to bones by tendons. **Tendons** are strong elastic bands of tissue.

You're most aware of skeletal muscles, probably because you can control the movement of these muscles. But you have two other kinds of muscles, too. The walls of your heart are made of cardiac muscle. **Cardiac muscle** pumps blood through the heart and forces blood through the rest of the body. **Smooth muscle** is found in many places inside your body, such as your stomach and intestines. Food moves through your digestive system by smooth muscle. How much control do you think you have over cardiac and smooth muscle? Compare the three kinds of muscles in Figure 7-12.

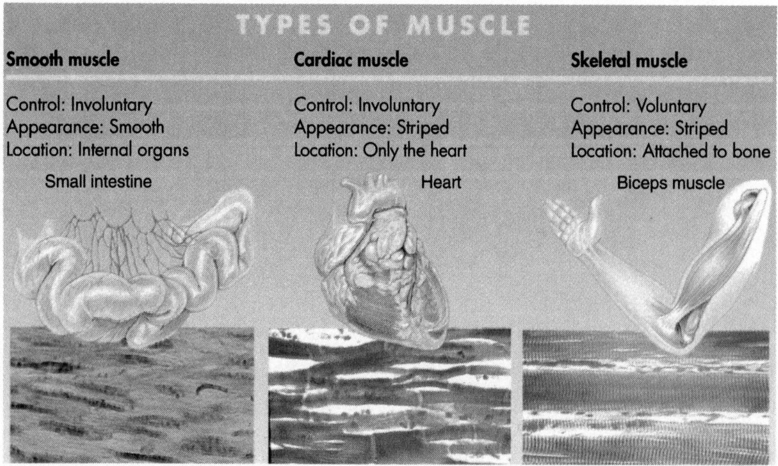

TYPES OF MUSCLE
Smooth muscle
Control: Involuntary
Appearance: Smooth
Location: Internal organs
Small intestine
Cardiac muscle
Control: Involuntary
Appearance: Striped
Location: Only the heart
Heart
Skeletal muscle
Control: Voluntary
Appearance: Striped
Location: Attached to bone
Biceps muscle

FIGURE 7-12. Smooth muscle can be found in blood vessels and internal organs, such as the small intestine; cardiac muscle is specialized muscle found only in the heart; skeletal muscles, such as the biceps, attach to the bones of the skeletal system.

MUSCLE ACTION

Body movement depends on the action of your muscles. But how do muscles work? Muscles are made up of bundles of long, stringlike structures called fibers, that can contract. When a muscle contracts, it gets shorter. In doing so, it pulls on the attached bone. The force of a muscle pulling on a bone moves a body part. Since work is done when a force moves an object a distance, the muscle does work when it contracts.

Like all things that do work, your muscles need energy. Fuel of some kind is always needed to obtain the energy to do work.

Glucose is your muscles' main fuel. In your muscles, chemical energy stored in glucose changes to mechanical energy, and your muscles contract.

Muscles also produce thermal energy when they contract. The heat produced by muscle contraction helps keep your body temperature at the same level. When your body temperature drops too low, your brain sends a message to your body muscles, and you begin to shiver and heat is produced. Shivering is actually the contraction of body muscles.

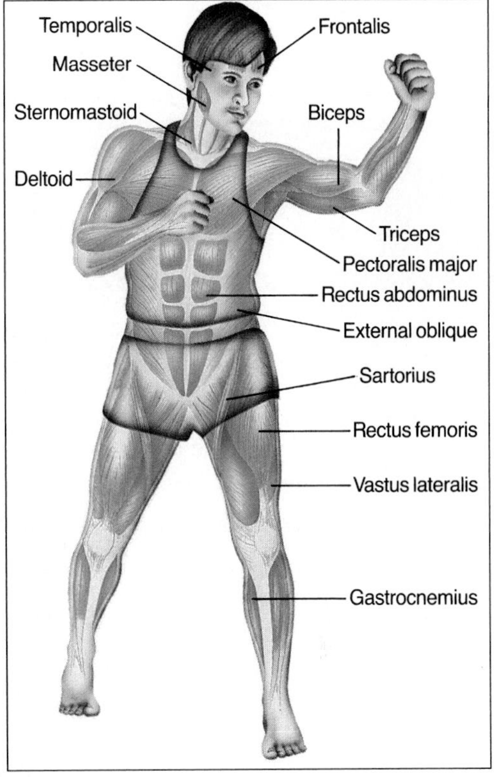

FIGURE 7-13. Major muscles of the human body.

Figure 7-13 shows some of the muscles of the human body. Observe one of your own muscles in action. Make a fist. Test the muscle on the top side of your upper arm called the biceps. Stretch your arm out straight and then bend it up at the elbow. Can you see your biceps get shorter and fatter? The far end of this muscle is attached by a strong tendon to the bone in your forearm at a spot just below your elbow. When your biceps contract, it pulls your forearm up. Contract your biceps again. Can you feel the strong tendon in your elbow? In the next activity, you will learn more about the action of muscles on bones.

How do we know?

Muscle Illustrations

Your body is made up of more than 600 muscles. During the Renaissance (1452–1519), a period of great advancement in the arts and sciences, Leonardo da Vinci gathered a great deal of knowledge about the muscular system and other parts of the human body. da Vinci carefully dissected human specimens to find out the locations and functions of the muscles of the body. His work led to a much greater understanding of bones and muscles.

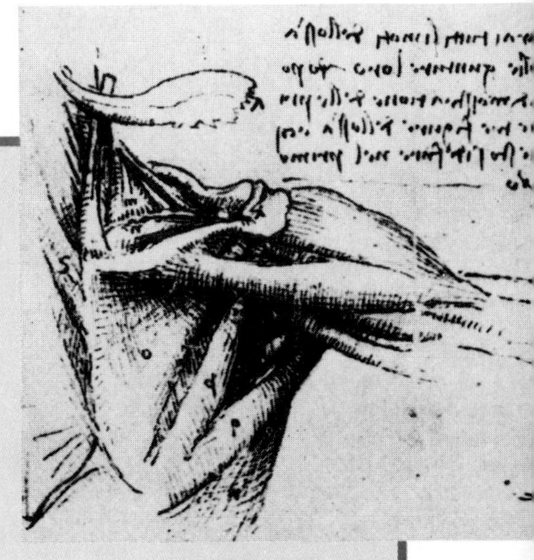

I N V E S T I G A T E !

7-2 MUSCLES AND BONES

Skeletal muscles pull bones at joints. That is how body parts are moved. In this activity, you will observe the relationships among bones, muscles, tendons, and joints.

PROBLEM

How do muscles move bones?

MATERIALS  

apron
paper towels
dissecting pan
human bone and muscle chart
forceps
scalpel
scissors
boiled chicken leg and thigh

PROCEDURE

1. Copy the data table.
2. Lay a chicken leg on paper towels in a dissecting pan. Use forceps to remove the skin.
3. Locate and **observe** the muscles and bones in the legs and thigh. How are the muscles connected to the bones? Draw and label what you see.
4. Bend and straighten the leg and thigh at the joint. **Observe** what happens to the muscles.
5. Use a scalpel and scissors to remove the muscles from the bones. Locate and **observe** the bones, joints, ligaments, and cartilage. Draw what you see and label these parts.
6. Record the parts of the skeleton and muscle systems that you located.
7. Give all sharp instruments to your teacher for proper disposal.

DATA AND OBSERVATIONS

BODY SYSTEMS	BODY PARTS
Muscular	
Skeletal	

ANALYZE

1. **Identify** which muscles lengthen and which shorten. **Compare and contrast** their movements.
2. What connects muscles to bones?
3. Did you locate any cartilage or ligaments? Where and how did they appear?

CONCLUDE AND APPLY

4. What kind of joint is between the thigh bone and the lower leg bone?
5. **Determine** how the bones in a chicken's leg move.
6. **Going Further**: How is your arm similar to a chicken wing in the way it moves?

You have observed the relationships among bones, muscles, tendons, and joints. To find out how muscles work together, make a model with an index card, a metal fastener, string, and tape.

FIND OUT!

How do muscles work together?

Cut an index card lengthwise into two pieces, one for a lower leg bone, and one for a foot. Punch holes in the card as shown. Attach the leg to the foot using a metal fastener as an ankle joint. Cut two 25-centimeter pieces of string and tape one in front and one behind the ankle as shown. Thread one string through each hole at the upper end of the leg. Look at the picture if you need help.

Now experiment with the foot. Pull up on the string behind the ankle. What happens to the foot? What about the string in front of the ankle? Now let go of this string to release the tension and pull up on the other string. What happens to the foot now? How about the string behind the ankle? Can both strings be pulled at the same time? Can they be relaxed at the same time? Why not?

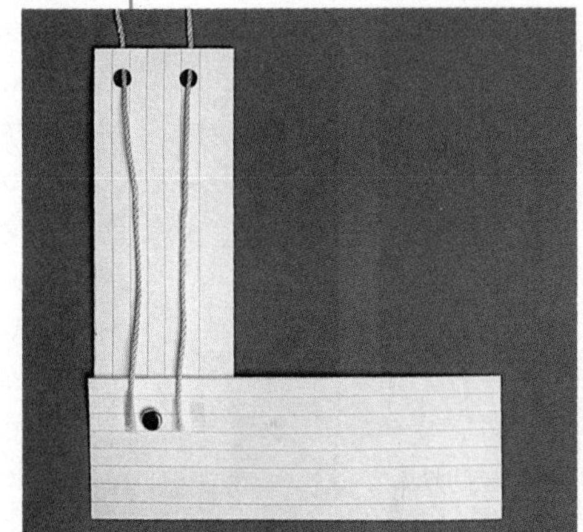

Conclude and Apply

1. What do the strings in your model represent?
2. What have you demonstrated about the action of muscles?

MUSCLES WORK TOGETHER

In the Investigate, you observed two different muscles bending and straightening a chicken leg. Muscles in your body work in a similar way. Your biceps muscle bends your arm. But how does your arm straighten out?

In the Find Out activity, you explored how muscles work together. When one muscle of a pair contracts, the other muscle relaxes, or returns to its original length. Because skeletal muscles move bones only when muscles contract, muscles only pull bones. Muscles never push.

Bend and straighten your arm a few times. What happens when your biceps contracts? When it relaxes? The

DID YOU KNOW?

Skeletal muscles are so powerful that if both muscles of a pair that works together were to contract at the same time, they could easily break a bone.

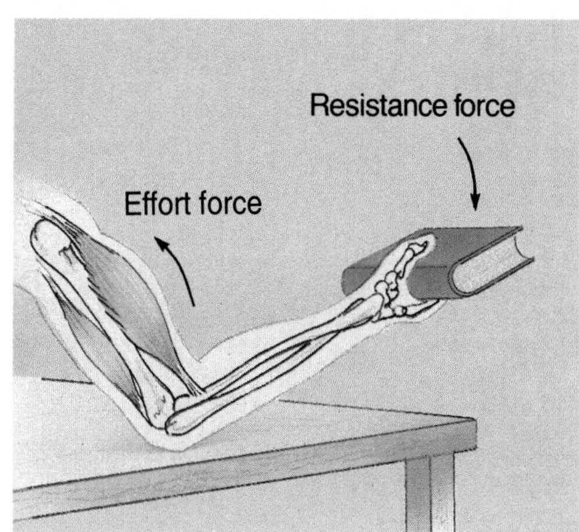

FIGURE 7-14. The biceps and triceps work together to help you coordinate your movements.

muscle on the underside of your arm is called the triceps. When the biceps is contracting, the triceps is relaxed. But when the triceps contracts, your biceps is relaxed, and you straighten your arm. This teamwork of muscle pairs makes it possible for you to coordinate your movements with the precision needed to hit a backhand in tennis, write a letter, or play a video game.

You can help your muscles be better coordinated and stronger by using them. Your muscles will become larger or smaller depending on how much you use them. Regular exercise increases the size of your muscles as well as their strength. When you exercise, the size of your muscle fibers increases, and this increases your muscles' strength. Exercise also increases muscle tone. Tone refers to the state of readiness of your muscles to contract. Muscles are usually slightly contracted so they're ready to go when you need them. Even when you think you aren't moving, some of your muscle fibers are contracting and relaxing to maintain tone. A well-toned body can help you have a better shape. Muscles, along with bones, support and shape your body.

Simple movements you probably take for granted, such as walking, aren't so simple after all. To move the bones and joints required to take just one step can involve the teamwork of up to 200 different muscles from your shoulders to your toes. That's one major reason why it takes a toddler so long to master it. But once learned, it can be expanded into a variety of movements and activities that can enrich your life.

SKILLBUILDER

SEQUENCING
How do your thigh muscles function to bend your leg at the knee? To straighten your leg? Write the sequence of muscle movement. Refer to the diagram of body muscles. If you need help, refer to the **Skill Handbook** on page 678.

Check Your Understanding

1. What do your heart, your stomach, and your thigh muscles have in common? How do they differ?
2. How do your arm muscles function to bend your elbow? To straighten your elbow?
3. How do muscles attach to bones?
4. **APPLY:** Suppose the biceps muscle was removed. What arm movement would not be possible?

EXPANDING YOUR VIEW

CONTENTS

A Closer Look
Bone Density 211

Physics Connection
Strong Bones 212

Science and Society
Spud Dud 212

How it Works
Robot Arms 214

Health Connection
Athletic Epidemic 215

Teens in Science
Lending a Helping Hand 216

A CLOSER LOOK

BONE DENSITY

The bones of various animals have many similarities, but as you might expect, they also have differences. A cow's bones are strong enough to support the cow as it lumbers across pastures. On the other hand, a finch's bones are light, enabling the finch to flit from tree to tree in search of food. This activity will show you one way in which animals' bones are different.

For this exercise, you will need to copy the data table. You'll also need water, a balance, a 100-mL graduated cylinder, and bones from a pig, a steer, a turkey, and a chicken. Use the balance to find the mass in grams of a steer bone and record this amount in the data table. Use the displacement method to determine the volume of the bone. Pour 50 mL of water into the cylinder and then add the bone to it. Record the volume of the water plus the bone.

Find the volume of the bone by subtracting the volume of water(50 mL) from the water plus bone volume reading. Record this amount on your data table. Calculate the density of the bone by dividing its mass by its volume.

Repeat the measurements using the bones of a pig, chicken, and turkey. Record the measurements and find the density of each bone sample. Which kind of bone had the highest density? The lowest?

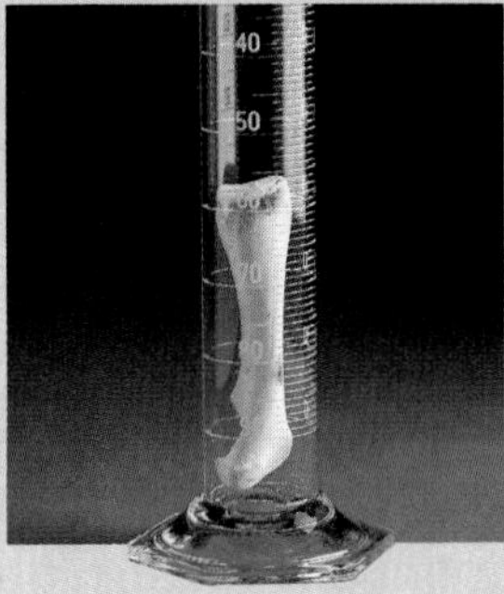

	Steer	Pig	Chicken	Turkey
Mass				
Water and bone volume				
Bone volume				
Density				

WHAT DO YOU THINK?

Bones from several types of dinosaurs have been found in the United States. How can bone density help researchers determine how large a dinosaur was? Do you think bone density is a reliable indicator of whether the animal could fly? Explain your position.

Physics Connection

STRONG BONES

Do you ever wonder how bones that are hollow can be so strong? This activity may give you some insight into bone strength. You'll need a few 4 × 6 note cards, some cellophane tape, and a stack of small books.

Fold one note card in half, then stand it on its edge.

Place a lightweight book on top to see if the card supports the book. If so, can you add another one? Take another card, fold it in half, then in half again. Using the four-folded card, form a square tube and secure it with tape. Stand this card on end and place one or two books on the card. What happens?

Next, roll a card into a cylinder and tape it. Add books, one at a time, to see how many the rolled card will support. Can you see how tubular structures—such as bones—may support a good deal of weight?

YOU TRY IT!

Find a lightweight piece of furniture that is supported by one of the shapes you've just tested. Discuss the design of the item, explaining how support is gained through its particular structure.

SCIENCE AND SOCIETY

SPUD DUD

This afternoon after school, keep track of how much time you spend watching television or playing video games. Do you think this is more or less time than you spent a year ago? Five years ago?

The terms *couch potato* and *spud dud* describe people who spend a lot of their free or leisure time just sitting.

The couch potato trend is taking its toll on the children and teens in the United States. Medical researchers are concerned that, while there is a trend toward physical fitness in adults, young people are more overweight and less physically fit today than ever before. Are you in danger of becoming a spud dud? Let's look at what happens to a couch potato's body.

If you sit for a long time, your pulse rate slows, much the way it does when you sleep. When you do get up and move—to get a snack—your system is moving slowly, and so you feel listless.

Muscles that don't get

enough exercise lack tone and flexibility. Infrequent or sudden strenuous activity may cause injury. On the other hand, muscles kept in shape through regular exercise give you the capacity for taking on unexpected activities.

Physical activity also builds cardiovascular endurance. Cardiovascular endurance is the ability of your heart, lungs, and circulatory system to work together to deliver oxygen to your body's cells and to take away waste products. To build this endurance, you have to condition your heart and lungs to work more efficiently. Good activities are those that require continuous movement, such as running, swimming, or cycling.

You may think, "I'm only a teenager. I'll get more exercise when I'm older." But the growth years can be the best time to develop strong muscle tone. Sitting in front of the TV won't do it. If you develop a couch potato pattern as a teenager, you may find it difficult to change as you get older.

Many physical activities bring you into contact with other people. You may make new friends and have a lot of fun while you're taking care of your body. You may develop physical abilities you never knew you had.

WHAT DO YOU THINK

Write a description—in about 100 words—of what you think the world might be like in the year 2020 if everyone became a couch potato today and remained one.

HOW IT WORKS

ROBOT ARMS

Most robot arms used in industry are jointed like the human arm. A typical robot arm may have five or more different movements. Each movement is controlled by a separate power source, usually an electric motor. Motors for these individual movements are controlled by computers. An interface connects the power source, the motors, and the computer. With an intricate electrical circuit, the interface directs power, switching motors on and off, as instructed by the computer.

A robot arm has a waist (or base), a shoulder, an elbow, and a wrist. You may expect that each of these joints might hold its own motor. However, in most robot arms, especially the smaller ones, the weight of these motors would make efficient movement of the arm difficult. Instead, many robot arms have their motors located near the base. Much like tendons, cords link the motors to the joints they operate. Pulleys are used to hold the cords and ease movement within the sections of the arm.

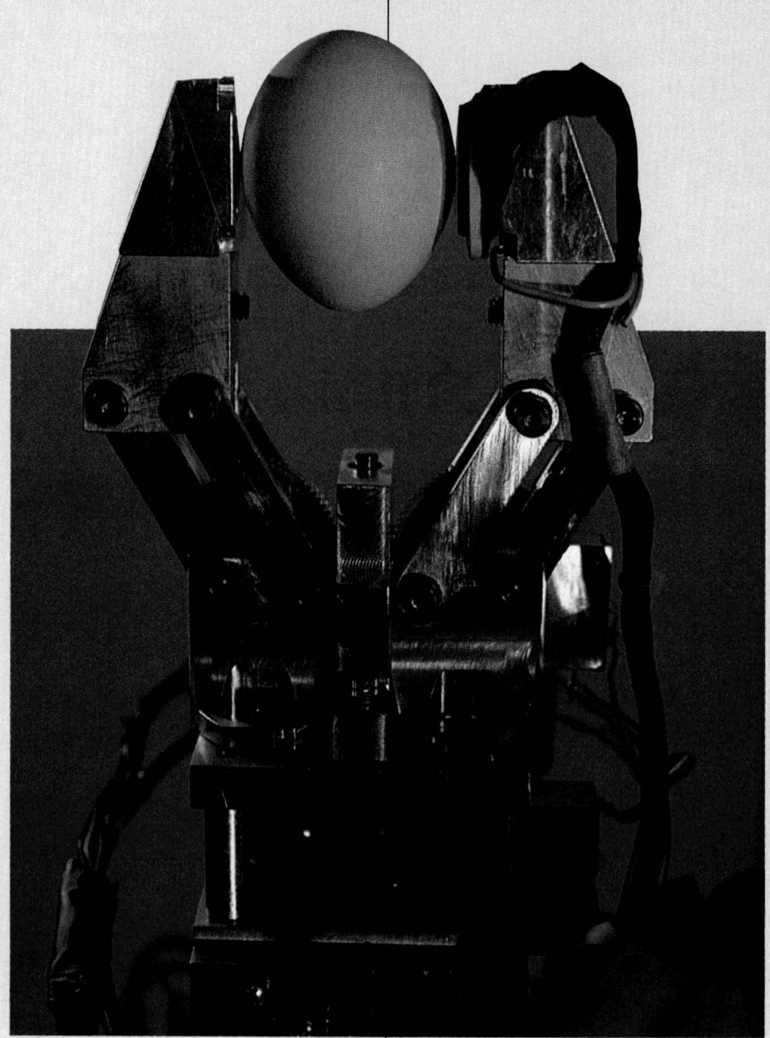

Frequently, the motors used to control joint movements are "stepping motors" or "steppers." These motors can turn on and off very rapidly, for quick changes in movement. Extremely fast changes in motion and function happen with step-by-step instructions from the computer. The robot arm can grip, lift, turn, and twist in seconds, much like your own arm.

YOU TRY IT

Imagine that you are designing a robot to assist you with your physical tasks at home. Think about the movements that the robot's arm could make. Then describe which chores the robot could help you accomplish.

Health CONNECTION

ATHLETIC EPIDEMIC

It's been called the athletic epidemic. Amateur, professional, even Olympic athletes have been stricken. It affects athletes of all ages and backgrounds. Some have lost valuable titles, others are barred from further competition, and all have lost respect within their sport and among their fans. What is this epidemic and how can it be stopped?

In recent years, athletes have increased their use of, and dependence on, drugs to aid their performance. Some take stimulants to get "high" and more alert, while others take beta-blockers to remain calm. There are athletes who have used growth promoters to encourage development of body tissue. But by far the most controversial and often discussed drugs are anabolic steroids.

Composed of natural body chemicals, or hormones, steroids (also called roids, gear, and juice) are taken to build body muscle for weight lifting and other sports that require fast, short-term strength. Anabolic steroids inflate muscles. Although the muscles look bigger, scientists have found no real evidence to support claims of increased strength. Many authorities feel that if an athlete believes the steroids are helping, the increased competitive urge and aggression may make that athlete train harder.

Aside from the possibility that steroids may not help the athlete, there is positive proof that steroids harm the athlete's overall health. Young people who take these drugs may stop growing altogether. On the other hand, their bones may thicken, leading to acromegaly (ak roh MEG e lee), a condition in which the body produces too much growth hormone. Steroids tend to increase fats in the bloodstream, and so, may contribute to heart attacks. Research is still being conducted on the long-term health risks of steroid use.

Some athletes, coaches, and trainers view these drugs as necessary for competition. They point to competitors who use drugs to aid their performance, implying that a drug-free athlete hasn't a chance against an athlete whose performance is drug-enhanced.

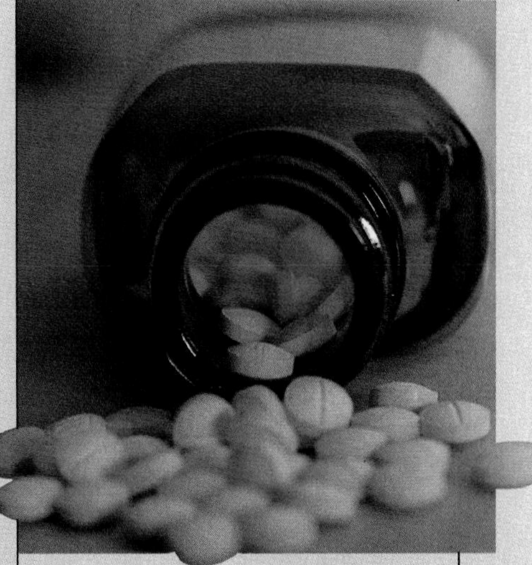

WHAT DO YOU THINK?

Many people feel that the increasing emphasis on competition and the high dollar value placed on winning is a major factor in steroid use. Based on the effects of steroids described here, or from your own outside reading, you may have developed a specific opinion of your own. Imagine that you are a junior-high athletic coach. Prepare a talk to discuss steroid use with your team.

TEENS *in* SCIENCE

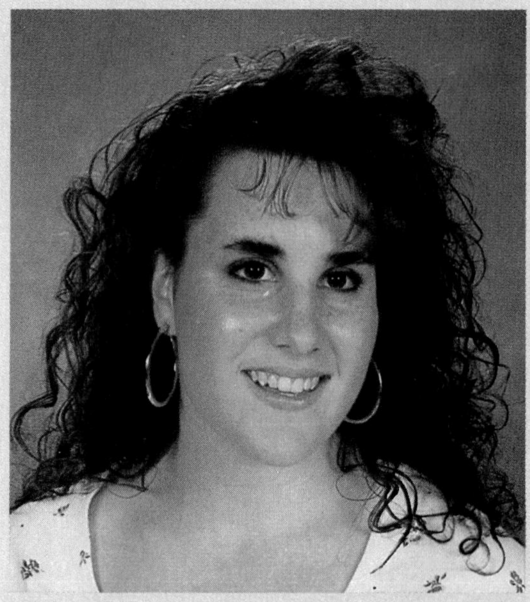

LENDING A HELPING HAND

Have you ever spent a few days in bed because you were ill? If so, you may have been surprised at how quickly muscles in your body began to lose their strength. Imagine how weak you might become if you were bedridden for months!

As a volunteer in a convalescent home, 16-year-old Jennifer November helps her patients keep their muscle tone. "I start at the hands, moving each finger five times. I'll move on until the entire body has been worked. This motion keeps the muscles from getting contractures, or shrinking."

Jennifer became involved in this work as part of a special vocational education program at her high school in Hacienda Heights, California.

"I had no plans to sign up for the Nursing Assistant Program. In fact, I did it because all the other elective courses were filled. I'd always thought I wanted to be a journalist. But as soon as I got involved in medicine, I knew that I'd found my career. I'm going to nursing school first and then on to become a doctor."

Although Jennifer is very comfortable on the job now, the first few days were tough. "I was frightened. Like most people, I hadn't spent a lot of time with disabled or elderly people. I didn't want to be afraid of them but I just was. It was confusing. But as soon as I got to know some of my patients, I found out that we had a lot in common. We're people."

In addition to making new friends, Jennifer has found a good deal of satisfaction in her work. "At first, it seemed like I was the one doing all the helping. But after a while, I realized how much I was being helped. I've learned a lot about life and courage from my patients."

YOU TRY IT!

Jennifer describes stumbling into nursing by accident. Write about an unexpected event that had a big impact on your life.

Do you know any disabled or elderly people? Write a brief description of your relationship. If you don't have any friends or relatives who fit this description, write about how you might meet such a person. If you feel you would be uncomfortable meeting a disabled or elderly person, describe why.

Chapter 7

Reviewing Main Ideas

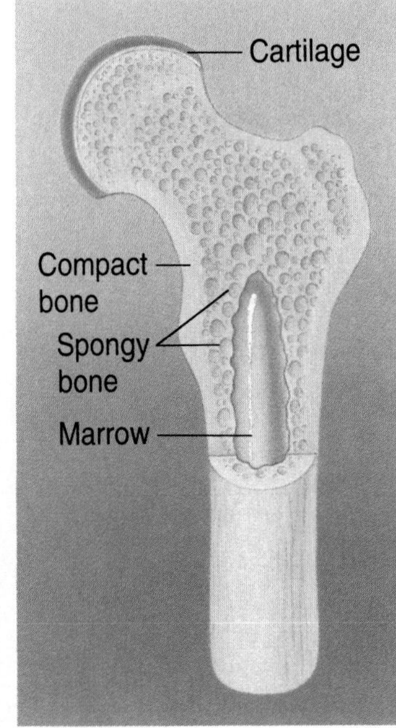

1. Bone is a vital, living tissue with numerous functions that gives the body a shape and supplies it with minerals.

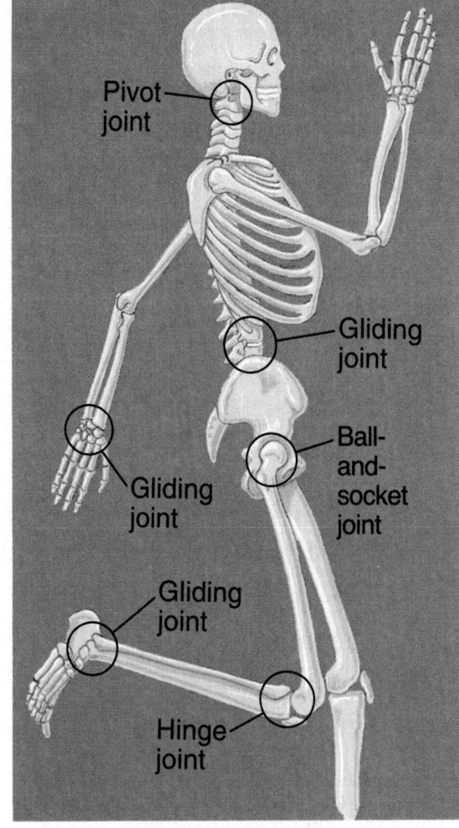

2. The skeletal system is able to move at certain points throughout the body because of joints.

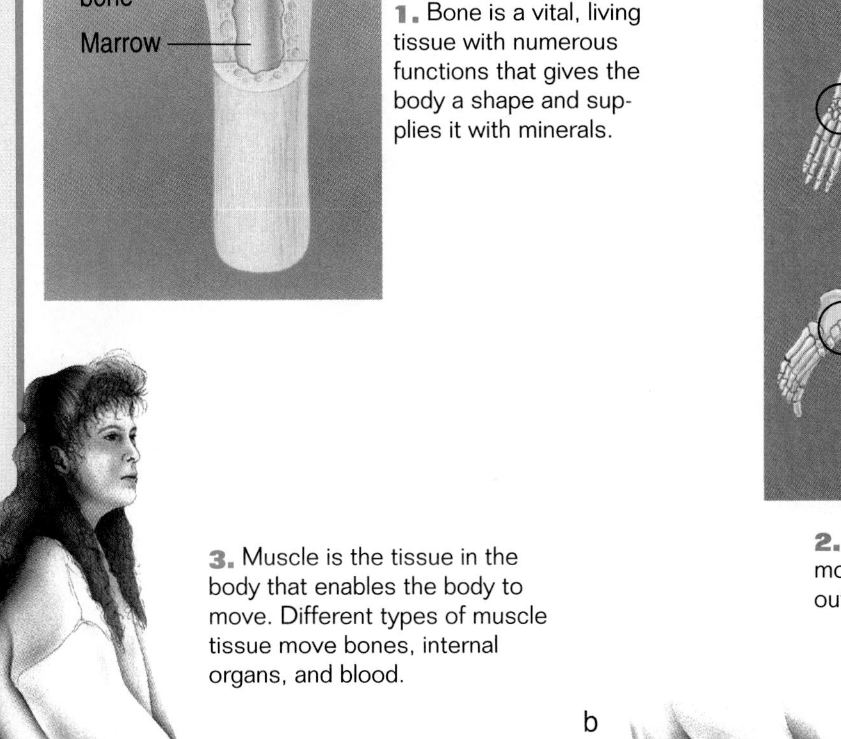

3. Muscle is the tissue in the body that enables the body to move. Different types of muscle tissue move bones, internal organs, and blood.

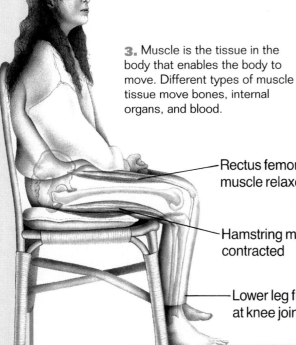

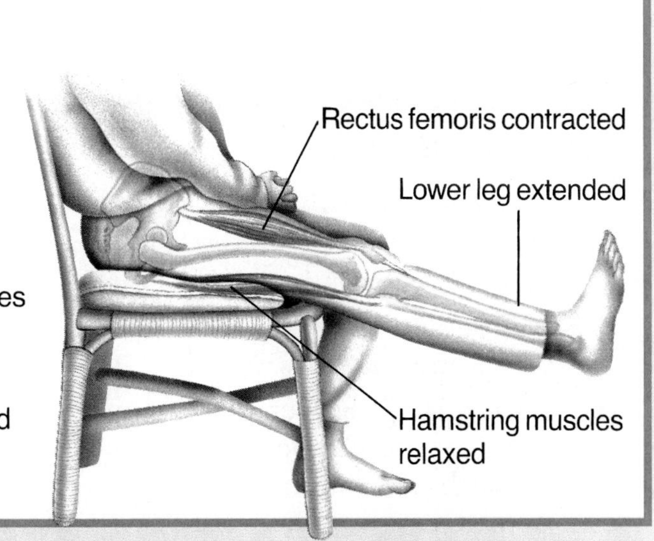

Chapter Review

USING KEY SCIENCE TERMS

bone marrow
cardiac muscle
cartilage
compact bone
joints
ligaments
skeletal muscles
smooth muscles
spongy bone
tendons

For each set of the terms below, choose the one term that does not belong and explain why it does not belong.

1. compact bone, spongy bone, marrow, ligament
2. tendon, skeletal muscle, smooth muscle, bone
3. joint, ligament, cardiac muscle, cartilage
4. jaw muscles, hand muscles, skeletal muscles, stomach muscles
5. support, compact bone, marrow, skeletal muscles

UNDERSTANDING IDEAS

Choose the best answer to complete each sentence.

1. Muscles are attached to bones by ____.
   a. cartilage **c.** tendons
   b. ligaments **d.** joints
2. Cardiac muscle makes up your ____.
   a. heart **c.** intestines
   b. stomach **d.** forearm
3. Before you were born, your skeleton was made up of ____.
   a. tendons **c.** cartilage
   b. compact bone **d.** ligaments
4. Red bone marrow produces ____.
   a. fat **c.** calcium
   b. blood cells **d.** spongy bone
5. The joint at your hip is a ____.
   a. hinge joint
   b. ball-and-socket joint
   c. pivot joint
   d. gliding joint
6. The joint at your knee is a ____.
   a. hinge joint
   b. ball-and-socket joint
   c. pivot joint
   d. gliding joint
7. The periosteum is the thin, outer layer of ____.
   a. cartilage **c.** joints
   b. skeletal muscle **d.** bone
8. Muscles make bones move when they ____.
   a. lengthen **c.** contract
   b. push **d.** relax
9. Rickets is caused by not enough ____.
   a. calcium **c.** iron
   b. blood cells **d.** glucose
10. The joints in your skull are ____.
    a. movable joints
    b. immovable joints
    c. gliding joints
    d. hinge joints

CRITICAL THINKING

Use your understanding of the concepts developed in the chapter to answer each of the following questions.

1. Pick up this book, and then put it down again. What enables you to do both with the same bones and joints in your arm?
2. What is the advantage of having immovable joints in your skull?
3. Why is there always some movement in your body?
4. How do the foods you eat affect your bones?
5. How does the part of the bone shown in the illustration help reduce the effect of pressure on your joints?

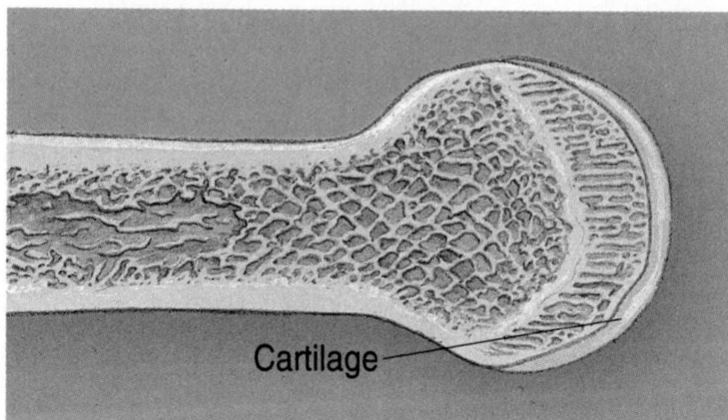

PROBLEM SOLVING

Read the following problem and discuss your answers in a brief paragraph.

On the last day of a fossil hunting expedition, Dr. Susman uncovers a remarkable find—an almost complete skeleton of an ape ancestor! After examining the newly found fossil in the lab, Dr. Susman discovers something very important to her research. She finds that all of the fossil's leg joints are perfectly intact and undamaged. She also finds that the leg joints are identical in size and shape to those of certain living species of apes. Dr. Susman wants to investigate how the ape ancestor used its legs to move around. Use your knowledge of the skeletal system to describe what Dr. Susman might do to find out how the leg joints of the fossil worked.

CONNECTING IDEAS

Discuss each of the following in a brief paragraph.

1. What forms of energy are involved in a muscle contraction?
2. How are your bones and muscles like machines?
3. Why do you think the face of a person who is exercising turns red?
4. **A CLOSER LOOK** How do you think your bone density compares to that of a robin's? Explain your answer.
5. **SCIENCE AND SOCIETY** Describe some of the benefits of exercise for your muscular system.
6. **HOW IT WORKS** Compare a robot arm with a human arm. What supplies the energy to move the joints of a robot arm? How is this similiar to a human arm?

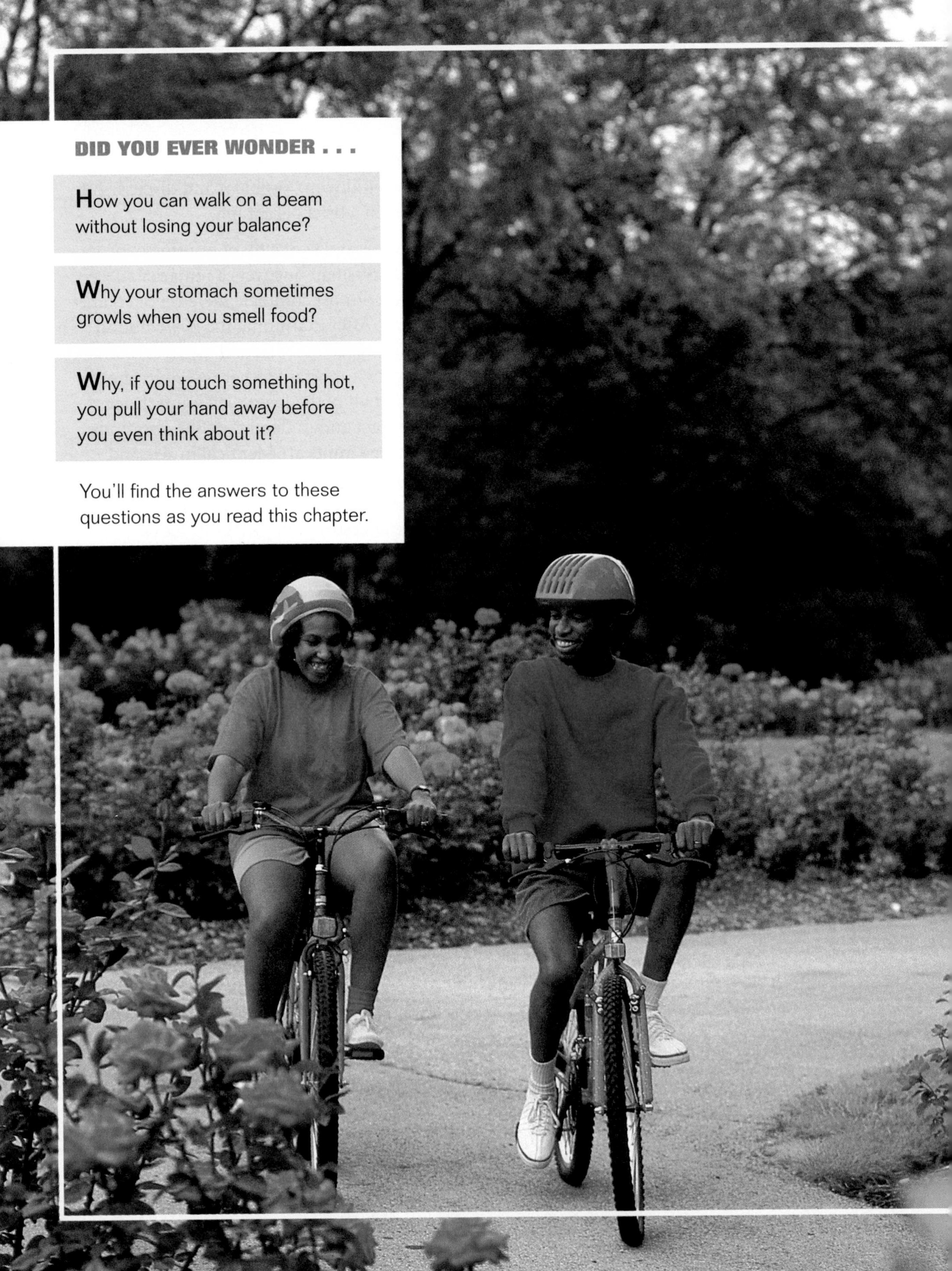

DID YOU EVER WONDER . . .

How you can walk on a beam without losing your balance?

Why your stomach sometimes growls when you smell food?

Why, if you touch something hot, you pull your hand away before you even think about it?

You'll find the answers to these questions as you read this chapter.

Chapter 8

Controlling the Body Machine

"The first time I tried to ride a bike, I wondered how anyone could do it. There was so much to remember all at once. Look straight ahead. Pedal. Don't lean sideways. Keep the bike straight. Time and time again, the bike leaned one way while I leaned the other. And time after time, the bike and I crash-landed. Then one Saturday morning, I got on, pushed away from the curb, and pedaled down to the corner and around the block without stopping or falling. Everything worked together. It was great!"

Riding a bike, walking, playing ball—in fact, every activity you do—requires coordination of the bones, joints, and muscles in your body. What controls the actions of these body parts? How are they coordinated?

Most living things have something that controls their behaviors and coordinates their body processes. In this chapter, you will explore the body system that controls and coordinates most of your behaviors. You'll examine how this system works to help you interact with the world around you.

EXPLORE!

Why does your dog bark?

Why do animals do the things they do? Why do some pets run to the kitchen when they hear a can opener? Why do some fish come to the top of the tank when you're about to feed them? These are behaviors. Try the following activity. Observe and record the behaviors of any animal for 30 minutes. It can be a pet or an outside animal, such as a bird or squirrel. Be sure to watch carefully what goes on around the animal. Did the animal do things at random, or did there seem to be a pattern to its behaviors?

8-1 The Nervous System: Master Control

OBJECTIVES

In this section, you will

- demonstrate the relationship between a stimulus and a response;
- describe the function of the nervous system;
- diagram the basic structure of a neuron;
- explain how impulses travel along nerves.

KEY SCIENCE TERMS

neuron
synapse

THE ROLE OF YOUR NERVOUS SYSTEM

While learning to ride a bike, you probably found yourself a little confused by all the things you had to remember to do all at the same time. Putting your feet on the pedals and learning how to brake were important. So was the slope of the street, the holes in the road, the car turning the corner, the stoplight, and so on. As you ride a bike, your body makes adjustments for each of these things. But all living organisms are constantly faced with situations in which they have to make adjustments to the changing world around them.

EXPLORE!

How do you keep your balance?

Have you ever tried walking on a balance beam? Try the following activity. Find a low wall or a long, secured two-by-four board that you can walk across. Make sure the part you are walking on is no wider than your foot. Try walking along your balance beam, slowly at first and then try to walk more quickly. What are some of the things you have to watch out for on a balance beam? What kinds of body adjustments did you make to keep yourself in balance?

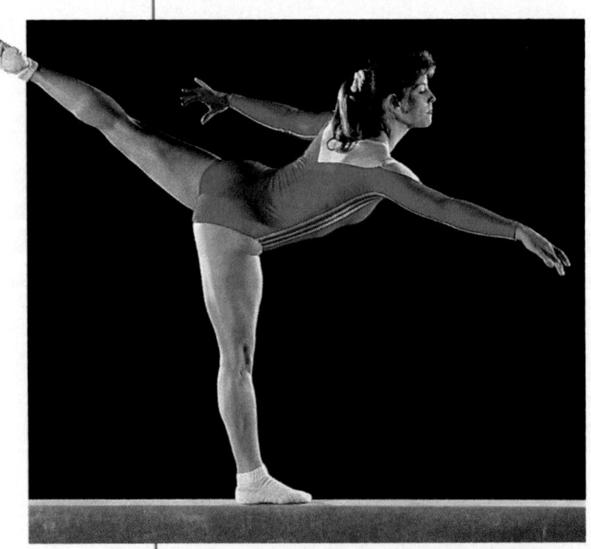

In order to make adjustments to changes around them, living organisms have systems that control all the parts of their bodies. On the balance beam, you probably had to constantly adjust the way you held your body so you wouldn't tumble off. Maybe you stuck your arms out or bent your knees. Your body has a system that permits you to make these rapid adjustments. The body system that makes adjustments by controlling parts of the body is your nervous system.

FIGURE 8-1. Your body makes several rapid adjustments to keep you from falling as you ride your bike.

Each behavior you perform during a typical day is the result of the work of your nervous system. A nervous system receives signals, or stimuli, from inside and outside your body. The smell of lunch is a stimulus. The ring of a telephone is also a stimulus. Once your nervous system receives a stimulus, it reacts. The reactions made by your body are called responses. Your stomach growling is a response to the smell of lunch, just as reaching for the telephone is a response to its ring. When you ride a bike or walk on a balance beam, you are faced with stimuli related to balance. You respond by adjusting how your body is held. What stimuli and responses did you observe in the animal you watched?

In many ways, your nervous system can be compared to the workings of a telephone service. A telephone system, like the one in Figure 8-2, receives incoming calls all day from telephone lines coming from all over. An information operator working at a computerized system enters incoming questions. The computer responds by giving the correct information or direction. Like a telephone service, the job of your nervous system is to receive stimuli, process them, and give directions to various parts of your body to coordinate responses.

FIGURE 8-2. Your nervous system, like a telephone system, processes information and gives directions.

NEURONS: YOUR BODY'S RELAY TEAM

You know that telephone messages are sent along telephone lines, but do you know how these messages, called impulses, travel throughout the nervous system? To

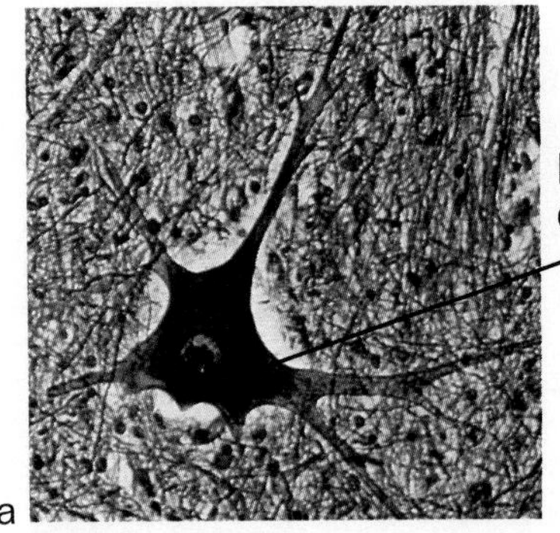

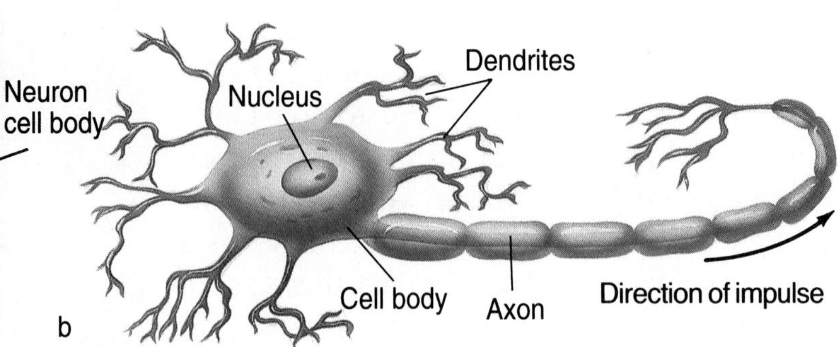

FIGURE 8-3. A neuron (a) is made up of a cell body, dendrites, and an axon (b).

understand this, we have to look at the working unit of the nervous system, the **neuron**.

Figure 8-3 shows a photograph and a diagram of a neuron. As you can see from the diagram, neurons have three main parts. The neuron is made up of a cell body and branches called dendrites and axons. The short twig-like dendrites receive messages and send them to the cell body, the largest part of the neuron. From the cell body, the messages, or impulses, are carried away by the long, string-like axon.

Each neuron is a separate cell, but neurons usually are grouped together in a bundle called a nerve. Neurons transmit impulses from one neuron to the next. How does this happen?

FIND OUT!

How does information move through your nervous system?

Out on the track field, or in the school yard, organize a relay team of six students spaced around the track. At the word *Go*, the student at the starting line runs and passes a stick to the second team member. The second team member runs to the next member and passes the stick. The race continues in this fashion until the last team member crosses the finish line.

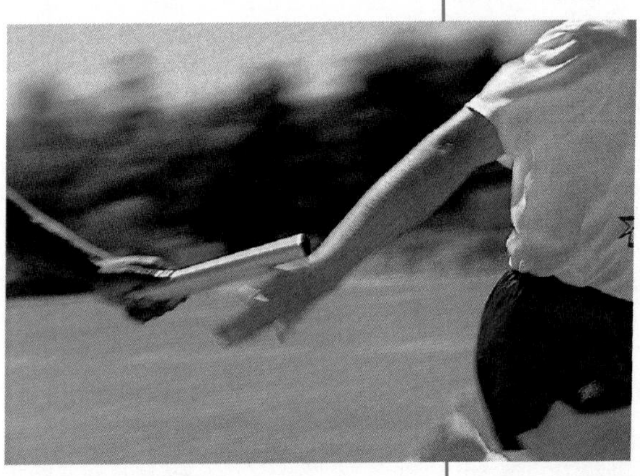

Conclude and Apply

1. Can the second runner begin before the first has come along?
2. What enables the second or third to run their parts of the race?

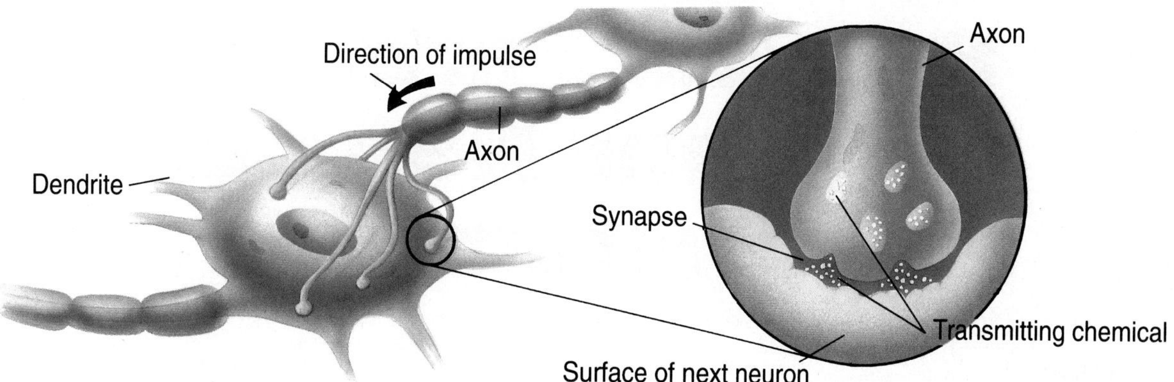

FIGURE 8-4. Impulses move from one neuron, across the synapse, to other neurons.

In your relay race, you never actually touched the next team member. The stick was simply passed to that person. Neurons work in a similar way. Look at the two neurons in Figure 8-4. As you can see, the neurons are close to each other, but they don't touch. Instead, the axon of one neuron is separated from the dendrites of the other neuron by tiny spaces. A space between neurons is called a **synapse**.

To move from one neuron to the next, an impulse has to cross a synapse. How is this done? Like the first runner passing the stick, when the impulse reaches the end of a branch of an axon, the axon releases a chemical into the synapse. The chemical crosses the synapse to a dendrite and an impulse starts in the next neuron.

You have seen that organisms have systems that enable them to respond to changes in their environments. The system that enables you to make organized responses to stimuli is your nervous system. Throughout this system, stimulus and response impulses are carried by neurons.

In the next section, you will look at the parts of the nervous system and how they work.

DID YOU KNOW?

An impulse can travel along a nerve at 270 miles per hour and cross a synapse in 1/10,000th of a second. In contrast, the fastest animal on Earth, the cheetah, runs at speeds of up to 70 miles per hour.

Check Your Understanding

1. Give an example of a stimulus you encounter every day and your response. What role does your nervous system play in this situation?
2. Diagram two neurons. Include the following—axon, body, dendrites, synapse. Show the direction an impulse travels.
3. How does an impulse move from one neuron to the next?
4. **APPLY:** Certain drugs prevent axons from releasing chemicals into a synapse. What effect would drugs like this have on the transmission of an impulse?

8-2 The Parts of Your Nervous System

OBJECTIVES

In this section, you will

- explain how the cerebrum and cerebellum work together during complex activities;
- compare and contrast the roles of the central and peripheral nervous systems.

KEY SCIENCE TERMS

cerebrum
cerebellum
brainstem
spinal cord

THE CENTRAL NERVOUS SYSTEM

When you play ball, like the students in Figure 8-5, or do any other complex activity, your nervous system receives and acts on many different stimuli all at the same time. For example, the clock is running down. You're being chased by opposing team members. Your own team members are signaling for you to throw the ball. There are so many stimuli. They all seem to happen at once, yet your body responds to all of them. What parts of the nervous system take care of the incoming stimuli? How does your body know what responses to make?

FIGURE 8-5. How does your body know to listen to the quarterback and to ignore the crowd?

EXPLORE!

What does a central information computer do for you?

Try the following game to help you understand how your nervous system responds to a stimulus. In this model, you and your classmates will simulate the working of a telephone information service. Students will take turns playing a central computer operator. The operator wins points by either answering science questions or redirecting the caller to where he or she can find the answer. Choose a classmate to be the operator and others to be callers.

Callers will each write one question and pass them to the operator, who will respond to each of the calls. Ten points are awarded for a direct answer and five points are awarded for redirected answers. How well did the operator handle the questions? Were many questions redirected?

THE BRAIN: OPERATOR OF THE NERVOUS SYSTEM

Think about what a telephone service would be like if there were no central computer operator present to process incoming phone calls. If you were to call for a phone number, your call would get through to the switchboard, but there would be no one there to answer your call and give you information.

Like the central computer operator who receives and processes hundreds of incoming calls a day, your nervous system contains structures that receive and process numerous stimuli every minute. This division of your nervous system is called the central nervous system. As shown in Figure 8-6, the central nervous system is made up of two structures: the brain and the spinal cord.

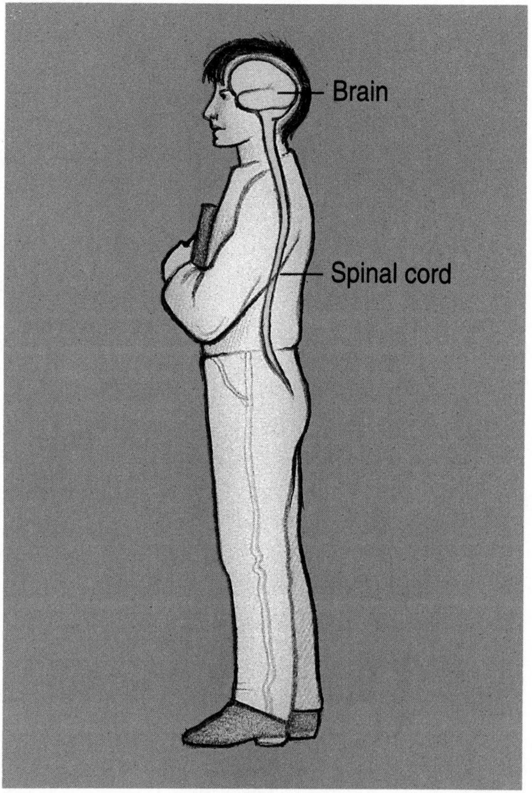

FIGURE 8-6. The brain and the spinal cord make up the central nervous system.

Your brain is composed of billions of neurons. From your knowledge of the skeletal system, you know that the brain is protected on the outside by the bones that form your skull. The brain is divided into three parts, as shown in Figure 8-7. The parts are the cerebrum, the cerebellum, and the brainstem, and each has a different function.

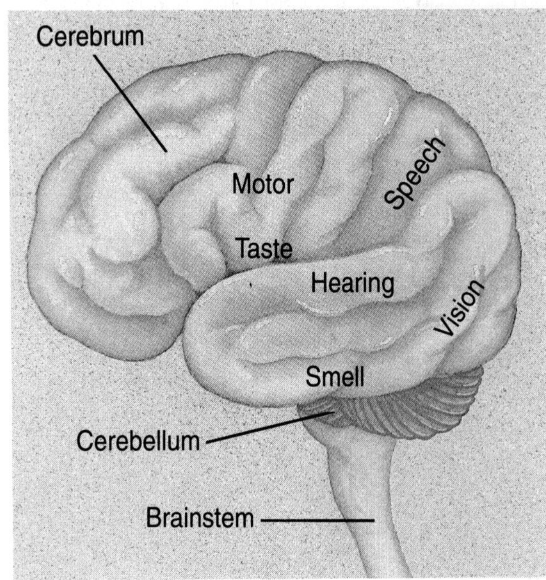

FIGURE 8-7. Different areas of the brain control specific body activities.

CEREBRUM

The **cerebrum** is the largest part of the brain. You may have noticed that the surface of the cerebrum is wrinkled. Different areas, or centers, in the wrinkled surface of the cerebrum interpret impulses that come to it from different parts of the body. For instance, there is a center for each of your senses: vision, touch, taste, smell, and hearing. When impulses are sent along nerves to one of these centers, the center interprets the impulse. If, for example, an impulse stimulated by popcorn travels from the nose to the smell center, it will be interpreted by that center as popcorn.

There are also centers for speech, memory, and for motor activities, which are activities that involve muscle movement. If you want to wave and say good-bye, your motor center sends impulses to your arm and hand muscles, and your speech center sends impulses to your vocal cords and the muscles of your mouth.

The size of the cerebrum differs from organism to organism. Figure 8-8 shows a human brain (a) and the brain of a cat (b). In the figure, the human cerebrum is much larger than the cat cerebrum. Do you think the size of different parts of the brain has anything to do with an organism's ability to perform different tasks? Animals such as cats apparently don't use the thinking center as much as humans do, but they do use other centers more frequently than humans. Which centers would you expect to be more active in a cat?

FIGURE 8-8. Compare the human brain (a) with the cat's brain (b). What differences do you see?

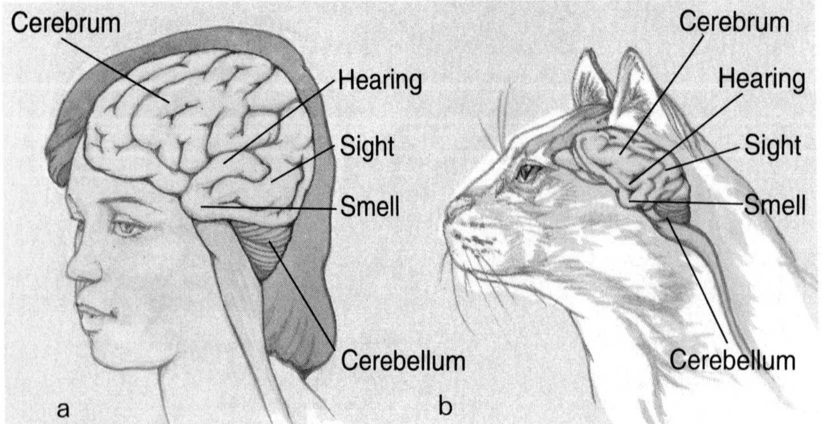

CEREBELLUM

You know that the motor center in your cerebrum sends impulses to the muscles you use when you ride a bike. But think for a moment about how many muscles you use when you ride a bike. How is it that you can use so many of these muscles at the same time? For instance, you use your back muscles to control balance. Arm and shoulder muscles help you to steer the bike. You use your leg and foot muscles to pedal. You can control a bike with ease, even though biking is actually a very complex activity. It requires the coordination and control of all of these muscles at the same time. How do you know how hard to pedal, where to steer, and how far you should tilt your body to balance?

During complex activities like those just described, your cerebellum coordinates the actions of all your muscles and maintains balance. The **cerebellum** is much smaller than the cerebrum and is located toward the back and bottom of the brain, as shown in Figure 8-9. When you are riding a bike, the cerebellum sends messages to the cerebrum that direct and coordinate the activity. These messages control how far to tilt from side to side and how much and in what order your arm, hand, and leg muscles should move to ride successfully. The cerebrum then sends out impulses to your muscles according to the directions given to it by the cerebellum.

Your cerebrum and your cerebellum work together when you need to move muscles in response to stimuli. For example, if somebody throws a ball toward you in gym class, you may move the muscles in your arms and hands to catch that ball. This type of response must be quick and well timed. In the next activity, you will investigate how quickly your brain causes you to respond to stimuli.

FIGURE 8-9. Your cerebellum coordinates your bike-riding actions.

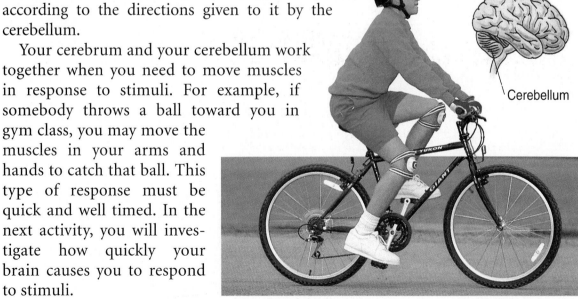

INVESTIGATE!

8-1 REACTION TIME

The time it takes the brain to react to a stimulus is called reaction time. In the following activity, you will test your reaction time.

PROBLEM

How fast do you react?

MATERIALS

penny
meterstick

PROCEDURE

Part A

1. Copy the data table.
2. While sitting, hold out your right arm (use your left arm if you are left-handed) with the palm down. Place a penny on the back of your hand.
3. Turn your hand so that the penny slides off. Try to catch the penny with the same hand before it lands.
4. Repeat Steps 2 and 3 nine more times. Record the number of times you caught the penny or dropped the penny.
5. Repeat Steps 2, 3, and 4 with your other hand.

Part B

1. Have your partner hold a penny 0.5 m above the palm of your hand.
2. When the penny drops, move your hand before the penny hits it.
3. Repeat Steps 1 and 2 nine more times. Record how many times the penny hit or missed your hand.
4. Repeat Part B, Steps 1, 2, and 3 with the penny 0.3 m above your palm.
5. Repeat all steps with your other hand.

Part C

1. Hold a meterstick between your thumb and index finger.
2. Have your partner **observe** the stick as you release it. Your partner should catch the meterstick before it hits the ground. In the data table, record the distance the meterstick fell.
3. Repeat Step 2 nine more times and record each result in the data table.
4. Repeat all steps using your other hand.

DATA AND OBSERVATIONS

PART A				
	RIGHT HAND		LEFT HAND	
TRIAL	CAUGHT	NOT CAUGHT	CAUGHT	NOT CAUGHT
1				
2				

PART B			
TRIAL	DISTANCE ABOVE HAND	HIT	NOT HIT
1			
2			

PART C		
	DISTANCE FALLEN	
TRIAL	RIGHT HAND	LEFT HAND
1		
2		

ANALYZE

1. List the stimulus in each of the three activities.
2. **Compare** and **contrast** your reaction times for each hand. Is there a connection between your response and your writing hand?
3. Did your reaction time improve after a few trials?

CONCLUDE AND APPLY

4. **Compare** your results with the results of your classmates. Can you **hypothesize** why some people had faster reaction times?
5. Why do you think the hand you use for writing had a quicker reaction time?
6. **Going Further:** Do you think it is advantageous for animals to have quick reaction times to stimuli? Explain your answer.

BRAINSTEM AND SPINAL CORD

In the last activity, you had direct control over the muscles of your hand. Activities that are under your direct control, such as moving arm or leg muscles, are called voluntary activities. But there are many body activities that you do not have control over. Digestion, heartbeat, and breathing, for example, occur without you having to think about them. These activities are called involuntary activities.

Even though involuntary body activities occur without you thinking about them, they are still controlled by a part of your brain. The **brainstem** controls involuntary body activities. As its name suggests, and as you saw in Figure 8-7, the brainstem is the part of the brain that connects with the spinal cord.

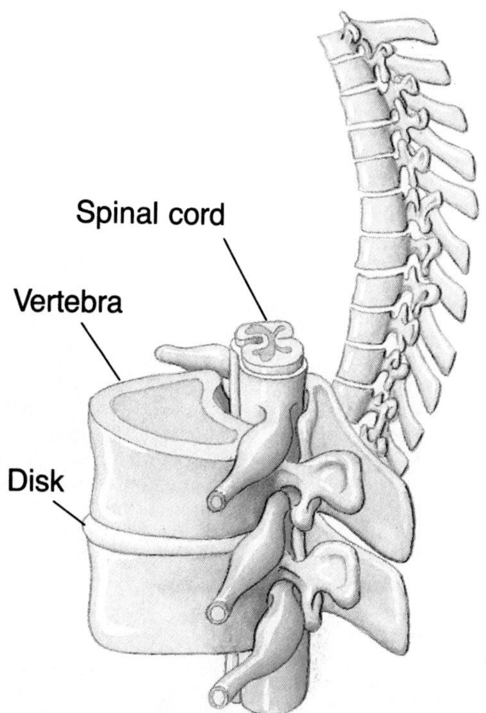

FIGURE 8-10. Impulses travel to and from the brain by way of the spinal cord.

The **spinal cord** is a long cord that extends from the brainstem down the back. In Figure 8-10, you can see that it is protected by the bony tube formed by the vertebrae of your spine.

Nerves can be compared to the telephone lines entering a computerized system. The brain is like the computer that controls the switchboard, and the spinal cord is like a thick cable of lines that go into and out of the computer. Telephone calls first enter on a line before the computer processes them. In the same manner, an impulse from a nerve first enters the spinal cord before it is carried to the brain for processing. Likewise, an outgoing impulse from the brain travels first to the spinal cord, and then out to parts of the body along nerves. The spinal cord acts as the connection between the brain and parts of the body.

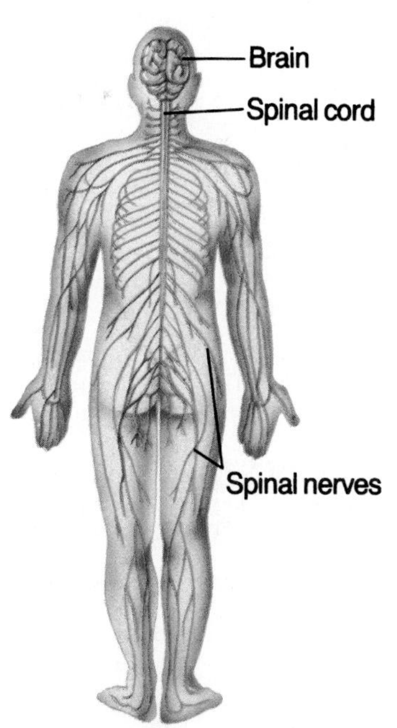

FIGURE 8-11. The brain and spinal cord make up the central nervous system. Spinal nerves are part of the peripheral nervous system.

THE PERIPHERAL NERVOUS SYSTEM

Your brain and spinal cord form the central nervous system. All of the nerves in your body make up the peripheral nervous system. *Peripheral* means to the side and away from. Therefore, the nerves of the peripheral nervous system, as shown in Figure 8-11, extend to and away from the central nervous system.

a

b

FIGURE 8-12. Sensory nerves are involved in smelling a flower (a). Motor nerves are involved in picking a flower (b).

In the peripheral nervous system, there are two types of nerves that carry impulses. These are sensory nerves and motor nerves. Sensory nerves carry the impulses from a stimulus to the central nervous system for processing. When you smell a flower, like the people in Figure 8-12, impulses for fragrance are carried by sensory nerves from your nose to your brain. How were sensory nerves involved when you grabbed the penny and the meterstick in the Investigate?

Motor nerves carry impulses from the central nervous system to activate the muscles in your body. When you pick a flower, the impulse is carried by a motor nerve from the central nervous system out to the muscles of the arm and hand. How was a motor nerve involved when you grabbed the penny and meterstick?

In this section, you have seen that the central nervous system is made up of the brain and the spinal cord. The function of the central nervous system is to receive an impulse from a stimulus, interpret it, and issue necessary responses to the stimulus.

SKILLBUILDER

MAKING AND USING TABLES

Make a table of the divisions and functions of the parts of the nervous system. Include the following: central nervous system, cerebrum, cerebellum, brainstem, spinal cord, and peripheral nervous system. If you need help, refer to the **Skill Handbook** on page 679.

How do we know?

Brain centers

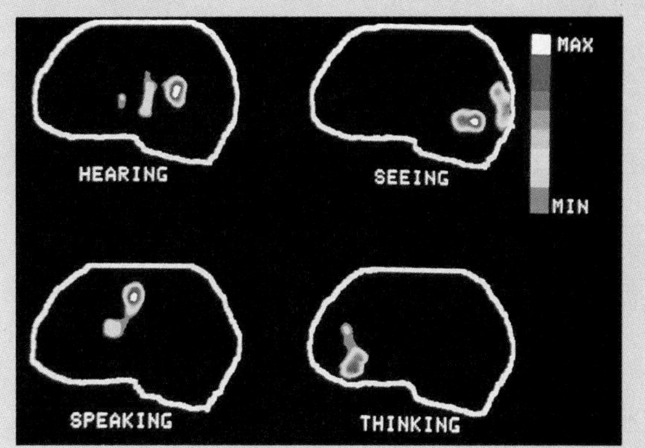

Many researchers are interested in knowing which activities take place in the different areas of the brain. In the past, researchers relied on persons who had had a brain injury. They could tell which part of the brain is related to which activity by the injury and by observing the person to see if he or she had any difficulty in seeing, hearing, speaking, moving muscles, and so on.

Now with the help of a technology called PET (positron emission tomography) that displays energy levels in brain centers when they are active, researchers have pinpointed the areas of the brain used for seeing, reading, hearing, speaking, and thinking.

Inside the brain, different stimuli are processed in different centers of the cerebrum. There are centers for each sense, as well as for speech, thinking, memory, and motor activities. The cerebrum sends out impulses along motor nerves to activate muscles. During complex activities, the cerebellum coordinates the speed and timing of muscle action, making the activity run smoothly.

Impulses to and from the central nervous system are carried by the nerves of the peripheral nervous system. Sensory nerves carry impulses from a stimulus to the central nervous system for processing. Motor nerves carry impulses from the central nervous system out to the muscles of the body. Next, you will explore the structures that gather stimuli from the world around you.

Check Your Understanding

1. Describe the roles of your cerebrum and cerebellum during a swimming exercise.
2. Describe the path of an impulse associated with lifting your arm. What part of your brain starts this impulse?
3. Describe the role your peripheral nervous system plays in responding to a stimulus.
4. **APPLY:** After a severe accident, a person can talk and write, but has to learn to walk all over again. What parts of the nervous system were probably affected by the accident? What parts of the nervous system were not affected?

8-3 Senses and Reflexes

OBJECTIVES

In this section, you will

- classify the different forms of energy that your senses respond to;
- trace the pathway of a reflex.

KEY SCIENCE TERMS

reflex

YOUR SENSES

Imagine walking through a crowded area like the one in Figure 8-13. What kinds of stimuli would your nervous system respond to? Colors? Smells? Sounds? You couldn't appreciate the sights, sounds, and smells of a busy area such as this without having some way for this information to get to your central nervous system.

Fortunately, your body is equipped with organs that react to each of these stimuli. These are your sense organs, found in your eyes, ears, nose, mouth, and throughout your skin. You use your senses to detect stimuli. How much do you depend on your senses to keep you in touch with the world around you?

EXPLORE!

How important are your senses?

Try the following activity. Have a friend place an object in a box and tape the lid securely. Without opening the box, see if you can guess the contents of the box in five minutes. Record the activities you tried when guessing the contents. Name the senses that you used while trying to solve this problem.

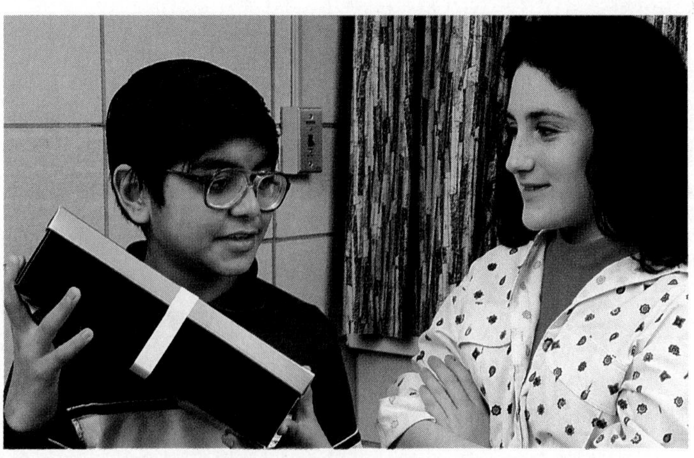

In this activity, you saw how important your senses are for detecting things around you. Maybe you shook the box so that you could hear the sound of the object bouncing around. Perhaps you used your sense of touch to feel the weight of the object in the box. You may have even decided to smell the box. Even if you quickly guessed what was in the box, your senses are so important that you probably still had to use at least one of them. How do your senses work?

FIGURE 8-13. In all situations, your body responds to several stimuli at one time.

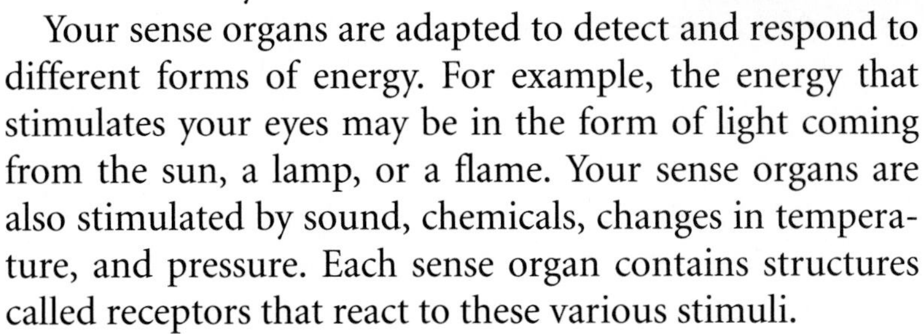

Your sense organs are adapted to detect and respond to different forms of energy. For example, the energy that stimulates your eyes may be in the form of light coming from the sun, a lamp, or a flame. Your sense organs are also stimulated by sound, chemicals, changes in temperature, and pressure. Each sense organ contains structures called receptors that react to these various stimuli.

As you can see from Figure 8-14(a), your sense of smell is possible because the nose contains receptors that are sensitive to the movement of different chemical molecules. In the same manner, the taste buds of your tongue, shown in Figure 8-14(b), work by responding to molecules in the foods you eat and drink.

FIGURE 8-14. Your nose contains receptors that react to the movement of chemical molecules in the air (a). Taste buds contain nerve endings that react to chemicals in food (b).

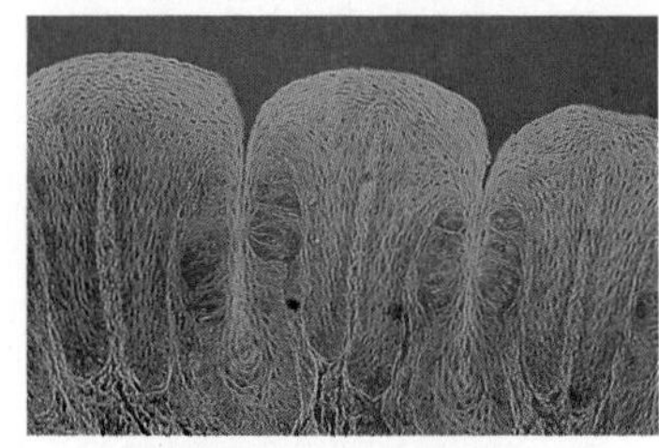

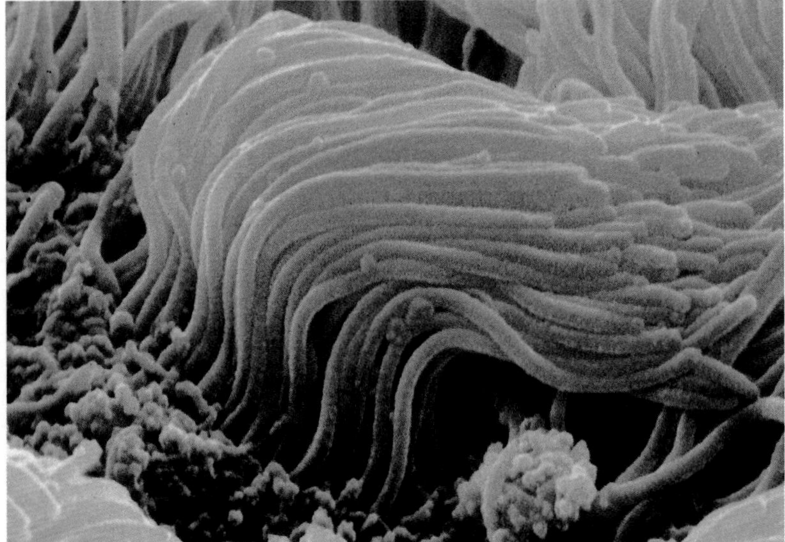

a

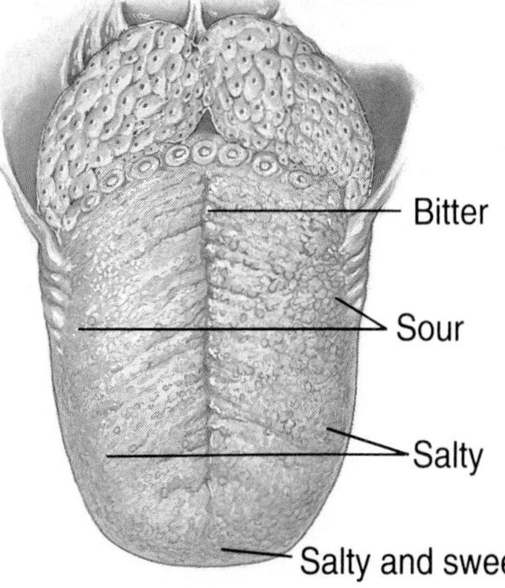

b

Sight is possible because your eye's retina contains receptors that capture the light energy reflected from objects. Receptors called rods respond to dim light. These are the receptors that help you see at night. Other receptors called cones respond to bright light and color. Because they don't work well without bright light, you can't distinguish colors well in darkened rooms or at night. Light energy stimulates impulses in these cells. The impulses pass to the optic nerve and then to the brain. Here they are interpreted, and you see what you are looking at.

You are able to hear different sounds because receptors in your inner ear are sensitive to the different frequencies of sound waves. As these receptors are stimulated, impulses are sent to the brain. Again, the brain responds and you hear the sound.

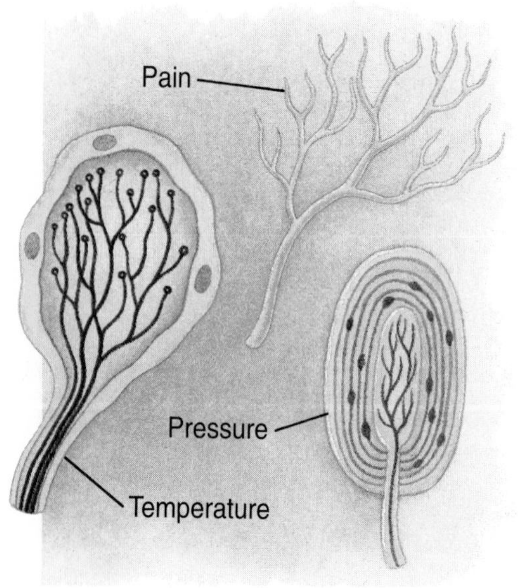

FIGURE 8-15. Your skin contains special receptors sensitive to pressure, pain, and temperature.

Imagine how difficult it would be to write with a pen or pencil without your sense of touch. Many of the activities you do every day rely on your ability to feel the things that you come in contact with. You wouldn't know how tightly to hold the pen or pencil, and your writing wouldn't come out very well.

Your sense of touch is a network of different types of receptors contained in the skin and throughout your entire body. As you can see in Figure 8-15, there are temperature receptors that are sensitive to the thermal energy given off by objects and pain receptors that warn you when your body is being injured.

Pressure receptors respond to the amount of force you apply to objects or that they apply to you. As you recall, pressure is defined as the amount of force applied over a given area. There are thousands of pressure receptors in your skin, scattered throughout your body. Pressure receptors permit you to feel the objects you come in contact with. When you feel something that you are touching, we say that your skin is sensitive. In the next activity, you will investigate how the pressure receptors on your hands and arms function as part of your sense of touch.

INVESTIGATE!

8-2 TESTING FOR SKIN SENSITIVITY

This activity will help you determine the relationship between the sensitivity of your skin and the location, number, and spacing of pressure receptors.

PROBLEM

How sensitive is your skin?

MATERIALS

large paper clip
metric ruler

PROCEDURE

1. Copy the data table.
2. Look at the test areas listed in the data table. **Predict** which parts of your arm will be the most sensitive to touch. Record your predictions.
3. Open a large paper clip and bend it into a U-shape. Push the two tips of the paper clip together until they are 1 cm apart.
4. Lightly touch your partner's fingertip with both points of the paper clip. Make sure your partner does not see what you are doing.
5. Ask your partner whether one or two points were felt. Record this response in your data table.
6. Fix the paper clip so that the points are farther apart and repeat Steps 2 and 3. Do this for 3 cm, 5 cm, and 7 cm. Record all responses in the data table.
7. Repeat Steps 4 through 6 for each location listed in the data table.
8. Switch jobs and have your partner test your skin sensitivity. Record the responses in a second data table.

DATA AND OBSERVATIONS

DISTANCE	PREDICTIONS	1CM	3CM	5CM	7CM
Fingertip					
Palm					
Back of hand					
Forearm					
Back of neck					

ANALYZE

1. **Interpret** the data in your table to determine which area of your arm was the most sensitive. Which was the least sensitive?
2. **Compare** the sensitivity of different parts of your arm.
3. How well did your predictions match your results?

CONCLUDE AND APPLY

4. Can you suggest a reason why it might be beneficial for your fingertips to have many receptors?
5. Can you suggest a reason why your upper arm and neck have fewer receptors than your fingertips?
6. **Going Further**: What parts of your body besides your arm would you **predict** to be the least sensitive? Explain your predictions.

As you observed in the activity, you have many types of receptors in the skin of your body. In the same manner, the receptors in your eyes, ears, nose, and tongue are sensitive to many different sights, sounds, smells, and tastes. Why is it advantageous to have different types of receptors that are more sensitive to stimuli around you? Just as your ability to detect stimuli is important, your ability to do something about the stimuli is just as important.

REFLEXES

Sometimes you encounter stimuli in your environment that are so strong they may be harmful to you. How does your nervous system protect you ?

FIND OUT!

How are you protected from light?

Try the following activity. After your teacher dims the lights in the classroom, lightly tie a blindfold around your partner's head so that the eyes are completely covered. Wait several minutes. Remove the blindfold and quickly shine a flashlight into your partner's right eye for about one second. **CAUTION:** *Do not shine the flashlight any longer than required.* Carefully observe the changes in the pupil of your partner's eye. Repeat the procedure on the left eye. What happens to the pupil?

Conclude and Apply

1. How does the eye respond?
2. Is this response protective?

Look at the photos in Figure 8-16. Is this what happened to your partner's pupils in the last activity?

Your eyes respond to brightness by controlling the size of the pupil. When you walk around in a dark room, your pupils become larger. As a result, more light enters the eye to strike the retina. If there is a lot of light, such as on a sunny day, your pupils get smaller. The changes in your pupil size happen automatically and involuntarily. You have no control over them. How is this response helpful? Can you identify another response that protects your eyes?

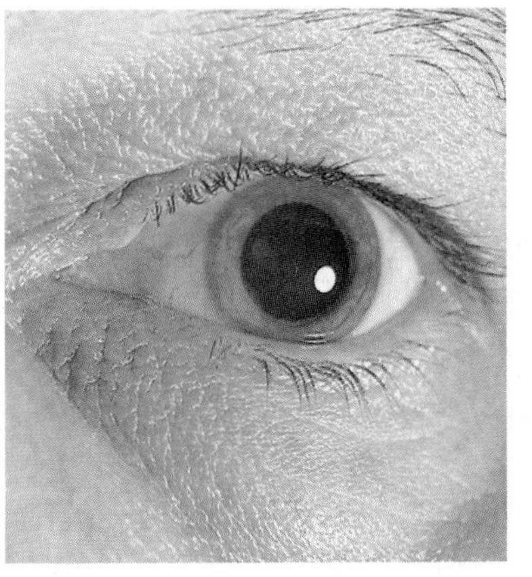

FIGURE 8-16. One of your eye's protective responses closes your pupil if too much light is entering the eye.

Other parts of your body also respond automatically to stimuli. Touch a hot stove and your hand is automatically pulled back! Step on a sharp object and you jump instantly! An automatic body response to a potentially harmful stimulus, such as a bright light or a hot object, is called a **reflex**. What do you do when you hear a sudden, loud noise? Do you think about your reaction before it happens? Can you think of some other reflexes that protect you? How are reflexes important for the survival of an organism?

Because reflexes are critical for the survival of organisms, they must occur very quickly and in the same way each time. These impulses are carried through the nervous system along set pathways. They are the shortest possible length and do not involve the brain. These pathways are called *reflex arcs*.

Reflex arcs involve several nerves. Figure 8-17 shows the pathway of an impulse from stepping on a sharp object. First, pain and pressure receptors in the foot produce impulses that are carried along sensory nerves to the spinal cord. One set of impulses circles back to the motor neurons

FIGURE 8-17. A reflex arc occurs when you step on a sharp object.

SKILLBUILDER

SEQUENCING

Make a sequence of the events that happen in your nervous system when you touch a hot stove. If you need help, refer to the **Skill Handbook** on page 678.

through a small neuron (interneuron) in the spinal cord and you rapidly move your foot away from the source of pain.

At a slightly later moment another impulse passes to the brain. It is at this time that you become aware of the pain. You actually react to the pain before you "feel" it—that is, before you are conscious of it.

In this chapter, you explored your nervous system and learned that it enables you to do your everyday activities. The central nervous system includes your brain and spinal cord. It receives an impulse from a stimulus, interprets it, and issues the necessary response to that stimulus. The peripheral nervous system includes the nerves that extend to and from the central nervous system.

Your nervous system has structures called receptors located in your sense organs, that respond to different forms of energy in the environment. Receptors send impulses along sensory neurons to the brain for processing. Finally, you learned that your body has built-in defense mechanisms called reflexes that work without involving the brain so you can respond rapidly to stimuli.

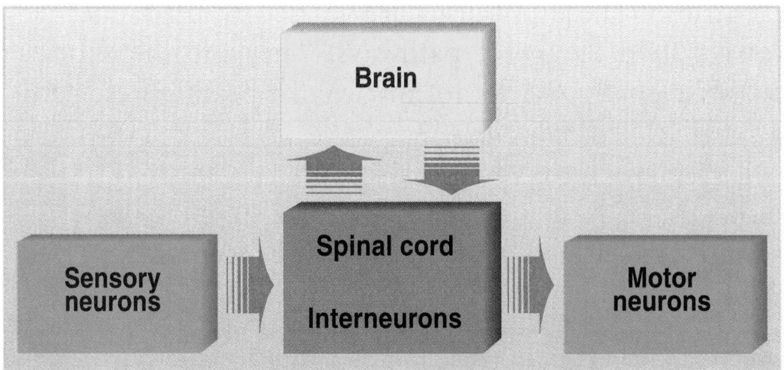

FIGURE 8-18. In your nervous system, sensory impulses are carried by sensory neurons to the central nervous system and then by motor neurons to the muscles of the body.

Check Your Understanding

1. For each energy stimulus listed below, provide the name of the sense organ(s) that responds to it.
   light energy thermal energy
   chemicals mechanical energy
   pressure
2. Trace the pathway of your reflex when you touch a hot stove.
3. **APPLY:** Discuss some reasons why reflexes are important for the survival of organisms.

EXPANDING YOUR VIEW

CONTENTS

A Closer Look
Teach Your Old Pet a New Trick 241

Physics Connection
Voice-Activated Computers 242

Science and Society
Alzheimer's Disease 243

Technology Connection
Watching the Brain 245

Psychology Connection
Infant Learning 246

A CLOSER LOOK

TEACH YOUR OLD PET A NEW TRICK

If you have a fish, cat, or dog, watch its behavior around feeding time. How does your pet respond when it anticipates food?

As you approach the fishbowl, the fish may swim to that "special" place where you usually drop its food. Your coming near the fishbowl is the stimulus, and the fish swimming toward the usual feeding place is the response. You've observed a learned response to a stimulus.

Cats and dogs have more freedom of movement than fish, so observing their responses can be more interesting. They, too, learn to recognize and respond to stimuli from their owners. The pets may come when they hear a cupboard open or a can opener turn. They may follow a person who picks up their food dish.

Your pets may even have learned stimuli that elicit a desired response from you. Some cats may learn to use a "sad" sounding meow because it has been an effective way, in the past, of getting a meal. Dogs sometimes linger by an empty food dish, pawing it and pushing it around the floor. In the past, someone usually filled the empty dish after seeing this behavior.

Try this experiment with your pet or a friend's pet. Move your pet's food dish to a new location. Store the food in a new location as well. See how long it takes your pet to adapt to the changes. Keep a record of the changes you made and how the pet responds to the new different stimuli. Remember though, this is an exercise designed to demonstrate learned response to stimuli—not to tease your pet!

WHAT DO YOU THINK?

1. If you could train an animal to do a very difficult stimulus/response behavior pattern, what would it be? Describe in detail.
2. Describe three stimulus/response patterns that are part of your behavior at school.

Physics Connection

VOICE-ACTIVATED COMPUTERS

Voice-activated computers may someday replace many of the personal computers that require typed instructions. How does a voice-activated computer work?

When you speak, a microphone converts the sounds into electrical signals. Special computer chips change these signals into digital data. The computer stores the data in its memory. When you speak into the computer the next time, it compares the new data with the data already in its memory. If the data matches, the computer will indicate that it has recognized a word. This process is called voice recognition.

Most voice-activated computers recognize only the voice of a particular operator. Sometimes, even clearly spoken words may confuse it. Because people have different speech patterns, stored data may not match the sounds of an unfamiliar operator. In fact, this speech pattern characteristic makes voice-activated computers a useful choice for security systems that depend on the spoken word. But by far the most exciting application of voice-activated computers is as a tool for the physically challenged. People with limited use of their hands or fingers will be among the first to benefit from the use of voice-activated computers. Voice-activated computers can assist these people in the workplace as well as at home. In the future, computers may even carry on conversations, with stored sounds converted into computer-voice sentences.

WHAT DO YOU THINK?

Imagine yourself sitting in front of a voice-activated computer. Your voice has been stored in its memory and is recognized by it. Still, some of the words that the computer has displayed are not the correct words as spoken by you. What do you think might cause this to happen?

SCIENCE AND SOCIETY

ALZHEIMER'S DISEASE

Mrs. Greeley was surprised and confused the other day when she realized she was outside in her nightgown. She couldn't remember coming down stairs or unlocking the door. A few blocks away, Maury Fishman is staring at his grandson. He can't remember the boy's name, and he doesn't know why the boy is familiar. Mr. Fishman reacts angrily.

Everyday scenes like these take place across the country. These people and others like them feel frightened, confused, and ashamed. After accumulating a lifetime of memories, memory has begun to slip away like sand along a beach. These people are experiencing the early symptoms of Alzheimer's (AWLTZ hi merz) disease.

At the present time, researchers have only a few concrete answers about the cause of Alzheimer's disease. Alzheimer's begins when nerve cells in the brain stop interacting. The nervous system uses a chemical called acetylcholine (as uh teel KOH leen) to move impulses from one neuron to the next. In Alzheimer's patients, the brain cells fail to produce this vital chemical. The neurons become inactive, then begin to die. It may be the inactivity that causes neurons to die, but researchers are not sure.

Many researchers believe that heredity plays a role in causing the disease. They point to a specific type of chromosomal abnormality in Alzheimer's patients as a probable cause. Also supporting the heredity theory are statistics showing that children of Alzheimer's patients are more likely to develop the disease themselves.

People with Alzheimer's are generally over age 65. However, some people in their 40s have also been affected by the disease. It doesn't occur more often in certain ethnic or economic groups nor has it been linked to the occurrence of any other diseases.

Because some brain cells die, the Alzheimer's patient suffers a loss of mental powers. Although 60 to 70 percent of the patients who suffer a loss of mental powers due to a physical cause have Alzheimer's disease, there is no specific test for it. Rather, patients undergo tests for many other possible causes, including thyroid disorders, anemia due to a lack of vitamin B_{12}, and

ministrokes. When the other possible causes have been eliminated, Alzheimer's disease is usually diagnosed.

While some patients have occasional periods of full awareness, others have difficulty feeding and dressing themselves. Many Alzheimer's patients suffer severe personality changes, leaving them unable to recognize family members or to control violent outbursts toward these people and other caregivers. The ultimate outcome for all, however, is the eventual loss of physical function, and then death. In the United States each year, Alzheimer's disease takes the lives of more than 100,000 people.

An Alzheimer's patient can linger from six to eight years, with an average care cost of $28,000 a year. However, until a cause is determined, it will be very difficult to find a cure for Alzheimer's disease.

Will there be a cure in your lifetime? Although intensive research has been done only since the early 1970s, much knowledge of the disease has been gained. Researchers do understand what happens to the brain of an Alzheimer's patient, yet no real progress toward a cure has been made. Drugs that produce the essential acetylcholine have been tested. However, these drugs have been found to cause serious side effects in most patients.

In 1986, test results were published that showed the drug THA produced a significant reduction in symptoms in Alzheimer's patients. The drug was studied by the Food and Drug Administration, the government agency that determines whether drugs work and whether they are safe and can be marketed in the United States.

Some patients were helped greatly by THA. Other patients showed no improvement, and others even suffered a harmful side effect that could cause liver damage. The FDA lowered the legal dosage of the drug to an amount that would reduce the risk of liver damage. At the lower dosage, however, the drug helped so few people that the FDA decided THA is not an effective treatment for Alzheimer's disease and did not approve its use. Other drugs are being developed and tested.

WHAT DO YOU THINK?

The FDA's decision not to approve the use of THA was very controversial.

1. How do you think Alzheimer's patients and their families would evaluate the possible risk of liver damage against the possible benefit of THA?
2. What do you think about the FDA's decision?

TECHNOLOGY CONNECTION

WATCHING THE BRAIN

For centuries, scientists have sought to view the activity within the brain in order to gain a better knowledge of its makeup and an understanding of disorders of the brain. The thickness of the skull made viewing the brain difficult. X rays provided information, but not of the brain at work. Delicate surgery was too extreme in most cases. However, recent development of the positron emission tomography (PET) now gives researchers the opportunity to see the brain at work.

A patient is given a simple sugar (glucose) solution which has been tagged with a radioactive element. The sugar with the tracer moves through the circulatory system and into the brain. Once in the brain, the radioactive tracer gives off particles like X rays that are detected by equipment outside the patient. A computer is able to trace the location of the tagged sugar. The PET machine shows the location on a color computer monitor. The greater the use of sugar by the brain, the brighter the spot on the monitor.

During this scan, the researcher may vary the patient's exposure to sound or sight in order to watch for changes in the brain's image. Recalling memories as well as other psychological stimuli may also cause visible changes in the brain. In comparing images of a patient's brain during different activities, researchers have identified specific areas of the brain used for seeing, hearing, speaking, and thinking.

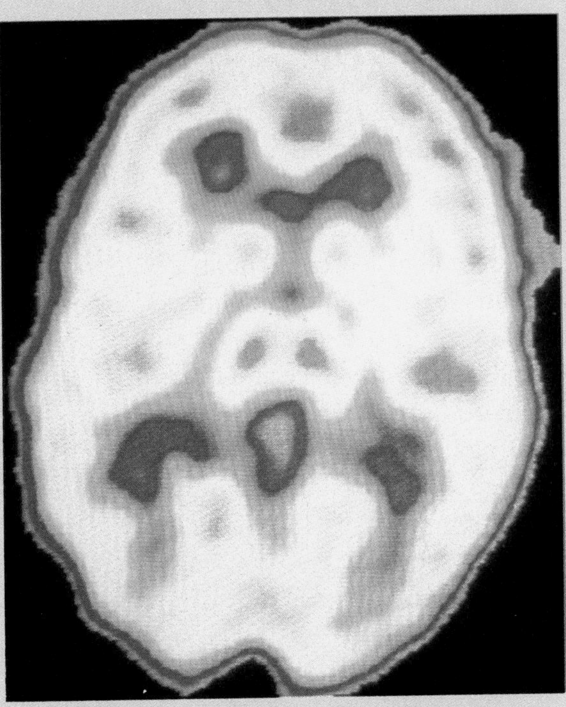

Victims of serious accidents involving brain damage are benefiting from the use of PET. Many stroke patients, especially those suffering loss of some senses, can be treated more effectively as a result of the scan. The PET scan has also become an important tool for researchers, who use it to learn about diseases that affect the brain.

YOU TRY IT!

In an anatomy book, find a diagram of the brain. Make your own PET scan drawing from the diagram. The right side of the brain controls a person's ability to perform household chores.

Make a second drawing, perhaps using different colors for detail, showing what the PET scan might look like of a person who is unable to do household chores due to a brain disorder.

Psychology CONNECTION

INFANT LEARNING

Early stimulation of a baby's five senses is essential to successful brain development and later learning. As an infant sees, hears, touches, tastes, and smells, specific areas of the brain become active and utilized. An infant's sensory development is most rapid between the second and fifth months of life. With each new bit of information learned, the child builds sensory pathways from one brain center to another. At this point, the child can't yet relate the senses to one another—that happens later in development.

Shortly after birth, an infant can see. The child receives visual stimulation from faces, shapes, patterns, colors, and light. Within the first four months of life, healthy babies learn a good deal from visual exploration of their surroundings.

A sudden, startling sound may make a baby jerk or blink his or her eyes. Gentle, soothing music may lull the baby to sleep. Most importantly, at a very early age the baby may learn to recognize the mother's voice. Although it is important to the development of an infant's capacity to hear a variety of sounds, too many different noises or too much loud sound may confuse the learning process.

By being touched, babies learn to touch, to identify the feel of objects, and to feel secure and safe. A gentle touch provides a baby with a sense of emotional well-being.

Using laboratory animals, researchers have found that infants raised in environments without stimulation suffer permanent damage to their nervous systems. Many of the lab animals grew to be unduly aggressive and unable to socialize and reproduce effectively.

Studies have shown that failure to fulfill a baby's sensory needs can weaken the ability to learn at a later time. A child whose sensory needs are not met as an infant may later be frustrated, angry, and impatient with attempts to learn. The resulting lack of confidence dims the child's desire to learn. Parents who want to raise a productive person with an active brain are encouraged to provide a sufficient amount of stimulation for their baby.

WHAT DO YOU THINK?

Imagine that you are a parent. You want your baby to develop the most productive learning system possible. Describe three or more things you would do to provide sensory stimulation for your infant during an average day.

Chapter 8

Reviewing Main Ideas

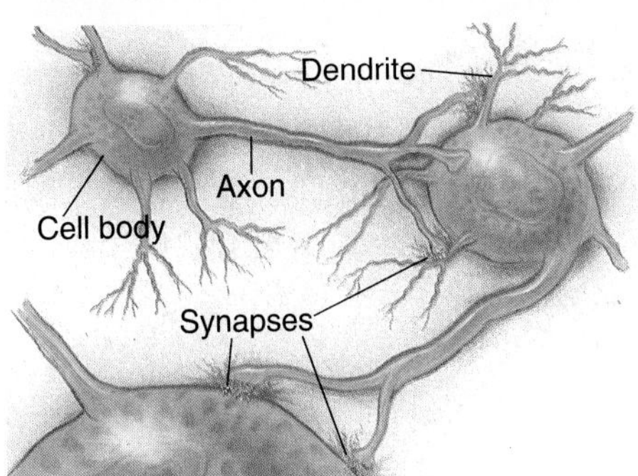

1. The neuron is the basic unit of the nervous system. Messages called impulses travel along neurons from dendrites to cell body to axons.

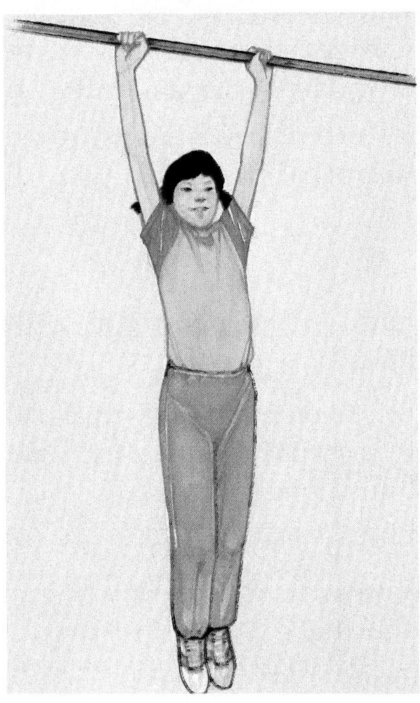

2. The central nervous system contains the brain and spinal cord, highly specialized organs containing billions of neurons that control and coordinate body activities. The spinal cord acts as a connection between the brain and the nerves of the body, which make up the peripheral nervous system.

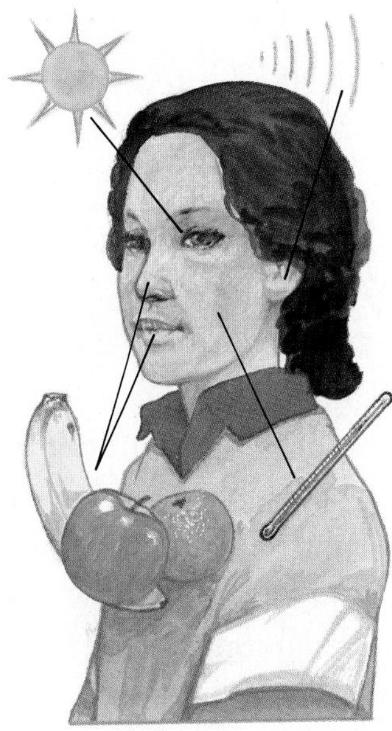

3. Impulses are started in different sense organs in response to different types of energy stimuli. Receptors in each sense organ detect energy stimuli and send impulses along sensory nerves to the central nervous system for processing.

4. Reflexes are automatic body responses to potentially harmful stimuli. Reflexes are important for the survival of organisms. The pathway of a reflex bypasses the brain.

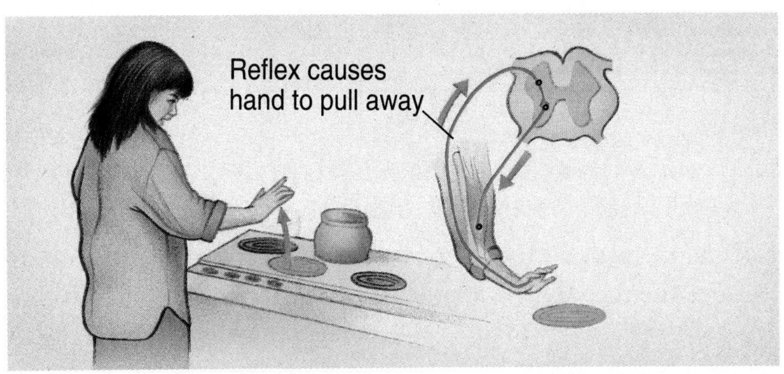

Chapter Review

USING KEY SCIENCE TERMS

brainstem
cerebellum
cerebrum
neuron
reflex
spinal cord
synapse

Using the list above, replace the underlined words with the correct key science term.

1. The <u>largest part of the brain</u> is active when you are reading this sentence.
2. The axon of one neuron is separated from the dendrites of another neuron by a <u>gap</u>.
3. Bundles of <u>the functional units of the nervous system</u> are called nerves.
4. The <u>part of the brain that controls breathing, digestion, and your heartbeat</u>, links the brain and the spinal cord.
5. <u>An automatic body response to a potentially harmful stimulus</u> can help you avoid serious injury.
6. You are able to perform complex activities because the motor center of your cerebrum receives help from <u>another part of your brain</u>, which coordinates muscle activity.

UNDERSTANDING IDEAS

Answer the following questions.

1. When you taste something, what type of nerve carries the impulse to the brain?
2. If neurons don't touch each other, how does the impulse continue on its course?
3. You hear a doorbell ring, and you get up to answer the door. In this situation, what was the stimulus? What was the response?
4. Compare your central nervous system to a centralized telephone. Which part acts like the operator?
5. What structures in the nervous system respond to different forms of energy?
6. Discuss the role of the cerebellum for performing activities involving many skeletal muscles all working at the same time.
7. Involuntary body activities are controlled by what part of the brain?

CRITICAL THINKING

Use your understanding of the concepts developed in the chapter to answer each of the following questions.

1. Suggest a reason why it is advantageous to have more receptors in the skin of your hands than in the skin of your feet.
2. Suggest a reason why some people have to learn how to speak again after serious brain injury.
3. Why do you think dogs and cats have larger centers in their brains for detecting odors than humans have?
4. Explain why an injury to the back of the head might affect the way you walk.
5. Can you hypothesize why it is sometimes difficult to smell things when you have a stuffy nose?

6. The blinking reflex is a reflex that occurs when someone flashes an object in front of your eyes without you expecting it. Suggest an explanation for the blinking reflex.
7. Is there an advantage to having pain receptors in your skin and throughout your body? Why or why not?
8. Look at the illustration of the nervous system in the figure. Which body parts might be affected if the spinal cord were injured at the area marked "X"—the arm muscles or the leg muscles?

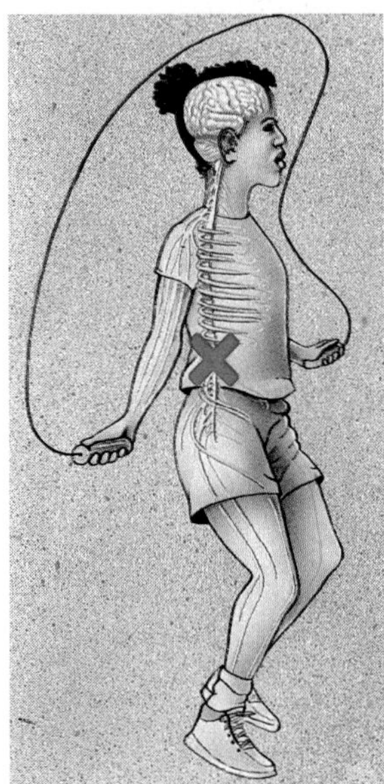

PROBLEM SOLVING

Read the following problem and discuss your answers in a brief paragraph.

During your dog's annual visit to the veterinarian's office, the doctor checks your pet's nervous system by testing a reflex that makes the dog's tail wag. During the test, the doctor finds that your dog's tail doesn't wag after the proper stimulus is given. Using your knowledge of the nervous system and skeletal muscles, suggest two reasons why your dog's tail-wagging reflex may not have worked.

CONNECTING IDEAS

Discuss each of the following in a brief paragraph.

1. What part of the brain is responsible for the pressure of blood as it moves through the circulatory system?

2. Impulses to activate skeletal muscles are carried by what kinds of nerves? Where do these impulses originate?

3. SCIENCE AND SOCIETY Describe what researchers believe happens in the brain cells of patients showing early symptoms of Alzheimer's disease.

4. TECHNOLOGY CONNECTION Compare a PET scan to a normal X ray. How does PET technology allow researchers to learn more about the brain?

5. SOCIOLOGY CONNECTION Use knowledge from this chapter to explain why a baby may become excited upon seeing its mother's face.

LOOKING BACK

UNIT 2 ENERGY AT WORK

CONTENTS

Chapter 4 Work and Energy
Chapter 5 Machines
Chapter 6 Thermal Energy
Chapter 7 Moving the Body Machine
Chapter 8 Controlling the Body Machine

UNIT FOCUS

In this unit, you learned that work is done on an object when force is applied and the object is moved in the direction of the force. You also learned that the Law of Conservation of Energy means that work can only be done if energy is put into a system. Systems such as machines or the bones and muscles of your body convert energy into work. Energy for machines may come from various sources, while your body relies on energy from food.

Try the exercises and activity that follow—they will challenge you to use and apply some of the ideas you learned in this unit.

CONNECTING IDEAS

1. As you ride your bike, an animal darts in front of you. You apply the brakes and come to a stop. Explain how your nerves and muscles acted, how machines in your body and bike stopped the bike, and where the bike's energy went.
2. An inventor claims that she can make a car more efficient by using the waste heat from the exhaust pipe. In fact, she says the modified car will be twice as efficient as the original car. Is this possible? Explain.

EXPLORING FURTHER

Build a model of your forearm using wood for the bones, a metal hinge for the joint, and cords for muscles. What is the mechanical advantage of your model? How does it compare to that of your arm?

LOOKING AHEAD

UNIT 3 EARTH MATERIALS AND RESOURCES

CONTENTS

Chapter 9 Discovering Elements
Chapter 10 Minerals and Their Uses
Chapter 11 The Rock Cycle
Chapter 12 The Ocean Floor and Shore Zones
Chapter 13 Energy Resources

UNIT FOCUS

In Unit 2, you learned how the human body works as a machine. You compared your arm to a lever as it used energy to perform work. As you study Unit 3, you will learn about Earth's materials and how some of these materials, such as coal and natural gas, can be used to produce energy that is used in machines such as stoves, tape players, and projectors to do work.

TRY IT

In this unit, you are going to learn about different kinds of materials. You use materials all the time without even thinking about where they come from or what they are made of. From your desk to your chair to the paper and ink in this book, you use materials all the time. What are some characteristics of common objects in your classroom? Observe a group of objects provided by your teacher. Answer the following questions about each object. Some questions may ask about things you haven't studied yet. Do the best you can to answer the questions about each object. Are the materials metal or nonmetal? What is the original or raw material from which the object was made? What properties of the raw material made it the best to use in the object? After you have finished this unit, you may want to review these questions again to see if you would answer them differently.

DID YOU EVER WONDER . . .

Why pennies are made of copper?

What happens to plants and animals after they die?

How video games can be so small?

You'll find the answers to these questions as you read this chapter.

Chapter 9

Discovering Elements

Omar collects model cars, Yolanda collects glass bottles, and Luis collects coins. What do you collect?

Whether buttons or baseball cards, the objects in your collection are made up of elements, or a combination of elements. The coins pictured in the photograph, for example, are made up of gold and silver. Luis may have a similar coin, but more likely he has coins containing a combination of elements, such as copper, zinc, and nickel. Omar's model cars and Yolanda's glass bottles also are made up of combinations of elements.

Everything around you, in fact, everything in the known universe is made of elements. The oceans and the forests, automobiles and clouds, stars and planets, even your body and the air you breathe—all are composed of fewer than 100 different elements. What are these elements and what combinations do they form? After completing this chapter, you'll think the answer to that question is elementary!

EXPLORE!

What elements are in your environment?

With your partner, make a list of as many elements as you can think of that are found in your body—in your muscles, bones, teeth, and blood. Where else in your environment are these elements found? What other elements exist in your environment?

9-1 Discovering Metals

OBJECTIVES

In this section, you will

- describe the physical properties of a typical metal;
- compare and contrast the terms *malleable* and *ductile*;
- explain how the properties of metals determine their uses.

KEY SCIENCE TERMS

metals
malleable
ductile
coinage metal

ELEMENTS AND SYMBOLS

As you have learned, elements are the simplest form of matter, the building blocks of the universe. An element can't be broken down into anything simpler. Every other form of matter is either a compound, produced when elements combine, or a mixture.

Sometimes, when we want to discuss these elements we use a kind of shorthand. You're already familiar with some shorthand notations. For instance, we use St. to stand for the word street, hr to stand for the word hour, or lb to stand for the word pound. Scientists use a similar type of shorthand to stand for elements. A symbol is an abbreviation which stands for an element. For example, the letter H stands for the element hydrogen. Symbols consist of either one capital letter or one capital and one or two small letters. Ca stands for calcium and Cl stands for chlorine. As you can see, two-letter symbols are not always the first two letters of the element. Sometimes, the symbol doesn't begin with the same letter as the element—Na stands for sodium while Fe stands for iron. Perhaps you are already familiar with some common symbols for abundant elements.

EXPLORE!

What element is it?

Match the symbols listed with the element you think they stand for.

Oxygen	Copper	Hg	Zn
Zinc	Aluminum	Al	Au
Nitrogen	Carbon	Ca	N
Gold	Mercury	C	Cu
Magnesium	Calcium	O	Mg

Can you think of a reason why symbols aren't always just the first letter of an element name?

As you picture the elements in the Explore, you may notice that some are solids, some are gases, and one, mercury, is a liquid at room temperature. Could you use any other properties to place them into groups?

EXPLORE!

How can you identify a metal?

Examine the element samples provided by your teacher. Separate them into two or more groups by using their properties. What properties did you choose? Did other students choose the same properties? In which group would you place gold? Explain.

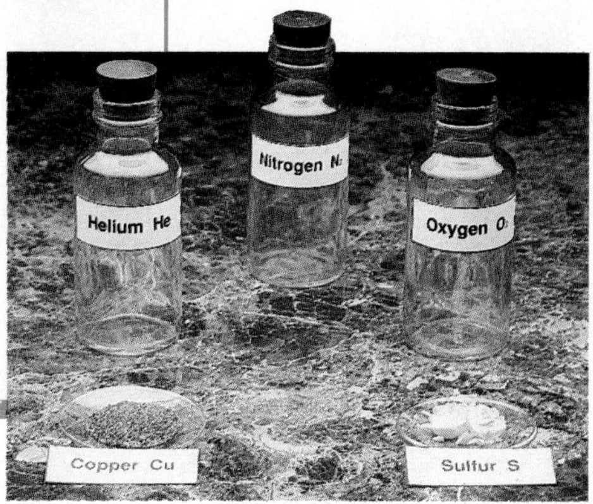

PROPERTIES OF METALS

There are several ways you might have grouped your elements in the Explore. Although all elements are important, one of the most important groups of elements is **metals**. Picture a metal. What does it look like? How do you know that it's a metal? Is it shiny and hard? In fact, many metals are hard and shiny solids. But some, like lead, are dull and soft enough to shape easily. One metal, mercury, is a shiny liquid.

Look at Figure 9-1. Which object has the greatest shine or sheen? The shine or sheen of an object is called luster. Luster is a measure of the way an object reflects light. Luster is one of several properties that many metals have in common. Silver is so lustrous that it can be used as a backing for mirrors. A new gold chain has a lot more luster than an iron pipe.

In Figure 9-1, some of the elements have been shaped into common objects, like a penny or a piece of foil. When an element can be hammered or pressed into various shapes without breaking, we say that it is **malleable**. Malleability is a property of most metals. What would happen if you tried to roll carbon or coal, which is made up of the element carbon, into a sheet?

FIGURE 9-1. These objects are all made of metals. What properties do they have in common?

Some metals are more malleable than others. Archaeologists and treasure hunters often find jewelry and other decorative pieces made of gold, silver, and copper. Early crafts people were able to work with these metals because of their malleability. The capitol dome shown in Figure 9-2 is covered with gold. The gold was hammered into sheets thinner than paper. These thin gold sheets, called gold leaf, are often used to decorate picture frames or sculpture.

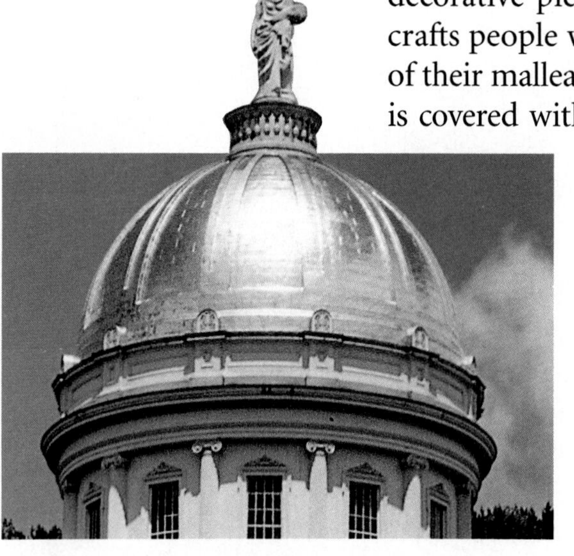

FIGURE 9-2. The dome of this building is covered with gold leaf.

In Figure 9-1, you can see that some metals have not only been shaped, they've been stretched as well. This is how copper and iron wire can be formed from chunks of metal. These two metals are ductile. A **ductile** metal can be pulled into a wire without breaking. For example, an ounce of gold can be pulled into a wire that is more than 75 kilometers long.

Many metals are good conductors of electricity. Metals that are both ductile and conduct electricity can be used in electrical devices. Which object in Figure 9-1 demonstrates the ductility of copper? Many metals are good conductors of thermal energy. Which object demonstrates copper's ability to conduct heat? What other metals are used to make cooking pans?

Not all metals are equally malleable or ductile, nor do they all conduct electricity or heat as well as copper, iron, or aluminum. Metals differ in other properties as well. Gold is yellow, iron is a grayish-silver, and copper is a reddish-orange, indicating that color is a characteristic property of metals. As you can see from Figure 9-3, there are metals, such as sodium and potassium, soft enough to be cut with a knife!

FIGURE 9-3. Freshly cut sodium is shiny, but it quickly reacts with oxygen in the air to become dull.

Metals such as gold, silver, and copper react less readily and can be found in their natural state in Earth, while other metals, such as sodium and calcium, immediately form compounds when they come in contact with air or water. Sodium and calcium combine so easily with other substances that they are never found as uncombined elements in nature.

When metals form compounds, those compounds often dissolve in water. Let's see if we can still identify those elements even though their appearance has changed.

I N V E S T I G A T E !

9-1 IDENTIFYING METALS

Centuries ago, the Chinese discovered what happens when a substance containing a metal is heated to a high temperature. The Chinese put this discovery to a use we still find exciting today. In this activity, you will discover this novel property of solutions that contain certain metals.

PROBLEM:

How can we identify the presence of certain metals in a solution?

MATERIALS

7 test tubes and rack
7 metal salt solutions
evaporating dish
wooden splints
wire gauze
matches

PROCEDURE

1. Copy the data table.
2. Label each test tube with a number of a metal solution.
3. Pour approximately 1 thumbnail full of each test solution into the correctly numbered test tube.
4. **Observe** the physical properties of each solution.
5. Using tweezers, place in an evaporating dish a piece of splint that your teacher has soaked in Solution 1 and then dried.
6. Place the evaporating dish on the wire gauze.
7. Ignite the splint with another full-length splint.
8. **Observe** and record your observations.
9. Clean the dish as instructed, disposing of the splint in the proper container.
10. Repeat Steps 5 through 9 for each of the other solutions.

DATA AND OBSERVATIONS

TEST	METALS	RESULT WHEN HEATED
1	Lithium	
2	Calcium	
3	Potassium	
4	Copper	
5	Strontium	
6	Sodium	
7	Barium	

ANALYZE

1. What did you **observe** when you heated each of the different solutions?

CONCLUDE AND APPLY

2. Can you **infer** how the Chinese used this property of metals?
3. If you were given an unknown metal compound solution, how could you identify the metal present?
4. **Going Further**: **Predict** what would happen if your test solution were a mixture of the compounds of two metals. Could each metal be identified?

FIGURE 9-4. What metallic compounds produce these spectacular colors?

In the Investigate, you weren't working with the metal elements themselves. Instead, you were working with solutions that contained compounds of the metals dissolved in water. As you recall, a solution is a homogeneous mixture and is so well blended that it is the same throughout. You saw that when each metal compound is heated, it produces a different, characteristic color. The color can then be used to identify the element. Use the results of the Investigate to decide which metals the fireworks in Figure 9-4 might contain.

How many different roles do metals play in your life? You might begin with what you're wearing, your room, how you got to school, and what you eat. Think of the properties of metals described in this section. What common objects are lustrous, malleable, or ductile? You know from the Investigate that not all substances containing metals look like metals. Your body contains metals. Can you guess where these metals might be found? Where else are metals found?

From your study of Earth science, you know which rocks are the most abundant on Earth. Again, there are particular chemical tests, much like the burning splint test you did with metals in the Investigate, that determine which elements are in the rocks and how much of the element is contained in the rock. From these types of experiments, researchers can make statements such as, "Calcium is the fifth most abundant element in Earth's crust," or "Iron is the second most abundant element in Earth's core."

METALS IN YOUR BODY

It may seem strange to think that you have metal in your body. Well, maybe in a tooth filling, but in your bones? Or blood?

You've probably heard about how important it is to have plenty of dairy products and green vegetables in your diet. What is the element that is always mentioned as being in milk, yogurt, and cheese? Right! It's calcium.

Most of the calcium in your body is in the compound calcium carbonate. Calcium carbonate makes your bones and teeth strong and healthy. It's found in animal skeletons and shells and in marble and limestone. Calcium is the fifth most common element in Earth's crust.

Calcium, along with sodium and potassium, is essential for the proper working of the nervous system. The concentration of these elements as they move in and out of your nerve cells determines what signals are transmitted from one nerve cell to another. We get sodium from foods that contain sodium chloride, or table salt. Bananas, oranges, and potatoes are good sources of potassium.

Iron is another metal important to the proper functioning of your body. A small amount of iron is contained in hemoglobin, a substance in red blood cells. When the iron in hemoglobin combines with oxygen, blood turns from dark red to very bright red. It is this ability of iron to combine with oxygen that makes it important. The iron in your blood picks up oxygen in your lungs and carries it to the rest of your body. When you don't have

DID YOU KNOW?

At today's prices, if the human body were reduced to its elements, it would be worth about \$3.88.

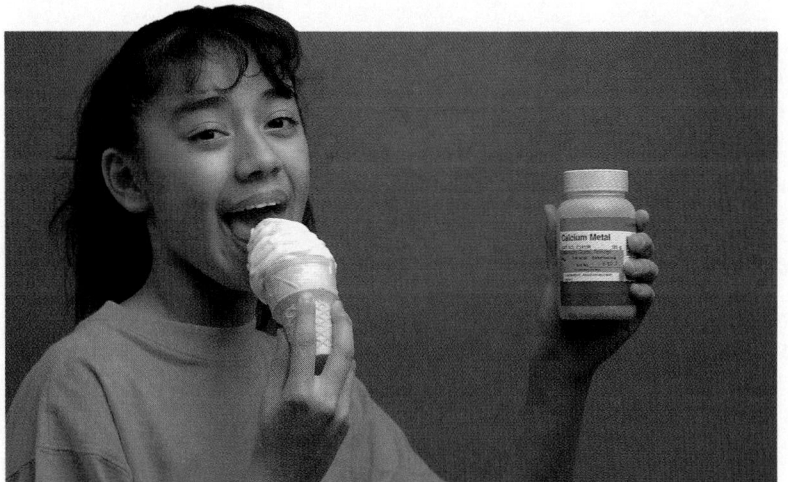

FIGURE 9-5. Find the calcium in this picture.

FIGURE 9-6. "What do you mean I need more iron in my diet?!"

enough iron, you are said to be anemic. Anemia makes people weak and tired because they don't get enough oxygen in their muscle tissue. Foods such as beans, peas, egg yolks, and, yes, liver and prunes are good sources of iron.

Another element important to your health is magnesium. Magnesium is found in very small amounts in the blood, muscles, and stomach juices.

Perhaps the most important use of magnesium in your life isn't in your body. Magnesium is found in the compound chlorophyll. You may recall that chlorophyll is the green pigment found in plants that allows them to make food. During this process, plants give off oxygen. Without magnesium, plants could not produce food for their survival. If the plants could not survive, they would no longer provide oxygen for our survival.

Magnesium burns very quickly and brightly. It is often used in photographic flashbulbs and fireworks displays. Magnesium's lightness and strength have made it popular for use in aircraft and sports equipment as well.

FIGURE 9-7. Magnesium has many uses.

METALS DANGEROUS TO YOUR HEALTH

Not all metals are beneficial for your body. Lead and mercury are both metals that can be poisonous to living things. Lead and mercury, called heavy metals, can take the place of iron in your red blood cells. Since they don't have the same ability to carry oxygen through your system as iron does, they can produce some of the same symptoms as anemia.

Lead is a very soft, dark gray metal that is quite dense. It was once used widely in paints and gasoline. Although lead has been removed from house paint available today, lead paint still poses a problem. Children playing with or eating flaking paint are very likely eating lead. These children often have problems in growing normally. In some cases, they have a great deal of difficulty learning. In ancient Rome, the water pipes were made of lead. Some historians believe that many Romans died from lead poisoning, since the lead contaminated the water as it flowed through the pipes. In fact, the name *plumber* comes from the Latin word for lead, *plumbum*. The symbol for lead is Pb.

Mercury is different from other metals in that it is a liquid at room temperature. Once called *quicksilver*, it is used in some thermostats, batteries, and thermometers. Many people think it's fun to play with the mercury from a broken thermometer, but mercury is poisonous. It can be inhaled or absorbed through the skin and collect in the body. People can become very ill, or even die, from eating fish that have been contaminated with mercury.

DID YOU KNOW?

At one time, workers who made felt hats treated them with mercury and mercury-containing materials to preserve the felt. Many of these people later went insane because of mercury poisoning. That's where the expression *mad as a hatter* came from.

COINAGE METALS

For centuries, three metals have been widely used as coins. Study Figure 9-8. Can you name these metals? If you said copper, silver, and gold, you're right. Together, these are called **coinage metals**. As mentioned earlier, these metals are often uncombined in nature and can be mined. They are also malleable and ductile. These metals are easily shaped and stamped into

FIGURE 9-8. Copper, silver, and gold are used in many coins.

SKILLBUILDER

MAKING AND INTERPRETING TABLES
Make a table listing six of the metals described in this section. Include column headings for four properties and a heading for uses of each metal. If you need help, refer to the **Skill Handbook** on page 679.

coins. The coins have a denomination imprinted on them, but the actual value may be different. By international agreement the value of gold and silver is determined by the amount of these metals available in the marketplace.

FIND OUT!

What are the current prices of silver and gold?

The price of gold and silver changes often, sometimes by the day or week. Find the current price of silver and gold by looking in the business section of a newspaper. Write down the date and the current price. Be careful to note whether the price is by the pound or by the ounce. Check again every day for a week.

Conclude and Apply

1. How much did the price change?
2. The weight of five quarters is about one ounce. Would it make sense to make quarters out of silver at the current cost of silver?

As you saw in the Find Out, silver and gold prices can vary a lot from day to day. The coins that you use today do not contain silver or gold. Silver and gold are so valuable that coins are now made from copper, nickel, and zinc. Gold and silver are saved for jewelry, ornaments, medical implants, and electronic circuits.

In addition, silver is used as a backing for mirrors, and in photographic film. Silver chloride or silver bromide is used in photographic film and turns dark when exposed to light. That's why film turns dark when it is exposed.

FIGURE 9-9. Iron, nickel, and cobalt are three metals with magnetic properties.

Although there is no silver in your silver money, there is nickel inside the nickel coin you may have in your pocket right now. Nickels are actually 25 percent nickel and 75 percent copper.

Nickel is a metal that can be magnetized. Iron and

cobalt are the only other abundant metals that have this property. Iron by far has the best magnetic properties.

Copper has frequently been mentioned in this chapter. Because of its low cost, its malleability, and its resistance to change, copper is used as a base for many coins. Sometimes it is mixed with other metals, other times it is covered with a thin layer of a more expensive metal. You can see this *sandwich* effect if you look at the edge of some dimes and quarters.

DID YOU KNOW?

In the United States, 70 percent of all metals used are discarded after a single use.

ALUMINUM—JACK OF ALL TRADES

The most common metal in Earth's crust is aluminum. Aluminum is strong, light, and isn't easily affected by oxygen or other substances that can destroy many metals. Aluminum is in soft drink cans, in the foil wrap in your kitchen, and in the siding you may have on your house. Aluminum compounds are used in medicines, deodorants, pigments, and dyes.

Because of our many uses of aluminum, we could face a worldwide shortage. Fortunately, aluminum can be recycled, but that depends on our willingness to save aluminum articles that we would once have thrown away.

Look around you. How many of the objects that you can see right now contain metals? They are in the things that you eat, touch, ride in, and wear. Think about how different your life would be without metals.

FIGURE 9-10. Recycling aluminum cans can help prevent an aluminum shortage.

Check Your Understanding

1. Given a substance, how would you test it to see if it is a metal?
2. Name some elements that are both malleable and ductile.
3. Why would silver be a good coinage metal, while calcium would not?
4. **APPLY:** Early civilizations used salt, glass, and sea shells as coins or money. Why do you think metals have replaced these materials as coins?

9-2 Discovering Nonmetals

OBJECTIVES

In this section, you will

- describe the physical properties of a nonmetal;
- compare and contrast metals and nonmetals;
- relate the properties of nonmetals to their uses.

KEY SCIENCE TERMS

nonmetal

PROPERTIES OF NONMETALS

In the last section, you grouped several elements together. These elements, metals, share properties such as luster, malleability, ductility, and conductivity. But what about the elements that do not have those properties? How can they be grouped together?

EXPLORE!

How can you identify nonmetals?

You have seen many different metals and can describe their properties. Not all elements, however, are metals. Some elements that are not metals are shown in the photo. What properties might you use to describe the elements that are not metals? What other elements can you think of that are not metals? What, if anything, do they have in common?

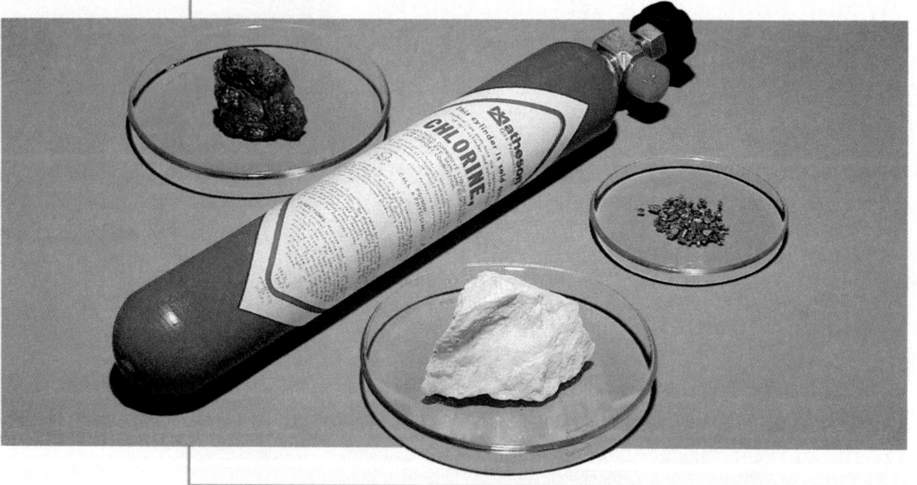

These elements, called **nonmetals**, are dull, rather than lustrous; brittle, rather than malleable and ductile. They are poor conductors of heat and electricity. Many are gases. You might say that the properties of nonmetals are just the opposite of metals.

Although there are many more metals than nonmetals, most living material is composed of nonmetallic compounds. Most of your body is made up of elements called nonmetals. In Figure 9-11, identify the elements that were not mentioned in the section on metals and add them together. What percent of your body is made of nonmetals?

The most common and important nonmetals are carbon, hydrogen, oxygen, nitrogen, sulfur, fluorine, and chlorine. Except for carbon and sulfur, these common nonmetals are gases. Just as metals have properties you could test for, these gases have properties you can test for.

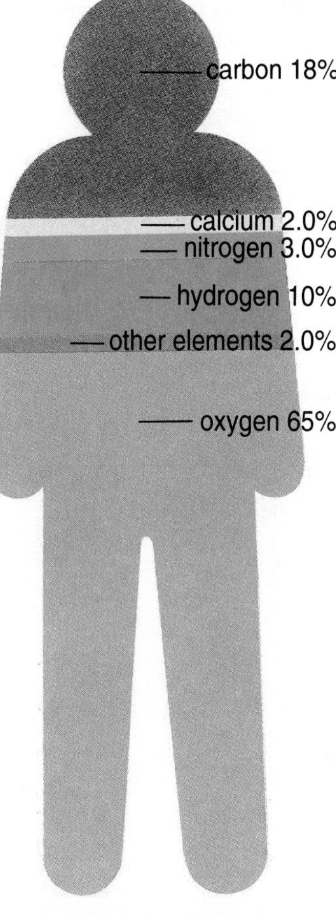

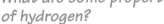

FIGURE 9-11. What percentage of the human body is composed of nonmetals?

EXPLORE!

What are some properties of hydrogen?

Drop a small piece of sanded magnesium ribbon into a test tube containing about an inch of white vinegar. Record what you observe. When the reaction is going well, put a cork stopper over the top of the tube. After a few moments, hold the tube at a slant, making sure you aren't pointing it at anyone. Just as you remove the cork, bring a lighted splint to the mouth of the tube.

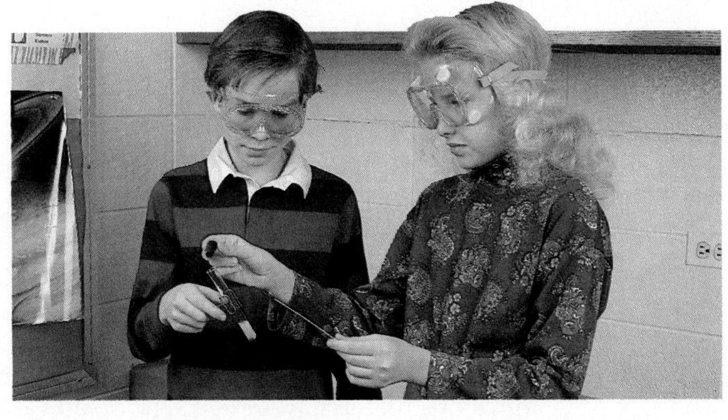

The material formed during the reaction in the Explore did not have a specific volume nor a specific shape. From your earlier studies you recognize this material as a gas. The gas was hydrogen. Based on your observations, what are three properties of hydrogen? You probably noticed that it is a colorless, odorless gas that explodes when lit.

FIGURE 9-12. Hydrogen was used to fill the *Hindenburg* so it would float in air.

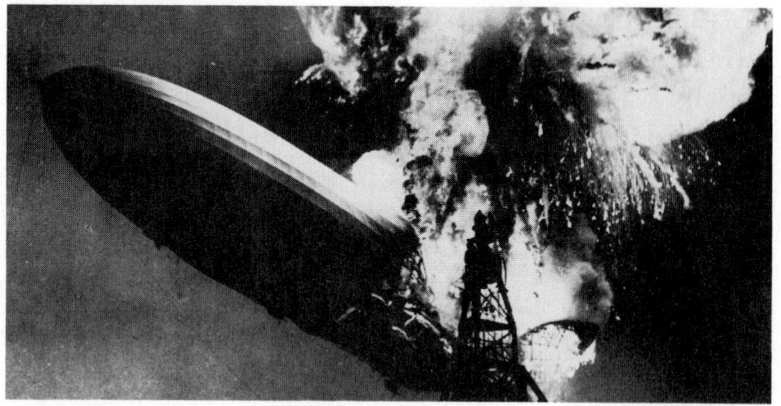

Hydrogen is much less dense than air, so balloons filled with hydrogen float. At one time, hydrogen was used to fill aircraft similar to the Goodyear blimps. One of these aircraft, the *Hindenburg*, exploded as it was approaching its New Jersey landing site in 1937. Can you imagine an explosion thousands of times larger than the test tube explosion you experienced?

Nearly all the stars we see are made entirely of hydrogen. Most of the hydrogen on Earth is found in the compound water. Hydrogen can also combine with nitrogen, carbon, or oxygen to form most of the compounds found in living things.

Each breath you take is about 80 percent nitrogen. Almost 80 percent of Earth's atmosphere is nitrogen. However, your body can't use nitrogen directly, but uses

How do we know?

What's the universe made of?

How do researchers know that the universe is 99 percent hydrogen? The process of spectroscopy is the chemist's most important tool in identifying what kind of material—and how much of a material—is contained in a sample. You may recall that using spectroscopy is a little like looking at a rainbow. In a rainbow, the colors appear because the light is affected as it passes through the rain drops. In spectroscopy, a researcher can look at light given off by a sample substance. The colored bands of light the substance produces can be matched to the colored bands given off by identified substances. In this way, the researchers can tell what elements are in a sample. The intensity of the colored bands helps researchers know how much of a material is present. The quantity of material present determines how strong the bands appear.

Researchers using spectroscopy and telescopes have been able to determine that our sun is made of hydrogen and that nearly all the stars are made of hydrogen. Earth is a very small part of the universe so that it is with confidence that researchers say hydrogen is the most abundant element in the universe.

compounds of nitrogen. Bacteria and plants play a key role in producing nitrogen your body can use. First, bacteria change the nitrogen in the soil into nitrogen compounds. Then plants take in these compounds and change them to proteins that your body can use. This process is called the nitrogen cycle, which you have studied previously.

FIGURE 9-13. Nitrogen-fixing bacteria are found in nodules on the roots of certain plants.

Although it supports life, nitrogen can produce problems in your environment. Nitrogen compounds from car and truck exhausts react with water in the air to form nitric acid. This contributes to acid rain, which corrodes metal and poisons soil and water in which living organisms exist.

Although, like hydrogen, nitrogen itself is colorless and odorless, nitrogen and hydrogen together form a strong-smelling compound, ammonia. Ammonia is found in many household cleaners. Nitrogen makes up a major portion of fertilizers because it promotes plant growth.

Carbon is found in all things that are or were living. When plants and animals die, they decompose. As layers of dirt are deposited on top of them, the pressure from the weight of the layers produces other forms of carbon, such as coal and petroleum. These fuels are still the basic form of energy used in our society.

What other nonmetal is absolutely necessary for you to survive? That's right. Oxygen. Let's investigate some of the properties of this element.

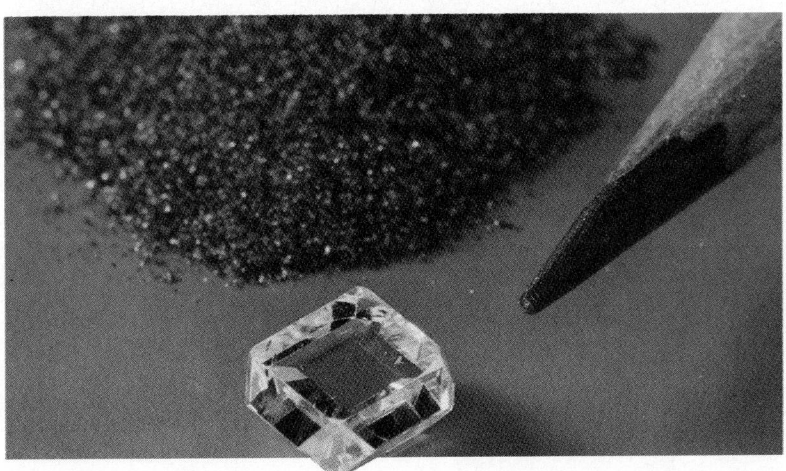

FIGURE 9-14. Diamonds and pencil lead are forms of the element carbon.

I N V E S T I G A T E !

9-2 PREPARING AND OBSERVING OXYGEN

Oxygen makes up about 20 percent of air. Animals and humans need it for respiration and plants release it as they produce food during photosynthesis. In this Investigate, you'll observe some of the important properties of this element.

PROBLEM

What are some of the properties of oxygen?

MATERIALS  

test tube
test-tube holder
wooden splint
matches
0.5 g cobalt chloride
balance
cork stopper
graduated cylinder
liquid laundry bleach
(5% sodium hypochlorite)

PROCEDURE

1. **Measure** 20 mL of bleach with the graduated cylinder and pour it into the test tube.
2. **Measure** 0.5 g of cobalt chloride on the balance.
3. Add the cobalt chloride to the test tube and **observe**. Record your observations.
4. Place the cork stopper loosely over the opening of the tube.
5. Tilt the tube at a 45° angle. **CAUTION**: *Do not point at anyone. Be sure you are holding the tube with tongs as shown in the picture.* Remove the stopper. Have your partner light a splint then blow it out. Then your partner should carefully lower the glowing splint into the mouth of the tube. **Observe** and record your observations.

ANALYZE

1. How did you **infer** that a gas was being formed in the test tube?
2. What happened when the glowing splint was placed in the tube?

CONCLUDE AND APPLY

3. What properties of oxygen did you **observe?**
4. **Compare and contrast** the properties of oxygen with those of hydrogen.
5. Why do you think you used a glowing splint rather than a lit one as you did for hydrogen? What property of oxygen does this demonstrate?
6. **Going Further**: Like cobalt chloride, sunlight can also release oxygen from bleach. How are bleach containers designed to stop this?

Oxygen is another colorless, odorless gas. In the Investigate, you used a glowing splint rather than a lit one to test the gas. The splint relit, didn't it? How do you make the fire burn more brightly? You fan it, don't you? That circulates more oxygen around the coals. Putting the glowing splint in the oxygen serves the same purpose. Burning takes place in the presence of oxygen, so the more oxygen present, the better the burning.

Without oxygen, you wouldn't be alive. Simple, but true. The oxygen that you inhale in every breath is carried throughout your body by your blood. Unlike nitrogen, your body uses oxygen in its elemental form. Just as coal or paper uses oxygen from the air to burn, so your body burns the foods you eat and the fats and carbohydrates you have stored. It does this by slowly combining these foods with oxygen from the blood. In this way, digestion provides you with the energy you need to live.

Oxygen is the other element present in water. Isn't it interesting that one element that burns explosively (hydrogen) and another that allows things to burn (oxygen) can combine into something that puts out fires—water?

You may have heard something about a hole in Earth's ozone layer. What is ozone? It's our old friend oxygen, but in a different form. Ozone is formed when radiation from the sun strikes oxygen high in our atmosphere. Ozone is necessary because it shields us from many harmful types of radiation from space. These types of radiation can cause sunburn and skin cancers. The ozone layer can be damaged by the use of some refrigerants and aerosol sprays. Ozone is just as necessary for your survival on Earth as the form of oxygen you breathe.

While ozone acts as a protective screen high in the atmosphere, it is undesirable closer to Earth. Ozone is produced near Earth by high-voltage generators and during electrical storms. It is one of the substances in smog. Ozone damages the leaves of plants and irritates the human respiratory system.

DID YOU KNOW?

Have you noticed the fire doors in your school? If there's a fire, these doors are used to close off one part of a building from another. Without fire doors, a fire could spread quickly because more oxygen would be available.

FIGURE 9-15. Why is Earth called the blue planet?

FIGURE 9-16. Elements such as bromine, chlorine and iodine have distinctive colors.

Two other nonmetals that shouldn't be inhaled are fluorine and chlorine. They have very strong odors. You may have had experience with this when you smelled chlorine from laundry bleach or swimming pool disinfectant.

In its pure form, chlorine is a poisonous, yellow gas. Because it reacts easily, it's usually found in compounds. There's one chlorine compound that you eat every day. Can you think of what it is? Remember our discussion of metals that are useful to the body? Yes, the compound is salt—sodium chloride.

In some areas, where there is a high concentration of bacteria in the water, chlorine may be added to the water to kill these microorganisms. Fluorine is also added to drinking water. Have you heard about fluoridated water? What does it do? A fluorine compound is added to water to slow tooth decay. It forms tough compounds with the enamel on the surface of your teeth, keeping cavity-causing bacteria from reaching the tooth. A fluorine compound is added to another common substance that you use every day. What is it?

THE NOBLE GASES

When they were first discovered, the gases helium, neon, argon, and xenon were thought to be the royalty among the elements. Like nobles who refuse to mingle with common folk, the noble gases rarely combine with other elements.

FIGURE 9-17. Sulfur is another nonmetal. Io, a moon of Jupiter (a) and areas around Mammoth Hot Springs in Yellowstone Park (b) have yellow sulfur deposits.

a

b

Figure 9-18 shows a display similar to those you may have seen in your neighborhood. Although these signs are usually called neon signs, they actually may contain any one or a combination of the noble gases. Each gas produces a different color as electricity passes through it, so a very colorful sign may contain all of the noble gases.

Life on Earth has developed around the elements that are present in the land, sea, and air—our environment. You've explored the properties of metals and nonmetals. Metals are the elements most often used for construction while nonmetals are the elements that make up most of your body's compounds. In the next section, you'll explore the properties of elements that are neither metals nor nonmetals.

INTERPRETING DATA

Use the information below to identify the noble gases used in Figure 9-18. If you need help, refer to the **Skill Handbook** on page 689.

Argon	purple
Helium	yellow
Neon	red
Xenon	blue

FIGURE 9-18. These colorful lights are filled with noble gases.

Check Your Understanding

1. If you were given a piece of the element sulfur, how would you test it to see if it is a metal or nonmetal?
2. Compare and contrast the properties and uses of metals and nonmetals.
3. Many of the nonmetals are gases. How does this observation relate to the most common uses of nonmetals?
4. **APPLY:** If you wanted to protect a historical document from damage, you might put it in an airtight case. Explain which of the nonmetals you would choose to replace the air in the case.

9-3 Understanding Metalloids

OBJECTIVES

In this section, you will

- distinguish among metals, nonmetals, and metalloids;
- relate the unique properties of metalloids to their uses.

KEY SCIENCE TERMS

metalloids

PROPERTIES OF METALLOIDS

What would you call something that was part human and part alien? You'd probably refer to this being as a humanoid, since it has some human characteristics, but is not human. In the same way, what would you call an element that had some characteristics of metals and some of nonmetals? Right! A metalloid. As a group, **metalloids** are elements that have properties of both metals and nonmetals. Although the properties of metalloids vary from one element to another, all metalloids show metallic luster. It is the one property all metalloids have in common. Although there are ten metalloids, we'll talk about the two most common ones.

BORON

Do you hate scrubbing away the dreaded bathtub ring? In hard water, soaps and laundry products combine with minerals in the water to produce soap scum. Borax, a

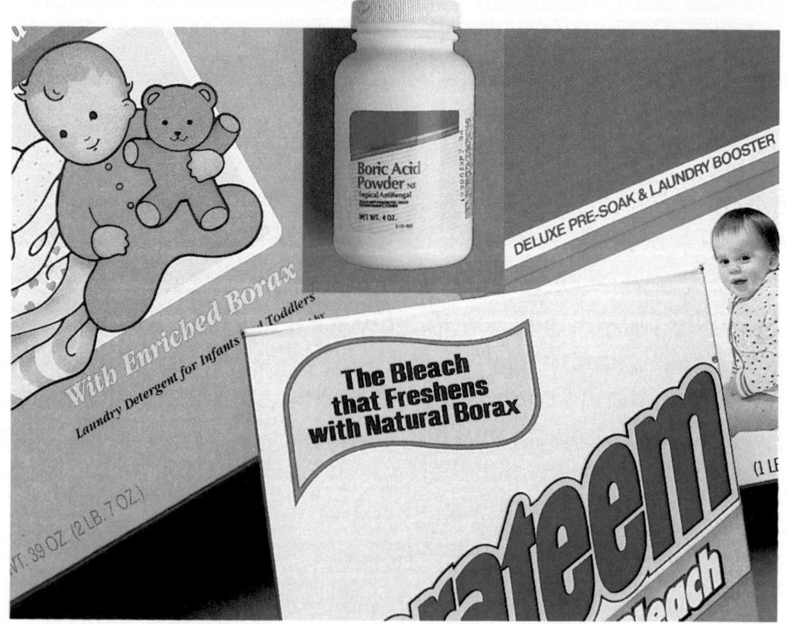

FIGURE 9-19. The metalloid boron is used in rocket fuels, laundry products, and as an antiseptic.

compound of boron, is added to laundry products to soften the water so that the minerals in the water don't interfere with dirt removal. If you add a little borax to your bath water, it helps prevent bathtub ring! Can you find the boron compounds on the laundry products in Figure 9-19?

Boron is also found in boric acid, a mild disinfectant that is sometimes used to treat infections. Boron is used in rocket fuels.

FIGURE 9-20. As beautiful as it is, opal is made of the same elements as common sand.

SILICON

Although the name may not be familiar, almost everyone has been in contact with silicon. Combined with oxygen, it is called sand. When sand is melted and allowed to cool, it forms glass. Ordinary glass is melted silicon dioxide with at least one metal, such as sodium, calcium, or aluminum added.

The element silicon is a perfect example of a metalloid. It comes in shiny gray chunks that look somewhat like a metal. But the chunks are rough and full of little holes—not smooth and dense like many metals. Silicon breaks apart easily, it is not malleable or ductile, but it does conduct an electric current.

If you have any kind of electronic or video game, a calculator, or even a watch that runs on batteries, you are probably carrying around some silicon right now. Because silicon doesn't conduct electricity as well as a metal, it is called a semiconductor. This semiconducting property of silicon makes it extremely important in the computer and electronics industry. The tiny electronic parts contained in the device in Figure 9-21 are based on silicon and other metalloids.

FIGURE 9-21. The use of semiconductors has allowed scientists to make electronic devices quite small.

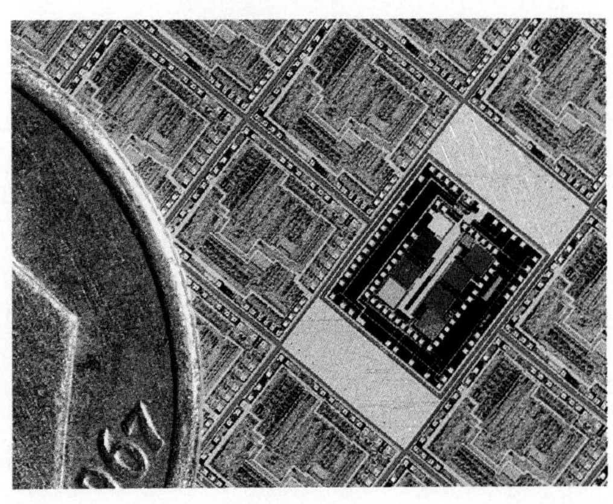

Metalloids include many useful elements used to manufacture items we rely on every day. But are metalloids, like metals and nonmetals, important to your health? The next Explore will help you answer that question.

EXPLORE!

What elements are in your mineral supplements? Compare the elements on this list with the label on one or more bottles of mineral tablets.

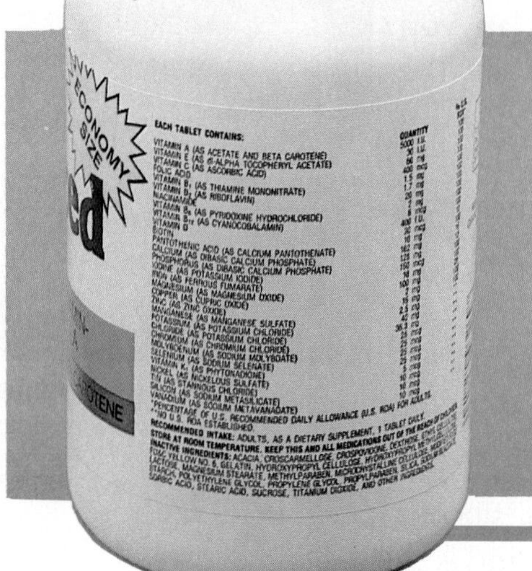

Aluminum
Calcium
Copper
Iron
Magnesium
Potassium
Selenium
Silicon
Zinc

How many can you find? Are they metals, nonmetals, or metalloids?

From the observations you made in the Explore, you saw that some metals, nonmetals, and metalloids are important to your health and well-being. But no matter what was listed on the label, the ingredients were all elements.

Everything within you and outside of you is composed of metals, nonmetals, or metalloids. No matter how complex a substance seems, it is some combination of these approximately 100 elements. From the gold, copper, and iron objects at the beginning of the chapter to the video games at the end, it's an elemental world.

Do you see now that, no matter what you or your friends might choose to collect, it's sure to be made of elements?

Check Your Understanding

1. Classify each of the following elements as 1) a metal, 2) a nonmetal, or 3) a metalloid:
   chlorine, carbon, calcium, boron, neon, sodium, aluminum.
2. In addition to metals, which group of elements is likely to contain elements that can conduct electricity?
3. **APPLY:** The basic component of most video games as well as most computers is the silicon chip. Why is this component called a chip rather than a wire?

EXPANDING YOUR VIEW

CONTENTS

A Closer Look
Thermostats 275

Earth Science Connection
Diamonds and Pencils 276

Science and Society
Recycling Aluminum 277

Consumer Connection
The Prices of Precious Metals 278

How it Works
Metalworking in Jewelry 279

Technology Connection
Neon Lights 280

A CLOSER LOOK

THERMOSTATS

The temperature in your home is probably regulated by a thermostat. Have you ever looked closely at one? A thermostat is a combination of a thermometer that measures the air temperature in a room and a switch that turns the heating and cooling systems on and off. A modern automated heating and cooling system uses a thermostat to provide safety and comfort and to conserve fuel.

A thermostat uses the expansion of metal to maintain the house at a constant temperature. The most common thermostat is a bimetal thermostat. This type uses two layers of metal held together. An increase in the temperature of the room causes each layer to expand at a different rate. The strip(metal layers)bends, closing a switch that controls the heating and cooling systems.

A clock thermostat allows you to change the temperature of the house automatically at specific times of the day. Gas ovens and heaters use a rod thermostat, as shown in the picture, to control the temperature. The control mechanism in this kind of thermostat is attached to a steel rod that sits inside a brass tube. When the temperature increases, the brass tube expands more than the steel rod. As the right temperature is reached, a spring closes the valve that controls the gas supply. When the temperature decreases, the brass tube contracts, pushing the rod back so that it opens the valve, allowing gas to flow.

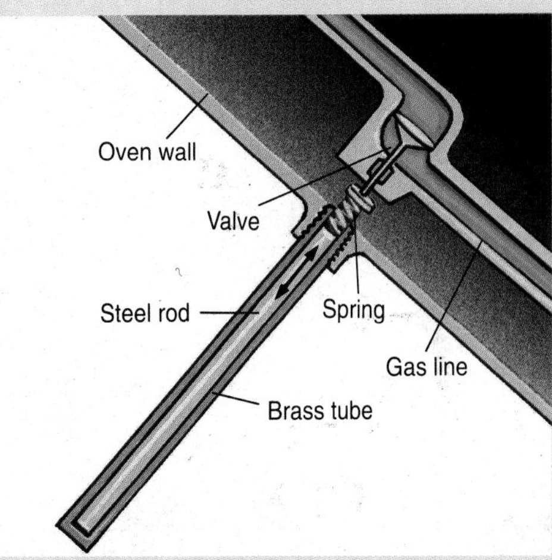

The thermostat is part of an automated system. An automatic furnace heats a home, but the temperature is kept in check by the thermostat. The thermostat measures temperature in the air and adjusts the heat by switching the furnace on and off.

YOU TRY IT!

Can you identify all the thermostats in your home? Remember, thermostats are switches that control heating or cooling. Make a list of the appliances and machines in the home that use thermostats.

EARTH SCIENCE CONNECTION

DIAMONDS AND PENCILS

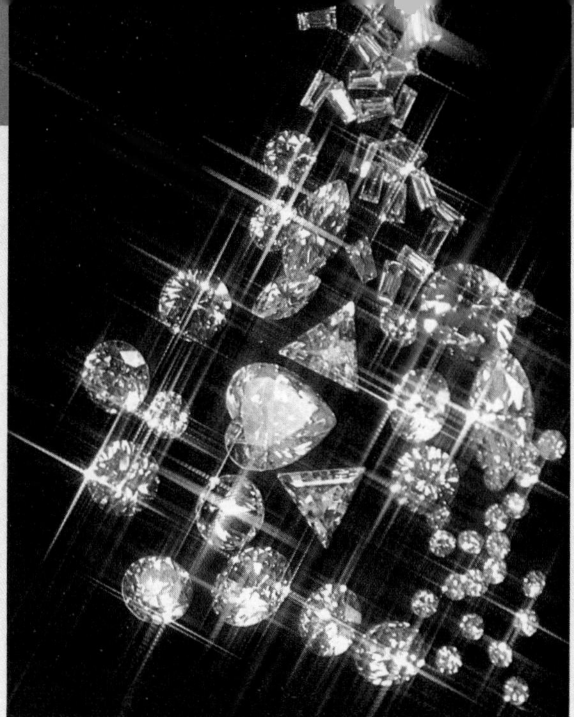

Did you know that a diamond and the graphite in your pencil have a lot in common? Diamonds are one of the hardest substances known. And yet, if exposed to temperatures exceeding 1830° F, a diamond will turn into graphite—the soft, black material found in a pencil. The pure natural form of carbon we know as a diamond is different from graphite only in the way the carbon formed. Although diamond and graphite are forms of carbon, their value and use in society are as different as two materials can be.

The rare, valuable, and much idolized diamond formed billions of years ago in dying volcanoes. When molten lava in the volcanoes became solid, heat and pressure changed the carbon present into diamond crystals. As Earth's crust and upper mantle moved, volcanic eruptions pushed the diamond deposits closer to the surface. Not all volcanoes contained carbon. For this reason, diamonds formed in only certain regions of the world.

The earliest diamond mine is believed to have been in central India. By the early 1700s, mines had been dug in Brazil. Over a century later, young children playing along the Orange River in South Africa discovered the first South African diamond. Today, most of the world's diamond production comes from Australia, Zaire, Botswana, and South Africa.

Only 20 percent of all diamonds mined are of gem quality. Of the five tons of diamonds mined yearly, only one ton can be used for jewelry. A diamond's value depends on its color and brilliance. The most valued diamonds give off light, are colorless or pale blue stones, and are relatively free of impurities. Rare diamonds can be red, blue, or green. The more common types of diamonds are orange, violet, yellow, and yellow green.

Diamonds are useful in industry. Their hard, solid state makes them resistant to chipping or cracking. For this reason, the better quality phonograph needles are tipped with diamond crystals. Because diamonds do not corrode or tarnish and are resistant to temperature changes, they are excellent as mechanical parts. For example, hospital and science laboratories use diamond bearings in their machines. Some of these machines rotate as many as 90,000 revolutions in a minute. But the hard, smooth surface of the diamond will not wear away.

YOU TRY IT!

Study a phonograph needle in class. Can you see that the needle is tipped with a diamond crystal? Test the hardness of the diamond by scratching it across an old glass bottle. Can you see why diamonds are very useful in industry?

SCIENCE AND SOCIETY

RECYCLING ALUMINUM

Did you know that the energy saved from recycling one aluminum can could keep a television running for three hours? It requires only five percent of the energy needed to mine aluminum to recycle it.

Aluminum is found in the form of bauxite. Although bauxite is still plentiful, easily mined deposits will disappear one day if we do not recycle the aluminum we use.

World production of aluminum in 1990 exceeded a total of 17 million metric tons. This extremely lightweight and malleable metal is an excellent conductor and has proved useful in industry, particularly when substituted for heavier, more costly materials.

Aluminum is used in making many cooking utensils. Heat spreads more evenly in aluminum pans, unlike pans made from other metals. Aluminum foil is used in roofing and insulating homes. Coating space suits with aluminum protects astronauts from the sun's dangerous rays because the rays tend to bounce off the aluminum.

The packaging industry uses about 30 percent of the total United States production of aluminum. Most of that is used for soft drink cans. More than 85 billion cans are produced yearly. These cans, like other aluminum products, are not biodegradable. Unlike iron, aluminum doesn't rust and break down. Once aluminum is exposed to air, it combines with the oxygen and forms a thin coat over the metal, protecting it from further change.

When aluminum is used and thrown away, it becomes solid waste. Solid waste includes all discarded products that biodegrade slowly or not at all. All materials in aluminum products can be used and reused.

Like other kinds of industrial waste materials, aluminum can also be reused in the manufacturing of new products. Recycling industrial materials such as aluminum requires separating it from other garbage before it finds its way into a stream, a waterway, or a landfill. In an attempt to slow down this kind of pollution, local communities have set up recycling programs.

Some newer solid waste recycling facilities have their own equipment for recycling materials. A conveyor belt carries trash past devices that separate aluminum and other metals from materials such as glass. Once separated, aluminum can be melted down and sold as scrap to be used again.

YOU TRY IT!

Identify recycling programs in your community. Find out how they recycle aluminum and other metals. What other products does your community recycle?

Consumer CONNECTION

THE PRICES OF PRECIOUS METALS

The prices of precious metals, such as gold, silver, and platinum, are listed daily in *The Wall Street Journal* and other major urban newspapers around the country. Under the heading Commodities Futures Prices, readers all over the world can see how these prices change from day to day. Why do these prices change?

Each day, individuals or groups of people buy and sell these metals. The prices of gold and silver increase, for example, when more people wish to buy than sell. Prices go down if more people want to sell their gold or silver than buy. Everyone is affected by these prices, including the jeweler who's commissioned to make a sterling silver necklace or the factory electronics manager. Precious metals are bought and sold under a contract for some present or future need.

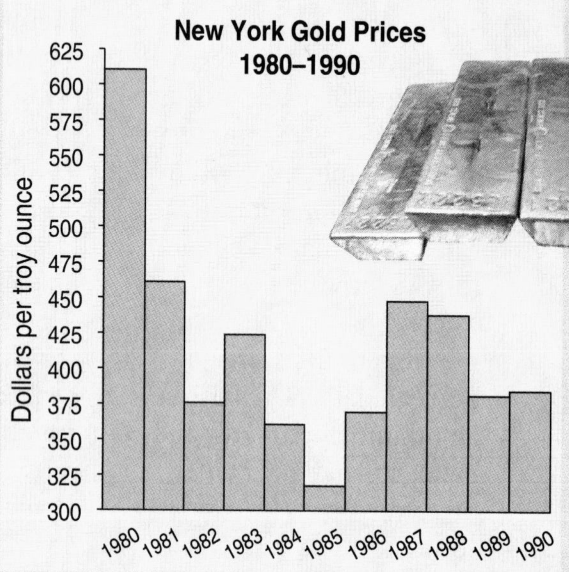

New York Gold Prices 1980–1990

One of the most important precious metals on the market today is gold. What are some of the uses of gold? The list is long.

Most of us have seen a gold ring or necklace. Gold has been valued as jewelry for thousands of years. It is also accepted all over the world as currency.

Recently, gold has become an important material in the industrial community. The metal's durability, malleability, and electrical conductivity make it useful in several ways. For example, gold is used to coat windows to reduce heating and cooling costs. It's been used in space equipment to reflect light. And, of course, dentists use gold to repair teeth.

YOU TRY IT!

Study the graph on this page. Can you tell which years gold prices increased? Why do you think the price of gold went up during these years? Ask a parent or teacher what might have happened during those years when gold prices increased.

CAREER CONNECTION

A metallurgist is trained in chemistry and engineering. Metallurgists study the way metals are extracted from ore, how the metals are formed, and how they might be used to make different products. An extractive metallurgist explores the ways to remove and refine metal.

An individual trained in production metallurgy would work for a company or a research lab developing the metals into some real product.

HOW IT WORKS

METALWORKING IN JEWELRY

Jewelry is made from a variety of rare and not so rare metals and gems. The more expensive jewelry is usually made from gold or platinum. Most gold contains some percentage of copper, zinc, or silver. Less expensive jewelry or costume jewelry is made from bronze or tin. Because consumers like gold, costume jewelry is sometimes given a gold wash or covered with a thin sheet of gold to make it look like pure gold. One of the most popular metals used in jewelry today is silver. But most silver jewelry will also have other metals mixed in. According to United States law, a sterling silver piece must consist of at least 92.5 percent silver.

Before machinery made it possible to mass-produce jewelry, metalworkers made jewelry by hand. As the machine took over, new methods improved the quality of manufacturing jewelry. Today there are several methods used to make jewelry.

One frequently used method is called casting. In this process, a jeweler or metalworker creates a number of pieces of a particular kind of jewelry. Once a design is developed, a master model, usually made of metal, is formed. A rubber mold is then made of the metal model. Molten wax is poured into the rubber mold, creating a wax model. After completing this process, a second mold is made by dipping the wax model in thinned clay, letting the clay dry, and then baking it in an oven until hard. The melted wax drips through a hole left in the clay. Liquid metal is then poured through the hole, filling up the cavity left by the wax. Once the metal has cooled and hardened, the ceramic mold is cracked open to reveal the cast piece. While the rubber mold can be used a number of times, each wax model can only be used once.

Although this process is faster than making each piece of jewelry separately, each step requires great patience and skill.

In another method called stamping, metal is squeezed between two steel pieces called dies. Stamping and other methods of mass production are used to make huge quantities of inexpensive costume jewelry.

YOU TRY IT!

Study some of your family's jewelry at home. Can you tell what kinds of metals were used to make the jewelry?

TECHNOLOGY CONNECTION

NEON LIGHTS

If you've ever been to Times Square in New York City or to Las Vegas, or seen pictures of them, you've seen the brightly colored flashing electric signs. Noble gases cause these signs to light up. Although they are called neon lights after neon gas, the colored signs contain a number of different gases including helium, argon, krypton, and xenon.

How do these signs work? Electricity passes through a tube filled with one of these gases. The color depends on the type of gas in the tube. For example, argon gives off a purple glow, neon a reddish orange, and krypton a pale violet.

These gases were discovered late in the 19th century. One reason that they went undiscovered for so long is that they make up a small fraction of Earth's atmosphere. Imagine, for example, having to process 88 pounds of liquid air to produce one pound of a neon gas. Noble gases are hard to observe. They are colorless, tasteless, and odorless. These noble gases were once called inert gases (completely inactive gases) because no one was able to combine them chemically to make compounds with other elements.

Where are the noble gases found? The chief source is in the air we breathe. To extract noble gases from air, the air is first chilled to a very low temperature, then liquefied. The liquid air passes through long towers and is gradually heated. As the air boils, each noble gas is individually separated from the air.

Before fluorescent lights became part of our culture, neon and lamps of other gases were used. The gas tubes weren't practical inside homes and offices because the color of the light is so unlike sunlight. These special gases were best used in creating glowing, lettered signs. By 1923, neon lights were used in Los Angeles to advertise automobiles. And in the 1970s, artists created a new medium using glass sculptures filled with different noble gases.

YOU TRY IT!

Look at the neon signs in your community. Can you classify the kinds of products or ideas marketed through the use of neon signs? How effective is this kind of advertising?

Chapter 9

Reviewing Main Ideas

1. All matter is made of elements. Elements can be grouped into metals, nonmetals, or metalloids.

2. Earth's crust contains a limited amount of metallic elements. They are prized for their luster, hardness, ability to be easily shaped, and ability to conduct heat and electricity.

3. In addition to many other uses, nonmetals form the basis of life cycles and play important roles in the processes of living organisms.

4. Metalloids have properties of both metals and nonmetals.

Chapter Review

USING KEY SCIENCE TERMS

coinage metal
ductile
malleable
metalloids
metals
nonmetal

For each set of terms below, choose the one term that does not belong and explain why it does not belong.

1. brittle, coinage metal, malleable, ductile
2. ductile, malleable, metal, nonmetal
3. gas, brittle, metal, nonmetal
4. metalloid, nonmetal, metal, gas

UNDERSTANDING IDEAS

Choose the best answer to complete each sentence.

1. A nonmetal found in all living things is ____.
   a. magnesium c. carbon
   b. iron d. aluminum
2. An invisible, explosive gas is ____.
   a. oxygen c. carbon dioxide
   b. hydrogen d. calcium
3. If a metal can be drawn into a wire, it is ____.
   a. strong c. ductile
   b. malleable d. electric
4. The noble gases got their name because ____.
   a. they were used by nobility
   b. they are very expensive
   c. they make neon signs
   d. they do not easily form compounds
5. Sand, glass, and semiconductors contain ____.
   a. silicon c. copper
   b. calcium d. iron
6. The coinage metals are ____.
   a. silver, copper, gold
   b. nickel, tin, silver
   c. copper and nickel
   d. silver and copper
7. Together, metals, nonmetals, and metalloids are called ____.
   a. compounds c. gases
   b. elements d. solids
8. Metalloids include elements used as ____.
   a. wires c. electronic parts
   b. jewelry d. coins
9. Most living material is composed of____.
   a. metalloids c. metals
   b. nonmetals d. noble gases

CRITICAL THINKING

Use your understanding of the concepts developed in the chapter to answer each of the following questions.

1. Explain the relationship between oxygen and iron in your body.
2. Compare and contrast the properties of the elements sodium and chlorine with those of salt.
3. From the properties shown in the picture, is this element a metal, nonmetal, or metalloid? Explain your answer.

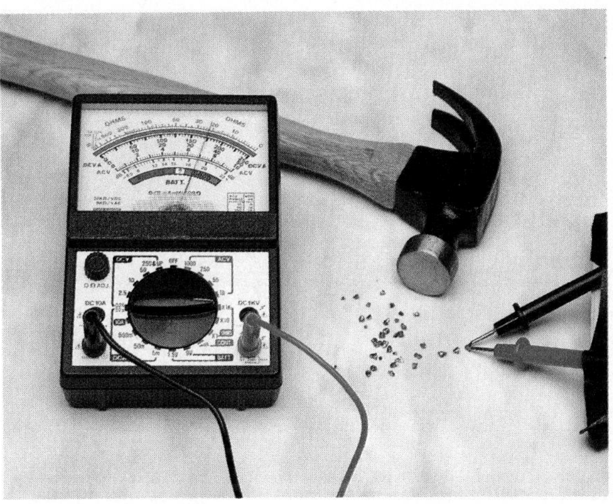

4. What is the most abundant element in your body? In the universe? In Earth's crust? Are they metals or nonmetals?
5. Why is it more useful to divide elements into metals, nonmetals, and metalloids than into solids, liquids, and gases?
6. Describe the relationship between ordinary glass and semiconductors in computers.

PROBLEM SOLVING

Read the following problem and discuss your answers in a brief paragraph.

You've been hired to design a new fireworks display for the 4th of July. The display must be in red, white, and blue.

1. What metals would you be sure are present in your fireworks? Why?
2. If you wanted a permanently lighted display instead of fireworks, which group of elements could you use to make it?
3. You accidently mix some sodium and potassium into your American flag display. What colors will be added to the flag?

CONNECTING IDEAS

Discuss each of the following in a brief paragraph.

1. How can lead or mercury affect your health?

2. Compare and contrast metals, nonmetals, and metalloids.

3. Why are silver and copper good materials for making electric wires?

4. **EARTH SCIENCE CONNECTION** Describe one way in which diamonds are formed.

5. **TECHNOLOGY CONNECTION** What physical property of matter is used to help collect noble gases from air? Explain the process.

6. **HOW IT WORKS** Explain why more inexpensive jewelry is made by stamping than by molding.

DID YOU EVER WONDER . . .

Where gold comes from and why it's so valuable?

Why some stones are called gems and others are called rocks?

How to tell the difference between real gold and "fool's gold"?

You'll find the answers to these questions as you read this chapter.

Chapter 10

Minerals and Their Uses

Here you are, looking at the beautiful items in a jewelry store's window. The first things you notice are the gleaming gold chains. You see several you wish you could wear.

You catch your breath a little as you move to the next section of the window. Blue sapphires, red rubies, green emeralds, and purple amethysts glisten at you from rings and bracelets. In the next window are the sparkling diamonds, with their brilliant dancing flashes of light. Light seems to stream from every point on their surfaces.

In this chapter, you'll see what these jewels are like before they reach the store windows and how they are related to many of the other substances on Earth.

EXPLORE!

What makes jewels valuable?
Are you a collector? Perhaps you have a collection of leaves, or insects, or baseball cards. No matter what you collect, you probably have one item in your collection that is special. What is the "real gem" of the collection? Why do you prize it over other items in the collection? List various qualities that may make some things worth more than others. Would these qualities be the same for someone else with the same kind of collection?

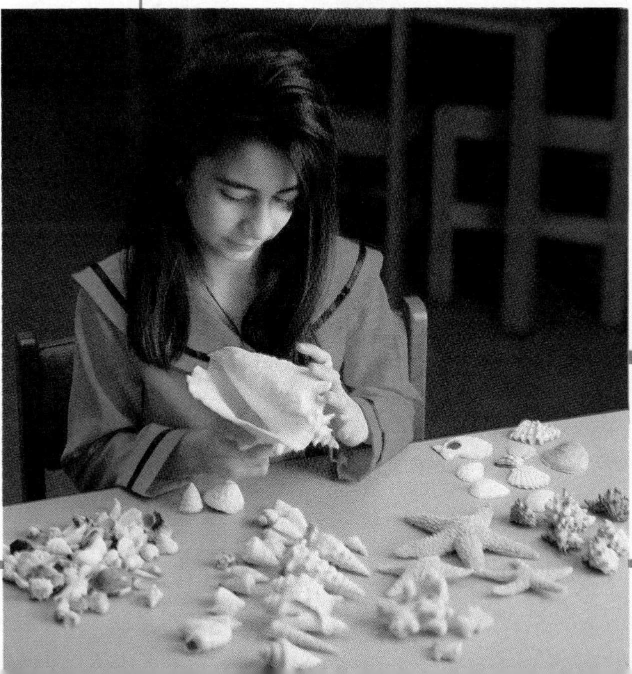

10-1 Minerals and Their Value

OBJECTIVES

In this section, you will

- name five conditions that define minerals;
- explain how rarity and beauty can affect the value of a particular mineral.

KEY SCIENCE TERMS

mineral

gem

FIGURE 10-1. Shown here are just a few examples of how we use minerals.

MINERALS CAN BE FAMILIAR

Without asking anyone or looking at any price tags, you know that the gold and jewels you see in store windows cost a good deal of money. You may decide that they cost a lot because they are so beautiful. You may also take into account that gold and jewels are rare and hard to find. Even the most beautiful, rare, and costly jewels, however, fall into a broad category of substances. These substances are called minerals.

Minerals are part of your life. Write your name with a pencil, and you use the mineral graphite, which is used in pencil lead. Lean against a plastered wall, and you rub against gypsum, a common mineral used in plaster and other building materials. Toss a penny, and you toss the mineral copper, one of several substances used in coin currency. Crunch a salted pretzel, and you eat the mineral halite, commonly referred to as table salt. If you wear any gold, silver, or perhaps turquoise jewelry, you are wearing minerals.

There are more than 4000 different minerals on Earth. Some minerals can be used in many different ways. Others we may not use at all. One of the most common minerals for which we have found many uses is quartz. If you have ever walked across a tan or light-colored sandy beach, you have stepped on tiny grains of quartz. Glass is made from quartz sand. Colorless quartz crystals are used in watches, radios, televisions, radar, and other electronic equipment. Quartz crystals can also be found in microscope and telescope lenses.

How can you know what substances are minerals? Even though there are thousands of minerals, they all meet five basic conditions. A **mineral** is a naturally occurring, nonliving solid, with a definite structure and composition.

HOW DO WE DEFINE MINERALS?

Let's look at the conditions that define minerals more closely.

1. **Minerals Occur Naturally** All minerals are formed by natural processes. Gold, halite, graphite, and other minerals are all formed from natural processes in Earth. You will learn more about the natural formation of minerals as you read this chapter.

2. **Minerals Are Inorganic** Minerals are not alive nor are they formed from anything that ever was alive. Some jewelry items are carved from coral. Because coral is formed from skeletons of tiny sea animals, it is organic. On the other hand, diamonds are made of carbon formed deep underground from inorganic matter. A diamond is a mineral, but coral is not.

3. **Minerals Are Solid** Petroleum and diamonds both contain the element carbon. But because petroleum occurs as a liquid, while diamonds are solid, petroleum is not a mineral.

4. **Minerals Have Unique Chemical Compositions** A mineral can be an element or a compound. Each type of mineral has a chemical composition that is unique to that mineral. The mineral quartz, for example, is a combination of two elements, silicon and oxygen. Although other minerals may also contain silicon and oxygen, the arrangement and proportion of the elements in quartz are unique to quartz.

5. **Minerals Have Crystal Structure** The atoms in a mineral are arranged in a regular geometric pattern repeated over and over again. Substances with this kind of inner structure have crystalline structure.

When natural conditions allow, a mineral grows and forms in such a way that it shows its crystal structure on its exterior. In this case, we can see smooth surfaces and sharp angles on a sample of the mineral. Crystals can form in many different sizes. Some are too small to be seen under a microscope. Many can be held in your hand. Others, such as some quartz crystals, may be too large for you to carry. Look at the mineral samples in Figure 10-2. How are they alike? How are they different? Crystals can also grow in a variety of shapes.

a

b

FIGURE 10-2. Some minerals show crystal structure on their outside surfaces (a). Even if a mineral sample does not show its crystal structure on the outside, the crystal pattern still exists within the mineral (b).

FIND OUT!

What shapes do halite and quartz crystals take? Slide a tiny amount of table salt—halite—under your microscope and separate the granules. Focus on just one granule as you examine the salt under your microscope. Now examine a quartz sample with evidence of its crystal structure visible on the outside. How does the shape of the quartz crystal compare with the shape of the halite crystal? Count the number of sides each crystal has. Make a sketch of the quartz crystal and of the halite crystal. The diagram below shows the six major crystal systems of minerals.

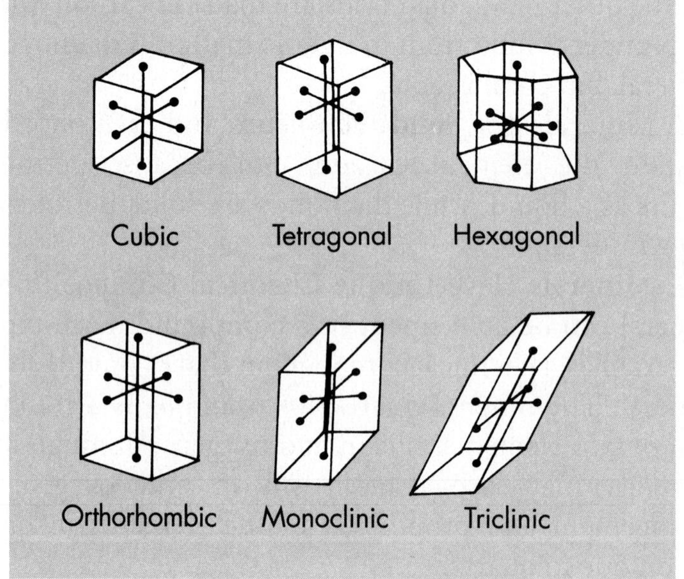

Conclude and Apply

Compare your sketches with the crystals diagramed here.

1. Which type of crystal is quartz?
2. Which type of crystal is halite?

DID YOU KNOW?

The state of Colorado is famous for its mineral resources. In 1894, the largest silver nugget ever found in North America was discovered there. The nugget had a mass of 835 kg. That's about 15 times the mass of the average person in your classroom.

There are six major crystal systems, as shown in the diagram above. These crystal systems refer to the set patterns that mineral particles form in a crystal. The simplest crystal system is cubic. Pyrite is an example of a mineral that has a cubic crystal system.

a

b

FIGURE 10-3. Rough, uncut minerals (a) sometimes look very different after they've been cut and polished (b).

SOME MINERALS ARE GEMS

A **gem** is a highly prized mineral because it is rare, durable, and beautiful. Suppose you were a gem explorer hoping to make your fortune in emeralds. Would you know what to look for? Look at the mineral in Figure 10-3. This is the way the mineral looks when it is extracted or mined from the ground. The mineral must be cut and polished before it becomes a sparkling gem. The same is true for other gems. The gem-cutting tools shown in Figure 10-4 are very specialized.

As indicated earlier, one reason gems are valued is because they are rare. What do you think would happen to the value of a gem if it were found to be abundant? Amethyst was once one of the most valuable gems. After many amethyst gems were discovered in Brazil, however, the value of amethyst fell because it was no longer as scarce.

DID YOU KNOW?

Gold samples rarely show their crystal structure outwardly. Those that do are so beautiful and priceless that they usually become museum pieces.

FIGURE 10-4. A gem cutter's challenge is to remove imperfections yet retain as much of the gem as possible.

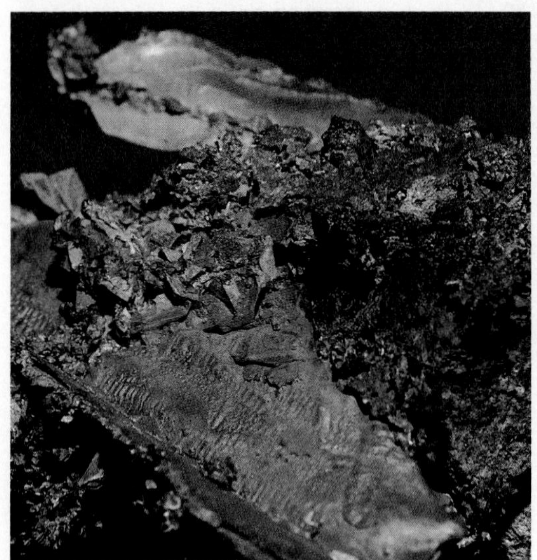

FIGURE 10-5. This sample of copper was found in Ajo, Arizona.

METAL AND NONMETAL MINERALS

Gold, silver, and copper are minerals that are metals. However, not all metals are minerals. Bronze is a metal that is not a mineral. Remember that a mineral is a naturally occurring, inorganic solid having a crystal structure and a unique chemical composition. Gold, silver, and copper meet these conditions, but bronze does not. Bronze is a human-made metal, produced by the combination of copper and tin. Therefore, bronze is not a mineral.

Most minerals are nonmetallic. Graphite, gypsum, and halite are all good examples of nonmetallic minerals.

Except for gold and silver, most of the minerals listed in Appendices K and L at the back of the book are fairly common. They may be found in large quantities—but not necessarily in all places—around the world.

EXPLORE!

How are metallic and nonmetallic minerals used?

Appendices K and L will introduce you to a few of the most common minerals. Read the names of the minerals listed. Which names are familiar?

Read the column that describes how the minerals are used. On this basis, list three minerals and the roles they have played in your activities today.

It's easy to see that our lives would be very different without Earth's minerals. As you read on, you will learn some ways to distinguish one mineral from another.

Check Your Understanding

1. What five conditions do minerals satisfy?
2. What factors help determine the value of a mineral?
3. **APPLY:** Coal is made of carbon from plants. Is coal a mineral? Tell why or why not.

10-2 Characteristics of Minerals

MINERAL CHACTERISTICS

Remember when you were thinking about collections in the Explore activity at the beginning of the chapter? Did you picture labels to identify each item in the collection? What characteristics help you distinguish between items in a collection?

Every mineral, like every item in a collection, has special characteristics that can help you distinguish it from other minerals. Suppose you had a collection of minerals. What characteristics would help you identify each one?

OBJECTIVES

In this section, you will

- differentiate between mineral characteristics such as hardness, color, streak, cleavage, and fracture;
- describe how physical characteristics are used to identify minerals.

KEY SCIENCE TERMS

hardness
streak
cleavage
fracture

FIND OUT!

How does a scratch test help identify minerals?
Your teacher will give you samples of the three minerals listed in the table. You will use the samples to do what is called a scratch test for hardness.

First, copy the table. Then choose one of the mineral samples and try to scratch the other minerals with it. For example, does calcite scratch quartz? If so, make a check mark in the calcite row where it intersects with the quartz column. Does quartz scratch calcite? If so, make a check mark in the quartz row where it intersects with the calcite column. Do the same for each mineral on the chart.

When you have performed the scratch test with each mineral and completed your table, analyze the results you have recorded.

Conclude and Apply

Sequence the minerals from softest to hardest by listing them in order, 1 = softest, 3 = hardest.

1. Which mineral is the hardest?
2. Can you scratch any of the minerals with your fingernail?
3. Which is the softest?

DATA AND OBSERVATIONS

	Calcite	Quartz	Talc
Calcite	X		
Quartz		X	
Talc			X

FIGURE 10-6. Minerals have many different characteristics.

HARDNESS

The Find Out activity shows one characteristic that helps distinguish one mineral from another. **Hardness** is a measure of how easily a mineral can be scratched. Talc is one of the softest known minerals and can be scratched with your fingernail. If you have ever rubbed talcum powder on you skin, you know how smooth and soft talc can be. In contrast, diamonds are so hard that they often are used in sharpening and cutting tools. A diamond can be scratched only by another diamond.

Remember how you sequenced the minerals in the Find Out activity according to hardness? You were working with minerals that had three distinctive hardnesses, so you used a scale of 1 to 3. In a similar way, you can use a scale of 1 to 10 to compare the hardnesses of all minerals. This scale is shown in Figure 10-7. The scale is named for the German scientist who devised it, Friedrich Mohs.

FIGURE 10-7. Minerals and other solids can be rated on the Mohs scale.

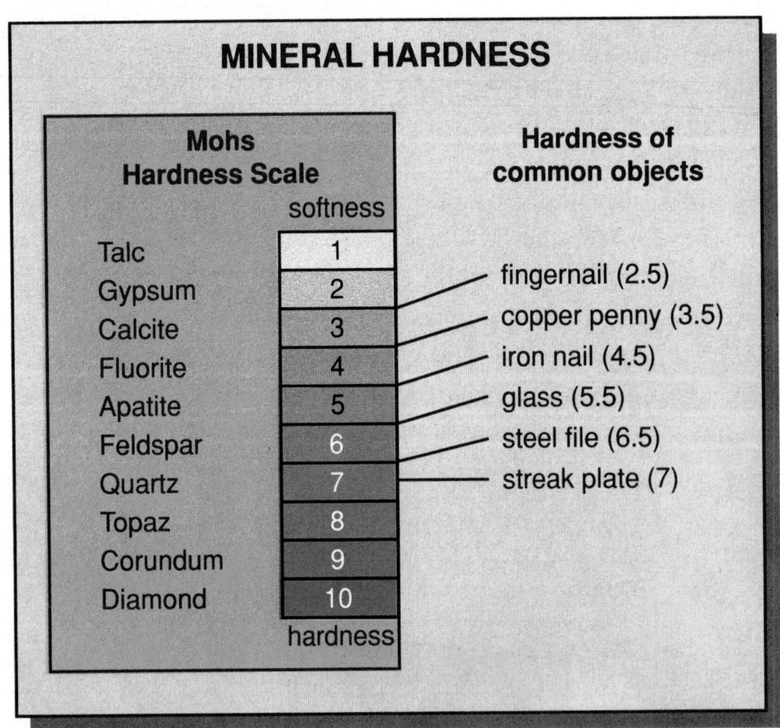

MINERAL HARDNESS
Mohs Hardness Scale
softness
Talc 1
Gypsum 2
Calcite 3
Fluorite 4
Apatite 5
Feldspar 6
Quartz 7
Topaz 8
Corundum 9
Diamond 10
hardness
Hardness of common objects
fingernail (2.5)
copper penny (3.5)
iron nail (4.5)
glass (5.5)
steel file (6.5)
streak plate (7)

The Mohs scale begins with 1 for the softest mineral and ends with 10 for the hardest mineral. The relative hardnesses of all minerals are classified within this scale. Minerals within any level of hardness also vary in hardness. Decimal numbers show these variations. A mineral that ranks 2.1 on the Mohs' scale, for example, would be softer than a mineral that ranks 2.2.

Common objects, such as your fingernail or a copper penny, can be used to determine hardness. Let's say you have a clear or whitish-colored mineral sample that you know is either calcite or quartz. You scratch it on your fingernail and then on a copper penny. You find that the mineral leaves a scratch line on your fingernail but not on the penny. You see from the scale that a fingernail has a hardness of 2.5 and a copper penny a hardness of about 3.5. From this, you can determine that the mineral's hardness is about 3. Using the list of sample minerals in Figure 10–7, determine if your mineral is calcite or quartz.

FIGURE 10-8. Some minerals are so soft that you can scratch them with your fingernail.

EXPLORE!

How does looking at minerals help identify them? Your teacher will display several different mineral samples. Examine them and discuss what they have in common and how they differ. Group the samples according to the similarities you can visually observe. Try to decide on only two groups, with the samples in each group all sharing one characteristic. Can you do it? What title would you give to each group?

If your class has difficulty agreeing upon two groups that include all the samples, try answering these questions. Is the mineral shiny? How does it reflect light compared to the other samples? Use your answers to determine two characteristics that separate the minerals into two groups. What titles can you come up with now?

LUSTER

The main difference between the two final groups of minerals in the Explore activity could have been how they reflect light. Minerals have luster, which determines how their surfaces reflect light. Minerals have either metallic or nonmetallic luster. The minerals in Figure 10-9 illustrate the difference between metallic (a) and nonmetallic luster (b).

a

b

FIGURE 10-9. A mineral may have a metallic luster (a) or a dull luster (b).

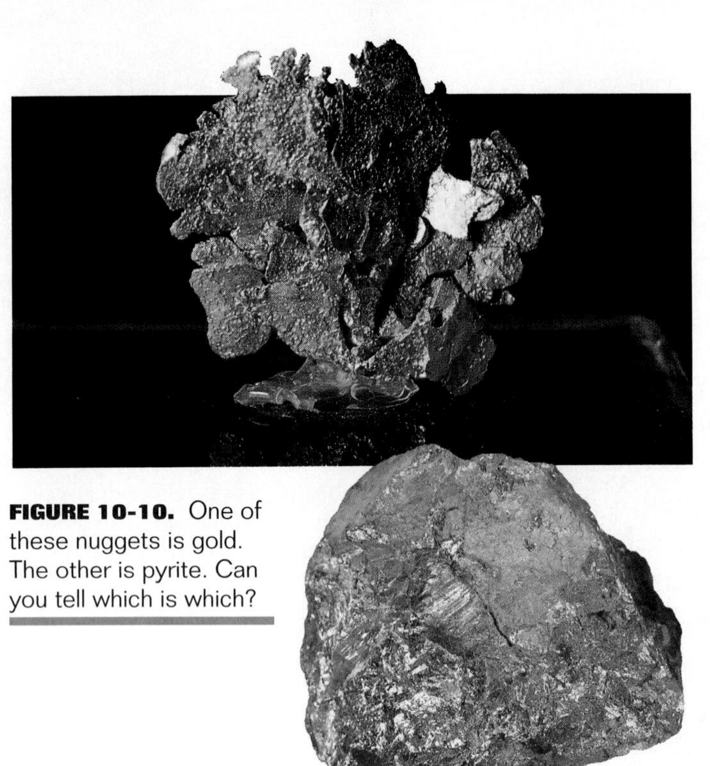

FIGURE 10-10. One of these nuggets is gold. The other is pyrite. Can you tell which is which?

Metallic luster can be compared to the shine of a fancy belt buckle or the shiny chrome trim on some cars. Minerals with a metallic luster shine, and look much like metal.

Some minerals do not shine like metal. These are minerals with nonmetallic luster. Nonmetallic luster can be described in a variety of ways—including dull, pearly, resinous, silky, glassy, and brilliant.

A mineral's luster has to do with its appearance only. For example, a mineral with a metallic luster is not necessarily a metal. By the same token, minerals with nonmetallic luster can be metals.

COLOR

A mineral's color is another clue to its identity. Sulfur, for example, has a very distinctive yellow color. Thus, sulfur can usually be identified fairly quickly among an assortment of minerals.

Color alone, however, isn't enough to distinguish one mineral from another. Often, different samples of the same mineral will have different colors—there are blue, purple, green, pink, and orange sapphires, which form from the mineral corundum. Also, two different minerals can have the same color. The minerals gold and pyrite, for example, are each gold in color and can look very similar. But gold is worth a lot more money than pyrite. Pyrite, as you have probably guessed, is the mineral name for "fool's gold." If you are not to be fooled by pyrite's color, you would have to use another test in mineral identification. Gold has a hardness of about 2.5, pyrite of about 6.5. So you might carefully try to bite a sample the way characters in Western movies often do. Which of the two minerals do you think will bend a little when you bite it? The next Find Out activity is another test you could use to tell the difference between similar-colored minerals.

FIND OUT!

What is a streak test?

Your teacher will give you a piece of unglazed porcelain called a streak plate and several samples of minerals, including pyrite, hematite, and graphite. First run the graphite across the streak plate. This is called streaking the graphite. Look at the color of graphite's streak on the streak plate. How does it compare with the color of the graphite itself?

Before you streak the pyrite, hypothesize what color the pyrite will streak on the streak plate. Now streak the pyrite. What color is its streak? How does the pyrite's streak color compare with its actual color? Were you correct in the hypothesis you made before you streaked the pyrite?

Conclude and Apply

When streaked, gold leaves a yellow mark. How could you use the streak test to make sure you weren't fooled by "fool's gold"?

DID YOU KNOW?

Some of the world's finest garnet crystals were found by construction workers at the site of a medical center project near the northern end of the island of Manhattan.

STREAK

When a mineral is rubbed across a streak plate, as you did in the Find Out activity, a streak is left behind. The streak itself is the powdered mineral. The color of a mineral when it is broken up and powdered is called its **streak**. Was the red brown streak of hematite what you expected to see?

As you also discovered in the Find Out activity, gold and pyrite can be distinguished from each other by using the streak test. Gold has a yellow streak, and pyrite has a greenish black streak.

FIGURE 10-11. A streak test reveals the color of a mineral in powdered form.

The streak test works for all minerals that are softer than the streak plate. Very soft minerals will even leave a streak on paper. Do you know the last time you did a streak test before you did the Find Out activity? The last time you used a pencil! Writing with a pencil is the same as doing a streak test of graphite. Graphite in pencils is soft enough to leave a streak on paper.

FIGURE 10-12. Mica's perfect cleavage allows it to be broken along smooth, flat surfaces.

CLEAVAGE AND FRACTURE

Minerals also differ in the way they break. You might perform this test by tapping a mineral sample against a hard surface or perhaps just picking at it with your fingernail if its hardness rating is low. Minerals that break along smooth, flat surfaces have **cleavage**. Mica is a mineral that has perfect cleavage. You can see in Figure 10-12 how it breaks along smooth, flat surfaces.

Minerals that have curved, rough, or jagged surfaces when they break apart have **fracture**. Quartz is a good example of a mineral with fracture.

OTHER PROPERTIES OF MINERALS

Some minerals have unique traits that set them apart from other minerals. They have special and interesting properties. In the following Explore activity, you'll be able to discover one of them.

EXPLORE!

How do clear minerals compare?

Your teacher will give you samples of some clear minerals. Place each sample over the print on this page. Can you read through each mineral?

Now your teacher will give you a clear piece of the mineral calcite. Place it over this page and try to read it. Is there a difference? What happens to light when it passes through calcite?

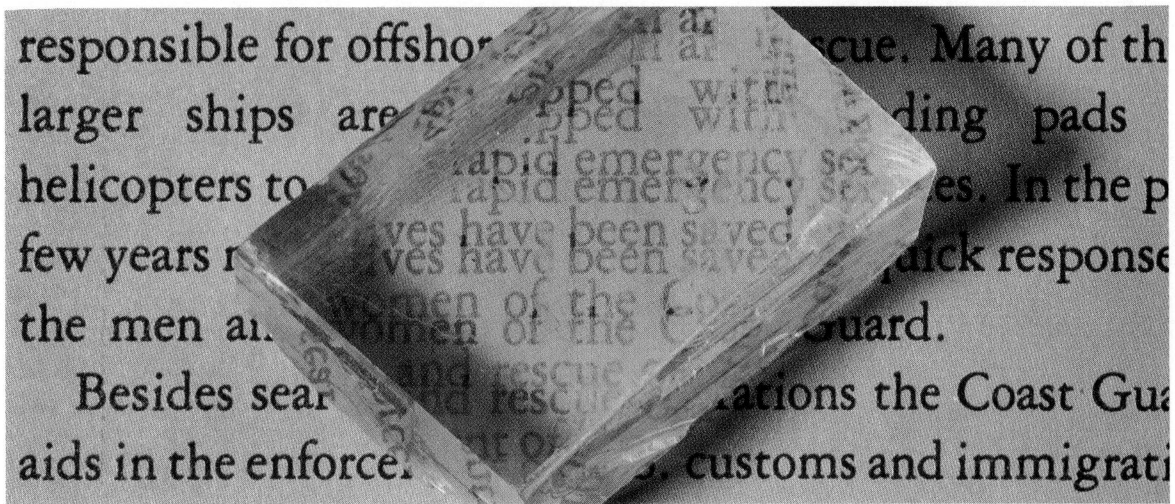

FIGURE 10-13. A clear specimen of calcite can be identified by its unique ability to cause a double image.

You discovered in the Explore activity that when light passes through some calcite samples, you see a double image. Calcite can also be distinguished from other minerals by putting hydrochloric acid on it; this acid causes calcite to dissolve and release bubbles of fizzing carbon dioxide.

Magnetite is another mineral with its own unique trait. As you may have already guessed from its name, magnetite has magnetic properties. In its lodestone form, magnetite has the ability to attract iron like a magnet. This was a material ancient mariners used to make compasses.

USING PHYSICAL PROPERTIES TO IDENTIFY MINERALS

You have discovered in this section that we usually need to know more about a mineral than just its color and appearance in order to identify it. We might also need to test it for streak, hardness, luster, and cleavage or fracture. Knowing some of its other, less common properties can help, too. In the next Investigate activity, you get a chance to put these tests to work as you identify some mineral samples.

INVESTIGATE!

10-1 HOW ARE MINERALS IDENTIFIED?

In this activity, you will use tests for several mineral properties discussed in this chapter. You will use your test results to decide the identity of various mineral samples.

PROBLEM

How can mineral identities be determined from tests?

MATERIALS

mineral samples
hand lens
steel file
goggles
apron
streak plate
5% hydrochloric acid with dropper
Mohs scale of hardness

PROCEDURE

1. Start a data table like the one shown below.
2. Use the hand lens to examine the mineral samples. **Observe** and record the luster and color for each sample.
3. Perform tests for hardness, streak, and fracture or cleavage. **Observe** and record the results.
4. Test the samples for other properties, such as reaction to hydrochloric acid. **CAUTION:** *Wear your goggles and apron. HCl may cause burns. If spills occur, rinse with water and notify your teacher.*

ANALYZE

1. **Analyze** the results you recorded in your table. **Compare** them with data in Appendices K and L. Then **infer** what each sample must be. Write the mineral's name in the appropriate space on your table.
2. Compare the usefulness of the different properties in identifying the given minerals. Which was most useful? Which property was least useful? Explain your answers.
3. **Compare and contrast** the ease of performing the various tests. Which test was the most difficult to do? Why?

CONCLUDE AND APPLY

4. How many tests should usually be performed before deciding what mineral a given sample is? Why?
5. **Going Further:** Pretend you are going on a geological expedition. Your purpose is to determine what minerals are abundant in the area of the expedition. What things will you pack to take along on your expedition? What activities will you be engaged in while you are on the expedition? How will you keep track of your observations? How might you share the data you obtain with others?

DATA AND OBSERVATIONS

MINERAL SAMPLE	COLOR	LUSTER	HARDNESS	STREAK	OTHER CHARACTERISTICS	THIS SAMPLE MUST BE:
A						
B						

Since you first started thinking about minerals at the beginning of this chapter, you've learned that five features set minerals apart from all other substances on Earth. You've learned to do six tests to help distinguish minerals from one another. To get the mineral samples you used in your tests, your teacher simply turned to the supplies in your classroom lab—or perhaps ordered them from a store or catalogue.

While you may be familiar with several minerals, you may not be familiar with how they are retrieved from Earth. Figure 10-14(a) shows a deep narrow mine such as the mines where diamonds and coal are found. Mining in the open pit in Figure 10-14(b), one of the world's largest open mines, takes advantage of the rich copper deposit close to Earth's surface. But how do minerals form in the first place? That's something you'll learn about in the next section.

FIGURE 10-14. Mining often takes place deep inside Earth (a). In contrast, other mines are large open pits (b), such as this one in Montana.

a

b

Check Your Understanding

1. Name five characteristics that can help distinguish one mineral from another.
2. **APPLY:** Pretend you're a prospector looking for gold. You find a nugget that you think may be gold. What tests can you use to determine whether you've discovered gold and "struck it rich"?

10-3 Mineral Formation

OBJECTIVES

In this section, you will

- examine mineral formation by evaporation;
- describe mineral formation by the cooling of magma.

HOW MINERALS FORM

Do you recognize any of the minerals in Figure 10-15? Think back to what you learned about minerals and their crystal structure in the first section. You'll see right away that the small, white cube is a halite crystal. Halite, of course, is the mineral that gives us the perfectly cubic grains we sprinkle on many foods. The other items in Figure 10-15 are crystals of other minerals.

There are two main ways that minerals form. One is from the cooling of magma. As the magma cools, elements in the magma may form minerals. Minerals can also form from elements dissolved in a liquid. When the liquid evaporates, the elements stay behind and may form minerals.

In the next activity, you'll watch crystals form. You will be able to see two processes of mineral formation in action.

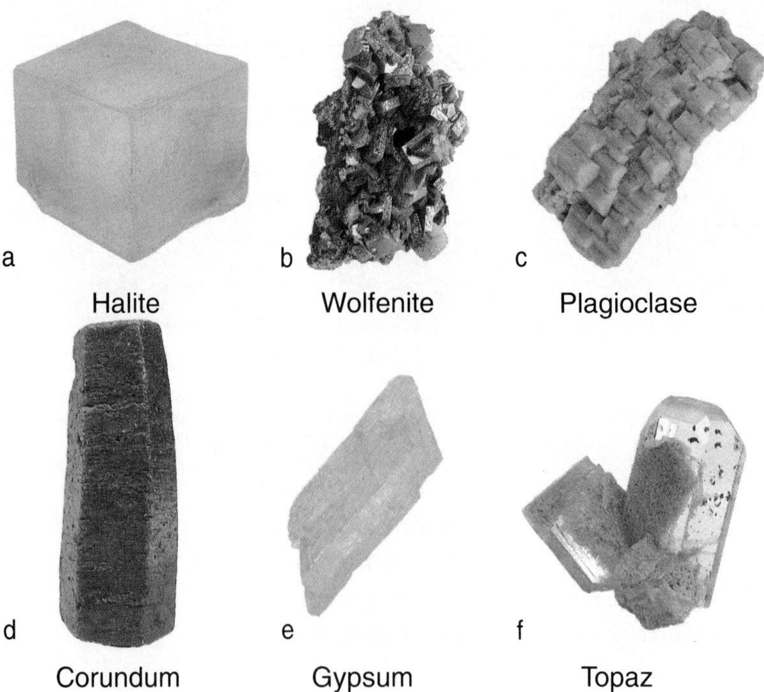

FIGURE 10-15. All of these minerals show their crystal structure on the outside.

INVESTIGATE!

10-2 HOW DO CRYSTALS FORM?

Earth's minerals were once elements in solution. How the minerals form crystals and take on the solid state in which they are found involves two processes.

PROBLEM

In what two ways can crystals form?

MATERIALS

salt solution
sugar solution
large test tube
toothpick
cotton thread
hand lens
2 shallow pans
thermal mitt
test-tube rack
cardboard
table salt
granulated sugar
hot plate

PROCEDURE

1. Pour the sugar solution into one of the shallow pans. Use the hot plate to gently heat the solution.
2. Place the test tube in the test-tube rack. Using a thermal mitt to protect your hand, pour some of the hot sugar solution into the test tube. **CAUTION:** *The liquid is hot. Do not touch the test tube without protecting your hands.*
3. Tie the thread to one end of the toothpick. Place the thread in the test tube. Be sure that it does not touch the sides or bottom of the tube.
4. Cover the test tube with a piece of cardboard. Place the rack containing the test tube in a location where it will not be disturbed.
5. Pour a thin layer of the salt solution into the second shallow pan.
6. Place the pan in a warm area of the room.
7. Leave both the covered test tube and the shallow pan undisturbed for at least one week.
8. Examine sample grains of table salt and sugar with the hand lens. **Observe** any similarities or differences.
9. At the end of one week, **observe** each solution and see if crystals have formed. Use a hand lens to examine any crystals.

ANALYZE

1. **Compare and contrast** the crystals that formed from the salt and sugar solutions. Make a sketch of each type of crystal.
2. **Infer** what happened to the salt water in the shallow pan.
3. Did this same process occur in the test tube? Explain.

CONCLUDE AND APPLY

4. What caused the formation of crystals in the test tube? What caused the formation of crystals in the shallow pan?
5. Are salt and sugar both minerals? Explain your answer.
6. In what two ways can crystals form?
7. **Going Further: Hypothesize** the results of your experiments if you had performed the test-tube experiment with the salt solution and the pan experiment with the sugar solution. Explain your hypotheses.

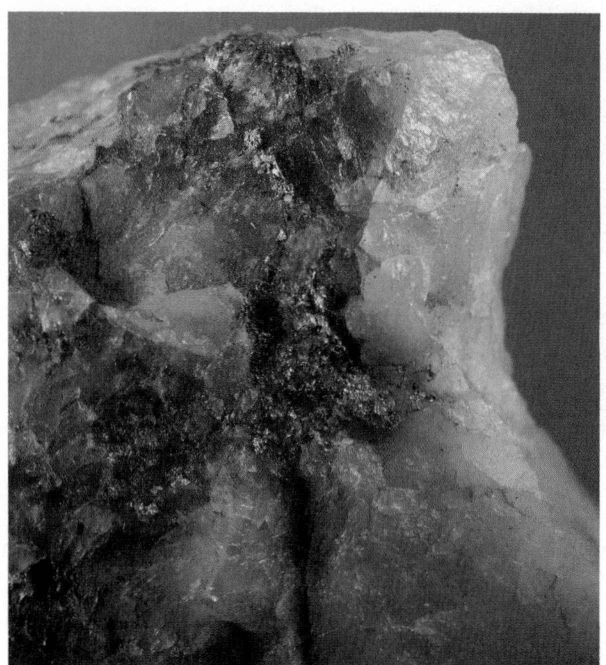

FIGURE 10-16. A vein of gold may form in a rock crack from which water evaporated.

Minerals Form From Evaporation

When you were adding sugar to the water to make a sugar solution in the Investigate activity, why did you stop? Why did the sugar stop dissolving?

You may remember from what you've learned about solutions that a given volume of water can dissolve only a certain amount of solid before the water becomes saturated. When the water is saturated, the next teaspoonful of sugar will not dissolve.

What happens to water when it is allowed to sit exposed to the air? Have you guessed that the water in your sugar solution will evaporate? As the water evaporates, there is less water in the glass—but there's still the same amount of sugar. So what happens to that extra sugar when the volume of water decreases through evaporation? What will be left behind when all the water evaporates? What do you expect to see on the string?

You read in the first section that many minerals are composed of more than one element. Before they become minerals, however, these elements are in solution. In some cases, this solution forms when elements are dissolved in water. When the water evaporates, the elements may combine in a mineral's characteristic crystal structure. If the mineral has an open space to form, crystals will form that show their crystal shape on the outside. If there is no open space for the mineral to form, the crystals will overlap. When this happens, the elements have still combined in an orderly pattern, but we just cannot see it on the outside of the crystal.

Sometimes water containing minerals in solution invades cracks in rocks and dissolves the minerals in the walls of the crack. When the water evaporates, these newly dissolved minerals and the minerals that were originally in the water may combine, forming new minerals. When the water is completely gone, the cracks in the rocks are filled with the mineral or minerals that the

DID YOU KNOW?

Artificial diamonds can be made in laboratories by applying a great deal of heat and pressure to graphite.

water left behind. Gold, copper, sulfur, and galena often form mineral-filled cracks called veins.

You have just learned how minerals can form by evaporation. Now let's look at another way minerals can form—the cooling of magma.

a

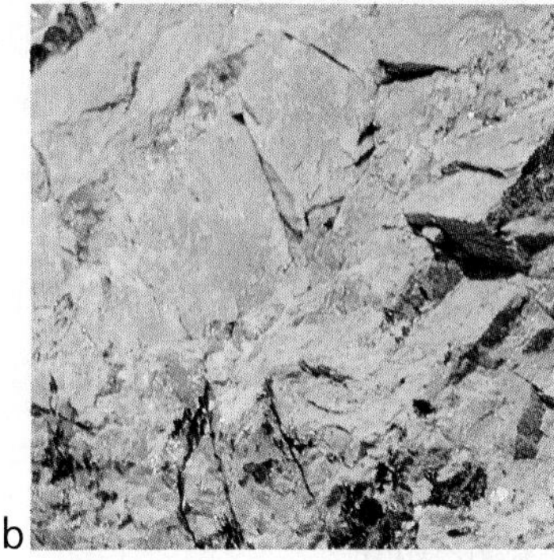

b

FIGURE 10-17. If magma cools slowly, large crystals form (a). If it cools quickly, small crystals form (b).

Minerals Form From Cooling Magma

Minerals deep below Earth's surface are also in solution. The solution is magma, the hot, molten material found beneath Earth's crust. When magma seeps upward into cooler layers of the planet's interior, it cools. As the magma cools, the elements in magma may combine chemically and form minerals. Again, if there is enough open space, the minerals form crystal shapes that are visible on the outside of the sample.

The cooling process can be slow or quick. This cooling rate determines crystal size. If magma cools slowly, as it is apt to do in Earth's warm to hot interior, large crystals form. Minerals such as mica, feldspar, and quartz are examples of minerals that often form large crystals. If the magma cools quickly, minerals form in small crystals. Lava, which is magma that reaches Earth's surface, escapes Earth's inner heat. On the surface, it is exposed to air and perhaps water. Lava cools quickly in air, so small mineral crystals form. If lava runs into water, it may cool so quickly that no crystals form at all.

How do we know?

Minerals' interior crystal structure

Humans have known about, experimented with, and used minerals for thousands of years. The study of mineral crystals, however, is less than 400 years old. Two centuries ago, scientists were almost certain that minerals had regular, repeating, interior structures. However, they could neither describe nor demonstrate them.

By the beginning of the twentieth century, scientists had X-ray technology to work with. A German scientist, Max von Laue, was the first to send an X-ray beam through a mineral crystal. The smooth, flat surfaces of the crystal fractured the X-ray beam. Thus, science got its first glimpse of the crystalline pattern of surfaces and sharp angles within minerals.

Now, in the late twentieth century, scientists work with electronic and computerized microscopes. They have actually photographed shadows and reflections made by the inner crystal pattern of minerals. Today's scientists hope to use their relatively new knowledge of crystals to help them understand how certain impurities within a mineral affect some of its special properties. They also hope to discover new uses for minerals.

FIGURE 10-18. Both sandpaper and ruby gems are made of corundum.

Sometimes flowing magma or lava will fill cracks in surrounding rock. The rock traps the heat from the molten material, causing it to cool very slowly and form large mineral crystals. Veins of some gems and rare minerals form in this way. Some examples are the mineral corundum, of which rubies and sapphires are examples; the mineral beryl, of which emeralds and aquamarine are examples; and topaz. Figure 10-18 shows a corundum source for rubies formed by magma that was slowly cooled.

The Investigate experiment showed you how both the evaporation of water from a solution and the cooling of a solution can form crystals. Valued minerals come from water and magma, are deposited in rocks, then extracted from rock, and, in many cases, returned to Earth to repeat the cycle. How is this so?

Minerals spend much of their existence in rocks. Humans sometimes go to great length and expense to extract them from the rocks. But, in fact, rocks are made of minerals. Put all the minerals of an area, valued and not so valued, together in a solid mass, and you have rock! Rocks are the next group of materials you will investigate as you go on to Chapter 11.

Check Your Understanding

1. What is the connection between evaporation and mineral formation?
2. Describe two ways in which a vein of a mineral may form in a rock.
3. **APPLY:** A volcano erupts in the middle of the ocean. Lava slips down the sides of its cone and eventually enters the ocean water. Will the mineral crystals formed be large or small? Explain your answer.

EXPANDING YOUR VIEW

CONTENTS

A Closer Look
Evolution of Iron 305

Life Science Connection
Minerals in the Body 306

Science and Society
Asbestos Debate 307

Technology Connection
Quartz and Computers 309

History Connection
Rewriting Prehistory 310

A CLOSER LOOK

EVOLUTION OF IRON

Iron is seldom found on Earth in its elemental form, but it can be extracted from iron-rich rocks known as iron ores. Ores are minerals or rocks that contain a useful substance. Like all ores, iron in iron ore does not usually exist by itself. Instead, it is combined with other substances, such as oxygen. Heating the iron ore separates the iron from these substances.

Although humans first began using iron thousands of years ago, it wasn't until about 1200 B.C.E. that humans were able to extract iron from its ore. The start of the Iron Age brought widespread use of iron in tools and weapons.

In ancient civilizations, people heated iron ore in a shallow pit dug in the ground. They produced a soft iron used to make crude tools, weapons, and ornaments. Through the ages, iron makers have learned to melt iron ore with more intense heat by blowing air into furnaces.

Today's blast furnace uses the same principle. A blast of heated air is blown into a mixture of iron ore, limestone, and a substance called coke that is made from coal. Coke produces an intense heat that, when mixed with oxygen, helps separate iron from ore. The iron that is extracted from ore in this heating process is called pig iron, consisting of about 93 percent of the metal. The rest is made up of carbon and other impurities.

Pig iron is harder than the soft iron that was made for centuries, but the carbon in pig iron makes it too brittle for many applications. Most iron today is made into steel. To make steel, the blast furnace is connected to a steel-making furnace. Here, oxygen is blown over pig iron to remove extra carbon. Steel is often an alloy, meaning that it is mixed with different elements, such as tungsten, to produce varying degrees of hardness.

WHAT DO YOU THINK?

Most metal things we use are made of steel. Steel is used for everything from buildings to safety pins. How many things can you observe from where you are sitting that you think are made of steel?

LIFE SCIENCE CONNECTION

MINERALS IN THE BODY

Your body needs many of the elements found in minerals to survive. Instead of chewing on rocks, we get the elements we need from plants or from animals that have eaten plants.

The elements in minerals help plants grow. Water seeps into the ground, passes through rocks, and dissolves minerals. The mineral-rich water is absorbed by the plant's roots and carried throughout the plant. The elements in minerals help the plant grow by assisting in photosynthesis and other processes.

The human body needs more than 20 different kinds of elements, but only in very small amounts. Iron, which is found in such minerals as magnetite and pyrite, helps blood carry oxygen throughout our bodies. Calcium, found in calcite and dolomite, helps make bones and teeth strong. Sodium, found in halite, helps regulate water in the body's cells.

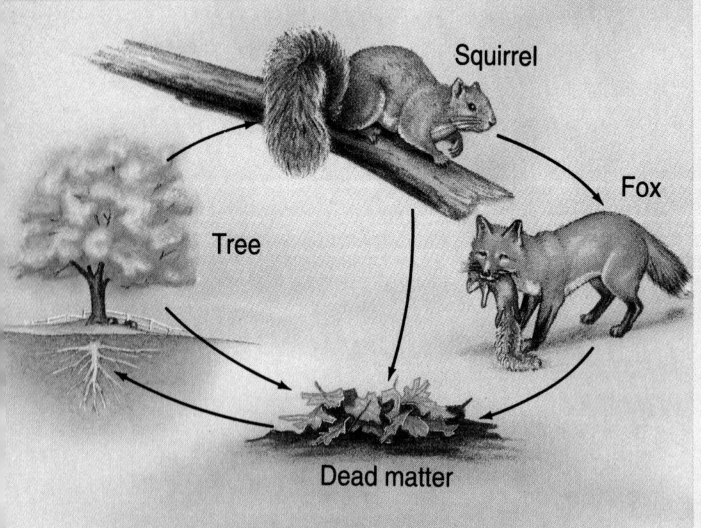

YOU TRY IT!

Calcium is the most abundant element in the body, making up about two percent of adult body weight in teeth and bones. Calcium is found in many foods, including dairy products and whole grains. Calcium helps build teeth and bones and aids in the clotting of blood. Try reading the labels on the foods you eat. How much calcium is contained in a slice of bread?

Minerals can be recycled. Plants absorb minerals from the soil, then animals eat the plants. When the animals—including humans—die and decompose, they return the minerals to the soil. But most of the plants humans eat come from large production farms, where there isn't enough time for this gradual cycle of returning minerals to the soil.

Farmers use different methods of returning minerals to the soil. Often, organic or inorganic fertilizers are used. Organic fertilizers, often referred to as compost, are fertilizers made from plant and animal remains and waste. Inorganic fertilizers are made from essential elements and minerals that have been extracted from rock.

Crop rotation is another method by which minerals in soil can be preserved or replaced. Farmers rotate the types of crops they plant each year to ensure that the minerals used by one type of crop are replaced the following year by a different crop. Farmers who plant crops year after year and don't replace the minerals absorbed by plants will soon discover that the soil will no longer support plant growth. Soil that is rich in minerals will grow plants that provide humans with the nutrients they need to live.

SCIENCE AND SOCIETY

ASBESTOS DEBATE

Asbestos has been the subject of debate for nearly 20 years. What is asbestos, and why is it so controversial?

Asbestos is a natural mineral often found in metamorphic rock. It is a lightweight, fibrous mineral that is white to green in color. Asbestos use dates back to ancient times, when Egyptians and Romans realized that asbestos is resistant to fire and heat. They wove asbestos into clothing and pressed it into paper.

More recently, asbestos has often been used to produce insulation for buildings and water pipes, because asbestos materials don't conduct heat or electricity very well. Asbestos is mixed with other materials to produce such things as plaster and cement. Since they don't burn easily and are resistant to acids, asbestos materials are used in products such as automobile brakes and fireproof clothing, shown on the next page.

As far back as the early 1900s, scientists were concerned with the possible harmful effects of inhaling asbestos fibers. Airborne asbestos fibers are like glass slivers, most so small they can't be seen without a microscope. Even when asbestos is mixed with other materials such as cement, the products can break down over time and release the fibers into the air.

Scientists first realized the dangers of asbestos by studying workers in plants where asbestos products were manufactured. Breathing some types of asbestos fibers can cause asbestosis, a disease that stiffens the lungs and makes breathing difficult. It can also cause lung cancer or cancer of the stomach lining. Sometimes these diseases don't show up until 20 or 30 years after a person has been exposed to asbestos.

The Environmental Protection Agency (EPA) has researched the effects of asbestos for the United States government since the early 1970s. Beginning with a ban on the use of asbestos in public schools in 1973, the EPA has sought to eliminate the use of asbestos. In 1975, the EPA banned the use of asbestos in new public buildings. However, this did not solve the problem of asbestos already in the buildings.

People were concerned

CAREER CONNECTION

The economic geologist uses a broad knowledge of all areas of geology and applies it to the exploration and development of mineral deposits. Working with other specialists, such as engineers and financial analysts, the economic geologist determines whether and how a mineral or fuel can be developed.

that children attending school in older buildings may be exposed to higher than normal levels of asbestos fibers. In 1986, Congress passed the Asbestos Hazardous Emergency Response Act, which directs local school districts to control or remove asbestos from public school buildings. The schools could cover the asbestos with sealants to prevent the fibers from becoming airborne, or could remove the asbestos altogether. In 1989, the EPA enacted a ban to eliminate almost all remaining uses of asbestos in the United States by 1997.

The debate over the government's anti-asbestos activities focuses on two issues. First, some studies show that the removal process may release more fibers into the air than if the asbestos was left in place.

Second, the asbestos industry and product manufacturers are concerned with the costs of eliminating asbestos. They say that substitute materials in the manufacture of products would cost $460 to $800 million to them and consumers. They also say that the banning of asbestos products would cost far more in dollars than society would gain in health benefits.

The asbestos industry won a major court victory in the fall of 1991, when a federal appeals court overturned the EPA ban on the use and manufacture of asbestos. The court said that the EPA failed to prove that the dangers of asbestos outweighed the costs of the ban and the possible health effects of removal. The EPA plans to do further research on asbestos, which may set the stage for yet another court battle in the years to come.

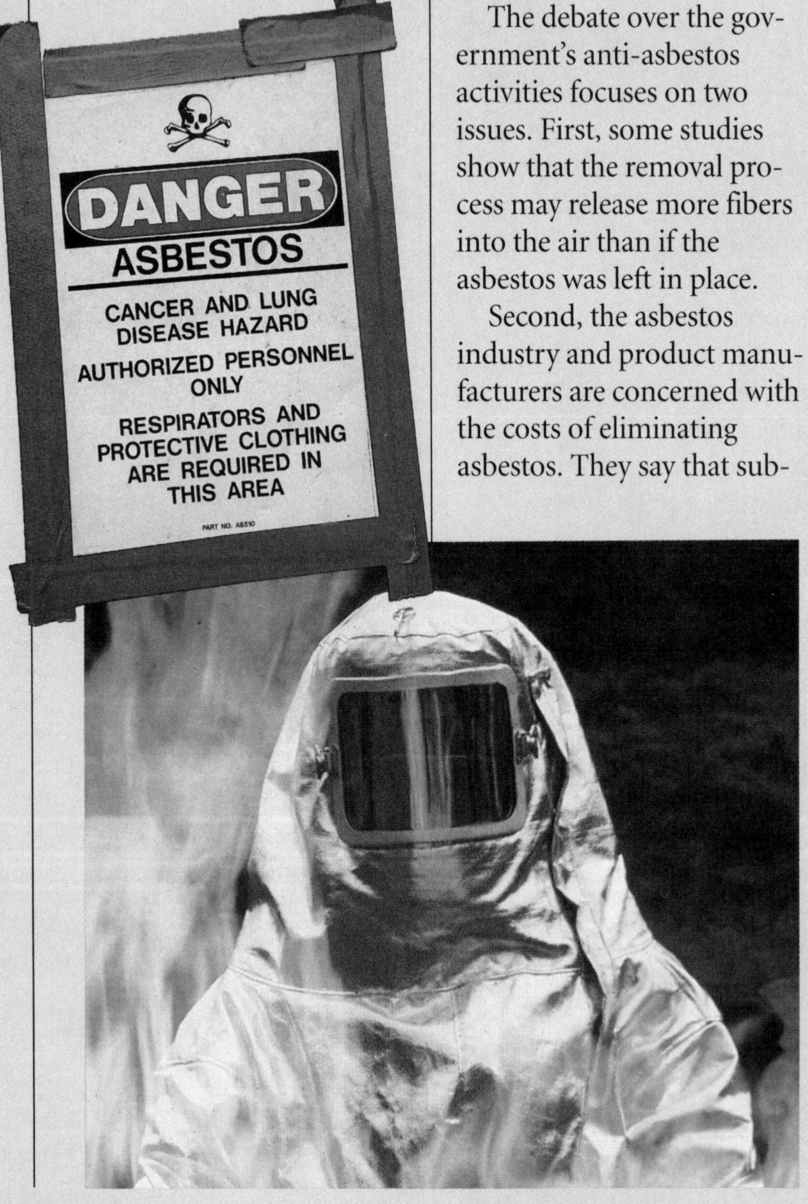

WHAT DO YOU THINK?

Research has shown that although asbestos is dangerous to people who mine or manufacture products from it, the risk of dying from exposure is very small. People are at least 100 times more likely to die in an airplane crash than from normal asbestos exposure. Do you agree with the ruling that the EPA went too far in trying to ban asbestos while ignoring the costs to society?

TECHNOLOGY CONNECTION

QUARTZ AND COMPUTERS

Quartz is a mineral made of the elements oxygen and silicon. Quartz may be found by itself, but it is often found in combination with other minerals. Pure quartz crystals are clear and have piezoelectric properties. This means the crystals become charged with electricity when mechanically compressed. Quartz is used to make one of the most important components of the computer age—the silicon chip.

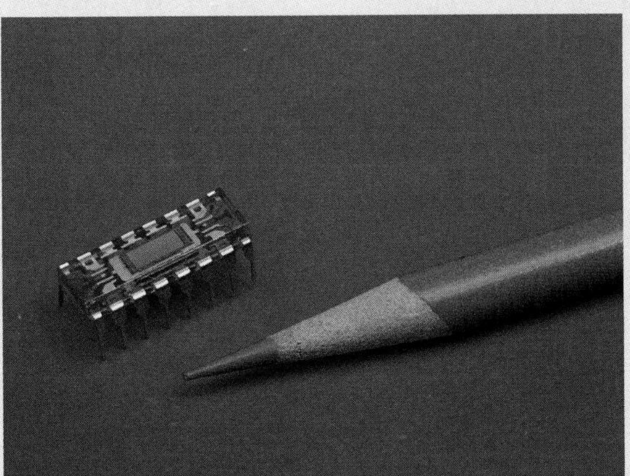

A chip is a tiny piece of silicon that is packed with thousands of electronic circuits. Silicon chips revolutionized computers because they can store and process huge amounts of information. The key to making silicon chips is that the quartz from which the silicon is refined must be very pure.

Quartz is mined and is then chemically altered so that all the particles of silicon are lined up. This creates crystals. The crystals are then heated and cooled to remove any remaining impurities. The end product is a pure silicon rod, which is sliced into thin wafers.

A computer-designed pattern is made of the electronic circuits that will be layered onto the silicon wafer. The pattern is reduced by a photographic process and becomes a "mask," which is then laid on the wafer. The mask on the wafer is copied several times, and many more layers of circuits are applied to the wafer. The wafer is then cut into individual chips, called microchips, which are attached to gold wires and sealed in a tiny frame. The microchips can be smaller than 1 centimeter on a side.

One microchip can contain thousands of electronic components. The tiny surface area of the chip makes it possible for electric currents to move incredibly fast between the components. The microchip revolutionized computers because of the speed with which it can do complex calculations and electronic processing. Microchips are used in everything from supercomputers to toasters.

WHAT DO YOU THINK?

The physical properties of quartz are unique. The piezoelectric effect that quartz exhibits makes quartz the material of choice in the transmitters of radio and TV sets. Quartz crystals can amplify energy and vibrate at a particular speed. The uniform number of vibrations per second is the basis for quartz watches and clocks.

Quartz crystals can be made artificially, and most quartz that is used in industry is synthetic. But can you imagine how our world might be different if scientists had never discovered the properties of quartz?

*H*istory CONNECTION

REWRITING PREHISTORY

From 5000 B.C. to 2500 B.C., human culture in Europe, Africa, and Asia depended on bronze, an alloy of tin and copper, to make most of the products of civilization. Bronze was used to make everything from tools and weapons to hairpins. Tablets written by the Assyrians 4000 years ago claim that they were very shrewd traders. The Assyrians made very profitable deals with their trade partners to the north in Anatolia (present day Turkey)—or so they claimed. Because the Assyrians were the only group at that time to leave written records, the Anatolians never got to tell their side of the story. However, a Turkish-American archeologist, Kutlu Aslihan Yener, is writing another chapter in this story based on newly found archeological evidence.

Although Yener was born in Turkey, she grew up in New York. In college, Yener studied chemistry, but an interest in traveling influenced her to switch to art history and to study in Turkey. While observing Turkish ruins, Aslihan developed an interest in past cultures. This led to the completion of a doctorate in archeology at Columbia University in New York.

Her original research involved identifying the sources of lead used in bronze objects. While searching for trade patterns for some of these sources, she made a far greater find in the Taurus Mountains of Turkey. Dr. Yener first found a cluster of eight hundred and fifty silver mines in a six-square-mile area. Surrounding hillsides have settlements and strongholds, many with slag heaps and stone mining tools still intact. In 1989, further research in this area yielded what she felt was a Bronze Age tin mine—just where the Assyrians said one couldn't be.

When the tin mine was found, little tin was left. Skeptics told Dr. Yener that she would have to find tin oxide to prove that the Taurus mine was actually originally mined for tin. Dr. Yener and her colleagues painstakingly searched for proof for six years before finding Turkish tin. The tin turned out to be burgundy colored rather than the usual black — one reason it may have been overlooked. As a final piece of evidence, in 1990 Dr. Yener discovered a vast underground city and tin processing center .

Dr. Yener's work has shown that the Bronze Age must have had some complex economic relationships. With competing sources of tin, there were probably price competitions and trade wars even then.

YOU TRY IT!

Many scholars relied upon the Assyrian tablets to give them an accurate picture of Bronze Age trade. Can it be misleading to learn about an event from only one source? Why or why not?

Chapter 10

Reviewing Main Ideas

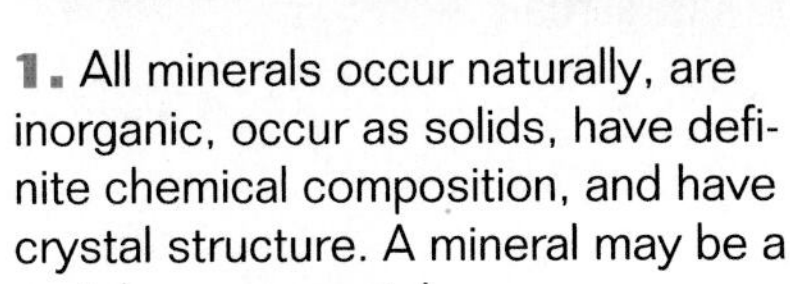

1. All minerals occur naturally, are inorganic, occur as solids, have definite chemical composition, and have crystal structure. A mineral may be a metal or a nonmetal.

2. Minerals can be identified by scratching them for hardness, observing their color and luster, streaking them for powder color, and noting their cleavage and fracture. Some minerals are also known for unique characteristics, such as magnetite's ability to attract iron.

3. When water containing dissolved elements evaporates or when magma cools, minerals form. If there is enough space, well-shaped crystals will form. If magma cools slowly, large crystals may form. If it cools quickly, as it will if exposed to air or water, smaller crystals will form.

Chapter Review

USING KEY SCIENCE TERMS

cleavage hardness
fracture mineral
gem streak

Use one of the terms above to complete each sentence.

1. A rating of 2 on the Mohs scale means that a mineral's ____ is comparatively low.
2. A mineral that breaks along smooth, flat surfaces as mica does has good ____.
3. A durable, rare, beautiful mineral may be a ____.
4. If a mineral breaks into pieces with sharp, jagged edges, it has the characteristic called ____.
5. The ____ test is useful because the color of a mineral's powder may differ from the color of its surface.

UNDERSTANDING IDEAS

Choose the best answer to complete each sentence.

1. All of the following terms correctly describe minerals except____.
   a. solid **c.** organic
   b. natural **d.** crystalline
2. The cubic shape of the mineral halite gives evidence of its ____.
   a. crystal structure
   b. metallic qualities
   c. water solution
   d. semiprecious value
3. People are most likely to use gems as ____.
   a. jewelry or ornaments
   b. sources of metals
   c. cleaning agents
   d. talcum powder
4. A mineral that does not exhibit cleavage exhibits ____.
   a. color **c.** metallic
   b. fracture **d.** streak
5. When you write with a graphite pencil, you have performed a kind of ____.
   a. scratch test
   b. cleavage and fracture
   c. streak test
   d. observation and conclusion
6. Calcite's fizzing reaction to hydrochloric acid is an example of its ____.
   a. perfect cleavage
   b. glassy luster
   c. metallic uses
   d. unique properties
7. All of the following can cause crystals to form except ____.
   a. slowly cooling magma
   b. decaying plant materials
   c. quickly cooling magma
   d. evaporating water
8. In order for mineral crystals to form, there must first be ____.
   a. metallic and nonmetallic powders
   b. veins and cracks in rocks
   c. elements dissolved in solution
   d. volcanic eruptions

CRITICAL THINKING

Use your understanding of the concepts developed in the chapter to answer each of the following questions.

1. Suppose you decide to enter the mineral mining business. You discover that there are five relatively abundant types of minerals near where you live. In the table, these five are ranked according to their abundance, 5 represents the most abundant and 1 represents the least abundant minerals. The table also gives the ease with which they may be extracted, 5 represents the most difficult and 1 represents the least difficult to extract.

Mineral	Abundance Ranking	Ease of Extraction
Aluminum	5	2
Iron	4	1
Sodium	3	3
Magnesium	2	5
Zinc	1	4

With one or two of your classmates, decide which mineral you would mine and explain why. Keep in mind the fact that the harder a mineral is to extract, the more it will cost to pay for the equipment and labor needed.

2. List at least five ways in which minerals are important to daily life.
3. Hypothesize what might happen to the value of gold jewelry if someone found an inexpensive way to manufacture gold.
4. Hypothesize what might happen to the value of automobiles if someone found an inexpensive way to manufacture the aluminum and iron used in automobiles.

PROBLEM SOLVING

Read the following problem and discuss your answers in a brief paragraph.

While hiking in the mountains, Helen found a pink rock. She took it home and tested it. It had no metallic luster and broke along a flat, smooth plane. The streak test was colorless. What did Helen decide that her rock was made of? Why?

CONNECTING IDEAS

Discuss each of the following in a brief paragraph.

1. Explain how mineral formation relates to forces inside Earth and thermal energy.
2. Explain why observing physical properties is important in identifying minerals.
3. When is a metal not a mineral?
4. **SCIENCE AND SOCIETY** Explain what asbestos is used for and why there has been some controversy regarding its use.
5. **LIFE SCIENCE CONNECTION** Describe how fertilization or crop rotation can help you get the minerals you need in your body.

DID YOU EVER WONDER . . .

Where rocks come from?

What is inside a rock?

Why some rocks are smooth and rounded while others have jagged edges?

Why there are so many different colors of rock?

You'll find the answers to these questions as you read this chapter.

Chapter 11

The Rock Cycle

In 1869, John Wesley Powell led companions down the Colorado River on the first recorded expedition into the Grand Canyon. Riding the rapids, he was awestruck by the grandeur you see pictured here. Never before had he seen rock so magnificent.

Powell marveled at how insignificant the great river appeared compared to the high wall of rock that rose above it. Isn't it amazing that this extraordinary canyon was formed little by little as the swiftly flowing Colorado River cut into many different rock layers? Here in the Grand Canyon, erosion has exposed many different types of rocks.

The Colorado River begins its journey in the Rocky Mountains. The Rocky Mountains are the largest mountain system in North America. Just as layers of rock in the Grand Canyon have been eroded, the peaks of the Rockies have been weathered and eroded to their present form.

Let's explore what makes the rocks of Earth's canyons, mountains, and other land features different.

EXPLORE!

How are rocks different?

Collect eight or nine different rocks from around your school. Examine them closely. In what ways are they the same? In what ways are they different? What characteristics could you use to sort them? Try to sort them into three separate groups.

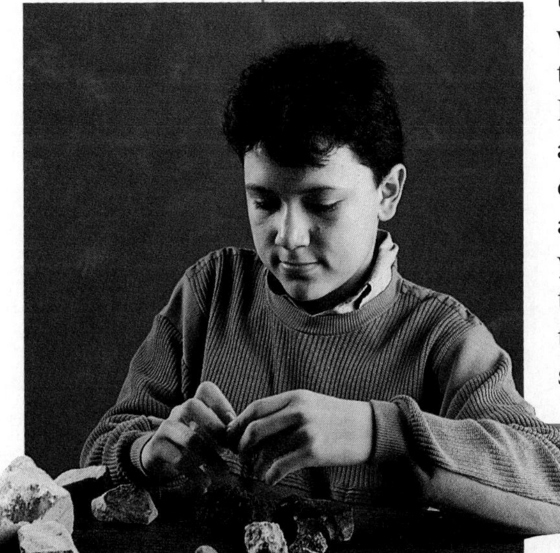

11-1 Igneous Rocks

OBJECTIVES

In this section, you will

- distinguish between a rock and a mineral;
- explain how igneous rock is formed;
- identify and classify igneous rocks.

KEY SCIENCE TERMS

rock
igneous rock
intrusive
extrusive

HOW DO IGNEOUS ROCKS FORM?

As Powell and his companions were carried along by the swift water at the base of the Grand Canyon, they noticed rocks that formed rows of irregular shelves, steep slopes, and sharp cliffs. Like Powell, you may see variations in the rocks along the sidewalk as you are walking to school. You might pick up an unusual rock and wonder why it looks different from most of the other rocks nearby. While most of the rocks are flat and dull, this one is rounded and has shiny black and white pieces in it. You put the interesting rock in your pocket and decide that you will ask your science teacher about it .

What exactly should you ask your teacher? You might begin by asking, "Why are rocks different from one another?" and "Is this a rock or a mineral?" You would probably also ask, "What kind of rock is this?"

EXPLORE!

What makes a rock unique?

You have noticed that rocks can be found with many shapes, colors, and textures. These characteristics can be used to classify and name rocks. One type of rock is called granite. Let's take a look at the characteristics of granite. Your teacher will provide you with several samples of granite. Some samples will be pink, and others will be speckled with pink, gray, and black color. You will also be given several minerals, including quartz, feldspar, hornblende, and mica. Use a magnifying lens to examine the granite. Do you notice any similarities between the small fragments in the rock and the mineral samples in front of you?

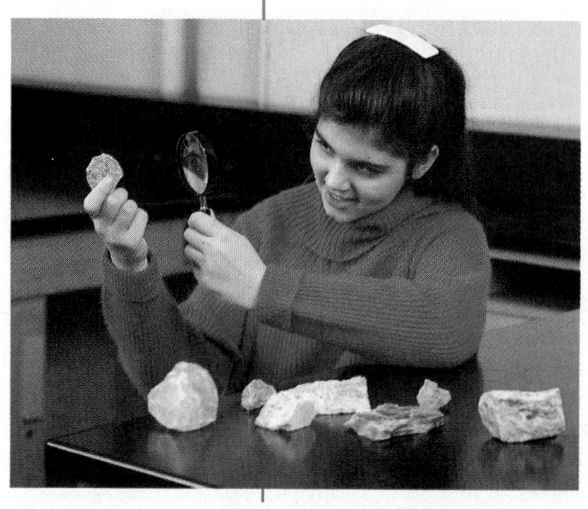

Suppose you were asked to assemble pieces of granite using the mineral samples. Which ones would you use to make pink granite? Which would make gray granite? Now examine a rock that isn't granite. Can you identify any of the minerals that make it up? Are they the same minerals you found in granite? Define the term *rock* based on your observations.

From the Explore, you discovered that a **rock** is a mixture of one or more minerals. Often several different minerals are mixed together, which gives a rock its color or texture. In granite, the mineral pieces are large enough to be seen without a microscope. Look at Figure 11-1. It shows a photograph of granite and its components. The granite is composed of a mixture of minerals that includes quartz, feldspar, mica, and hornblende.

The photo helps you see that a rock can be made up of different minerals, but how do minerals combine to create granite and other types of rock? Recall from Chapter 10 that minerals have crystal forms. When examining a rock, some of the mineral crystals may be too small for you to see the shapes that you recognize as characteristics of crystals. The following activity will help you see how minerals may crystallize to form rock.

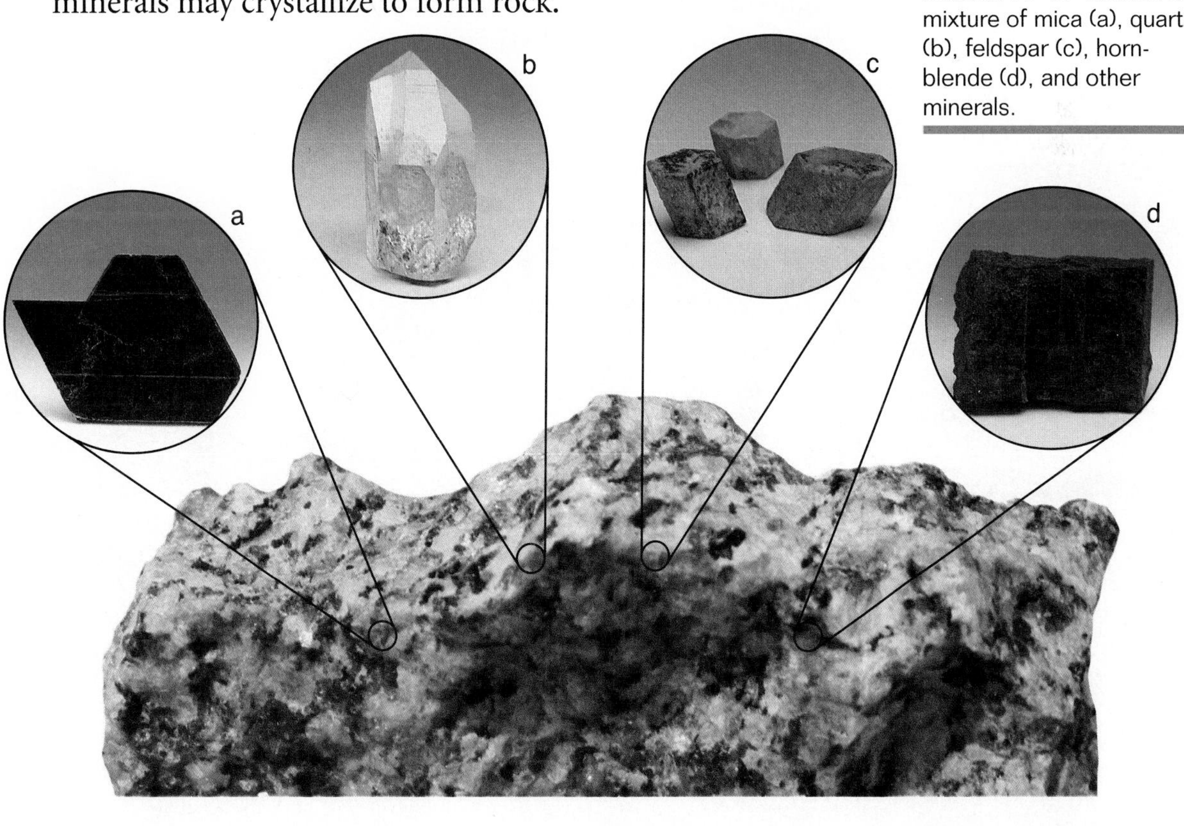

a

b

c

d

FIGURE 11-1. Granite is a mixture of mica (a), quartz (b), feldspar (c), hornblende (d), and other minerals.

FIND OUT!

What happens as a mineral cools?

Place a small piece of the mineral alum on a microscope slide. Wearing a thermal glove, set the slide on a hot plate for a few seconds—just until the alum melts. Then quickly place the slide under a microscope. What do you observe?

Conclude and Apply

1. What is happening to the alum?
2. What happens to the mineral as it cools?

In the activity, the alum behaved like lava from a volcano or like magma that is trapped below Earth's surface. As the lava or magma cools, it becomes solid similar to the way fudge candy hardens as it cools. Many crystals of various minerals form from the cooling of lava or magma. The crystals grow together and form one solid igneous rock. An **igneous rock** is a rock that formed as molten material cooled.

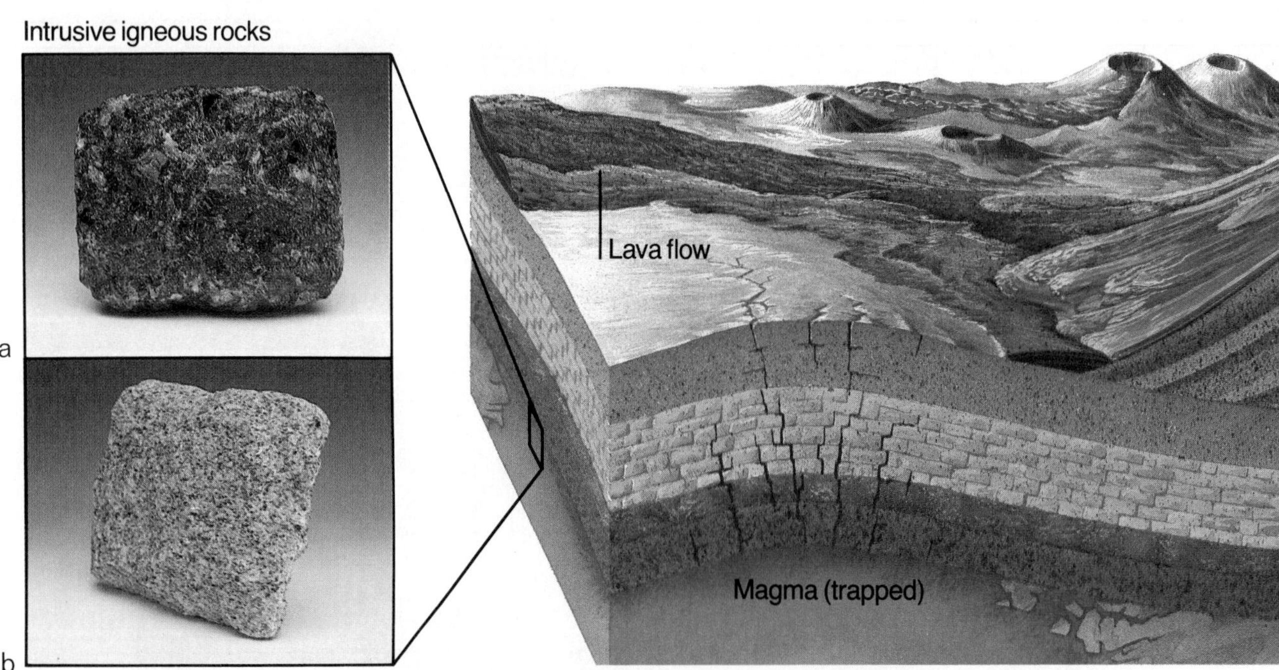

Intrusive Igneous Rocks

When igneous rocks are formed by magma that cools beneath Earth's surface, they are called **intrusive** igneous rocks. Intrusive rocks are found at Earth's surface when rock and soil that once covered them have been removed by erosion. They may also be found at the surface when forces in Earth such as compression or tension have pushed them to Earth's surface. Figure 11-2 shows you examples of two intrusive igneous rocks and where they might form.

Extrusive Igneous Rocks

When igneous rocks are formed by lava that cools on Earth's surface, they are called **extrusive** igneous rocks. This lava is exposed to air and moisture, and it cools quickly. The quick rate of cooling usually doesn't allow time for large crystals to grow. For this reason, some extrusive igneous

FIGURE 11-2. Intrusive rocks such as gabbro (a) and diorite (b) form from magma that cools slowly. Extrusive rocks such as rhyolite (c) and andesite (d) form from fast-cooling lava.

FIGURE 11-3. Basalt is the most common extrusive rock. Black sand beaches in Hawaii are made of tiny particles of basalt.

rocks have individual mineral crystals that are too small to be seen without magnification. Observe the size of the individual minerals of the extrusive igneous rocks in Figure 11-2. Compare this size with the size of the individual minerals in intrusive igneous rocks.

Basalt, the most common extrusive igneous rock, is shown in Figure 11-3. Notice that basalt is made of small, dark minerals. It is a common rock of the Hawaiian Islands. The photograph also shows an unusual beach in the Hawaiian Islands. It has black sand. Recall that weathering breaks down rocks and erosion carries the rock particles away. Can you apply what you know about igneous rocks and the processes of weathering and erosion to explain where the black sand came from?

Other extrusive igneous rocks include pumice, obsidian, and scoria. Notice in Figure 11-4 that these rocks contain no individual crystals. Can you describe a situation in which lava would cool but no crystals would form? The lava

FIGURE 11-4. Pumice (a), obsidian (b), and scoria (c) contain no individual crystals.

a

b

c

that formed the pumice, obsidian, and scoria cooled so quickly when exposed to the atmosphere and water on Earth's surface that there was no time for crystals to form. See how obsidian, in Figure 11-4, resembles smooth black glass. Now observe the holes in pumice and scoria. The holes formed when pockets of air and other gases were trapped in the molten material as it cooled.

COMPARING AND CONTRASTING
Examine samples of obsidian, pumice, and gabbro. In what ways do obsidian and pumice differ from gabbro, another igneous rock? In what ways are they similar? If you need help, refer to the **Skill Handbook** on page 683.

CLASSIFYING IGNEOUS ROCKS

Unless we're near an erupting volcano, we can't actually observe the formation of igneous rocks to see whether they were created below or above Earth's surface. Yet we can identify igneous rocks as either intrusive or extrusive by the size of their crystals. Look at the sizes of the crystals in the two sides of the rock shown in Figure 11-5. Rocks that have large, visible crystals are called coarse-grained rocks. Rocks that have crystals so small that we cannot see them are referred to as fine-grained rocks. Coarse-grained, fine-grained, glassy, and porous are examples of rock textures.

FIGURE 11-5. Notice the different textures in this rock. Which side was formed intrusively? Which side was formed extrusively?

Igneous rocks can also be identified and grouped by their overall color. Look at the photographs of the igneous rocks in Figure 11-6. Why is one of the rocks so lightly colored? It must be composed of light-colored minerals such as quartz and some feldspars. Notice the other rock is very dark. It is composed of dark-colored minerals such as pyroxene and labradorite.

a 

b 

FIGURE 11-6. What gives rhyolite (a) its light color? Why is the gabbro (b) dark-colored?

INVESTIGATE!

11-1 CLASSIFYING IGNEOUS ROCKS

Here is a chance to apply what you know about igneous rocks. In this Investigate, you will **classify** igneous rocks by **observing** their texture, color, and visible minerals.

PROBLEM

How are igneous rocks classified?

MATERIALS

igneous rock samples, A–F
hand lens

PROCEDURE

1. Copy the data table.
2. Examine each rock sample with a hand lens. Determine the texture of each rock sample. Remember, if the crystals are large and easily seen, the texture is coarse. If the crystals are so small that they are not easily distinguished, the texture is described as fine. Rocks can also be glassy or porous in texture. **Classify** the rocks into groups based on texture.
3. Answer Question 1 under Analyze.
4. Determine the overall color of each rock.
5. Answer Questions 2 and 3 under Analyze.
6. Examine the coarse-grained rocks to determine the minerals present.
7. **Classify** each sample according to its composition and grain size. Then, **interpret the table** and name each sample.

ANALYZE

1. Which samples are intrusive or extrusive?
2. What minerals may be responsible for the color of sample B?
3. Name at least two other igneous rocks that owe their colors to the presence of these minerals.

CONCLUDE AND APPLY

4. Why do igneous rocks of the same composition sometimes have different sizes of grains?
5. What characteristics help you identify an igneous rock as extrusive or intrusive?
6. **Going Further:** How does obsidian differ from most other igneous rocks?

DATA AND OBSERVATIONS

ROCK SAMPLE	TEXTURE	OVERALL COLOR	MINERALS VISIBLE	ROCK NAME
A				
B				
C				
D				
E				
F				

TABLE 11-1. Common Igneous Rocks

Overall Color	Intrusive Coarse Texture	Extrusive Fine Texture
Dark	Gabbro	Basalt
		Scoria
Intermediate	Diorite	Andesite
Light	Granite	Rhyolite
		Pumice

Granite, rhyolite, gabbro, and basalt are individual types of igneous rock. Use the table to describe their characteristics. There are also some igneous rocks that are classified as intermediate in color. They are neither dark nor light in overall color. Diorite and andesite are examples of these intermediate rocks.

Igneous rocks are the most abundant type of rock on Earth. They've been classified to make them easier to identify and to study. By studying all types of rocks, geologists and other scientists have been able to hypothesize how Earth formed. They have been able to determine how mountains such as the Rockies were formed from an upheaval of Earth's crust, and how the rock layers of the Grand Canyon have accumulated and eroded over millions of years.

How do we know?

The History of the Rockies

In the Rocky Mountains, geologists have found igneous rocks that were formed deep within Earth's hot interior. From this, geologists have determined that the peaks of the Rockies were formed during an upheaval of Earth's crust.

In the southern half of the Rockies, geologists find much extrusive igneous rock. Such rocks indicate that this section of mountains was once volcanic.

FIGURE 11-7. The Rocky Mountains formed when Earth's crust was forced up.

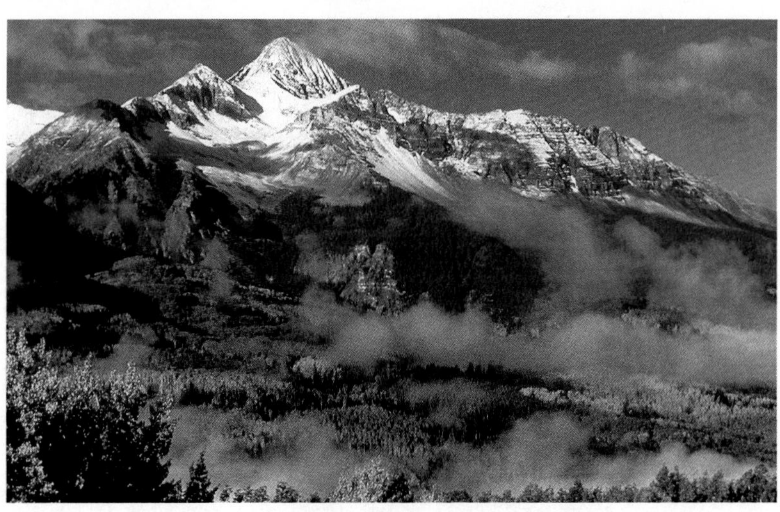

Check Your Understanding

1. What is the difference between a rock and a mineral?
2. How do igneous rocks form?
3. Describe the differences between intrusive and extrusive igneous rocks.
4. **APPLY:** How are granite and rhyolite similar? How are they different?

11-2 Metamorphic Rocks

OBJECTIVES

In this section, you will

- explain how metamorphic rock is formed;
- identify and classify metamorphic rocks.

KEY SCIENCE TERMS

metamorphic rock
foliated
nonfoliated

HOW DO METAMORPHIC ROCKS FORM?

Suppose you discovered that the rock you found on your way to school is an igneous rock. It formed when crystals of one or more minerals grew together as magma or lava cooled. Will the minerals in the rock remain unchanged forever? You know that weathering can change rocks, but are there other ways that rocks can change?

To understand a different way that rocks can change, think about how the contents of your lunch bag might change after it's been in your locker all day. The apple you packed has been resting on your sandwich and cream-filled cake since early this morning. The heat in your locker has turned the cake into a gooey mess. The pressure from the apple has flattened your sandwich. In the following activity, observe what changes occur when pressure is similarly applied to a model of rock layers.

FIND OUT!

What can happen to a rock when it is exposed to pressure?

To find out, you will first need to make a crayon rock using four to six of each color of crayon—red, green, blue, and yellow. Use a pencil sharpener to make a pile of crayon shavings on a sheet of aluminum foil. They will represent different minerals in an igneous rock. Fold the edges of the foil toward the middle to enclose the shavings within a rectangular packet. Gently flatten the packet by squeezing it between your palms. Now unfold the foil packet and examine your rock.

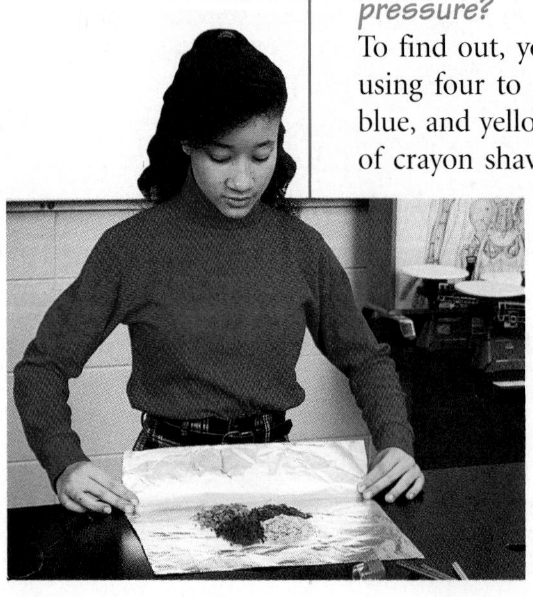

Return the crayon rock into its foil packet and see what happens when you squeeze it between two boards using a vise or two C-clamps.

Conclude and Apply

1. How did the crayon rock change?
2. Recall that the individual shavings represent mineral crystals. What do you think would happen to the crayon minerals if heat was applied? Would the minerals melt? Would the colors run together? Recombine?

You have seen what happens to minerals in rocks when they are exposed to increases in pressure. **Metamorphic rock** forms when rock is changed by heat or pressure or both. Figure 11-8 shows what can happen when pressure is applied to the igneous rock granite. The minerals in granite are flattened and form the metamorphic rock gneiss (NIS). What occurs in Earth to change these rocks?

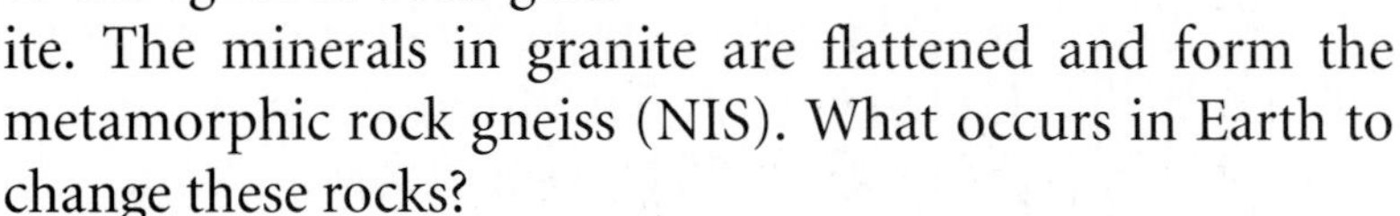

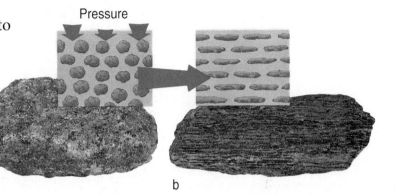

FIGURE 11-8. The mineral grains in granite (a) are flattened and aligned when pressure is applied to them. Gneiss (b) is formed.

Rocks beneath Earth's surface are under great pressure from overlying rock layers. They are also exposed to heat from magma. If the heat and pressure are great enough, the rocks melt and magma forms. If the heat and pressure are not great enough to melt the rocks, the mineral grains in the rock may change in size or shape. Some are flattened, and some combine with surrounding minerals to form new or bigger minerals.

Metamorphic rocks can also form from rocks other than igneous rocks. In the following activity, you'll compare metamorphic rocks with nonmetamorphic rocks.

EXPLORE!

From what do metamorphic rocks form?

Your teacher will provide you with samples of four metamorphic rocks and four nonmetamorphic rocks. Each of the metamorphic rocks formed from one of the nonmetamorphic rocks. For each metamorphic rock, determine which nonmetamorphic rock it might be related to.

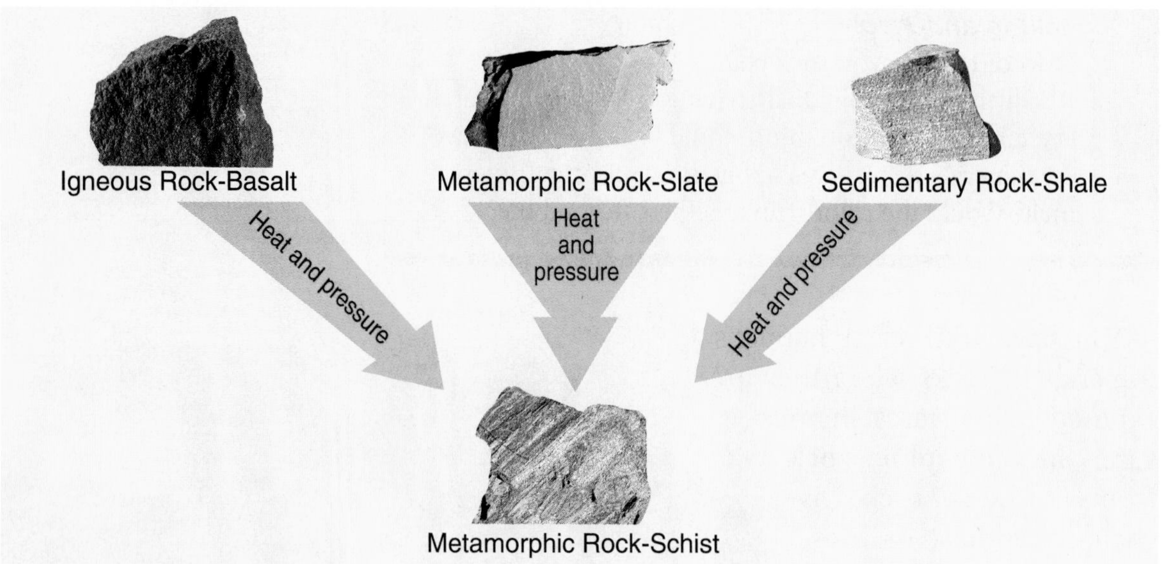

FIGURE 11-9. The minerals within a rock can be altered by heat and pressure until a new metamorphic rock is formed.

The Explore activity helped you see the similarities and differences between rocks before and after metamorphism. The same kind of metamorphic rock can form from different kinds of rock. For example, the metamorphic rock schist (SHIHST) can form from the metamorphic rock slate. As you can see in Figure 11-9, schist can also form from the igneous rock basalt or from the sedimentary rock shale. You will learn more about sedimentary rocks later in this chapter.

CLASSIFYING METAMORPHIC ROCKS

In any of the samples you observed in the Explore, did the mineral grains flatten and line up in parallel bands? Metamorphic rocks with this kind of **foliated** texture form when minerals in the original rock flatten under pressure. Two examples of foliated rocks are slate and gneiss.

Slate forms from the sedimentary rock shale. Under heat and pressure, the minerals in shale become so tightly compacted that water can't pass between them. Slate is easily separated along its foliation layers.

Gneiss, another foliated rock, forms when a great deal of pressure is applied to granite or a few other types of rocks. Quartz, feldspar, mica, and other minerals in granite aren't changed much in the process, but they are rearranged into alternating bands.

FIGURE 11-10. The differing amounts of minerals in shale result in many different colors of slate. Slate is often used for patio floors, stepping stones, and roofing shingles.

In some metamorphic rocks, the mineral grains change, combine, and rearrange, but they don't form visible bands. This process produces a **nonfoliated** texture. Such rocks don't separate easily into layers. Instead, they fracture into pieces of random size and shape.

One nonfoliated metamorphic rock is marble. Marble forms from the sedimentary rock limestone, which is composed of calcite. Marble can be carved and polished, making it a popular material for sculpture. Besides calcite, marble contains several other minerals that may lend color to marble. Hornblende and serpentine give marble a greenish tone, while hematite makes it red.

So far, we've discovered how two types of rock are formed. Next we'll observe how sedimentary rocks are formed and how some igneous and metamorphic rocks are formed from them. The next section will complete our investigation of different kinds of rock.

FIGURE 11-11. Sculptors . work with marble because it's relatively soft and easy to shape.

Check Your Understanding

1. How do igneous rock and metamorphic rock differ?
2. By what characteristics are metamorphic rocks classified?
3. **APPLY:** Slate is sometimes used as building material for roofs. What properties make it useful for this purpose?

11-3 Sedimentary Rocks

OBJECTIVES

In this section, you will

- explain how sedimentary rock is formed;
- identify and classify sedimentary rocks;
- use a diagram of the rock cycle to explain how rocks form and change.

KEY SCIENCE TERMS

sedimentary rock
rock cycle

HOW DO SEDIMENTARY ROCKS FORM?

So far, you've explored two major types of rocks: igneous and metamorphic. In this section, you will learn about a third type of rock, which is composed of sediments. Not surprisingly, this rock is called sedimentary rock. Most of the rocks *below* Earth's surface are igneous rocks, but most of the rocks exposed *at* Earth's surface are sedimentary rocks. Where do sedimentary rocks—and the sediments that form them—come from?

You may recall from your earlier studies that weathering and erosion are two major processes that change Earth's surface. Weathering breaks rocks or remains of plants and animals into smaller pieces called sediments. These sediments are transported to new locations by the agents of erosion—water, wind, ice, and gravity. Under certain conditions, deposited sediments recombine to form a solid rock called **sedimentary rock**.

Table 11-2 lists various sizes of sediments and shows examples of the various sedimentary rocks formed from these sediments. How do deposited sediments form rock?

TABLE 11-2. Samples of Various Sedimentary Rocks

Sediment	Clay	Silt	Sand	Pebbles
Size range of grains	< 0.004 mm	0.004 – 0.06 mm	0.06 – 2 mm	2 – 64 mm
Examples of rock formed	Mudstone	Siltstone	Sandstone	Conglomerate

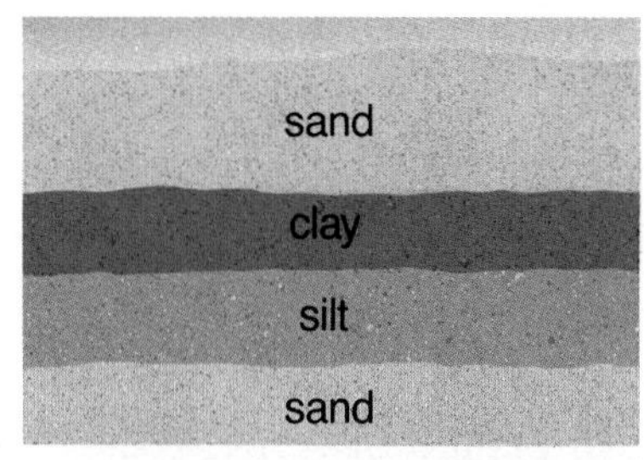

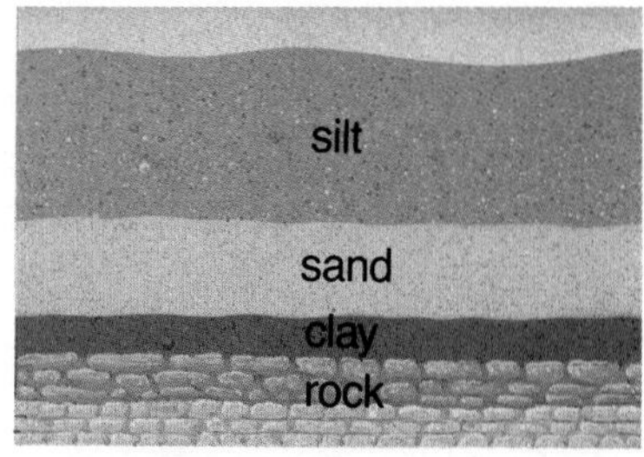

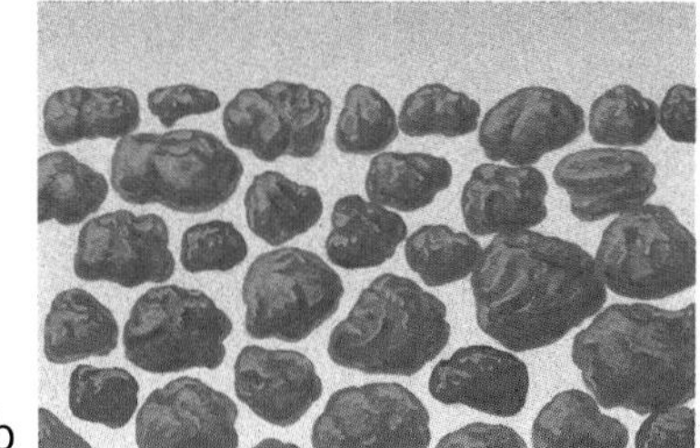

FIGURE 11-12. Two processes that form sedimentary rocks are compaction (a) and cementation (b).

Think of an area where layer after layer of sediments are deposited. The pressure from the upper layers pushes down on the lower layers. If the sediments are very small, they can compress and form rock. This process is called compaction, and is shown in Figure 11-12 (a). How else can sediments form rock?

FIND OUT!

How can sediments become cemented together?

Fill a paper cup with sand. In a second cup, mix one part white glue and one part water. Poke small holes in the sand-filled cup large enough for the glue solution to drain through, but not large enough for much sand to run out.

Suspend the paper cup with the sand over a bowl. Pour the glue solution into the cup and allow it to drain through the sand for several days. Then tear away the paper.

Conclude and Apply

How is this block of sand similar to a sedimentary rock?

Pressure alone cannot make large sediments like sand stick together. Look again at Figure 11-12. It shows how a process called cementation holds large sediments together with naturally occurring substances that act like the glue you used in the Find Out.

To identify a sedimentary rock, examine it to see if it contains sediments that have been compacted or cemented.

CLASSIFYING SEDIMENTARY ROCKS

Sedimentary rocks can be composed of any type of weathered and eroded rock material and sometimes even particles from plants and animals. To classify sedimentary rocks, you must look at the sediments they contain as well as the way in which the rocks were formed.

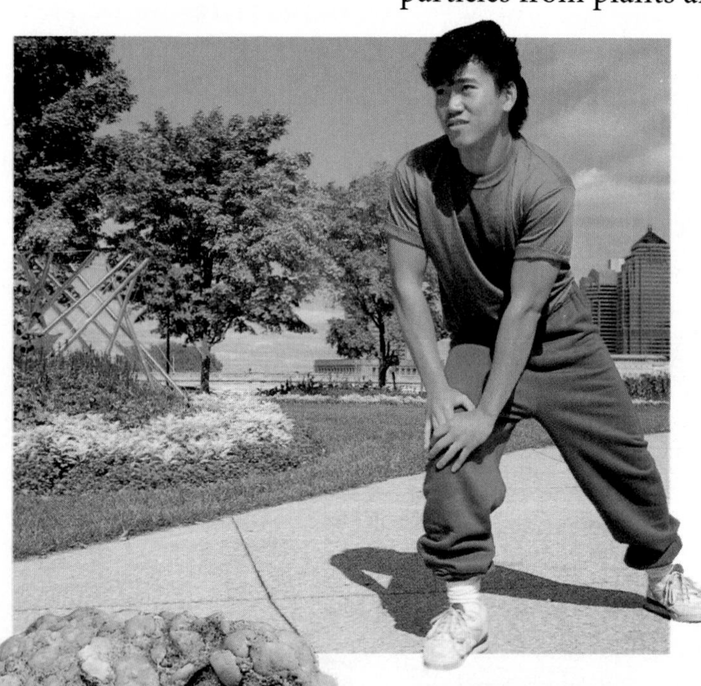

FIGURE 11-13. The concrete making up the sidewalk is similar to a naturally occurring detrital sedimentary rock.

Detrital Sedimentary Rocks

Detrital (dih TRIT uhl) sedimentary rocks are made of the broken fragments of other rocks. They may also contain small amounts of plant and animal remains. These sediments, which are the solid products of weathering, have been compacted and cemented together.

In some detrital rock, the sediments are large and well rounded. In another kind, the sediments are large but have sharp angles.

The pebble-sized sediments in both kinds of detrital rock may consist of any type of rock or mineral. Often, they are chunks of the mineral quartz or feldspar. They can also be pieces of rocks such as gneiss, granite, or limestone.

Although not a rock, concrete is made by pebbles and sand grains that have been cemented together. Look at Figure 11-13. Notice how similar the concrete sidewalk looks to naturally occurring detrital rock.

FIGURE 11-14. Why does this sandstone look so much like desert sand dunes? This rock formed from sand deposited in layers by desert winds.

Another detrital sedimentary rock is sandstone. Can you infer from Figure 11-14 which agent of erosion deposited the sediment in this rock? Its sand-sized sediments are usually grains of the minerals quartz and feldspar. These sand grains can be compacted together if clay particles are also present, or they can be cemented.

Shale is a detrital sedimentary rock that requires no cementation to hold its particles together. Its sediments are clay-sized minerals. Clay-sized sediments can be compacted together by pressure from overlying layers.

DID YOU KNOW?

Layers of sandstone beneath Earth's surface transport large volumes of groundwater. People drill wells into some sandstone deposits to obtain drinking water.

Chemical Sedimentary Rocks

The sediments of detrital sedimentary rocks originate from weathering and are transported as solid particles. But what happens to rock particles when weathering causes some of their minerals to dissolve?

FIND OUT!

What can happen to dissolved minerals?
Dissolve 1 teaspoon of salt in 2 tablespoons of water to make a saltwater solution. Pour the solution into a shallow pan and allow it to evaporate.

Conclude and Apply

Now look at the bottom of the pan. What do you think happens when ocean water evaporates?

FIGURE 11-15. Based on what you've learned, can you explain how the rock salt shown here might have formed?

As you have just observed, some layers of sediment come from minerals that were once chemical compounds dissolved in solution. Chemical compounds become concentrated when the water in seas or lakes evaporates. Layers of deposited minerals are left behind when solutions evaporate and the chemical compounds that were within them precipitate. These mineral layers can form into chemical sedimentary rocks.

Limestone is an example of a chemical sedimentary rock. Although it usually contains several other minerals and sediments, limestone is at least 50 percent calcite. Limestone can form when calcite is carried in solution in ocean or lake water. As the water evaporates, the concentration of calcite increases until the point of saturation is reached. The calcite then precipitates onto the ocean or lake floor, where it may eventually form limestone. We know that oceans once covered much of the United States for millions of years because of the huge amounts of limestone that are present over much of the United States.

When lakes and seas evaporate, they often leave deposits of the mineral halite. Halite, mixed with a few other minerals, forms another chemical sedimentary rock called rock salt. Rock salt deposits range in thickness from a few meters to over 400 meters. People mine these deposits because rock salt is an important resource. It's used in the manufacturing of glass, paper, soap, and dairy products. It's the same salt used in home-made ice cream makers and on streets in the wintertime to melt snow and ice. You even use the halite in rock salt in your kitchen as table salt!

DID YOU KNOW?

Many of the earliest trade routes between continents were established for the purposes of trading salt. Gold and salt were considered of equal value—salt was even used as currency in early China.

Organic Sedimentary Rocks

Other sedimentary rocks have large amounts of the remains of once-living things, also known as fossils. They are classified as organic sedimentary rocks. One of the most common organic sedimentary rocks is fossil-rich limestone. Like chemical limestone, it is made of the mineral calcite. But fossil-rich limestone consists mostly of the remains of once-living aquatic organisms, together with calcite.

FIGURE 11-16. The White Cliffs of Dover, England, are composed mostly of chalk.

Ocean animals such as mussels and snails make their shells from the mineral calcite and a few other minerals. When the animals die, their shells accumulate on the ocean floor. When these calcareous shells are compacted and cemented together, layers of sedimentary rock are formed.

If the rock is composed entirely of shell fragments that are relatively large and unbroken, the rock is called coquina (koh KEE nuh). If the shells are microscopic, the rock is called chalk. When we use naturally occurring chalk to write with, we're actually crushing and smearing the calcareous shells of once-living ocean organisms called protozoa.

Now that you've explored three different types of sedimentary rocks, you can use your knowledge and power of observation to identify the unknown sedimentary rocks you'll examine in the following Investigate activity.

I N V E S T I G A T E !

11-2 SEDIMENTARY ROCKS

In this activity, you will identify and **classify** sedimentary rocks.

PROBLEM

How can you **classify** sedimentary rocks?

MATERIALS   

sedimentary rock samples
5% hydrochloric acid (HCl)
dropper
water
hand lens
goggles
paper towels
apron
calcite sample

PROCEDURE

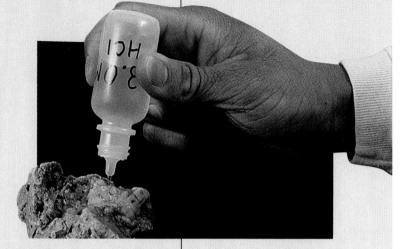

1. Copy the data table.
2. Identify the sediments in each sample as detrital, chemical, or organic. **Classify** the size of the sediments in the rocks as pebbles, sand, silt, or clay. Refer back to Table 11-2.
3. Put a few drops of HCl on your sample of calcite. **CAUTION:** *HCl is an acid and can cause burns. Wear goggles and an apron. Rinse any spill with cold water.* **Observe** what happens. Use a paper towel to remove remaining acid.
4. Put a few drops of HCl on each rock sample. Which samples contain calcite?
5. Describe any minerals present.
6. **Classify** your samples. Then identify each rock.

ANALYZE

1. How did examining the sediments help you to identify the detrital rocks?
2. Why did you test the rocks with HCl?

CONCLUDE AND APPLY

3. Contrast detrital rocks with chemical and organic rocks. How do they differ?
4. **Going Further:** Acid dissolved some minerals in the rock. Explain why this is a weathering process.

DATA AND OBSERVATIONS

SAMPLE	SEDIMENT SIZE	OBSERVATIONS	MINERALS PRESENT	DETRITAL, CHEMICAL, OR ORGANIC	ROCK NAME
A					
B					
C					
D					
E					

Pictured in Figure 11-17 is a very useful organic sedimentary rock—coal. Coal forms when pieces of dead plants are buried under other sediments. These plant materials are first decomposed by microorganisms. The resulting sediments are compacted. Over millions of years, the buried sediments form coal. Like obsidian, coal has no mineral crystals. However, it is still often classified as a rock.

You've learned about igneous, metamorphic, and sedimentary rocks. Within and on Earth, these rocks are continually changing from one form to another.

FIGURE 11-17. A valuable layer of coal is located under deep layers of sediment in this strip mine.

THE ROCK CYCLE

By now, you have an idea about what processes made the variety of rocks Powell observed as he explored the Grand Canyon. You know that rocks form in different ways from a variety of minerals, giving them unique characteristics.

What has happened to the rocks that Powell observed over a hundred years ago? Some of the rocks have probably been broken apart and carried away by weathering and erosion. Have some of the rocks changed into other kinds of rocks?

Figure 11-18 shows how weathering, erosion, compaction, cementation, melting, and cooling all interact to form and change rocks. The processes by which Earth materials change to form different kinds of rocks make up the **rock cycle**. Can you explain why the rock cycle has no beginning and no end?

On Figure 11-18, you can trace the formation of different types of rock. Metamorphic rock forms when heat, pressure, or both are applied to either sedimentary or igneous rock. Sedimentary rock forms when metamorphic or igneous rock is weathered and eroded into sediments and then compacted and/or cemented. Igneous rock forms when magma or lava cools. You can

SKILLBUILDER

SEQUENCING
Put the following events in a sequence that could explain how a metamorphic rock might form from an igneous rock. (HINT: Start with igneous rock forms.) Use each event just once. If you need help, refer to the **Skill Handbook** on page 678.
sedimentary rock forms
weathering and erosion occur
heat and pressure are applied
igneous rock forms
metamorphic rock forms
sediments are formed
compaction, cementation occur

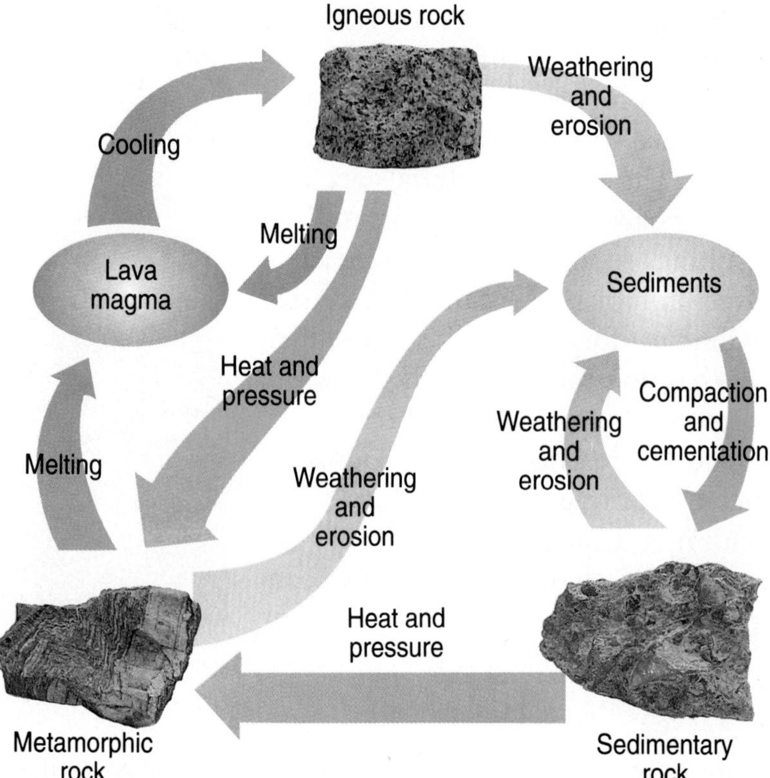

FIGURE 11-18. This model of the rock cycle shows how one rock changes into another.

see the relationship between these rocks and the processes that form them in Figure 11-18. When a rock changes into another type of rock, its minerals can flatten, grow, dissolve, melt, or combine with other minerals.

All the rocks you've learned about in this chapter formed through the processes of the rock cycle. And all the rocks around you, including those used to make buildings, monuments, and even sidewalks, are part of the rock cycle. They are all changing.

Check Your Understanding

1. How is sedimentary rock formed?
2. Why can limestone be classified as either a chemical or an organic sedimentary rock?
3. Explain how limestone can change into several other rocks in the rock cycle.
4. **APPLY:** How can both granite and slate be found in the same detrital rock?

EXPANDING YOUR VIEW

CONTENTS

A Closer Look
Natural Glass 337

Life Science Connection
Animals Eat Rocks! 338

Science and Society
Who Owns the Rocks? 339

Leisure Connection
Collecting Rocks 341

Teens In Science
Caving Clan 342

A CLOSER LOOK

NATURAL GLASS

Natural glass forms when thick, slow-flowing lava is rapidly cooled. One kind of lava that typically forms natural glass is rhyolitic (ri uh LIHT ic) lava. This lava contains a lot of silica, which is a mineral made of the elements silicon and oxygen. When rhyolitic lava cools on the surface of Earth, it forms crystals. The size of the crystals determines the texture of the igneous rock. Some scientists compare rhyolitic lava to cold honey. The lava is a thick liquid that flows very slowly. Sometimes rhyolitic lava cools so quickly, crystals do not have time to form. This lava pours out of a volcano, resists flowing, and cools quickly. The result is a smooth, shiny, glossy volcanic glass called obsidian.

Obsidian is natural glass, sometimes referred to as frozen liquid. To understand this idea of frozen liquid, picture a windowpane. Window glass is also considered frozen liquid. It is smooth and glossy in texture. The difference between window glass and obsidian is window glass contains no impurities, so it is clear in color. Obsidian contains metallic impurities, and so is usually black in color. The presence of iron oxide will turn obsidian red. Other colors of obsidian do occur, but are rare. Obsidian is found in abundance where volcanoes erupted in cool climate areas. One of the most famous obsidian sites is a nine-mile-long and five-mile-wide formation in Yellowstone National Park.

When obsidian fractures, it breaks into pieces that are angular and sharp. For this reason, ancient cultures found obsidian useful for arrowheads and knives.

Scientists estimate that humans began making their own glass about 6000 years ago. Some scientists theorize that human-made glass was discovered by accident, when rocks and sand were melted by fire, creating a product similar to nature's own glass. Today's glass is made in a similar way. Sand, soda (sodium oxide) and lime (calcium oxide) are mixed and melted in a furnace.

WHAT DO YOU THINK?

Today, obsidian is often used in surgical instruments. Describe how the properties of obsidian make this rock useful for surgery.

LIFE SCIENCE CONNECTION

ANIMALS EAT ROCKS!

Imagine that part of your regular diet was swallowing rocks—whole. Hard to imagine? Scientists know that certain species of birds and other animals swallow small rocks to help digest food.

More than 300 years ago, scientists discovered that the stomachs of birds are very different from other animals' stomachs. A bird's stomach is usually a sac with two sections, or chambers. One of the chambers is where juices are produced. The juices begin to break down food for digestion. The other chamber is known as the gizzard. The gizzard is a muscular, thick, strong sac that contracts and expands, grinding hard foods much like the teeth and mouth of other animals.

Birds that eat mostly insects or fruit have small gizzards, but birds that eat hard foods have large, powerful gizzards. Hard foods may include seeds, nuts, and shellfish. Because birds do not have teeth, they often swallow hard foods whole, or nearly whole. If you watch birds in your yard or neighborhood, you may see them peck at hard foods, breaking off bite-sized pieces. Most birds that eat plant parts or seeds swallow large pieces of hard foods.

The gizzard moves in rhythmic contractions to grind up food for digestion. To help with the grinding action, many birds swallow small stones or grit. Grit is a mixture of sand and very tiny pebbles from rocks that have weathered. In the gizzard, grit mixes with the digestive juices, and the grinding action of the gizzard walls works with the grit to break up food. A bird's gizzard can be as powerful as a mammal's mouth. The gizzard is like the jaw, while the grit acts like a set of teeth.

Until recently, scientists thought only birds and a few small animals such as earthworms swallowed rocks to help them digest food. However, some scientists now believe that certain species of dinosaurs also ate rocks to aid in digestion. This discovery was made by paleontologists, scientists who study fossils and the remains of extinct animals. Paleontologists found what they call stomach stones in the fossil of a dinosaur. The placement of the stones in the skeleton led scientists to conclude that the dinosaur had a gizzard similar to that of modern birds. The discovery of this dinosaur is an important scientific find. Before the discovery, paleontologists were unable to learn much about the internal organs of these extinct creatures.

WHAT DO YOU THINK?

Most scientists believe that modern birds are the living descendants of dinosaurs. How does the discovery of stomach stones in a dinosaur support this hypothesis?

SCIENCE AND SOCIETY

WHO OWNS THE ROCKS?

Let's say you lean over your back fence and pick up an interesting rock from your friend's yard. Does this rock belong to you or to your friend? Did you know that there are laws to decide questions like this?

Let's say you own a house and the property on which your house is built. You decide to build a swimming pool in your backyard. While digging a hole for your pool, you discover oil right there in your own backyard! The newspaper publishes a story on your lucky find, but you don't really know anything about the oil business. Then the phone starts to ring. People are offering you money in return for the rights to the oil in your yard. What would you do?

In the United States, the law says that if you own the land, you own anything buried beneath that land. If you live in an urban area, chances are that as a landowner you have restricted rights, meaning you can't, for example, just stick an oil well in the middle of a busy city. But many landowners do own the land, the rocks beneath the land, and any mineral deposits found there. Actually, the law says that, in theory, as a landowner, you own your property all the way to the center of Earth.

You could let someone pay you to drill for oil in your backyard. What you are doing is selling the mineral rights to your land. The person who buys your mineral rights can drill for oil, but they have only bought the rights to the minerals, not to your land. You still own the land and the surface of that land. But the person who bought your mineral rights does have the right to enter your property, build roads to get to the drilling site, and move in whatever equipment is necessary to get those minerals out of the ground.

You as a landowner own your land, and the rock formations underneath the ground. But you don't automatically own all the resources—such as gas, oil, and water—on the land or embedded within the rock layers beneath the surface. That's because such resources may shift in position, even when they are located underground. If your neighbor started drilling an oil well and was able to drain the oil from your land through his well, that is legal. It is legal because of the *law of capture.* This law says that if you stay on your own land but can capture such a resource, it now belongs to you.

The law of capture has become more controversial in this country in recent years because of the growing shortage of fresh water. It is legal for someone to drain water from an underground source on someone else's land. Such an action, however, may leave others without groundwater, and some people don't think this is fair. The law of capture is also an issue now because some oil companies have discovered ways to drain the oil from miles of underground oil fields.

Our government owns thousands of acres of land across the country, some of it in very remote areas. When it comes to the question of who should have the right to search rock formations for mineral deposits in these areas, there is disagreement among different groups in American society. Environmental groups are opposed to mining and drilling in these areas because of possible environmental damage. Corporations fight for the chance to search for mineral deposits on those properties because of the profit involved and the fact that most of the easy-to-find mineral deposits in the United States have been mined already.

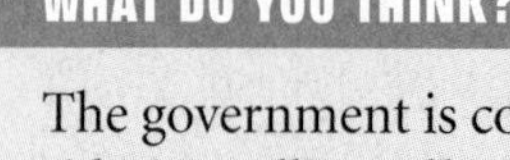

WHAT DO YOU THINK?

The government is considering selling off more of its mineral rights. The oil industry is in favor of more land becoming available to them to use. But some people are opposed to the idea because some of the methods used to extract oil from the ground have caused damage to the surface land.

Environmentalists want the government to keep certain wilderness areas pure and unspoiled. They want the government to find alternative energy sources.

How do you think the government should respond to the oil industry's and environmentalists' requests?

Leisure CONNECTION

COLLECTING ROCKS

You can learn about the history of Earth, understand the work of geologists, and uncover fossils while exploring your environment—just by collecting rocks. Rock collecting is a fun way to get early experience as a scientist.

You will need a few tools. A geologist's hammer and chisel are available at a hardware or camping store. A sturdy knapsack will carry tools and any specimens you collect. A pocketknife is handy for scraping rocks. Take along pen and paper to keep notes on where you find your rocks and on identifying characteristics of each specimen.

Most important for the serious collector are a pocket guidebook for collecting and a map of the area in which you'll be collecting, preferably a topographical map. Look for rocks where natural forces have uncovered them. Streams and cliffs are good places to look. You can also look in places where human activity has exposed rock, such as railroad cuts and quarries.

You can catalog rocks by using what you've already learned. Reveal the true luster of the rock with a freshly made break in the specimen. Rub the rock over a hard surface to find the streak color. Your field guidebook will list a simple hardness test to help you identify your finds.

You may be lucky enough to uncover fossils to add to your collection. Look for places where sedimentary rock is exposed. Chip away carefully at the rock and try to keep the fossil intact. Fossil collecting is more difficult than finding rocks. But if you become familiar with the rock formations, and are patient in your search, fossil collecting is an exciting way to make your own historical discoveries.

YOU TRY IT!

Marble, granite, and limestone are just some of the common rock materials used for buildings in most towns and cities. If you live in an urban area and can't find a natural place to collect rocks, use a magnifying lens to examine the materials on buildings around you. You can also determine the geological history of your town by learning which rock materials are from the region, and which are imported. Old stone buildings may even have fossils "built" right into them!

TEENS *in* SCIENCE

CAVING CLAN

If you ask Mike Bittinger and his dad, Craig, to take you along when they explore caves, they'll ask you to take a little test first. They'll take a wire coat hanger, bend it to form a large circle, and ask you to fit your entire body through it. They want to be sure you can crawl through some tight places.

Cave exploration, or caving, is also known by its technical name—spelunking. Spelunking comes from the word *speleology*, which is the science of caves. Mike, a fourteen-year-old who lives in Austin, Texas, has been caving most of his life. Craig started caving with his father when he was Mike's age.

Mike and his dad go caving at least once a month. Austin has a lot of caves because of the large volume of underground water and the high acid content in the soil. When the water mixes with the soil, it becomes a mild acid. This acidic water wears away the limestone in Earth's crust, forming caves over thousands of years. The Bittingers are interested in the limestone formations called stalactites and stalagmites that decorate the caves. They also find gypsum crystals that stand over a foot tall.

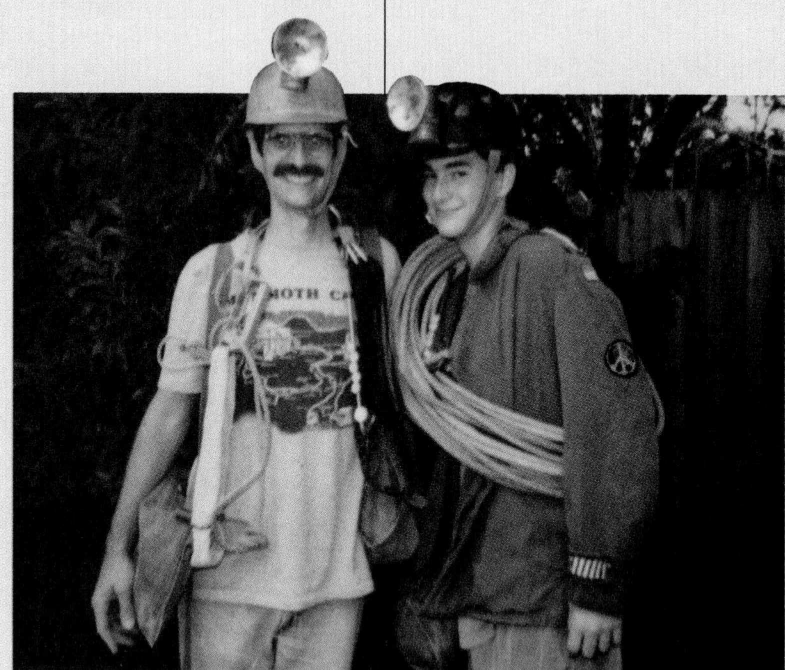

Mike and Craig have explored caves in five states. One thing they don't like to find in caves is other people's garbage. "Mike and I live by the cavers' motto," says Craig, "and we wish everyone else would follow it, too." The motto says: Take nothing but pictures, leave nothing but footprints, kill nothing but time.

YOU TRY IT!

Mike listed the basic rules of caving:

1. Always tell someone where you are going.
2. Always tell someone when you'll be back.
3. Never go caving alone—groups of three are best.
4. Always bring three sources of light.
5. Follow the cavers' motto.
6. Real cavers don't use string.

Can you explain these rules of caving? What do you think rule number six means?

Chapter 11

Reviewing Main Ideas

1. Intrusive igneous rocks form below Earth's surface and generally contain large mineral grains. Extrusive igneous rocks form on Earth's surface and generally have small mineral grains.

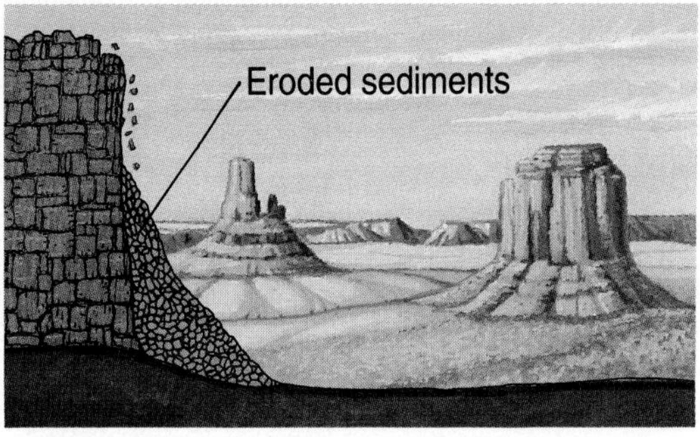

2. Weathering breaks rock and plant and animal remains into small sediments.

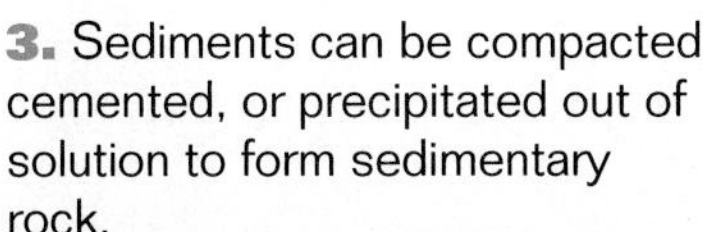

3. Sediments can be compacted, cemented, or precipitated out of solution to form sedimentary rock.

Pressure

4. Pressure and heat can change minerals to form metamorphic rock.

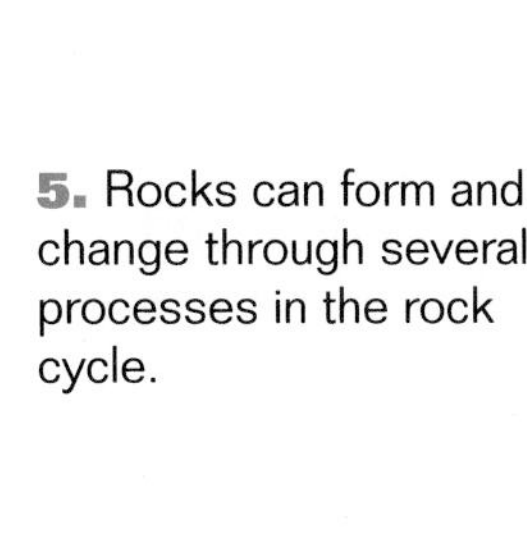

5. Rocks can form and change through several processes in the rock cycle.

Chapter 11

Chapter Review

USING KEY SCIENCE TERMS

extrusive
foliated
igneous rock
intrusive
metamorphic rock
nonfoliated
rock
rock cycle
sedimentary rock

Using the list above, replace the underlined words with the correct key science term.

1. Crystals are small in <u>fine-grained</u> igneous rocks.
2. Erosion, heat, pressure, and weathering are part of the <u>series of events that change rocks</u>.
3. <u>Gneiss</u> is formed when intense pressure changes minerals in existing rock.
4. The texture of metamorphic rocks can be <u>banded</u> or <u>nonbanded</u>.
5. Conglomerates are examples of <u>rock made up of small bits of other rocks</u>.

UNDERSTANDING IDEAS

Complete each sentence.

1. Rocks have different colors because of their ____.
2. Erosion, weathering, cementation, and ____ are some of the processes of the rock cycle.
3. *Extrusive* and *intrusive* describe types of ____ rock.
4. Two kinds of extrusive igneous rock are basalt and ____.
5. Metamorphic rocks form as a result of heat and/or ____.
6. An example of a nonfoliated metamorphic rock is ____.
7. Sediments form through the ____ of rock.
8. *Chemical* and *organic* are ways to describe ____ rock.
9. Detrital sedimentary rocks can be recognized by their ____.
10. You can distinguish organic from chemical limestone by its ____.

CRITICAL THINKING

Use your understanding of the concepts developed in the chapter to answer each of the following questions.

1. Describe some effects of heat and pressure on mineral crystals.
2. What might cause intrusive igneous rocks to appear at Earth's surface?
3. Hypothesize why some rock fragments in detrital sedimentary rock might be rounded.
4. How can concrete be part of the rock cycle if it is not a true rock?

5. Look at the two igneous rocks in the photographs. Which is an extrusive igneous rock? Which is an intrusive igneous rock? Explain your answers.

PROBLEM SOLVING

Read the following problem and discuss your answers in a brief paragraph.

While on a class field trip in the city, you and your classmates observed rocks used as building materials. In the city square, you noticed flowers arranged in a rock terrace, that is, layers of rock and soil with plants growing among the rock. The rocks were light-colored and contained many small fossils.

Soon, your class left the square and entered a historical district with an assortment of buildings. The first building you noticed was light pink with small crystals of quartz that felt gritty to the touch. Continuing down the street, you observed another building with columns. This building was constructed of a light-colored, highly polished rock. Next, you saw a wooden building with a roof made of dark tiles. Some of the tiles had been broken off in layers.

Using what you have learned about minerals and rocks, name the rocks that you observed. What rocks or rocklike materials do people use for buildings and other structures?

CONNECTING IDEAS

Discuss each of the following in a brief paragraph.

1. Explain what the difference is between a rock and a mineral.
2. How do igneous rocks form with various colors and textures?
3. Why are metamorphic processes difficult for scientists to study?
4. Why can both sedimentary and metamorphic rocks have bands of colors?
5. **LEISURE CONNECTION** How can rocks tell us about events in Earth's history?
6. **LIFE SCIENCE CONNECTION** Explain how small rocks can help some animals digest food.

DID YOU EVER WONDER . . .

Where beach sand comes from?

Why beaches must sometimes be closed for health reasons?

What land beneath the ocean looks like?

You'll find the answers to these questions as you read this chapter.

Chapter 12

The Ocean Floor and Shore Zones

What do you think about when you hear the word *Earth*? If you're like many people, you think about the land portions of our planet. After all, the land is where we live and play. Very few people stop and think that nearly three-fourths of Earth's surface is covered by water.

Most of the water on Earth is found in the oceans. The oceans affect the climate in your area and around the world. People obtain food from ocean waters, and they use the oceans for recreation. People even use the oceans as a huge dump for wastes.

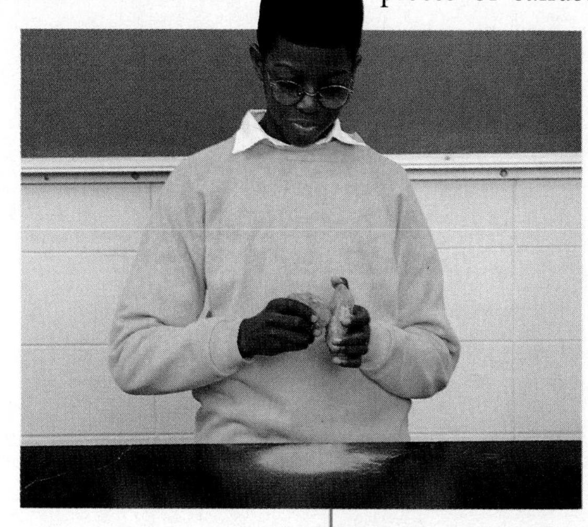

In this chapter, you will explore the land regions that contact the ocean, from the rocky coasts and sandy beaches of the shore zones to the ocean floor beneath its waters.

EXPLORE!

From rock to sand—how can it happen?

Hold a piece of sandstone in one hand and some sand in the other. Feel the differences between these two rock materials. Now rub two pieces of sandstone together. Describe what happens. How do the particles of sandstone compare with the sand? Think of what forces in nature could possibly cause large rock surfaces to become as small as gravel or even sand.

12-1 Shore Zones

OBJECTIVES

In this section, you will

- describe how longshore currents form;
- contrast steep shore zones and flat shore zones;
- list some origins of beach sand.

KEY SCIENCE TERMS

longshore current

HOW SHORE ZONES FORM

If you went to the seashore, would you be interested in looking at beautiful scenery and watching the waves pound against rocks? Or would you rather play on a sandy beach and swim? Different kinds of land areas come in contact with ocean waters, but all are called shore zones. These shore zones are where most of the interaction between people and the ocean takes place.

Changing Shore Zones

Shore zones are regions of constant change. Imagine yourself sitting on the beautiful beach shown in Figure 12-1. You can hear the gentle surf, feel the breeze that sways the trees above your head, and see lovely homes and resorts resting atop rocks and sand dunes yards away from the ocean's edge.

Now examine Figure 12-2, which shows another beach. Much of the sand on this beach seems to have disappeared. No structures stand for very long without special supports. As one local citizen explains, "The water takes them." In other words, the sand dunes that form their base are gradually carried away, bit by bit, by the ocean.

FIGURE 12-1. Sand and vegetation as well as humanmade structures are found along many beaches.

FIGURE 12-2. Beach erosion is a problem for people who have houses along coastlines.

Shore zones are constantly changing. They change because waves and currents are constantly eroding and depositing sediments along a shore. The next activity will show you how this happens.

EXPLORE!

How do waves affect the shoreline?

Waves constantly wash against the land. Most waves strike the shoreline at an angle. In this activity, you will determine whether the angle at which waves strike the shore makes any difference in their effects on the land.

Pour enough fine sand into one end of a rectangular cake pan to form a small beach. Then add water to the pan until it is half full. At the end of the pan away from the sand, move a ruler back and forth on the surface of the water to create a series of waves that move directly toward your beach. Observe what happens to the sand. Now change the angle of your ruler to form waves that strike the beach at an angle. Once again observe what happens to the sand.

What happened to the shoreline when waves moved directly on shore? Do waves striking the shore at an angle change the shape of the shoreline?

As you continue with this section, you will be able to apply what happened in your model shoreline in the previous activity to actual events. When a low, gentle wave breaks on the shore, it moves sand onto the beach. Large storm waves carry sand away from the beach. Water that flows back into the ocean after a wave breaks is called backwash. In some places, waves bring in more sand than they carry away, and a beach grows. At other times, as during a storm, waves remove more sand than they bring in, and the beach is eroded. This is what happened to the beach in Figure 12-2.

In most places, waves approach at a slight angle to the shore. Therefore, the sand is pushed along the beach. A **longshore current** is a flow of ocean water that runs close to the shore and parallel to it. Figure 12-3 diagrams such a current for you.

On beaches, longshore currents have enough mechanical energy to carry away many tons of loose sediments, thus eroding the shore. These currents are like rivers of sand. A longshore current may carry the sediments for several kilometers before some obstacle causes it to slow down and deposit its load. Then features such as those shown in Figure 12-4 are formed.

All shore zones are affected by waves. Yet some shore zones are steep and rocky, with little if any beach area, while others have relatively flat stretches of sandy beach. Let's look into some reasons for these differences.

FIGURE 12-3. Waves approaching the shoreline at an angle cause a longshore current. Rip currents form where longshore currents meet and flow out to sea.

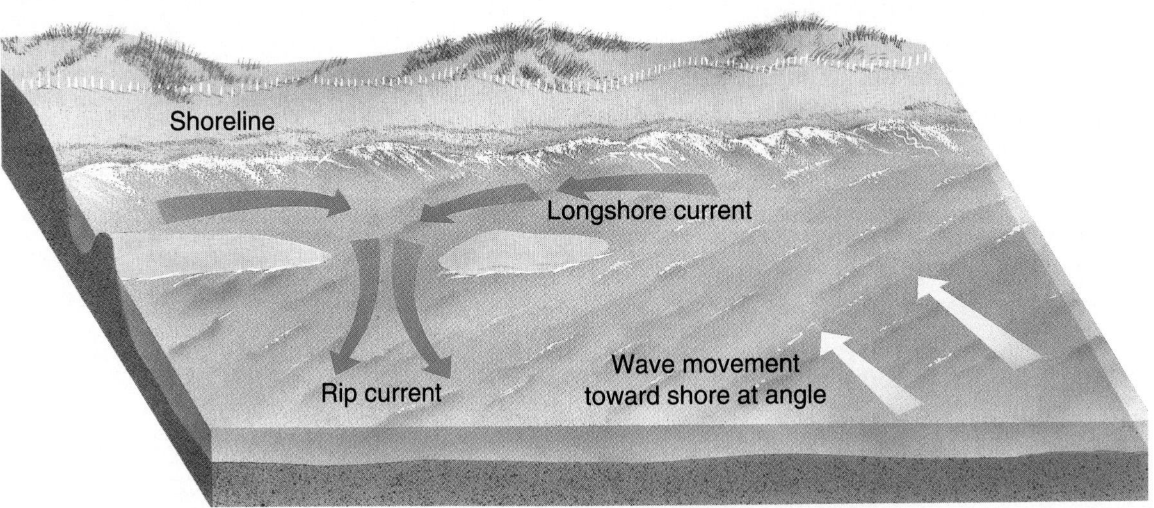

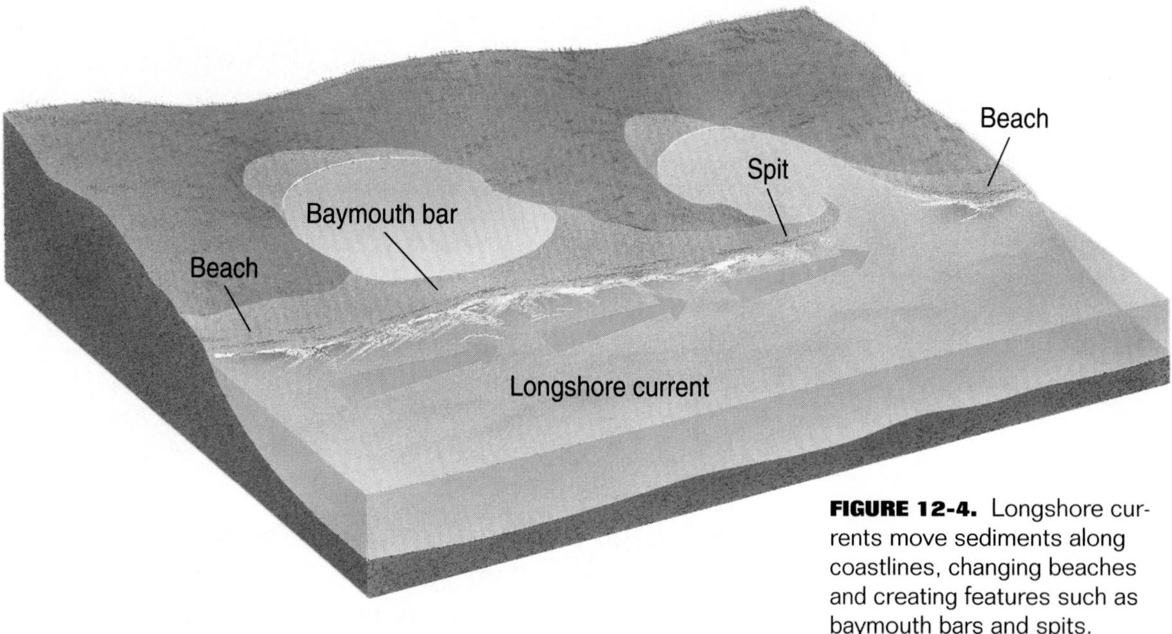

FIGURE 12-4. Longshore currents move sediments along coastlines, changing beaches and creating features such as baymouth bars and spits.

STEEP SHORE ZONES

If you plan to visit the shore to enjoy the scenery, you should probably go to a steep shore zone, where rocks and cliffs are the most common features. You know that some types of rock are harder than others. For example, granite is much harder than sandstone. The harder a rock is, the more difficult it is to wear down. Hard rock, such as granite, resists the constant pounding of waves and therefore wears down very slowly.

However, over time even the hardest rock will show signs of weathering. After all, the ocean never stops its weathering processes. In your lifetime, more than 200 million waves will crash onto any given shore! Imagine how many waves have left their mark since that shore was formed thousands or even millions of years ago.

In a steep shore zone, the action of waves against the rock produces interesting and beautiful formations. Rock fragments are broken from the cliffs and ground up into small pieces by the endless motion of the waves. As these fragments pound against the cliffs, they act like chisels, constantly grinding and chipping away the rocks of the cliffs. This grinding action produces sea caves, arches, and small islands of rock.

SKILLBUILDER

MAKING AND USING GRAPHS

Look at a world map or globe and estimate the percent covered by water and the percent not covered by water. Make a pie graph showing these percentages. If you need help, refer to the **Skill Handbook** on page 680.

FIGURE 12-5. The action of waves and small particles sometimes produces beautiful formations along steep shore zones.

Rock fragments produced by the waves become sediment. But the constant pounding motion of the water in a steep shore zone prevents most of the sediment from settling at the base of the cliffs. Where do you think this sediment goes? Waves and longshore currents carry it away and deposit it in quieter waters somewhere along the coastline. This quieter area is the shore zone to visit if you are interested in playing in the sand and surf.

FLAT SHORE ZONES

If you like a sandy beach, a flat shore zone is the place for you. On a sandy beach, you can play volleyball, build a castle, cover your friends with sand, or just stroll along the water's edge.

Beaches are the main feature of flat shore zones. Every beach is made up of sediments that have been deposited parallel to the shoreline by ocean water. Some beaches are narrow strips of sand, while others are hundreds of meters wide. A beach extends as far inland as the tides and waves can deposit sediments. It also extends some distance out below the surface of the water.

FIGURE 12-6. Beach fragments vary in size.

Beaches are made of different materials. Some are made up of small stones, while others consist of shell fragments. You can find beach fragments ranging in size from fist-sized rocks to grains of sand almost as fine as powder. Look at Figure 12-6. Most beaches have sand-sized particles that have been rounded off by the waves that deposited them.

INVESTIGATE!

12-1 BEACH SAND

You have learned how to identify different types of rocks and minerals by looking for certain characteristics. In this activity, you'll learn how to identify the compositions of different beach sands by observing the characteristics of their grains.

PROBLEM

What are some characteristics of beach sand?

MATERIALS

samples of 3 different types of beach sand
stereomicroscope
magnet

PROCEDURE

1. Use the stereomicroscope to **observe** the sand samples. Copy the data table and record your observations of each sample.
2. Describe the color of each sample.
3. Using the drawing of sand grain shapes, describe the average roundness of the grains in each sample.
4. Place sand grains from one sample in the middle of the circle of the sand gauge shown below the sand grain shapes. Use the upper half of the circle for dark-colored grains and the bottom half for light-colored grains. Determine the average size of the grains.
5. Repeat Steps 2–4 for the other two samples.
6. Pour a small amount of sand from one sample into your hand. Describe its texture as smooth, rough, or sharp. Repeat for the other two samples.
7. Describe the luster of the grains as shiny or dull.
8. Determine if a magnet will attract grains in any of the samples.
9. Try to **classify** the types of fragments that make up your samples. Use categories such as shape and size. Record the compositions in a table like the one on this page.

Sand Shapes

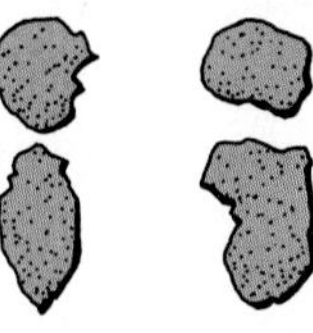
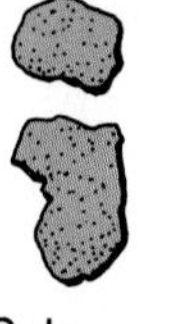
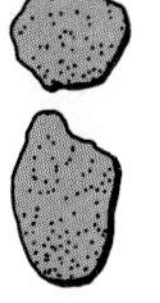
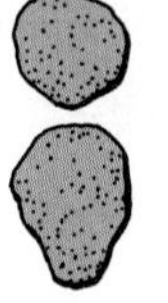

Angular | Sub-angular | Sub-rounded | Rounded

Sand Gauge

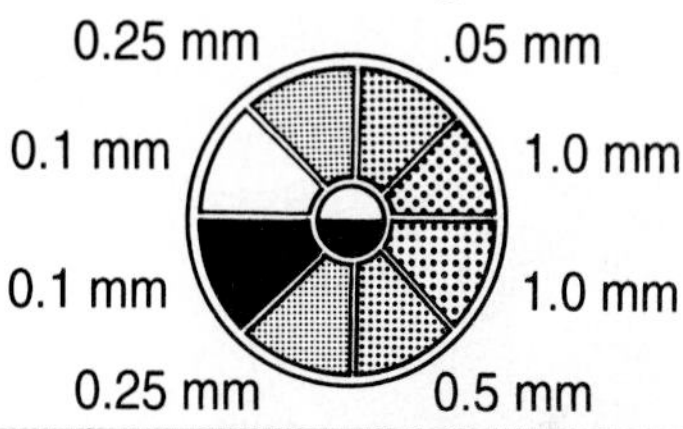

ANALYZE

1. Were the grains of a particular sample generally the same size? Explain.
2. Were they generally the same shape?

CONCLUDE AND APPLY

3. What are some characteristics of beach sand?
4. **Going Further: Hypothesize** as to why there are differences in the characteristics of different sand samples.

DATA AND OBSERVATIONS

SAMPLE	COLOR	ROUNDNESS	GRAIN SIZE	TEXTURE	LUSTER	COMPOSITION
1						
2						
3						

a

b

FIGURE 12-7. Beach sands vary in composition, ranging from the white shell and coral fragment beaches of Jamaica (a) to the black basaltic beaches of Hawaii (b).

The characteristics of the sand found on a given beach depend on many factors. Perhaps the most important factor is the source of the material.

Where do you think beach sand comes from? It comes largely from sediment carried to oceans by rivers. Many beach sands contain a lot of quartz, a hard, resistant mineral present in many common rock types. Other types of sand are made up of organic materials. Warm ocean waters, such as those of the Caribbean Sea, contain abundant marine life. Look at Figure 12-7(a) and (b). The beautiful white beaches of a Caribbean island like Jamaica are made up of many fragments of seashell and coral. You learned in the last chapter that the black sand found on some beaches in Hawaii is composed of basalt, an igneous rock that is formed when lava hardens. Some sand is formed as waves weather the rocks, shells, or coral found in the shore zone.

Perhaps the next time you visit the seashore, or see scenes of the shore in a movie or magazine, you'll stop and think about the type of shore zone you're looking at and some of the factors that formed it. Keep in mind, however, that all shore zones are subject to constant change. In addition to the daily effects of winds, waves, and currents, humans have a great effect on shore zones. You will learn about some of these effects in the next section of this chapter.

Check Your Understanding

1. How do longshore currents form?
2. Contrast the characteristics of a steep or rocky shore zone with those of a flat shore zone.
3. Are all beach sands alike? Explain your answer.
4. **APPLY:** At a nearby lakeshore, you notice that a long, low wall, just a little above the water's surface, is being built about a hundred meters from shore. What effect might this construction have on the lake's shore?

12-2 Humans Affect Shore Zones

OBJECTIVES

In this section, you will

- relate the ways in which human activities pollute shore zones;
- describe the effects of ocean pollution on sea life.

KEY SCIENCE TERMS

pollution

POLLUTION

How would you feel if people came into your home, removed all the things they could use, and then spilled oil on your floor? What if they threw cans, bottles, and plastic bags all around? What would you say if they sprayed bug killer and built a stone wall halfway up your doorway? Would you want to or even be able to stay in your home after it was treated this way? Organisms that live in and near shore zones experience this kind of treatment all the time. People take food and minerals from the shore and water, leave harmful materials behind, and reshape the shore zone.

Imagine going to the beach in Figure 12-8. You notice a sign has been posted. It states that the beach is closed because waste materials have washed ashore. Swimming has been banned because the water is unhealthful. Does this story sound familiar? You may have heard of such an incident on the news. Every year beaches around the world are spoiled by careless treatment of shore zones.

Shore zones are very popular areas. In the United States, three out of every four persons live in a coastal state. Many of these people spend at least some of their time at the shore each year. Coastal cities and towns are active places. Commercial shipping and fishing are important industries, and factories often line the waterfronts. Unfortunately, one side effect of these many human activities is pollution. **Pollution** is unwanted or harmful materials or effects in the environment. Pollution may range from a

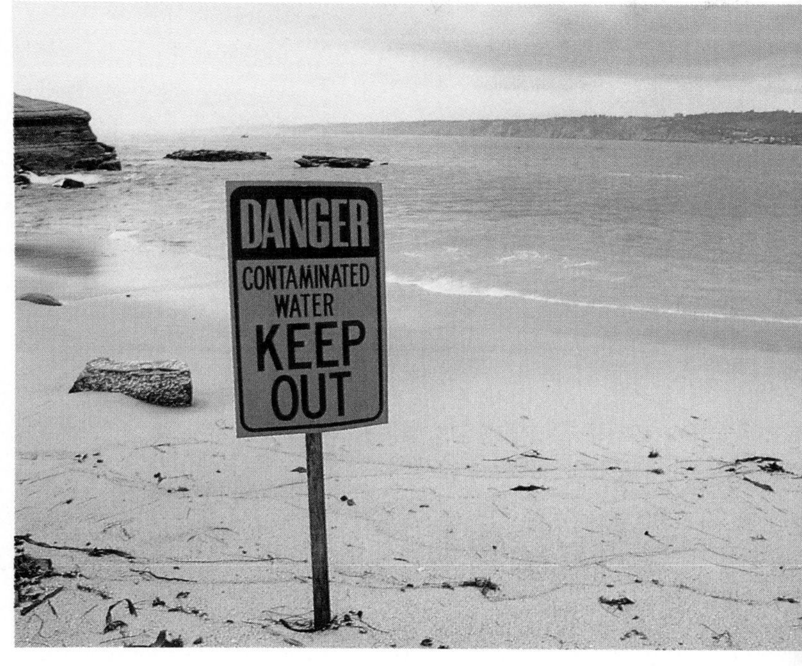

FIGURE 12-8. Some beaches must be closed because of pollution.

plastic cup left behind by a picnicker to heat released into the water by a factory or power plant.

Some pollution is just annoying and ugly, such as litter left behind along beaches. Yet other types of pollution, such as wastes from factories, homes, and businesses, can cause great harm when they get into streams, lakes, or ocean water. These materials include toxic chemicals and metals from factories along with plastic, paper, and garbage from homes and businesses. This refuse is dumped directly into the sea or in landfills near the shore. Medical wastes, such as used needles and plastic tubes, have washed up onto beaches, where they threaten humans with disease. Even something as simple as the plastic rings that hold six-packs of aluminum cans can be harmful. Birds have become trapped when they stick their necks through the rings.

Some of the most serious cases of ocean and shore zone pollution have been produced by oil spills. Oil spills are usually caused when offshore oil wells leak, oil tankers collide at sea, or accidents occur at oil refineries. The largest oil spill in U.S. history occurred in March of 1989, when the Exxon *Valdez* oil tanker struck a reef in Alaska's Prince William Sound. More than a quarter million barrels of crude oil escaped from the tanker. In less than a

FIGURE 12-9. Oil slicks from spills are some of the most serious forms of ocean and shore zone pollution. Here, you can see oil spreading out from a leak near the shore at Galveston Bay in Texas.

week, the spill extended more than 75 kilometers from the site of the accident. Rocks and beaches along tens of kilometers of shoreline were coated with oil, which killed or injured thousands of birds and animals living in the area. In addition to these major sources of oil pollution, waste oil from motor vehicles and industrial machinery is sometimes dumped in landfills. This oil seeps into the ground and is carried by groundwater to the sea.

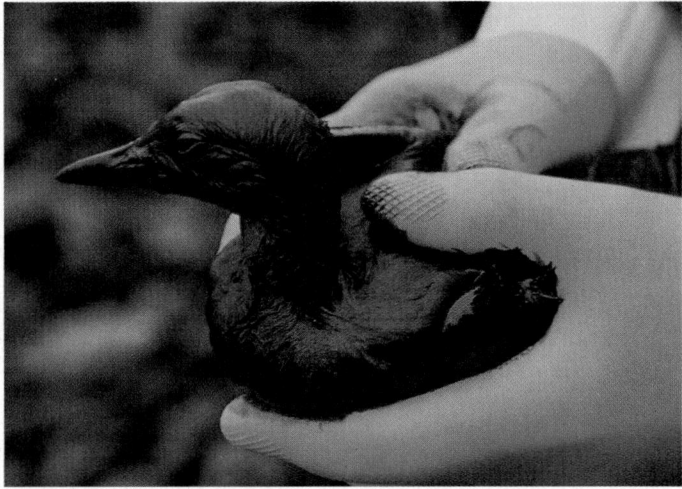

FIGURE 12-10. Oil pollution can harm or kill animals that live in or near the ocean.

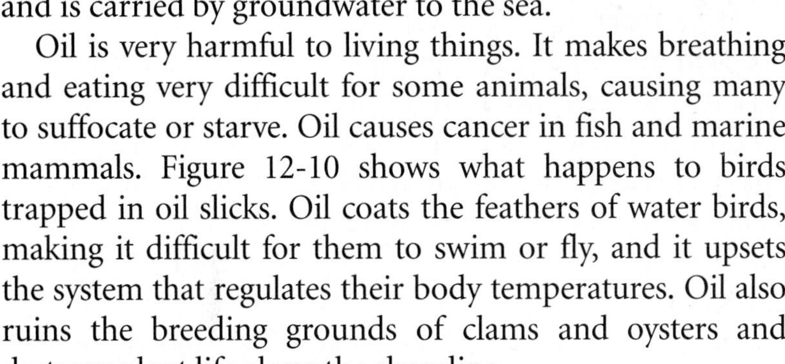

Oil is very harmful to living things. It makes breathing and eating very difficult for some animals, causing many to suffocate or starve. Oil causes cancer in fish and marine mammals. Figure 12-10 shows what happens to birds trapped in oil slicks. Oil coats the feathers of water birds, making it difficult for them to swim or fly, and it upsets the system that regulates their body temperatures. Oil also ruins the breeding grounds of clams and oysters and destroys plant life along the shoreline.

Once oil has been spilled, what can be done about cleaning it up and restoring the environment?

FIND OUT!

How do you clean up an oil spill? 

Cleaning up an oil spill presents a problem because of the nature of oil. It floats on the water's surface and forms a sticky coating on everything it touches. The following activity will help you appreciate the difficult job people have in cleaning up an oil spill.

Place a few small rocks at one end of a shallow baking pan to represent a shoreline. Pour water into the pan until it is half full. Next, pour 10 mL of motor oil into the water. Gently slosh the water back and forth to make sure that the rocks become wet. Then try using the following materials to clean up the oil: tongue depressors, cotton balls, detergent, paper toweling, and feathers. Describe your efforts to remove the oil from the water and the rocks.

Conclude and Apply

1. An additional problem in cleaning up an oil spill is that the oil seeps into the soil and rocks along the shore. In cleaning up your oil spill, did you remove each rock and clean it off?
2. If not, what will happen the next time water covers the rocks?

As you learned in the Find Out, oil pollution isn't easy to clean up. But at least you can see oil. Imagine how difficult it is to clean up harmful materials you can't see. Two examples of such materials are the chemicals used to kill insects (insecticides) and weeds (herbicides). These chemicals are widely used in treating lawns and in farming, as you can see in Figure 12-11. They can be very harmful to animals and plants.

Figure 12-12 shows how insecticides and herbicides, among other kinds of pollution, reach the oceans. When rain falls on fields treated with these chemicals, some of them are picked up by the rainwater. The insecticides and herbicides are then carried to streams as runoff or into the soil and its groundwater. The polluted streams and groundwater carry these chemicals to the ocean, where

FIGURE 12-11. Insecticides and herbicides are sprayed on crops and eventually find their way to the ocean.

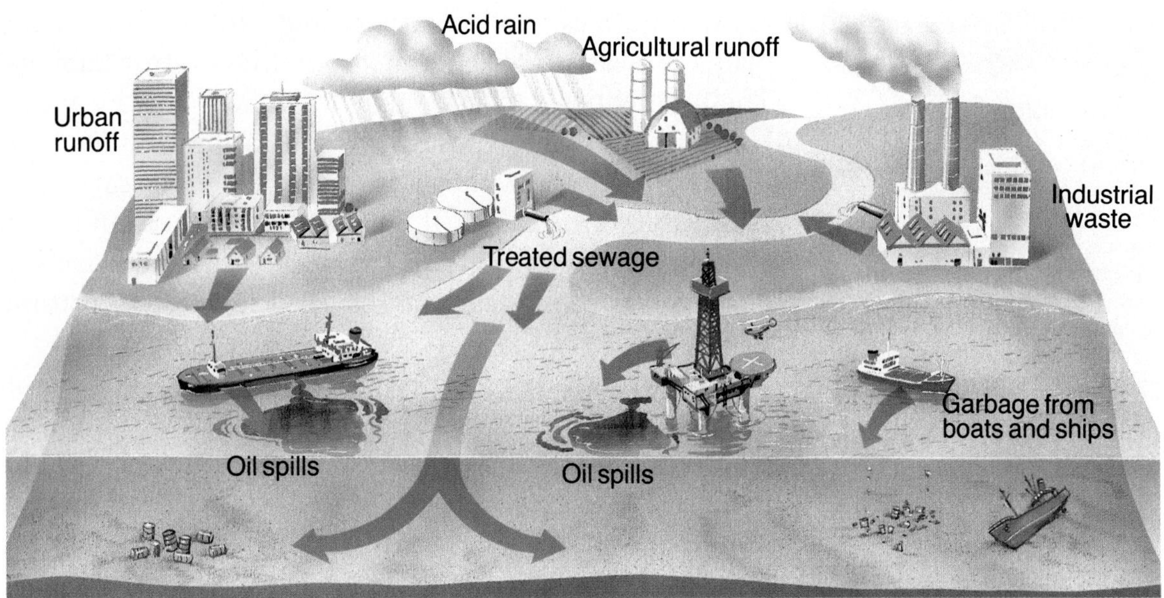

FIGURE 12-12. Ocean pollution has many sources.

fish and other marine organisms can be exposed to them. The chemicals can be poisonous both to the organisms themselves and to any creatures that eat them.

Crop fertilizers and human sewage present a different kind of problem. These materials actually add nutrients to the water. These nutrients act as fertilizer for some marine organisms, such as algae and plankton, helping them grow very rapidly. When these organisms die, their remains are decomposed by bacteria. During this process, the bacteria use up large amounts of oxygen in the water. This deprives fish and other organisms of the oxygen they need to survive, so they die.

When the waters near shore zones become polluted, everyone and everything is affected. Food chains are disrupted, and the oxygen supply in the region is reduced. Marine algae are an important source of oxygen for many organisms. If the marine algae die, the organisms that depend on those algae will soon follow.

DID YOU KNOW?

Sludge is dumped from sewage treatment plants onto the ocean floor. In some areas off the eastern coast of the United States, this sludge has accumulated to a thickness of almost 11 meters.

HABITAT DESTRUCTION

The place where an organism lives is called its habitat. If one part of a habitat is altered or destroyed, all members are affected. Many human activities, such as farming,

SKILLBUILDER

RECOGNIZING CAUSE AND EFFECT

You've learned how many human activities are polluting the ocean. As the human population grows, these activities will increase in size and number. Think of ways that increased population will affect the ocean. Make a cause-and-effect chart listing these effects. If you need help, refer to the **Skill Handbook** on page 683.

removing trees, and clearing land, involve uprooting plants. It's easy to see how such activities destroy habitats. These activities can also help to pollute nearby water. Uprooting a plant exposes bare soil to the weather. This makes it easy for wind and moving water to carry fine sediments to the ocean. If these sediments accumulate in tidal areas, they can interfere with the cells and organs of marine organisms, such as clams and oysters, causing them to die.

Another way people destroy shore habitats is to fill them in. Have you ever added dirt or sand to a puddle or a muddy spot to help dry the spot so you could play ball there? If so, you have reclaimed that wet area and made it more useful to you. Humans have been doing the same thing on a large scale for years.

As populations in many flat shore zones grow, the need for more land becomes urgent. Huge areas of coastal wetlands are filled in with soil, rock, construction materials, and even garbage. The newly created land is used for buildings, roads, and airports, while thousands of acres of shore zone habitats have been destroyed.

Thus far in this chapter, you have learned about shore zones and the harmful effects humans can have on these important regions. But the shore zones make up only a small part of Earth's surface. Most of the solid Earth lies beneath the ocean waters, largely unexplored. Many people feel that the ocean basins will become more important as the world's population continues to increase. We certainly will look to the ocean floor for new sources of minerals. But some people suggest that we should start developing ways to build communities on the ocean floor in which people can live. What do you think it's like down there? You'll learn about the ocean floor in the next section of this chapter.

Check Your Understanding

1. Describe some things an individual might do to reduce shore zone pollution.
2. Describe some of the effects of pollution on organisms in and near the shore zone.
3. **APPLY:** How can planting trees and grass help to preserve a shore zone habitat?

12-3 The Ocean Floor

EXPLORING THE OCEAN FLOOR

Can you imagine living on the ocean floor—sleeping and eating and going to school hundreds of meters below the ocean's surface? What's it like down there? If you're like most people, you probably think of the ocean floor as a vast, flat region covered with a thick layer of sediments. You may be surprised to learn that the highest mountain peaks and the deepest canyons in the world are located on the ocean floor! It's also very dark, because sunlight can't reach it.

How do we know what the ocean floor is like? Most of the information comes from making indirect measurements. Humans can't measure features of the ocean floor directly because they can't withstand the very high pressure exerted by the water at great depths. The following activity will help you to understand how indirect measurements are made.

In this activity, you will attempt to determine the shape of a surface without seeing it. Your teacher will provide you with a sealed shoe box having a series of numbered holes in a straight line along the lid of the box. You will insert a soda straw into each hole to determine the shape of an ocean-floor model on the bottom of the box. Once the shape has been determined, you will construct a graph to represent the shape of the model in the box.

OBJECTIVES

In this section, you will

- describe some of the methods used to map the ocean floor;
- name and describe some features of the ocean floor.

KEY SCIENCE TERMS

continental shelf
abyssal plain
rift zone
mid-ocean ridges

FIND OUT!

How can you determine the shape of something you can't see?

When exploring something you can't see, you often must use evidence based on indirect observations. This approach is especially true in science, when you have to consider such questions as what the inside of Earth is like and how stars produce light.

First construct a graph like the one shown here. The graph should be as long as the shoe

DATA AND OBSERVATIONS

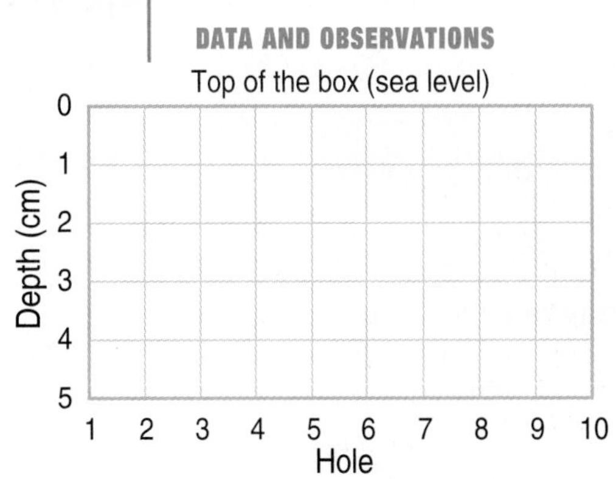

box, and the vertical lines should line up with the holes in the lid. The vertical scale should be marked off in centimeters as shown. Next, place the soda straw beside a ruler and, starting with zero, mark the straw at 0.5-cm intervals. Label each mark.

Now make your measurements. Insert the zero end of the straw into hole 1 until it touches the ocean-floor model on the bottom of the box. Record this measurement on your graph by placing a dot on line 1 at the depth measured. Repeat this procedure for holes 2–10. Then connect the points on your graph to produce a side-view drawing of your ocean floor. After completing this activity, you can understand how the shape of an unseen surface can be found.

Conclude and Apply

1. What do the highest points on your model represent?
2. What do the lowest points represent?

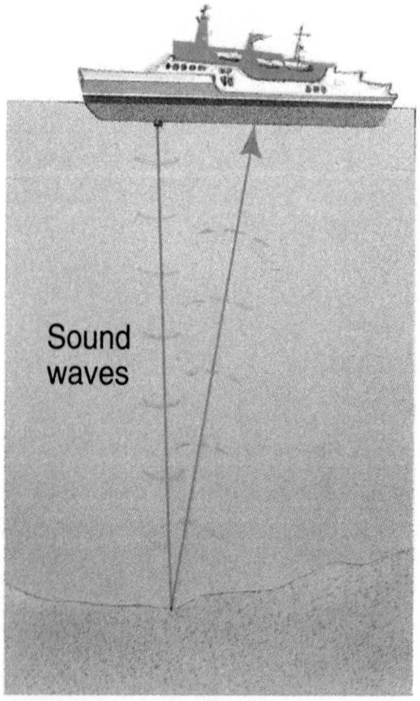

Early measurements of the ocean floor were made in a manner similar to the one you used in the Find Out. Instead of a soda straw, a long rope tied to a lead weight was used. Sailors tied knots in the rope at measured intervals. They lowered the rope over the side of a ship, and when it touched bottom, they recorded the length of the rope. The ship then moved to a new location, and the process was repeated.

Today more modern methods are used to learn about the ocean floor. On board ship, an instrument called sonar sends sound waves toward the ocean floor, as shown in Figure 12-13. When the waves hit the bottom, they bounce back and are received by a recorder on the ship. The recorder measures the time it took for the waves to travel from the ship to the ocean floor and back. Scientists use this information to determine the depth of the floor at the point where the signal hit.

FIGURE 12-13. A profile of the ocean floor can be produced using sound waves to measure depth.

OCEAN FLOOR FEATURES

Now you know how the shape of the ocean floor can be determined. The next question is, what are some of the features found on the ocean floor?

As you leave the shore zones and move out under the water, the first part of the ocean floor is the **continental shelf**, a flat part of the continent that extends out under the ocean. Along some coasts, the continental shelf is quite wide. For example, along the east coast of North America, the continental shelf is 100–200 kilometers wide. But along coastal areas where mountain ranges run close to shore, as in California, the shelf is only 10–30 kilometers wide. Each continental shelf slants gently down and out into the ocean. But at the outer edge of a shelf, it dips steeply, forming a continental slope.

If you think of the ocean basin as being a very large swimming pool, the continental slopes would be the sides of the pool and the seafloor would be its flat bottom. The seafloor is where you find the flattest areas on Earth. Ocean currents carry sediments from the continental shelves and slopes and deposit them on the ocean bottom. These deposits fill in valleys, creating a flat seafloor called an **abyssal** (uh BIHS uhl) **plain** in the deepest part of the ocean basin.

An interesting way to study the shape of the ocean floor is to look at a side view across the entire width of an ocean basin. Imagine that you are traveling across the Atlantic Ocean from New Jersey to Portugal in a glass-bottomed boat that allows you to see the ocean bottom all the way across. What ocean features would you see? To find out, do the following activity.

FIGURE 12-14. The ocean floor has a variety of features.

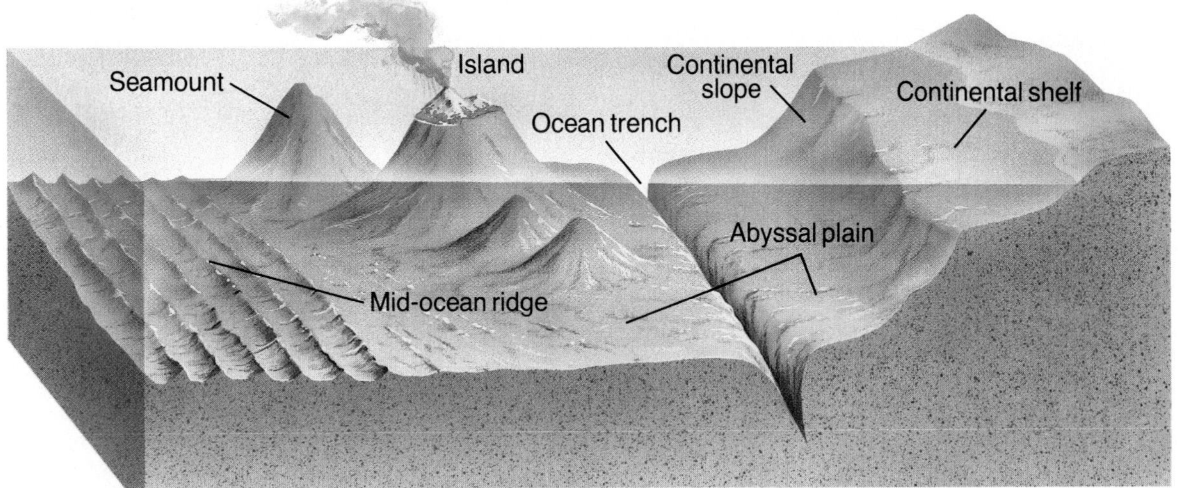

I N V E S T I G A T E !

12-2 OCEAN-FLOOR PROFILE

In this activity, you will construct a profile, or side view, of the features of the ocean floor between New Jersey and Portugal. To make your profile, you will **interpret a table** of data that were collected by a depth-sounding technique similar to the sonar technique described earlier.

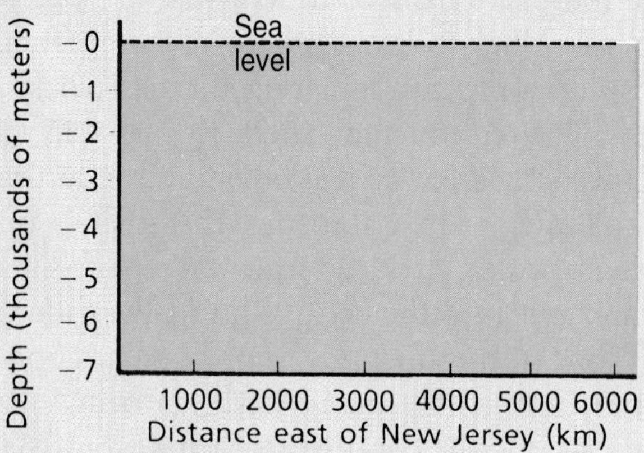

PROBLEM

What does the ocean floor look like?

MATERIALS

graph paper
blue and brown pencils

PROCEDURE

1. Set up a graph as shown.
2. Examine the data listed in the table. This information was collected at 29 locations across the Atlantic Ocean. Each station was along the 39° north latitude line from New Jersey to Portugal.
3. Plot each data point listed on the table. Then connect the points with a line.
4. Color the ocean bottom brown and the water blue.

DATA AND OBSERVATIONS

STATION NUMBER	DISTANCE FROM NEW JERSEY (KM)	DEPTH TO OCEAN FLOOR (M)
1	0	0
2	160	165
3	200	1800
4	500	800
5	800	4600
6	1050	5450
7	1450	5100
8	1800	5300
9	2000	5600
10	2300	4750
11	2400	3500
12	2600	3100
13	3000	4300
14	3200	3900
15	3450	3400
16	3550	2100
17	3600	1330
18	3700	1275
19	3950	1000
20	4000	0
21	4100	1800
22	4350	3650
23	4500	5100
24	5000	5000
25	5300	4200
26	5450	1800
27	5500	920
28	5600	180
29	5650	0

ANALYZE

1. What ocean-floor features would you **infer** occur between 160 and 1050 km from the coast of New Jersey? Between 2000 and 4500 km? Between 5300 and 5600 km?

CONCLUDE AND APPLY

2. You have constructed a profile of the ocean floor along the 39° latitude line. If a profile is drawn to represent an accurate scale model of a feature, both the horizontal and vertical scales will be the same. What is the vertical scale of your profile? What is the horizontal scale?
3. **Going Further: Compare and contrast** your profile with the actual ocean floor. See Figure 12-15. How accurate do you think it is? Explain.

In the activity just completed, you learned that the Atlantic Ocean floor has many interesting features. Now study the map shown in Figure 12-15. Down the middle of the Atlantic Ocean, you can see a system of cracks in the seafloor called a rift zone. A **rift zone** marks a region where the seafloor is spreading apart. One rift zone extends southward from Iceland through the center of the Atlantic Ocean floor. From these cracks, hot lava from Earth's interior oozes onto the seafloor. The lava is cooled very quickly by the seawater and becomes solid rock, forming new seafloor. Can you spot the rift zones in the Indian Ocean and the Pacific Ocean?

Alongside the rift zones extend chains of underwater mountains called **mid-ocean ridges**. Active volcanoes are common along the mid-ocean ridges. By depositing material from the interior of Earth, these volcanoes build up mountains on the seafloor, just as they do on land. When a volcanic mountain extends above the surface of the ocean, an island is formed. Find the mid-ocean ridges in Figure 12-15.

FIGURE 12-15. This map shows the mountains, valleys, and plains of Earth—those on dry land as well as those on the ocean floor.

FIGURE 12-16. Lying in the Pacific Ocean is the Marianas Trench, a trench so deep that Mount Everest could be submerged in it.

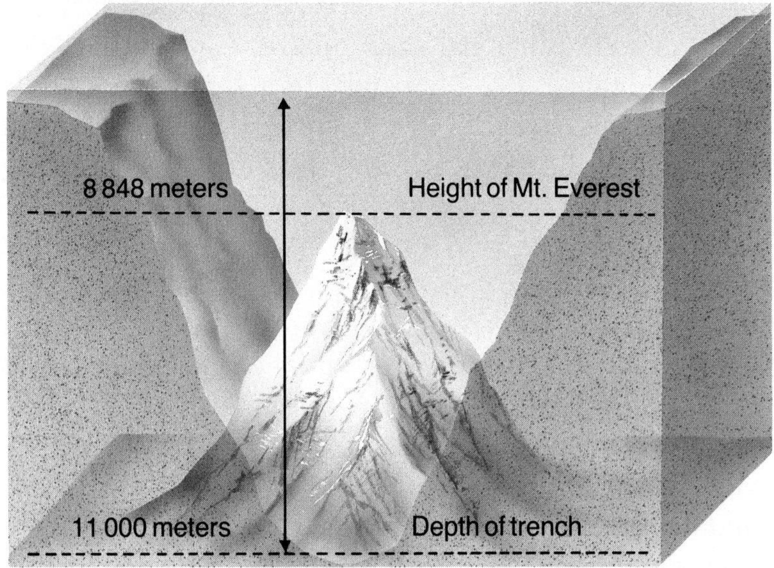

Another interesting feature of the ocean floor is the deep, canyonlike ocean trench. Many ocean trenches are longer and deeper than any canyon on the continents. For example, the Marianas Trench in the Pacific Ocean is the deepest spot known on Earth, almost 11 kilometers deep. By contrast, the Grand Canyon is only about 1.6 kilometers deep. In fact, the Marianas Trench is so deep that Earth's highest mountain above water, Mount Everest, could fit inside it. Look at Figure 12-16. About how many meters of ocean water would still lie above Everest's peak if it could be placed within the Marianas Trench?

In this section, you have learned quite a bit about the ocean basins and the features on the ocean floor. Now think again about the possibility of people living on the ocean floor. What do you think about this idea? On what part of the ocean floor would you choose to live? Why?

Check Your Understanding

1. How could a long pole be used to determine the shape of a lake floor?
2. Where is the flattest part of the ocean floor? Why is it so flat?
3. What features would you expect to find extending above the ocean surface along a mid-ocean ridge?
4. **APPLY:** Why is most of our information about the ocean floor based on indirect evidence?

EXPANDING YOUR VIEW

CONTENTS

A Closer Look
Mining Minerals at the Rift Zones 367

Life Science Connection
Adaptation of Marine Life in the Rift Zones 368

Science and Society
Beach Erosion 369

Technology Connection
Offshore Oil 371

Teens In Science
Rescue Team Is All Wet 372

Literature Connection
A Real Find 372

A CLOSER LOOK

MINING MINERALS AT THE RIFT ZONES

The year 1848 will always be remembered as the start of the Gold Rush. Hundreds of prospectors—people who search the ground for valuable minerals—headed out west to search for gold in the mountains of California. There may be another gold rush in the 21st century, except this time it will be to mine precious metals at the bottom of the ocean. Oceanographers say that a good place to look for metals will be at rift zones, where undersea surveys have already discovered huge amounts of such metals.

Where do they come from? It's a slow process, beginning when seawater passes through cracks in rocks at the rift zone. Beneath the ocean's crust, the seawater encounters deposits of magma, a hot volcanic rock containing metallic ore. The hot seawater mixes with particles of metal and then rises back up to the surface. Some vents, called black smokers, are chimneys of rock up to 30 meters tall. The seawater pours out of them in black plumes. Then the dissolved metal particles in the plumes solidify and sink to the bottom of the ocean.

Finding precious metals might not be half as troublesome as trying to figure out who has a right to own them. If a silver deposit is found in the middle of the Atlantic Ocean, which country has a right to claim it?

In an attempt to prevent such disputes, the United Nations drafted a treaty—The Law of the Sea. The treaty states that a nation has a right to minerals found within 370 kilometers of its shoreline. Any metals found beyond that boundary line are "the common heritage of humankind."

WHAT DO YOU THINK?

In 1983, 117 countries signed the United Nations treaty. Yet, many industrialized countries, such as the United States and Japan, refused to sign. They feel that only countries that participate in undersea mining should have the right to claim any profits. Do you agree? What do you think would be the fairest way to distribute metals found at the bottom of the ocean?

LIFE SCIENCE CONNECTION

ADAPTATION OF MARINE LIFE IN THE RIFT ZONES

It is always dark in the deepest parts of the ocean. There is no sunlight, and the temperature is only a few degrees above freezing. For many years, biologists believed that it was impossible for any form of life to exist in such an environment. Without sunlight, plants would be unable to carry on photosynthesis. Without plants, there would be no food or oxygen.

Then, in 1977, marine biologists made a startling discovery. In a Pacific Ocean rift zone, 2500 meters under water, they found a thriving colony of bizarre sea creatures. Giant clams the size of footballs were piled on top of one another. Bright red worms, as thick as a person's wrist, were encased in white tubes more than two meters long. Pale, ghost-white crabs that had never seen a ray of sunlight, crawled along the rocks hunting for food.

All of these creatures were living in the vicinity of a hot-water vent—a tall chimney of solid rock that spewed forth water heated by volcanic magma beneath the ocean floor. The hot water warmed the surrounding ocean, with temperatures climbing as high as 30°C. The animals clustered around the vent like people huddled around a camp fire on a cold winter night.

Although the geysers provided heat, they did not provide sunlight. That left biologists puzzled. How could this community of creatures survive without plants, and how could plants grow without sunlight? In the deepest parts of the ocean, there is a substitute for sunlight. The black smokers produce a rotten-egg-smelling gas known as hydrogen sulfide. Through a chemical process called chemosynthesis, certain species of bacteria can convert hydrogen sulfide into food and oxygen. So, deep-sea dwellers feed upon the bacteria, the way animals living in shallow waters feed upon small, floating green plants.

WHAT DO YOU THINK?

Chemosynthesis is just one example of how animals have had to adapt in order to survive in a harsh environment. Can you think of any other examples?

SCIENCE AND SOCIETY

BEACH EROSION

Imagine that you take a trip to the ocean. You walk down to the beach and lay down your towel, only to discover that there's no more sand. Everywhere you look, you see nothing but rocks and cobblestones. It's hard to believe that anything as large as a beach can simply vanish. Yet, in some places, longshore currents carry away tons of sand each year.

How does this happen? Waves and currents can cut away at the land that slopes toward the sea, eventually shaping the shoreline into steep cliffs. Land that is eroded in this way may form a flat underwater terrace. This type of formation permits the waves to pound directly at the base of the cliff. Finally, the overhanging portion above the notch may crumble, and more land is carried out to the sea.

Wave action and other currents can shape the shore in other dramatic ways. They can build up sandbars directly offshore. The sandbars then absorb much of the

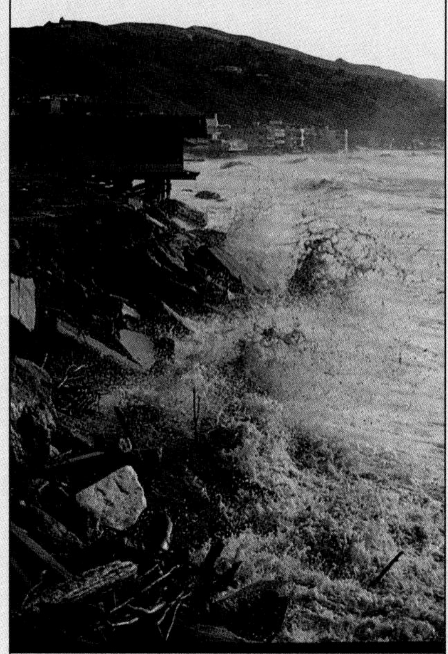

force of the waves, altering the effects of the waves' impact on the shore. Sandbars, once formed, may show continual and rapid change—eroding at one end and getting longer at the other as the sand particles are deposited differently.

A fierce storm or hurricane may magnify the effects discussed above, by generating huge waves and strong currents. And the effects of a storm are further magnified if it happens to hit when tides are especially high—tides are highest when the moon is full or new. At such times, homes along the threatened beach may be flooded or destroyed. The day after such a storm, an onlooker can often notice a visible change in the shore's configuration from the day before.

There are less obvious natural causes of beach erosion as well. Ocean levels all over the world are rising, at a rate of about 10 to 15 centimeters per century. Furthermore, geological processes cause coastlines to very slowly sink. When shorelines submerge, water may flow into valleys, and hilltops may become islands. This makes for a ragged, uneven-looking coastline. Coastlines that have become elevated, on the other hand, are much straighter.

What would you do if you had a home by the beach, and you found out that your property was slowly eroding away? You might want to construct a groyne. Groynes are short walls built at right angles to the shore that trap sand being carried away by longshore currents.

Sometimes, however, human efforts to stop beach erosion can be detrimental. The problem with groynes is that they work too well. They capture so much sand that beaches down-current from the wall are deprived of sand. You would trap sand at your own beach, but meanwhile sand would continue to be eroded from the next beach area down-current from your beach. In Westhampton, New York, the loss of sand caused by the construction of groynes resulted in high tides coming in right under people's houses. The houses had to be placed on elevated supports to prevent them from being completely flooded.

Some property owners try to minimize the effects of shoreline erosion simply by contructing more groynes. On the New Jersey shore, for example, more than 300 such walls have already been built. Seen from above, such beaches take on the appearance of a wavy line, with alternating peaks and valleys.

Other communities have decided to stop building groynes altogether. Instead, they try to prevent sand erosion through a technique known as beach nourishment. Truckloads of sand are dumped on the beach to replace sand that has been washed away. Unfortunately, beach nourishment is only a temporary solution, and it can be very expensive. In the early 1980s, it cost $65 million to restore 24 kilometers of beach along the shores of Miami.

Beach nourishment can also pose a serious hazard for the environment. In Miami, for instance, coarse quartz sand was replaced with a muddier, softer sand. When the waves broke upon the shore, they picked up a lot of mud, and the water became thick and cloudy. This natural pollution killed many coral reefs off the coast of Miami.

Another important cause of beach erosion is destruction of coastal vegetation. Plant cover stabilizes sand dunes and helps prevent the loss of beach sand or dirt. The low shrubbery and beach grasses that are common along shorelines can be damaged or lost for many reasons. Off-road bikers or too many recreational hikers may harm the vegetation. So can real estate development and road building.

The twentieth century has seen more erosion than any other period in history. This is largely because of all the construction that takes place on our beaches. Bulldozers clear away tons of sand every time someone decides to build a hotel, restaurant, parking lot, or highway. This aids the process of erosion.

WHAT DO YOU THINK?

Some environmentalists believe that our government should pass laws that would place restrictions on beachfront construction. Do you think that would be a good idea? What other ways can you think of to halt the process of beach erosion?

TECHNOLOGY CONNECTION

OFFSHORE OIL

Did you know that 35 percent of the world's supply of oil is provided by the ocean? Large oil deposits are located under the oceans.

When searching for deposits of oil, the first step is to send out a survey ship. The ship explores the bottom of the ocean by generating underwater sound pulses. These sound pulses are reflected by layers of rock beneath the ocean floor, creating an echo. The sound pulses bounce back up to the surface, where they are recorded by a series of hydrophones, instruments used to detect sound under water and to determine the source and its position. They are attached to a cable being towed behind the ship. By studying the pattern of these sound echoes, geologists can tell whether there is a pool of oil trapped in rock layers beneath the ocean.

When geologists think that they have found oil, an exploration rig is sent to confirm the discovery. The exploration rig is a mobile oil drill, which floats. The crew aboard the rig will drill several wells in order to figure out the exact size and location of the oil field. If the rig strikes oil, the well is capped until a permanent oil production platform can be built.

In just one oil field, there might be several production platforms, each one costing at least $100 million. The deck of the platform sits on top of steel scaffolding, which may be as high as 150 meters. The scaffolding is built onshore, and then towed to the site of the oil field, where it is installed on the ocean floor.

A single oil platform can drill as many as 40 wells, slanting off in different directions. The oil is pumped through a series of pipelines. If the platform is close enough to land, then the oil is pumped directly to tanks onshore. If the platform is too far from land, then the oil is pumped into huge underwater storage tanks, where it waits until it is picked up by a tanker.

CAREER CONNECTION

Chemical oceanographers investigate the different elements and chemical compounds present in seawater. They study chemistry and oceanography, but they also have a working knowledge of geology and biology. Chemical oceanographers are sometimes hired by government agencies and environmental organizations to assess the changes caused by oil spills, pesticides, and other types of pollution.

YOU TRY IT!

A large amount of the world's oil supply is provided by countries in the Middle East, such as Saudi Arabia and Kuwait. Why is there so much oil in these countries? The next time you visit the library, pick up a book about geology. You may be surprised to learn that millions of years ago, these deserts were part of the ocean. Read to see how this is true.

TEENS *in* SCIENCE

RESCUE TEAM IS ALL WET

Imagine that your telephone has just rung. It's the Pod Squad alerting you to another rescue. Fifteen-year-old Marc D'Anto is a member of a volunteer whale rescue team. He works with marine biologists, environmentalists, and veterinarians in Key Largo, Florida.

"To me the ocean is very exciting. It's a whole new world. Like a real-life video game," Marc says. "I guess Trish and Alex, two pilot whales, are the biggest rescues I've been involved in.

Trish weighed close to 1200 pounds and Alex nearly 700 pounds. When we found them, they were floating in shallow water."

The rescuers used a crane and specially made harness to lift the whales to safety. They transported them in a moving van to a nearby canal. "The whales had to be given antibiotics to combat pneumonia. The medication made them sleepy. If we didn't watch them closely, they would sink."

Marc and other volunteers stayed in the water 24 hours a day to keep the whales afloat. After months of care, both whales were strong enough to be set free. "It felt really good to watch them go, but a little sad, like losing a friend," Marc said. "But whenever I think of them, I just look out over the water. I know they are there somewhere."

WHAT DO YOU THINK?

Marc describes the ocean as a "real-life video game." What do you think he means by this?

Literature CONNECTION

A REAL FIND

Shell collecting is a hobby enjoyed by many people. They like to search the seashore at low tide for new and unusual shells that wash up at high tide. The empty shells are called dead shells. But sometimes shells are found that are still "alive"—an animal is attached to it and lives inside.

"The Strombus," by Latino author Sylvia C. Peña, is the story of a father and daughter who find a shell on the beach after a hurricane. Read the story to learn how the strombus inside the shell feels in the ocean during the hurricane and after being washed ashore. Also learn how finding a prized strombus shell, and then realizing the animal is still alive, affects the girl.

WHAT DO YOU THINK?

What do you think about the girl's behavior? How would you have reacted to finding the strombus?

Chapter 12

Reviewing Main Ideas

1. Land areas in contact with the ocean are called shore zones. Steep shore zones are rocky and have cliffs and other unusual rock formations. Flat shore zones are made up largely of gently sloping beaches.

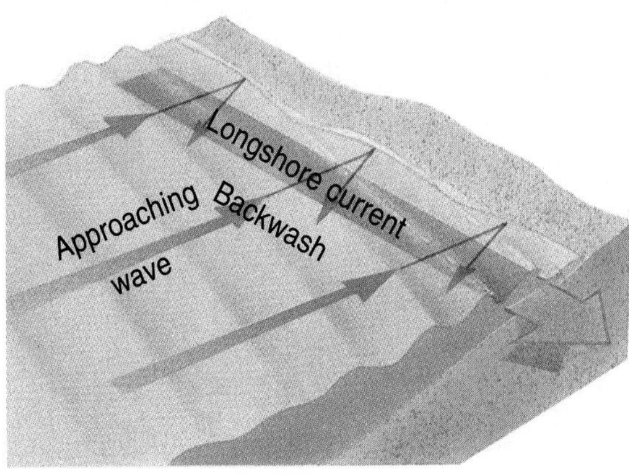

2. Longshore currents play a major role in shaping the features of shore zones.

3. Many human activities contribute to the pollution of the oceans. Pollution can be harmful to plants and animals that live in the ocean and on land in the shore zones.

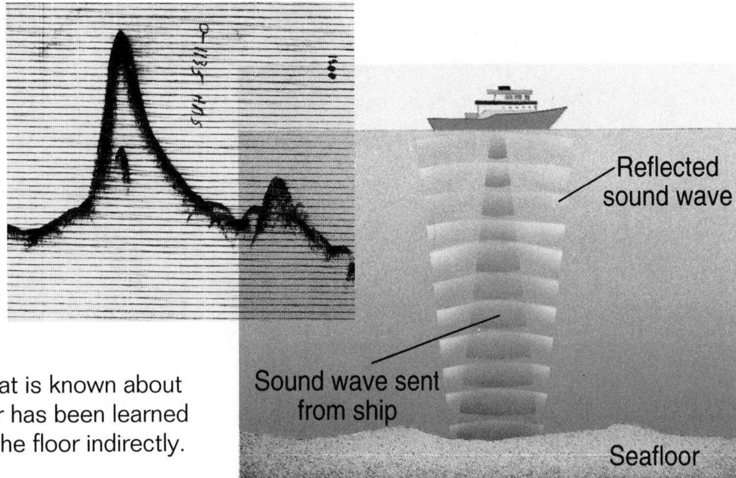

4. Most of what is known about the ocean floor has been learned by measuring the floor indirectly.

Chapter Review

USING KEY SCIENCE TERMS

abyssal plain
continental shelf
longshore current
mid-ocean ridges
pollution
rift zone

Read each statement. If the statement is true, write T. If false, replace the underlined term with the correct key science term to make it true.

1. Ocean currents carry sediments from the continental shelf and deposit them on the <u>mid-ocean ridges</u>.
2. New ocean floor forms from hardened lava that rises in the <u>rift zone</u>.
3. The <u>abyssal plain</u> is the flattest part of the ocean floor.
4. Volcanic activity is most apt to be found along the <u>continental slope</u>.

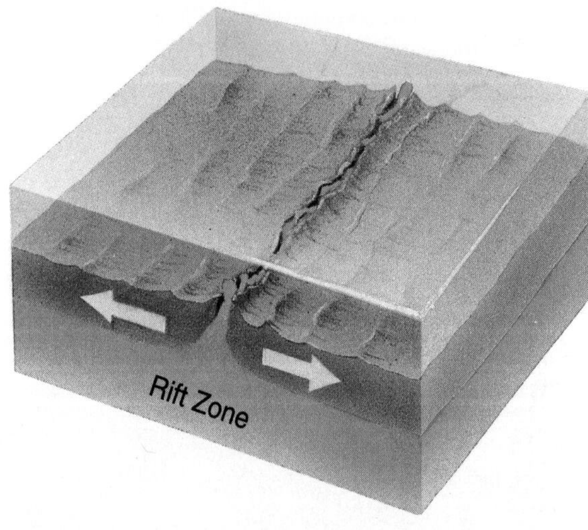

5. A <u>rift zone</u> often forms where waves coming in at an angle meet the shoreline.

UNDERSTANDING IDEAS

Complete each sentence.

1. When a longshore current ____, it deposits sediments.
2. The composition of the ____ in a shore zone depends on the original source of the material.
3. Islands can form from ____ that rise up from the seafloor.
4. Oil spills and fertilizers are often sources of ocean ____.
5. Ocean ____ are the deepest places on Earth.
6. The action of waves is the most important factor in forming and changing ____.
7. Most beach sand is composed of ____, a hard, resistant mineral.
8. ____ are the most common feature of flat shore zones.
9. The movement of water back toward the sea after a wave hits the shore is called ____.
10. ____ shore zones generally have hard rocks that resist being worn down.

CRITICAL THINKING

Use your understanding of the concepts developed in the chapter to answer each of the following questions.

1. How can pesticides used on a field far from the coast pollute ocean water?

2. Explain why beach sand in different shore zones may be different.
3. Specialized submarines called submersibles have been developed that can carry people safely to some of the deepest parts of the ocean, where they can make direct observations of the ocean floor. Why don't scientists use these machines to map the ocean floor?
4. The distance "as the crow flies" from North Point to South City is 15 km. The table shows how much coastline lay between the two cities in the years 1894, 1924, 1954, and 1984. What could account for the differences in distance? What do you think the distance might be in 2004?

Distance Between South City and North Point	
Straight Line Distance	15 km
1894	27 km
1924	26 km
1954	22 km
1984	19 km

5. Phosphates are chemicals that contain phosphorous, which is a plant nutrient. Why is it a good idea to use phosphate-free laundry detergents?

PROBLEM SOLVING

Read the following problem and discuss your answers in a brief paragraph.

Scientists use sound waves produced by sonar to map the ocean floor.

1. In using these waves, what two factors must they know in order to calculate how deep the floor is in a particular place?
2. How would you use the factors named in Question 1 to calculate the depth of the ocean floor?
3. Sound travels through ocean water at an average speed of about 1500 meters per second. If a sound wave takes 4 seconds to travel from the machine to the ocean floor and back, how deep is the ocean floor at that location?

CONNECTING IDEAS

Discuss each of the following in a brief paragraph.

1. What kind of rock would most likely be found on the ocean floor near the continental slope? What kind might be found along a rift zone? Explain your answers.
2. Explain how the waste water that leaves your home might pollute a shore zone.
3. How might a steep shore zone become a flat zone over time?
4. **LIFE SCIENCE CONNECTION** On what parts of the ocean floor is there probably an adequate amount of sunlight for ocean plants to photosynthesize? What parts may be so deep that only chemosynthesis is possible?
5. **SCIENCE AND SOCIETY** What effect do groynes have on longshore currents and their movement of beach sediments?

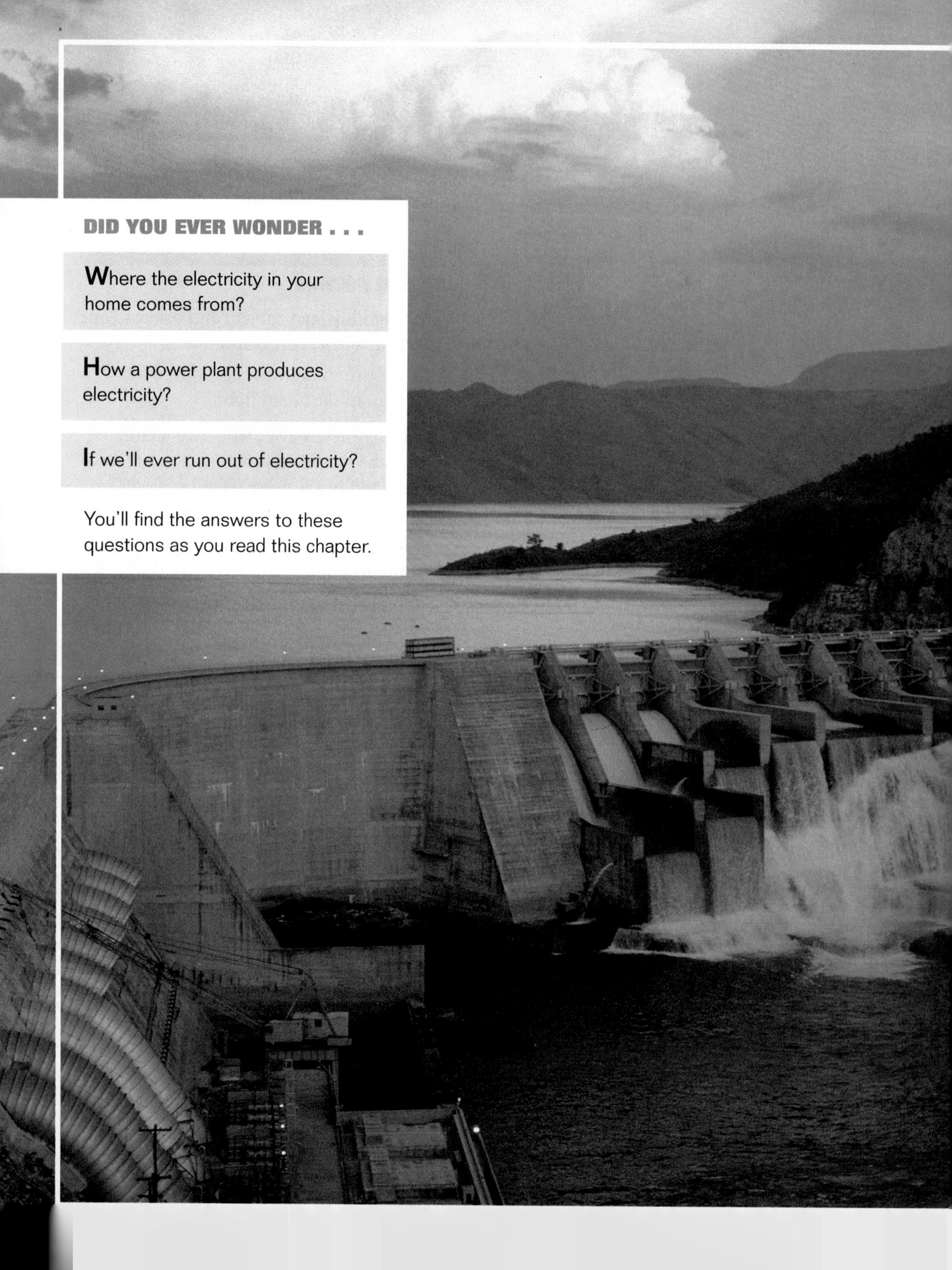

DID YOU EVER WONDER . . .

Where the electricity in your home comes from?

How a power plant produces electricity?

If we'll ever run out of electricity?

You'll find the answers to these questions as you read this chapter.

Chapter 13

Energy Resources

Remember the last time the electricity went out? Where were you? At school? At home? At school, the lights blinked out, and your class may not have been able to read in the dimmed room. At home, the television suddenly went blank and silent. If it was nighttime, someone may have quickly rummaged through a drawer looking for candles to light. In towns and cities, stores and buildings almost seemed to disappear.

How long did the last electrical power failure in your area last? The longer it lasted, the more apt it was to have serious effects, such as traffic lights not working or food defrosting inside freezers. When the power was returned, you and others may have breathed a sigh of relief. Life could return to normal with a flick of a switch.

In this chapter, you will read the story behind that flick of the switch that brings us electricity. You'll read about power plants like the one shown here. Day and night, they are responsible for providing people with the electricity they need to live normal modern lives.

EXPLORE!

How much does electricity mean to you?

Mentally walk through each room of your home. List all of the items that use electricity. Then classify the items as things you cannot do without (refrigerator), things that make your life easier (blow dryer), or things you have just for fun (TV set). Describe how you might live if the items in each category did not exist.

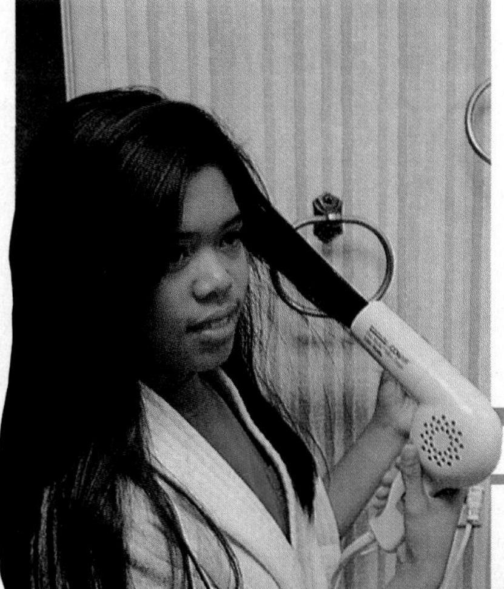

13-1 The Electricity You Use

OBJECTIVES

In this section, you will

- trace the source of the energy that runs common appliances you use all the time;
- describe what water and steam do in an electric power plant;
- relate the roles of turbines and generators in producing electricity.

KEY SCIENCE TERMS

turbine
generator

THE SOURCE OF ELECTRICITY

When you wake up in the morning and reach for a lamp or wall switch, you take it for granted the light will come on. You may flick a number of appliances on and off as you get ready for school without even thinking about the electricity you're using. You'd probably be shocked, in fact, to find one morning that your blow dryer wouldn't blow or your toaster wouldn't toast. These appliances, after all, run on electricity.

Where does the electricity in your home come from? Imagine jumping through one of those handy outlets to see for yourself. Once behind the outlet, you find that you are inside electrical wires. You follow the wires to a box on an outside wall of your home. From there, more electrical wires may go underground or high up to a power line pole. Finally, you arrive at a power plant. The wires

FIGURE 13-1. As homes are constructed, they are wired for electricity.

FIGURE 13-2. Electrical wiring reaches from homes and businesses to power plants such as this coal-burning facility.

take you right on inside the big concrete building at the power plant. Finally you have arrived at the source of the electricity. What goes on there? Do this Find Out activity to discover one way electricity is generated.

FIND OUT!

How can thermal energy be converted to mechanical energy?

Fill a teakettle about three-fourths full with cool water and place it on a burner. Turn on the burner. What happens to the water as energy from the burner is transferred to the kettle? Is the transferred energy still thermal energy? When steam begins coming out of the kettle's opening, hold a pinwheel in the path of the steam and observe. **CAUTION:** *Steam causes severe burns. Do not hold your arm or hand near the steam.*

Conclude and Apply

1. What happens to the pinwheel?
2. Explain why the following statement is true: The demonstration you have just done shows that energy changes forms.

ENERGY CHANGES FORMS AT A POWER PLANT

According to the law of conservation of energy, energy can change form, but it cannot disappear. The total amount of energy does not change. You worked with the law of conservation of energy as you completed the activity with the teakettle and the pinwheel. You neither created nor destroyed energy. You simply caused it to change form. First you transferred thermal energy from the burner to the water. Steam from the boiling water acted on the blades of your pinwheel, changing internal energy to mechanical energy.

Electricity can be generated at power plants using the same principles of energy transfer and change as your teakettle and pinwheel. Figure 13-3 shows some of the equipment at a power plant and how it works. Find the combustion chamber on the drawing. Think of it as the burner in your demonstration. This power plant uses coal as its fuel. Coal is burned in the combustion chamber to produce the thermal energy.

Now find the pipes inside the combustion chamber in the drawing. Thermal energy in the combustion chamber causes the water inside these pipes to turn into steam. The steam is then directed at the turbine. A **turbine** is a machine with blades arranged around a central axle. When the steam from the combustion chamber comes in contact with the turbine blades, the turbine spins just as your pinwheel did—only incredibly faster! And just as in your demonstration, the spinning turbine means that

FIGURE 13-3. Energy changes form at a coal-burning electrical power plant.

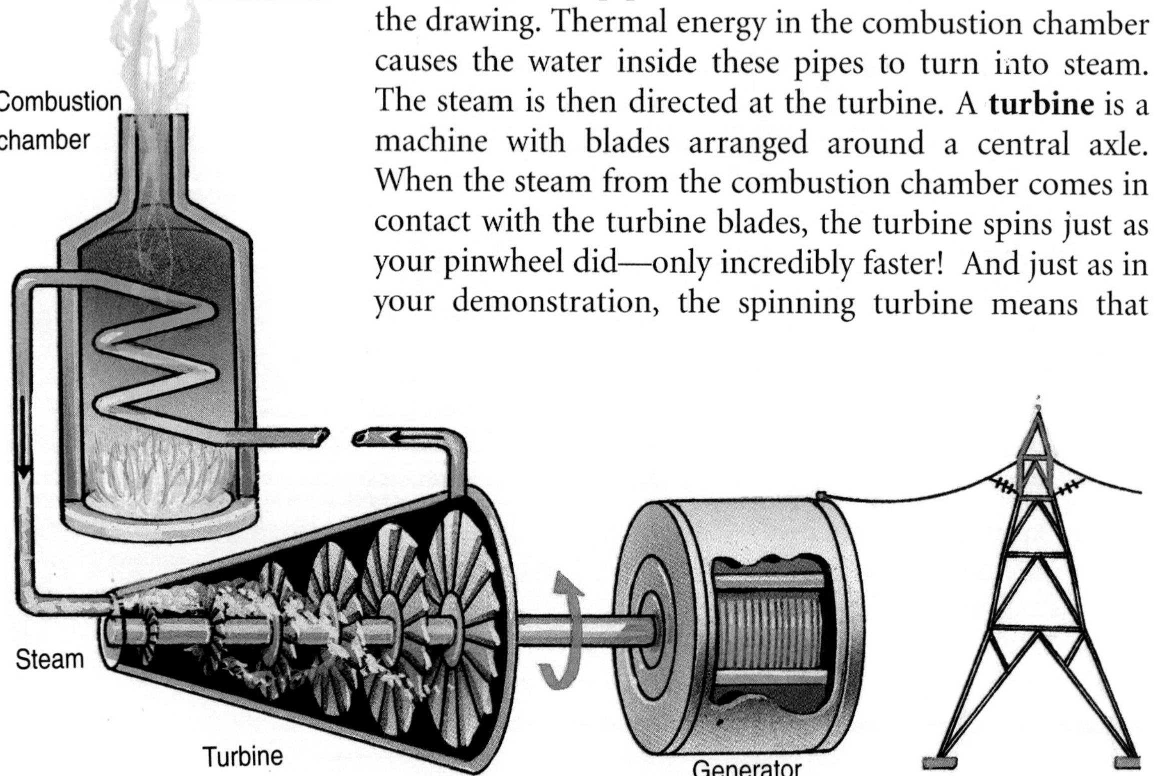

some of the steam's internal energy has been converted into mechanical energy. The mechanical energy from the turbine, in turn, spins the axle of a generator. The generator is yet another piece of power plant equipment that makes energy change forms. A **generator** is any machine that converts mechanical energy into electrical energy.

Find the axle that runs through the turbine in the power plant diagram. See how it projects into the generator in the final stages of the power plant's operation. Notice the wires that lead out of the generator and away from the power plant. "Isn't this where we came in?" you ask. Indeed it is. If you could hop back into the wires leading away from the generator, you could return to the outlet in your home.

It takes a lot of pretending to make a trip through electrical power lines. There's nothing imaginary, however, about the role electricity plays in our lives. You found that out when you listed all the appliances in your home. A world without electricity might be interesting to imagine in a story, but would you want to live in it?

SKILLBUILDER

SEQUENCING

Use the information in the text to show the chain of events, or sequence, connecting the burning of coal with turning on a light in your room. Use the light turning on as your final outcome and work backward toward the starting event. If you need help, refer to the **Skill Handbook** on page 678.

FIGURE 13-4. When energy is transferred from a turbine to a generator, it changes from mechanical energy to electrical energy.

Check Your Understanding

1. How does a blow dryer or other appliance you might use every day at home get the power to operate?
2. Use the terms *water, steam, mechanical energy,* and *electrical energy* to discuss how steam helps generate electricity.
3. What is the relationship between a turbine and a generator in an electric power plant?
4. **APPLY:** Do you think it would be possible to generate electricity without coal? Explain.

13-2 Fossil Fuels

OBJECTIVES

In this section, you will

- compare and contrast three different fossil fuels;
- trace the steps in the formation of fossil fuels.

KEY SCIENCE TERMS

fossil fuel

THE ENERGY IN COAL

Power plants use a number of different resources for the energy needed to operate turbines and generators. Some power plants, for instance, get their energy from the force of rushing water or blowing winds. Others derive thermal energy from burning oil or natural gas. In the United States, more than 57 percent of the electric power plants rely on burning coal. That makes coal very important.

EXPLORE!

What does a piece of coal look like?

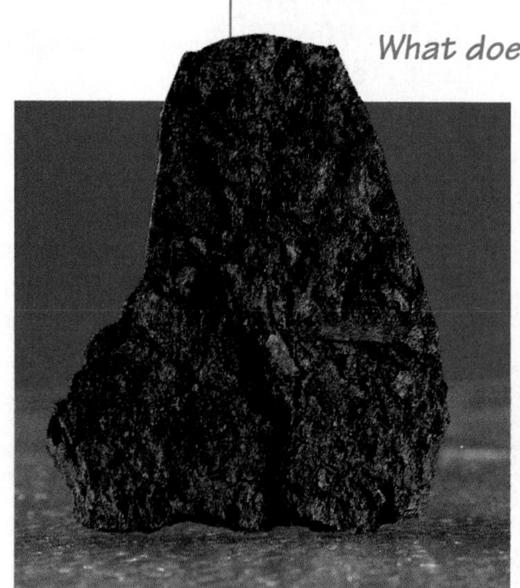

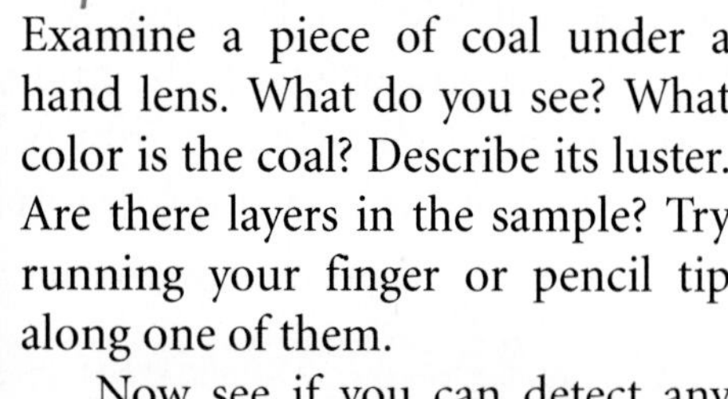

Examine a piece of coal under a hand lens. What do you see? What color is the coal? Describe its luster. Are there layers in the sample? Try running your finger or pencil tip along one of them.

Now see if you can detect any fossils in the sample. A fossil is any evidence of past life. It might be the imprint of either plant or animal life. If your coal sample has any fossils, decide whether they are remains of plants or of animals.

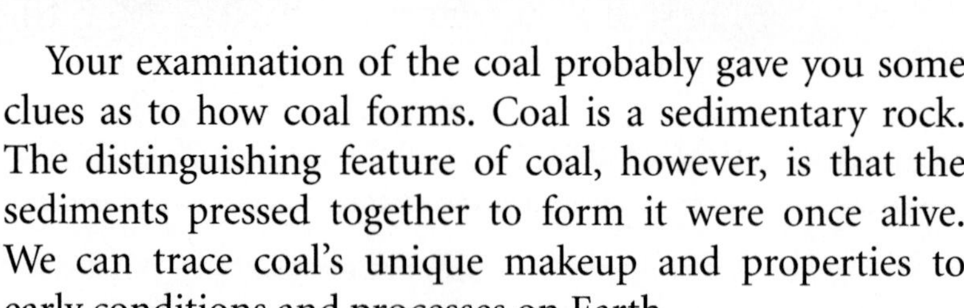

Your examination of the coal probably gave you some clues as to how coal forms. Coal is a sedimentary rock. The distinguishing feature of coal, however, is that the sediments pressed together to form it were once alive. We can trace coal's unique makeup and properties to early conditions and processes on Earth.

Formation of Coal

The swamp pictured in Figure 13-5 looks like nothing any of us has ever experienced. That's because it's 300 million years old. Most of the coal mined in the United

FIGURE 13-5. The first stage of coal formation took place in ancient swamps like the one pictured here.

States began forming about that long ago, when swamps covered much of the land. Huge green ferns and mosses competed for space. Giant reptiles lumbered among the plants. Crawling insects, some the size of mice, crept about. Flying insects with wingspans as wide as your desktop flew through the warm, humid air.

When it was time for each green, leafy plant to die, it would fall over, slip into the watery swamp floor, and begin to decay. The elements carbon, hydrogen, and oxygen make up plants. During the decaying process, bacteria break up the plant material to release the hydrogen and oxygen. This process leaves carbon behind. The carbon combines with plant material in various stages of decay to form coal.

It took a hundred million years or so and many cycles of dying and decaying plants for the coal to take form. As old plants died and fell into the swamp, new ones grew up in their place. In time, the new plants died and likewise fell over, adding layer upon layer of plant debris. The layers sank into the swamp under their own weight. Pressure from this weight, in combination with heat, promoted coal formation.

Coal subjected to the greatest amount of pressure and heat during its formation is anthracite. Anthracite is very hard and black. It burns with very little smoke and produces large amounts of thermal energy. Bituminous coal, which makes a lot of smoke as it burns, was subjected to less heat and pressure. Lignite, which is brown and very smoky to burn, was subjected to the least amount of pressure. It still contains pieces of woody plant material.

Because of its link with living plants from the past, coal is one among several kinds of fossil fuels. A **fossil fuel** is the remains of ancient plants or animals that you can burn today to produce thermal energy. Think back to the electrical power plant. Steam turned the turbine, which in turn spun the generator to produce electricity. What was being burned to provide the thermal energy to change liquid water into steam? In many power plants, the fuel being burned is coal.

OIL AND NATURAL GAS

You may have figured out that the other fossil fuels are oil and natural gas. What makes these two energy resources fossil fuels? Both formed millions of years ago from the remains of ancient organisms. Unlike coal, however, which came from land plants, oil and natural gas are thought to have formed from plants and animals that lived in ancient shallow oceans.

FIGURE 13-6. Oil is brought to the surface by pumps, shown here in an oil field in California.

As ancient sea organisms died, their remains fell down to the ocean floor. Most organisms that settled on the ocean floor decayed. But in some places, they became buried under thick layers of sand and mud. Just as layers of decaying plants were compressed during the formation of coal, so the thick layers of sediment and partly decayed organisms on the ocean floor compacted over time. Slowly, chemical reactions changed the organisms into oil and natural gas. How are these fuels found within the ground now? This activity will help answer that question.

EXPLORE!

How do water and oil react?

Pour equal amounts of water and salad oil into a small bottle or jar. Shake the container. Describe the appearance of the mixture. Observe what happens after the container is allowed to rest for a few minutes. What does the oil do? What does the water do?

As you have just seen, oil and water don't mix. Oil will always float to the top because it is less dense than the water. Figure 13-7 shows you that a similar process takes place underground. Oil, gas, and water often get squeezed into the spaces of porous sandstone. If there is a space for oil and gas to collect and accumulate, an oil or gas reservoir is formed. See how the oil, gas, and water are arranged in Figure 13-7. Which is the least dense? How can you tell?

To get oil and gas from the ground, engineers must drill through the rock layers to reach the reservoir. Many of the reservoirs in the United States would yield too little oil to make drilling worthwhile. Also, not all the oil and gas in a reservoir can be pumped out. Oil drillers often want to know how more oil could be pumped out of a well. Let's find out what methods an oil driller uses.

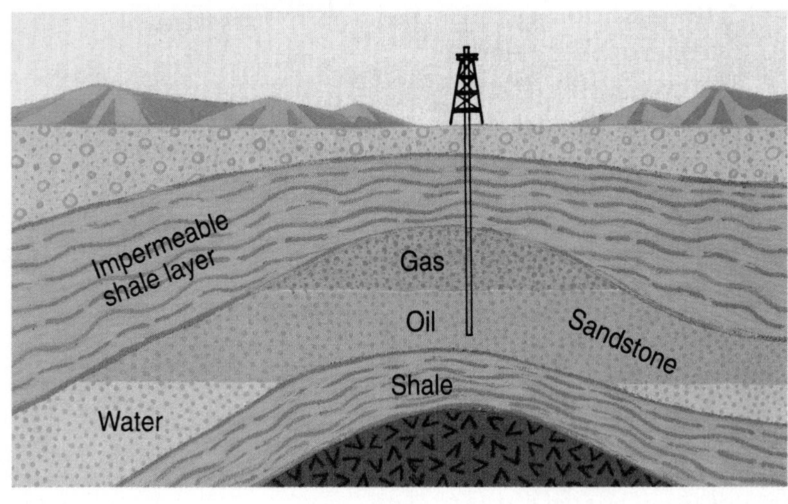

FIGURE 13-7. Oil and gas, along with water, can be trapped in layers of sandstone.

I N V E S T I G A T E !

13-1 RETRIEVING OIL

In this activity, you'll be an oil driller. Your objective is to find methods for pumping out the maximum amount of oil your well has to give.

PROBLEM

What methods can be used to remove the most oil from a reservoir?

MATERIALS 

clear plastic bottle with spray pump
1 to 2 cups of small, clean pebbles
clear plastic tubing
100-mL graduated cylinder
100-mL vegetable oil
50 mL cold water
100 mL hot water
liquid detergent

PROCEDURE

1. Copy the data table.
2. Study the picture. Then use the plastic pump bottle, plastic tubing, and pebbles to build your oil well. The plastic tubing should be inserted deep into the pebbles.
3. Pour 100 mL of oil into your well.
4. Now pump as much oil as you can get out of your well. **Measure** the amount in your graduated cylinder and record the amount on your data table.
5. Empty the oil out of your graduated cylinder.
6. Pour 50 mL of cold water into your well. **Observe** the reaction in the bottle. Again, pump out as much oil as you can. Give the oil and water time to separate in the graduated cylinder. Then record the amount of oil you recovered. Empty the cylinder.
7. Using 50 mL of hot water, repeat Step 6.
8. Using 50 mL of hot water and 8 drops of liquid detergent, repeat Step 6.

DATA AND OBSERVATIONS

PUMPING STRATEGY	OIL RETRIEVED (IN ML)
Oil only	
Oil with cold water	
Oil with hot water	
Oil with hot water and detergent	

ANALYZE

1. How many milliliters of oil did you retrieve by pumping alone?
2. What did the oil do when you added the cold water to your well? How much oil did you pump out?
3. How much oil did you pump out using hot water?
4. How much oil did you pump out using hot water and detergent?

CONCLUDE AND APPLY

5. Tell how you would support this statement: Pumping alone is not adequate for removing all the oil from a well.
6. **Going Further: Predict** the results of using detergent alone. Then try the experiment this way.

FIGURE 13-8. We use oil to make a large number and variety of everyday products.

Oil as it is pumped from the ground is sometimes called crude oil. Manufacturers break down the crude oil into many different stages, and from that breakdown comes an array of things close to all our lives. Fuels, such as the gasoline we burn in our car engines, are one of the biggest products derived from oil. Natural gas is a fuel widely used for heating and cooking. Altogether, the amount of fuel energy derived from oil and natural gas in the United States is double the amount provided by coal. Considering the amount of coal used in electric power plants, it is easy to see that the United States consumes an enormous amount of oil.

Oil also has many uses that go even beyond energy. Look at the items in Figure 13-8. Each item contains a basic ingredient derived from oil. Which items relate most closely to your life?

Check Your Understanding

1. In what ways are each of the fossil fuels used in the United States?
2. How was the formation of coal like the formation of oil and natural gas? How was it different?
3. **APPLY:** Natural gas is often taken from the same locations where oil is drilled. Why do you think this is true?

13-3 Resources and Pollution

OBJECTIVES

In this section, you will

- classify energy resources as either renewable or nonrenewable;
- discuss the environmental effects of burning fossil fuels.

KEY SCIENCE TERMS

renewable resource
nonrenewable resources

FOSSIL FUEL: HOW MUCH AND HOW LONG?

The processes that caused coal to form ages ago are probably continuing in some places on Earth. The same may be true for the formation of oil and natural gas. This does not mean, however, that the planet will continue producing all the fossil fuels people may demand. Fossil fuels are natural resources. A natural resource is anything that occurs naturally and for which people have found one or more uses. Some natural resources occur in virtually endless supplies. Others do not. Fossil fuels are among those that do not.

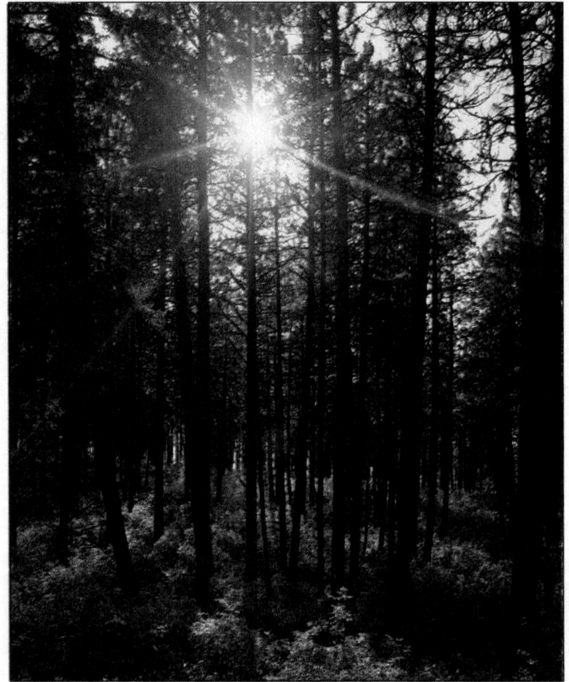

FIGURE 13-9. Sunlight and forests are renewable resources.

RENEWABLE RESOURCES

Those natural resources that cannot be used up are called renewable resources. A **renewable resource** is one that can be replaced. In other words, there is little danger that we will run out of that resource in the future.

Think about the sun. It will continue to shine for millions of years. Energy from the sun will continue to warm the planet and provide light for growing plants. New trees will be able to replace dying ones. Therefore, forests are a renewable resource. The sun's energy also keeps water moving back and forth between land and bodies of water in the water cycle. Sunlight and water also make it possible for people to grow the same crops year after year. A field of corn harvested and used in the fall can be replanted in the spring. Thus, crops become a renewable resource too.

NONRENEWABLE RESOURCES

Resources that people are using up much faster than nature can replace them are **nonrenewable resources.** A nonrenewable resource is one that can be replaced only over a very long time.

Take coal as an example. It took millions of years for decaying plants to change into a small seam of coal. An electric power plant burns that much coal in a single day. Plants dying in today's swamps won't become coal until millions of years from now. Our supplies of coal, therefore, are limited. Even so, we may be able to rely longer on coal than on any other fossil fuel. The United States once had supplies of anthracite coal. Most of it was used up decades ago. The United States still has a great supply of bituminous coal, however—more than 430 billion tons of it are still in the ground. The United States recovers and burns well over 900 million tons of coal each year. Of that 900 million, electric power plants burn more than 750 million tons. Even at this rate of usage, the United States would still have enough coal to last hundreds of years.

Supplies of other fossil fuels are much more limited. The United States and some other countries of the world still have reserves of oil and natural gas. Reserves are places people know of where natural resources are deposited. According to some estimates, all the world's oil reserves could be emptied within the next 25 years if people continue to use oil at current rates. There are also estimates on the limited supplies of natural gas. What do they show? Do the next Investigate to find out.

SKILLBUILDER

MAKING TABLES

Use the information in the following paragraph to make a table. If you need help, refer to the **Skill Handbook** on page 679.

In 1970, vehicles used 52.9 percent of all the oil consumed in the United States. By 1989, vehicle consumption had increased to 62.9 percent. In contrast, industry's consumption dropped from 25.9 percent to 24.7 percent, power plant use went from 6.3 percent to 4.3 percent, and homes and businesses reduced their consumption from 14.8 percent to 8.1 percent.

FIGURE 13-10. Coal near the surface is "strip" mined. Rock and soil covering the coal is stripped off, revealing the coal layers.

INVESTIGATE!

13-2 PREDICTING NATURAL GAS RESERVES

In this activity, you will **interpret a graph** showing how much natural gas we currently consume and how much our reserves still hold. You will use this information to **predict** how long these reserves will last.

PROBLEM

How much natural gas do we consume in the United States?

MATERIALS

graph of reserves vs. production
pencil
paper

PROCEDURE

1. Examine the graph closely. It shows the billions of cubic meters of natural gas in United States reserves and in marketed production (pumped out and sold) from 1925 to 1985.
2. Study the directions the curves take from 1925 through 1985. Assume that the slopes of the curves will continue in mostly the same pattern. Keep this assumption in mind as you answer these questions.

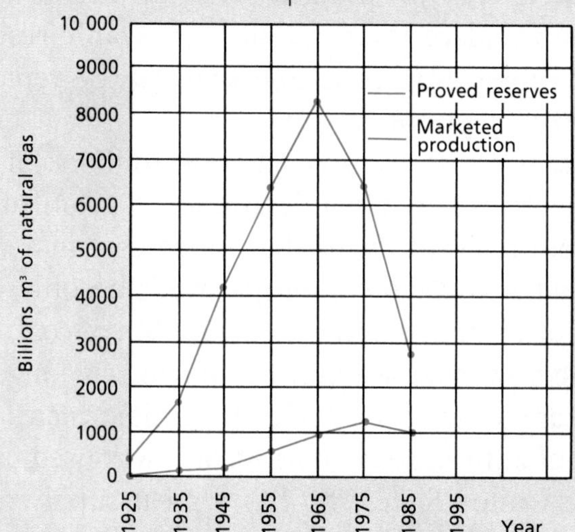

ANALYZE

Use the words *increased, decreased,* or *remained the same* to answer Questions 1–4 below.

1. What trend in proved reserves occurred between 1925 and 1965?
2. What trend in proved reserves occurred between 1965 and 1985?
3. What trend in marketed production occurred between 1945 and 1975?
4. What trend in marketed production occurred between 1975 and 1985?

CONCLUDE AND APPLY

5. Why do you think the United States gas reserves increased from 1925 to 1965, but decreased from 1965 to 1985?
6. Why did marketed production increase between 1945 and 1975 and then drop off?
7. Assuming past trends continue in both reserves and marketed production, **predict** the status of United States natural gas reserves for the year 1995.
8. **Going Further: Predict** what could happen to the reserves if consumers started conserving natural gas so that the marketed production fell back to its 1945 level.

BURNING FOSSIL FUELS: COSTS TO BE PAID

People are concerned about the limited supplies and possible scarcities of fossil fuels in the years and decades ahead. People are working on plans for a time when we may have to rely on other sources of energy. There is also a more immediate danger connected with fossil fuels. That danger is air pollution. Although natural gas burns with a clean flame, both coal and oil products release harmful pollution when they burn.

Most of the air pollution traced to oil comes from the gasoline burned in our cars' engines. Because electric power plants burn so much coal, most of the air pollution traced to coal comes from them. Burning coal gives off nitrogen oxide, which is made of nitrogen and oxygen, and carbon dioxide, which is made of carbon and oxygen. Carbon dioxide and nitrogen oxide are both greenhouse gases. They get that name because they collect in layers in the

FIGURE 13-11. Thousands of tons of coal wait to be burned at this coal-fired electricity generating plant.

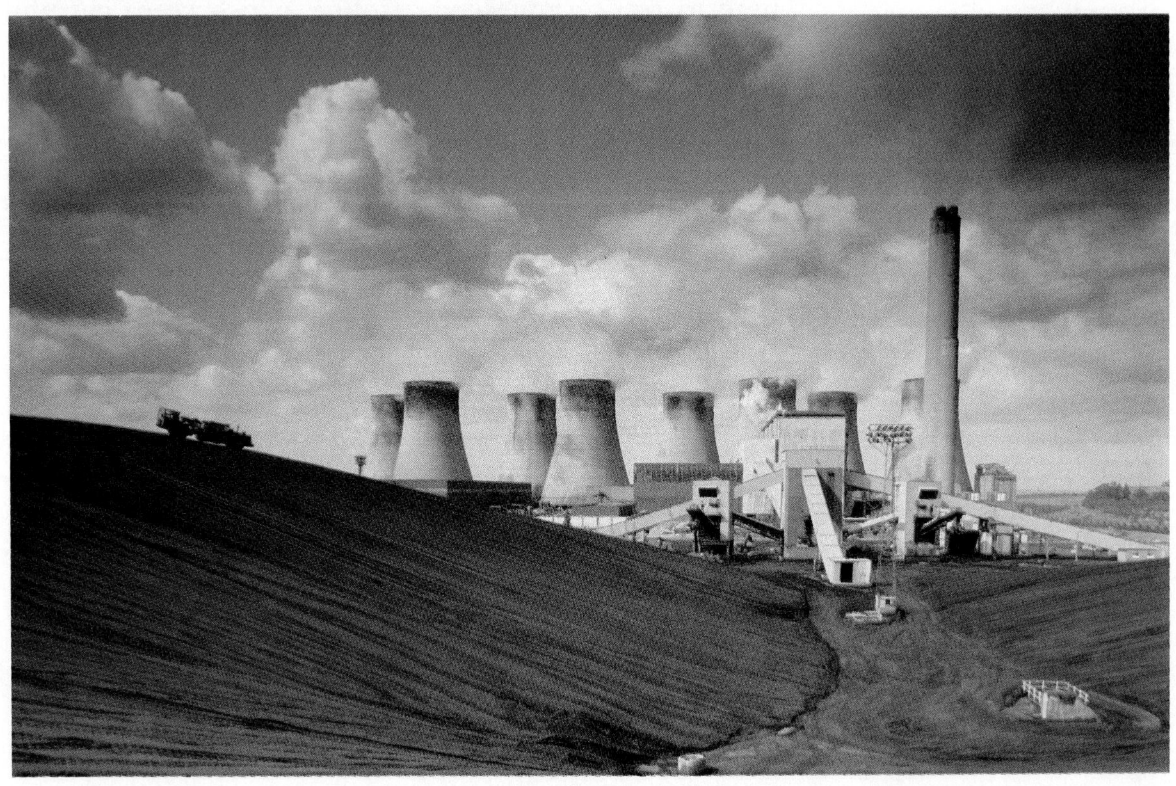

DID YOU KNOW?

In one year, burning the coal to light one 100-watt light bulb for 12 hours a day creates more than 936 pounds of carbon dioxide and 7.8 pounds of sulfur dioxide.

atmosphere and keep reflected solar heat from escaping from Earth, much as a greenhouse retains solar heat inside. An accumulation of greenhouse gases may contribute to global warming. You will study more about greenhouse gases and global warming in Chapter 15.

Some coal contains high amounts of sulfur. When high-sulfur coal burns, it releases sulfur dioxide. The sulfur dioxide combines with water vapor in the air to form tiny droplets of sulfuric acid. These droplets gather together to form acid rain, which has eaten away at the walls of buildings in cities and poisoned water and forests in the countryside.

Now many coal-burning power plants have special pollution-control equipment inside their smokestacks. Often said to scrub the coal smoke, this equipment prevents harmful pollutants from reaching the atmosphere by mixing sulfur dioxide with chemicals that react with it to form solids. Solids are then removed and disposed of. Car manufacturers attach a device called a catalytic converter to the pipe that carries exhaust from a car engine. Catalytic converters change irritating exhaust pollutants into carbon dioxide and water vapor. In addition, cars are now built to run on unleaded gasoline, which keeps harmful lead pollutants out of car exhausts.

Only time will tell what the future of our fossil fuel resources will be. We can be certain, however, that our need for energy will always be there. What qualities would the perfect energy source have? First, it should be clean. It should provide energy without adding harmful pollutants to the environment. Second, it should be plentiful. Finally, it should be renewable. Can you think of an alternative form of energy to fossil fuels? In the next section, you will read about several.

Check Your Understanding

1. What makes coal a nonrenewable resource?
2. Why might the burning of fossil fuels be considered a costly practice?
3. **APPLY:** Would it be possible for us to solve our fossil fuel pollution problems by burning natural gas rather than coal or oil? Why or why not?

13-4 Alternative Energy Resources

IF NOT FOSSIL FUELS, WHAT?

Imagine that you are responsible for developing the power source for a new city. You know you will have to build a power plant to generate the electricity. You decide that you will not use fossil fuels as your source of energy. But where do you go from there? What alternative sources of energy might you use to turn the turbine and generator in your power plant? The following activity may help you develop some ideas.

OBJECTIVES

In this section, you will

- describe alternative sources of energy;
- differentiate among the ways alternative energy resources are used to produce electricity.

KEY SCIENCE TERMS

hydroelectric
solar cell
geothermal

EXPLORE!

How many different methods can you use to make your pinwheel spin?

Demonstrate some of the ways. Try this one. Fill a 250-mL beaker with water. Hold the pinwheel over the sink or a bucket. Pour the water on the pinwheel, being careful that the water falls into the sink or bucket. Did you get the pinwheel to turn?

HYDROELECTRIC ENERGY

Now you have proved to yourself that there is more than one way to get a pinwheel to spin. The same must be true of turbines in electric power plants, you think. You are pleased to discover that a number of alternative sources of energy are already at work generating electricity. One of them is waterpower. Power plants that use waterpower to generate electricity are called **hydroelectric** plants.

People in southern Canada and the eastern United States use the rushing river waters at Niagara Falls to generate electricity for a number of large cities. In other places, where there are no natural waterfalls, people have built concrete dams to produce hydroelectric power. The Shasta Dam, in northern California's Sacramento River, is the tallest structure of its type in the world. What happens to the waters of the Sacramento River behind the dam?

FIGURE 13-12. Shasta Dam and its hydroelectric power plant (a) turn the potential energy of the water in the reservoir into mechanical energy and then into electricity. The diagram of the dam and plant (b) illustrates how.

The river water that backs up behind a dam makes up the hydroelectric plant's reservoir. Most reservoirs are the size of lakes. Lake Shasta extends 56 kilometers up the Sacramento River. Now look at Figure 13-12 of the dam and power plant. The water in the reservoir stands rather still, but it has potential energy. Because of the water's depth, the water at the base of the dam is under great pressure. This water pressure turns the turbines, and they convert potential energy into mechanical energy. That mechanical energy pushes against the turbines that turn the generators. Power plant operators open or close the gateways in the dam to control when the generators will run and how much electric power they will produce.

a

b

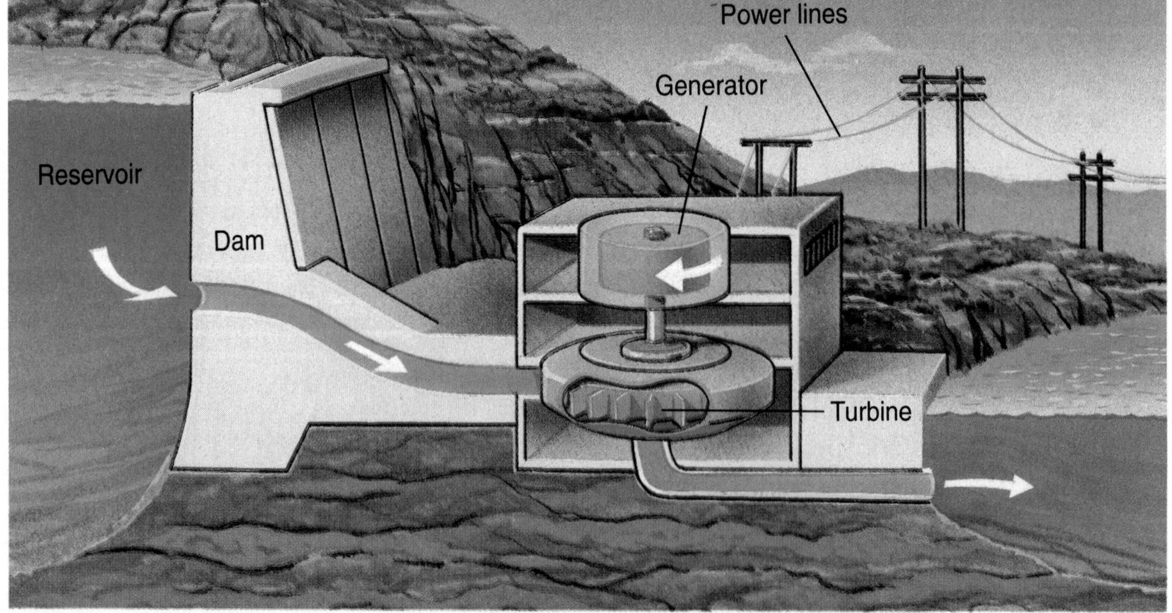

Hydroelectric power is a clean, renewable source of energy. If you were to use it in your new city, however, you would have to make sure your city is close to a river with enough water to build a dam and reservoir. In the United States, hydroelectric power plants are already operating in many locations. About 10 percent of the electricity used in the United States comes from hydroelectric power plants.

SOLAR ENERGY

Suppose your new city could find a single source for all its energy needs—power to generate electricity, run cars, and even operate computers. This source might be the sun. The sun sends as much energy to Earth's surface in 40 minutes as humans use all around the world in one year. Energy from the sun, called solar energy, is clean and renewable. Hour after hour, year after year, the sun bathes the planet in energy. There are several ways to use energy from the sun.

Perhaps you have seen large, flat boxes on the rooftops of homes or buildings. These are solar collectors. Energy from the sun hits the black lining of a solar collector and heats air or water held inside under a glass lid. The heated air or water is then piped into the building to provide heat as needed. You can see solar energy being used this way in Figure 13-13.

Another way to use the sun's energy is to concentrate it with the aid of mirrors. For example, a towering structure of flat mirrors stands just outside the town of Odeillo, France. It is a solar power tower that provides the energy for Odeillo's electric power plant. The mirrors are positioned so that they focus energy from the sun on one part of the tower. Heat from that concentrated solar energy boils water in the tower. The boiling water turns to steam, and the steam turns a turbine, which leads to a

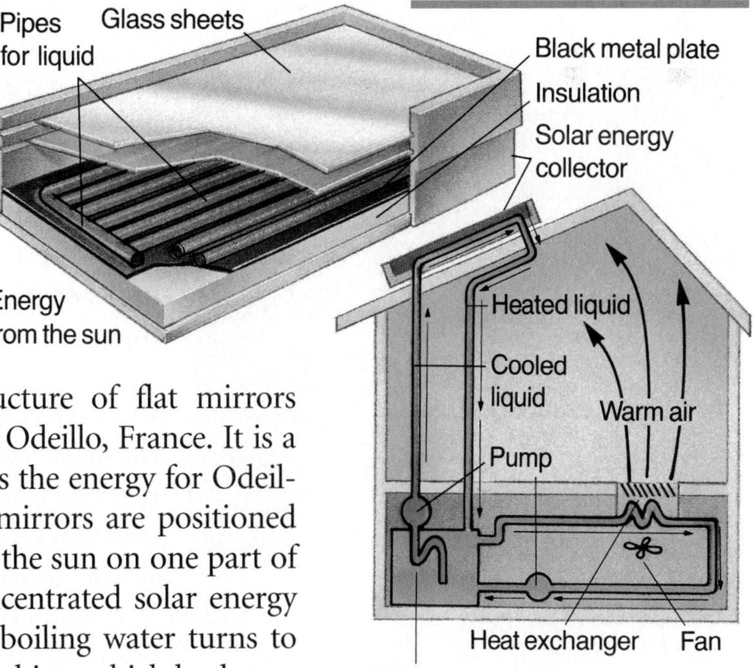

FIGURE 13-13. In a solar heating system, the liquid heated in the solar collector is circulated throughout the house.

FIGURE 13-14. The solar power plant at Odeillo, France, uses energy from the sun rather than from burning coal to produce enough heat to turn water into steam. The steam then turns a turbine, which transmits energy into a generator.

generator. You can see the solar power tower of Odeillo in Figure 13-14. But there are other uses for solar energy closer to home, and on a much smaller scale.

For example, you probably have used a calculator similar to the one in Figure 13-15. A **solar cell** in the casing turns solar energy into electricity, which powers the calculator. In one type of solar cell, thin layers of silicon are sandwiched together and attached to tiny wires. As light strikes the different layers, it causes an electrical current to flow. Silicon is a hard, dark-colored element found almost everywhere. Solar cells are also very efficient because they generate electricity in just one step. The cells turn solar energy directly into electricity. Compare that with the number of steps at an electric power plant that uses coal as an energy source.

FIGURE 13-15. The solar cell in this solar calculator turns energy from the sun directly into electricity.

Solar energy seems like a perfect energy source, doesn't it? But there are some disadvantages of solar power. Solar energy is received only when the sun is shining. Solar collectors and cells work less efficiently on cloudy days. They don't work at all at night. And during winter, when days are short, the collectors and cells generate less energy. Finally, although silicon is cheap and plentiful, solar cells are still expensive to make.

WIND ENERGY

What source of energy takes a kite soaring overhead or a sailboat bobbing through the waves? It is wind power, perhaps the oldest energy source in use. The Egyptians used wind power to propel their sailing barges along the Nile River at least 5000 years ago. The Dutch have used windmills to drive the pumps that drain seawater from their low-lying lands for centuries.

FIGURE 13-16. Energy from the wind is used by these windmills and combined to generate electricity.

Just as with a pinwheel, moving air can turn the blades of a windmill. Before electric lines brought electricity to the country, farmers often used windmills to drive small generators. The generators produced enough electricity for lights in the farmhouse and small machines the farmer used. Today, people are using windmills to generate electricity on a much larger scale. How many windmills can you see in the photo of California's windmill farm in Figure 13-16? There are actually hundreds, standing in parade formation, each turning its own generator. Together, these hundreds of windmills can produce enough electricity for a small city.

Wind energy is another clean and renewable alternative energy source. Like waterpower, it can be used only at certain locations. Winds must reach speeds of about 32 kilometers per hour or more if they are to turn the blades of windmills. The winds must also blow steadily the year round to make them a reliable source of energy.

DID YOU KNOW?

The earliest windmills were probably built in Iran in the 600s. They were used to grind grain. These windmills had sail-shaped arms that revolved around a vertical axis.

GEOTHERMAL ENERGY

Wind power, water power, and energy from the sun are all apparent to us from our positions on the surface of the planet. But what about alternative sources of energy underground? As you saw in Chapter 11, there is enough heat deep below Earth's surface to hold the material of igneous rock in a liquid state. In some

FIGURE 13-17. Steam from Earth's interior reaches the surface in certain regions, where it can be used to generate electricity. These facilities are in California.

places, usable energy can indeed be derived from this heat. It is called **geothermal** energy, which means energy extracted from Earth's internal heat.

The hot, molten rock inside Earth heats the layers of rock that rest above it. Groundwater that comes in contact with these heated rock layers is also heated, often to high enough temperatures to turn to steam. In some locations, vents in Earth's crust conduct the steam to the surface naturally. People need only pipe the steam to a geothermal power plant, where it turns a turbine generator that produces electricity. People can harness geothermal energy only in places where hot rock is very close to Earth's surface. Iceland, New Zealand, Japan, and northern California use geothermal energy to run electric generators. Powerhouse turbines spun by geothermal energy provide about 50 percent of San Francisco's electricity.

Which of the alternative energy sources do you think you might like to use in your new city? You know now that there are a number of choices. You know also that planning and new ways of looking at energy issues can keep electricity coming out of every outlet in every home for as long as we need it. And we do need it—every day—to light classrooms, refrigerate food, warm homes, and even entertain us. As time goes on, we'll still use electricity in the same ways, but the energy resources that help generate it will be different from most of those we now use.

Check Your Understanding

1. List what makes each of the four alternative energy resources in this lesson renewable.
2. Think about the ways in which the four alternative energy resources can be used to generate electricity. What factor do solar and geothermal energy have in common? In what major way do all four alternatives differ from fossil fuel generation of electricity?
3. **APPLY:** Do you think solar energy could serve well as an alternative energy resource where you live? Why or why not?

EXPANDING YOUR VIEW

CONTENTS

A Closer Look
Electric Expense 399

Physics Connection
Promises and Problems 400

Science and Society
Using Coal Resources 401

How It Works
Solar Panels 402

Technology Connection
Clean, Cheap, Fast! 403

History Connection
Lights Out! 404

Health Connection:
Bicycle Fuel 404

A CLOSER LOOK

ELECTRIC EXPENSE

The electric company charges your family for the electric energy you use. The company sells energy in units called kilowatt hours (kwh). A kilowatt hour is equal to 1000 watts of power used for one hour.

For example, one 100-watt light bulb left burning for ten hours uses one kilowatt hour of electric energy. If that bulb burns day and night for a month, it uses 72 kilowatts of energy.

To figure out your monthly bill, an electric company employee comes to your home and reads the electric meter. The meter might have dials like those on the one shown. It works something like a clock. The hands on the dials move to measure the amount of electricity used.

Read the meter from left to right. If the needle is between numbers, read the smaller number. This meter reads 18,432 kilowatt hours. It read 17,268 kilowatt hours last month. The difference between the two readings (18,432 – 17,268 = 1164) is how much electric energy was used this past month.

In this particular city, using one kilowatt hour of electricity costs 10.658 cents. Multiplying the cost of one kilowatt hour by the number of kilowatt hours used (10.658 cents per kwh × 1164 kwh) gives the amount of the bill — $124.06.

WHAT DO YOU THINK?

What can you and your family do to reduce your electric bill by $10.00 a month? Do you think you can reduce your bill by $25.00 a month? How?

Physics Connection

PROMISES AND PROBLEMS

About 20 percent of the electricity in the United States comes from nuclear energy. One kind of nuclear energy is released when tiny particles of the element uranium are split apart. The particles fly apart at high speed and collide with other particles, giving off thermal energy. The heat is used to boil water, which makes steam. The steam drives a turbine, which turns a generator. In this way, electricity is produced.

With nuclear energy, just a small amount of fuel can produce a great amount of energy. In fact, the nuclear energy released by one kilogram of uranium is a million times greater than the energy that one kilogram of fossil fuel can create. Nuclear energy does not release air pollution, such as CO_2, like coal-burning power plants do, nor does it release sulfur emissions that cause acid rain.

However, there are disadvantages to nuclear energy. Uranium releases invisible radioactive particles. Therefore, the fuel in nuclear reactors must be handled with extreme care. Even though nuclear power plants are designed to contain radiation, accidents have occurred.

A serious accident happened at the Chernobyl reactor in the Ukrainian Republic of the former Soviet Union in 1986. Temperatures inside the fuel chamber got too high. Steam pressure built up in the pipes and exploded, sending pieces of fuel rods through the roof. The roof caught fire, sending radioactive materials into the air. The wind carried this radioactivity for many kilometers over neighboring countries. As a result, nearly 135,000 people were evacuated from nearby towns, more than 200 suffered severe radiation injury, and at least 30 died. More may die from sickness and cancer caused by the radiation exposure.

Even the most safely run nuclear power plant produces harmful waste products. No entirely safe way has been discovered to store these waste products, which remain very dangerous for thousands of years.

Some government officials and scientists have suggested putting the waste in storage areas deep underground, in rural areas away from cities and towns. But others have said there is no way to make sure the storage area won't leak in the thousands of years the waste will remain dangerous.

Many people think that the use of nuclear power should not be expanded until the serious problems connected with it are solved. Others believe that nuclear power should continue to be developed and that safety and environmental problems can be solved as they occur.

WHAT DO YOU THINK?

Do you think we should continue to use nuclear power? Would you be willing to live near a nuclear power plant? Why or why not?

SCIENCE AND SOCIETY

USING COAL RESOURCES

An ordinary black lump of coal may once have been a patch of ferns that swayed in breezes 300 million years ago. The ferns could have been brushed against by passing land snails, cockroaches, and giant dragonflies—but not by dinosaurs. Dinosaurs didn't make their appearance until 230 million years ago.

As the ferns and their neighboring plants died, the swampy environment prevented bacteria from completely breaking down the plants. A soggy material called peat formed. Over hundreds of years, sediments were deposited atop the peat, and the resulting pressure squeezed water and gases out of the peat. The resulting material was coal.

Some coal lies within 200 feet of Earth's surface. To mine this coal, the tons of soil and rock lying above the coal must be moved out of the way. It's a simple but dirty process. First, bulldozers clear off an area and make it level. Then, many

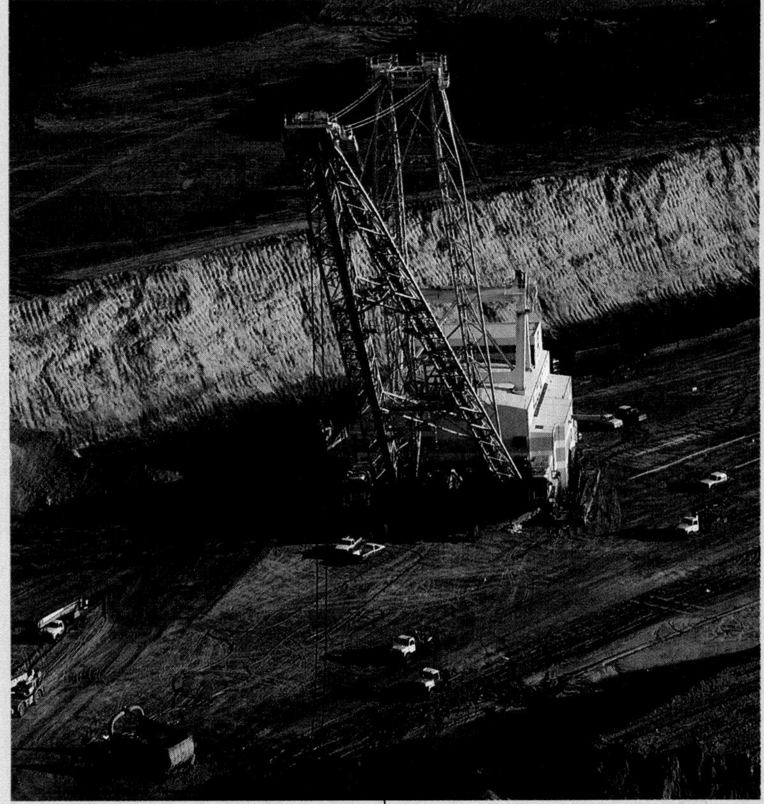

small holes are drilled in the rock and soil above the coal. The holes are filled with explosives, and when the explosives are set off, the rock is shattered. Next, earth movers, some as tall as a 20-story building, clear away the rock and soil, shoving it into massive heaps. The exposed coal is then scooped up and loaded into huge trucks. This process is called strip mining.

For over a hundred years, the huge expanses of land were scarred by strip mining as the mining companies moved from one coal-rich area to another. Once the coal was removed, the mined areas, looking like landscapes from some barren planet, were abandoned. The abandoned strip mines were more than just an eyesore. Serious environmental problems, including erosion, resulted.

Since 1978, companies wishing to strip mine in the United States have been required by law to restore the land they disturb. In this process, the open coal pit is leveled, and the rock and soil that were removed to expose the coal are placed back in the leveled pit. Topsoil is replaced and replanted. This restored area looks better than the abandoned pits, but it isn't quite as good as new. For one thing, the original coal seams are natural storage areas for underground water. Removing coal often causes wells in the area to go dry. Furthermore, without groundwater, plants cannot live. As plants disappear, so do the food and shelter needed by wildlife. Several years may pass before plants and animals can again flourish on a strip-mined area.

What about coal that isn't strip mined? Coal buried deeper than 200 feet below Earth's surface can only be removed by a process called underground mining. Shafts are dug 300 to 1000 feet into Earth, and miners and their equipment go underground to extract the coal. This kind of mining is far more hazardous for miners than strip mining. Shafts cave in, and tunnels can collapse. Hundreds of miners have lost their lives when they were trapped underground.

In addition, poisonous gases—some explosive—gather underground. "Fire in the hole," is a cry dreaded by miners and their families. Breathing coal dust and gases can cause serious lung diseases, among them the dreaded black lung disease.

Environmental effects of mining are substantial as well. Wastes from underground mines pollute water. Abandoned mines have caused the settling and sinking of two million acres of land in the United States. This has resulted in broken roads and sewer lines, as well as collapsed buildings.

About 35 percent of the world's coal reserves lies beneath the ground in the United States. This natural resource could provide a way for the United States to lessen its dependence on oil, much of which is purchased from faraway countries. As a country lessens its dependence on foreign sources of oil, it strengthens its own economy, providing jobs and security for its citizens. Making decisions about energy sources and their use is difficult. Many complex political, economic, and environmental factors must be considered.

WHAT DO YOU THINK?

Coal is currently a valuable energy resource in the United States. If coal were a clean-burning fuel, would the problems of mining be justified? Which do you think the United States should do—find alternate sources of energy or find a clean way to use coal?

HOW IT WORKS

SOLAR PANELS

Have you seen shallow boxes like these on the roofs of some buildings? These boxes have glass in front of a black material that absorbs the heat of the sun. Inside, a sheet of copper transfers the collected heat to water pipes that twist through the glass box. The water inside the pipes gets hot and is piped into the building to provide warmth and hot water. These glass boxes are solar panels, and they offer a way to provide warmth and energy. Solar panels

work well in places that receive a lot of sun. But can you imagine what happens in places that have long stretches of gray, overcast days?

YOU TRY IT!

You can capture some of the sun's energy. On a sunny day, get two plastic or glass containers of the same size, one white and one dark-colored. Fill each with water and set them outside in the sun. After a few hours, use a thermometer to check the temperature of the water in each container. Which one is warmer? Why is it warmer?

TECHNOLOGY CONNECTION

CLEAN, CHEAP, FAST!

Would you buy a used car that traveled at 132 miles an hour? What if the dealer claimed the exhaust was clean enough to drink? Would you believe it?

Well, it's been done. An engineer set a land speed record in a car at the Bonneville Salt Flats and then spent just $12.32 to convert the speedy vehicle to run on hydrogen.

Hydrogen is readily available from a very ordinary substance—water. As you may know, the recipe for water is H_2O, which means it is made up of two parts hydrogen and one part oxygen. An electric current can convert water into the two elements. So can a solar water splitter. Using solar power for the job results in zero pollution.

If hydrogen power is so great, why aren't hydrogen powered cars available? Hydrogen powered cars need more storage space for hydrogen than ordinary cars use for gasoline. That means more frequent stops for fuel.

WHAT DO YOU THINK?

Do you think having cleaner air by using hydrogen powered cars would be worth the inconvenience of more frequent stops?

History CONNECTION

LIGHTS OUT!

"The whole city is missing!" exclaimed a pilot flying over New York City. The pilot expected to see a scene similar to the one shown in the photograph. Instead, he saw nothing but blackness. A disruption in power darkened parts of eight states and Canada for several hours one November day in 1965.

It was rush hour. People were leaving work to go home. Thousands were stranded in subways and highrise elevators. The city came to a standstill. Although it was a difficult and sometimes frightening twelve hours, people rallied to help one another, and few crimes were committed.

However, another New York City blackout 12 years later didn't bring out the best in people. During that incident, millions of dollars worth of property was looted and burned.

WHAT DO YOU THINK?

Imagine all the power being cut off in your city or town. Describe what you think might happen.

Health CONNECTION

BICYCLE FUEL

How much energy do you think you produce as you pedal around on your bike? Scientists estimate that a person pedaling steadily for seven days puts out energy equal to that contained in one gallon of gasoline. To produce that energy, the human body burns the fuel contained in food. Like the burning of coal or oil, burning that food produces some carbon dioxide. This gas contributes to the greenhouse effect, a gradual warming of Earth's surface. But all in all, bicycling is a fuel-efficient, low-polluting way to travel.

WHAT DO YOU THINK?

What other advantages are there to traveling by bicycle? Can it benefit you personally? How?

Chapter 13

Reviewing Main Ideas

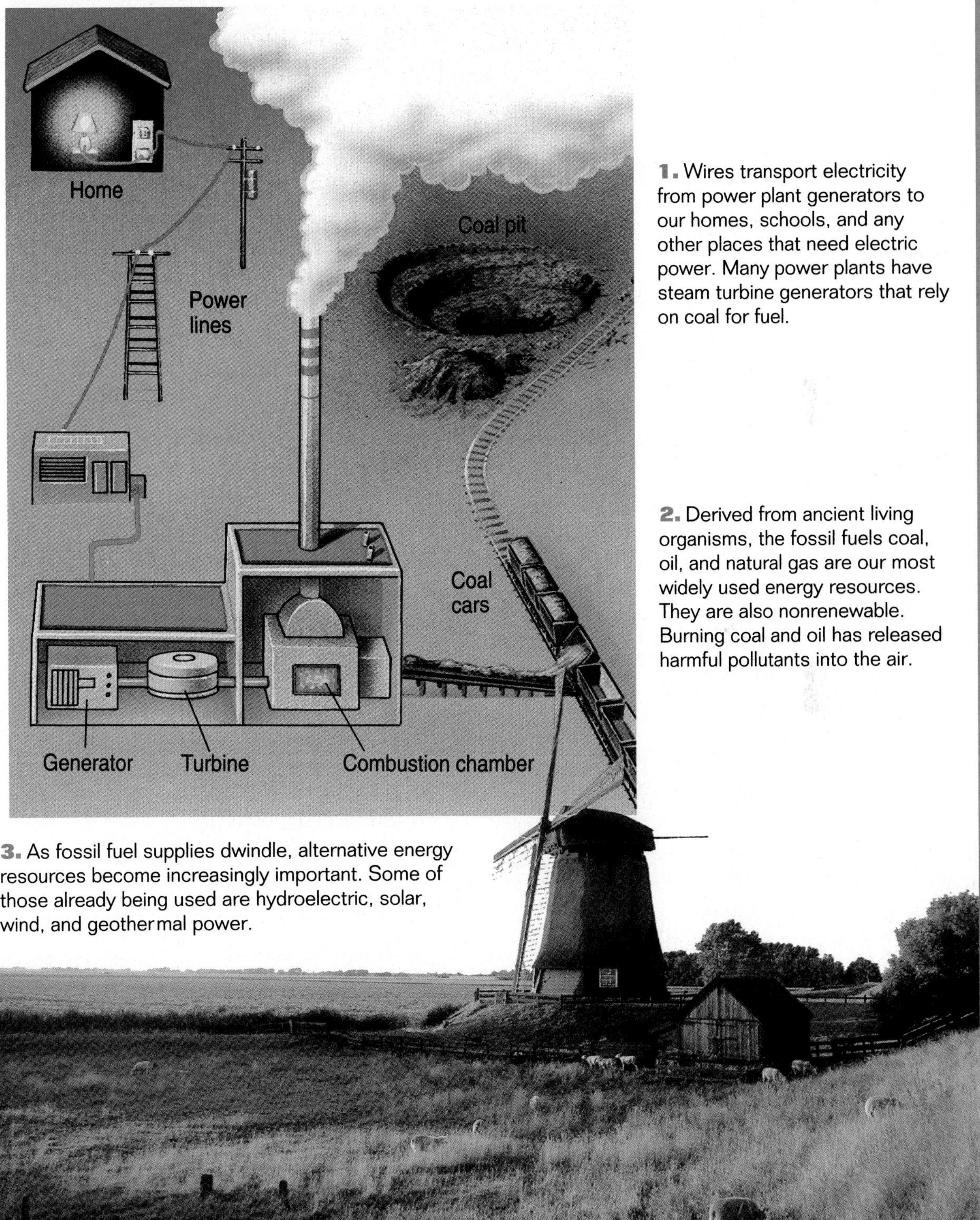

1. Wires transport electricity from power plant generators to our homes, schools, and any other places that need electric power. Many power plants have steam turbine generators that rely on coal for fuel.

2. Derived from ancient living organisms, the fossil fuels coal, oil, and natural gas are our most widely used energy resources. They are also nonrenewable. Burning coal and oil has released harmful pollutants into the air.

3. As fossil fuel supplies dwindle, alternative energy resources become increasingly important. Some of those already being used are hydroelectric, solar, wind, and geothermal power.

Chapter 13

Chapter Review

USING KEY SCIENCE TERMS

fossil fuel
generator
geothermal
hydroelectric
nonrenewable resource
renewable resource
solar cell
turbine

Use one or more of the key science terms listed above to write a sentence explaining the following phrases.

1. the function of steam in a coal-burning electric power plant

2. why swamps of 300 million years ago have importance to people today
3. one of the best aspects of the power produced by Shasta Dam
4. why some calculators may not operate at night
5. why Iceland's electric power plants do not pollute the air

UNDERSTANDING IDEAS

Choose the best answer to complete each sentence.

1. Electrical output at a coal-burning power plant depends on the fact that energy can be ____.
   a. either renewable or nonrenewable
   b. stored in solar cells
   c. obtained from the sun
   d. transmitted through wires
2. You could use all the following terms to explain how electricity is most commonly generated at an electric power plant except ____.
   a. solar   c. mechanical
   b. turbine   d. thermal
3. The materials from which coal, oil, and natural gas formed were once ____.
   a. hydroelectric   c. anthracite
   b. burned   d. alive
4. Oil reserves are stored naturally under layers of ____.
   a. sea organisms
   b. gasoline deposits
   c. impermeable rock
   d. bituminous coal
5. All of the following resources are renewable except ____.
   a. coal   c. solar energy
   b. farm crops   d. wind
6. Greenhouse gases and acid rain are air pollutants resulting from ____.
   a. scrubbing power plant chimneys
   b. burning fossil fuels
   c. recycling Earth's water supply
   d. installing catalytic converters in cars

CRITICAL THINKING

Use your understanding of the concepts developed in the chapter to answer each of the following questions.

1. You find a fossil in a chunk of coal. Could it be a coral or a twig? Explain your answer.
2. What geographic limitations do the four alternative energy resources have?

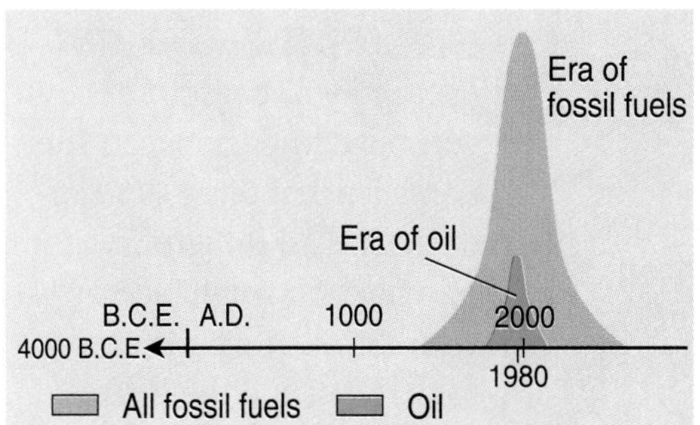

3. The diagram above shows one geologist's idea of the place fossil fuels will occupy in human history. What statement is the geologist making about the use of all fossil fuels today, in our own time? What statement is he making about oil in particular? Why might you agree or disagree with the geologist's view of the future of fossil fuels?
4. Imagine that there is a natural resource you need called a barghopper. Using barghoppers at the rate of 5000 a year for the past 20 years, you have now used up all of the existing barghoppers. Nature is still producing barghoppers at the rate of 2000 a year. What change do you make to change the barghopper from a nonrenewable to a renewable resource?

PROBLEM SOLVING

Read the following problem and discuss your answers in a brief paragraph.

Dmetri lives with his family in a multiroom cabin high atop a mountain. The cabin is well above the tree line. The cabin is so far away from the nearest city that there is no electric service and no natural gas. Much of the year, the mountain is covered with snow. During the spring and summer, the snow melts, forming rapidly moving meltwater streams in the nearby valleys.

Knowing what you do about sources of electricity, write a list of suggestions for Dmetri, telling him what to do to get electricity to power his house throughout the year.

CONNECTING IDEAS

Discuss each of the following in a brief paragraph.

1. Why is geothermal energy probably most readily available in regions of frequent volcanic activity?
2. Why can we accurately say that fossil fuels are a form of solar energy?
3. How is oil related to air pollution? How is it related to pollution of the ocean?
4. **PHYSICS CONNECTION** How is a hydroelectric power plant similar to a coal-burning power plant? How is it different?
5. **TECHNOLOGY CONNECTION** Would hydrogen as a fuel be considered a renewable or a nonrenewable resource? Explain your answer.

LOOKING BACK

UNIT 3 EARTH MATERIALS AND RESOURCES

CONTENTS

Chapter 9 Discovering Elements

Chapter 10 Minerals and Their Uses

Chapter 11 The Rock Cycle

Chapter 12 The Ocean Floor and Shore Zones

Chapter 13 Energy Resources

UNIT FOCUS

In this unit, you learned how to distinguish among metals, nonmetals, and metalloids. You compared minerals based on properties, such as hardness, luster, and cleavage. You classified rocks as sedimentary, igneous, and metamorphic. You learned how some of Earth's materials can be used as sources of energy.

You also investigated the structure of Earth's oceans and learned about features of Earth's shorelines and the ocean basin floor.

Try the exercises and activity that follow—they will challenge you to use and apply some of the ideas you learned in this unit.

CONNECTING IDEAS

1. Explain why sedimentary rocks will likely form on ocean floors. What types of natural resources would you expect to find within the layers of sedimentary rocks on the ocean floor? Explain your answer.
2. Arrange the following groups in order from the simplest to the most complex of Earth's structures: a) Rocky Mountains and the Mid-Ocean Ridge; b) silicon, aluminum, and oxygen; c) granite and basalt; and d) quartz, feldspar, and mica. Identify a natural Earth resource from the group with the simplest structure and from the group with the most complex structure.

EXPLORING FURTHER

Pretend you could reduce your size to fit between the particles in a piece of granite. Write an imaginary story of what you might see in your travels through the rock. Describe the different particle sizes, elements, minerals, crystals, gas molecules, liquids, colors, lusters, or any other properties you might see.

LOOKING AHEAD

TRY IT

Can you place a paper towel in an aquarium full of water and still keep it dry? Fill half an aquarium with water. Crumple a paper towel and put it in a baby food jar so the towel won't fall out when you turn the jar over. What do you think will happen if you put the upside-down jar in the aquarium? Write down, then test, your prediction.

What will happen if you fill half the jar with water, place a plastic coffee can lid over the jar, and turn it upside down in the aquarium? Write down, then test, your prediction.

Now, add 30 mL of water to a soft drink can and heat until the water boils. What will happen if you use a thermal mitt to turn the can upside down over the aquarium, placing the rim of the can just below the level of water? Write down, then test, your prediction.

After you've learned more about gases, do this activity again and explain your observations.

UNIT 4 AIR: MOLECULES IN MOTION

CONTENTS

Chapter 14 Gases, Atoms, and Molecules
Chapter 15 The Air Around You
Chapter 16 Breathing

UNIT FOCUS

In Unit 3, you learned that properties of metals and nonmetals are quite different. You learned how to identify rocks and minerals based on their properties. In Unit 4, you will learn how the structure of atoms not only affects whether or not they are classified as a metal, but also how they react to form molecules. You will learn how some elements combine to form gases that are affected by temperature and pressure. You will relate what you learn about gases to their importance to the respiratory systems of living things.

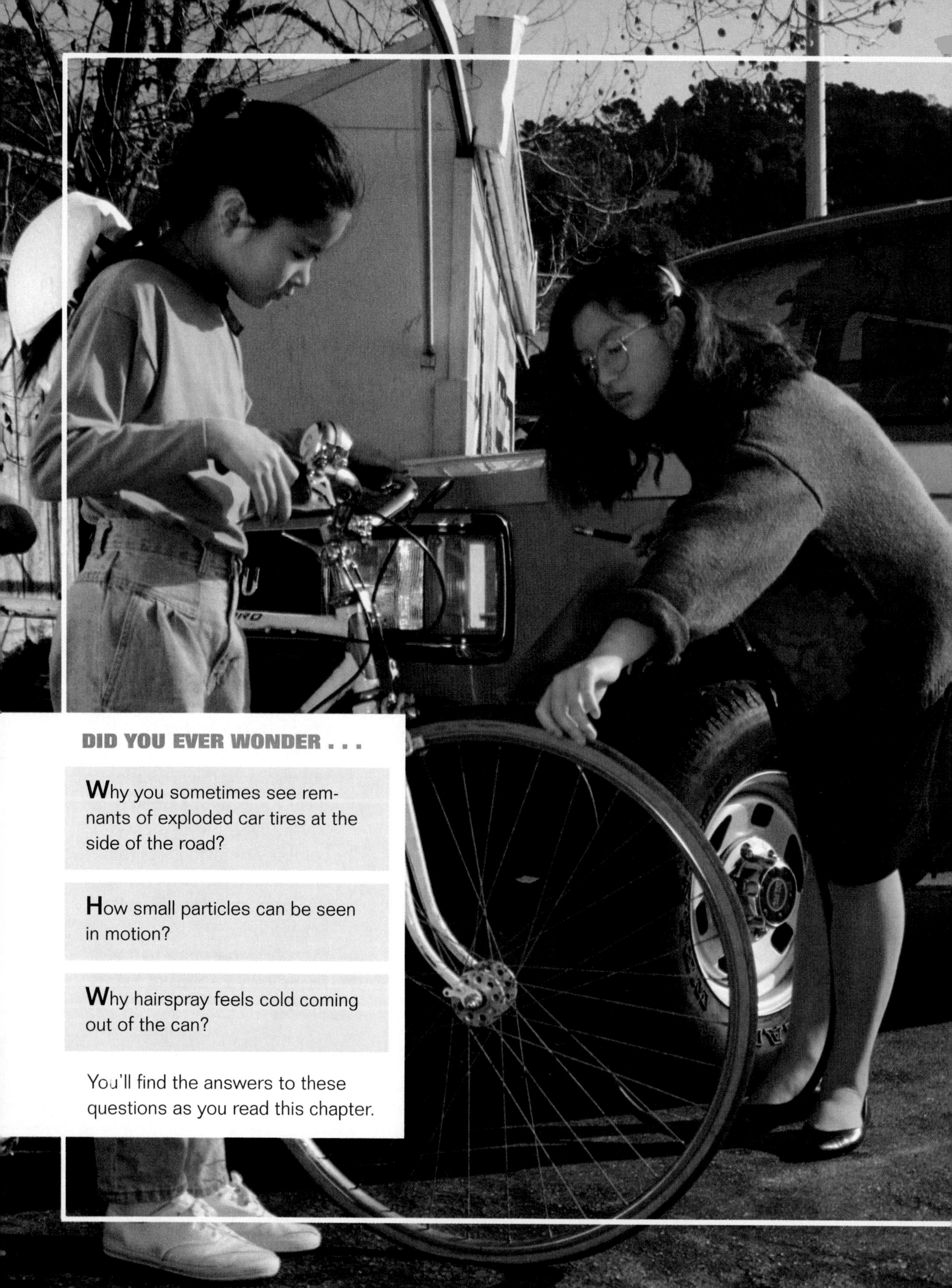

DID YOU EVER WONDER . . .

Why you sometimes see remnants of exploded car tires at the side of the road?

How small particles can be seen in motion?

Why hairspray feels cold coming out of the can?

You'll find the answers to these questions as you read this chapter.

Chapter 14

Gases, Atoms, and Molecules

Imagine you are casually riding your bike through the neighborhood. In the alley behind one building, you cannot avoid some broken glass. A loud "Thwop!" and your front tire is flat. As you walk your bike home, you see your older sister at the gas station. She is putting air in her car's tires. You remember she had said that the tires squealed when she turned corners and that they probably needed more air. She looks up and sees your plight, and you gratefully accept her offer to drive you home. Together, you lift the bike into the car's trunk.

On the way home, the fresh breeze through the window dries the water beads from your sweaty face. As you round the corner toward home, you notice that the car's tires no longer squeal. You begin to wonder what made the difference. As you know, the air pumped into your tires is a gas. Air is useful because, like other gases, it has certain characteristic properties. In this chapter, you will explore these useful properties of gases.

EXPLORE!

Does air exert pressure?

Wet the surface of a chair. Put the cup of a plunger on the wet portion and push down on the handle. What does pushing down on the handle do? Lift up on the plunger handle. What happens? How can you remove the plunger from the chair?

14-1 How Do Gases Behave?

OBJECTIVES

In this section, you will

- identify the gas phase of matter by its properties;
- find the relationships involving pressure, volume, and temperature of a gas.

KEY SCIENCE TERMS

Boyle's law
Charles' law

IDENTIFYING PROPERTIES OF GASES

You know that matter exists in three physical phases—solid, liquid, and gas. Each phase has its own characteristic properties and behaviors. In this section, you will study gases. Gases are important parts of your everyday life. Table 14-1 shows some ways that different gases are used. How many do you recognize?

TABLE 14-1. Selected Gases and Their Uses

Gas	Uses
Argon	as the inactive gas inside light bulbs
Ammonia	in fertilizers and cleaning compounds
Carbon dioxide	to make carbonation in beverages; to make baked goods rise; as a solid (dry ice), keeps things cold
Chlorine	to kill bacteria in water at treatment plants; in liquid bleach; in pool chemicals
Fluorine	as anticavity agent in toothpaste; in drinking water to help prevent tooth decay
Freon	the cooling gas in air conditioners and refrigerators
Helium	in parade and weather balloons; in gas mixture breathed by deep-sea divers
Hydrogen	bubbled through crude oil to remove sulfur; bubbled into vegetable oils to make margarines
Krypton	produces pale violet color in illuminated lights; in high-speed flash bulbs
Neon	produces orange color in illuminated lights
Nitrogen	to make ammonia; to preserve flavor in dried foods such as instant coffee; in liquid state, as a coolant
Oxygen	in life-support systems; to burn off impurities in molten steel; to purify water at treatment plants; as rocket fuel
Ozone	helps filter dangerous ultraviolet light from the sun; as a bleach for fabrics and paper

EXPLORE!

Do gases move?

With your classmates, arrange chairs facing away from a small table or desk like four equally spaced spokes of a wheel. Everybody except the experimenter should sit in one of the chairs. The experimenter then will put on the small table something that has an odor. The sitting students are to raise their hands as soon as they can smell whatever is on the table.

Which hands are raised first? How long is it before everyone can smell the odor? In what direction does the odor travel?

Vapors from the thing you smelled moved without any help from a fan or any other outside source.

You will recall that gases have other characteristic properties.

1. *Expansion.* A gas doesn't have a shape of its own or a definite volume. It occupies the space of whatever container it is in. The shape and volume of the gas are determined by the container. The gas *diffuses,* or moves through the air or other substance already present in the container. Examples of gas containers include light bulbs, tires, and air mattresses.

2. *Pressure.* When a balloon is inflated, it gets larger because the gas pressure on its inside surface has increased. If the air is let out, the pressure decreases and the balloon becomes smaller. When the tire on your bike punctured, the air escaped, the pressure decreased, and the tire went flat.

3. *Low density.* We know that air must have a very low density. We and everything around us are at the bottom of a sea of air, and yet we don't float. What does it take to float in air? Something very light. Air and all gases at normal temperature and pressure have very low densities.

SKILLBUILDER

OBSERVING AND INFERRING

As you leave your apartment building, you notice a neighbor washing her apartment door with a cleaner containing ammonia. An hour later, you walk into the building and you can smell ammonia cleaner almost everywhere. The smell is strongest near your neighbor's door. State an inference to explain your observations. If you need help, refer to the **Skill Handbook** on page 682.

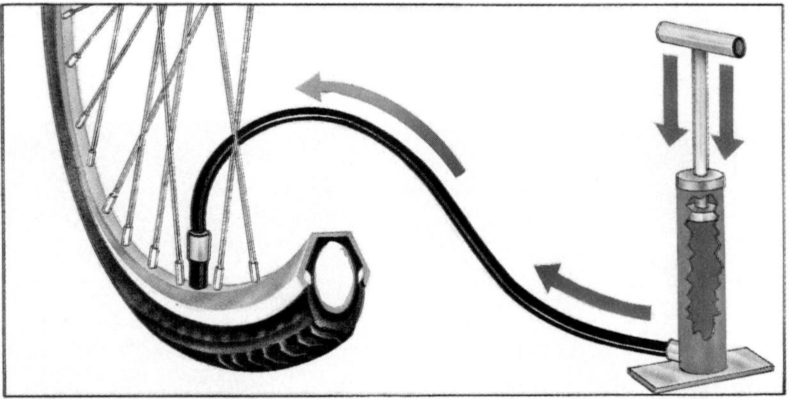

FIGURE 14-1. When you inflate a tire, you decrease the volume of air in the pump and increase its pressure and temperature.

RELATING GAS PRESSURE AND VOLUME

You know something of how gases behave. Some of your knowledge is from experience. Some is from what you have read in science books. You know that gases can be compressed. You compress air to get it to go into a balloon or to put air in a tire. You learned that when you compress air with a tire pump, the air gets warm. Compressing the air in the pump increases the pressure of the gas. Since you are compressing the air, you are also decreasing its volume. This is shown in Figure 14-1. The air you put into the tire must be decreased in volume to fit into the fixed volume of the tire. Both the pressure and the volume in the pump are changing. You also feel a temperature change. And the amount of air being added to the tire is changing.

There are four variables that are important in describing gases: amount of gas, pressure, volume, and temperature. How can you understand what causes these four quantities to change? The only way to understand how the variables are related is to keep all but two of them constant. Then find out how one of the two changes as you change the other.

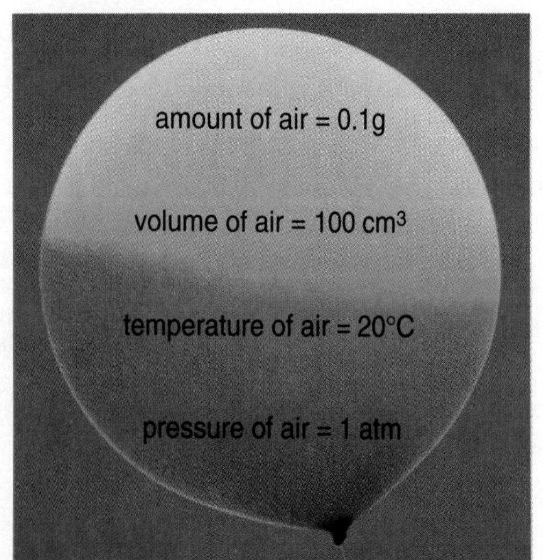

FIGURE 14-2. There are four variables that can be measured when working with gases.

Suppose you start with a certain amount of gas and want to control the temperature. What does control mean here? It means that you prevent the temperature from changing. Since the amount of gas and the temperature stay the same, only two variables are left to change—pressure and volume. To see how these two are related, you must be able to change one of them while watching what happens to the other. This process of controlling the number of variables is called a controlled experiment. You will perform an experiment on gases that will show the relationship between the volume and pressure of a gas.

INVESTIGATE!

14-1 PRESSURE AND VOLUME

In this activity, you'll measure the pressure and volume of a gas and discover how they are related.

PROBLEM

How are the pressure and volume of a gas related?

MATERIALS

large air cylinder with piston or plastic syringe
petroleum jelly
4 weights, such as bricks or books

PROCEDURE

1. Copy the data table.
2. Remove the cap from the air piston. Lightly lubricate the plunger of the air piston with petroleum jelly. Insert the plunger into the cylinder. Make sure the plunger is snug but moves easily.
3. Pull the plunger back so that the cylinder contains 30 mL of air. Replace the cap.

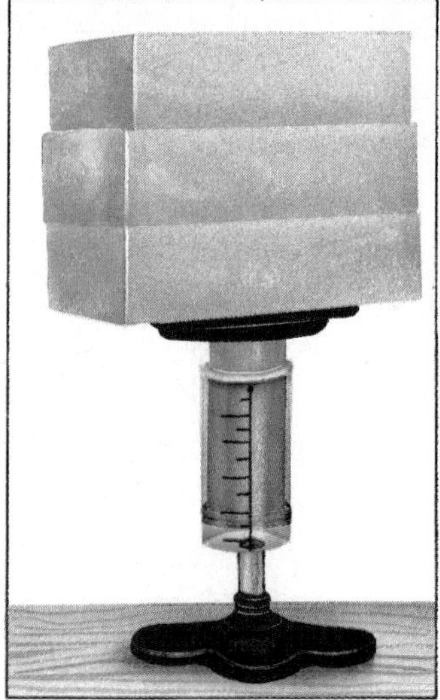

4. Set one weight, such as a brick or large book, on the piston's platform. Twist the plunger a bit in case it is sticking. Read the volume of air in mL from the marks on the cylinder. Remember that pressure on a gas can raise its temperature. Wait a minute or so for the air inside the cylinder to return to room temperature. Record the reading under Trial 1 for one weight.
5. Remove the weight. Then remove the cap and pull out the plunger. Repeat Steps 3 and 4 for Trial 2 and Trial 3.
6. Repeat Steps 3, 4, and 5 using two, three, and four weights. Record your data after each trial.
7. Find the average of the three trials for one weight. Put this number in the Average Volume column for one weight. Do this for two, three, and four weights as well.

DATA AND OBSERVATIONS

NO. OF WEIGHTS	VOLUME OF AIR			AVERAGE VOLUME
	TRIAL 1	TRIAL 2	TRIAL 3	
1				
2				
3				
4				

ANALYZE

1. Why is it a good idea to do several trials with the same number of weights?
2 **Identify the variables.** How were they controlled? What was the function of the weights?
3. **Determine the effect** of increasing pressure on the volume of a gas.

CONCLUDE AND APPLY

4. **Going Further:** Graph your data, putting pressure on the horizontal axis and volume on the vertical axis. By **interpreting your graph**, what relationship can you find between pressure and volume of an enclosed gas?

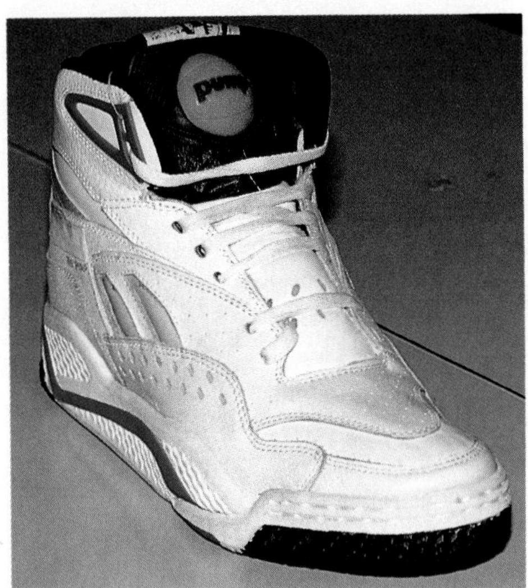
FIGURE 14-3. This shoe can help demonstrate Boyle's law.

In the Investigate, you observed the same result that scientists discovered over 300 years ago. They found that the pressure and volume of gases are inversely proportional. What does that mean? It means that when one goes up, the other goes down. If one variable is doubled, the other variable is halved. If one variable increases by three times as much, by how much does the other one decrease? That's right, one-third.

For this relationship to be true, the amount of gas in the system and the temperature of the system must be held constant. This relationship has been called Boyle's law, after a British chemist who performed many experiments with gases. **Boyle's law** can be stated thus: The volume of a certain amount of gas is inversely proportional to the pressure, if the temperature remains constant. The law is illustrated in Figure 14-4.

Relate what you just learned to air pump sports shoes. Suppose two athletes have the same brand and the same size of air pump shoe. The tennis player weighs 120 pounds, and the football player weighs 240 pounds. If they both put five pumps of air into their shoes, which athlete will have a thicker cushion of air under his or her feet? Why?

You now have a better understanding of how pressure and volume are related. More important, you have a sense of what it means to carry out a controlled experiment. Boyle's law tells how pressure and volume are related, but it does not tell why. You will learn why later.

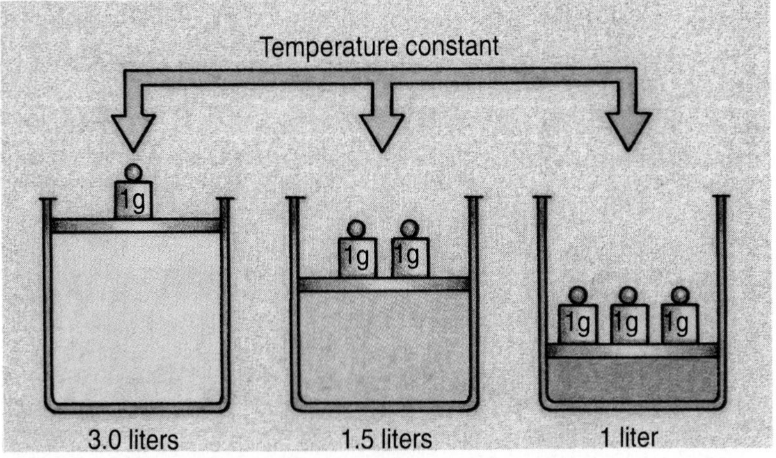

FIGURE 14-4. As pressure increases, volume decreases proportionally.

EFFECT OF TEMPERATURE ON GAS PRESSURE AND VOLUME

What happens to the tires on your bike in hot weather? They probably get harder. What's going on inside the tire? The same thing that goes on in the tires on cars and trucks that travel roads and highways. You know that there is air inside the tires. What happens to that air as the tire pounds against the road? The tire heats up because of the friction with the road. As the tire heats up, so does the air inside the tire. If it heats up too much, the tire may explode. How could this happen if no additional air was pumped into the tire? How is the volume of a gas affected by a change in its temperature?

FIGURE 14-5. Because trucks travel for many hours without stopping, it is not uncommon for their tires to explode.

FIND OUT!

How does the volume of a gas depend on its temperature? 

Copy the data table. Obtain a capillary tube and thermometer from your teacher. In this activity, you will record the temperature reading on the thermometer and the length of the column of air trapped below the oil plug in the capillary tube. Measure only the air, not the glass bead at the bottom of the tube. Prepare a mixture of crushed ice and water in a deep beaker. Place the thermometer and tube into this beaker. Be sure the air column is below the water level. Wait until the temperature becomes constant and bring the thermometer close to the side of the beaker. Read and record the temperature. Place a ruler in the water next to the tube and record the length of the air column. Replace the ice water with tap water and heat the water until it is boiling. Repeat the measurements. Using beaker tongs, pour out some of the boiling water and add tap water until you get a temperature of about 80°C. Repeat the measurements of temperature and length of the air column. Adjust the water

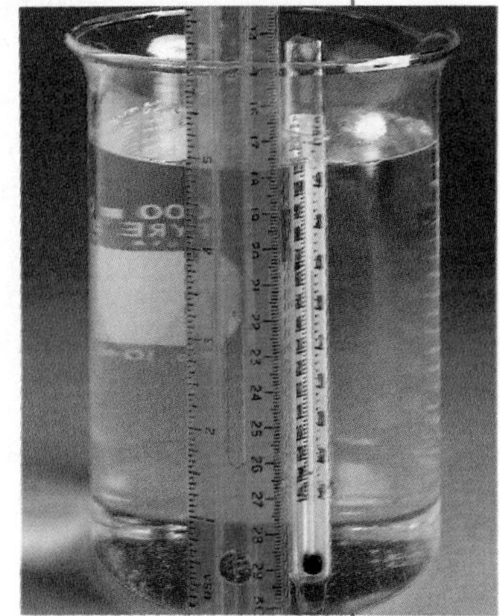

DATA AND OBSERVATIONS

	near 0°C	near 20°C	near 40°C	near 80°C	near 100°C
Temp °C					
Volume represented by length of air columns					

temperature until it is about 40°C and repeat the measurements. Finally, measure the length and temperature when in water at room temperature.

Conclude and Apply

1. We can assume that the diameter of the tube is constant, so that as the length increases, the volume increases proportionally. Since we're looking for a relationship between temperature and volume, let's use the length of the column in place of the volume to make our calculations easier. Plot a graph with volume (length) on the vertical axis and temperature on the horizontal axis.
2. As the temperature increases, what happens to the volume? What is the relationship between the temperature and volume of a gas?
3. How did you hold the variables of pressure and amount of gas constant in this activity?

You've seen that an increase in the temperature of a gas produces an increase in volume. Where else does this happen? Tires get harder when the air inside them heats up. Bread dough rises when put into a hot oven. The increase in temperature causes the bubbles of carbon dioxide gas in the dough to expand. The large increase in the volume of the dough during baking shows that the gas must expand a lot as the temperature increases. In fact, gases expand many times more than liquids and solids for a given temperature rise.

The relationship between the temperature and volume of a gas is called Charles' law, after a French scientist who suggested it. **Charles' law** can be stated thus: Gases increase or decrease their volume at the same rate that temperature changes, provided pressure and amount of gas are held constant. Charles' law is shown in Figure 14-6.

If, instead of allowing the volume to change, you had just a solid, immovable plug in the capillary tube, what would have happened when you heated the air column?

SKILLBUILDER

INTERPRETING TABLES

Use Table 14-2 to answer the following question. If you need help, refer to the **Skill Handbook** on page 679. What would happen to the volume of a gas if you doubled the pressure and doubled the temperature?

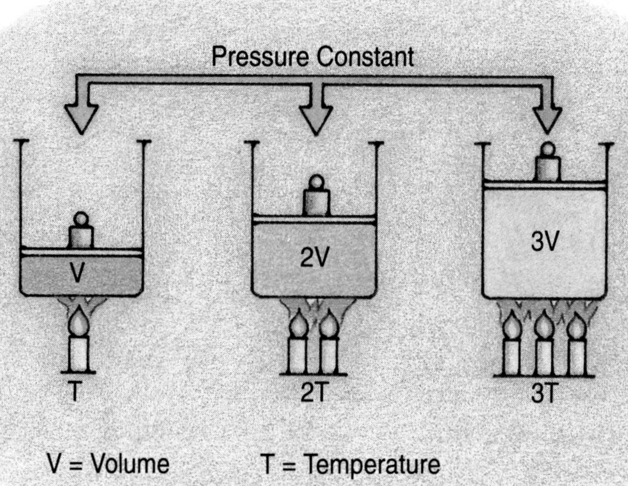

FIGURE 14-6. As temperature increases, volume increases, if the pressure on a gas remains constant.

Right. The tube probably would have shattered. The pressure inside the tube must have increased as the temperature increased or it couldn't have pushed the oil plug up. If volume is held constant, pressure and temperature are directly proportional.

You have discovered that the relationship between the volume of a gas and its pressure is inverse: as one goes up, the other goes down. You have seen that the relationship of the volume and temperature of a gas is direct: as one goes up, so does the other, and vice versa. You also found that the relationship between the temperature and pressure of a gas is direct: as one goes up, the other goes up too, and vice versa. These relationships are shown in Table 14-2. These relationships were found by careful experiments. In each case, two variables were held constant and the other two allowed to change. The results tell how the gas behaves. But they do not tell why. That will require more investigation.

TABLE 14-2. Pressure, Volume, Temperature Relationship in a Fixed Volume of Gas

Boyle's Law	P↑ P↓	V↓ V↑
Charles' Law	T↑ T↓	V↑ V↓
Pressure and Temperature	P↑ P↓	T↑ T↓

Check Your Understanding

1. Give an example for each of the characteristics of a gas.
2. As you pump more air into a basketball, what happens to the pressure in the ball? What happens to the temperature of the air in the ball?
3. **APPLY:** One way to fill up a balloon is to blow air into it—increase the inside air pressure. Can you think of another way to expand a balloon?

14-2 What Are Gases Made Of?

OBJECTIVES

In this section, you will

- relate how the behavior of gases can be explained by a particle theory of matter;
- describe evidence for an atomic theory of matter.

KEY SCIENCE TERMS

atomic theory of matter

DESCRIBING GASES

You've seen huge trailer trucks on the road supported by nothing but the air in the tires. You know air is supporting all that weight. But it's hard to imagine how. Using a model can help.

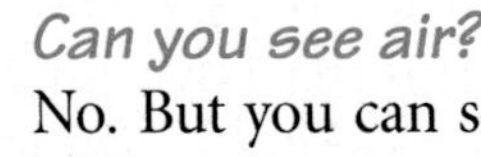

Can you see air?

No. But you can see what air can do, such as bend trees and blow dust around.

Push a deflated balloon into an empty soda bottle or flask and stretch the open end of the balloon back over the bottle's mouth, as shown in the picture. Try to blow up the balloon. What happens? Remove the open end of the balloon from the bottle's mouth but keep the balloon in the bottle. Try to blow up the balloon now. What happens? Insert a straw into the bottle between the balloon and the glass. Now try to blow up the balloon in the bottle. What happens?

No matter how hard you huff and puff, you cannot blow up the balloon—until the straw is put in. As you try to inflate the balloon, it takes up more space in the bottle. But the bottle is already full—of air. Even though you cannot see it, air takes up space. When you try to inflate the balloon, the air trapped inside the bottle prevents you from doing so. The straw allows an escape route for the air inside the bottle, so you then can inflate the balloon.

You've observed a lot about gases. You know how they behave under certain conditions. But how can that behavior be explained? A model will help you picture the behavior of gases. Remember when your bike tires ran over the broken glass? How small were the pieces of glass? How small can glass pieces get? You could crush the glass pieces until they became small enough to look like a powder. Are powder-sized particles as small as anything can get? What if gases were made up of tiny particles too small to be seen? Would this model explain the phenomena you have observed? The tiny particles could spread out or move together to make gases fill their containers. The particles could spread out or move together when gases become hot or cold. Yes, particles could explain some of the phenomena you've observed.

FIGURE 14-7. Gas particles exert pressure as they collide with the walls of a container.

EXPLAINING PRESSURE AND TEMPERATURE

What if gas particles were in motion? Moving gas particles could bang into the walls of a container and cause pressure. The energy of these moving particles could be measured. In fact, if you measure the temperature of a gas, you are measuring the kinetic energy of the gas particles. How can we observe gas particles in motion?

EXPLORE!

How do gas particles move?

If gas particles are too small to see, how can anyone see them moving? Try this activity to find out.

Light a flashlight in a darkened room. Watch the dust specks in the beam of light. Do the specks ever change speed? Set a tray of ice cubes in the light beam and watch the dance of the dust specks now. What happens?

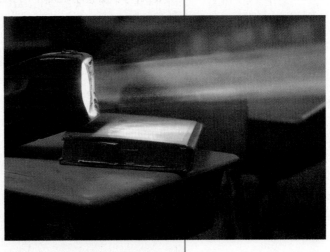

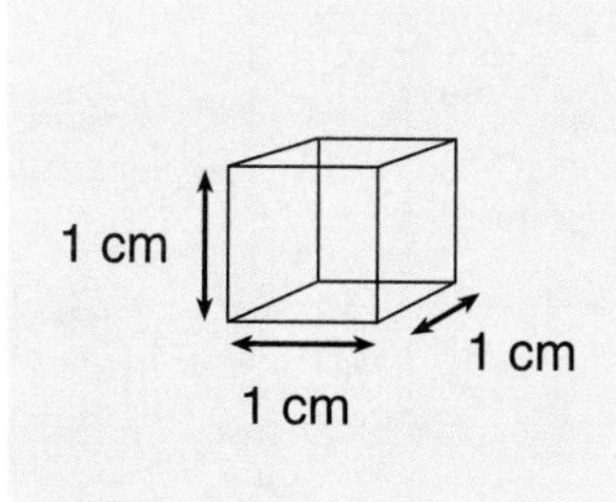

FIGURE 14-8. There are 2.7×10^{19} gas particles in 1 cm^3 of air at 20 ^{0}C and 1 atmosphere.

The dust specks you saw were never still. Although dust is not a gas, it seems reasonable to assume that gas particles in the air around the dust are also moving.

The idea that gas particles are in motion could help explain how a gas expands to fill a space. You've probably observed that shortly after a bottle of perfume is opened, the fragrance seems to fill the room, too. The gas particles of the perfume spread rapidly. This suggests that the particles of a gas are in motion. It also suggests that there are relatively large spaces between the gas particles.

So you've seen evidence that tiny gas particles have energy and are constantly moving very rapidly. This can also be used to explain pressure. The particles continually collide with one another and with the walls of any container they are in. As each particle of gas strikes the container wall, it exerts a push, or force—like that caused by a baseball hitting a wall. There are billions of gas particles in even a cubic centimeter of space. The push of that many particles adds up to quite a force being exerted.

How do we know?

Thinking about atoms

Democritus was a philosopher, a thinker. He wasn't what we would call a scientist. You might wonder how someone living so long ago and without the benefit of experimental testing that we do today could imagine something like the atom.

Early thinkers had to rely on their experience—with rain, snow, and wind; heat and cold, salt water and fresh water; and the lives of animals and plants around them. Lucretius, a Roman poet, helped us understand how Democritus reasoned in these lines about atoms.

... Their nature lies beyond our range of sense,
Far, far beyond. Since you can't get to see
The things themselves, they're bound to hide their moves.
Especially since things we can see, often
Conceal their movements, too, when at a distance.
Take grazing sheep on a hill, you know they move,
... Yet all this, far away, is just a blur,
A whiteness resting on a hill of green...

These ancient philosophers knew that even things they could see would disappear when at a great distance. They reasoned that matter could appear as solid as the flock of sheep on the hillside, if it were made of very tiny particles. Like the sheep, these particles could be moving, and yet that movement would be invisible. While we can follow their thinking, it is still remarkable that the idea of atoms has not been disproved in over 2000 years.

The air in the soda bottle illustrated this. The air particles in the bottle exerted enough force in their collisions with the surface of the balloon to keep the balloon from inflating in the bottle.

Air does not have to be trapped in a bottle or tire to exert pressure. The air molecules in the atmosphere constantly collide with one another and with different surfaces. They exert pressure on you, on your books, on the floor and ceiling and walls of your classroom—on everything. As shown in Figure 14-9, the Explore activity you did at the beginning of the chapter was an example of air pressure in action. You pushed the air from under the plunger. The air in the room exerted pressure on the plunger and held it to the chair.

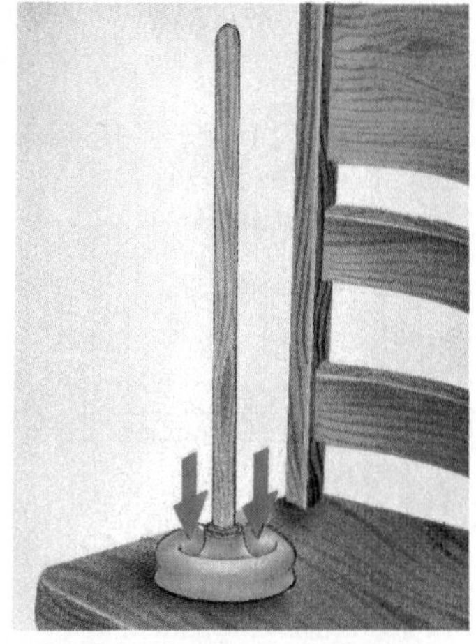

FIGURE 14-9. Particles of air in the room exerted pressure on the plunger.

THE ATOMIC THEORY OF MATTER

It seems that particles could be used to explain what you have observed and to accurately predict the behavior of matter. For this reason, scientists have theorized that such particles exist and make up all gases, as well as solids and liquids. In fact, they make up your body. What are these particles called? Atoms.

The theory that matter is composed of small particles called atoms is the **atomic theory of matter**. It was first suggested by a Greek named Democritus. An expanded theory building on Democritus' idea of the atom was put forth by the chemist John Dalton. His theory will be explained as the chapter continues.

In the next section, you will examine more about atoms and some of the evidence that has led to the atomic theory of matter.

Check Your Understanding

1. How does a particle theory of matter explain diffusion?
2. How does a particle theory of matter explain gas pressure?
3. What evidence do scientists have that gases are made of particles?
4. **APPLY:** When weather balloons are sent up from Earth, only a small amount of gas is added to the balloon. As the balloon rises, it expands until it appears full. Use the particle theory to explain why this happens.

14-3 What Is the Atomic Theory of Matter?

OBJECTIVES

In this section, you will

- describe evidence that pure substances are made up of identical particles;
- specify what is meant by element, compound, and atom.

KEY SCIENCE TERMS

atom

PURE SUBSTANCE—ELEMENTS AND COMPOUNDS

You have seen evidence that there are pure substances. Aluminum metal has certain properties. If you cut aluminum into smaller and smaller pieces by ordinary means, you can never find a piece of this metal that differs from the larger piece. When you try to break down aluminum by any chemical or electrical means, you are unable to do so. Aluminum is an example of an element.

Is there some pattern in the way elements combine when they form other substances? Let's find out.

FIND OUT!

How do hydrogen and oxygen make up water?

You know that hydrogen and oxygen are gases and that they are elements. How much of each gas is needed to make water?

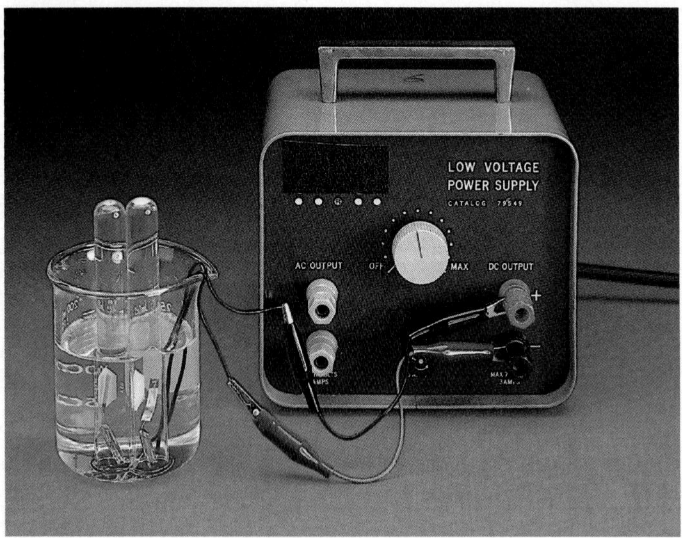

Partially fill a 250-mL beaker with concentrated washing soda solution. Overfill two test tubes with the same solution. Insert an electrode into each test tube. Holding your thumb over the mouth of one test tube, invert it into the beaker. When you let go, there should be no bubble at the top of the tube. Repeat with the second test tube. **CAUTION:** *Wash your hands thoroughly after touching the solution.*

Connect the electrodes with alligator clamps to a power supply. What happens? Let the setup run for at least 15 minutes. Use a ruler to measure the amounts of gas collected in the tubes. Record these measurements.

Conclude and Apply

What do you notice about the relationship between the amounts of gas in the test tubes?

The gases you collected in your test tubes were hydrogen and oxygen. The proportion should have been very close to, if not exactly, twice as much volume of hydrogen gas as oxygen. Experiments like this show that when you break up water, you always end up with the same volume ratio of hydrogen to oxygen.

Think about water like you thought about a piece of aluminum. If you try to separate pure water into smaller and smaller drops, the water always behaves like water. But, unlike aluminum, water can be broken down by electricity into simpler substances—the elements hydrogen and oxygen. Water is therefore a *compound* of two other elements.

You've studied enough about matter to understand the meaning of the terms *element* and *compound.* An element is a pure substance that cannot be changed into any other pure substance by ordinary chemical means. Similarly, a compound is a pure substance, but it can be broken down by chemical means into two or more other pure substances. These substances are often elements, but may be other compounds.

The smallest particle of water, a compound, is a molecule of water. A molecule is two or more atoms chemically combined. If you break up that molecule, you

FIGURE 14-10. Some of the most familiar substances are elements. Others are compounds.

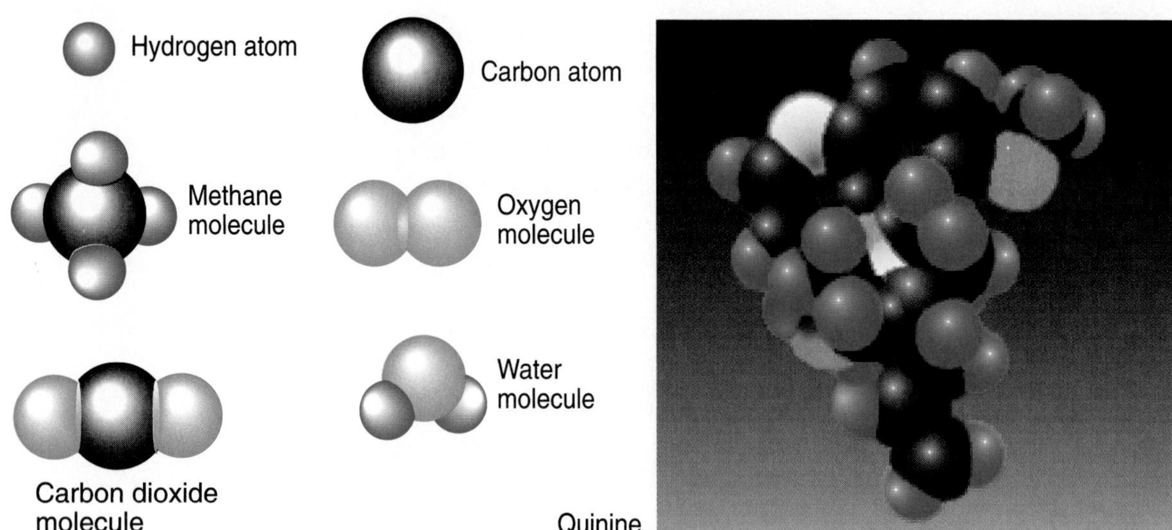

FIGURE 14-11. What elements are in the gas methane?

no longer have a compound, but atoms of the elements out of which it is made.The **atom** is defined as the smallest particle of an element.

The atomic theory of matter is based on the idea that all matter is made of atoms. What evidence leads us to such a theory?

HOW DO WE KNOW THAT MATTER IS MADE OF ATOMS?

When you think about an element, you can understand how the idea of matter consisting of small basic particles arises. Imagine that you break copper into smaller and smaller pieces. In reality, you can't divide a microscopic piece of copper, since you don't have the tools, and you couldn't see it anyway. But you can imagine doing it.

Imagine that you keep dividing copper. Would you ever reach a point that you could no longer divide the copper? It would seem natural that copper, or any element, would have a smallest particle that could not be further divided and still be regarded as that element. But this is not evidence. Interestingly, evidence that there is a smallest particle comes only when considering how elements combine chemically. It is chemical reactions that lead us to the concept of atoms and molecules.

DID YOU KNOW?

Atoms are so small that 150 billion of them would fit on the period at the end of this sentence.

FIXED RATIOS IN CHEMICAL REACTIONS

If you were preparing a saltwater solution, you know that you can use different percentages of salt. You can make a one-percent solution or a ten-percent solution. You can make such solutions any concentration you want up to the point of saturation. In alloys, you can use whatever ratio of one element to another you want, and you will get that alloy as a solid solution. But you know that these are examples of mechanically mixing substances rather than chemically combining them. Can any amount of elements be used in chemical reactions?

You know that if hydrogen is burned in the air, it will combine with oxygen to form water. If you were able to weigh the hydrogen and oxygen that combine, you would find that for every one gram of hydrogen that burns, eight grams of oxygen are required. Likewise, if you take pure water apart, regardless of where it comes from, you will always get one gram of hydrogen for every eight grams of oxygen. When hydrogen combines with oxygen to form water, it always does so in a mass ratio of 1 g of hydrogen to 8 g of oxygen.

If you take apart ordinary table salt, you get 1.54 g of chlorine for each 1 g of sodium—no more and no less. It makes no difference where you get the salt. It can be from a salt mine, or table salt that you made in the lab. You always get a fixed ratio of 1.54 to 1.

Copper sulfide, CuS, is always produced by combining 1.98 grams of copper with 1 gram of sulfur. When you combine carbon with oxygen to make carbon dioxide, you always need 2.67 g of oxygen for every 1 g of carbon—again, never more and never less. Two elements combine to make a compound. When they do, the ratio of mass of one element to the other is always the same. This statement is a law of science called the law of definite proportions. The following activity will help you to understand this law.

FIGURE 14-12. The ratio of copper to sulfur in copper sulfide is always 1.98:1.

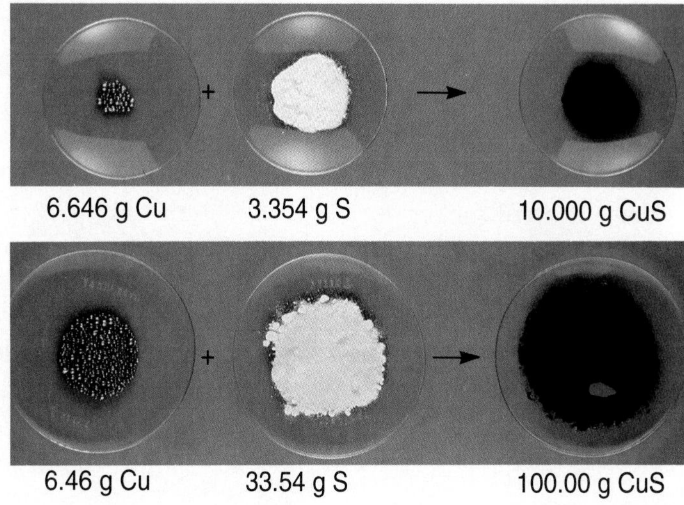

INVESTIGATE!

14-2 DEFINITE AND MULTIPLE PROPORTIONS

In this activity, you will discover the relationships among the masses of coins individually and in combination.

PROBLEM

What is the relationship between the numbers and masses of objects as they combine?

MATERIALS

30 1-cent coins
15 5-cent coins
balance

PROCEDURE

1. Copy the data table.
2. **Measure the mass** of fifteen 1-cent coins and fifteen 5-cent coins. Record. **Measure the mass** of eight 1-cent coins and eight 5-cent coins. Record.
3. Make 6-cent coins by placing a drop of rubber cement on the center of each of the 5-cent coins. Press a 1-cent coin on each of these fifteen 5-cent coins. You now have fifteen 6-cent combinations.
4. **Measure the mass** of the 15 6-cent coin combinations. Record.
5. **Measure the mass** of eight of the 6-cent combinations. Record.
6. Using a small drop of rubber cement to stick a 1-cent coin on the other side of the 6-cent coin, prepare six 7-cent combinations. The 7-cent combinations are made of the same two types of coins as the 6-cent combinations, but the ratios of the two coins are different. Find the mass of the six 7-cent combinations. Record.

DATA AND OBSERVATIONS

	15 1¢ COINS	15 5¢ COINS	15 6¢ COINS	6 7¢ COINS
Mass				

ANALYZE

1. How does the mass of 15 6-cent coin combinations compare with the sum of the masses of the 15 separate 1-cent and 5-cent coins? What is the ratio of the total mass of 15 5-cent coins to the total mass of 15 1-cent coins?
2. In Step 2, what is the ratio of the mass of eight 5-cent coins to the mass of the eight 1-cent coins? Predict the ratio of the mass of one 5-cent coin to one 1-cent coin.
3. What is the ratio of 1-cent coins to 5-cent coins in the 6-cent combination? What is the ratio of 1-cent to 5-cent coins in the 7-cent combinations?

CONCLUDE AND APPLY

4. **Predict** the ratio of the mass of 1000 5-cent coins to that of 1000 1-cent coins.
5. What would you calculate that the ratio of the masses of 1-cent coins to 5-cent coins in the 7-cent combinations would be? Would this ratio change if you had 1000 7-cent combinations?
6. **Going Further:** If you had made ten 8-cent combinations, what would you predict to be true about the ratio of the masses of the 5-cent coins and 1-cent coins?

Can you draw certain conclusions about coins that make up certain combinations? First you observed that the mass ratios of 5-cent to 1-cent coins is always the same when you make 6-cent combinations, no matter how many 6-cent combinations you have. The same is true for 7-cent combinations. You saw that you could combine two coins in a one-to-one ratio and a two-to-one ratio but that it is impossible to combine them in ratios that are not whole number multiples.

When John Dalton, a chemist, analyzed the masses of elements involved in chemical reactions, he could see the same kinds of ratios as you found in the Investigate. In fact, he created a model or theory to account for the ratios he was observing. This model is called the atomic theory of matter.

Dalton proposed that different elements would be composed of different atoms. The atoms of different elements would have different masses, just as the mass of a 1-cent coin is different from the mass of a 5-cent coin. Also, the ratios of the masses of the individual elements would be the same as the ratio of masses needed to make a compound, just as the ratio of the masses of 5-cent and 1-cent coins stayed the same whether you made eight, fifteen, or 1000 6-cent combinations.

You also found that you could get more than one combination from 5-cent and 1-cent coins. You could get a 6-cent combination or a 7-cent combination. But the ratio of masses in one combination to masses in the other combination was a small whole number. Dalton found that the same was true for atoms in compounds. For example, carbon can combine with oxygen to form carbon dioxide and carbon monoxide. The ratio of the mass of oxygen to the mass of carbon in carbon dioxide is 2.66:1. In carbon monoxide, the ratio is 1.33:1. The mass of oxygen in CO_2 is two times that in CO (2.66 is twice 1.33). Thus, the ratio of oxygen in these compounds is 2:1. The ratio of masses of carbon is 1:1.

Just as you could get a number of combinations from 5-cent and 1-cent coins, so can you get several combinations when

DID YOU KNOW?

Most molecules are made up of small numbers of atoms, but some molecules contain many more. An aspirin molecule contains 21 atoms; a rubber molecule may have up to 65,000 atoms.

FIGURE 14-13. Evidence that atoms exist comes from the way elements combine.

Molecule	Composition
Nitrogen oxide	N O
Nitrogen dioxide	O N O
Dinitrogen oxide	N O N

○ = oxygen ◐ = nitrogen

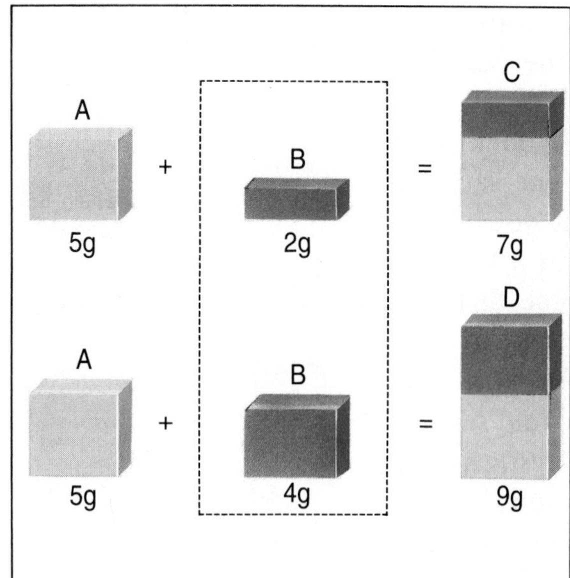

FIGURE 14-14. Elements combine in small whole number mass ratios.

combining atoms. You can see that the 5-cent and 1-cent coins could be arranged 5:1, 5:2, 5:3, and so on, but the ratio of the 1-cent coins is always some small whole number—2:1, 3:1. The idea that atoms combine in this same way is called the *law of multiple proportions.* Notice that this law is different from the law of definite proportions which states that the ratio of one element to another element is fixed. The important idea in both these laws is that atoms always combine as whole atoms, never as fractions. An atom can't be broken into anything smaller as it forms compounds.

So far this theory only tells us that there are smallest units or particles of matter that make up every element. We have not seen any evidence yet that these atoms can or cannot be broken down further into other particles. This will have to wait until later in the course.

The atomic theory of matter is based upon three laws of science: the law of conservation of mass; the law of definite proportions; and the law of multiple proportions. It can be summarized in the following statements:

1. Matter consists of atoms.
2. All atoms of a given element are identical.
3. Different elements have different atoms.
4. Atoms retain their identity in chemical reactions.
5. Compounds are formed by combinations of atoms in small whole-number ratios.

Check Your Understanding

1. What evidence do you have that every water molecule is alike?
2. Table salt is made up of sodium and chlorine. Is it an element or a compound? Why?
3. A 9 g sample of distilled water in Los Angeles contains 8 grams of oxygen and 1 gram of hydrogen. How many grams of hydrogen would a 90 g sample of distilled water in London contain? Explain.
4. **APPLY:** Draw 4 particles of hydrogen and 1 particle of carbon. Draw 1 particle of methane (made up of 1 carbon and 4 hydrogens). Which of the particles that you drew is a molecule? How do you know?

EXPANDING YOUR VIEW

CONTENTS

A Closer Look
The Density of a Gas 431

Earth Science Connection
Research Giants 432

Technology Connection
What Is a Vacuum? 433

Health Connection
Breathing Underwater 434

Leisure Connection
Cooking Under Pressure 435

History Connection
The Gas Laws 436

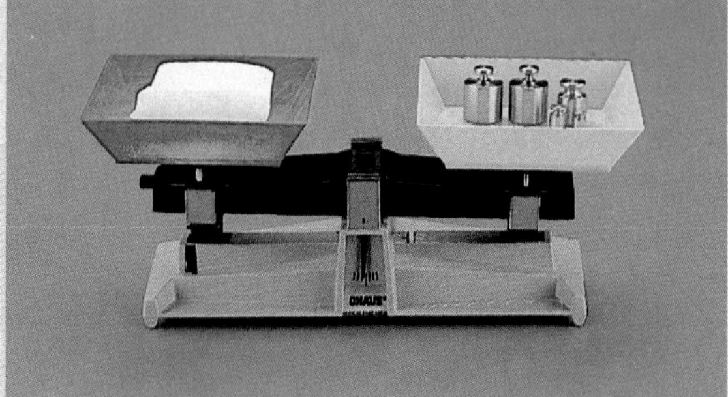

A CLOSER LOOK

THE DENSITY OF A GAS

We move through a gas, air, all the time. Rarely are we aware of its presence. We know that gases exist and that they are made of atoms and molecules. How can we measure other properties of this generally invisible substance?

YOU TRY IT!

The purpose of this activity is to compare the density of dry ice, which is solid carbon dioxide (CO_2), with that of gaseous CO_2. Flatten a tall kitchen trash bag so there is no air in it.Use a cube-shaped piece of dry ice so you can measure its dimensions. **CAUTION:** *Dry ice is very cold and must be handled with extreme care because it could freeze your skin. Do not touch dry ice with your fingers. Always use tongs when handling the dry ice.* Quickly use a balance to find the mass of the dry ice cube. Then measure its dimensions, and immediately place the dry ice in a large plastic bag. Seal the bag tightly as soon as you put the dry ice in. Try not to let any gaseous CO_2 escape.

Once the dry ice is sealed in the bag, you may begin your calculations of the volume and density of the dry ice. The volume is equal to the length times the width times the height, or $V = l \times w \times h$. The density is the mass divided by the volume, or $D = \text{g/cm}^3$.

While you are doing your calculations, the dry ice will be changing into a gas inside the plastic bag, so the bag will appear to be partially inflated. When you are sure there is no longer any solid dry ice in the bag, put the bag into a shape that is as boxlike as possible. When it is in this shape, measure its dimensions as well as you can. Then calculate the volume and the density. Since the bag is not perfectly boxlike, you will not be able to get measurements that are extremely accurate. However, with patience and care, you will get a close approximation. Because no CO_2 was allowed to escape, the mass of the dry ice will be about the same as the mass of the gaseous CO_2.

How does the volume of the gaseous CO_2 compare with the volume of the dry ice? Is the number of molecules the same in the dry ice and in the gaseous CO_2? Why do the molecules in gaseous CO_2 take up more space?

EARTH SCIENCE CONNECTION

RESEARCH GIANTS

Have you ever heard of an aerostat (AIR oh stat)? An aerostat is an aircraft that is supported by the buoyancy of a gas that is less dense than air.

Aerostats include blimps and dirigibles. The simplest kind is the balloon, because it has no means of propulsion or steering. In other words, a balloon just goes wherever the movement of the air takes it.

Basically, a balloon is a large bag that is filled with a gas that is lighter, or less dense, than air, for example, hot air or helium. This large bag displaces a lot of air, and has an upward force on it—called a buoyant force—that is equal to the weight of the displaced air.

These giant balloons can lift a load of instruments higher than a jetliner but lower than an orbiting satellite. The volume of helium needed to lift the load could be equal to the volume of a small house on the ground. Once the balloon reaches the altitude it's designed for, the volume of the gas could be the volume of 283 houses.

What kind of information can be obtained by balloons? Balloons carry many different kinds of instruments. Some have telescopes for viewing objects in space. Others collect and analyze the gases in space. Still others measure and record temperature, pressure, and the amounts and kinds of radiation from space. Ground-based radar can track balloons to find out about the speed and direction of high-altitude winds.

Information collected in these studies helps scientists understand the makeup and behavior of the gases in our atmosphere. As we learn more about this important part of the environment, we will be able to predict the atmosphere's behavior and to know how we can protect and preserve it.

WHAT DO YOU THINK?

What would be an advantage of taking pictures through telescopes on high-altitude balloons, rather than through ground-based telescopes? What are the disadvantages? In what ways are research balloons different from the multicolored balloon shown above?

TECHNOLOGY CONNECTION

WHAT IS A VACUUM?

Vacuum cleaners, vacuum-sealed containers, vacuum-packed foods—just what is a vacuum?

A vacuum is a space that has no matter in it. There is no such thing as a complete vacuum because no one has ever been able to remove all the air molecules within a given space. Even in the near-vacuum of outer space, it is estimated that there are about 100 molecules of matter in every cubic meter of space.

Why would anyone want to create a vacuum in the first place? Have you ever used a straw to drink from a glass or can? When you draw on the straw, you remove some of the air inside the straw. This produces a lower pressure inside the straw than in the air outside—a partial vacuum. The greater air pressure of the air on the liquid pushes the liquid up the straw.

How else are partial vacuums used? A vacuum conducts heat poorly, so it's a good insulator. This property is used in devices such as

insulating bottles. These bottles contain a double-walled glass container that has had the air removed from between the walls. Thermal energy can't pass through this space from either direction and so the liquid inside stays hot or cold.

You may recall when you studied sound that sound is a result of vibrations of molecules. Because there are no molecules—or atoms—in a vacuum, it does not conduct sound well.

Light bulbs contain a partial vacuum and nitrogen or argon gas, which is why a light bulb will pop when it breaks. Since there is little oxygen in the light bulb, the burning filament lasts longer than it would if surrounded by air. You will learn more about this in a later chapter.

One of your favorite uses for a vacuum may be the television. The television tube works because there are very few air molecules in the tube. The beam inside the television tube would be too fuzzy and blurred to see if it had to travel through air molecules.

YOU TRY IT!

Roll a wax coated paper straw between your fingers a few times to remove the stiffness. Be sure to leave the straw open. Now press your finger tightly over one end so that no air can enter. Put the other end of the straw in your mouth and suck on it. What happens? Why did this happen?

Health CONNECTION

BREATHING UNDERWATER

In 1943, the famous French oceanographer, Jacques-Yves Cousteau and his associate, Emile Gagnan, invented the SCUBA (Self-Contained Underwater Breathing Apparatus). This opened the way for people to freely explore and enjoy large areas of our planet that lie underwater.

Unlike fish, a person's body has no way to draw oxygen from water. We must take our environment with us when we travel in the depths of the oceans or the vacuum of space. As you know, the pressure on your body due to the mass of air around you is one atmosphere. This is as if a weight of almost 15 pounds is pressing on every square inch of your body. Underwater, the pressure increases due to the added mass of water above you. Every ten meters adds one atmosphere pressure. At a depth of ten meters, the total pressure on your body would be 2 atm. At 30 meters, it would be 4 atm. That's nearly 60 pounds of pressure per square inch! If the palm of your hand were about 20 square inches, that would be like holding a compact car in your hand.

The muscles controlling your lungs and diaphragm evolved to work in 1 atm pressure. At a depth of 40 meters, the pressure on your chest would make it impossible to inflate your lungs to breathe, even if you had a supply of air available. SCUBA equipment provides air to the lungs at a pressure that matches the underwater environment. Therefore, you can breathe comfortably.

If the pressure in your lungs is increased to match the outside pressure, what happens when you swim toward the surface? The average human lung capacity is about six to seven liters. Boyle's law tells us that if the amount of a gas remains constant, as the pressure decreases, volume increases. If you went from an outside pressure of 5 atm to a pressure of 1 atm without exhaling to reduce the amount of air in your lungs, the air would expand to 30 to 35 liters, certainly enough to rupture your lungs.

When you breathe the air under increased pressure for 30 minutes or longer, more nitrogen from the air dissolves in your blood than normal. Your blood becomes like a carbonated beverage in a sealed bottle but with N_2, not CO_2. As you move up to the surface, reducing the outside pressure, the nitrogen becomes less soluble and comes out of your blood as bubbles. This is much like what happens when you

WHAT DO YOU THINK?

If SCUBA equipment can provide air at a pressure equal to that underwater, why do people still have to use enclosed diving vessels at depths below 100 m?

release the cap from the beverage bottle and you see bubbles rising in the liquid.

If you rise to the surface too quickly, these bubbles of nitrogen form in joints and muscles and cause pain. If they form in the spinal cord, brain, or lungs, they can cause death. This effect is called "the bends" or decompression sickness. If a diver rises slowly, decreasing the pressure gradually, the nitrogen can be released through the lungs as in normal respiration.

When divers are forced to rise quickly to the surface after spending a considerable time underwater, they must be placed in a decompression chamber. The pressure in the chamber is then raised to match the pressure at which they were diving. Over a period of hours, it is lowered to 1 atm.

You can see why it takes many hours of training to become certified to use SCUBA equipment. While exploring underwater is a very enjoyable activity, it is also one that requires a good understanding of gases and pressure to be safe.

Leisure CONNECTION

COOKING UNDER PRESSURE

Sometimes, foods—such as eggs and potatoes—are cooked by boiling them in water. The time it takes for them to cook varies depending on factors such as the temperature of the boiling water. But water does not always boil at the same temperature.

The temperature at which water boils depends on the pressure on the surface of the water. This pressure is usually the air pressure. As the molecules in the air bounce against the surface of the liquid, they exert pressure. The water molecules must have enough energy to overcome that pressure before they leave the liquid.

Air pressure varies inversely with altitude—that is, the greater the altitude, the less the pressure. For example, the air pressure in Miami, which is very near sea level, is greater than the pressure in Denver, the mile-high city.

And so, a cook in Denver must increase cooking times for everything from boiled eggs to baked cakes.

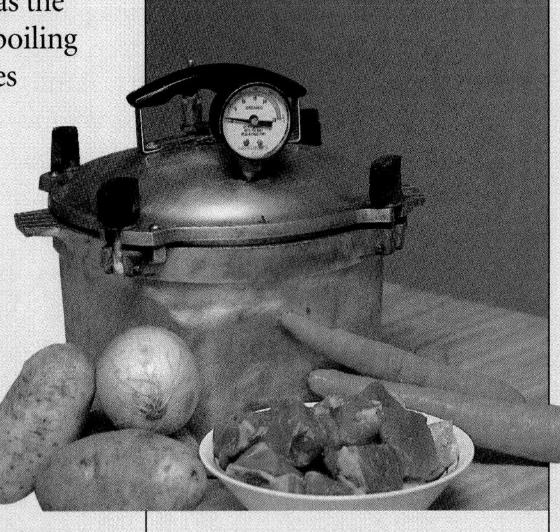

WHAT DO YOU THINK?

A pressure cooker, like the one pictured here, increases the pressure in the pot. What do you think that does to the temperature at which water boils? Will foods cook more quickly or more slowly in a pressure cooker?

History CONNECTION

THE GAS LAWS

Does it seem strange that some of the earliest experiments were done on gases? Most gases are, after all, invisible. How did these early scientists even know they were there?

One of the most important characteristics that a scientist possesses is curiosity. If you hold a glass upside down and push it into a container of water, what happens? If you are a curious person, you might begin to wonder what is in the glass that won't allow the water to enter.

Robert Boyle, although he is described as a chemist, was very curious about nature. The relationship between pressure and temperature that you know as Boyle's law was first published in 1662. But Boyle didn't spend his life working with gases. He went on to study blood circulation, water expansion, color, electricity, the bending of light in transparent objects, as well as the way sound travels in air.

Jacques Charles, a French physicist, was another scientist who was interested in how and why things happened. When he heard about Benjamin Franklin's experiments with electricity, he immediately attempted to repeat them. Franklin was so impressed with Charles' work that he paid him a visit.

But a scientist doesn't always spend his time doing fancy experiments. When the French Academy of Science, for whom Charles worked, decided to experiment with balloon flight, Jacques Charles was given the job of making the hydrogen gas and filling the balloon. He was so fascinated by the idea that, within a month of the first flight, Charles and his brother built their own balloon and flew for 90 minutes. Charles took along several scientific instruments, but managed to show only that air pressure decreased as the balloon rose.

Even though his interest and research in the behavior of gases continued, Charles never published his experiments, but explained them to the French chemist, Joseph Gay-Lussac. Gay-Lussac repeated the experiments and published the results in 1802. For this reason, Charles' law is sometimes called Gay-Lussac's law. Gay-Lussac also published results on the relationship between the pressure and temperature of a gas when the volume is constant. This law completes the circle of laws relating pressure, volume, and temperature of gases.

WHAT DO YOU THINK?

Some of the greatest discoveries in science have been made when something went wrong! If you were doing an experiment and something unexpected happened, would you just assume you'd done something wrong or would you try to figure out why the unexpected occurred? Why is curiosity an important quality for a scientist to possess?

Reviewing Main Ideas

1. Gases expand to fill their containers, exert pressure, and have low density.

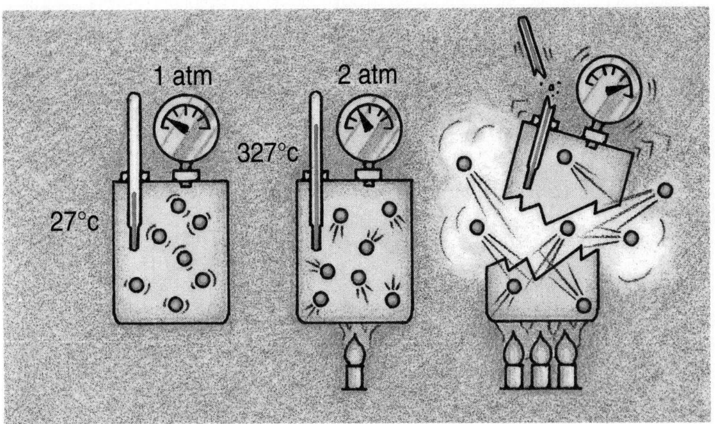

2. The temperature, volume, pressure, and amount of a gas are all related. As one changes, so do the others.

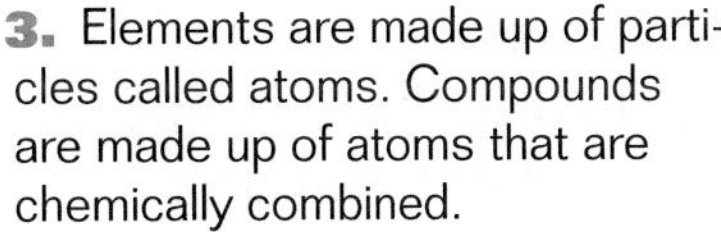

3. Elements are made up of particles called atoms. Compounds are made up of atoms that are chemically combined.

Element (Atom)		Compound (Molecule)		Atoms
Carbon	●	Magnesium Oxide		
Hydrogen	⊙			
Nitrogen		Carbon Dioxide		
Magnesium				
Oxygen	○	Ammonia		

Atoms of element A	Atoms of element B	Mixture of atoms of elements A and B	Compound of molecules made from uniting atoms of elements A and B	Another compound of elements A and B

4. The atomic theory states that matter consists of atoms, all atoms of an element are identical, different elements have different atoms, and compounds are formed by combinations of atoms in small whole number ratios.

Chapter 14

Chapter Review

USING KEY SCIENCE TERMS

atom
atomic theory of matter
Boyle's law
Charles' law

Using the list above, replace the underlined words with the correct key science term.

1. Compounds are formed by combinations of the smallest particle of an element.
2. The ideas of John Dalton about atoms were written down in order to help explain the behavior of matter, including gases.
3. The volume of a gas decreases as the pressure on it increases if the temperature is constant is a gas law.
4. The volume of a gas increases as the temperature increases if the pressure is constant is a gas law.

UNDERSTANDING IDEAS

Answer the following questions.

1. Suppose you blow up a brown paper lunch bag, you hit it hard, and it explodes. Use what you have learned in this chapter to explain why the bag exploded.
2. How much pressure is required to cut the volume of a gas by one-third? How much would the pressure of a gas change if its volume were four times greater?
3. Is it possible to find an atom of water? Why or why not?
4. What part(s) of the atomic theory of matter helps explain why the air ship that takes overhead pictures of football games stays inflated?
5. Hydrogen peroxide contains two hydrogen and two oxygen atoms. If the ratio of the mass of oxygen to the mass of hydrogen in water is 8:1, what would you expect this ratio to be in hydrogen peroxide? What law does this demonstrate?

CRITICAL THINKING

Use your understanding of the concepts developed in the chapter to answer each of the following questions.

1. Explain why diffusion is not a property of solids and liquids.
2. You have a weak spot in the wall of your bicycle tire. Is your tire more likely to tear on a hot day or a cold day?

3. When a dry test tube full of hydrogen is ignited, there is a loud pop and a film of water forms on the inside of the tube. Where does this come from? Why isn't the tube filled with water?
4. Compare the piece of bread and the piece of volcanic rock shown in the picture. How may their formations have been similar?

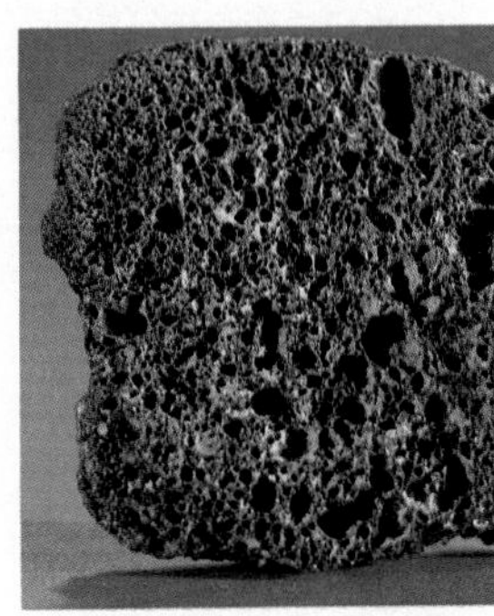

5. The pressure on a gas in a closed container was increased. What can you say about the volume of the gas? Explain.
6. Sugar and alcohol are each made of carbon, hydrogen, and oxygen. Sugar and alcohol have very different properties. Does this violate the atomic theory of matter? Explain.
7. You are taking a bouquet of inflated balloons to a friend in the hospital on a winter day with the air temperature near freezing. You blew the balloons up in your house, but by the time you got to the hospital, they appeared shriveled and smaller. Why did this happen? What will happen when you take the balloons into the hospital?

PROBLEM SOLVING

Read the following problem and discuss your answer in a brief paragraph.

Juan and Sam were camping and a rainstorm during the night got their tent bottom wet. The next day was warm and bright so Sam left his inflatable air mattress in the sun to dry while they went hiking. When they returned, the mattress had a jagged hole in it and all the air was gone.

Sam thought that an animal had ripped the mattress. How did Juan explain what happened using what he learned in this chapter?

CONNECTING IDEAS

Discuss each of the following in a brief paragraph.

1. On TV, the weather map shows a large air mass moving into your area. Its volume is increasing, but its pressure is staying the same. What is happening to its temperature?

2. Explain how gas from digesting food in the intestines can cause a stomach ache.

3. **EARTH SCIENCE CONNECTION** How do aerostats help scientists learn about gases in the atmosphere?

4. **LEISURE CONNECTION** Describe how cooking with a pressure cooker might speed up the process of cooking.

5. **TECHNOLOGY CONNECTION** Describe how you are able to drink liquids through a straw.

DID YOU EVER WONDER . . .

What the air is made of?

What is meant by *outer space*?

Why the wind blows?

You'll find the answers to these questions as you read this chapter.

Chapter 15

The Air Around You

Red and white colors soar overhead. This is a hang gliders' meet. It's your first, and you're quite excited.

"How do they stay afloat?" you wonder. "How can they turn or go up and down without any machinery or visible power?"

You remember that last weekend the meet was scheduled but called off because of very high winds. Earlier today, you overheard two of the glider pilots saying that the air was perfect for a great flight.

You know it's air that enables the gliders to soar through the sky. What properties of air can support the weight of the glider and the pilot? What properties of air allow the pilot to turn and change direction?

In this chapter, you will study the properties of air that enable gliders to fly as you learn about one part of Earth, its atmosphere.

EXPLORE!

Does air have mass?

Use a pan balance to determine the mass of a completely deflated ball. Record your measurement. Then use a bicycle pump to inflate the ball to its recommended maximum pressure. Predict what you think the mass of the inflated ball is. Use the pan balance to determine the mass of the air-filled ball.

Were there any changes in mass? If so, what were they? What conclusions can you draw?

15-1 So This Is the Atmosphere

OBJECTIVES

In this section, you will

- describe the composition of the atmosphere;
- discuss ways people affect air composition.

KEY SCIENCE TERMS

atmosphere
smog

WHAT'S IN THE ATMOSPHERE?

Imagine yourself waking up on a typical morning twenty years from now. It's early morning, and you decide to check the weather report coming over the computer screen. The smog is bad today! Once again, you will need to wear your air-filter mask. Pollution in the atmosphere has raised the temperature, and it could reach 104°F today! You will have to wear clothes designed to keep you cool. The ozone layer is thinner than it was last week, so you will have to use extra-strong lotion to protect your skin from the harmful rays of the sun. You sigh and remember attending a hang gliding rally when you were a teenager. It was on a beautiful day before the atmosphere became so polluted.

Could this be your future? It's one possible future you could face. Your life depends on the air you breathe and the condition of the atmosphere in which you live. The layer of gases hundreds of kilometers thick around Earth is its **atmosphere**. In this chapter, you'll study the atmosphere and some of the ways the atmosphere is polluted.

Every time you take a breath, you breathe in a mixture of gases, including oxygen and nitrogen. Your body needs oxygen to live. How much of the atmosphere is made up of oxygen? Let's investigate!

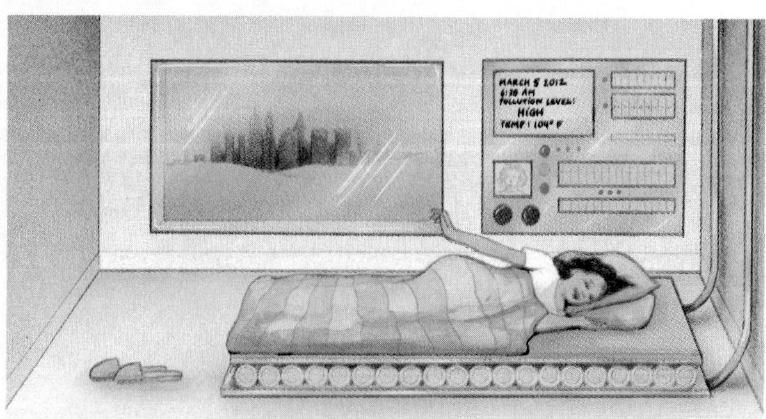

FIGURE 15-1. In a world with severe air pollution, you might have to check pollution levels before you can go outside.

INVESTIGATE!

15-1 HOW MUCH OXYGEN IS IN THE AIR?

Steel wool, which is mostly iron, reacts with the oxygen in air. The steel wool will combine with oxygen in a test tube to form rust. This reaction will continue until all of the oxygen has been used. In this activity, you will determine how much oxygen was used.

PROBLEM

How can the amount of oxygen in the air be measured?

MATERIALS 

measuring cup with mL gradations
clear plastic metric ruler
2 rubber bands
2 pencils
white vinegar
test-tube stand
test-tube clamp
test tube
paper towels
graph paper
scissors
steel wool
water
tongs
beaker

DATA AND OBSERVATIONS

TIME ELAPSED (MINUTES)	WATER LEVEL (MM)
2	
4	
6	
8	

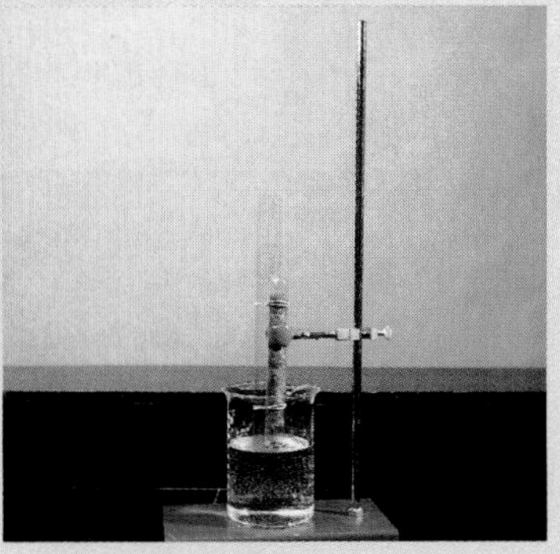

PROCEDURE

1. Copy the data table.
2. Mix 30 mL white vinegar with 20 mL water in the beaker.
3. **Measure** the length of the test tube in millimeters. Use rubber bands to attach the ruler to the test tube so the opening in the beaker is at 0 mm on the ruler.
4. Unroll a bale of steel wool. Cut a strip that is 2 cm wide and 20 cm long. Soak the steel wool in the vinegar solution for 1 minute.
5. Using tongs, remove the steel wool from the vinegar solution. Use the tongs to stretch out the strip of steel wool.
6. Dry the steel wool thoroughly between two paper towels.
7. Pour out the vinegar solution, rinse the beaker, and fill it about 2/3 full of water.
8. Using two pencils, push the steel wool into the bottom 2/3 of the test tube, keeping it as loose as possible.
9. Turn over the test tube and insert it into the beaker so the opening is just below the surface of the water. Then attach the tube to the stand, using the clamp. Adjust the ruler so that the 0 mm mark is at the water line.
10. **Observe** and record the level of the water in the test tube, in millimeters, every 2 minutes until the water level stops changing.

ANALYZE

1. Use this formula to calculate the percent of oxygen in the air.

$$\frac{\text{final water level (mm)}}{\text{tube length (mm)}} \times 100 = \%\ 0^2$$

2. About what percent of the air in the test tube was oxygen?

CONCLUDE AND APPLY

3. Why was it important to stretch the steel wool and pack it loosely before inserting it in the water?
4. Based on your observation, do you think the air is mostly oxygen?
5. **Going Further:** What do you **predict** will happen to the steel wool after you remove it from the test tube and expose it to air?

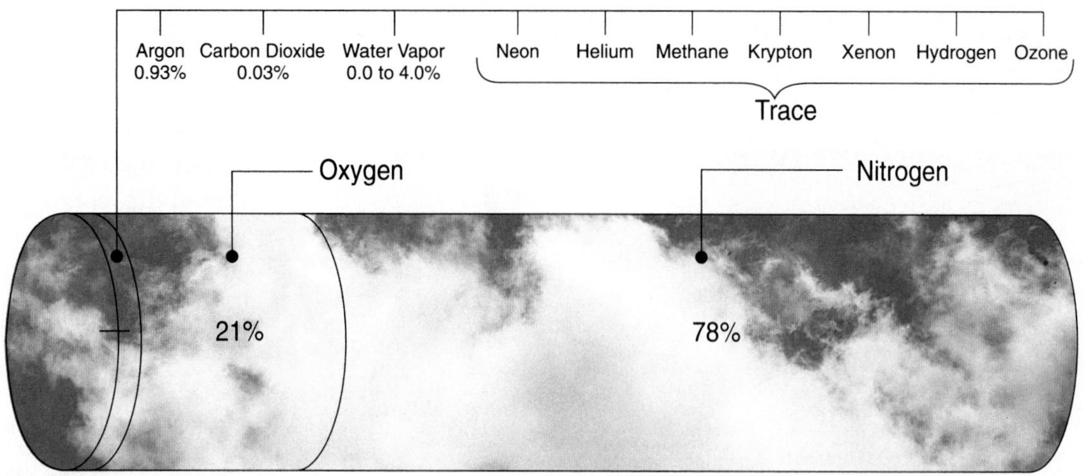

FIGURE 15-2. The diagram illustrates the percentages of gases in our atmosphere. All trace gases combined make up about 1 percent of the atmosphere when moisture levels are low.

From the Investigate activity, you found that oxygen makes up about 20 percent of the gases in the test tube. The gases in the tube are the same as the gases in the atmosphere. Therefore, you've shown that the atmosphere is about 20 percent oxygen. What gases make up the other 80 percent?

Figure 15-2 shows the percentages of gases that occur naturally in the atmosphere. However, human activities can increase the amount of certain gases in the atmosphere. Have you ever enjoyed watching the dancing flames of a roaring fire in a fireplace? The fire seems to make a room warm and cozy. At the same time, burning wood releases carbon dioxide into the air. This causes the amount of carbon dioxide in the atmosphere to increase. Burning coal, oil, and natural gas, three important fossil fuels, also releases carbon dioxide into the atmosphere.

Burning fossil fuels releases other gases into the atmosphere as well. Sulfur dioxide and nitrous oxides are among these gases. When these gases build up in the atmosphere, they can result in smog. **Smog** is a mixture of sulfur, nitrogen, and oxygen. It is a type of air pollution that is visible as a smokelike haze. Breathing smog is unhealthy for everyone. Smog can irritate the eyes and damage the tissues of the lungs, making them more susceptible to disease. Smog is also harmful to plants, because it prevents plants from absorbing the carbon dioxide they need.

When people pollute the air, they alter the mixture of gases in the atmosphere. In addition to gases, Earth's

SKILLBUILDER

INTERPRETING SCIENTIFIC ILLUSTRATIONS

Use the graph in Figure 15-2 to help you answer the following questions. If you need help, refer to the **Skill Handbook** on page 689.

1. What is the most abundant gas in the atmosphere? What percentage of the total volume of gases is it?
2. When added together, what percentage of the total volume of gases are nitrogen, oxygen, and carbon dioxide?

atmosphere contains liquid and solid matter. The most common liquid is water. Solids make up only a small portion of the atmosphere. What are some of these solids? Do they all come from nature, or are some the result of human activity?

DID YOU KNOW?

The amount of carbon dioxide in the atmosphere has increased by nearly 15 percent since 1900 as a result of burning fossil fuels.

FIND OUT!

What solids are in the air around you?

Smear thin layers of petroleum jelly onto four plastic lids. Place the lids in four outdoor locations around your home and school. After one week, collect the lids. Be sure to mark each lid to indicate the location from which it came. Examine each lid with a magnifying glass. On a sheet of paper, record the types of solids you can identify. Sort the solids—large pieces of dust, plant pieces, seeds, insect parts, and so on—taken from each sample site. Place the materials on microscope slides and examine each slide with a microscope.

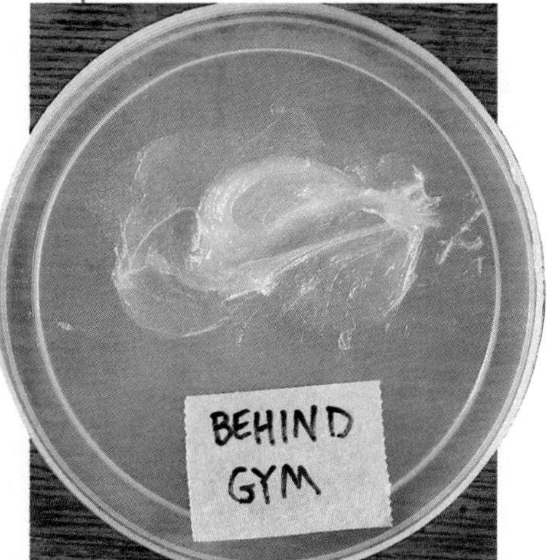

Conclude and Apply

1. Which of the solids collected could have been a result of human activity?
2. If you collected seeds, do any of them suggest how some plants disperse their seeds?
3. Do you think any of the materials might be harmful to people? Explain your answer.

From the activity, you may have discovered that dust and pollen are the most abundant solids in the air. Together, gases, solids, and liquids make up the atmosphere we live in. In the next section, you'll learn how the atmosphere of Earth is structured.

Check Your Understanding

1. Which gas in the atmosphere is most important to people? Why?
2. Why can driving a car be harmful to the atmosphere?
3. **APPLY:** Why do you think smog is more likely to form over cities than over rural areas?

15-2 Structure of the Atmosphere

OBJECTIVES

In this section, you will

- describe the structure of Earth's atmosphere;
- explain what causes atmospheric pressure.

KEY SCIENCE TERMS

troposphere
ozone

LAYERS OF THE ATMOSPHERE

Return for a moment to your future. After breakfast, you leave your home to travel downtown. You join several people at the tram stop. As you wait together for public transportation, you join in a discussion about the atmosphere's ozone. In the past, an outer ring of ozone shielded Earth's life-forms from the sun's harmful rays. Now the ozone provides very little protection. You recall that the loss of ozone protection was already a major environmental concern when you were a child. Air pollution from human activities in the last half of the 1900s was at the heart of the concern. But where is this ozone and how does it relate to the atmosphere as a whole?

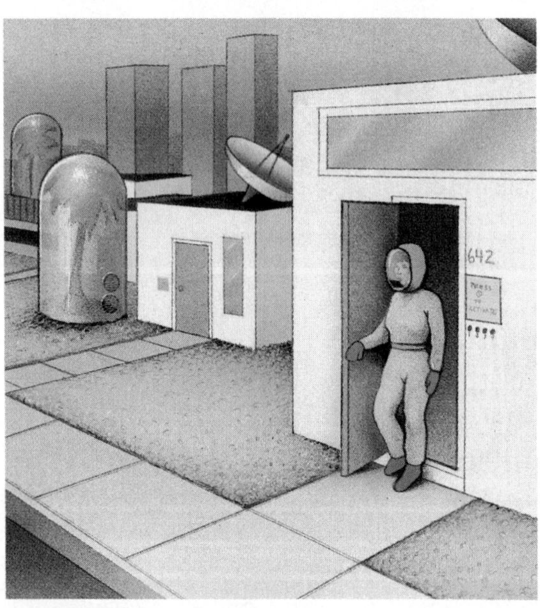

FIGURE 15-3. In a world without ozone protection, people would dress to protect themselves from the sun.

Just as sedimentary rock is layered on Earth's surface, the atmosphere wraps in layers around Earth. Some layers contain gases that easily absorb energy from the sun, while others do not. As a result, some layers are warmer than others. Based on the temperature differences, we can describe the atmosphere in terms of four layers.

You live in the **troposphere**, the layer closest to the ground. The troposphere contains 75 percent of all the gases in the atmosphere as well as dust, ice, and liquid water. Raging thunderstorms, sizzling heat, numbing cold, and all other kinds of weather occur in this layer. All clouds, from fluffy, white puffs to gray sheets of storm clouds, appear in this layer. It is also where smog forms.

Just above the troposphere is the stratosphere. It is within the stratosphere that the ozone layer is found. Use Figure 15-4 to locate the ozone layer in the atmosphere. About how far above Earth's surface does it lie? **Ozone** is a gas that absorbs some of the harmful radiation from the sun. As a layer in the atmosphere, ozone acts much like a sponge. Just as a sponge absorbs water, the ozone layer absorbs many of the sun's harmful rays, keeping them from reaching the troposphere. If you poured a large glass of water over a thin sponge on a table, the sponge could not hold all of the water. Some of it would seep through the sponge onto the table. In the same way, thinning areas and holes in the ozone layer let harmful rays pass into the troposphere. High concentrations of these rays can promote skin cancer and other diseases.

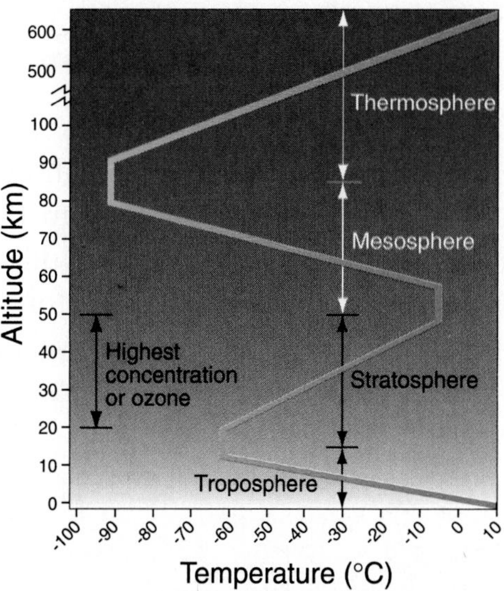

FIGURE 15-4. Although Earth's atmosphere extends nearly 700 km upward, 75 percent of all the gases are in the lowest 15 km, the troposphere.

Beyond the stratosphere are the mesosphere and the thermosphere, shown in both Figures 15-4 and 15-5. These two levels of the atmosphere are used for radio transmission.The thermosphere is the uppermost part of Earth's atmosphere. Beyond it is outer space. Unlike states or countries with defined boundaries, the upper part of the atmosphere has no special ending point. The air just becomes less and less dense until there is no air at all. We call the point where there is no atmosphere at all *outer space.*

FIGURE 15-5. This diagram shows where various phenomena occur in Earth's atmosphere.

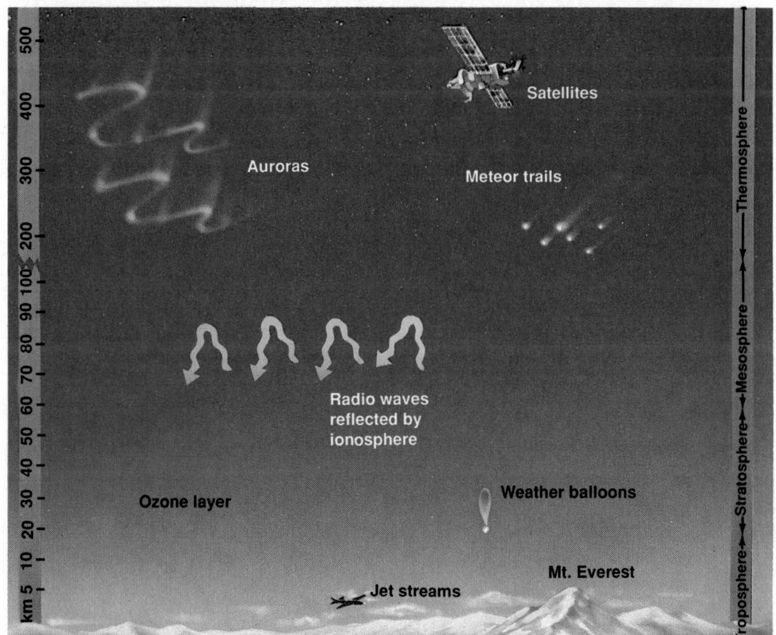

ATMOSPHERIC PRESSURE

The layers of the atmosphere are made of different amounts and combinations of gases. The gases that make up the air take up space and have mass. Earth's gravity pulls the air toward the ground the same as it does a stone, water, or any other mass, including you. Air has weight too, but we usually refer to air's weight as atmospheric pressure, or simply air pressure.

EXPLORE!

Is atmospheric pressure the same in all layers of the atmosphere?

Use four textbooks to represent layers of the atmosphere. Place a ball of clay on your desk. Place a piece of waxed paper over it and a book on top of the clay. Alternate balls of clay, waxed paper, and books until you have a pile of all four books. One by one, remove the books. Note the appearance of the clay. What differences do you see in the four lumps of clay? How would you account for these differences?

DID YOU KNOW?

The word *troposphere* comes from the Greek word *tropos*. It means "to turn or to mix." In this lower layer, there is a mixing of gases.

Think of your desktop as Earth's surface. The closer the air is to the surface, the more compressed the air becomes under the weight of the layers pushing down from above. On Earth, air pressure tends to be greatest at sea level. There is more air pressing down from above at sea level than on a mountaintop.

It takes more than just elevation, however, to determine what the air pressure is at any given spot on Earth. Temperature is also a factor. When air is warmed, it expands, and the same air mass occupies a greater volume. This means the air becomes less dense. The warmer the air, the less density and pressure it will have.

You've probably read a thermometer to learn the temperature of the air. Did you know that there is also an instrument that measures air pressure? This instrument is called a barometer. The next activity will help you understand how a barometer works.

INVESTIGATE!

15-2 ATMOSPHERIC PRESSURE

In this activity, you will make a simple barometer and take readings from it.

PROBLEM

How can a barometer measure atmospheric pressure?

MATERIALS 

small coffee can
drinking straw
rubber balloon
heavy paper (28 cm x 21.5 cm)
transparent tape
scissors
metric ruler
rubber band

PROCEDURE

1. Copy the data table.
2. Turn a piece of paper so that its long edges are at the top and bottom. Using the diagram shown as a guide, draw a vertical line 8 cm from the right edge of the paper. Draw a second line through the center of the paper and at right angles to the first.

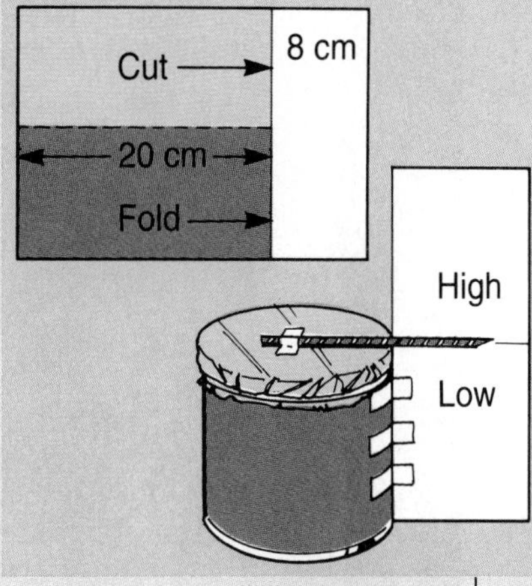

The two lines should form a letter T on the paper.

3. Cut away the light blue section indicated on the diagram. Fold the paper along the 8-cm line.
4. Wrap the section shown in blue around the can. Fasten it with tape. The long edge of the paper should now be sticking up above the can as the gauge.
5. Cover the top of the coffee can with the rubber balloon. Stretch the balloon tightly over the top of the can so that the barometer will work properly. Secure the balloon with the rubber band.
6. Trim one tip of the straw to a point. Position the straw so that the pointed end is alongside the gauge. Tape the other end of the straw to the balloon stretched over the coffee can. DO NOT tape the straw to the gauge.
7. Make a horizontal mark on the gauge showing the position of the straw. Write *high pressure* above the mark and *low pressure* below the mark.
8. **Observe** and **measure** the straw's movement for a week. Is it pointing to *high* or to *low pressure*? Also note the weather conditions for each day.
9. Record your data.

DATA AND OBSERVATIONS

DATA	BAROMETRIC READINGS (HIGH OR LOW)	WEATHER CONDITIONS

ANALYZE

1. Explain how your barometer works.
2. If the atmospheric pressure changed in your area over the week, what was the weather like on the days when it changed?

CONCLUDE AND APPLY

3. **Hypothesize** what you might record if your barometer were placed on a mountaintop. What type of readings would you expect in the stratosphere? Why?
4. **Going Further:** Would you **predict** that the air pressure would be greater at sea level or on a mountaintop if both places had the same air temperature? Why?

FIGURE 15-6. When pollution levels are high, it is important to protect ourselves from the harmful side effects of breathing smog.

DID YOU KNOW?

In 1991, the volcanic eruption of Mount Pinatubo, in the Philippines, spewed gases and ashes into the atmosphere. Material from such an eruption can remain in the lower stratosphere for months or even years because of the stratosphere's fairly constant temperature.

You have probably seen weather reports on the television news or have listened to them on the radio. One of the tools forecasters use is the barometer. It helps them predict what the weather will be like by analyzing the changes in air pressure.

The atmosphere has mass, just as all matter does, and gravity pulls on this mass, resulting in atmospheric pressure. The pressure varies in each of the four layers of the atmosphere. You live in the layer closest to Earth, the troposphere, where all weather takes place and where atmospheric pressure is the greatest. In the next section, you will explore more about how the air and the sun work together to produce the climate around you.

Check Your Understanding

1. Tell which layer has each of these characteristics—(**a**) a raging thunderstorm, (**b**) a blurred boundary with outer space, (**c**) a protective ozone layer.
2. What is air weight called?
3. **APPLY:** Would you expect air pressure to be greater in the thermosphere than in the stratosphere? Why?

15-3 Air and the Sun

ENERGY FROM THE SUN

OBJECTIVES

In this section, you will

- explain what causes wind;
- describe Earth's wind systems.

KEY SCIENCE TERMS

greenhouse effect
trade winds
prevailing westerlies

Once again, think ahead to the future. The workday ends, and you return to your home. You place your dinner in the microwave oven. While waiting for your dinner to cook, you flick on the electronic news scanner and request to see the news about the planetary atmospheric program. The space agency runs the program that is studying the atmospheres of Venus and Mars. The agency hopes to find solutions to Earth's atmospheric problems through the study. The atmosphere on Mars is too thin to support life. As Figure 15-7 shows, Mars cannot hold much of the heat that radiates from the sun. As a result, Mars is a very cold, lifeless planet. Venus is a very hot, lifeless planet. Its atmosphere is so dense that most of the heat coming

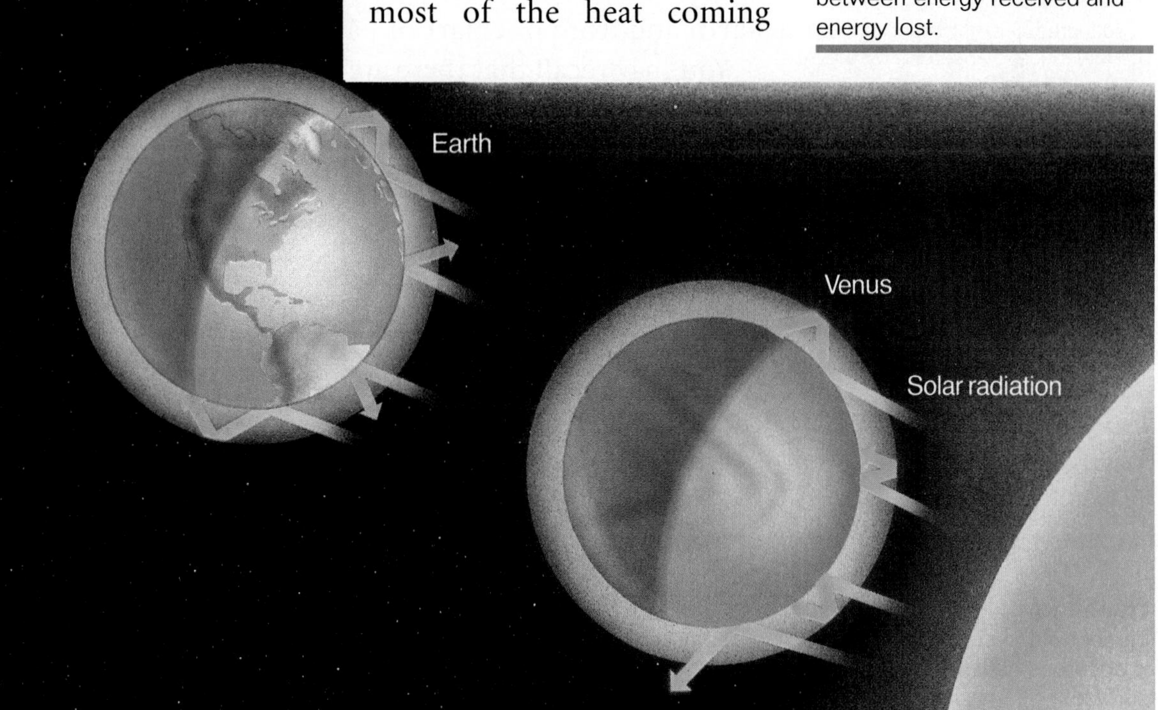

FIGURE 15-7. Most radiation entering Venus's atmosphere is trapped by thick gases and clouds. On Mars, a thin atmosphere allows much radiation to escape. Earth's atmosphere creates a delicate balance between energy received and energy lost.

FIGURE 15-8. Radiation, conduction, and convection all account for the heat in the atmosphere.

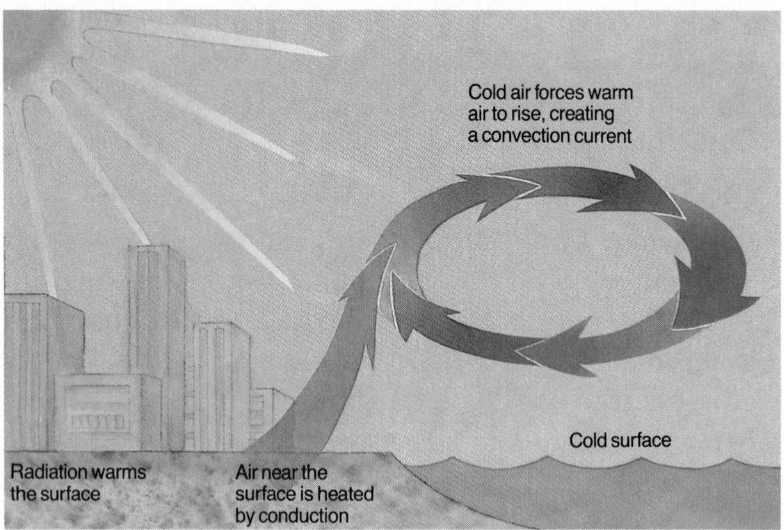

INTERPRETING SCIENTIFIC ILLUSTRATIONS

Use Figure 15-9 and its caption to help you answer these questions. If you need help, refer to the **Skill Handbook** on page 689.

1. How much of the sun's radiation is absorbed by Earth's surface?
2. How much of the radiation is reflected back into space?
3. How much is absorbed by the atmosphere?
4. How much radiation, from any source, is absorbed by the atmosphere?

into the atmosphere from the sun cannot escape. Venus is so hot that a living thing would instantly melt if it were put on its surface.

Venus, Mars, and Earth are only three of the nine planets in our solar system, and Earth is the only one known to support life. Earth's atmosphere and the sun interact to provide an environment that can support life. How do they do this? The sun is the source of most energy on Earth. Heat is transferred from the sun to Earth and from one part of Earth to another.

You may recall that there are three ways to transfer heat from one object to another. Radiation, conduction, and convection are also at work in the atmosphere, as shown in Figure 15-8.

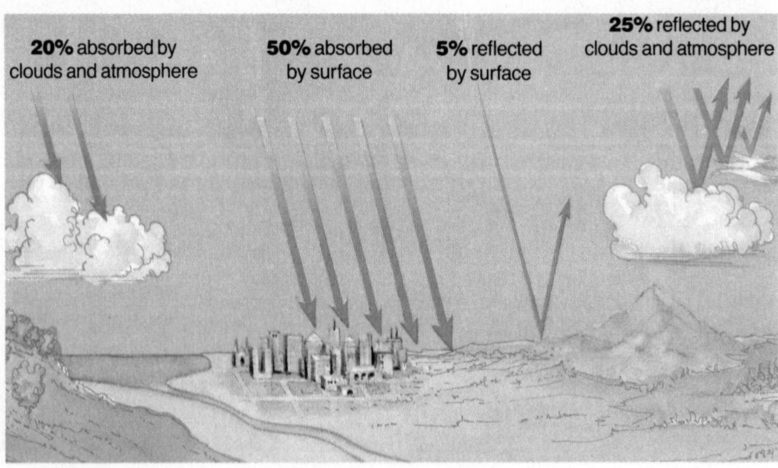

FIGURE 15-9. Only about 50 percent of the sun's radiation is absorbed on the Earth's surface.

Heat Transfer Through Radiation

Radiation from the sun travels through space on its way to Earth. Once it enters the atmosphere, some of the radiation is absorbed by Earth's atmosphere.

Not only can the atmosphere absorb radiation, but on Earth plants, buildings, and ground surfaces, including asphalt and dirt, can also absorb radiation. The objects can then transfer this heat back into the atmosphere. Much of the radiation from the sun to Earth passes through Earth's atmosphere. Much of the radiation coming from the surface of Earth passes back out into space.

The radiation trapped by the atmosphere affects temperature in much the same way a greenhouse does. You can demonstrate this warming effect by doing the next Find Out activity.

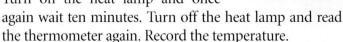

FIND OUT!

How does a greenhouse trap heat?

To demonstrate how heat is trapped in Earth's atmosphere, you will need a clear plastic storage box and lid. Fill the bottom of the storage box with about 3 cm of soil. Insert a stiff piece of cardboard into the soil at about half the length of the box. Use the cardboard as a prop for a thermometer. The bulb of the thermometer should be facing up. Overhead, about 30 cm from the box, place a heat lamp.

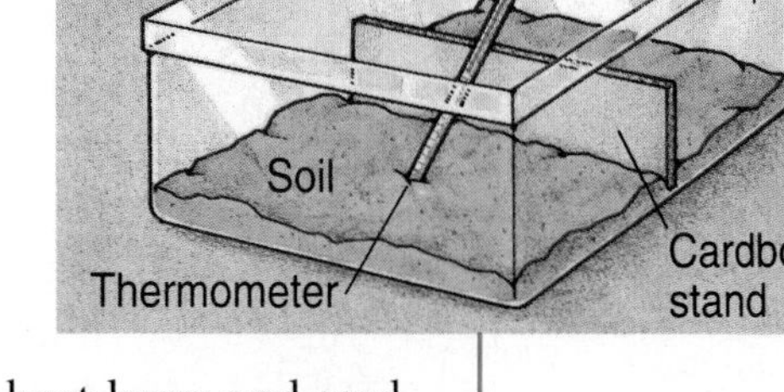

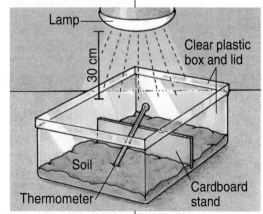

Do not cover the greenhouse with the lid. Turn on the heat lamp and wait ten minutes. Turn off the heat lamp and read the thermometer. Record the temperature on a sheet of paper. Allow the greenhouse to return to room temperature. Then put the lid on the greenhouse. Turn on the heat lamp and once again wait ten minutes. Turn off the heat lamp and read the thermometer again. Record the temperature.

Conclude and Apply

Compare the two temperatures. In which situation was the temperature higher? Why?

FIGURE 15-10. Greenhouses trap heat, allowing flowers to bloom in winter.

Once heat gets inside the atmosphere, it cannot escape easily, just as in the greenhouse. The trapping of heat by the atmosphere is called the **greenhouse effect**. The balance of heat entering the atmosphere and escaping back into space is delicate. Gases, such as carbon dioxide, can trap additional heat and upset this balance. The result could be global warming, meaning an increase in average temperatures all over Earth. Such a change would likely disrupt present climate patterns, melt polar ice caps, and raise ocean levels.

Conduction Transfer

Radiation is one way that heat is transferred in Earth's atmosphere. Heat is transferred from Earth's surface to the atmosphere by conduction. Have you ever left a metal spoon in a hot pan? If you have, you know that the spoon handle becomes hot. This is an example of conduction. Conduction is the transfer of heat through a material from a higher temperature to a lower temperature. The atmosphere is not a good conductor of heat. Only air that directly touches hot surfaces, like a hot road, becomes heated by conduction. As the air moves over Earth's surface, it picks up heat from the surface. Can the atmosphere gain heat in any other way? Let's do an Explore to find out.

EXPLORE!

Why does hot air move?

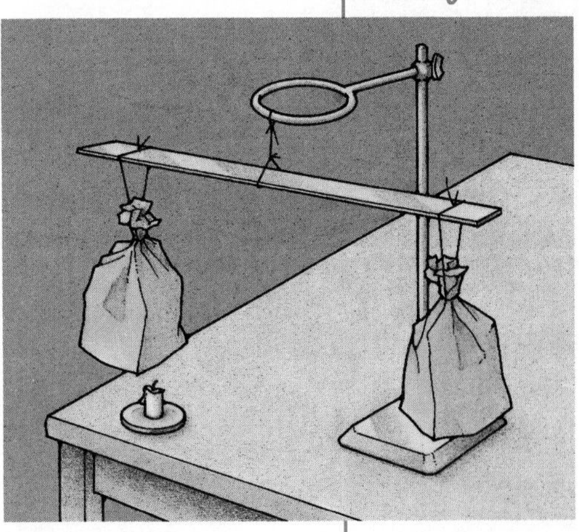

Tie two small paper bags filled with air closed with string. Hang the bags from the ends of a meter stick with more string. Suspend the meter stick on a ring stand and adjust the strings and meter stick until the meter stick is balanced. Light a candle and place the candle below one of the bags. **CAUTION:** *Make sure the candle is far enough from the bag so that it does not catch on fire.* Watch what happens to the balance. Why do you think this happens?

Convection Transfer

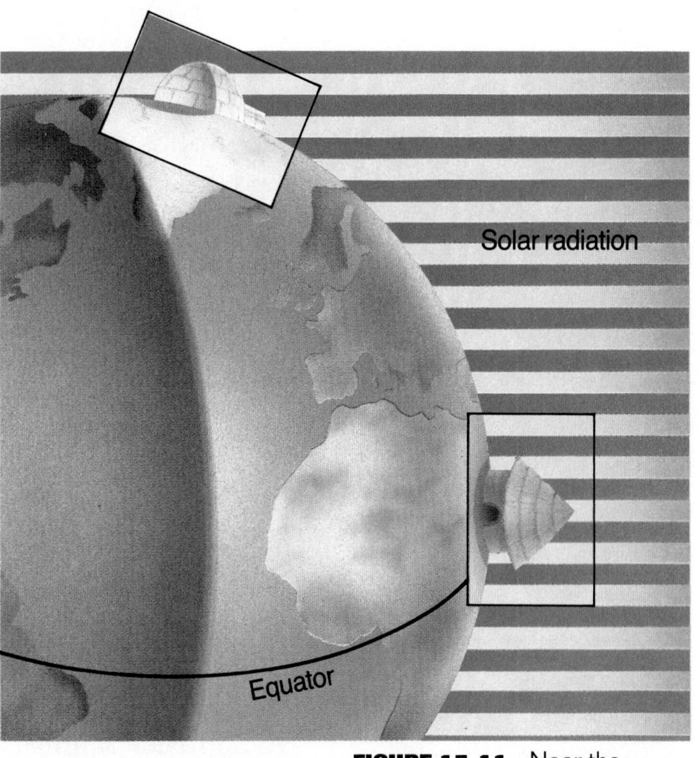

FIGURE 15-11. Near the poles, the sun's rays are spread out more than at the equator. So, equal amounts of energy don't heat equally—each square meter of land at the poles receives less energy than each square meter at the equator.

When the air inside the bag over the candle was heated, it became less dense and had less air pressure than the unheated air in the other bag. The unheated bag contained denser air at a greater pressure than the heated bag. This pressure caused the unheated bag to move down, in turn, causing the bag with less dense air to rise. As a result, the meter stick tilted. Convection causes movement of air masses in the atmosphere in a similar manner. Convection is the transfer of heat by the movement of an air mass from one place to another. Warm air in the atmosphere is less dense and has less air pressure than cooler air. It's pushed up by cooler, more dense air below it. In the atmosphere, as the warm air is pushed up, that air cools and again becomes more dense. The cooled air sinks and once again pushes less dense air upward. This up-and-down cycle sets up a convection current of moving air. This current of moving air is wind.

GLOBAL WINDS

You might want to stop a minute and think about how temperature, density, and pressure are related. Remember that temperature affects the density of air. Density, in turn, affects the pressure of air. Finally, pressure differences cause air movement, or wind. From this we can see that temperature can affect wind. Differences in temperature on Earth can be explained in part by the curved shape of its surface.

Look at how the sun's radiation strikes different places on Earth, shown in Figure 15-11. Where are the sun's rays more direct, at the North Pole or at the equator? Because the equator receives so much solar radiation, it is usually warmer than any other place. The unequal heating of places all over Earth results in large, global wind systems. The trade winds and the prevailing westerlies are examples of wind systems that can have a great effect on global climate.

Trade Winds

Cooler air coming into the equatorial area forces the heated air up. Staying aloft, the heated air moves toward the poles. As it moves, it cools and sinks, then rushes back toward the equator to force up heated air. The winds caused by the air sinking and returning to the equator are called **trade winds**. Do you think the trade winds make it all the way to the North and South poles?

The trade winds are warm and steady. In the Northern Hemisphere, early ship captains were able to use these winds to help them sail southwest and to explore the Americas. In the Southern Hemisphere, the trade winds would help a sailing ship glide northwest. Even today, airplane pilots use the trade winds to help save fuel. If you travel from Miami, Florida, to Ecuador in a jet, the pilot might ride the trade winds to increase the plane's speed and save fuel.

Prevailing Westerlies

Earth's rotation on its axis affects other air movements. Some of the warm air traveling away from the equator

FIGURE 15-12. European sailors took advantage of the trade winds as they sailed to the Americas.

does not cool enough to sink back to the surface. It continues to move toward the North and South poles. At the same time, cold, polar air is moving along the surface of the land toward the equator. Earth's rotation prevents either one of these masses from moving in a straight southerly or northerly direction.

Do you use a fan to circulate air when it is hot? What do you think would happen if you threw small pieces of paper toward the fan? That's right, the movement of air caused by the spinning blades would scatter the papers in a different direction. In the same way, the rotation of Earth deflects air from its original path. Look at a globe or world map. Find the area in the Northern Hemisphere between 30° and 60° north latitude. At these latitudes, wind is deflected to the right. It seems to move from a southwestern direction to a northeastern direction. In the Southern Hemisphere between 30° and 60° south latitude, the wind is deflected to the left. It appears to move from a northwestern to a southeastern direction. The winds between 30° and 60° latitude are called the **prevailing westerlies**. The northern prevailing westerlies are responsible for much of the weather movement in the United States and Canada.

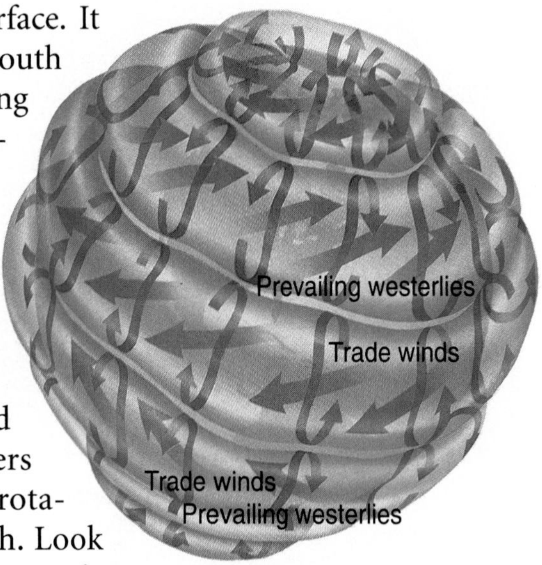

FIGURE 15-13. Arrows show the major wind systems created when air moving across the surface is deflected by the spinning of Earth.

Local Winds

Because they are global, trade winds and prevailing westerlies can affect weather patterns around the world. Within those patterns, smaller wind systems also exist. Whether you enjoy a bright, sunshiny day or a cold, rainy one often depends on the wind systems in your local area.

Do you live by a large lake or the sea? If you do, you have probably enjoyed days and evenings at the beach. Have you ever noticed that during the daytime a cool breeze seems to blow gently toward the beach from the water? Then at nighttime, the cooling breeze seems to blow from the land toward the water. There's a good reason that this happens.

During the day, radiation from the sun heats up both land and water. Conduction transfers some of the heat to the air. Because the land heats up faster than the water,

DID YOU KNOW?

In 1934, winds of 372 km/h were recorded at the top of Mount Washington, New Hampshire.

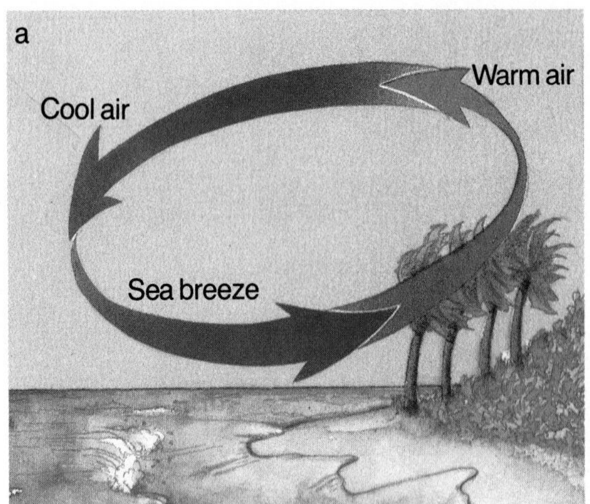

FIGURE 15-14. Cool air forces warm air to rise, creating a sea breeze during the day (a) and a land breeze at night (b).

the air over the land is warmer than the air over the water. The cooler, denser air from the water moves toward the land. It forces the land's warmer, lighter air up and so creates a convection current. This current blows cooler air from the water toward the land and your spot on the beach. During the nighttime, without radiation from the sun, the land cools faster than the water does. What do you think happens to the wind direction then? Use Figure 15-14 to confirm your answer. According to the figure, where is the warmer air at nighttime? Where is the cooler air?

Land and sea breezes are only one example of the different wind patterns that help make weather special in local communities. No matter what the locality, however, the air around us makes Earth a special planet in our solar system—the only planet with a life-supporting atmosphere.

Check Your Understanding

1. Describe three ways heat is transferred in the atmosphere.
2. Why do weather patterns tend to move from west to east across the United States?
3. **APPLY:** Why does it seem as if a cool breeze comes from the water during the day and from the land at night?

EXPANDING YOUR VIEW

CONTENTS

A Closer Look
Global Warming and the Greenhouse Effect 459

Life Science Connection
City Smog and Our Health 460

Science and Society
The Disappearing Ozone Layer 461

Health Connection
Cigarette Smoke and the Air We Breathe 463

Literature Connection
What Happened to the Animals? 463

Teens in Science
Flying High and Loving It 464

A CLOSER LOOK

GLOBAL WARMING AND THE GREENHOUSE EFFECT

The greenhouse effect, or the trapping of heat by the atmosphere, is becoming a serious environmental concern. Since 1900, average temperatures on Earth have risen by 0.5°C. That sounds insignificant, but even small temperature changes can mean big changes in climate. This global warming might melt enough of the polar ice to raise sea levels everywhere. Weather patterns also might shift.

Carbon dioxide is one of the main gases that causes the greenhouse effect. Pollution caused by human activities adds extra carbon dioxide to the atmosphere. The worldwide loss of trees and plants has an effect because trees and plants remove carbon dioxide from the air and give out oxygen. Destruction of forest lands has a double impact—less carbon dioxide is taken out of the atmosphere than before, and more

is put back in when the forests are burned.

Although the cause of global warming is not completely understood, many people feel humans should take action regarding the possible causes. Positive actions would include reduced use of fossil fuels and recycling paper products.

WHAT DO YOU THINK?

What would happen if global warming were to continue? Would our planet become like Venus—too hot for life as we know it to exist?

LIFE SCIENCE CONNECTION

CITY SMOG AND OUR HEALTH

If you've ever been hiking or camping in a forest, you've probably enjoyed taking deep breaths of fresh, pine-scented country air. The air in large urban areas, on the other hand, often doesn't smell too great. In fact, polluted air doesn't just smell bad—it's also bad for our health.

Athletes who train in big cities have to get up early—often before 5 A.M.—for their daily run. Later on, smog levels are too high. Recall that smog is a type of air pollution, made up mostly of sulfur, nitrogen, and oxygen. Breathing in dirty air during such strenuous activity would be dangerous for the athletes' bodies, as smog is harmful to the lungs as well as the heart.

What exactly makes the air dirty? Two of the worst gases we can breathe in are ozone and carbon monoxide. The ozone layer high up in the stratosphere absorbs solar radiation and is crucial to our existence. But the ozone gas released by industry and automobile exhaust into the air we breathe is a serious pollutant. Breathing in ozone is irritating, causing a burning sensation in your nose and throat. It can give you a headache, make your eyes sting and, if levels are high enough, blur your vision. Ozone can also damage sensitive lung tissue, reducing your ability to fight infection, and leading to diseases like pneumonia, chest colds, bronchitis, and the flu.

Carbon monoxide, a gas produced by vehicle exhaust fumes, is absorbed by red blood cells when we breathe in. Red blood cells are supposed to be absorbing oxygen, and are less efficient at this when carbon monoxide gets in the way, so the body receives less oxygen than it needs. Decreased oxygen levels can cause heart trouble and chest pains. This is why, on days when pollution levels are extremely high, the elderly, young children, and people with heart or chest problems are warned to stay indoors and rest.

Low levels of oxygen in the brain can impair coordination and motor functions. When we exercise, we need even more oxygen than usual to keep our bodies running. That's why it's dangerous to exercise when smog levels are high.

Smog is also affected by the weather. Usually, air temperature decreases with altitude, but sometimes a layer of warm air lies above a mass of cooler air. This is known as a temperature inversion, and when this happens, the upward circulation of the air below is limited. Pollutants get trapped and smog increases.

YOU TRY IT!

There are lots of stories on TV and in the newspapers about pollution. Using newspapers and other resources, find out which cities in the United States are most severely affected by smog. Are the biggest cities always the dirtiest? What about a city's location? You may be surprised to find a city like Denver, Colorado, on your list. Did you know that Denver is one mile above sea level? What special problems might this cause?

SCIENCE AND SOCIETY

THE DISAPPEARING OZONE LAYER

As you'll remember from reading this chapter, the ozone layer is part of the stratosphere—it lies about 24 kilometers above your head. This layer of ozone gas absorbs some of the portion of the sun's radiation that is considered harmful. The harmful radiation that manages to pass through the ozone layer makes you tan or sunburn—and too much of it can cause skin cancer, as well as other health problems. Currently, as many as 27,000 Americans develop skin cancer every year, and as many as 6000 die from it per year.

What would happen if something happened to the ozone layer and more of the sun's dangerous rays reached Earth? There could be a sharp increase in rates of skin cancer, resulting in more deaths. People who sunbathe would have to be more careful too, as a small amount of exposure could lead to a very painful sunburn. It's a frightening thought—but the ozone layer is already starting to develop holes. In 1986, scientists discovered two holes in the ozone layer—a small hole over the North Pole, and a much larger hole over Antarctica. Since that time, the holes have disappeared, then reappeared at certain times of year. No one is quite sure what's causing the holes, or why they open and close. But most scientists do agree that the holes are gradually getting bigger, and that the ozone layer has become thinner all around Earth.

One of the possible causes of the holes is a group of chemicals called chlorofluorocarbons (CFCs), which destroy ozone. Do you know how common they are? They're used in automobile air conditioners, in some aerosol sprays, in refrigerators, bicycle seats, foam cups, polystyrene egg cartons, and foam packaging for fast food containers. CFCs enter the

WHAT DO YOU THINK?

What conveniences would you be willing to give up if you knew they were destroying the ozone layer?

atmosphere when these products are manufactured and used.

CFC gases rise slowly from Earth to the ozone layer, where the sun's rays are very powerful. The CFCs break down in the intense heat and release chlorine. It is the free chlorine gas that destroys ozone. We used to think CFCs were ideal for consumer products—they're nonflammable, nontoxic, and decompose very slowly.

You may have heard that some major fast-food chains recently converted from using foam packaging to cardboard hamburger containers, in an effort to stop using CFCs. Several countries, including the United States, have introduced laws to restrict the use of CFCs, and some manufacturers have promised to stop CFC production by the year 2000.

Environmentalists think that despite these laws and promises, not enough is being done to get rid of CFCs. It can take up to 150 years for CFCs to decompose, and a further 15 years for the gas to rise to the stratosphere. They say that even if we stopped using CFCs tomorrow, the breakdown of the CFCs currently in use would make the ozone layer continue to thin for the next 100 years.

Sometimes looking at a global problem makes us feel helpless because so many things are beyond our immediate control. We feel we can't change laws or influence the policies of international companies. But politicians and businesses can be affected by the way we act. If people stopped buying products containing CFCs, the companies that make them would need to find an alternative—and that process is already starting. Imagine you do some grocery shopping for your family, and you have to buy a box of eggs. If you buy eggs packed in a recycled paper container, instead of in a foam container that contains CFCs, you've made a decision that will help the environment.

Health CONNECTION

CIGARETTE SMOKE AND THE AIR WE BREATHE

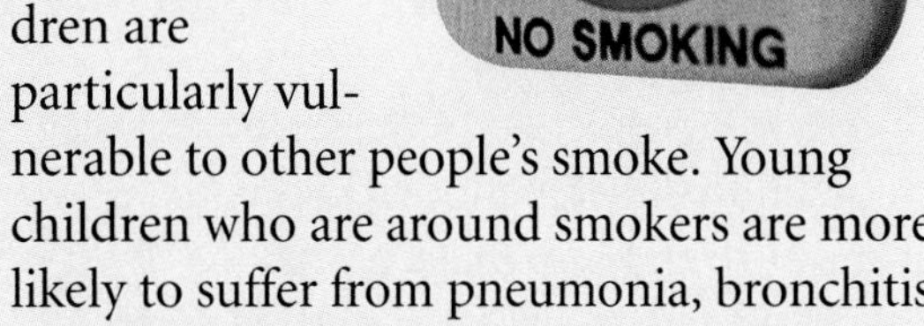

Human beings pollute the air in their own homes and offices by smoking cigarettes. Everyone knows smoking is a health hazard. Smoking is the leading cause of the deadliest cancer in the United States—lung cancer, which kills approximately 143,000 people each year. Smoking can also cause other cancers, as well as heart disease, chronic bronchitis, and emphysema.

About 400,000 Americans die each year of smoking-related illnesses, but smokers find it hard to quit because cigarettes contain the addictive drug nicotine. People who stop using a drug they're addicted to can feel very uncomfortable physically.

About 3800 lung cancer deaths each year in the United States are caused by passive smoking—breathing in other people's cigarette smoke. People with breathing problems, unborn babies, and children are particularly vulnerable to other people's smoke. Young children who are around smokers are more likely to suffer from pneumonia, bronchitis, and chronic coughs than other kids.

Most states have laws to control smoking in public places. Smoking is prohibited on airline flights in the United States that are less than six hours. Many smokers think these new, tough regulations violate their rights. At the opposite extreme, some people feel cigarettes should be made illegal.

WHAT DO YOU THINK?

Do you think no-smoking regulations violate people's rights? Explain.

Literature CONNECTION

WHAT HAPPENED TO THE ANIMALS?

The release of chemicals into the air we breath is a major concern in the world today. People can suffer respiratory problems and other ill effects from breathing in pollutants. People, however, are not the only living things that suffer from a lack of clean air.

Obtain a copy of the poem "Vision Shadows" by Simon Ortiz (Baym, Nina, ed., et al. W. W. Norton. *The Norton Anthology of American Literature*). He is a Native American author and poet who is concerned about the destructive things humans are doing to nature. Read the poem to see how animal life—particularly the eagle—suffered after a chemical was sprayed from helicopters to control the rat population that was harming farmers' crops.

WHAT DO YOU THINK?

What other ways might there be for farmers to control the rat problem without harming wildlife in the area?

TEENS *in* SCIENCE

FLYING HIGH AND LOVING IT

Have you ever let go of the string holding a helium-filled balloon? Did your balloon shoot straight up like a rocket, or did it seem to drift in the direction of the wind? Having trouble remembering? Just ask 18-year-old commercial hot-air balloon pilot, David Bair. He ought to know.

David took his first ride in a hot-air balloon at the age of four. His hometown of Albuquerque, New Mexico is host to an annual festival called the International Hot-Air Balloon Fiesta. "My family met a pilot who had no crew. We volunteered to help out."

But not all the flights have been so smooth. "Navigating is tricky. You don't steer a balloon as you would an airplane."

Why is navigating a hot-air balloon so difficult? As you know, if the temperature of a gas is increased, air molecules become more active and they begin to move away from each other. When the heat source in the balloon is turned on, air in the balloon heats up. Molecular action in the balloon makes air in the balloon less dense than the surrounding air, and the balloon is pushed upward by the colder air. To go down, the heating source is simply turned off. Air in the balloon becomes more dense, and the balloon sinks. Balloon pilots can only control the up and down movements of the balloon.

"To move side to side, you have to depend on wind currents. This past summer I got caught in a severe wind. Even though I kept the balloon at a stable temperature, this wind current tossed my balloon at a speed of 400 feet a minute. Normally, ballooning is very safe, but weather is part of what makes ballooning so exciting."

YOU TRY IT!

Warm air rises because cooler, denser air pushes it upward. Hot-air balloons work on this same principle. In this activity, you can see how hot air rises in your own classroom.

Materials

- Room thermometer
- Meterstick
- Masking tape
- Step ladder

Procedure

1. Tape the thermometer to one end of the meterstick. Hold the meterstick so that the thermometer is at ankle level. Wait two minutes and take a temperature reading.
2. Hold the meterstick so that the thermometer is at shoulder level. Again wait two minutes and record the temperature.
3. Climb up a few steps of the ladder and hold the meterstick so that the thermometer is as close to the ceiling as possible. Wait two minutes and record the temperature.

How does the temperature change relate to hot-air balloon navigation?

Chapter 15

Reviewing Main Ideas

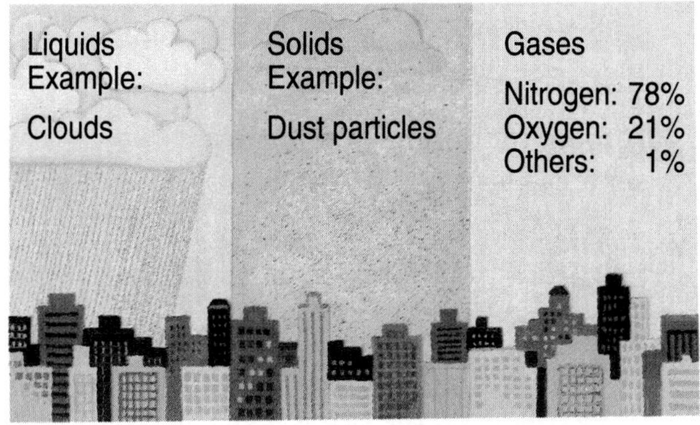

1. The atmosphere is made up of liquids, solids, and gases.

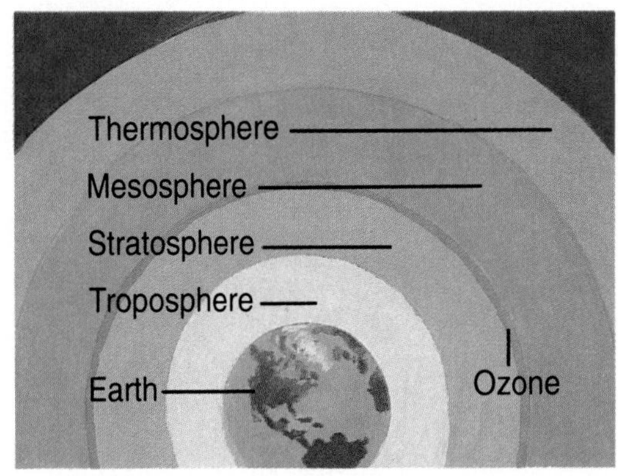

2. The atmosphere has four layers. You live in the troposphere, and a protective layer of ozone is in the stratosphere.

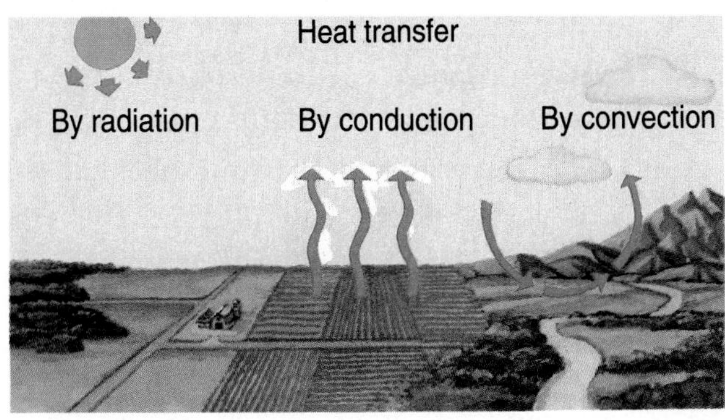

3. Heat is transferred by radiation, conduction, and convection in the atmosphere.

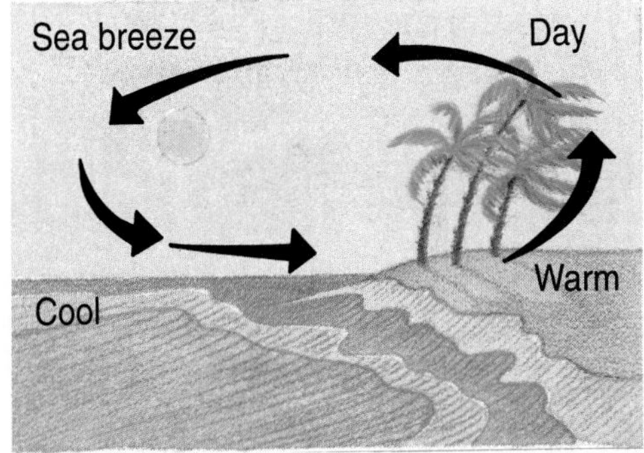

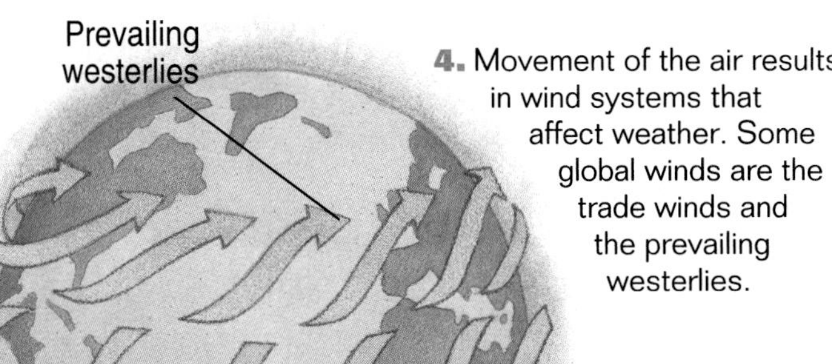

4. Movement of the air results in wind systems that affect weather. Some global winds are the trade winds and the prevailing westerlies.

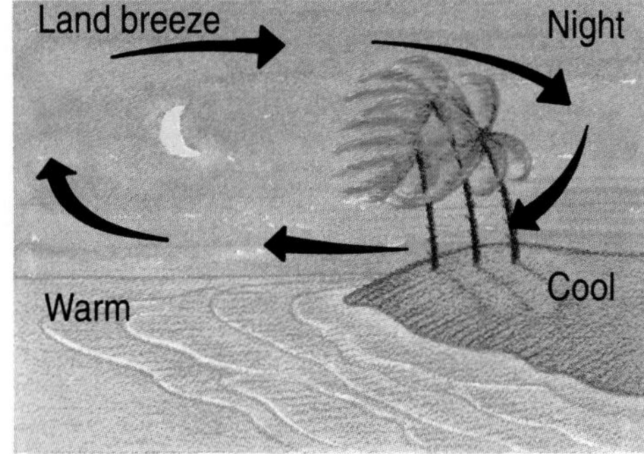

5. Sea and land breezes can create local weather patterns.

Chapter 15

Chapter Review

USING KEY SCIENCE TERMS

atmosphere
greenhouse effect
ozone
prevailing westerlies
smog
trade winds
troposphere

Each phrase below describes a key science term from the list above. Write the term that matches the phrase describing it.

1. layer of atmosphere nearest Earth's surface, weather layer
2. layer in the stratosphere, absorbs harmful rays from the sun
3. warm and steady global winds

4. global warming, trapped heat
5. global winds, northeastern direction in the Northern Hemisphere
6. polluted air, effect of burning fossil fuels
7. layers of gases, hundreds of kilometers thick

UNDERSTANDING IDEAS

Choose the best answer to complete each sentence.

1. The most common gas in the atmosphere is ___.
   a. dust
   b. nitrogen
   c. oxygen
   d. liquid
2. Energy from the sun is transferred to Earth by ___.
   a. conduction
   b. light
   c. convection
   d. radiation
3. Weather and smog are found in Earth's ____.
   a. stratosphere
   b. ozone layer
   c. troposphere
   d. thermosphere
4. The temperature of the atmosphere affects all of the following except ____.
   a. mass
   b. pressure
   c. density
   d. movement
5. The trapping of thermal energy in the atmosphere is known as ____.
   a. the ozone layer
   b. the trade winds
   c. smog
   d. the greenhouse effect

6. A land breeze over water is most likely to occur ____.
   a. globally
   b. at night
   c. during the day
   d. in cold weather
7. A barometer is used to measure air ____.
   a. mass
   b. quality
   c. temperature
   d. pressure

CRITICAL THINKING

Use your understanding of the concepts developed in the chapter to answer each of the following questions.

1. Why do you think European explorers took one route to the Americas and a different route on the return voyage?
2. Study the figure shown. Where would you have to be to feel a breeze during the daytime? During the nighttime? Is this a global or local pattern?

Daytime

Nighttime

3. Jet airliners have pressurized cabins. This means that a constant air pressure is maintained. Why do you think this is so?
4. Holes in the ozone layer have been found near the poles. Why is this dangerous?
5. From what you have learned in this chapter, explain why windsurfers and hang gliders are usually found near the water's edge or shoreline.
6. Based on your understanding of the atmosphere, why do you think helium balloons float?

PROBLEM SOLVING

Read the following problem and discuss your answers in a brief paragraph.

Alicia and her friends are hiking in Rocky Mountain National Park. They are experienced hikers, but Alicia has never hiked at such a high altitude. They begin their hike at the base of a mountain. By noon, they are three kilometers higher. Alicia begins having trouble keeping up with the others. She feels weak and is gasping for air. She tells her friends that she cannot continue.

1. What do you think is happening to Alicia? Why?
2. What can she do to help herself?

CONNECTING IDEAS

Discuss each of the following in a brief paragraph.

1. Relate Newton's law of inertia to the movement of air.
2. Why do you think Denver, Colorado, banned wood-burning fireplaces?
3. Would you expect atmospheric pressure to be greater at the poles or at the equator? Why?
4. **A CLOSER LOOK** How are the Amazon rain forest, carbon dioxide, and global warming related?
5. **LIFE SCIENCE CONNECTION** What factors about a city and its location might make it an unhealthful place for people with breathing disorders?

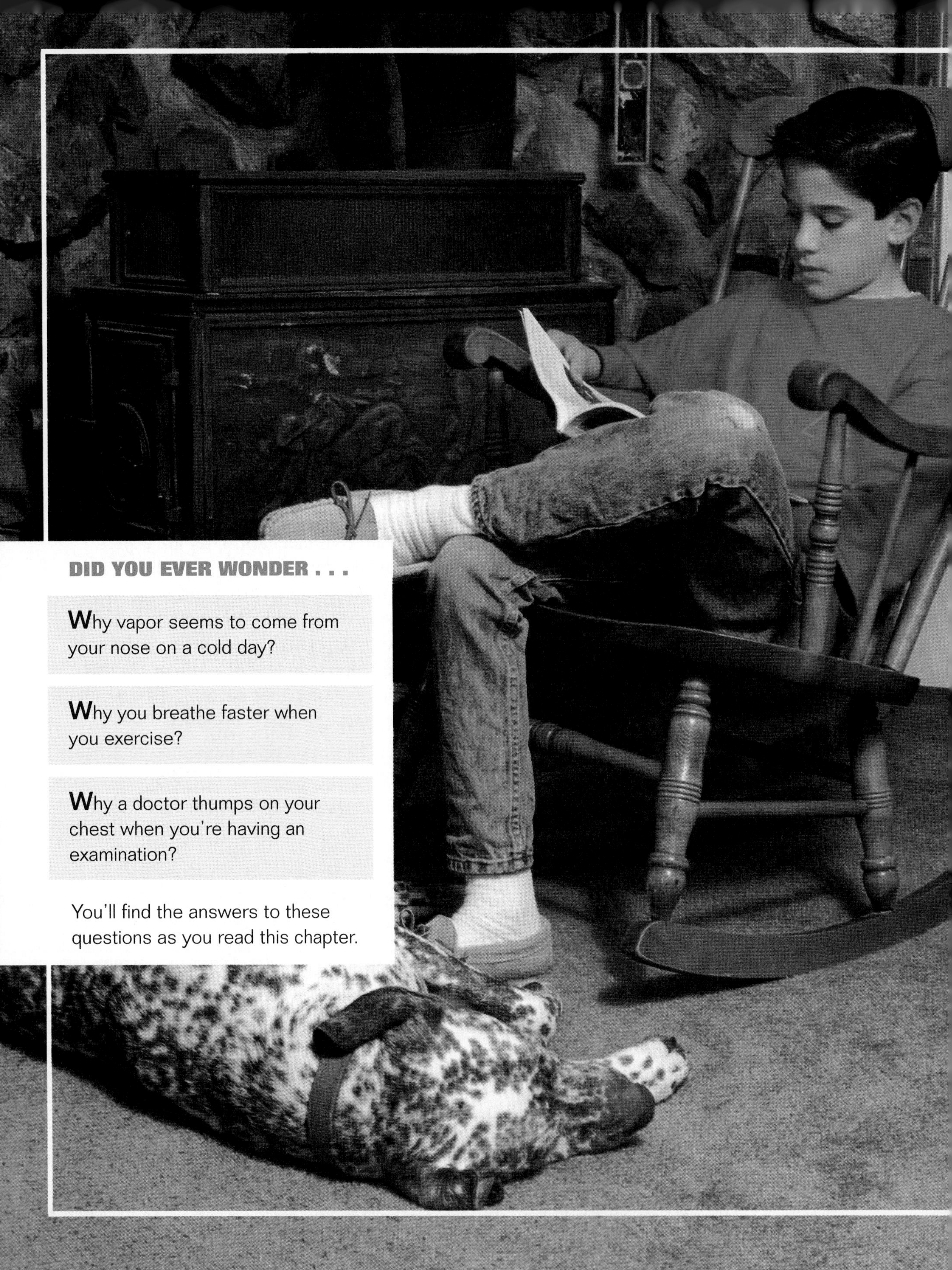

DID YOU EVER WONDER . . .

Why vapor seems to come from your nose on a cold day?

Why you breathe faster when you exercise?

Why a doctor thumps on your chest when you're having an examination?

You'll find the answers to these questions as you read this chapter.

Chapter 16

Breathing

It's a rainy day. You're relaxing by reading a magazine while your dog is asleep at your feet. As you finish a page, you become aware of a big sigh and the dog's rhythmic breathing. In and out, in and out, he breathes deeply and slowly. Occasionally, he even snores. You're aware of the dog's breathing, but he isn't. Come to think of it, most of the time you're probably not aware of your own breathing. You don't have to be. From the moment you're born until the moment you die, air enters and leaves your body automatically. You don't have to think about it. Breathing is actually one step in supplying your body with the oxygen it needs. In this chapter, you will discover how and why you and some of the organisms around you breathe. You'll also find out what happens to the air you breathe in. Where does it go? Finally, you will learn about some disorders of the respiratory system and how they may be prevented.

EXPLORE!

What happens when you breathe?

Put your hand on your chest. Notice your breathing. Feel your chest move up and down. Take a deep breath. Notice how your rib cage moves out and upward when you inhale. Count your breathing rate for one minute. How does your breathing rate compare with the rates of your classmates?

16-1 How Do You Breathe?

OBJECTIVES

In this section, you will

- compare how different organisms take in oxygen;
- trace the pathway of air into and out of the lungs;
- describe how air is inhaled and exhaled and the pressure changes that occur within the chest cavity.

KEY SCIENCE TERMS

trachea
gills
lungs
alveoli
diaphragm

HOW SOME ORGANISMS TAKE IN OXYGEN

If you compare the way you and the dog discussed on the previous page breathe, you'll find two very similar respiratory systems. However, while most organisms need oxygen, not all of them obtain it the same way. One-celled organisms, such as the paramecium in Figure 16-1(a), take in oxygen directly from their watery environment. Oxygen in the water diffuses into the body through the paramecium's thin outer covering. Carbon dioxide wastes move out through this covering and into the water.

Most complex organisms have specific body structures to take in oxygen and release carbon dioxide. For example, an earthworm moving through moist soil exchanges oxygen and carbon dioxide right through its skin. Amphibians also breathe through their skins. An insect has a more complex respiratory system. Unlike the paramecium and earthworm, oxygen doesn't diffuse

FIGURE 16-1. Oxygen enters a paramecium through its membrane (a), while oxygen and carbon dioxide diffuse through an earthworm's skin (b). The grasshopper has tracheae that carry air in and out of its body (c).

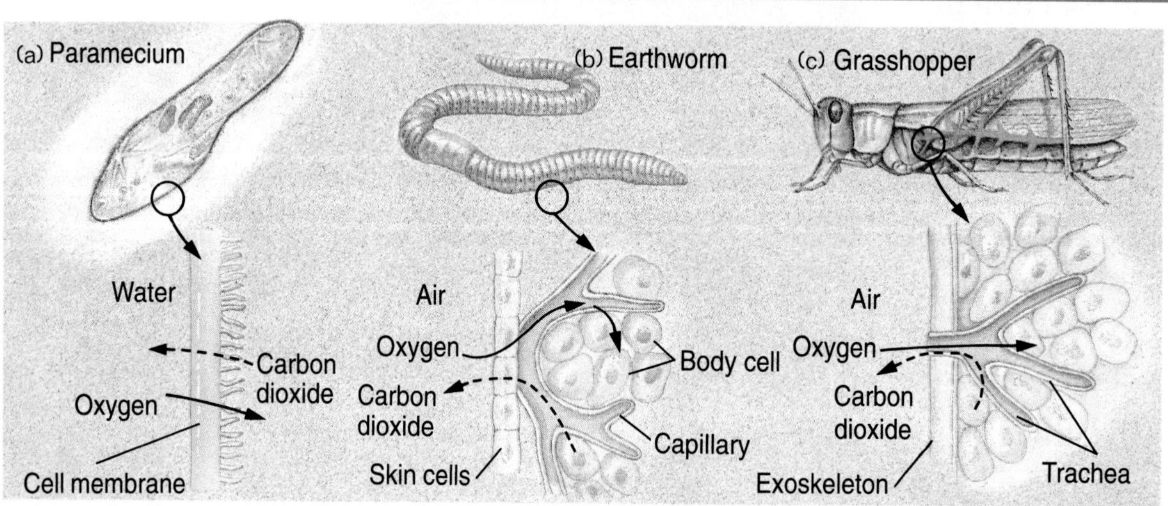

through an insect's outer body covering. Instead, oxygen enters an insect's body through tiny openings along its sides. Each opening connects to a tube called a trachea. The **trachea** is a passageway through which air travels into and out of the body. But not all complex organisms possess a trachea. In the next activity, you will explore how fish obtain oxygen.

EXPLORE!

What can you learn by watching a goldfish?

Observe goldfish in an aquarium. Watch the overall behavior of the fish for several minutes. Note any body parts that move. Which body parts moved while you watched the fish? Did any of the movements seem to be related to each other?

Fish have body structures that extract oxygen from the water. When you observed the goldfish in the last activity, you probably noticed the flaps on either side of its head. Beneath these flaps are gills. **Gills** are respiratory structures of some aquatic animals through which oxygen is removed from water. When a fish opens its mouth, water flows in at the same time as a cover, or

How do we know?

What makes air vital?

People have always taken for granted that air and food are needed for life. However, no one knew what it was about air that made it so vital. In 1771, a British chemist, Joseph Priestley, published the results of some experiments he did with air. He discovered that a mouse couldn't live in a container in which a candle had previously been burned. He reasoned that some substance in the air was destroyed when the candle burned. He also discovered that if he put a mint plant into the container for eight or nine days, and then returned a live mouse to the container, it lived. The substance necessary for life had returned. It was later to be called oxygen.

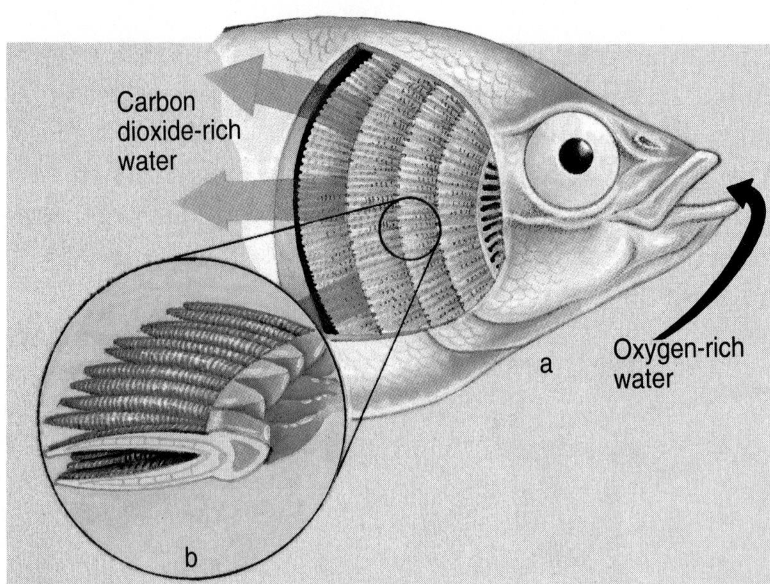

FIGURE 16-2. Water and oxygen enter the fish's mouth and pass over the gills, where oxygen diffuses into the capillaries. Water and carbon dioxide are then released (a). Gill filaments increase the surface area. As a result, more oxygen can diffuse into the capillaries (b).

flap, over the gills closes. When the mouth closes, the water moves through the mouth, over the gills, and out past the flap that is now opened. Figure 16-2 shows a fish's respiratory system.

Each gill is made of several spongy structures called gill filaments. Because the filaments are feathery in nature, they provide increased surface area for water to pass over. Tiny capillaries extend throughout each filament. When the water passes over the filaments, oxygen diffuses from the water into the fish's blood as it travels through the capillaries. This oxygen-rich blood is then delivered to all parts of the fish's body. At the same time, carbon dioxide moves from the capillaries of the gills out into the water. The water then flows out of the fish through the opened gill covers.

DID YOU KNOW?

Most fish breathe by means of gills. However, one type of fish, the lungfish from Australia, South America, and Africa, has the ability to breathe as you do, with its lungs, when water is scarce.

YOUR PATHWAY FOR AIR

Just like Priestley's mouse, you need oxygen for life. Your body has its own structures through which it receives oxygen and expels carbon dioxide wastes. These structures make up your respiratory system. The major parts of your respiratory system are shown in Figure 16-3.

Refer to this diagram as you follow the path of air from your nose to your lungs.

Air enters your body through two openings in your nose called nostrils. As the air moves into the nasal cavity behind the nostrils, your body heat raises the temperature of the air, and the moist tissues in the cavity raise the humidity. This warm, moist air then moves to the pharynx, a passageway at the back of your nose and mouth. Just below the pharynx is the larynx, or voice box. A protective flap of tissue, called the epiglottis, covers the top of the larynx. When you breathe, the epiglottis is open. When you swallow, the epiglottis closes so that food or liquid moves toward your esophagus and not toward your lungs. Why do you think it's important not to talk while eating?

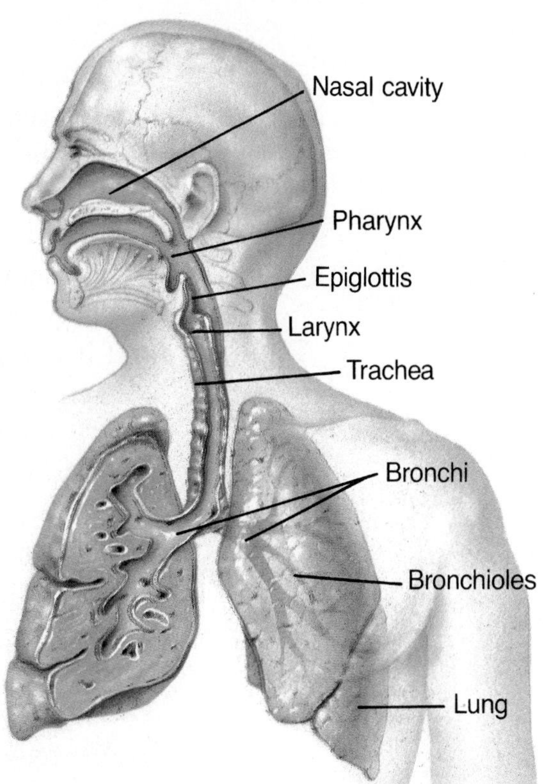

FIGURE 16-3. The Structures of the Human Respiratory System

EXPLORE!

What is your trachea like?

Feel the structure of your trachea by gently placing your fingers on the front of your neck. What do you feel? Turn your head from side to side and continue breathing. How does this structure help keep you alive? Now, gently cough while keeping your fingers on your neck. What happens when you cough? How might this action help keep you alive?

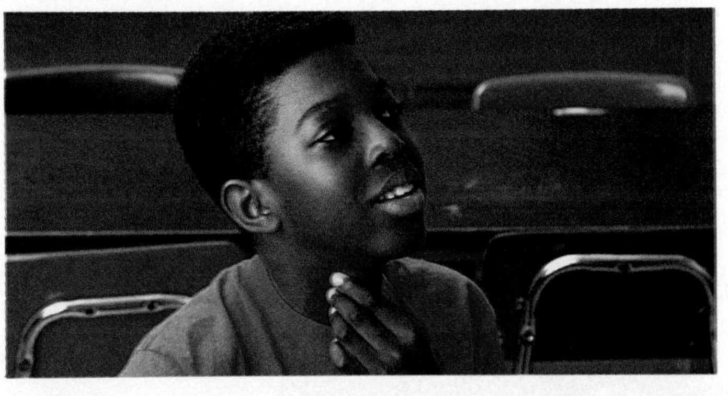

When you ran your fingers up and down your throat, you felt the top of your trachea. Remember an insect's

DID YOU KNOW?

When you cough, air can be forced out of the trachea at a speed of 160 meters per second.

trachea carries air in and out of its body. Your trachea is also a passageway for air moving into and out of your body. The rings you felt are C-shaped rings of cartilage that keep the trachea open. What advantage is there to having a trachea that is open all the time?

In Chapter 15, you learned that air is matter that takes up space. When you cough, you exert pressure on this air, and it is forced quickly out of your body. Have you ever choked on food or water? Sometimes food or water will accidentally go down the trachea. Coughing is your body's way of dislodging the food or water from this tube.

At the lower end of the trachea are two short branches called bronchial tubes through which air moves into the lungs. The **lungs**, which are located in the chest cavity, are the main organs of your respiratory system. Here in the lungs, the exchange of oxygen and carbon dioxide takes place.

Within your lungs, the bronchial tubes branch into increasingly smaller and smaller passageways. At the ends of the narrowest tubes are clusters of tiny thin-walled sacs called **alveoli**, which are shown in Figure 16-4. You can get an idea of what a mass of alveoli looks like if you imagine a tight cluster of grapes. Your lungs contain millions of alveoli that are surrounded by capillaries. Just as oxygen and carbon dioxide pass between the gills and capillaries in fish, the exchange of these gases takes place between the alveoli and capillaries in your body. Oxygen and carbon dioxide pass easily, or diffuse, through the thin walls of the alveoli. In addition, the large number of alveoli provides a huge surface area for gases to be exchanged.

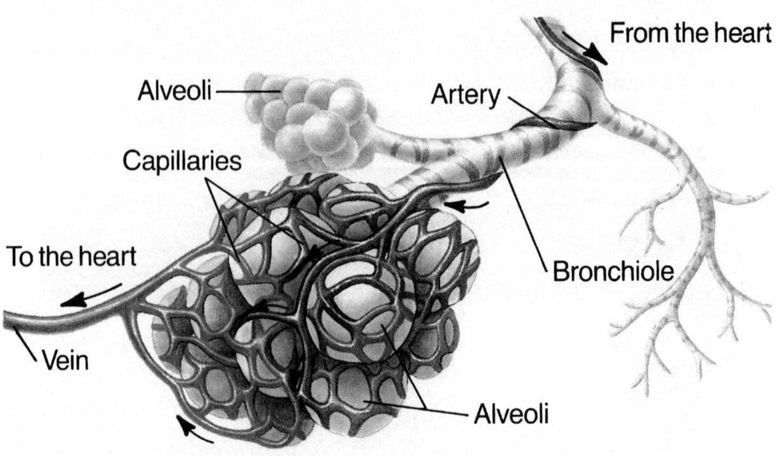

FIGURE 16-4. In the lungs, alveoli are surrounded by capillaries.

HOW AIR MOVES IN

You learned in Chapter 14 how gases act under certain conditions. Air is a mixture of gases. It follows the same laws in your lungs as it would in a laboratory. For example, you know that according to Boyle's law, if you decrease the volume of gas in a container, the pressure of the gas will increase. Under normal conditions, a gas moves from an area of high pressure to an area of low pressure. This can be demonstrated as air rushes out when you squeeze an empty plastic bottle, as is illustrated in Figure 16-5. This happens because pressure inside the bottle is greater than outside the bottle. As you release your grip, pressure inside the bottle drops below the pressure outside, and air rushes back in.

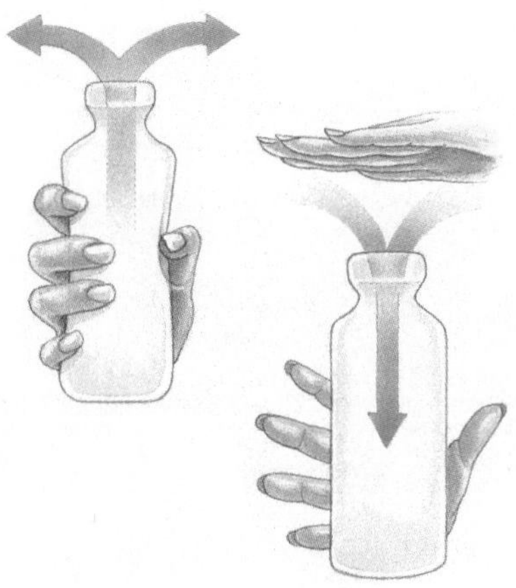

FIGURE 16-5. When the bottle is squeezed, pressure forces air out. When the bottle is released, pressure forces air back in.

EXPLORE!

How does your chest size change when you breathe?

Inhale and use a metric tape measure to find the size of your own chest. When measuring, place the tape around your chest and directly under your armpits. Then measure the size of your chest when you exhale. Compare the results. What do you think caused the differences in the measurements?

As you found out in the Explore activity, the size of your chest changes as air moves in and out of your lungs. Like hands on a plastic bottle, something in your chest cavity exerts pressure or relieves pressure on your lungs. These pressure changes are caused by your **diaphragm**, a thin sheet of muscle under your lungs.

When you inhale, your diaphragm contracts, causing it to flatten out and move lower in your chest. At the same time, your rib cage expands. The volume of your chest cavity is increased, and the pressure on your lungs is relieved. Air pressure outside your body is now greater than that inside your lungs, and air rushes in to fill them. The following investigation will show you how much air moves in and out of your lungs.

INVESTIGATE!

16-1 HOW CAN YOUR LUNG CAPACITY BE MEASURED?

Vital capacity is the largest amount of air your lungs expel after taking a deep breath. In this activity, you will find your vital capacity.

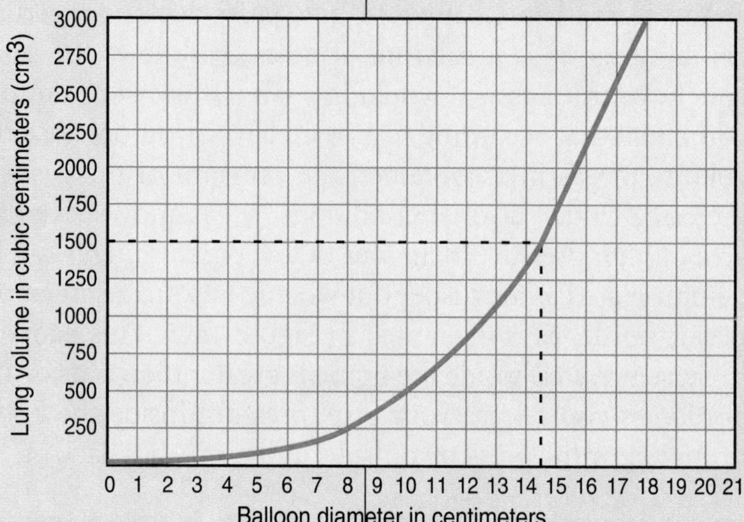

PROBLEM

What is your vital capacity?

MATERIALS

round balloon
metric ruler

PROCEDURE

1. Copy the data table.
2. Stretch a balloon several times. Take a deep breath. Exhale into the balloon only as much air as possible. **CAUTION:** *Do not force your breathing.* Pinch the balloon closed.
3. **Measure** the diameter of the balloon in centimeters as shown. Record the data.
4. Repeat Steps 2 and 3 four more times.
5. Lung capacity is expressed in cubic centimeters. To calculate lung capacity, find the balloon diameter on the horizontal axis of the graph. Follow this number up to the red line and move across to the corresponding capacity.
6. Record the capacity for each trial.
7. Calculate and record your average vital capacity.

DATA AND OBSERVATIONS

TRIAL	DIAMETER IN CENTIMETERS	VITAL CAPACITY IN CUBIC CENTIMETERS
1		
2		
3		
4		
5		
Total		
Average		

ANALYZE

1. Were there differences in the diameters of the balloon during the five trials?
2. How does your average **compare** with the averages of other class members?

CONCLUDE AND APPLY

3. How could you improve the accuracy of this activity?
4. Can you **infer** how this activity could be used to find people who might have a lung disease?
5. **Going Further:** Tidal volume is the amount of air that you exhale after drawing a normal breath. Design an experiment to find your tidal volume.

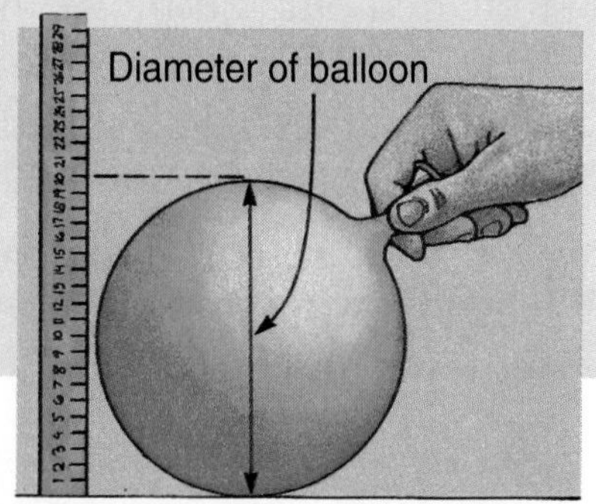

HOW AIR MOVES OUT

In the Investigate activity, you determined your vital lung capacity by measuring how much air you exhaled during a large breath. But what causes you to exhale during normal breathing? As shown in Figure 16-6, when you exhale, your diaphragm relaxes and moves upward. The muscles between your ribs also relax. These two actions reduce the size of your chest cavity and exert pressure on your lungs. Now the pressure inside the lungs is greater than the outside pressure. The increased pressure causes the gases in your lungs to be pushed out.

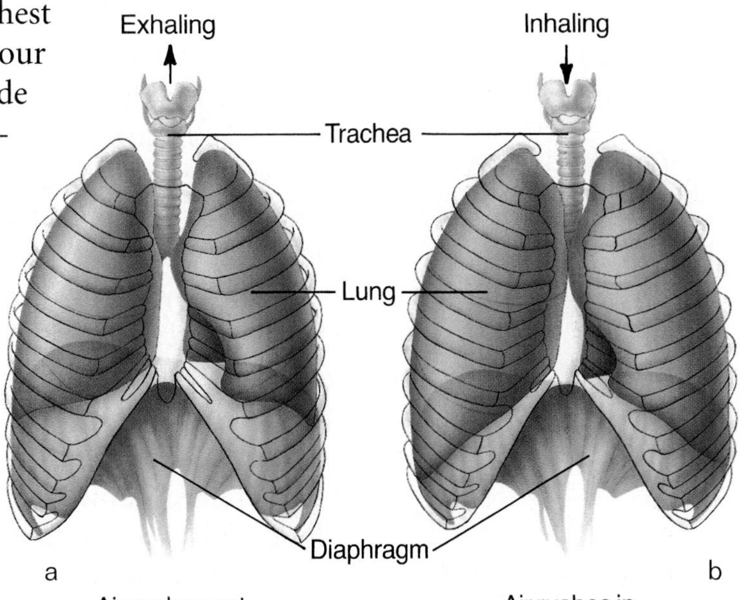

FIGURE 16-6. When you exhale (a), your diaphragm relaxes and pushes up on your lungs. When you inhale (b), your diaphragm contracts and lowers.

You found out how much air you normally exhale. During times of quiet activity, such as reading or doing homework, you might inhale up to 500 milliliters of air with every breath. When you exercise vigorously, you may inhale and exhale as much as 2000 milliliters of air per breath! Even when you exhale forcefully, a little air is always left in your lungs.

In this section, you learned the pathway air follows into your lungs. You also learned what causes you to inhale and exhale. In the next section, you will learn how the air you breathe in differs from the air you breathe out.

Check Your Understanding

1. Compare how a paramecium and a fish obtain oxygen.
2. Draw a diagram of the respiratory system indicating the direction of air flow in and out.
3. Explain how air pressure relates to inhalation and exhalation.
4. **APPLY:** Describe what occurs inside your chest cavity when you blow out the candles on a birthday cake.

16-2 The Air You Breathe

OBJECTIVES

In this section, you will

- compare air that is inhaled with air that is exhaled;
- explain respiration and the exchange of gases that takes place between your body and the environment.

KEY SCIENCE TERMS

hemoglobin
respiration

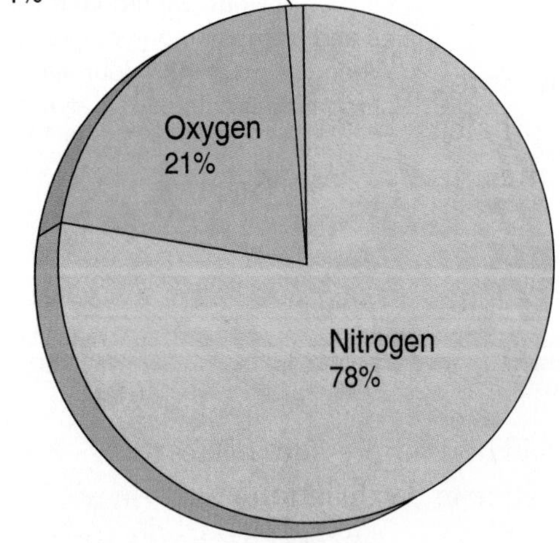

FIGURE 16-7. Air is a mixture of gases, with nitrogen and oxygen making up the largest percentage.

HOW OXYGEN GETS TO ALL PARTS OF YOUR BODY

Remember that in the last chapter you learned that Earth's atmosphere is a mixture of gases. As shown in Figure 16-7, nitrogen makes up about 78 percent of the atmosphere, and oxygen makes up about 21 percent. The remaining one percent is a combination of carbon dioxide, water vapor, and a few other gases. Because only 21 percent of the air you inhale is oxygen, your body needs to move a steady supply of air into and out of your lungs. You learned the path air travels into your lungs, but how does your body remove the oxygen it needs?

Your blood contains an oxygen-binding substance called **hemoglobin**. Hemoglobin is found in the red blood cells and contains iron, which easily bonds with oxygen. As blood moves through the capillaries around the alveoli, oxygen diffuses from the alveoli into the capillaries and then into the red blood cells. Once inside the red blood cells, oxygen binds with molecules of hemoglobin. After leaving the lungs, the oxygen-rich blood moves to the heart, which then pumps it to the rest of the body.

The hemoglobin and oxygen remain bonded as the red blood cells move through your body. As the blood passes body cells that have low amounts of oxygen, the oxygen in the red blood cells is released by the hemoglobin and diffuses from the red blood cells into individual body cells. At the same time, carbon dioxide wastes diffuse from the body cells into the blood. About 30 percent of the carbon dioxide attaches itself to passing hemoglobin. The rest travels back to your lungs in plasma, the watery substance in blood. Once the blood is back in the lungs, the carbon dioxide diffuses from the plasma and red blood cells into the alveoli. Your lungs release this waste gas from your body whenever you exhale.

In the following activity, you will learn that other things are released with the air you exhale.

FIND OUT!

What other gas do you exhale?
Use a towel to wipe off your hands. Hold the palm of your hand up to your mouth and exhale into it. Feel the palm with your other hand. Then hold a mirror up to your mouth and breathe onto it. Observe what happens to the mirror.

Conclude and Apply

1. How did your hand feel after you breathed into it?
2. What did you see on the mirror?
3. What other gas is released from your body when you exhale?

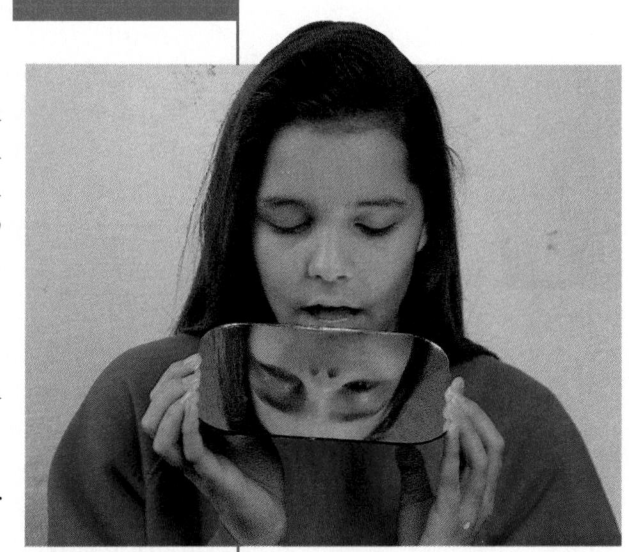

COMPARING AIR INHALED WITH AIR EXHALED

Remember that only about 21 percent of the air you breathe in is oxygen. Carbon dioxide makes up less than 1 percent of air in the atmosphere. As air moves through the respiratory system, its chemical composition changes.

You discovered in the Find Out activity that water vapor is one gas that is evident when you exhale. Where does this water vapor come from? Tissues lining the respiratory system are very moist. When you inhale atmospheric air, it is immediately exposed to these moist tissues, and it becomes more humid. But the amount of water vapor in this air is not the only thing to change when you breathe. The amount of carbon dioxide and oxygen gases changes as well.

FIGURE 16-8. Oxygen easily bonds to molecules of hemoglobin within red blood cells.

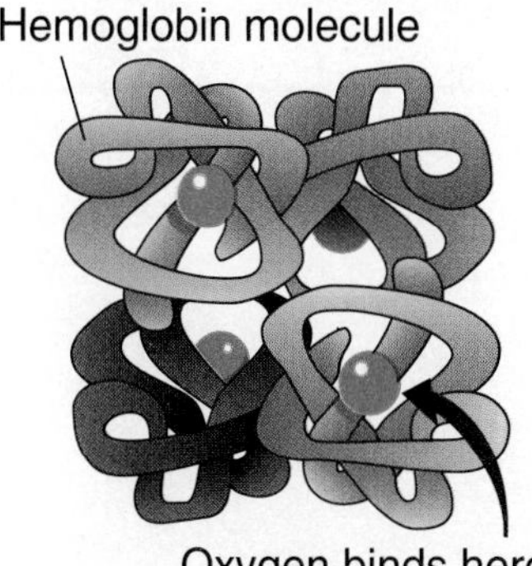

TABLE 16-1. Composition of Air

Gas	Atmospheric Air	Inhaled Air	Exhaled Air
Nitrogen	78.62%	74.1%	74.5%
Oxygen	20.84%	19.7%	15.7%
Carbon dioxide	.04%	.04%	3.6%
Water vapor	.50%	6.2%	6.2%

Table 16-1 shows the difference in the composition of the air you inhale and exhale. As you can see, air you inhale has more oxygen than air you exhale. It has less carbon dioxide and water vapor. What happens to cause this change in composition?

RESPIRATION

Think about what is needed before machines can run, lamps can be turned on, or microwave ovens can cook. Doesn't energy have to be available for all of these objects to work? Just as machines need energy to run, your body needs energy to operate. Your body gets this energy from a chemical reaction that happens within its individual cells. This process is called respiration. During **respiration**, oxygen combines with stored nutrients in cells to release energy, carbon dioxide, and water. The function of your respiratory system is to continuously supply the oxygen and remove the carbon dioxide produced in this process.

The rate of respiration varies with the types of activities that you do. Do you think reading and sleeping require the same amounts of energy as walking or swimming? Increased physical activity causes your cells to break down stored nutrients at a greater rate. Does this mean that the volume of waste products also increases? You'll explore this question in the following Investigate activity.

FIGURE 16-9. Your rate of respiration depends on the type of activity you are doing.

INVESTIGATE!

16-2 WHAT EFFECT DOES EXERCISE HAVE ON RESPIRATION?

You may have noticed that when you exercise or play a sport, your breathing rate increases. Is the amount of carbon dioxide you exhale related to your body's level of activity?

PROBLEM

How does exercise affect the amount of carbon dioxide exhaled by the lungs?

MATERIALS 

clock or watch with second hand
2 drinking straws
200 mL bromothymol blue solution
2 400-mL beakers
graduated cylinder

PROCEDURE

1. Copy the data table.
2. **Predict** how exercise will affect the amount of carbon dioxide exhaled by the lungs.
3. Label beaker A and beaker B. Pour 100 mL bromothymol blue solution into each of the beakers. Bromothymol blue will first turn green and will then turn yellow as carbon dioxide is added to it.
4. Record the starting time. Exhale through a straw into the bromothymol blue solution in beaker A. **CAUTION:** *Do not inhale through the straw.* Continue exhaling until the bromothymol blue solution changes to the color green. Record the time it takes for the color change to occur. Set beaker A aside.
5. Run in place for three minutes.
6. Repeat Step 4 with beaker B. Stop when the color in beaker B matches the color in beaker A.
7. **Compare** your data with the data of your classmates.

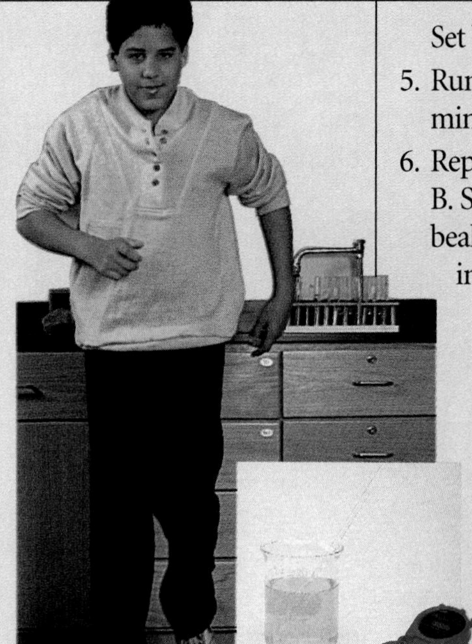

DATA AND OBSERVATIONS

BEAKER	TIME
Beaker A	
Beaker B	

ANALYZE

1. **Infer** what caused the bromothymol blue to change color?
2. **Compare** the time it took the bromothymol blue solution to change color before exercising and after exercising. Explain any difference.
3. What was the control in this experiment?

CONCLUDE AND APPLY

4. How does exercise affect the amount of carbon dioxide exhaled?
5. Why does exercising cause you to breathe faster than usual?
6. **Going Further:** Design an experiment to see if a person's height is related to the amount of carbon dioxide exhaled. Use the same materials as in this experiment.

You know that when you exercise you use up energy at a faster rate. Your body cells use more oxygen to release the energy. As a result, they produce more carbon dioxide. Didn't you find that you exhaled more carbon dioxide after exercising? You'll find that your breathing becomes more rapid and deep to supply the added oxygen. Eventually, as you rest, your breathing rate returns to its before-exercise rate. Chemically, the rate of use of oxygen by your cells has also slowed down.

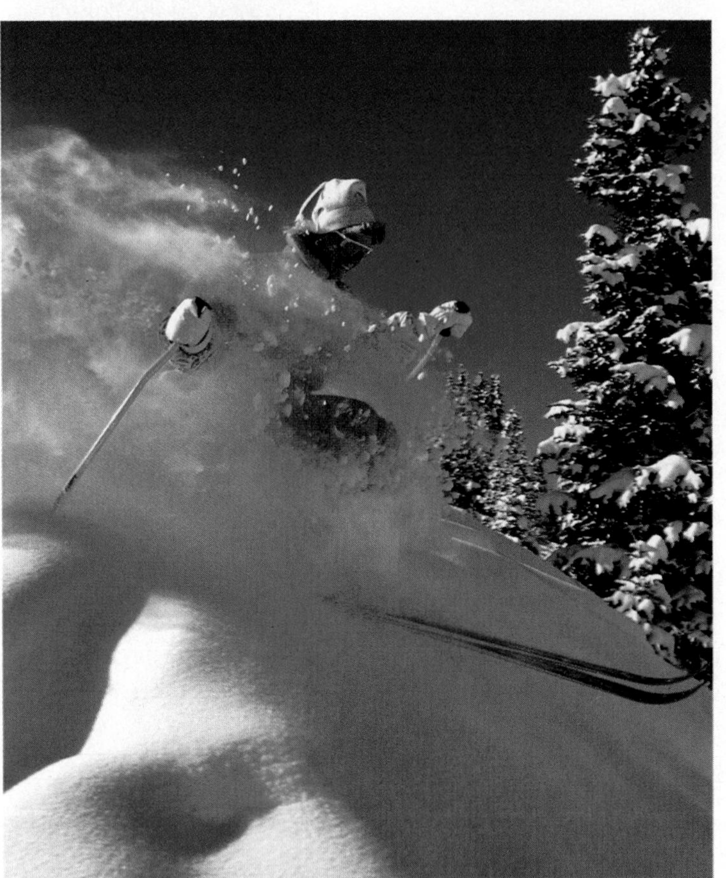

FIGURE 16-10. The respiratory system works efficiently when air is fresh and clean.

In this section, you discovered how two body systems, the respiratory and circulatory systems, work together to transport oxygen and carbon dioxide throughout your body. You have also learned about the process of respiration and why it must occur for you to stay alive. Your respiratory system is very efficient, especially when you have clean, fresh air to breathe. What happens if the air is not so fresh and clean? What if a disease prevents the efficient transfer of oxygen to your lungs and body cells? In the next section, you will learn how these problems affect your respiratory system.

Check Your Understanding

1. How does the air you inhale differ from the air you exhale?
2. What role does hemoglobin play in the transfer of oxygen between your lungs and body cells?
3. Why is the amount of water vapor higher in air you exhale than in air you inhale?
4. **APPLY:** Explain why both your heart rate and breathing rate increase with exercise.

16-3 Disorders of the Respiratory System

OBJECTIVES

In this section, you will

- discuss respiratory disorders and their causes;
- determine how to keep your lungs healthy.

KEY SCIENCE TERMS

cilia

asthma

emphysema

lung cancer

LUNG DISEASE

As you learned, air is a mixture of gases, but it also contains particles of dirt, pollen, dust, and smoke. These pollutants can damage your respiratory system and interrupt the flow of oxygen to your body's cells. Every year thousands of people in the United States die from diseases related to smoking and air pollution.

Your body has some defenses against the particles that mix with the different gases in air. When you inhale, these particles become stuck in a moist lining in the trachea and lungs. This lining is covered with tiny hairlike structures called **cilia**, shown in Figure 16-11. Cilia beat in an upward direction, causing a current that carries the particles to the throat, where they are swallowed and disposed of by acid in the stomach. What do you think happens if your cilia stop working?

When inhaled air contains large amounts of dust, pollen, smoke, or smog particles, cilia lining the respiratory system can be affected. Smoke from cigarettes, for example, temporarily paralyzes cilia, preventing them from performing their sweeping jobs. Particles not swept out by cilia usually reach the alveoli, where they are engulfed by white blood cells. White blood cells help prevent infections by consuming both dirt and bacteria. However, some substances such as asbestos, a material used for insulation, can't be consumed by white blood cells, and the substance remains in the lungs. In the following activity, you can determine how a classmate's lungs sound.

FIGURE 16-11. Cilia help trap and move foreign matter.

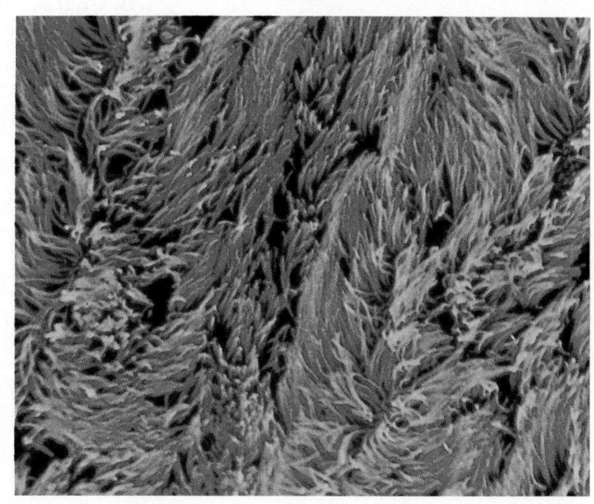

EXPLORE!

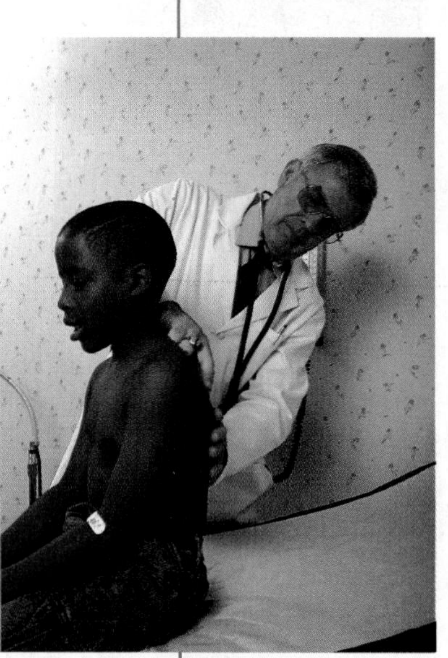

What is percussing?

Have you ever gone to a doctor and had him or her thump on your back? This is called percussing. A doctor can tell whether a body part is solid or air filled by percussing. Put one hand flat on your partner's back. Tap the third finger of that hand with the three middle fingers of your other hand. Healthy lungs should make a clear, hollow sound. Pneumonia patients have fluid around their lungs. How can percussing help a doctor diagnose if a patient's lungs are healthy or filled with fluid?

Did you ever see a person who was having a difficult time breathing? That person may have been having an asthma attack. **Asthma** is a disorder of the lungs in which there may be shortness of breath, wheezing, or coughing. When a person has an asthma attack, the bronchial tubes become constricted very quickly. As a result, the flow of air to the lungs is reduced. Asthma is often an allergic reaction. An attack can be caused by breathing certain substances such as plant pollen. Stress and eating certain foods also have been related to the onset of asthma attacks.

Smoking has been shown to cause severe damage to lungs. One disease that is closely linked with smoking is emphysema. **Emphysema** is a disease that occurs when air passageways or alveoli lose their ability to expand and contract. When a person has emphysema, air becomes trapped in the alveoli. Eventually the alveoli stretch and rupture. As a result, the overall surface area of the lungs is decreased. The lungs become scarred, and less oxygen moves into the bloodstream. The amount of oxygen carried by the blood decreases while the amount of carbon dioxide increases, resulting in a shortness of breath. Some people affected with emphysema can't blow out a match

DID YOU KNOW?

Tobacco was first introduced into Europe by Christopher Columbus, who found it growing on the islands he discovered when he sailed to the New World.

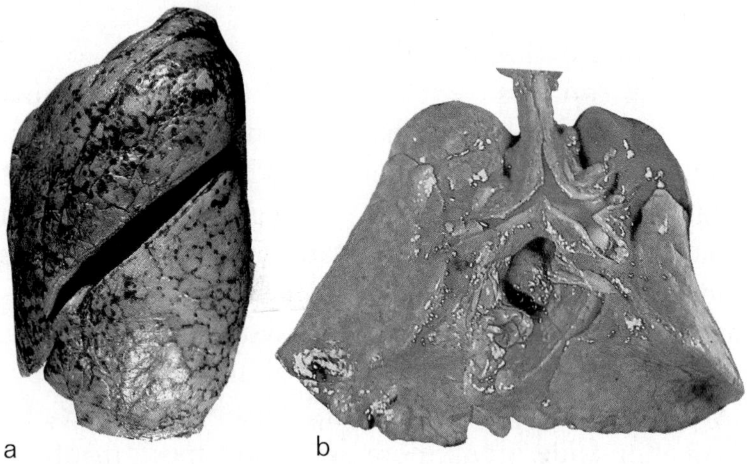

FIGURE 16-12. A diseased lung (a) cuts down on the amount of oxygen that can be delivered to body cells. A normal, healthy lung (b) can exchange oxygen and carbon dioxide effectively.

or walk up a flight of stairs. Because the heart works harder to supply oxygen to body cells, people who have emphysema often develop heart problems as well.

If you were asked which cancer caused the most deaths among men and women in the United States, would you know that the answer is lung cancer? When cilia are damaged, the lungs lose a defense against disease and **lung cancer** can develop. Inhaling the tar in cigarette smoke is the greatest contributing factor to lung cancer. Tar is a black, sticky substance that builds up on the linings of the

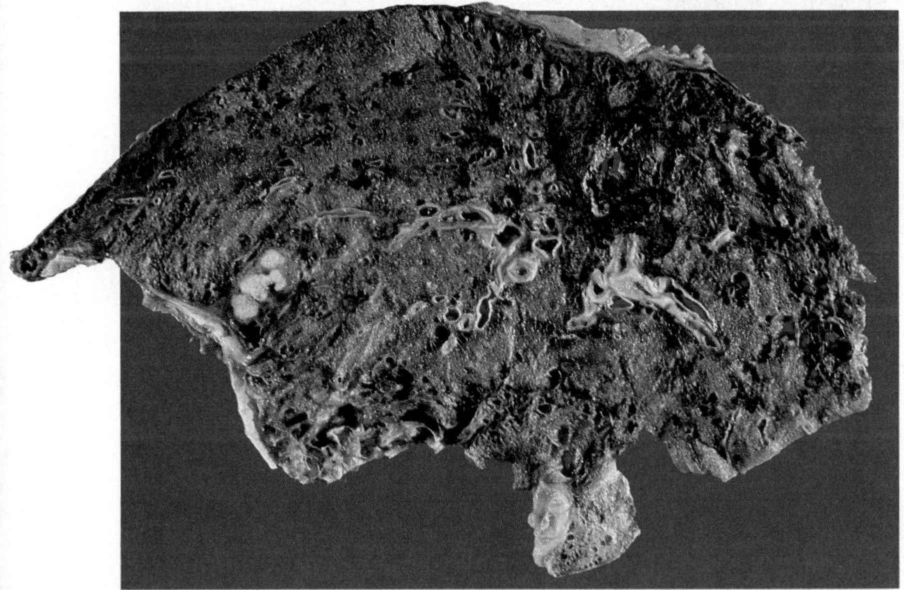

FIGURE 16-13. Lung cancer, which has been linked to smoking, can disrupt the functioning of the cilia.

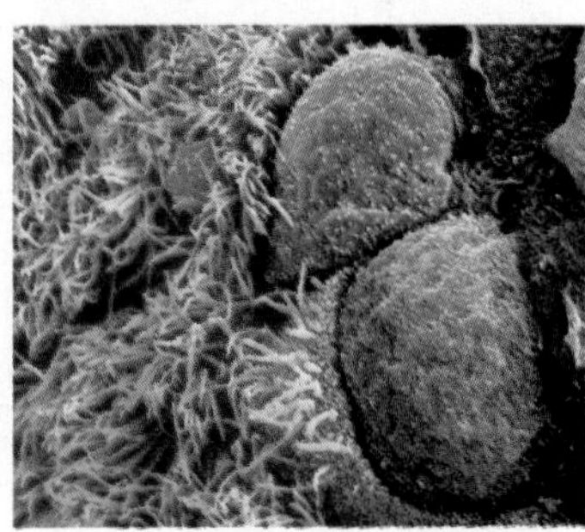

SKILLBUILDER

DETERMINING CAUSE AND EFFECT

Volcanoes produce massive amounts of ash, dust, and gases, such as carbon dioxide, when they erupt. Infer what would happen in your body if you were near a volcano that had erupted and the carbon dioxide level of the surrounding air had risen sharply. If you need help, refer to the **Skill Handbook** on page 683.

smoker's mouth, throat, and lungs.

While tar contains compounds that are known to cause cancer, it's not the only harmful substance found in cigarette smoke. Carbon monoxide is another poisonous substance found in the smoke. You might be familiar with the name of this compound, because it's one of the gases found in the exhaust of cars. When a smoker inhales, carbon monoxide enters the respiratory system. Here this poisonous substance interferes with the ability of hemoglobin to carry oxygen to the body's cells. This happens because carbon monoxide binds more easily and more firmly to hemoglobin than oxygen bonds. Thus, the smoker's body cells receive less oxygen than they need. This puts a great strain on the smoker's heart. Cigarette smoking damages the circulatory system as well as the respiratory system.

Cigarette smoking is not the only contributor to respiratory disease. It is also known that people living in crowded, urban areas suffer from higher rates of respiratory disease than people who live in the country. Can you see how urban living might contribute to respiratory disease?

FIGURE 16-14. X rays can help doctors identify respiratory diseases.

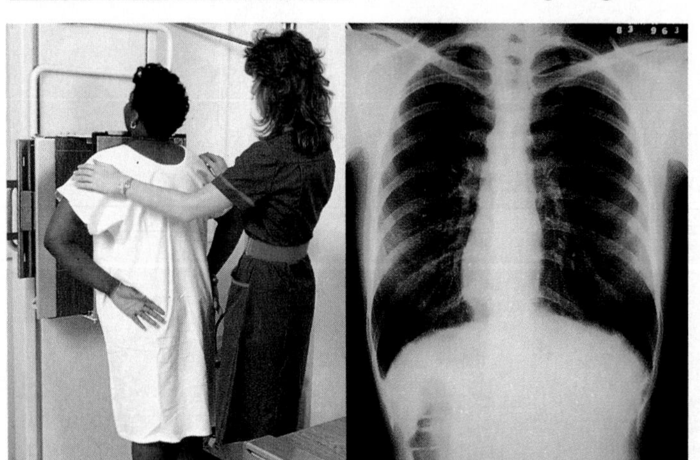

So far as is known, except for certain bacteria, all living things would die without oxygen. Your respiratory system takes in oxygen and gets rid of carbon dioxide. You can keep your respiratory system healthy by avoiding smoking and polluted air. Also, regular exercise helps you increase your body's ability to use oxygen. This makes your breathing more efficient.

Check Your Understanding

1. What two diseases of the respiratory system are linked to smoking?
2. What happens during an asthma attack?
3. How does the quality of air affect respiration?
4. **APPLY:** Why are people with respiratory disorders warned to stay indoors during days of high air pollution or pollen counts?

EXPANDING YOUR VIEW

CONTENTS

A Closer Look
Unusual Breathers 487

Physics Connection
Your Larynx 488

Science and Society
Lifesaving Techniques 489

Technology Connection
Garret A. Morgan:
Gas Mask Inventor 490

Health Connection
Plants—
Natural Air Purifiers 491

History Connection
Keeping a Nation Healthy 492

A CLOSER LOOK

UNUSUAL BREATHERS

Human beings and many other animals obtain oxygen through breathing with lungs. Have you ever explored some of the ways that animals get the oxygen they need to sustain life? Consider a few of nature's many examples.

A grasshopper has pairs of small openings called spiracles that lead to thousands of tracheal tubes. Through the spiracles, air travels into the tracheal tubes, then to all cells of the grasshopper's body. By using muscles to squeeze its abdomen, the grasshopper forces air out of the tracheal tubes. When it relaxes these muscles, air enters again, repeating the breathing process.

Mosquito larvae, also known as wrigglers, live in pools of water. Wrigglers swim near the top of the water and poke tiny protruding tubes through to the air. Air enters these tubes and moves to tracheal tubes throughout their bodies. Other marine animals have spiracles on the ends of sharp spines that they use to pierce underwater leaves for the oxygen trapped in the leaves.

Beetles carry extra oxygen in large bubbles within their thick hairs. When beetles are

underwater, oxygen passes from these bubbles to the tracheal tubes leading to all parts of their bodies. The oxygen bubbles also give them added buoyancy for traveling up to the water's surface.

Spiders and scorpions have book lungs connected to tracheal tubes. Book lungs look a lot like gills, and they work in a similar way, removing oxygen from air instead of water. Book lungs are a series of thin "plates" full of blood vessels that catch and carry oxygen throughout the animal's body. The European water spider carries bubbles of air within its book lungs to bell-shaped webs that it builds under water. It uses these webs to store oxygen for future use.

YOU TRY IT!

Imagine that you are writing a science fiction novel about a creature with an unusual way of getting oxygen. Write a description of what this animal looks like and exactly how it breathes.

Physics Connection

YOUR LARYNX

What kinds of sounds can you make with your voice? You may be able to sing or to imitate the sound of a door creaking, a dog growling, or a bass drum booming. You may have noticed that when you get excited, the pitch of your voice goes up or that when you're depressed, the pitch goes down. Your larynx makes a wide range of sounds possible.

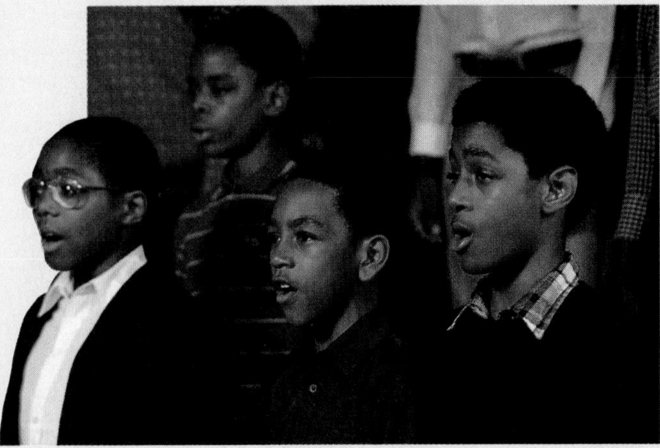

When you speak or sing, air pushed up by your diaphragm vibrates your vocal cords to produce sound. Muscles in your throat control the length and shape of the cords. Loose, relaxed vocal cords produce a low sound. Tightened, stretched cords make higher pitches.

Try building a model of the vocal cords. Find a metal, plastic, or cardboard tube one inch in diameter. Find a rubber stopper for one end of this tube, fitted with a smaller glass or metal tube through its center. Connect this smaller tube to an air pump. A foot pump, like the one you might use to inflate a bike tire, would be a good choice. Cut two pieces of rubber from toy balloons. Stretch these pieces across opposite sides of the open end of the tube, securing them with tape or rubber bands. Rubber bands may be better, as they will allow you to make alterations more easily. Be sure to leave plenty of width in the pieces of rubber for further alteration.

As you pump air through the tube, the rubber sheets should vibrate—producing sound. Loosen or tighten the sheets as you wish. Looser sheets should produce a low pitch. Tighter sheets, with the rubber pieces stretched thinner, will produce a higher pitch.

If you have easy access to the materials, construct more than one of these models. You may be able to combine different sounds, or even to play a tune, alternating use of the models or by sounding them at the same times.

YOU TRY IT!

See if you can match the pitch of your own speaking or singing voice with that of your model vocal cords. Also, take note of the effects of different quantities of air on the pitches and volumes of sounds from the model.

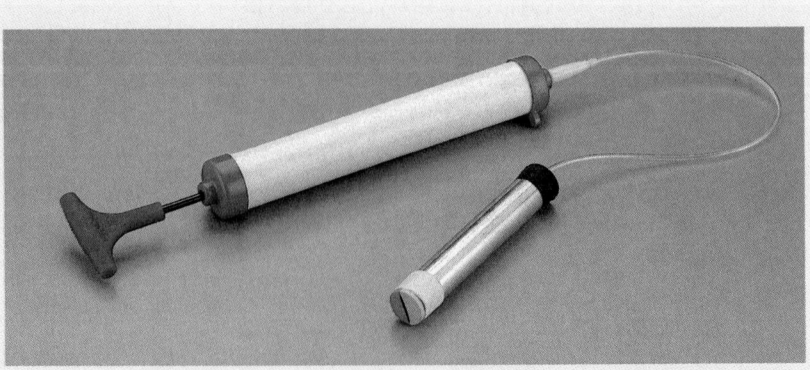

SCIENCE AND SOCIETY

LIFESAVING TECHNIQUES

If you were near someone who had stopped breathing, what would you do? What if that person were choking on a piece of food? What can be done for a victim of a heart attack, drowning, or an automobile accident if that person has stopped breathing?

Knowledge of basic techniques of resuscitation can be a valuable tool for you and the people you care about. While a technique known as artificial respiration, pictured here, was popular a number of years ago and is still useful in some cases, newer techniques such as cardiopulmonary resuscitation (CPR) and the Heimlich maneuver may be more useful in certain circumstances. A rescuer must act quickly in order to save a person's life. If a person is deprived of oxygen for even a few minutes, there may be permanent damage to the brain and other organs.

When it is apparent that a person is choking on a piece of food and cannot take a breath, the Heimlich maneuver is very fast and effective. In this technique, you would stand behind the person with your arms stretched out in front of them. Make a fist with one hand and cup the other hand over the fist. Place this two-handed fist at the top of the V formed where the ribs meet at the breastbone. Pull your fist sharply up and in. This action forces air upward and helps dislodge the piece of food. Continue this action, making sure that you quickly pull and release, until the food is dislodged and the person is breathing freely.

When both the heartbeat and breathing have stopped due to a heart attack or accident, a trained person can often help by using CPR. This technique combines forcing air into the person's lungs by blowing through their nose and mouth with alternating pressure on the heart area of the chest. Training sessions on CPR and other lifesaving techniques are offered through the local Red Cross and through schools. A number of lives could be saved if more people were trained in the proper use of these techniques.

YOU TRY IT!

In teams of three, practice the Heimlich maneuver. One person should play the victim, the second should perform the technique, and the third should observe and make suggestions. Switch so that everyone gets a chance to practice. It is not necessary to exert a great deal of pressure as you practice. The victim will be able to feel the air escape.

Note: Other lifesaving techniques should not be practiced without training. Contact your local Red Cross for information on classes.

TECHNOLOGY CONNECTION

GARRETT A. MORGAN: GAS MASK INVENTOR

African-American inventor Garrett A. Morgan (1877–1963) developed "The Safety Hood" in 1912—the predecessor of the gas mask. A patent was granted to Morgan in 1914 for a device consisting of a hood placed over the head of the user. A tube from the hood featured an inlet opening for air, with the tube long enough to enter a layer of air underneath dense smoke or gas. The tube could be placed beyond the reach of gas fumes and dust, and through it pure air could be furnished to the user. The lower end of the tube was lined with an absorbent material, such as a sponge, that was moistened with water before use. This lining prevented smoke and dust from penetrating the tube and cooled the outside air entering the tube. A separate tube contained a valve for exhaled air.

The original intent of Morgan's invention was to allow fire fighters to enter fires without suffocating from smoke and gases. Morgan had an opportunity to personally prove the value of his invention following a tunnel explosion in the Cleveland, Ohio, Waterworks. Morgan, his brother, and two volunteers saved several men trapped in the smoke and gas-filled tunnel under Lake Erie from almost certain asphyxiation. The men entered the burning tunnel wearing Safety Hoods and carried the trapped workers to safety. After 1914, many fire departments across the country were using the Morgan Safety Hood to save lives and property.

During World War I, Morgan's Safety Hood was improved and used as a gas mask by the United States Army. Thousands of lives were saved during this war thanks to Garrett Morgan's invention.

YOU TRY IT!

Research the type of "gas masks" used by fire fighters today in resource books at the library. Write a report on how fire fighters' respiration equipment has changed since the time of Morgan's Safety Hood.

Health CONNECTION

PLANTS—NATURAL AIR PURIFIERS

If you think that those plants sitting around in the living room, the kitchen, and the doctor's office are just taking up space and gathering dust, think again. Scientists are finding that houseplants are surprisingly useful in absorbing potentially harmful gases and cleaning the air inside buildings.

In studying ways to keep air pure in space stations, environmental specialists at the National Aeronautics and Space Administration (NASA) have found that many common houseplants reduce the amounts of formaldehyde, benzene, carbon monoxide, and nitrous oxide—all poisonous gases—in indoor air.

We have known for years that plants, as part of their growth mechanism, remove carbon dioxide from the air and give off oxygen and water vapor. Now scientists are finding that plants also take in other harmful gases through tiny openings on the leaves and return purified oxygen and vapor. Efforts to plant trees are often prompted by the knowledge that they help reduce pollutants and provide more oxygen to the atmosphere.

Although plants can't completely clean a room polluted by smoke and dirt, they can help keep a room's air fresher. Adding plants to your indoor world, as well as to the outdoor world, can make those worlds healthier places to be.

WHAT DO YOU THINK?

Observe the places you visit in the course of your day. Do the rooms where there are plants seem fresher and smell better? Do you have plants in rooms in your home? Can you tell a difference between the rooms with the plants and the rooms without plants? What factors might affect whether or not there is an observable difference?

History CONNECTION

KEEPING A NATION HEALTHY

Health problems come from many sources, such as contaminated food or water supplies. Some behaviors encourage ill health, too, as has been shown with smoking and the abuse of drugs and alcohol. What does an entire country do to protect the health of its people?

In the United States, the Public Health Service, a division of the Department of Health and Human Services, works to provide services that maintain health, treat illness, and devise methods to prevent the spread of disease. To accomplish these goals, the Public Health Service works on many fronts. It provides educational programs and funding for research. It also provides suggestions for improved health-care delivery systems, and protection of consumers against unsafe food, drugs, and cosmetics.

Within the Public Health Service, the spokesperson for the nation's health is the surgeon general. Most people are familiar with the surgeon general through the health warnings that appear on cigarette packages. The office of surgeon general came into being by an act of Congress in 1870. Its original purpose was to oversee the health care of American sailors. Over time, the duties of the office have expanded beyond the health of sailors so that now the surgeon general has become the advisor and spokesperson for anything that affects the health of anyone in the nation.

In 1990, the first woman and first Hispanic surgeon general was appointed by President Bush. She is Dr. Antonia Novello. Dr. Novello was born in Puerto Rico. She received her MD from the University of Puerto Rico in 1970 and has specialized in pediatrics with an emphasis on nephrology. Dr. Novello has been on the staff of several large hospitals in the United States and has directed research projects dealing with kidney diseases in children. As surgeon general, Dr. Novello has spoken out against advertising that entices children to smoke, but she is

also interested in pursuing other health risks that affect children, such as underage drinking and AIDS, as well as the health problems of all Americans.

WHAT DO YOU THINK?

Pretend you are a doctor and have a job at the public health office in your home town. You become aware of a pollution site that is a health threat to the people of the area. Explain how you would go about helping to make people aware of this problem. Whom would you contact? What services would you use?

Chapter 16

Reviewing Main Ideas

1. Most living things have specialized body parts that help organisms obtain the oxygen they need to live.

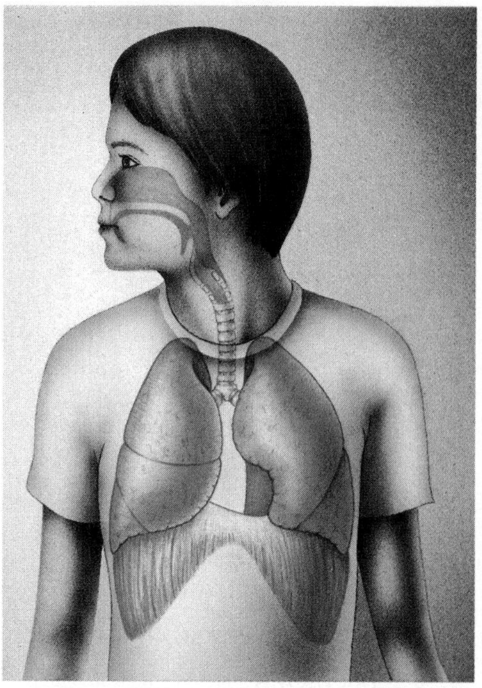

2. The lungs are the main organ of your respiratory system. An exchange of gases occurs in the lungs.

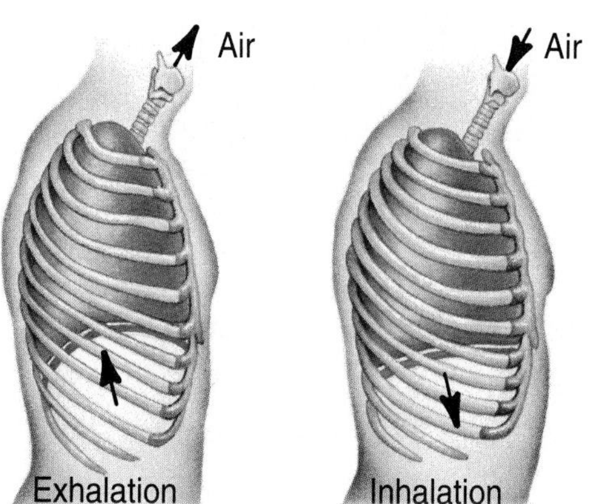

3. Changes in the position of the diaphragm and size of the chest cavity cause differences in the amount of air pressure inside the lungs and outside the body.

4. Respiration occurs in the body's cells when oxygen combines with food to release energy and produce carbon dioxide and water.

Word Formula
Oxygen
+
Food
↓
Energy
+
Carbon dioxide
+
Water

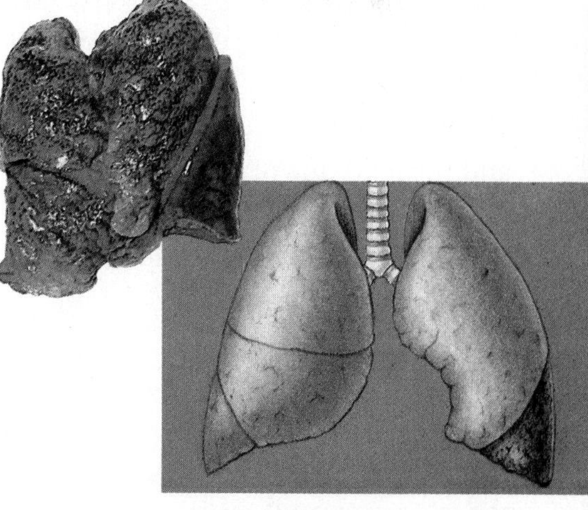

5. Lung diseases and disorders reduce the amount of oxygen that can be transported to the body's cells, thereby affecting the rate of respiration in cells.

Chapter Review

USING KEY SCIENCE TERMS

alveoli	hemoglobin
asthma	lung cancer
diaphragm	lungs
emphysema	respiration
gills	trachea

For each set of terms below, choose the one that does not belong and explain why it does not belong.

1. gills, alveoli, diaphragm, trachea
2. asthma, respiration, emphysema, lung cancer
3. gills, lungs, hemoglobin
4. lung cancer, asthma, emphysema
5. alveoli, diaphragm, trachea

UNDERSTANDING IDEAS

Choose the best answer to complete each sentence.

1. When you inhale, your ____ contract(s) and move(s) down.
   a. bronchioles **c.** alveoli
   b. diaphragm **d.** lungs
2. Air is first moistened, filtered, and warmed in the ____.
   a. larynx **c.** nasal cavity
   b. pharynx **d.** trachea
3. Exchange of gases occurs between the ____ and capillaries.
   a. alveoli **c.** bronchioles
   b. bronchi **d.** none of these

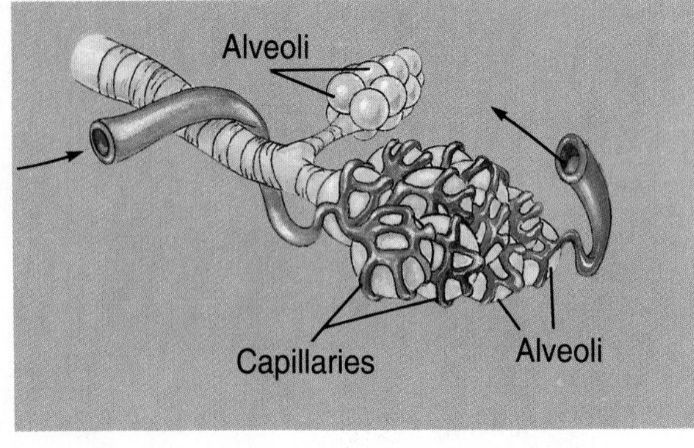

4. The rib cage ____ when you exhale.
   a. moves up **c.** moves out
   b. moves down **d.** none of these
5. ____ is a lung disorder that may occur as an allergic reaction.
   a. Asthma **c.** Emphysema
   b. Lung cancer **d.** All of these
6. A condition worsened by smoking is ____.
   a. asthma **c.** emphysema
   b. lung cancer **d.** any of these
7. The ____ blocks food from entering the larynx.
   a. pharynx **c.** epiglottis
   b. trachea **d.** alveoli
8. ____ and ____ are waste products of respiration.
   a. Carbon dioxide, oxygen
   b. Oxygen, nitrogen
   c. Oxygen, water
   d. Carbon dioxide, water
9. Your trachea is made of ____.
   a. bone **c.** cartilage
   b. blood **d.** none of these

CRITICAL THINKING

Use your understanding of the concepts developed in the chapter to answer each of the following questions.

1. Explain where the air pressure is greater, inside the chest cavity or outside the body, when you inhale and when you exhale.
2. Why is it an advantage to have cilia in your respiratory system?

3. What is the advantage of the lungs having many masses of air sacs instead of two large sacs?

PROBLEM SOLVING

Read the following problem and discuss your answers in a brief paragraph.

People who are physically active have a larger lung capacity than those who are less active. The largest possible amount of air which can be exhaled after drawing a deep breath is called the vital capacity. A relationship exists between a person's height and vital capacity. The average adult male's vital capacity is 5000 cm^3 while that of an adult female is 4000 cm^3.

1. To find your calculated vital capacity, multiply your height (in centimeters) by one of the following factors:
   20 for females 22 for female athletes
   25 for males 29 for male athletes
2. How does your calculated vital capacity compare with the average adult of your same sex? What could account for any differences in the figures?
3. Explain how exercise can increase one's vital capacity.
4. How can information about vital capacity be used to evaluate physical fitness?

CONNECTING IDEAS

Discuss each of the following in a brief paragraph.

1. What happens to your breathing rate when you sleep? Why?
2. People trapped in fires often die of smoke inhalation rather than from burns. How is smoke inhalation fatal?
3. **PHYSICS CONNECTION** Briefly describe how the larynx produces low and high sounds.
4. **SCIENCE AND SOCIETY** When someone chokes on a piece of food, you can grab the person around the waist from behind and squeeze hard under the rib cage. This action, called the Heimlich maneuver, often dislodges the food. What features of the respiratory system does this take advantage of?
5. **A CLOSER LOOK** How is a grasshopper's respiratory system different from yours? How is it similar?

LOOKING BACK

UNIT 4 AIR: MOLECULES IN MOTION

CONTENTS

Chapter 14 Gases, Atoms, and Molecules

Chapter 15 The Air Around You

Chapter 16 Breathing

UNIT FOCUS

In this unit, you investigated how the structure of an element's atoms determines how the element is classified and how it reacts with other elements to form molecules, such as the gases in Earth's atmosphere.

You also saw that your respiratory system interacts with the gases in Earth's atmosphere by taking in oxygen when you breathe in and releasing carbon dioxide when you breathe out. The oxygen taken into your body during respiration is very important because it allows cells to carry on life processes.

Try the exercises and activity that follow—they will challenge you to use and apply some of the ideas you learned in this unit.

CONNECTING IDEAS

1. The surface area of the palm of your hand is about 15 square inches. Air pressure is about 15 pounds per square inch. Calculate the amount of air pressure on your hand. Explain why you do not feel this pressure on your hand.
2. What are the most common gases in Earth's atmosphere? Which of these does the human body use? Describe several examples of how human activities affect the concentration of gases in Earth's atmosphere. How do you think human respiration might change if Earth's atmosphere were all oxygen?

EXPLORING FURTHER

Draw a diagram of the respiratory system. Use an arrow to show where cold air is heated before it reaches the lungs. What method of heat transfer is involved? Describe the process that enables your lungs to take in gases from the atmosphere. How is this related to the process that causes winds to occur?

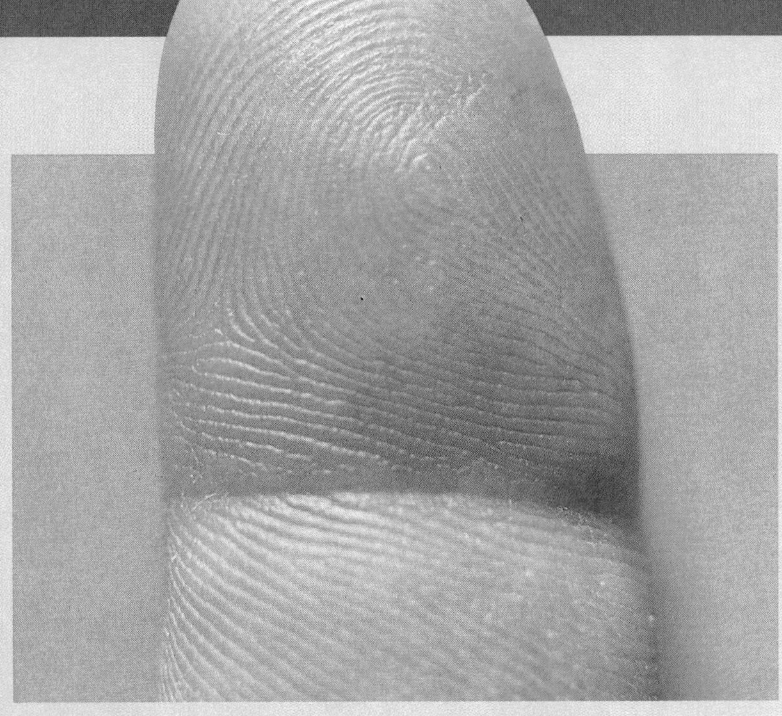

UNIT 5 LIFE AT THE CELLULAR LEVEL

CONTENTS

Chapter 17 Mirrors and Lenses
Chapter 18 Basic Units of Life
Chapter 19 Chemical Reactions
Chapter 20 How Cells Do Their Jobs
Chapter 21 Simple Organisms

UNIT FOCUS

In Unit 4, you learned that the oxygen taken into your body during respiration is used by cells to carry out life processes. As you study Unit 5, you'll use lenses in microscopes to observe the workings of the cell. You will learn about the chemical reactions that take place within the cell. You will realize how chemical reactions in nature enable life functions to go on.

TRY IT

What does the skin on your finger look like? Hold your index finger about six inches in front of your face and draw what you see on a sheet of paper. Now place your finger under a hand lens. Magnify the image of your finger as much as the hand lens will allow. What do you see? Can you see any flakes of skin? What do you notice about the lines and rings that make up your fingerprint? If you rub your hands back and forth quickly over a dark sheet of paper, you may see some dead flakes of skin that fall off. Make a wet mount slide using the flakes. Look at the slide under a microscope and describe what you see. After you've learned more about cells, try this activity again and see if you can observe any more detail on your finger or the flakes of skin that fall from it.

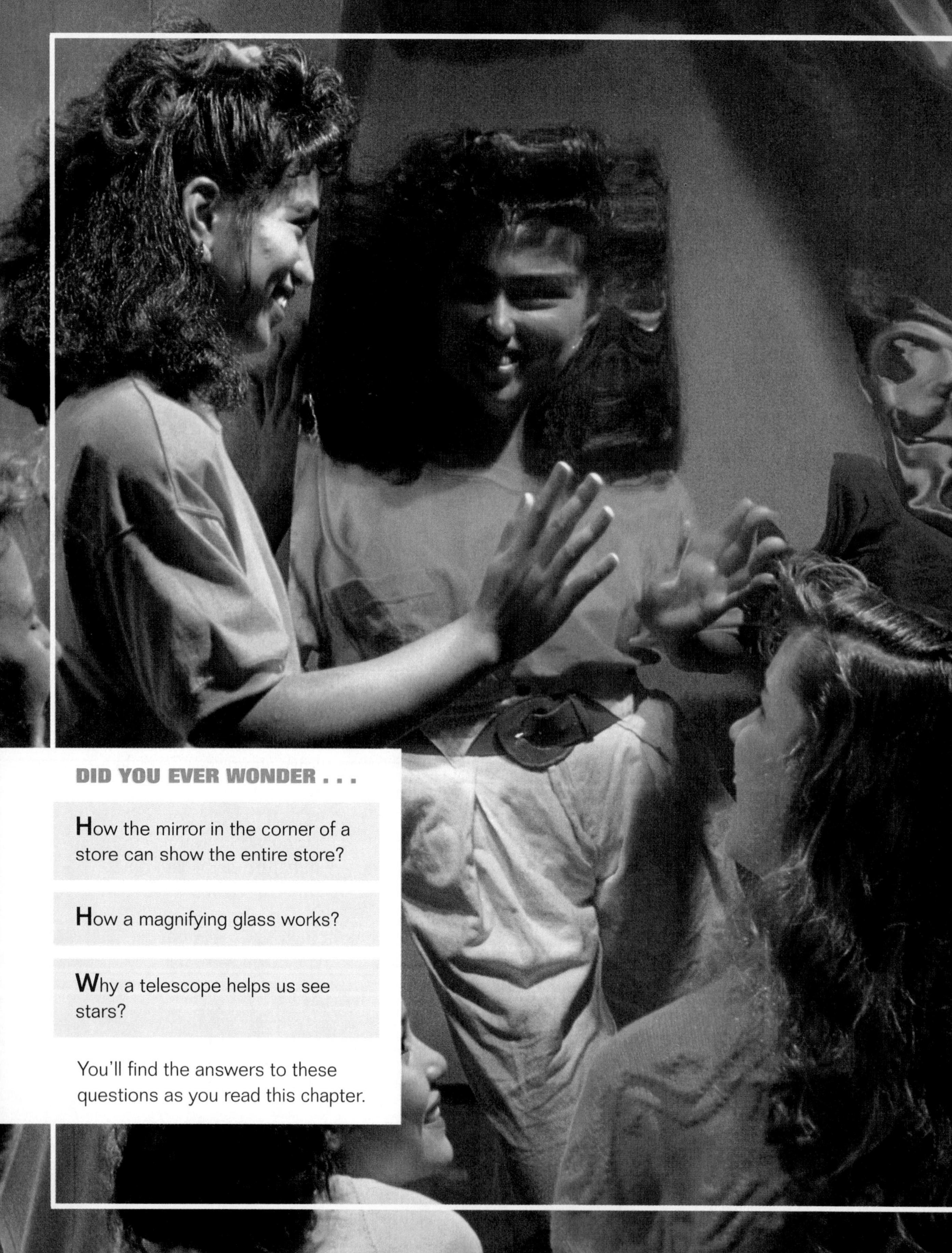

DID YOU EVER WONDER . . .

How the mirror in the corner of a store can show the entire store?

How a magnifying glass works?

Why a telescope helps us see stars?

You'll find the answers to these questions as you read this chapter.

Chapter 17

Mirrors and Lenses

Perhaps you've heard people say "It's all done with mirrors" and wondered what the sentence meant. If you've ever walked through a carnival fun house, you probably can guess the meaning.

What would happen if the mirror over your bathroom sink were curved like the mirror in the fun house? Your morning routine would turn into a real adventure! Yet curved mirrors are useful. They help us see beyond Earth to the stars.

Mirrors are not the only objects that help us see. Lenses help to magnify objects too small or too far away for our eyes to see and recognize.

This chapter explores how mirrors and lenses produce images and how mirrors and lenses can help us to see small or distant objects.

EXPLORE!

How do mirrors change your reflection?

Look at your reflection in a flat mirror. How does the size of your reflection compare with the size of your face? Is your reflection right side up? What happens as you move the mirror closer to your face? Farther away?

Now look at your reflection in the back of the spoon. Move the spoon close to your face, then far away. What change do you see as you move the spoon away from you?

Look into the bowl of the spoon. Move the spoon close to your face and then far away. Which side of the spoon is most like the fun house mirror?

17-1 Reflection of Light

OBJECTIVES

In this section, you will

- describe a plane mirror;
- explain the law of reflection.

KEY SCIENCE TERMS

plane mirror

MIRROR ЯOЯЯIM

Think back to this morning when you looked into the mirror as you brushed your teeth and combed your hair. You're familiar with the image you see in the bathroom mirror. As you placed the comb in your hair, the image placed the comb in its hair. As you checked for toothpaste on your chin, the image had toothpaste on its chin too. The mirror gave you a relatively realistic image. It wasn't particularly funny or odd-shaped like the image in a fun house mirror. The following Explore activity will help you describe the image you see in a plane mirror.

EXPLORE!

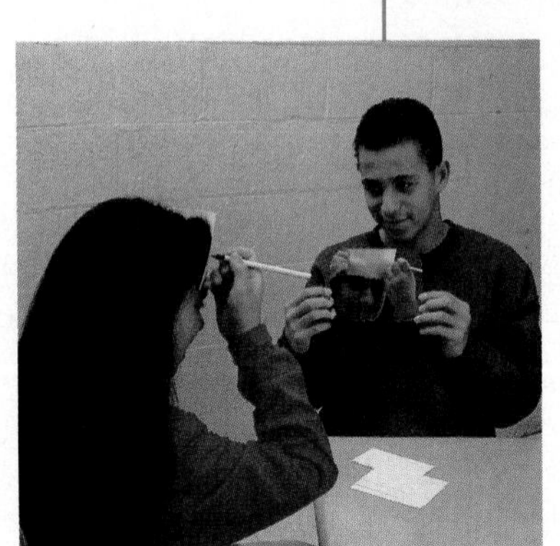

How do you look in a mirror?

Have a partner hold a mirror so you can see your face in it. Hold an index card to your forehead, as shown in the illustration. While looking in the mirror, write your name on the card.

After you're finished writing your name, remove the card from your forehead and look directly at the card. What do you observe about your writing? Describe the reflection you saw in the mirror.

What did you observe about yourself and the image in the mirror? If you stand in front of a mirror and snap the fingers of your right hand, your reflection seems to snap the fingers on its left hand. As you look into the mirror, the left and right sides of the reflection appear to be the reverse of your own left and right sides.

In a plane mirror, the left-to-right order of the original object is reversed in the image. A **plane mirror** is a flat piece of glass with a metallic coating on one side. The reflection image is upright and the same size as the original object.

In the first Explore, you saw that your reflection was reversed. You've probably noticed that windows, calm water, and shiny automobiles are some of the many objects that will produce reflections that are reversed. But what, exactly, do these objects do to light that results in the reflections and images? How does light act as it strikes the water or the shiny car?

FIGURE 17-1. You already know that you can see reflections in a variety of surfaces.

MIRROR MODEL

Because it's sometimes difficult to directly observe how light behaves, we often use a model to describe light's behavior. In the following activity, you will observe a bouncing ball. Later, you will form a model of reflected light that will help explain how a plane mirror works.

FIND OUT!

How does light behave?

Take a basketball or volleyball to your gymnasium or an outdoor area. Form teams of three students. The first student should bounce the ball, using no spin, toward the second student. The third student should observe the path of the ball as it bounces. Notice the angle the ball makes with the ground as it hits the ground and as the ball bounces or is reflected toward the second student. The student receiving the ball should observe the path of the ball as it is thrown, as it bounces, and as it travels toward him or her.

Throw the ball several times. The thrower and the receiver should stand close together for some trials, far apart for others. For each trial, describe the angles the

SKILLBUILDER

OBSERVING AND INFERRING

On the hood of an emergency vehicle, you notice the following lettering: ƎƆИAJUBMA. Why do you suppose this is done? If you need help, refer to the **Skill Handbook** on page 682.

ball makes as it bounces. Take turns at each position. Each of you should draw several diagrams showing your observations of the path of the ball as it moved toward the surface and then moved away from the surface. Pool your team's observations.

Conclude and Apply

1. For each throw, how does the angle at which the ball strikes the ground compare to the angle at which the ball leaves the ground?
2. What generalization can your team make about how the ball is reflected from a smooth surface?

Your observations and generalizations about the angles made by the bouncing ball are probably similar to the observations shown in Figure 17-2. If the ball was thrown toward the floor at an angle, it bounced off the floor or the ground at the same angle. Three examples of this are shown in Figure 17-2(a), (b), and (c). For each angle, small or large, the angle at which the ball left the surface was the same as the angle at which the ball approached the surface. If the ball were thrown straight onto the surface, it would bounce straight back, as shown in Figure 17-2(d).

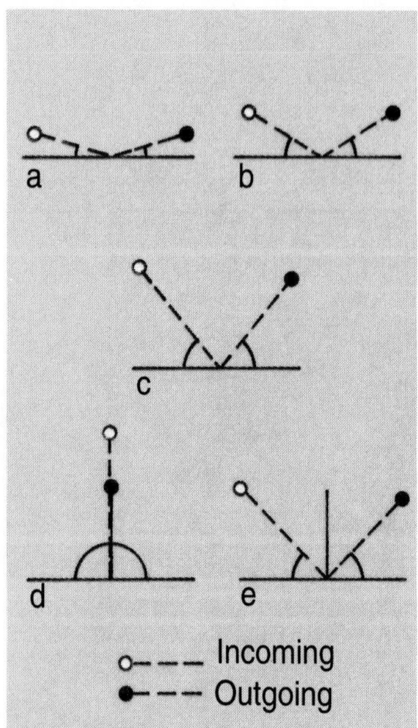

FIGURE 17-2. The angle at which the ball approaches the surface is equivalent to the angle at which the ball leaves the surface.

There is another important observation to be made. Imagine a glass wall along the path of the ball extending from the point at which the ball was thrown, to the spot where the ball bounced, and continuing to the receiver. This is shown in Figure 17-2(e). You may recognize this path as a plane. You probably observed that the ball traveled in the same plane before, during, and after it bounced.

From your earlier science studies, you may recall that reflection occurs if light strikes a surface and bounces off. Suppose you could diagram what happens as light strikes a surface, as you did with the ball. How do you think this would help you describe how light bounces and reflects?

To diagram what happens as light strikes a surface, you can represent the light with a ray. A ray is a straight line that represents the path of a very narrow beam of light. As you work through the next activity, you will see that reflected light acts very much like the bounced ball.

INVESTIGATE!

17-1 ANGLES OF REFLECTION

Light as it reflects from a plane mirror can be compared to the behavior of a bouncing ball.

PROBLEM

How does the angle of the incoming light compare to the angle of reflected light?

MATERIALS

flashlight
scissors
lump of clay
metric ruler
unlined paper
masking tape
small plane mirror
protractor
black construction paper

PROCEDURE

1. Copy the data table.
2. To make a narrow beam of light, first make a 5-mm slit in the black paper. Tape it over the flashlight lens so that the slit is in the center of the lens.

DATA AND OBSERVATIONS Sample data

MEASURE OF INCOMING ANGLE	MEASURE OF REFLECTED ANGLE
0°	
30°	
60°	

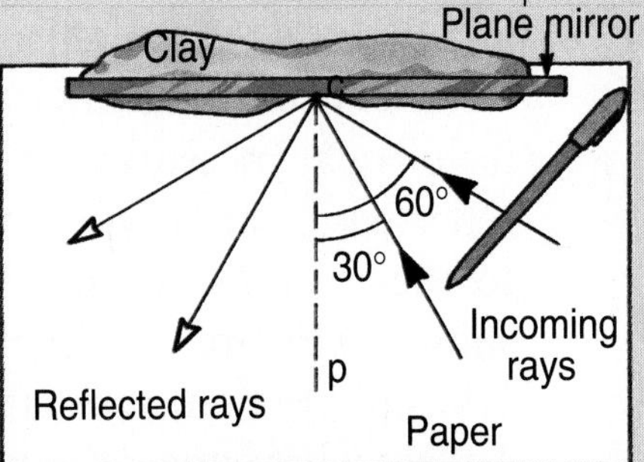

3. Place the clay at one end of the unlined paper. Push the mirror into the clay so that the mirror stands up.
4. Find the center of the bottom edge of the mirror. Mark the center by pressing the scissors into the clay. Label the center *C*.
5. Draw a line perpendicular to the mirror at *C*. Label this line *p*.
6. Draw a line that starts at *C* and forms an angle with the edge of the mirror that measures 30°. Draw a second angle with the mirror's edge measuring 60°. Label the angles.
7. Place the lighted flashlight on the line *p*. Find the measures of the angle of incoming light and the angle of the reflected light. Record the values in your table.
8. **Predict** the angle of the reflected light when the flashlight is placed on the 30° line. Make a prediction about the reflection angle when the flashlight is placed on the 60° line.
9. Place the flashlight so that the incoming light makes an angle with the mirror measuring 30°.
10. Mark the angle of reflection. Measure and record the angle.
11. Repeat Steps 9 and 10 for an incoming angle measuring 60° and for two other incoming angles.

ANALYZE

1. When light was directed along line *p*, where was the reflected ray?
2. How do the angles of the incoming light compare with the angle measures of the reflected light?

CONCLUDE AND APPLY

3. How does your prediction **compare** with your observations?
4. How did the bouncing ball model help you **interpret** the behavior of light?
5. **Going Further:** Use your diagrams to show that these rays are in the same plane as a line drawn perpendicular to the mirror's surface?

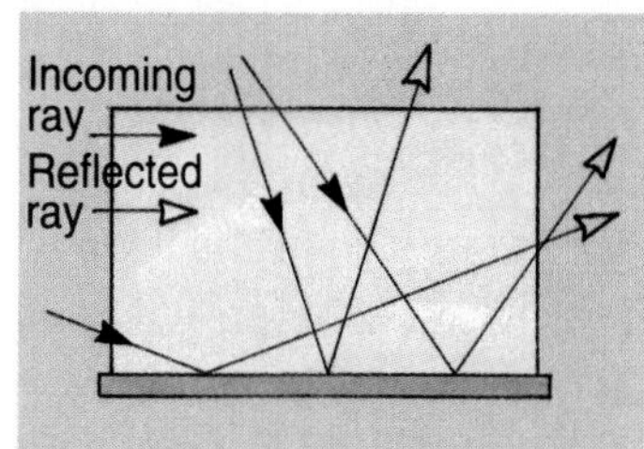

FIGURE 17-3. The incoming and reflected light rays form angles of equal measure with the reflecting surface

Your observations in the Investigate showed that there was a relationship between the angle of the incoming rays and the angle of the reflected rays. First, if light is reflected from a surface, the angles of incoming and reflected rays have equal measures. Second, the incoming ray and the reflected ray are in the same plane as a line perpendicular to the mirror's surface. Together, these two conditions, shown in Figure 17-3, make up the law of reflection.

In this section, you used a bouncing ball as a model to explain what happens as light reaches a plane mirror and is reflected from it. Most of the mirrors you use are plane mirrors. You are probably most familiar with mirrors that help you see if your hair looks the way you want it to. However, you use mirrors for other things as well. How does a car's rear-view mirror help you see? At some driveways, there are mirrors to help you see around corners. Can you use a diagram to explain how these mirrors work? In the next section, you will work with images formed by light as it is reflected by curved mirrors, such as those often seen in a carnival fun house.

FIGURE 17-4. How could a mirror help these two students see each other?

Check Your Understanding

1. Describe a plane mirror.
2. If light is reflected, how are the incoming angle, the reflected angle, and the perpendicular line to the surface related?
3. **APPLY:** Draw a diagram to show how a mirror can help the people in Figure 17-4 see each other.

17-2 Curved Mirrors

CAPTURING IMAGES

Remember the mirror in the fun house? It curved both inward and outward. The images of the student were distorted—larger than life in some places and smaller than life in others. How, you might ask, are these oddly shaped images formed?

OBJECTIVES

In this section, you will

- describe concave and convex mirrors;
- distinguish between a real and virtual image;
- identify the type of image produced by a concave and a convex mirror.

KEY SCIENCE TERMS

concave mirror
real image
focal point
convex mirror
virtual image

FIND OUT!

What happens as light strikes a mirror that curves inward?

Use a very shiny spoon or a mirror that curves inward for this activity. Hold the spoon near a bright light so that the light reflects from the bowl of the spoon toward an index card, as shown in the figure. Move the card back and forth a few centimeters, while looking for the image. What do you notice about the bright spot, or image, on the card?

When the image is clearest, measure the distance from the card to the mirror. Observe what happens if the distance between the index card and the spoon is less than or greater than this distance.

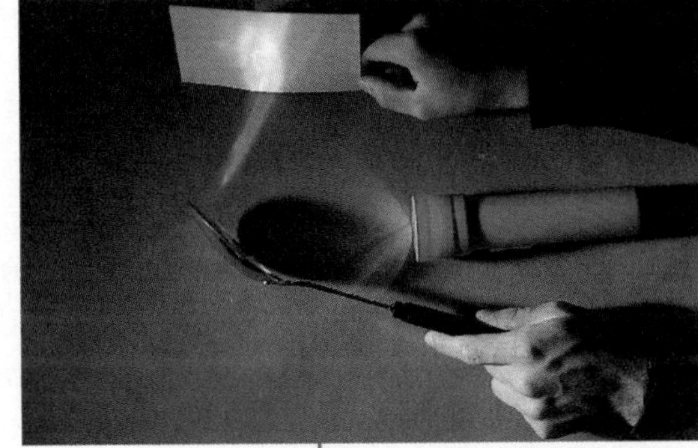

Conclude and Apply

1. What generalization can you make about distance from the spoon and brightness of the spot on the index card?
2. How does this mirror and the image formed compare with what you observed about plane mirrors?

In the Find Out, you saw that if the card was close to the spoon, the card had a bright spot reflected on it. But if the card was too close to the spoon, there was no bright spot on the card. Instead, the image was fuzzy and unclear. The image was also fuzzy and unclear if the card was too far from the spoon.

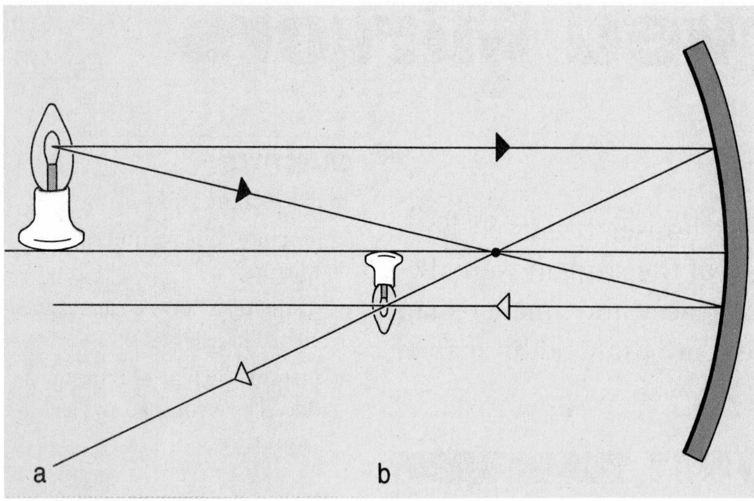

FIGURE 17-5. Light leaves the light source in all directions (a). Some rays reach the mirror and form an image (b). Beyond the image, the rays again spread apart.

You have seen that the image formed by a curved mirror is different from the image formed by a plane mirror. A mirror surface that curves inward is called a **concave mirror.** We can use a light bulb and a diagram to describe what happens to the rays of light as they are reflected from a concave mirror.

As shown in Figure 17-5(a), rays of light are continuously leaving the light bulb, traveling outward in all directions. Some of those light rays reach the concave mirror and follow the law of reflection. Figure 17-6(b) shows that the reflected rays gather or converge at a point. After the rays converge and form an image, they begin to spread apart. What is the relationship between the point at which the reflected rays gather and the observations you made in the Find Out?

As you moved the index card closer to and farther from the mirror in the Find Out, the bright spot on the card changed size. The brightest spot, or image, is called a **real image** and occurs at the point where the the light rays converge and pass through the image. A real image has another characteristic—it can be projected onto a screen, such as the index card.

FIGURE 17-6. The light rays reaching this concave mirror are parallel. The image forms at a constant distance from the mirror.

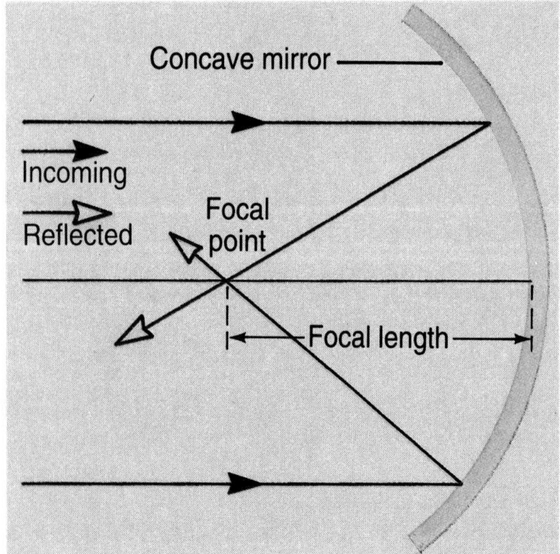

In Figure 17-5, light rays from several directions reach the mirror. Compare that figure with Figure 17-6, which shows parallel light rays reaching the mirror. Parallel light rays approaching a concave mirror are reflected from the mirror and gather at a single point. This point is called the **focal point.**

The distance from the mirror to the focal point is called the focal length and is always measured along a straight line drawn through the center of the mirror. The focal length of a curved mirror depends on the curvature of the mirror, and therefore varies from mirror to mirror. As shown in Figure 17-7, mirrors that are more curved cause the rays to gather closer to the mirror. These mirrors have a shorter focal length than mirrors that are less curved.

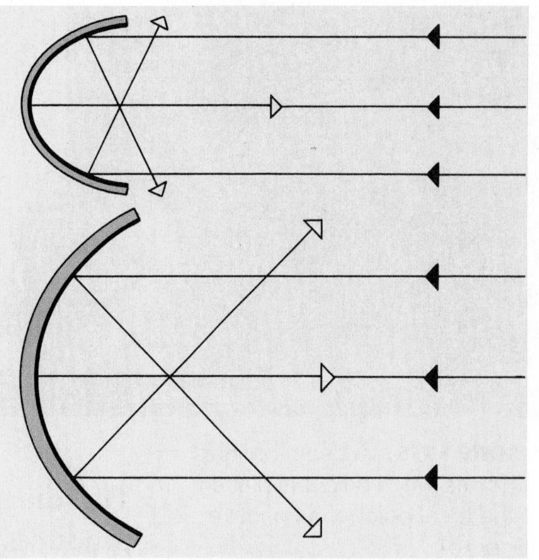

FIGURE 17-7. Mirrors with more curve focus light at a point closer to the mirror (a). Mirrors with less curve focus light farther from the mirror (b).

WORKING MIRRORS

Concave mirrors have many uses that depend on parallel light reaching the mirror. Because the sun is such a great distance from Earth, light rays reaching Earth from the sun are nearly parallel. Researchers use the concave array of mirrors in Figure 17-8(a) to explore the possibilities of using concave mirrors to harness the sun's energy.

You can find several other applications for concave mirrors around your own home. For these applications, the light source is placed at the focal point of the mirror.

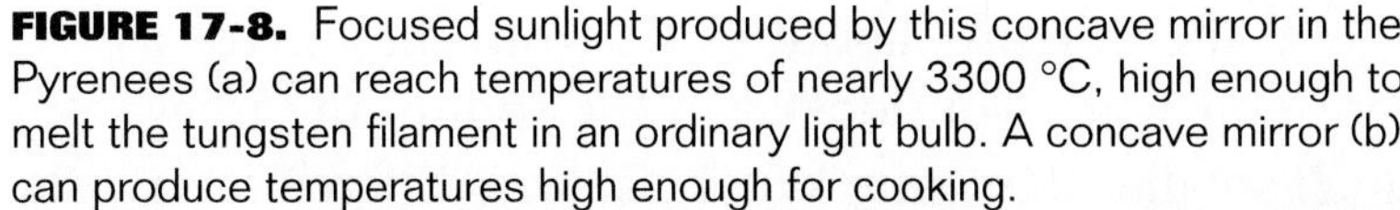

FIGURE 17-8. Focused sunlight produced by this concave mirror in the Pyrenees (a) can reach temperatures of nearly 3300 °C, high enough to melt the tungsten filament in an ordinary light bulb. A concave mirror (b) can produce temperatures high enough for cooking.

a

b

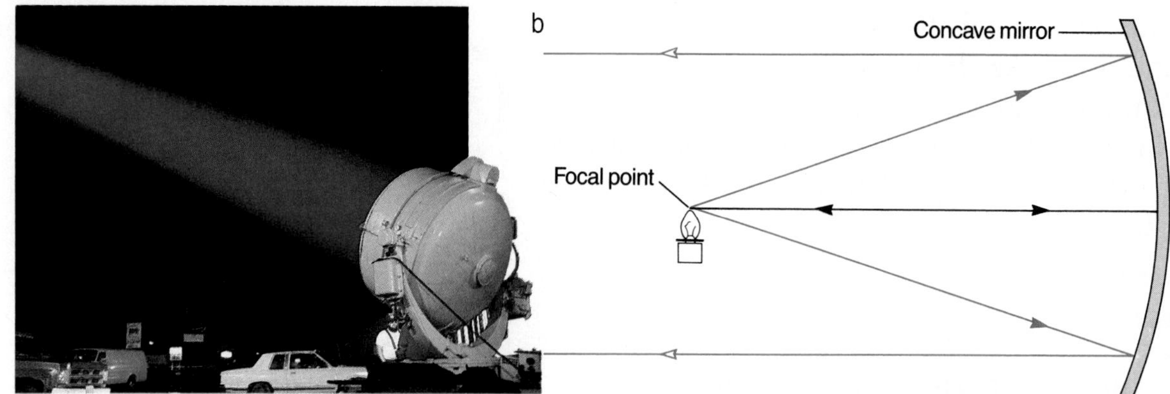

FIGURE 17-9. A beam of light (a) forms when a light is placed at the focal point of a concave mirror (b).

The diagram in Figure 17-9 shows how this placement produces a single beam of light. What familiar objects use a concave mirror and light source in this way?

FOLLOWING LIGHT RAYS

Think back to the images you saw in the plane and concave mirrors at the beginning of the chapter. You'll recall that your image in a plane mirror was upright and about the same size as you. The image looked as if it were behind the mirror—about as far from the mirror as you were. But when you looked in the spoon, the image was much smaller than you. What else was different about the image from the concave spoon?

EXPLORE!

How can you bring a building indoors?

Use a concave mirror or large spoon for this activity. Choose a building or tree located outside a window. As you did with the light source in the previous activity, try to capture the image on an index card or paper screen. You may need to darken the room and most of the window to see the image, but you'll need to allow some light to come in. Describe the image.

In the Explore, you were able to see an image of a faraway object using a concave mirror. The image was real—you were able to project it on a paper sheet. And it was smaller than the building. But probably most puzzling was that the image was upside down.

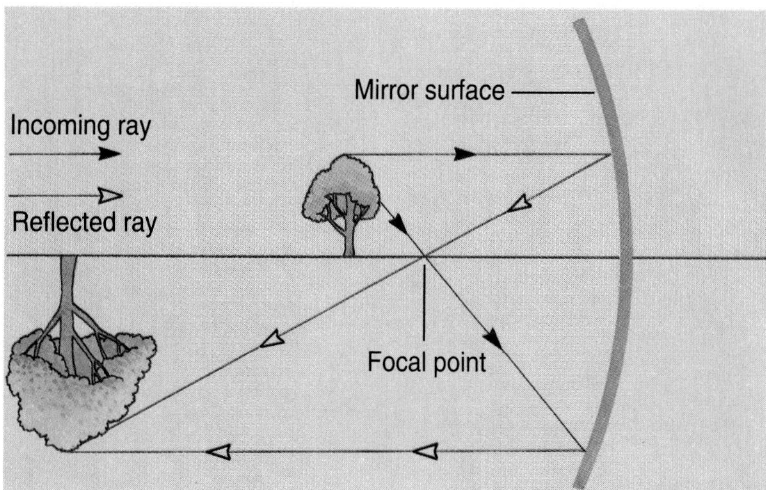

FIGURE 17-10. When the distance from the object to the concave mirror is a little greater than the focal length, the image is larger than the object, upside down, and real.

How does a concave mirror form an upside-down image? Figure 17-10 shows a diagram for an image formed with a concave mirror. You can see that if the object is beyond the focal point of the concave mirror, the image is larger than the original object and is upside down. You also know from your observations in the Explore, that the image is real.

You probably realize that concave mirrors are not the only curved mirrors you have seen. The last time you went to a store you may have noticed a large rounded mirror. No matter where you stand in the store, your image can be seen in the mirror. We can use the back of a spoon to learn more about the image formed by an outwardly curved mirror called a **convex mirror**.

EXPLORE!

Can you capture every image?

Hold a spoon in front of you so that you can see your image on the back of the spoon. Observe the size of the image. Be sure to observe other characteristics of the image as well. Now hold the spoon near a light and try to capture the image on an index card. Try some of the same mirror-to-image distances you used when you captured the image from the front of the spoon. What are your results and conclusions?

After a few tries, you may have decided that you couldn't capture a bright-spot image with a reflection from the back of a spoon.

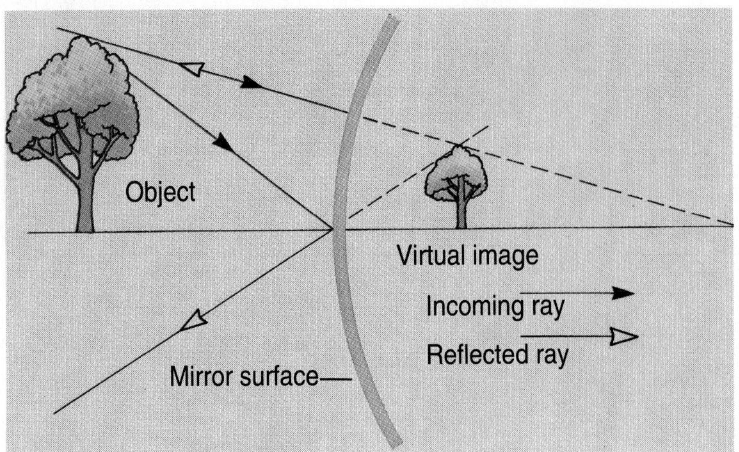

FIGURE 17-11. As reflected rays leave a convex mirror they spread apart. A virtual image is formed that is always upright and smaller than the object.

A diagram, such as the one shown in Figure 17-11, can help explain why you had difficulty in capturing the image. Unlike light that is reflected from a concave mirror, the light reflected from a convex mirror spreads apart as it leaves the mirror. The reflected rays give the impression that they originate behind the mirror. The image you see is not real. Light does not actually pass through it. It cannot be captured on a piece of paper or a screen. This image is called a **virtual image**. Another important characteristic of an image from a convex mirror is that the image is upright and smaller than the object.

Convex mirrors spread out the reflected light. This allows large areas to be viewed. Convex mirrors can increase the field of view in places such as stores and factories, and they can widen the view that can be seen in the rear- or side-view mirrors of automobiles.

In this section, you have read about two types of curved mirrors that can reflect light and form images. Concave mirrors can be used to focus and concentrate light at a single point or to reflect light into a single beam. The images from the concave mirrors tend to be real and upside down. Images from convex mirrors tend to be upright, virtual, and smaller in size when compared to the object. In the next section, you'll learn how lenses form images.

Check Your Understanding

1. If you see your reflection in a shiny balloon, what type of mirror is the balloon? What kind of image will you see?
2. Name two ways a real image is different from a virtual image.
3. If you could see only the image of a candle, not the mirror or the candle itself, how could you tell if the image was formed by a concave or a convex mirror?
4. Draw a diagram to explain how a concave mirror forms an image.
5. **APPLY:** You are looking at your reflection in the plate-glass window of a store. Is the image real or virtual? Explain.

17-3 Refraction and the Optics of Lenses

BENDING LIGHT

Perhaps you or members of your family have glasses or contact lenses. If your vision is less than perfect, you know that you are able to see everything more clearly when you wear your glasses or contact lenses than when you don't. You may have even tried on someone else's glasses—just to see how you would look in them. You probably noticed that your friend's glasses don't really help your vision. In fact, they may make things look very funny indeed.

OBJECTIVES

In this section, you will

- explain refraction;
- compare and contrast the images formed by concave and convex lenses.

KEY SCIENCE TERMS

refraction
convex lens
concave lens

EXPLORE!

What do lenses do to light?

Wrap a book in a piece of white paper and tape the paper securely. Place a comb, teeth standing above the book's surface, along one short edge of the book, as shown. Tape the comb in place. On the opposite edge of the book, tape an index card to the book. If you shine a flashlight through the comb and across the book, you will see the straight-line pattern made by the rays of light on the index card.

Obtain two lenses from your teacher. Hold one lens between the comb and the index card. Have your partner shine the flashlight through the comb and the lens from about 2 m away. What happens to the rays of light as they pass through the lens? Repeat this procedure with the other lens. What happens?

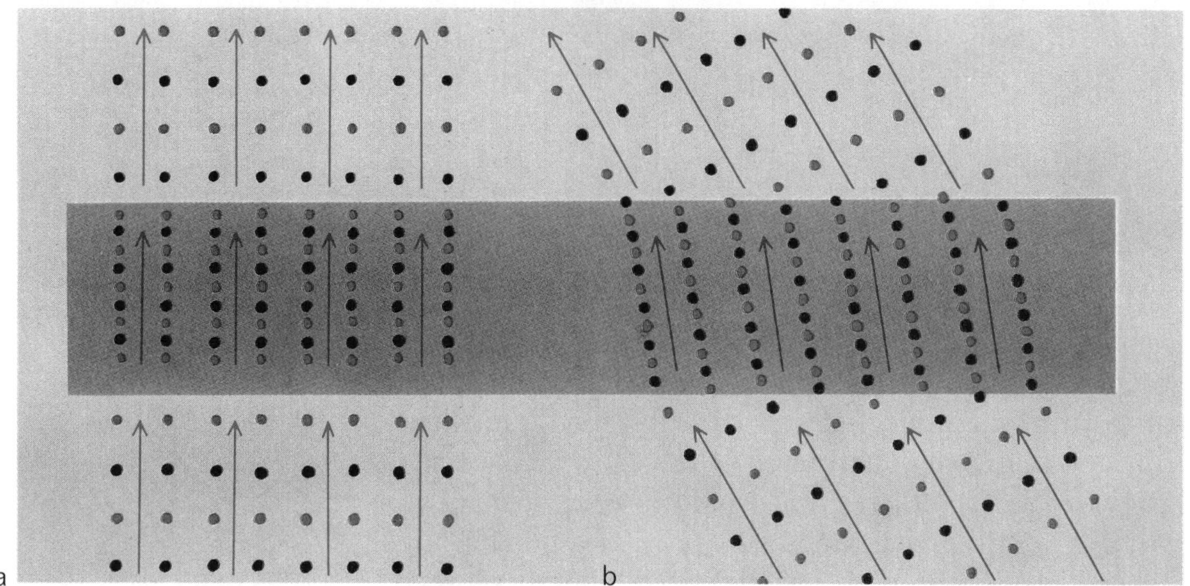

FIGURE 17-12. A line of marching soldiers stays straight as the soldiers march across concrete (a), but bends as they march into mud (b).

FIGURE 17-13. Light moves more slowly through glass and water than it does through air, so the handle of the fishnet appears bent.

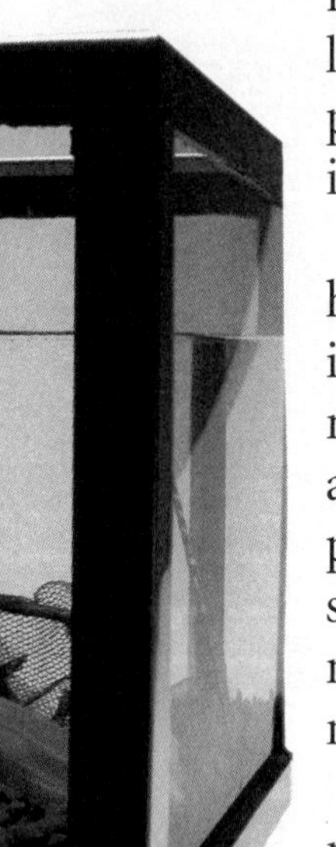

During the activity, you saw the light bend as it entered and left each lens. The bending of light as it passes from one material to another is called **refraction.** In the Explore, refraction occurred as the light passed from the air into the glass or plastic of the lens. Refraction occurred again as the light passed from the glass or plastic of the lens into the air.

Why did the light bend? Because it's pretty hard to imagine the behavior of light, let's imagine a line of marching soldiers as a model. Suppose a line of soldiers is marching along a concrete parking lot. At the end of the parking lot is a muddy field. When the line of soldiers reaches the field, they continue to march across it—but at a slower speed. The mud slows them down.

Now imagine that the line of soldiers marched across the parking lot at an angle. They have orders that they must stay in a straight line. Look at Figure 17-12(a) and decide what would happen when one end of the line reaches the mud. The line slows down, doesn't it? But the rest of the line is still on the concrete, so the soldiers in that part of the line keep going at the same speed—until they also reach the mud. What you would see is the whole line turning a little.

Once all the soldiers are in the mud, everyone in the line would go at the same, although slower, speed. But what happens when the first soldier begins to march on concrete again? The soldier speeds up! The rest of the line is still going slower so, again, the line turns. What would happen if there were waist-deep water beyond the mud? Which direction would the line turn this time?

Light behaves in much the same way. Light must slow down a little as it passes from air into glass or plastic. The light returns to its original speed as it moves back into the air. Figure 17-12(b) gives us a model of what happens as a line of light beams move from the air into glass and back out into air. How does this model help explain what you observed in the Explore?

If you looked closely at the lenses in the Explore, you'll notice that, as in some mirrors, the lenses were curved. The lenses may be thicker in the middle than at the edges, or they may be thicker at the edges than in the middle. In other words, lenses, like mirrors, may curve inward or outward.

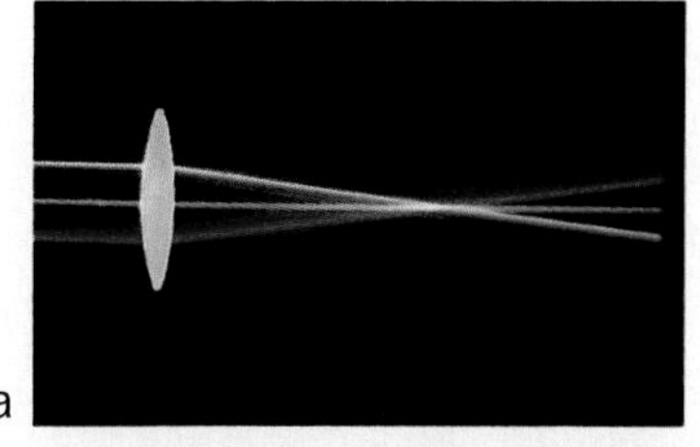

a

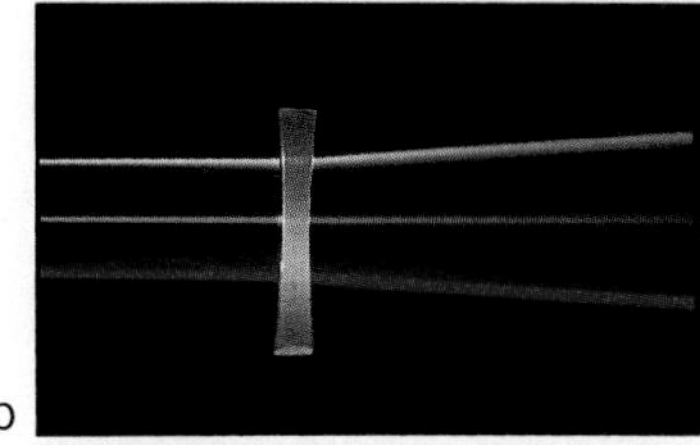

b

FIGURE 17-14. A convex lens (a) curves outward and is also thicker at its center. A concave lens (b) curves inward and is thicker at the edges.

FIGURE 17-15. Light is bent or refracted as it travels through a lens.

CONVEX LENSES

A **convex lens** is a piece of transparent material, such as glass or plastic, that is thicker in the middle than at the edges. A convex lens curves outward. Figure 17-15 shows what happens when light enters a convex lens. Remember that each light ray shown is like an individual soldier in a marching line. You may use a short length of pencil lead—about a centimeter long—to follow the line. Move the length of pencil along the line of light. Which end enters the glass first? What does it do? Turn the pencil just a little to show this. Which end of the pencil comes out of the lens first? Now what happens?

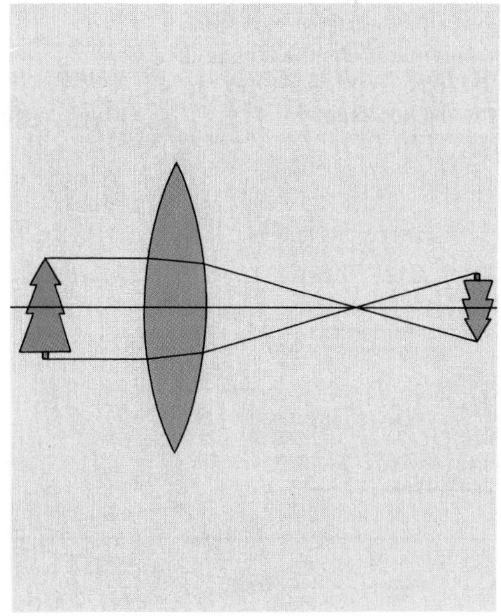

FIND OUT!

What shape of lens makes light bend more?

Set up the book, white paper, comb, and flashlight the way you did for the previous Explore. Obtain two convex lenses from your teacher.

Have your partner hold one lens 1 or 2 cm from the comb. In a darkened room, stand about 2 m from the comb and book and shine the light through the comb toward the lens. Describe what happens to the light.

On the paper covering the book, draw a line around the lens showing its location and thickness. Mark the point at which the refracted light rays converge. This is the focal point of the lens. Repeat the procedure using the second lens. This time, use a different colored pencil to draw around the lens and to mark the focal point. Which lens was thicker? Which lens' focal point was closer to the lens?

Conclude and Apply

1. Which lens bent the light more?
2. How is the distance from the focal point related to the thickness of the convex lens?
3. What two actions did you take to make sure the light reaching the lens was nearly parallel?

FIGURE 17-16. A thick convex lens (a) bends light more than a thin convex lens (b). Notice that the focal length is shorter for the thicker lens.

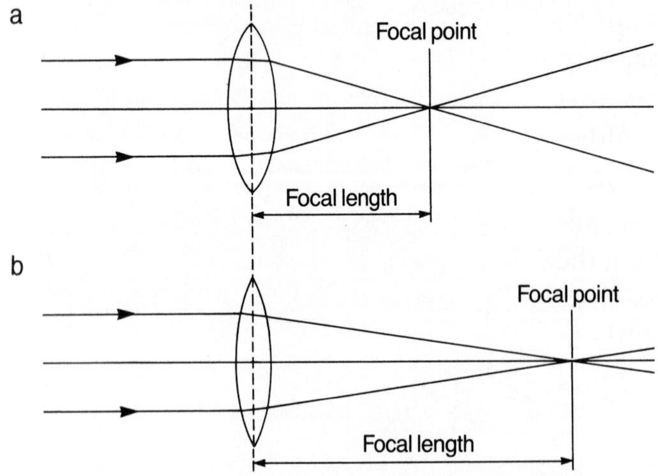

a

Focal point

Focal length

b

Focal point

Focal length

From the Find Out, you could see that a lens can help focus the light passing through it. The point at which the light focused is called the focal point. The convex lens you used in the Find Out had two outwardly curved surfaces. Light is refracted as it passes through each of these surfaces.

But what about an image made by a convex lens? Where is it? Is it upright, virtual, and smaller, like the image from a convex mirror? We can draw the same kind of diagram we used with mirrors to determine the characteristics of an image formed by a convex lens.

We know that every ray reaching the lens will be refracted. However, we know how two specific light rays behave as they pass through the lens. We can choose to draw those rays in our diagram.

First, let's choose a ray from the top of the tree traveling parallel to the lens' axis. In the Find Out, you saw that this ray will bend and pass through the focal point of the lens.

DID YOU KNOW?

The earliest eyeglasses were made of thick convex lenses. The lenses reminded their makers of lentil beans. The Latin word for *lentil beans* is *lens*—hence the name.

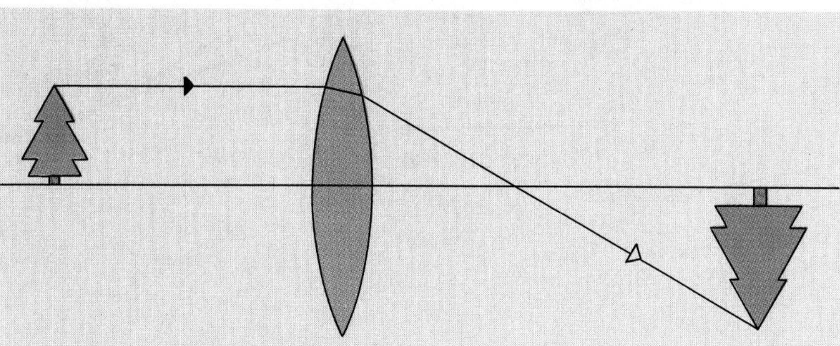

The second ray we can choose to draw is the ray from the top of the tree passing through the lens at its center. Because this ray passes through the center of the lens, it travels in a straight line.

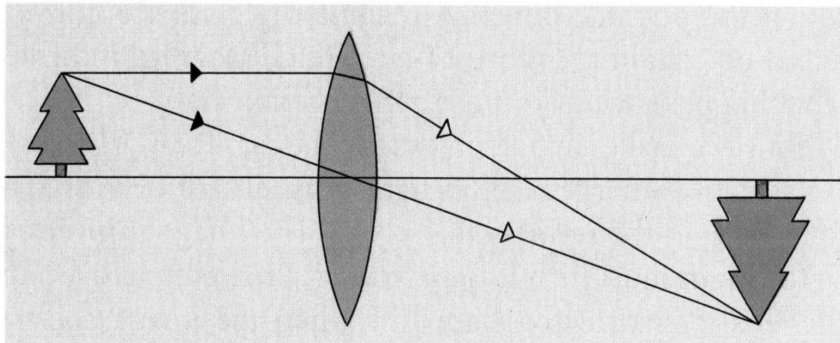

The ray diagram for the convex lens shows that the refracted rays of light meet after passing through the lens. Therefore, the image is real. The image was also upside down and smaller than the original. However, just as with concave mirrors, where you place the object can affect the image. Look at Figure 17-17. How can you use a convex lens to make a real image that is larger than the original?

If an object is placed between one and two focal lengths from the lens, the real image will be larger than the object. This is the method used to project the small pictures from movie film onto the big theater screen.

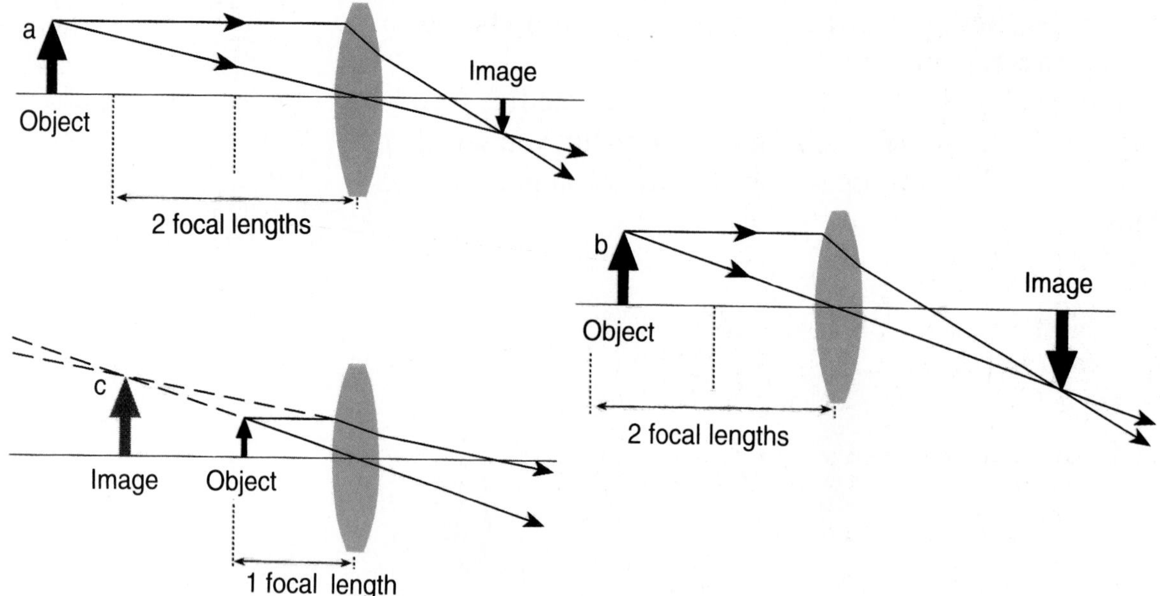

FIGURE 17-17. The image formed by a convex lens depends on the location of the object in relation to the focal length of the lens.

What other examples can you name in which an image larger than the object is desired?

Have you ever used a magnifying glass to closely examine an object? You usually wanted to see something in greater detail, and you probably wanted to see it upright rather than upside down. A magnifying glass is a convex lens. Look again at Figure 17-17. Which diagram matches what happens when you use a magnifying glass?

Your eye makes images in exactly the same way. The convex lens of your eye receives light from distant objects and focuses it on the retina—the screen. The image is inverted so the brain must turn it right side up. Problems arise when the lens is incorrectly shaped or when the image doesn't focus on the retina. That's when glasses are in order.

SKILLBUILDER

MAKING AND USING TABLES

Making a table of the similarities and differences among mirrors and lenses will help you to organize this information. You may want to use the following headings for your table: convex mirror, concave mirror, convex lens, and concave lens.

Under each heading, record information about the image, curve, and focal point associated with each lens or mirror. If you need help, refer to the **Skill Handbook** on page 679.

SPREADING LIGHT

From your first Explore in this section, you may recall that the rays of light converge as they pass through a convex lens. And you probably remember that a convex lens is thicker in the middle than at the edges. But you also know that some lenses are thicker at the edges than in the middle. This type of lens is called a **concave lens.** What kind of image would you expect to see with a concave lens?

EXPLORE!

Is a concave lens' image real?

Hold a concave lens so that you can see the image of a lamp or door in the room. Observe the size of the image. Make certain to observe other characteristics of the image as well. Now try to capture the image on an index card. Try different lens-to-object distances. What are your results and conclusions?

Figure 17-18 shows light passing through a concave lens. What kind of image is formed by a concave lens? The refracted light rays never really cross. If you extend the refracted rays, you will see that the image is virtual and upright. When the eye follows the light back to where the brain believes it came from, the object looks erect and much smaller.

FIGURE 17-18. Light rays passing through a concave lens diverge.

Concave lenses are also found in eyeglasses, but otherwise, they have fewer uses than convex lenses. One example is the peephole that is placed in doors to help you see who is outside without opening the door.

You now have some background on concave and convex lenses and the types of images they form. Can you recall what all lenses have in common? They bend or refract light that passes through them. You've seen several ways in which these properties of lenses can be used. As you read the next section, you'll see how these two kinds of lenses are used in telescopes and microscopes.

Check Your Understanding

1. Explain what happens as light passes from one material to another.
2. How are the images formed by convex and concave lenses different?
3. **APPLY:** You always put the slides in a slide projector upside down. Why?

17-4 Optical Instruments

OBJECTIVES

In this section, you will

- compare refracting and reflecting telescopes;
- explain how a microscope creates an image.

USING MIRRORS AND LENSES

Some of the most exciting uses for mirrors and lenses are in instruments that enable us to see out into the universe with great clarity. Meanwhile, other instruments allow us to see creatures so small that thousands of them could fit on the head of a pin. This is possible because of remarkable instruments such as telescopes and microscopes.

Telescopes

One common type of telescope is the refracting telescope. A simple refracting telescope uses two convex lenses to gather and focus light from distant objects. Figure 17-19(a) is a diagram of a refracting telescope. The light enters the telescope through a convex lens with a long focal length. This lens is called the objective lens. The real image formed by this lens is magnified by a second convex lens called the eyepiece. What you view through the eyepiece is an enlarged, virtual image of the real image. The image is also inverted.

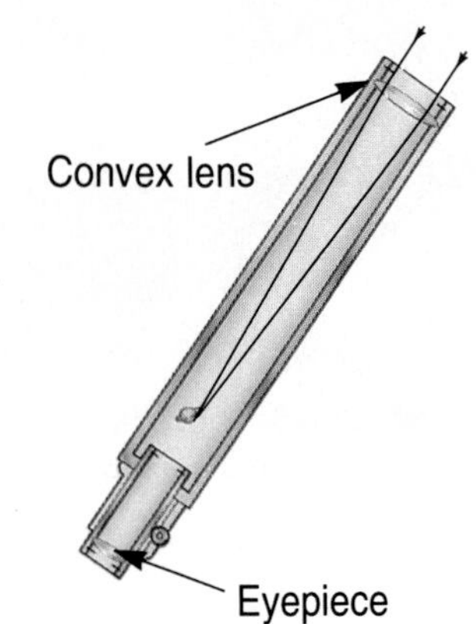

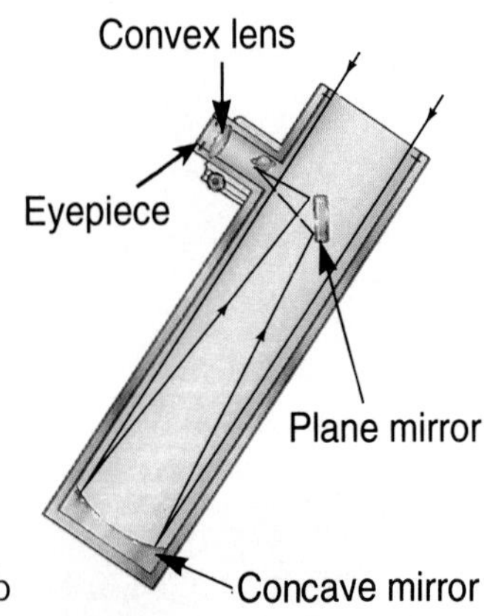

FIGURE 17-19. A simple refracting telescope (a) uses two convex lenses, while a reflecting telescope (b) uses a concave mirror, and a plane mirror, and a convex lens.

The lenses for a refracting telescope must be quite large to gather enough light to form a bright image. Such lenses are heavy, hard to make, and very expensive. They can weigh so much that they sag and distort much of the image. Because of this, most new, large telescopes are reflecting telescopes.

A reflecting telescope uses a concave mirror, a plane mirror, and a convex lens to magnify distant objects. Figure 17-19(b) shows how light enters the telescope and is collected and reflected by the concave mirror to the plane mirror inside the telescope. The convex lens in the eyepiece then magnifies this image.

The reflecting telescope uses mirrors, and the refracting telescope uses convex lenses to focus light. Let's investigate in more detail how a refracting telescope works.

INVESTIGATE!

17-2 MAKING A REFRACTING TELESCOPE

A refracting telescope uses a combination of lenses to help us see distant objects.

PURPOSE

How does a simple refracting telescope work?

MATERIALS

meterstick
thin and thick convex lenses
index card
clay
unshaded light source

PROCEDURE

1. Copy the data table.
2 Place a small piece of clay on the 60-cm mark on the meterstick. Press the thick convex lens into the clay so that the clay holds the lens securely in place.
3. Stick a piece of clay into the side of the index card. Hold the index card upright at the 5-cm mark. Point the lens side of the meterstick at an electric light or a window. **CAUTION:** *Do not look at the sun through the lens. Do not focus the lens at anyone.*

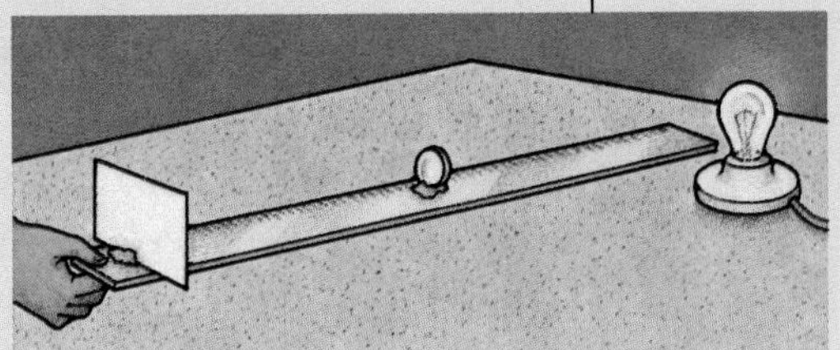

4. Move the clay with the index card back and forth until a clear sharp image is formed on the card. When you have an image, press the clay on the meterstick so that the index card doesn't move.
5. **Measure** the distance between the image and the thick lens. This is the focal length. Record it in the data table.
6. Stick a piece of clay onto the edge of the thin convex lens. Hold the lens upright at the 80-cm mark. Point the thin lens at the source of light. This time, move the clay with the thin lens back and forth until a clear sharp image is formed on the card. Press the clay down so it doesn't move.
7. **Measure** the distance between the image and the thin lens. Record the focal length in the data table.
8. Remove the index card.
9. Point the lens with the longer focal length toward a distant object. View the object through both lenses. If the image is not clear, you may have to move the lens nearer you to focus the image.

DATA AND OBSERVATIONS

LENS	FOCAL LENGTH (CM)

ANALYZE

1. Which lens has the longer focal length?
2. Use each lens to look at the print on this page. Which lens has the greater magnifying power?
3. Describe the effect of lens thickness on magnifying power.

CONCLUDE AND APPLY

4. Use the data in your table to **infer** the relationship between lens thickness and focal length.
5. **Predict** what could happen if you used another thick lens as the eyepiece.
6. **Going Further:** When you have a photographic negative enlarged, what type of lens would be used to project the negative onto the film? Draw a diagram of this device.

DID YOU KNOW?

Microscopes millions of times more powerful than ordinary optical microscopes are used in research. The most powerful microscope is the IBM scanning tunneling microscope with the magnifying ability of 100 million times. This instrument resolves down to 1/100 the diameter of an atom and the tip of its probe is a single atom.

Microscopes

What instrument would you use to look at a skin cell, a strand of hair, or an amoeba? A microscope would give you a good view of these objects. A microscope uses two convex lenses with relatively short focal lengths to magnify very small, close objects. A microscope, like a telescope, has both an objective lens and an eyepiece. It is designed differently, however, because the objects viewed are not far away. Figure 17-20 shows how the lenses in a microscope form images.

Notice in the figure that the object to be viewed is placed on a transparent slide, and the slide is lit from below. Light travels through the objective lens and a real, enlarged image is formed. The real image is magnified again by the eyepiece. The image you see is actually a virtual, enlarged image of the already magnified real image. This results in an image several hundred times larger than the actual object.

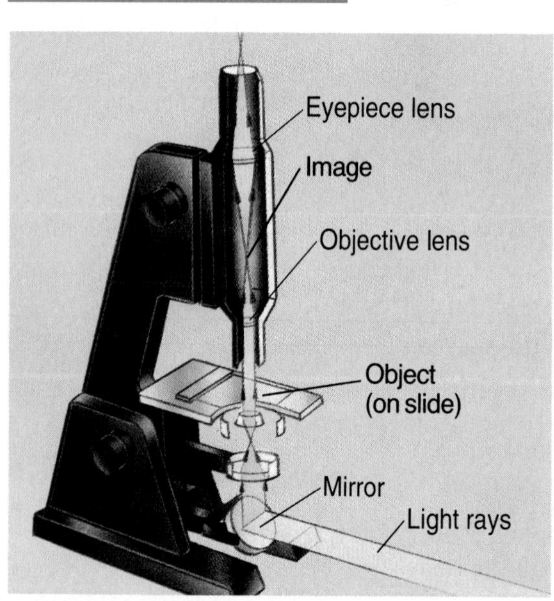

FIGURE 17-20. Unlike a telescope, a microscope views objects very close to the focal length of its lens.

You've seen how it is possible to see millions of miles into space. At the other extreme, you can now see tiny creatures and objects that once were not even imagined.

Understanding and applying the behavior of lenses will continue to increase what you can see and understand in your world. In the next chapter, you will use a microscope in your study of cells and cell reproduction. It is the microscope that makes possible our knowledge of how objects as small as cells look and behave.

Check Your Understanding

1. Compare and contrast reflecting and refracting telescopes.
2. How does a microscope use real and virtual images to magnify small objects? Explain.
3. **APPLY:** Could you make a microscope with the lens from a refracting telescope? Explain your answer?

EXPANDING YOUR VIEW

CONTENTS

A Closer Look
Cameras 521

Earth Science Connection
Mirrors for Radio Waves 522

Science and Society
Telescopes in Space 523

Health Connection
Lenses and Vision 525

How It Works
The Periscope 526

A CLOSER LOOK

CAMERAS

Have you ever wondered how cameras make pictures? Maybe you have seen or used a simple fixed-focus camera, an instant camera, or even a video camera. The word *camera* itself comes from the Latin words for *dark chamber.*

Convex lenses are used in cameras. A camera uses a lens to focus an image on a screen—the film.

When you take a picture, the light reflects off the subject of the photograph, and enters the opening in the camera, which has a lens in it. A shutter, which is controlled by the little button you click, opens behind the lens to allow light to enter the camera.

The light passes through the lens of the camera, which focuses the image on photographic film. The image, like the image in your eyes, is real, inverted, and smaller than the actual object. The size and sharpness of the image depends on the focal length of the lens, how close the lens is to the film, and how far away the object is.

Nearly all photographs are made with cameras. *Photography,* a word that comes from the Greek words meaning *write with light* or *draw with light,* has become a medium of communication that is all around us. It helps to shape the way people view our world.

The history of this medium of expression is relatively short, however. Cameras weren't really developed until the early 1800s. In fact, the oldest surviving photograph in the United States is of a type called a daguerreotype, similar to the one pictured, and it was taken in Philadelphia in 1839.

YOU TRY IT!

Make a pinhole camera. First, punch a small hole in the middle of the bottom of a coffee can (or a clean, dry 1/2 gallon milk carton). Then stretch a piece of waxed paper over the other end and secure it with a rubber band. Point the smaller hole at a distant, brightly lit house or tree from inside a darkened room. The image of the object should appear on the waxed paper screen. Compare the image to the object.

EARTH SCIENCE CONNECTION

MIRRORS FOR RADIO WAVES

You can see an image in a mirror because the mirror reflects light. Light is one kind of radiation that comes to Earth from the sun, moon, and stars. There are many kinds of radiation that come to Earth from space, including radio waves, microwaves, and X rays.

About 60 years ago, an accidental discovery opened up a new window to the universe! Karl Jansky was studying static in radio communication. He built an apparatus for locating the source of radio waves. He was surprised to find the source not something on Earth, but the sun. He didn't realize it, but he had built the first radio telescope.

What is a radio telescope? What does it do? Look at the sketch of a large radio telescope. Just as a concave mirror can reflect and focus light to a point, the large, curved surface of a radio telescope reflects radio waves and focuses them to a point on an antenna. The antenna feeds the signals into an amplifier and a recording device. The signals are then interpreted, and astronomers can locate places in the sky that are producing the radio waves.

Radio waves have a wavelength that is many times—up to a million times—longer than light waves. Because radio telescopes do not need a surface that looks shiny to reflect radio waves, the reflecting surface is usually a wire mesh or screen. To collect enough energy from distant stars, it must be very big.

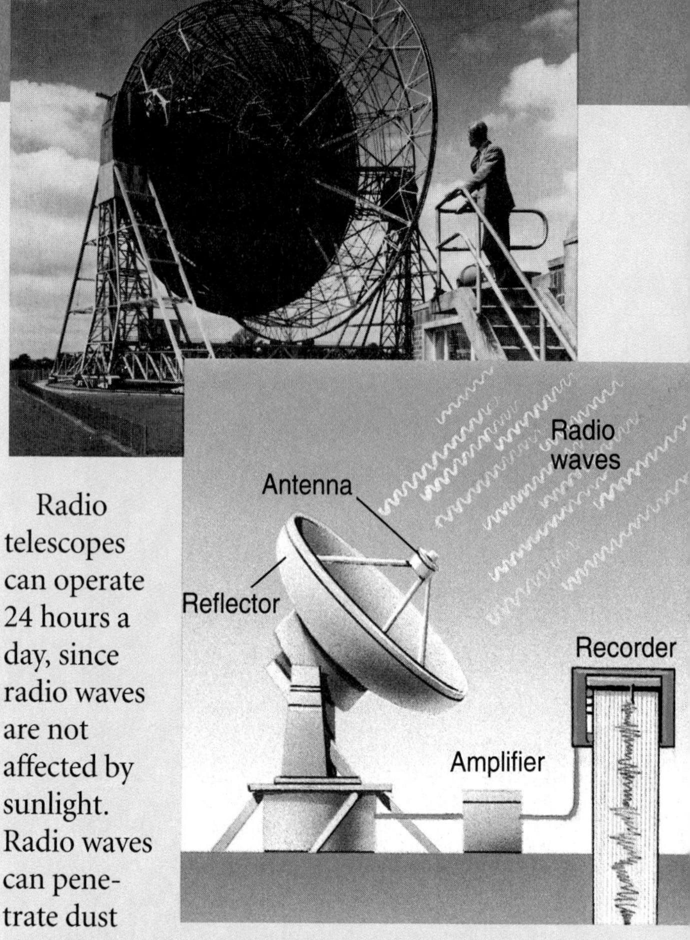

Radio telescopes can operate 24 hours a day, since radio waves are not affected by sunlight. Radio waves can penetrate dust clouds in space that light cannot penetrate.

Radio telescopes have some limitations. The objects that emit the waves cannot be seen in great detail. Also, radio signals reaching Earth from space are very weak. Each of these limitations can be overcome by making radio telescopes very large or by connecting distant ones together with radio signals. But, as you can imagine, there is a limit to how large such a telescope can be made.

YOU TRY IT!

Find out about the Jodrell Bank radio telescope in Great Britain, pictured above, and the radio telescope at Arecibo, Puerto Rico.

SCIENCE AND SOCIETY

TELESCOPES IN SPACE

Is there anyone who has not, at one time or another, looked up at the sky on an especially clear night and wondered about what is up there? In early times, people may have thought that the universe was pretty uncomplicated. But discoveries made during the last century or so tell us that it isn't simple at all. There are huge, violent reactions among the stars. The distances in space are immense. The whole universe seems to be expanding as the galaxies move farther and farther away from one another. Even though more is known about space with every passing year, mysteries remain. Scientists want to make more precise measurements. They want to better understand the features of the universe they observe, such as distant stars, dust clouds, and galaxies. They would also like to observe things that have never been seen but whose existence is suspected, such as planetary systems around other stars.

And they are always looking for better ways to make observations of such features of the universe.

The Hubble Space Telescope (HST) pictured above is the result of the search for a more effective device for observing the universe. Astronomers had long wondered about the value of a large telescope in space. Hundreds of miles up, a telescope would be above most of Earth's atmosphere. There would be little or no distortion due to turbulence, dust, or the reflected glow of city lights. Even better, a space telescope could be used to study infrared and ultraviolet radiation that is not able to get through the atmosphere to Earth-based telescopes.

So, astronomers envisioned this great instrument, but then had to figure out how to get it up there. It was not until after World War II that rocket technology had advanced to the point that the idea of a telescope in space became feasible.

In 1973, the first designs of a space telescope were proposed. Of course, many scientists from many institutions were involved. The government's space agency, NASA, would coordinate the plans, build, and launch the telescope.

When construction began, there were many problems. Technical problems were greater than expected. The cost went far beyond the original budget. All these problems caused the project to get far behind schedule. There were far fewer space shuttle launches than planned. The launch scheduled for 1983 was postponed time after time until 1986. Then, a tragic space shuttle explosion in 1986 caused another four year delay.

On April 24, 1990, HST was finally launched. It weighed 11,600 kilograms and was placed in orbit 614 kilometers above Earth. By then, some of its parts were 15 years old. It had cost 1.5 billion dollars and was the most expensive tool ever built for astronomical research. HST differed from any previous telescope because it could detect and measure a wide range of radiation, from ultraviolet to infrared. Hopes were high that many of the troubles and the high cost would be forgiven, if not forgotten, when HST began to send back data and pictures. But more disappointment was ahead.

About two months after the launching, scientists learned that HST's main mirror was improperly shaped and would not be able to produce results in the detail that had been hoped for. The equipment that needed sharp images would not be as effective as planned. Some people thought that the HST should be regarded as a very expensive failure.

Now, even its critics do not think of HST as useless. Because a great deal of the ultraviolet radiation from hot stars is blocked from reaching Earth's surface by a layer of ozone in the atmosphere, some scientists feel that HST, which orbits *above* the atmosphere, is the best telescope to study it. Also, fuzziness of images produced by the improperly shaped mirror can be reduced—but not eliminated—by computer processing. NASA has released some images from HST, such as the one of Pluto and its moon Charon. These images appear to be better than any produced by ground-based telescopes. HST is producing top quality work—just at a slower rate than expected. Other good news is that a space mission to repair or replace some of HST's instruments is scheduled for 1993.

Some people think the long awaited debut of HST has been an expensive embarrassment to many of those responsible for it. But in spite of its flawed mirror, many scientists don't consider it a failure.

WHAT DO YOU THINK?

Using what you've read, make a list of the positive and negative aspects of HST. Do you think that this telescope is a success or a failure? Why or why not? If you were on the team for the 1993 space mission, what suggestions would you make to improve the planning process?

Health CONNECTION

LENSES AND VISION

You have learned how concave and convex lenses refract light. Now let's find out how lenses can affect your vision. What determines how well you can see the words on this page? You need to be able to focus, and what enables you to focus on these words is the way your eye is designed.

Light enters the eye through the cornea, the transparent covering of the eye. From the cornea, light travels through the pupil, the dark hole in the center of the eye. The size of the pupil is determined by the iris, the colored part of the eye. The iris adjusts the pupil size, controlling how much light passes through the convex lens behind the pupil. The light then passes through the lens and forms an inverted image on the retina. Your brain then turns it right side up.

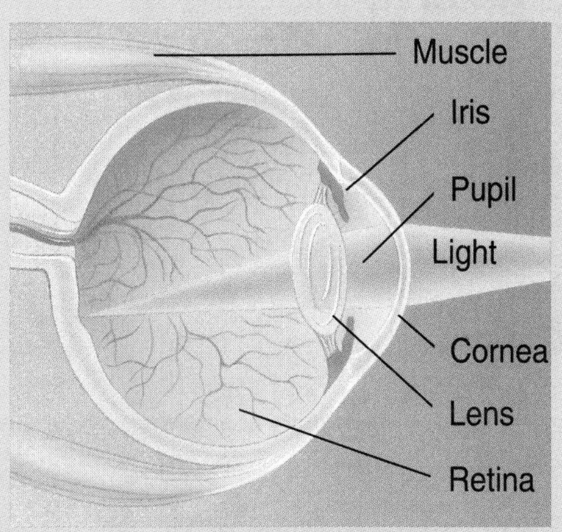

When you look at a distant object, your eye muscles pull the lens into a flatter shape. But when you look at the words on this page, your eye muscles increase the curve of the lens and shorten the focal length.

If you have healthy vision, you should be able to clearly see objects at a distance of about 25 centimeters or more. But many people need their vision corrected with lenses to enjoy normal vision. To have normal vision, the image of whatever is being looked at must be focused on the retina. As you get older, the lens becomes less flexible and its shape is not as easily changed. It becomes more difficult to focus on objects at different distances.

Some people are nearsighted. They have difficulty seeing distant objects clearly. The problem for nearsighted persons is that the eyeball is too long, as shown in diagram (a). The cornea, which, like the lens, helps to focus the light rays, bulges out. This causes the image to focus in front of the retina. A concave lens corrects this problem by spreading out the light rays before they enter the eye, as in diagram (b).

Other people can see distant objects clearly but they can't focus clearly on nearby objects. Their eyeballs are too short or the lenses aren't convex enough to bring the rays together on the retina. As a result, the image is focused behind the retina, as in diagram (c). A convex lens, shown in diagram (d), helps the eye focus the image on the retina.

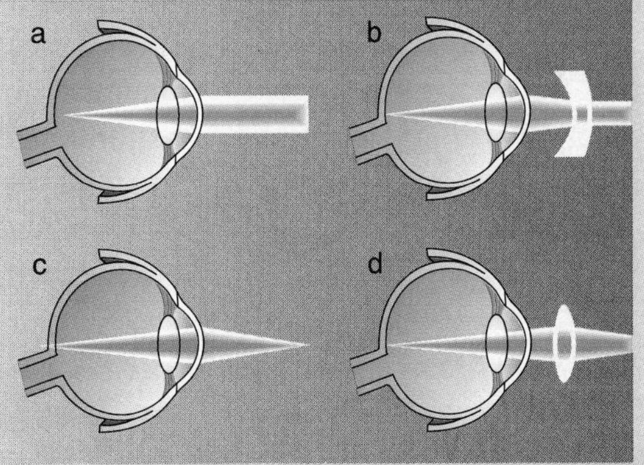

YOU TRY IT!

If you have difficulty reading the chalkboard from the back row, are you nearsighted or farsighted? Draw a diagram of how the vision problem could be corrected with lenses.

HOW IT WORKS

THE PERISCOPE

A periscope is a device that enables a person to see over or around an obstacle. The simplest kind is a tube or a long box in which a mirror has been placed at each end. The mirrors are set at an angle of 45 degrees, and their surfaces are parallel. Light enters a hole near the end of the periscope, strikes the top mirror, and reflects down to the second mirror. The observer views the image in the second mirror.

Some periscopes are much more elaborate. For example, lenses can be used to enlarge the image that is seen or to enlarge the field of view.

Such periscopes have important military and naval uses. For example, a commander can see and direct action in a battle situation from inside a tank. A soldier can look over a wall or out of a trench without being exposed. A submarine commander can observe what is happening at the surface while the submarine is underwater.

Periscopes have uses in science, too. Some experiments are dangerous and can only be viewed from behind protective walls. At the National Reactor Testing Center in Arco, Idaho, a periscope 90 feet long—perhaps the world's longest—is used to observe nuclear reactors in operation.

YOU TRY IT!

Use two plane mirrors and a shoe box to make a simple periscope. Cut holes in the sides of the box and tape the mirrors as in the diagram. Then put the lid on the box. Try using the periscope to see around corners or over some object.

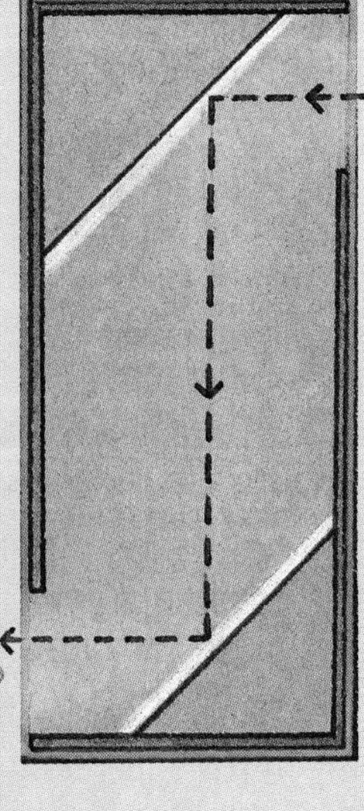

Chapter 17

Reviewing Main Ideas

1. Light reflected from flat and curved mirrors has many practical uses.

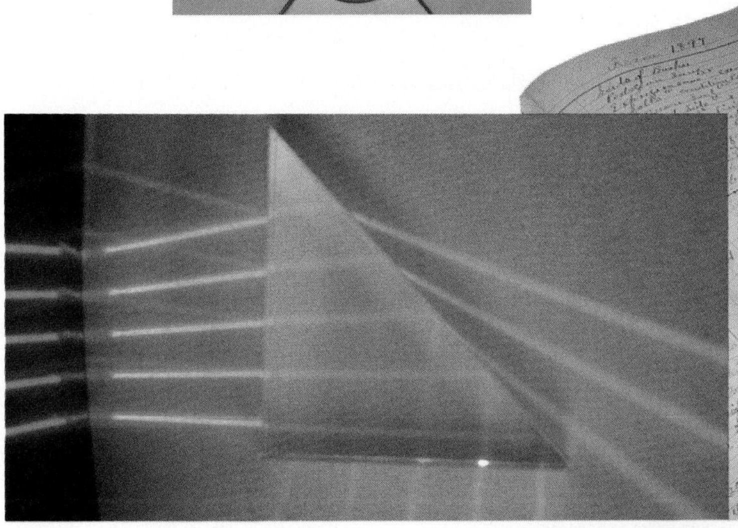

2. A lens refracts light and forms a real or a virtual image.

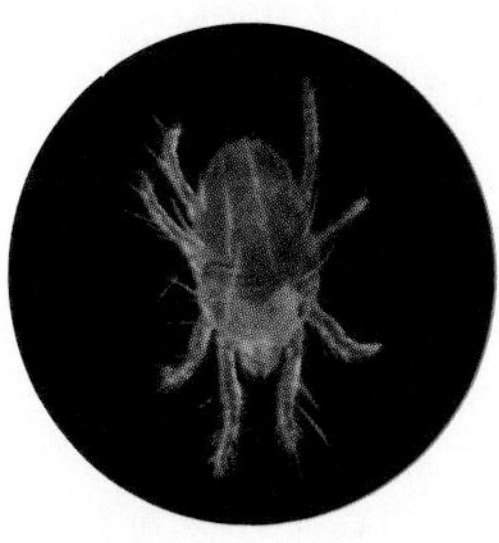

3. We use optical devices to increase our ability to see very distant and very small objects.

Chapter Review

USING KEY SCIENCE TERMS

concave lens
concave mirror
convex lens
convex mirror
focal point
plane mirror
real image
virtual image

Using the list above, replace the underlined words with the correct key science term.

1. A curved shiny surface that focuses light into a beam is used as a reflector in a car headlight.
2. A piece of clear glass that is thinner in the middle than at the edges spreads light apart.
3. Parallel light rays reflected from a curved mirror gather at a single point.
4. A reflecting telescope uses a flat shiny surface and a lens that produces a real image.
5. An image that cannot be projected on a screen and is smaller than the object is created by an outwardly curved mirror.

UNDERSTANDING IDEAS

Choose the best answer to complete each sentence.

1. The image usually seen in a convex mirror is ____.
   a. upright and smaller
   b. virtual and upside down
   c. larger and real
   d. virtual and larger
2. A wide angle mirror is ____.
   a. concave **c.** plane
   b. convex **d.** wide
3. Images in a plane mirror are ____.
   a. enlarged **c.** virtual
   b. inverted **d.** real
4. An object that reflects light and curves inward is called a ____.
   a. plane mirror
   b. concave mirror
   c. convex mirror
   d. concave lens
5. The light bulb in a flashlight or spotlight is placed at the focal point of a ____.
   a. concave lens
   b. convex lens
   c. concave mirror
   d. convex mirror
6. When light rays travel from one material to another they ____.
   a. reflect
   b. refract
   c. gather at a point
   d. spread apart
7. As the thickness of the middle of a convex lens increases, the ____.
   a. focal length increases
   b. image size decreases
   c. principle axis decreases
   d. image size increases and the focal length decreases

CRITICAL THINKING

Use your understanding of the concepts developed in the chapter to answer each of the following questions.

1. A concrete block wall is painted with shiny paint. Why can't you see a reflection from the wall? Draw a diagram to explain your answer.
2. A kaleidoscope uses mirrors to form symmetrical patterns. Look at the kaleidoscope image below. How many mirrors do you think are in the tube?

3. The magnification of a microscope is figured by multiplying the amount of magnification on the objective by the amount on the eyepiece. If the eyepiece magnifies 5 times and the objective magnifies 12 times, what will the overall magnification be?
4. Convex mirrors, such as those on cars, are printed with the words, *Warning, objects in mirror are closer than they appear.* Explain why this warning is needed.

PROBLEM SOLVING

Read the following problem and discuss your answers in a brief paragraph.

You are the head of the ski patrol at Happy Valley Ski Resort. The green meanies from space begin focusing a beam of sunlight on Happy Valley and slowly vaporize the snow. How are they doing this and what can you do to make their effort unsuccessful?

CONNECTING IDEAS

Discuss each of the following in a brief paragraph.

1. A refracting telescope may use a third lens to invert the upside-down image so it is upright. Draw a diagram of such a telescope showing where the third lens should be placed.

2. Would we have pictures of Mars, Venus, and the moon if telescopes formed virtual images?

3. **A CLOSER LOOK** How can you prove that a camera forms a real image?

4. **HEALTH CONNECTION** If you have trouble reading the chalkboard from the back of your classroom, what is your vision problem? How can it be corrected?

5. **HOW IT WORKS** There is a high wall behind your house with mysterious things going on behind it. Diagram and describe how you could use a mirror and lenses to observe what is going on.

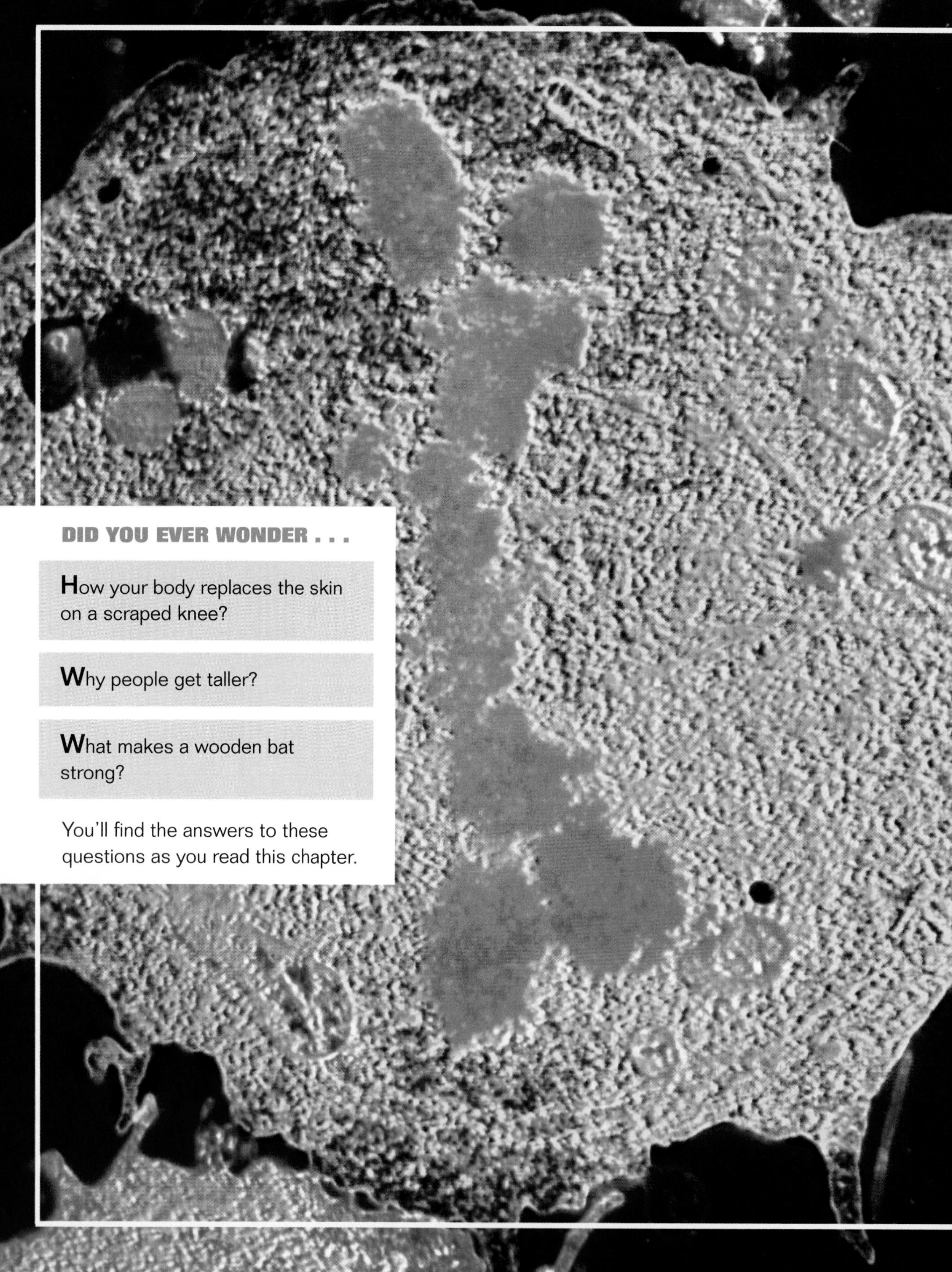

DID YOU EVER WONDER . . .

How your body replaces the skin on a scraped knee?

Why people get taller?

What makes a wooden bat strong?

You'll find the answers to these questions as you read this chapter.

Chapter 18

Basic Units of Life

Did you know that you were only about the size of a grain of sand when you started your life? You began life as a single cell. That first cell then divided into two. Those two became four. The dividing continued on and on until that original cell had become about two trillion cells by the time you were born nine months later!

But you're not the only thing made up of cells. All living things—from whales to chipmunks, from a giant redwood tree to a blade of grass—are made up of these remarkable structures. Cells are structures so small that most of them can't be seen without the help of a microscope.

What do cells do? Cells are the smallest units of life. They carry out the processes that are important to living organisms. This chapter will take you on a voyage into the inner world of the basic unit of life—the cell. You will see how vital cells are to small organisms, as well as large ones.

EXPLORE!

What are living things made of? Nearly everything in our world is made up of many smaller parts. Take a look at the honeycomb in the photograph. What does the whole comb look like? How would you describe the individual structures that make up the honeycomb? In many ways, the structures that form the honeycomb can serve as a model of the basic structure that makes up all living things.

18-1 The World of Cells

OBJECTIVES

In this section, you will

- identify cells as structures common to all living things;
- conclude that different cells usually have different functions;
- draw conclusions about why most cells are small.

KEY SCIENCE TERMS

cell

WHAT IS A CELL?

When you first looked at the honeycomb in the Explore photograph, what did you notice about it? You may have noticed that it looked very organized because it is made of many small units that were about the same general size and shape. It was also easy to see each unit, wasn't it? Living things, or organisms, are also made up of many small units. But, in most organisms, these units aren't easy to see because they are so small. You need a tool called a microscope to be able to see what these very small structures look like.

FIND OUT!

What is everything made of?

Look at several different types of materials to find out what they are made of. Using the directions at the end of this chapter, make separate wet mount slides of talcum powder, salt, and *Elodea* (an aquarium plant). Your teacher can also give you a permanent stained slide of frog blood. Carefully follow the directions, also at the end of this chapter, on how to use a microscope. Look at each slide first under low, then high power on the microscope.

Conclude and Apply

1. Describe the appearance of each sample.
2. Which of the samples looks as if it is made up of many small organized units?

Of the samples you just looked at, you probably saw small organized units in the *Elodea* and blood and maybe even in the salt, but not in the talcum powder. Would you say that any of these samples were alive? Or were they

How do we know?

How were cells discovered?

Until the microscope was invented, no one had been able to see what living things were made of. In 1665, Robert Hooke, an English scientist, looked at a thin slice of cork under a microscope. The lenses of the microscope magnified the image of the cork, allowing Hooke to see what looked like a collection of little empty boxes. He called these boxes *cells*. At the time, he had no idea how important his discovery was. Over the next two hundred years, lenses were improved and in 1838 and 1839, two German scientists, Matthias Schleiden and Theodor Schwann, both stated that the cell was the basic unit of all life. They had observed that both plants and animals are made up of cells. These observations, and those of others, have become part of what is known as the cell theory.

alive at one time? How could you know? You would have to put them to some sort of test, wouldn't you? In order to know if these units were from a living thing, you would have to know if the organism they came from had cells. You would also need to know if the organism could grow, reproduce, use food for energy, and respond to changes. These are features of living things. The salt you used was in the form of crystals. Crystals grow, but they do not show the rest of the features of living things. The units you saw in the *Elodea* and blood samples, however, are all cells. A **cell** is the basic unit of life in all living things.

ARE ALL CELLS ALIKE?

With the help of a microscope, you've been able to see the cells that make up *Elodea* and frog blood. Did these two types of cells look like each other? Are the cells that make up the flowers on a rosebush the same as the cells that make up the wings of a butterfly?

SKILLBUILDER

CLASSIFYING

Make a list of ten things in your classroom. Classify the things on your list as either "Made Up of Cells" or "Do Not Have Cells." Be sure to think about the features of living things when classifying. If you need help, refer to the **Skill Handbook** on page 678.

FIND OUT!

Do all cells look the same?

In this activity, you will look at cells from different types of organisms. You will need prepared slides of guard cells on the surface of a leaf, human cheek cells, and yeast cells. These slides may have been stained with different colors so that the parts of the cells can be seen more easily.

Place each slide on the microscope stage and focus with the low power objective in place. Draw what you see on each slide and label your drawing.

Conclude and Apply

1. How are the cells alike?
2. How do they differ?

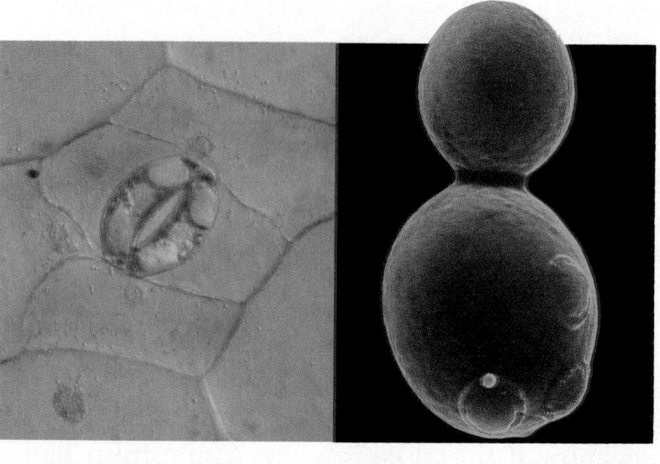

You've just observed an important fact about cells—cells from different organisms are not necessarily alike. Cells come in different sizes and shapes. Your body contains many different kinds of cells, each with its own unique job to perform. The shape of a cell may tell you something about the job of the cell. The nerve cell in Figure 18-1(a) has extensions that look like electric wires, doesn't it? If you have studied the nervous system, you may have learned that this is a neuron, a cell that transmits nerve impulses throughout your body. When you touch a hot stove, this type of cell enables you to sense the heat. It sends a message to the muscles of your hand to pull away.

FIGURE 18-1. Nerve cells are shaped like wires to transmit impulses throughout the body (a). Plant stem cells are shaped like tubes to carry water throughout the plant (b).

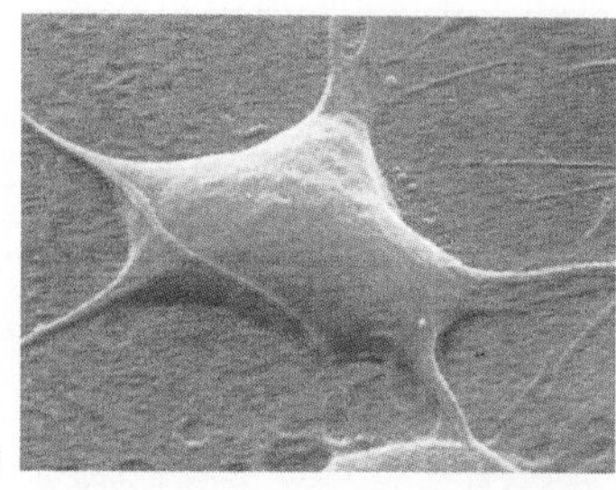

a

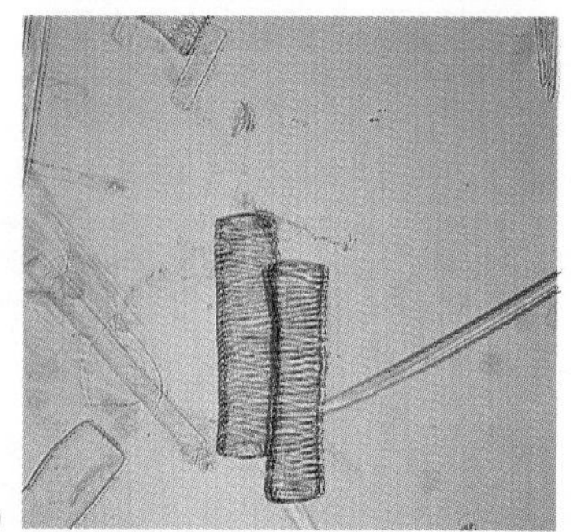

b

Now look at the cell from the plant stem in Figure 18-1(b). It looks different from the nerve cell, doesn't it? Notice the tubelike shape of this cell. What do the traits of this cell help tell you about its job?

HOW BIG IS A CELL?

Think back to any organisms you have seen on your way to school. Some of them, like trees, dogs, or your classmates, are large. Others, like a blade of grass or a mosquito, are quite small. Are their cells large and small as well?

FIND OUT!

Does the size of a living thing tell you anything about the size of its cells?

Your teacher will give you two slides. One slide has human cheek cells. The other slide is of *Elodea* cells. Look at the cells with a microscope using low power for each slide. Notice the size and shape of each. You must use the same power each time to be able to compare the cells. Draw two circles the exact same size on your paper. Then draw each cell exactly as you see it in relation to the circle. Are the cells on each slide the same size?

Conclude and Apply

What does the size of an organism tell you about the size of its cells?

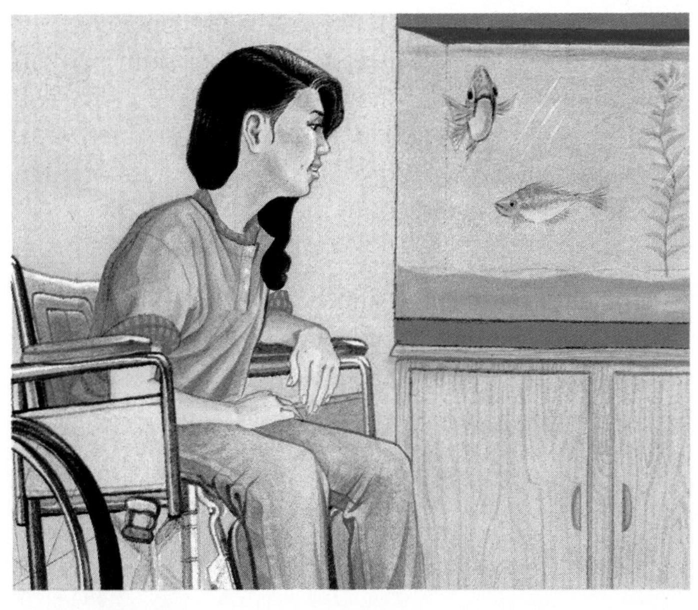

The two types of cells you just looked at were about the same size. Yet one slide contained cells from a human being, while the other slide contained cells from a small plant. You could also look at cells from a frog and your own skin and make the interesting discovery that although your body is a lot bigger than a frog's body, most of your cells aren't any bigger than those in a frog. You merely have more of them.

DID YOU KNOW?

A single yeast cell is an organism all by itself, but your body is made up of more than 10 trillion (10,000,000,000,000) cells, none of which can exist alone for very long.

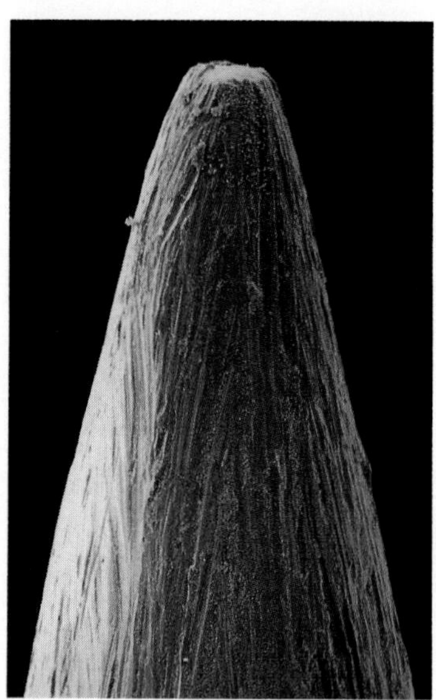

FIGURE 18-2. Most cells are ten to twenty times smaller than the point of a pin.

Most cells are quite small—about 0.01 mm to 0.02 mm in diameter. Just how small is this? Well, look at the point of a straight pin. The point measures about 0.20 mm in diameter. That means that most cells are 10 to 20 times smaller than the pinpoint!

Is there some advantage to a cell being so small? Why, for instance, aren't you made up of just one large cell instead of trillions of tiny cells? Let's think for a minute about objects, their sizes, and distance.

FIND OUT!

What is the relationship between the size of an object and the distance to its center? 

Obtain a small clear plastic container and a larger clear plastic container. Fill each container with water that is the same temperature. Your teacher will place potassium permanganate crystal in the smaller container. Note the amount of time it takes for the potassium permanganate to spread throughout the water. Then have your teacher place a crystal in the larger container. Once again, note how long it takes for the potassium permanganate to spread throughout the water.

Conclude and Apply

What is the relationship between the size of a substance and the amount of time needed for a material to spread through the substance?

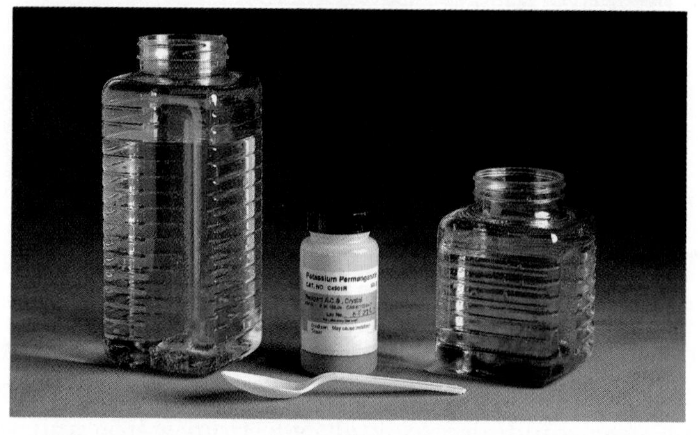

DID YOU KNOW?

Growing cells usually divide when they reach a certain size. This increases the likelihood that the cell will receive the materials it needs to exist. Yet, some very large cells do exist. A chicken yolk is actually a single cell! It measures about 45 mm in diameter. The prize for size, however, goes to the ostrich yolk, another single cell, which can measure up to 450 mm in diameter!

In the Find Out activity, you discovered that the greater the size of the container of water, the longer it took for the potassium permanganate to spread through it. Think about why this is so. It's because as the size of an object increases, so does the distance from its sides to its center. Now let's use this knowledge in our study of cells.

Look at the cells in Figure 18-3. Notice that each cell has something inside it. You may even remember seeing something moving around in the live *Elodea* cells when you looked at them. This material is constantly moving around within the cell. Materials that the cell needs move into the cell and then randomly move around in the cell, eventually reaching all parts of the cell.

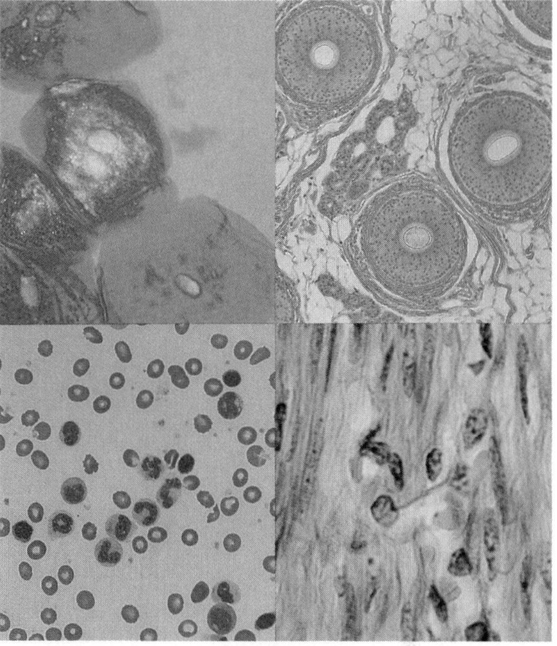

FIGURE 18-3. The shape and size of cells may tell you something about their function. Cells are adapted to work efficiently.

Suppose the plastic containers you observed in the Find Out activity were cells. Materials would travel from the center of the smaller cell to its edges in a shorter length of time than materials moving from the center of the larger cell to its edges. The ability of a cell to function well depends on the efficient flow of materials around it and into and out of it. Materials travel at the same rate in a large cell as in a small cell, but they must travel farther before they are available for work in the cell. So, it appears that materials may be supplied more efficiently in small units—such as small cells—than in larger ones.

FIGURE 18-4. Bird egg yolks, like this chicken yolk, are the largest known cells.

I N V E S T I G A T E !

18-1 EXPLORING CELL SIZE

In this activity, you will measure the size of a period at the end of a sentence, then compare the size of cells with the size of that period.

PROBLEM

How many cells can fit on a sentence period?

MATERIALS 

newspaper
scissors
slide
slide cover
microscope
metric ruler
paper and pencil
prepared slides of frog skin
flower petals

PROCEDURE

1. Copy the data table.
2. Cut out a piece of newspaper page that has a period on it.
3. Make a wet mount and locate the period under low power of your microscope. 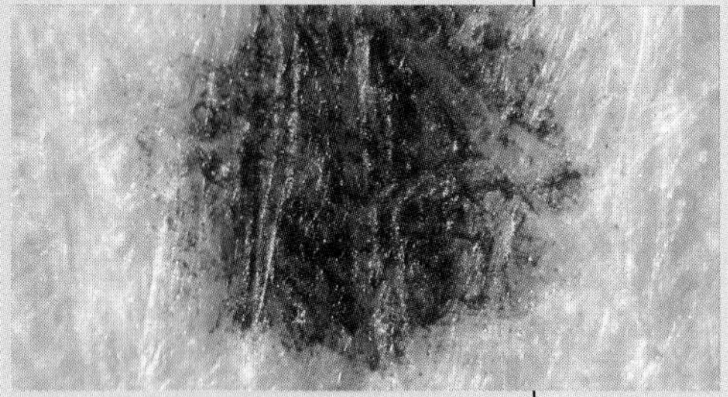
4. Draw a circle with a diameter of exactly 100 mm to represent the field of view you see through the microscope.
5. Look through the eyepiece. **Observe** how much space the period takes up. Draw the period in the circle as it appears in your viewing field. If the period takes up half of the space in the eyepiece, it should take up half of the space in the circle. This is called drawing to scale.
6. **Measure** the width of the period in your drawing in millimeters and multiply it by 0.015. Your answer is the actual size of the period in millimeters. Record the data in the table.
7. Now **observe** frog skin cells under high power. Draw a frog skin cell to scale in your circle.
8. **Measure** the diameter of one frog skin cell in your drawing in millimeters and multiply by 0.0035. Record the data in the table.
9. Repeat Step 4. Observe the flower petal under high power. **Measure** the width and multiply by 0.0035. Record the data in the table.

DATA AND OBSERVATIONS

TYPE OF CELL	DRAWING MEASUREMENT	MULTIPLY BY	ACTUAL SIZE OF OBJECT VIEWED
Period			
Frog Skin			
Flower petal			

ANALYSIS

1. How many times larger is the period than the frog skin cell?
2. **Sequence** the cells studied in order from smallest to largest cell size.

CONCLUDE AND APPLY

3. What do your observations tell you about the size of cells?
4. **Going Further**: A compound light microscope can magnify an object up to 2000 times its normal size, while an electron microscope can magnify images more than 300,000 times. How do you think electron microscopes have helped researchers understand cells?

In the Investigate activity, you used a microscope to observe cells. Due to the invention and improvement of the microscope, scientists are able to compare the cells of various organisms. They have discovered that while cells may vary in size and function, all cells have the same basic structure. Knowledge about cells was greatly advanced due to the development of the electron microscope. There are several types of electron microscopes, each with its own benefits to a cell scientist. One type of electron microscope is the transmission electron microscope (TEM). This type is used to study the inside parts of cells. A photograph of a cell taken with a TEM is shown in Figure 18-5(a).

Equally important to cell researchers today is the scanning electron microscope, or SEM. Scanning electron microscopes are used to study the details on the surfaces of objects. SEM's have helped scientists learn about the shapes of cells, as well as some details inside and outside of cells. In the next section, you will learn more about the features of cells.

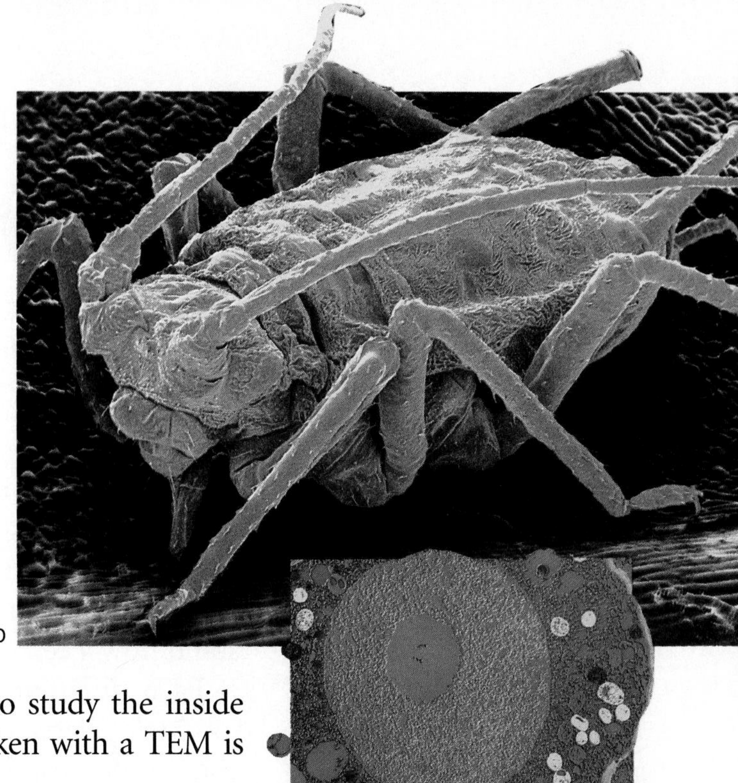

FIGURE 18-5. The transmission electron microscope, or TEM (a), shows details inside cells. The scanning electron microscope, or SEM (b), shows details of the surfaces of objects, such as this insect.

Check Your Understanding

1. How could you determine whether a green patch found on an orange is living or nonliving?
2. You are given two slides labeled "Rabbit cells." You examine them briefly and observe that they are very different from each other in size and shape. Explain why two cells from the same animal might have different sizes and shapes.
3. Through which type of cell, a chicken egg yolk or an ostrich egg yolk, might material move more efficiently? Explain.
4. **APPLY:** In the Find Out activity on page 536, you compared the amount of time it took for potassium permanganate to spread throughout different containers of water. While the size of the containers differed, the temperature of the water was the same. Now suppose you repeated the activity but filled the larger container with hot water and the smaller container with cool water. Would your results be the same? Explain your answer.

18-2 The Inside Story of Cells

OBJECTIVES

In this section, you will

- identify the parts of a typical cell;
- describe the jobs of cell parts;
- compare and contrast plant and animal cells.

KEY SCIENCE TERMS

cell membrane
cytoplasm
nucleus
chromosome
mitochondria
cell wall
chloroplast

THE PARTS OF A CELL

You've learned that all living things are composed of the same basic units—cells. As you begin to explore the world of cells, you've discovered that cells differ from one another in size, shape, and function. Even with these differences, however, most cells share some common traits. An understanding of these features will help you understand how a cell does its job.

Each different type of cell in your body has a specific job to do. Nerve cells transmit impulses. Muscle cells contract and cause bones to move. A cell and its activities might be compared to a business that operates 24 hours a day, making different products. It operates inside a building. Only materials that are needed to make specific products are brought into the building. Finished products and waste products are then moved out onto loading docks to be carried away. A cell has similar functions. A cell, of course, doesn't have a concrete wall to enclose it, as a business might, but it does have a barrier that encloses it. Try this next activity to see what that barrier is like.

EXPLORE!

What holds a cell together?

You can make a model of a cell using semi-solid gelatin and a clear plastic resealable sandwich bag. Fill the bag with the gelatin and close it. Gently poke the center of the bag. What happens to the gelatin inside? Do the bag and its contents have a definite shape? Can you change the shape of the gelatin by changing the shape of the bag? Does the shape stay changed? What helps keep the shape of the bag?

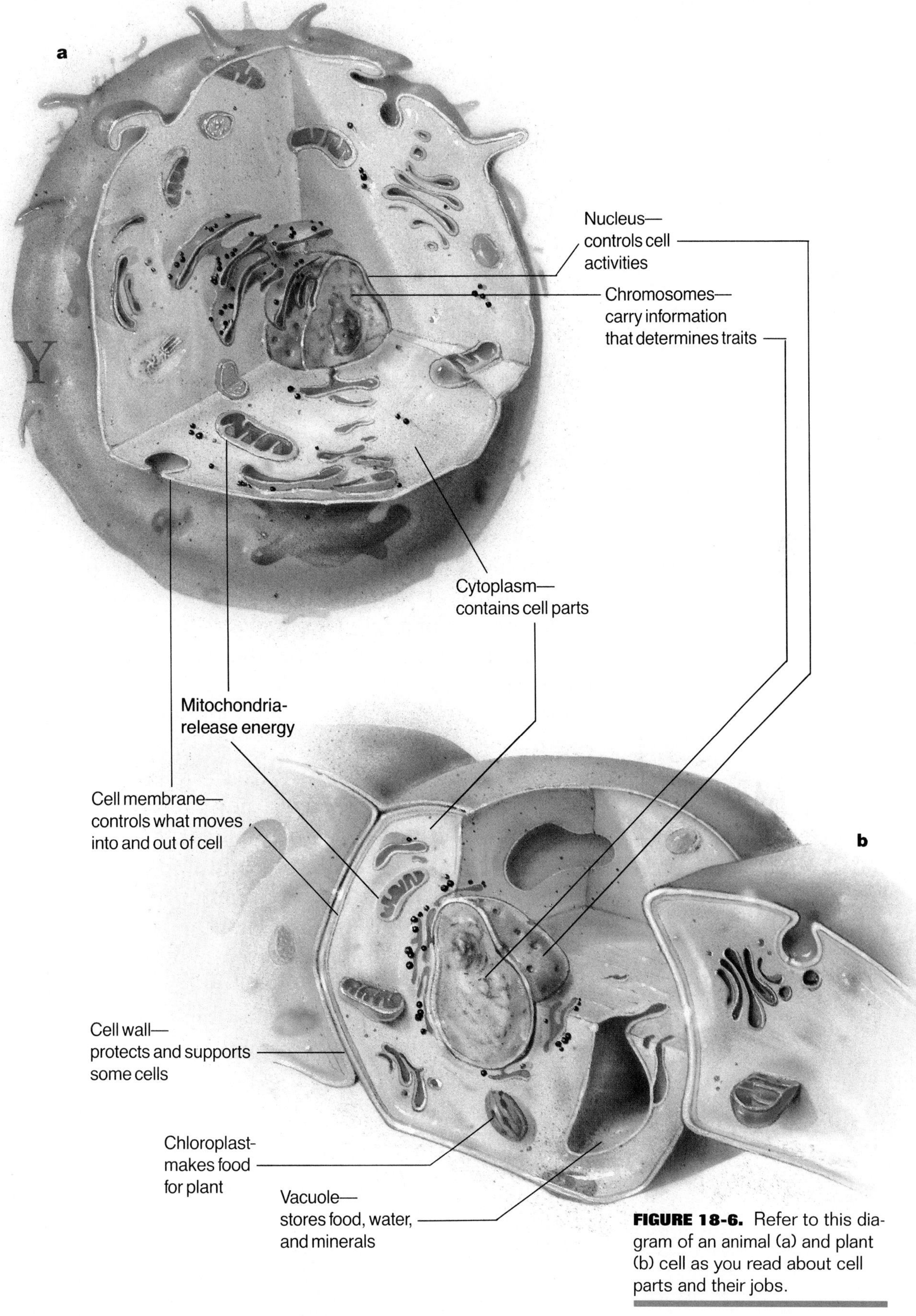

FIGURE 18-6. Refer to this diagram of an animal (a) and plant (b) cell as you read about cell parts and their jobs.

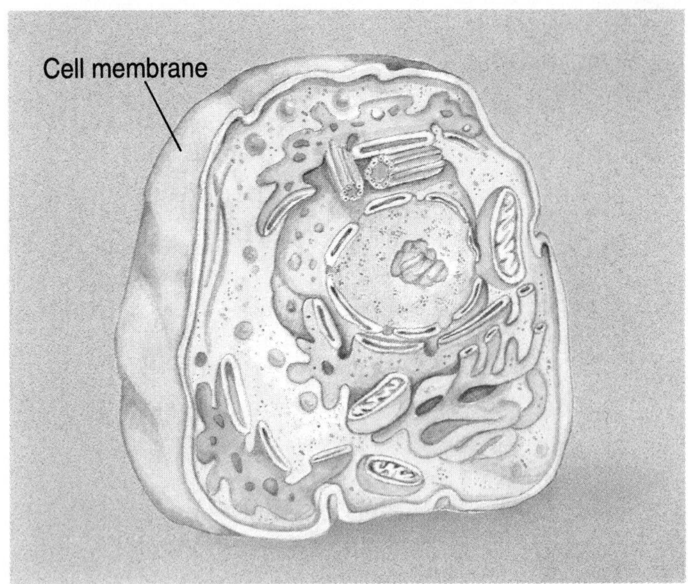

FIGURE 18-7. The cell membrane forms a boundary between a cell and its environment.

Cell Membranes

In the model of a cell you made in the Explore activity, a plastic bag represented the outer covering or barrier of a cell. Most cells are surrounded by an outer covering called the cell membrane. Figure 18-7 shows the cell membrane of a cell. The **cell membrane** is a flexible structure that forms the outer boundary of the cell. You can't see a cell membrane using a regular light microscope. However, by using chemical tests and the electron microscope, scientists have found out a cell membrane is a double-layered structure that surrounds the contents of the cell. In the Explore activity, you made a model of a cell using a plastic sandwich bag and gelatin. The part of the model that represented the cell membrane was only a single-layered structure. How could you have more accurately represented the structure of a cell membrane?

The cell membrane has several very important jobs. It is similar to the walls of the building from which a business operates. It is partly responsible for the shape of the cell and it regulates what goes into the cell and what leaves it. The materials the business needs to operate enter the building through a receiving department, while the products of the business leave the building through the shipping department. The cell membrane is like the receiving department. It allows food and oxygen needed by the cell to enter. It allows water and other products made by the cell to exit. You will learn more about how materials pass through the cell membrane in Chapter 20.

Cytoplasm

Think back to the photograph of the honeycomb you examined at the beginning of this chapter in the Explore activity. What filled each part of the comb? Honey, of course. Think about these rooms located inside the building a business operates from. Does some common substance fill these rooms? Air, of course. What about cells? Are they filled with anything? In the Find Out activity that follows, you will discover the answer to this question.

FIND OUT!

What's inside cells?

Take a piece of a leaf from a red onion. Bend it so that you can peel off a single, paper-thin layer from the inside of the leaf. Prepare a wet mount slide of this layer of cells. Observe the sample under low power and make a drawing of what you see. If you watch long enough, you may be able to see a clear liquid moving around inside each rectangular cell.

Conclude and Apply

How would you describe the material (cytoplasm) from looking at these cells?

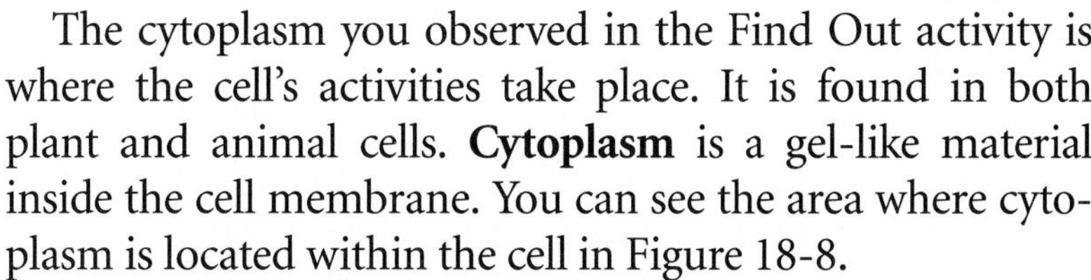

The cytoplasm you observed in the Find Out activity is where the cell's activities take place. It is found in both plant and animal cells. **Cytoplasm** is a gel-like material inside the cell membrane. You can see the area where cytoplasm is located within the cell in Figure 18-8.

You probably noticed that quite a large portion of the cell you observed in the Find Out, as well as the cell shown in Figure 18-8, is made up of cytoplasm. Cytoplasm is colorless and contains a large amount of water,

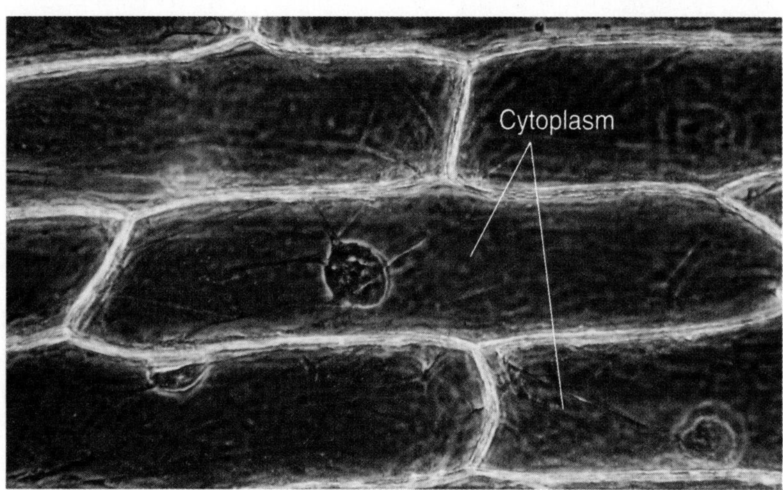

FIGURE 18-8. Cytoplasm is the gel-like component of cells where cell processes occur.

but it also contains chemicals and cell structures that carry out life processes for the cell. Some structures found in the onion cell have a small amount of color. The red onion cells contain the red color in a large storage area in the cell called a vacuole. Just as air surrounds the workers in a factory, cytoplasm surrounds the structures in a cell. Just as the air inside a building is constantly circulating, the gel-like cytoplasm constantly moves around the structures, or streams, within the cell. What use does this movement probably serve for the cell?

Nucleus and Chromosomes

Factories generally have a manager who directs everyday business for the company from a central office. A cell also has a command center that controls its activities. Just where is this center? What does it look like?

FIND OUT!

Where is the cell's command center located? 

Observe a layer of onion skin again, this time using a white onion. Make a wet mount slide of onion skin and look at it first under low power, then under high power. With your teacher's help, let a small drop of iodine seep under the coverslip. **CAUTION:** *Iodine is poisonous. Wash your hands to remove any iodine that gets on your skin.* Look for a large round structure in the cytoplasm that takes on color. Draw what you observe. Now look at a prepared slide of an onion root tip under high power.

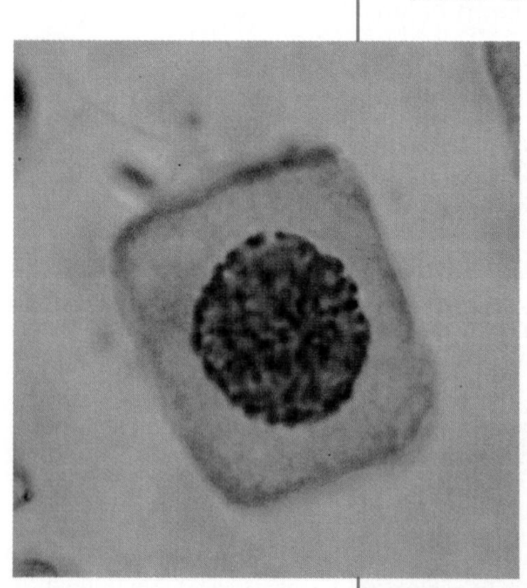

Conclude and Apply

1. What structure(s) in the cytoplasm became colored by iodine?
2. Did you see any movement in the living tissue?
3. How did your observations compare with the prepared, stained slide?

When you saw a large sphere in the cells you examined, you were looking at the nucleus of the cell. In many cells, the nucleus is the largest part you can see in the cytoplasm. The **nucleus** of a cell is its command center—the structure that directs all the activities of the cell.

Located inside each nucleus is complex chemical information that controls all of the cell's activities, including its ability to reproduce. These chemicals are in the form of long strands of material and they are called chromosomes. **Chromosomes** are threadlike structures made up of proteins and DNA, the molecule that controls the activities of the cell. Look at Figure 18-9, and identify the nucleus and the chromosomes.

Chromosomes aren't visible all the time. When a cell is not reproducing, the nucleus looks grainy. The only time you can observe chromosomes is when a cell is reproducing. What does this tell you about the cells you observed in the onion root tip? Look at them again if you need to.

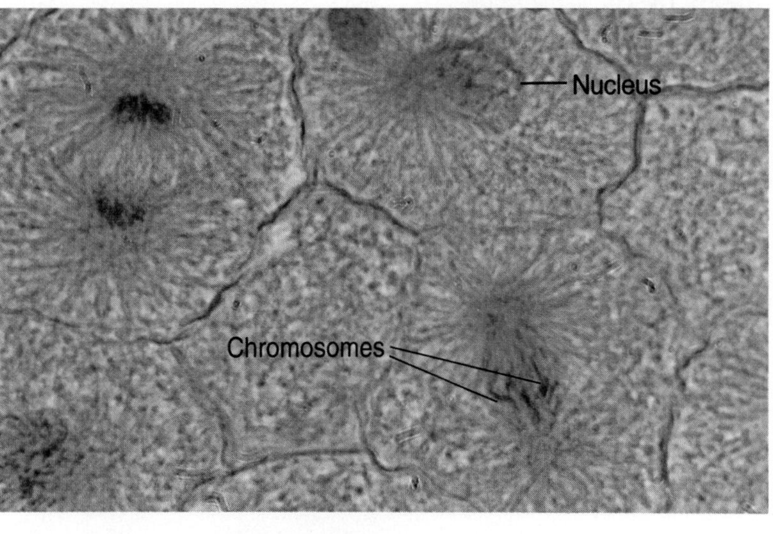

FIGURE 18-9. Chromosomes contain DNA, the substance that determines the traits an organism will have.

Mitochondria

Almost any factory uses some type of machine to do work. Whether it is a drill press, a computer, or a conveyor belt, machines run on energy. Located somewhere in or near your town is a power plant that supplies energy to the businesses we've been talking about. Cells work, so they require energy, too. Inside each cell are structures that enable the cell to release energy from food.

Look at Figure 18-10. The round to rod-shaped structures you see are called mitochondria (mi toh KAWN dree uh). **Mitochondria** are a cell's power plants—structures in which food molecules are broken down and chemical energy is converted to forms that can be used by the cell, such as mechanical energy. The energy that you use each day comes from the breakdown of food in the mitochondria of the cells of your body.

Some cells use more energy than others because they are more active. It appears that often the more active a cell is, the more mitochondria it has. Muscle cells, for example, have more mitochondria than do the cells that produce your fingernails. Why do you think that's so? Muscle cells exert force to move bones even small distances. Therefore, muscle cells seem to work harder than do the cells that produce fingernails. A larger number of mitochondria located in muscle cells supplies the energy needed for these cells to do their job.

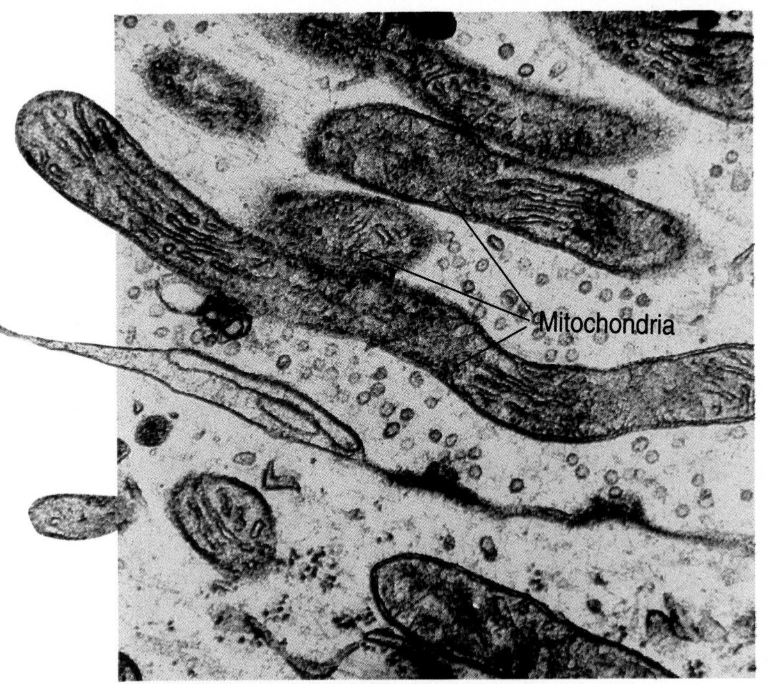

FIGURE 18-10. In mitochondria, energy that powers cell processes is released from stored nutrients.

In your trip through the structure of a cell, you have observed the cell membrane, cytoplasm, nucleus, chromosomes, and mitochondria of sample cells. Animal cells contain all these structures. Plant cells, however, contain some additional cell parts. In the next activity, you will make a model of a plant cell to learn about these cell parts.

EXPLORE!

How do plant and animal cells differ?

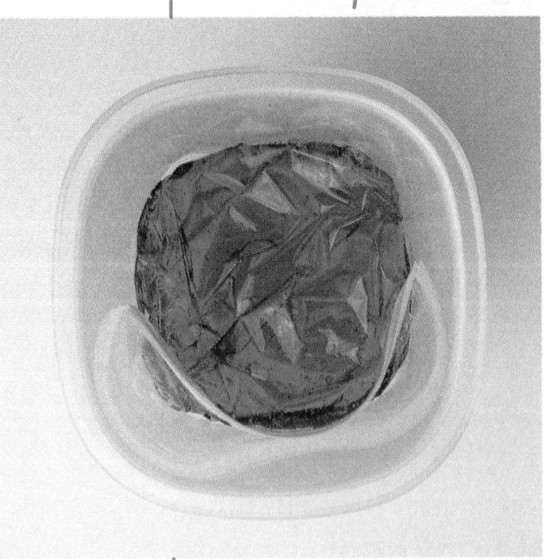

Take a clear food container and a plastic bag filled with semi-solid gelatin. Place the bag inside the container, pressing gently so that the plastic bag fits snugly up against the sides of the container. How does the shape of the bag now compare with the shape of the container? If the bag were placed in a different type of container, would its shape change?

Cell Walls

In your model, the plastic container represents a cell part found in plant cells, fungi, and bacteria. This structure, the outermost rim of the cell, is called the cell wall. The **cell wall**, shown in Figure 18-11, is a rigid structure located outside the cell membrane that supports and protects the cell. Tiny openings, or pores, in the cell wall permit substances to pass through and move up against the cell membrane so they can be used by the cell. In your model of the cell, the plastic bag represented the cell membrane and the plastic container represented the cell wall.

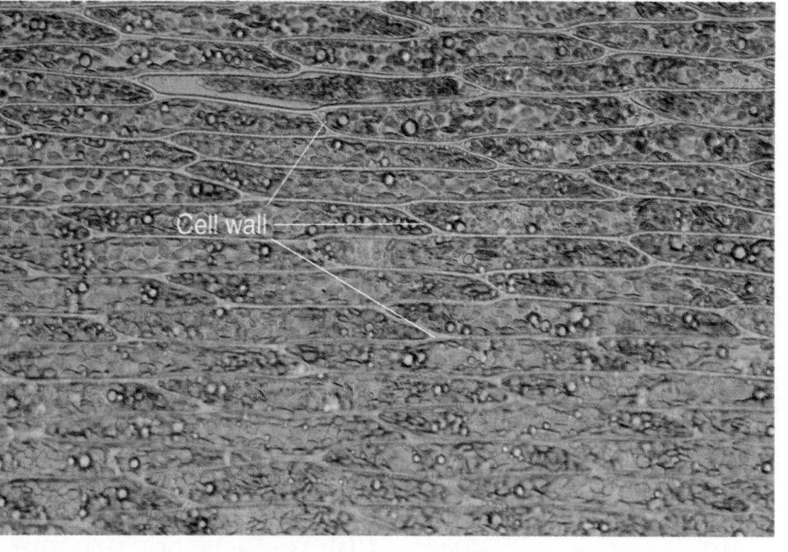

FIGURE 18-11. Cell walls are structures that make plant, fungus, and bacterial cells rigid.

The cell wall is made up of bundles of tough fibers produced by the cell itself. The fibers in some plant cell walls contain substances that are so strong that even after the plant dies, the fibers remain intact. Cell walls from dead plants are used as wood that can be cut up and made into furniture and buildings. If you play baseball, cell walls may have helped you "muscle" a ball over the pitcher's head. The wooden bat you may have used is made up of the dead cells from an ash tree. Cell walls remain strong even though the contents of the cells are no longer there. Just imagine what would happen if your Louisville Slugger had been made from animal cells whose only outer covering was a flexible cell membrane.

Chloroplasts

You already know that plant cells have a structure that animal cells do not, namely, a cell wall. But when you studied plant and animal cells under the microscope and compared their structures, you may have made an interesting discovery. Green plant cells have another structure that animal cells don't. In the next activity, you can find out what's different about green plant cells.

FIND OUT!

What structures are unique to green plant cells? Prepare a wet-mount slide of a moss leaflet or *Elodea* leaf. Observe the slide under both low and high power. Look for small green bodies within each cell. Where in the cell are these structures located? How many are present in each cell? Make a drawing of what you see.

Conclude and Apply
What is the relationship between the color of these structures and the color of the plant?

The small green bodies you observed in the cytoplasm of the moss cells are chloroplasts (KLOR uh plasts). **Chloroplasts** are structures that contain chlorophyll, a green pigment that allows plants to make their own food by converting light energy into chemical energy in the form of a sugar called glucose.

You have now completed your journey through the major parts of plant and animal cells. The structures in these cells carry out certain life processes. In the next section, you will learn more about one of these processes—reproduction.

SKILLBUILDER

MAKING A TABLE
Make a table that lists the parts of a cell and each of their jobs. If you need help, refer to the **Skill Handbook** on page 679.

Check Your Understanding

1. Compare the job of a cell membrane with that of a cell wall.
2. What cell parts are found in most green plant cells?
3. Describe the relationship that appears to exist between the job of a cell and the number of mitochondria it contains.
4. What cell parts are more clearly visible when a cell is dividing?
5. **APPLY:** Suppose a disease destroyed all the chloroplasts in a green plant. Explain what would happen to the plant and why.

18-3 When One Cell Becomes Two

CHANGE AND GROWTH

What happens to the tiny green shoots that, in spite of traffic, push through the cracks in playgrounds and parking lots? They often grow tall and strong, and produce roots that are hard to pull out. Puppies grow too, maturing into full-grown adult dogs. A green and black banded caterpillar sealed inside a pale green cocoon emerges as an orange and black monarch butterfly. All living things change and grow, often right before your eyes. Are you also changing? Think about that during the next activity.

OBJECTIVES

In this section, you will

- describe the process of mitosis and its end products;
- give examples of instances where cell reproduction takes place.

KEY SCIENCE TERMS

mitosis

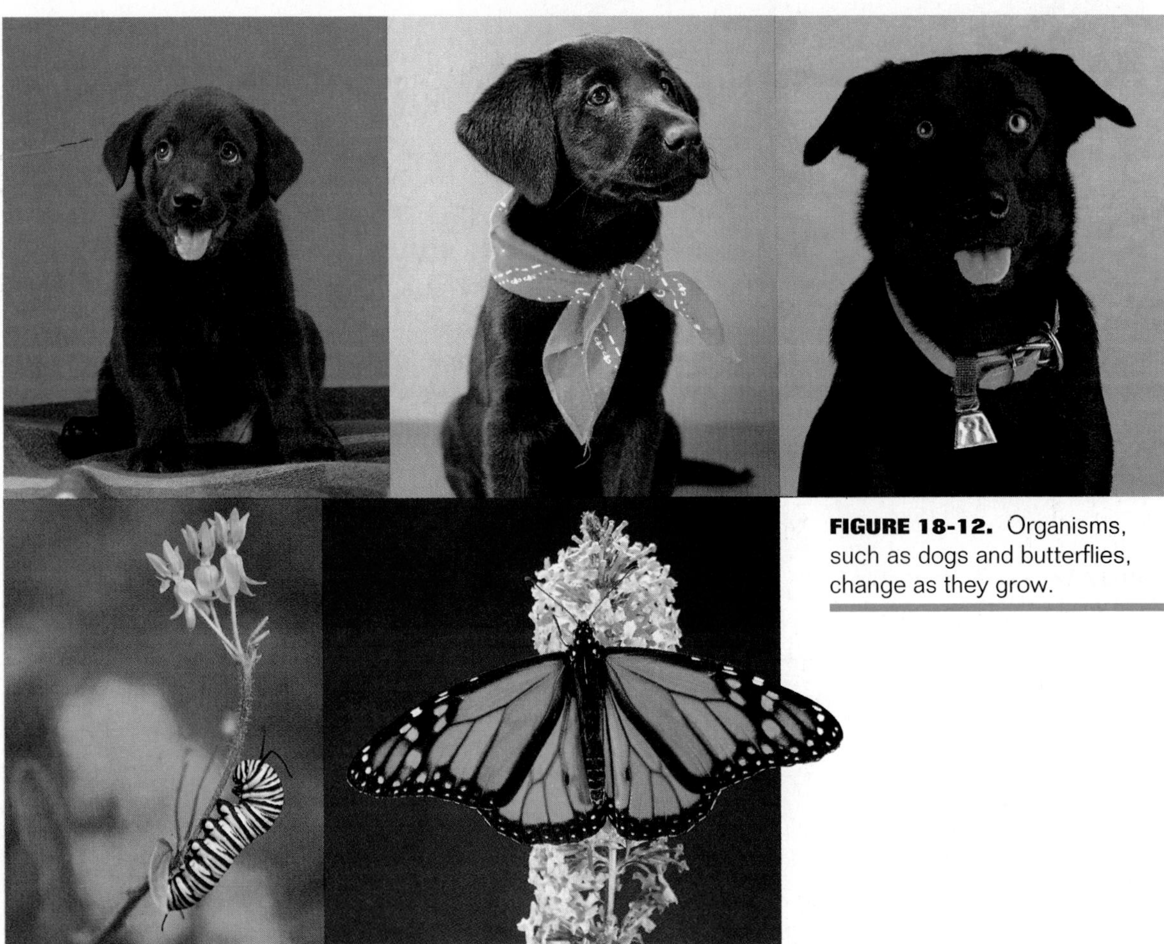

FIGURE 18-12. Organisms, such as dogs and butterflies, change as they grow.

FIND OUT!

How do you grow taller?

The growth of bones is controlled by many processes, including the production of new cells. One of the things that happen as you grow taller is that the number of bone cells in your body increases. A single bone cell is about 0.01 mm long. Suppose your height increased by 40 mm and that this gain in height was caused by the production of additional cells in your thigh bone.

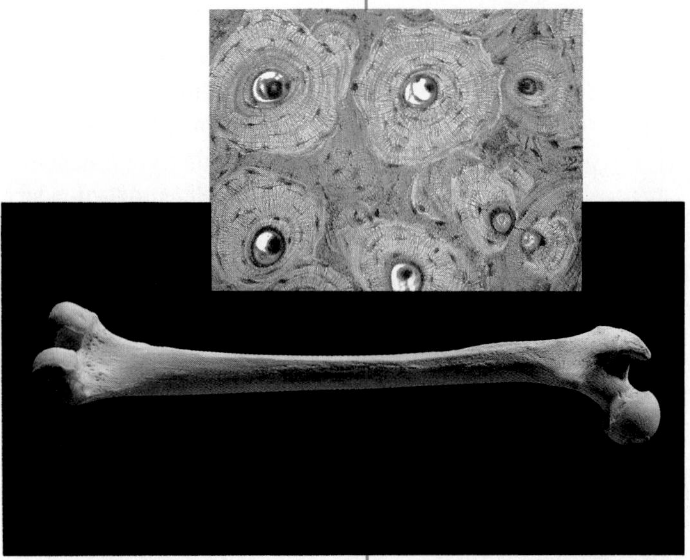

Conclude and Apply

1. Approximately how many new bone cells were produced to cause this gain in your height?
2. Provide two other examples of growth in your body.

Besides growing taller, you can find other evidence that the cells in your body are increasing in number. When you cut yourself, you see dramatic evidence of cell reproduction. A cut is a break in your skin. Have you ever scraped your knee on the ground? As you know, when a cut occurs, blood initially flows through the opening. But in time, the tear in your skin is no longer visible. Why? Your body actually repaired itself by sealing off the flow

FIGURE 18-13. A cut healing is an example of cell reproduction.

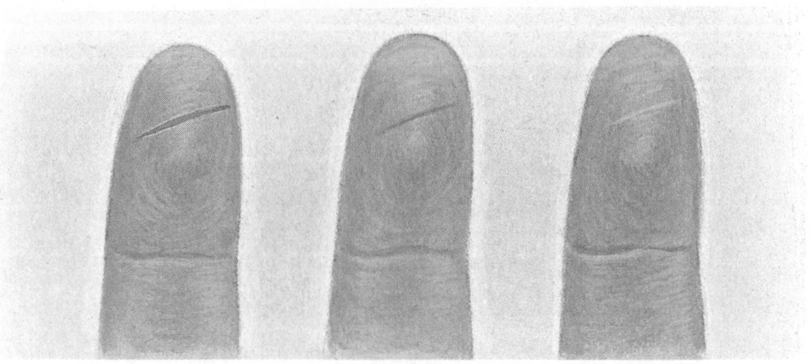

of blood and then producing new skin cells. The new cells filled the break in your skin as the dead cells were replaced. Cuts heal as new cells are produced.

> **DID YOU KNOW?**
>
> The word mitosis comes from the Greek word *mitos* which means thread. Chromosomes look somewhat like threads during mitosis.

AN INTRODUCTION TO CELL REPRODUCTION

In order to understand how your body makes new cells, you first need to review the features of a nucleus and chromosomes. In the following Find Out activity, you will take a closer look at these cell structures.

FIND OUT!

When are chromosomes visible?

Chromosomes are generally visible only when a cell is undergoing cell reproduction. If you can see a cell's chromosomes, then the cell is reproducing. Examine a prepared slide of an onion root tip under both low and high power. Look at cells that are undergoing reproduction. Make a drawing of a reproducing cell. Then make a drawing of a cell that's not reproducing.

Conclude and Apply

1. How do your drawings differ?
2. What structures indicated that the cell was undergoing reproduction?

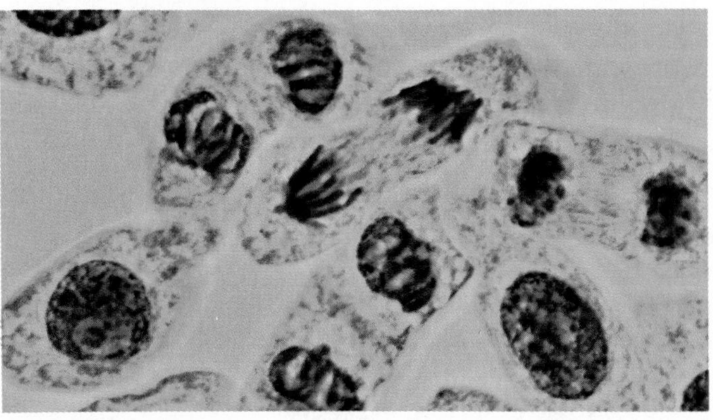

Did you see chromosomes in the onion root tip cell? Chromosomes are threadlike structures located in the nucleus of the cell. In most cells, chromosomes play an important role in the reproduction of cells.

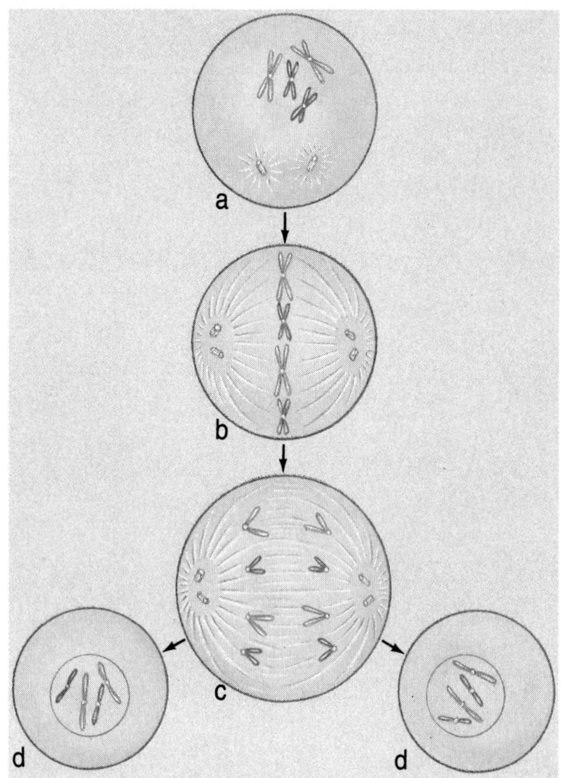

FIGURE 18-14. Mitosis produces two new cells, each identical to the parent cell.

HOW BODY CELLS REPRODUCE

Have you ever watched a magician at work? Objects seem to disappear or reappear with sleight of hand. Such tricks can even make one object appear to become two. When a cell reproduces, one cell becomes two identical cells. It's not magic, however—it's mitosis (mi TOH sus).

Mitosis is the process by which the nucleus of a cell divides to produce two nuclei, each with the same type and number of chromosomes that the parent cell had. After the nucleus divides, the cytoplasm also usually separates. Follow the steps in Figure 18-14 as this process is described.

Mitosis begins with a single cell. It could be a skin cell or a cell on the tip of an onion root. First, each chromosome in the cell makes a copy of itself (a). The identical chromosomes remain joined together. Threadlike spindle fibers stretch across the cell, making a football-shaped network of fibers in the cytoplasm. The chromosomes move toward the center of the cell and attach to the fibers. All the chromosomes line up along the center of the cell (b). Each chromosome and its copy then separate. The fibers seem to guide or pull the chromosomes to opposite ends of the cell (c). The fibers then disappear and the cytoplasm divides in half. The result? Each new cell is identical to the original cell (d).

Cell reproduction by mitosis has been taking place in your body from the moment you were conceived, and it continues even now. As you read this page, many cells in your body are dividing through mitosis. What evidence do you have that this is true?

All of your body cells reproduce by the same process—mitosis. But, the rate at which mitosis occurs in different types of cells may vary. In the next activity, you will observe the rate of mitosis in a young plant root.

INVESTIGATE!

18-2 24-HOUR CELL REPRODUCTION

You have learned that cells reproduce through the process of mitosis. In the following activity, you will observe how many new cells are formed by a young, growing root during a 24-hour period.

PROBLEM

How many new cells does a young, growing root produce in a day?

MATERIALS

5 young corn seedlings
permanent marking pen (not water-soluble)
metric ruler
paper towels
plastic bags
labels

PROCEDURE

1. Copy the data table.
2. Obtain five young corn seedlings from your teacher.

3. On the first seedling, locate the growing root. See the illustration.
4. Use the marking pen to place a dot on the root 10 mm from the tip end. Label this specimen Seedling 1. Record this measurement in the table under Original Length.
5. Repeat Steps 3 and 4 with the other four seedlings. Label each seedling with a number and record its length in the table.
6. Wrap each seedling individually in moist paper towels. Place them in a plastic bag.
7. After 24 hours, **measure** the length of each root from its tip to the dot you made. Record measurements in the table under Final Length.
8. Subtract the original length from the final length. Record this measurement in the table under Growth of Root.
9. Calculate the average growth of a root tip. Record this number in the table under Average Growth of Roots.

DATA AND OBSERVATIONS

SEEDLING	ORIGINAL LENGTH (MM)	FINAL LENGTH (MM)	GROWTH OF ROOT (MM)	AVERAGE GROWTH OF ROOTS (MM)
1				
2				
3				
4				
5				

ANALYZE

1. What evidence do you have that mitosis occurred in the corn roots?
2. How much, on average, did the roots grow in 24 hours?

CONCLUDE AND APPLY

3. **Predict** the amount of growth that would occur in an average corn root after a week.
4. Water is a nutrient needed by all living things. How did you supply the seedlings with the water they need to exist?
5. **Going Further:** Suppose you had found that the length of the seedlings had not changed during the 24-hour period. **Hypothesize** about some possible explanations for this lack of growth.

In the Investigate activity, you observed growth in the corn root seedlings. This growth occurred due to mitosis, a process that occurs in most living cells. Through mitosis, the corn plants produced new cells that were identical to their parent cell.

FIGURE 18-15. Roots of plants grow quickly through mitosis.

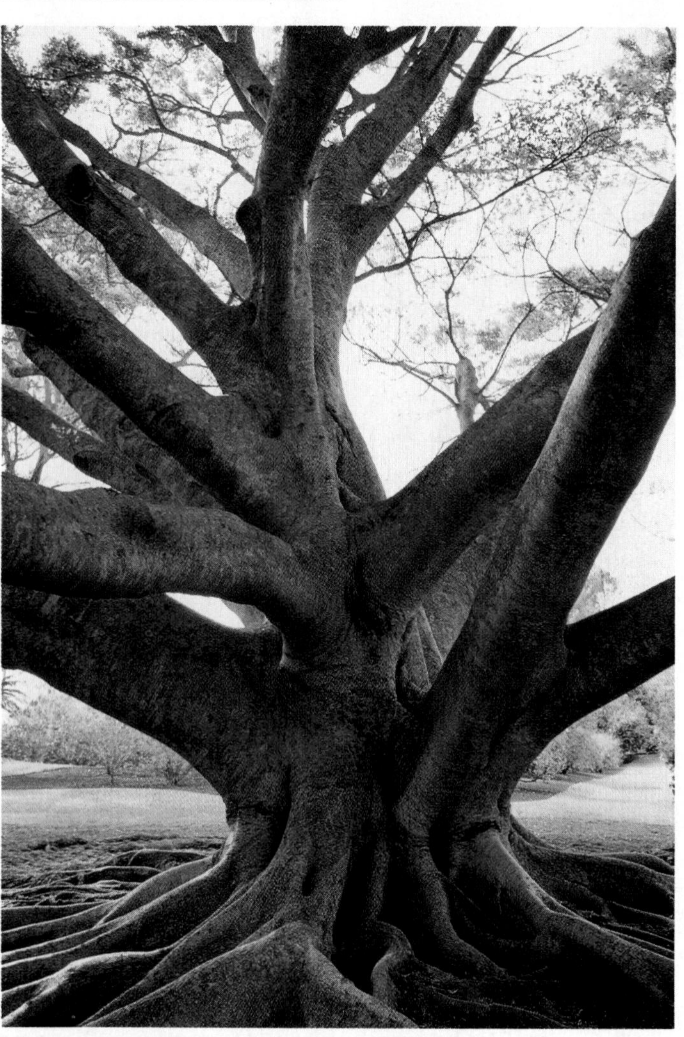

Why do root cells of young plants divide through mitosis so rapidly? As you know, cells divide to replace dead cells and to allow organisms to grow. Roots are important structures to plants, just as your skin is to you. Roots anchor plants and remove water and minerals from the soil. By growing rapidly, roots bring plentiful supplies of water and minerals to developing plants. This allows the plant to remain healthy. What would happen if tears in your skin healed slowly rather than rapidly?

Once a new cell forms, how does it stay alive? How does a cell maintain itself within its environment? In Chapter 20, these questions will be answered as you discover how cells obtain the materials they need for life.

Check Your Understanding

1. How do the end products of mitosis compare with the original cell?
2. You know that each new nucleus produced by mitosis contains the same number of chromosomes as the original cell. A cell from the body of a frog contains a nucleus with 26 chromosomes. If one of these cells undergoes mitosis, how many chromosomes will be in each new cell produced? Explain your answer.
3. How could you tell whether or not a cell was undergoing mitosis? Which structures are visible during mitosis?
4. **APPLY:** What cell process causes hair to constantly increase in length?

EXPANDING YOUR VIEW

CONTENTS

A Closer Look
How Temperature Affects Cells 555

Physics Connection
Light Microsope 556

How It Works
Using a Microscope 557

Health Connection
Skin Cell Mitosis and Cancer 558

Science and Society
Our Aging Population 559

A CLOSER LOOK

HOW TEMPERATURE AFFECTS CELLS

Cells are often described as tiny living factories. Like real factories, they require energy to operate efficiently. Cells do produce a kind of energy, called thermal energy. This energy is released by the process of respiration. The temperature of an organism is a measurement of the thermal energy being released. Most cells can operate at temperatures between 10°C and 40°C, but if the temperature of an organism gets as high as 45°C or as low as 5°C, the cell factories could shut down!

Different kinds of animals and plants have different ideal temperatures at which their cell factories operate. For example, humans maintain a body temperature of 37°C by breaking down foods. At this temperature, our cells have the right amount of energy to operate efficiently. If our cells reach a temperature that's too low, they may be damaged or even die. Respiration slows down when cells get too cold. Reptiles and other cold-blooded creatures cannot regulate their own body temperature but instead depend completely upon energy from their environment to keep them warm. They usually go into hibernation when their body temperature becomes too low for their cells to operate.

You may never have thought of plants running a temperature, but cells of some plants also produce thermal energy. Most plants, however, are very dependent on energy from the environment. Plants, such as broccoli, do poorly in hot weather but grow well in cool weather. Others, such as corn, are just the opposite. Nevertheless, they all need a certain degree of warmth for their seeds to germinate and grow.

WHAT DO YOU THINK?

Why do you think farmers and gardeners wait until the ground has warmed up in the spring before sowing their crops?

Physics Connection

LIGHT MICROSCOPE

It's easy to think of a microscope as a super magnifying glass, but a microscope is much more complex. Unlike a magnifying glass, which has only one lens, a microscope usually has at least three lenses and sometimes more. First, there is the lens closest to your eye, called the eyepiece. Then there is the lens closest to the item you want to see, called the objective lens. Finally, there is the lens closest to the light source that illuminates the item so you can see it, called the condenser.

Here's what happens when you look into a microscope. Light, from either a mirror or a built-in light bulb, passes through the condenser lens where it is intensified and focused on the specimen you are looking at. The light then passes through the specimen and is collected by the objective lens, which shapes the light to form a magnified image of the specimen. That light image is then gathered by the eyepiece lens, which magnifies it again. Finally, the light carries the image into your eye, where it is projected on the layer at the back of your eye called the retina. As a result, you see an onion cell, a skin cell, bacteria, or whatever else you may be looking at through the microscope.

Most microscopes actually have more than one objective lens. Usually, they have three objective lenses with different powers of magnification—10x, 40x, and 100x—meaning they enlarge the image of an item to 10 times, 40 times, or 100 times its natural size. Some microscopes also have changeable eyepiece lenses with different powers of magnification. If you multiply the power of the objective lens by the power of the eyepiece lens, you get the total magnification power of the microscope. For example, if your microscope has an eyepiece of 10x and objective lenses of 10x, 40x, and 100x, it can magnify items from 100 to 1000 times their natural size!

WHAT DO YOU THINK?

The image produced by a microscope is backwards, like the reflection in a mirror, and upside down. For example, if you move a specimen slide to the right, the image you see through the eyepiece will look like it is moving to the left. Or if you move the slide down (toward you), the image will look like it is moving up (away from you). Why does this happen? Can you think of a way to correct the visual image you see so that it operates the same way as the real item?

HOW IT WORKS

USING A MICROSOPE

As you may already know, microscopes contain fragile lenses and must be handled carefully. Always carry the microscope holding the arm with one hand and supporting the base with the other hand. Do not touch the lenses with your fingers.

Place the microscope on a flat surface. Look through the eyepiece and adjust the diaphragm so that light comes through the opening in the stage. Place a slide on the stage. Looking through the eyepiece, make sure the specimen is within your field of view. Then use the spring clips to hold the slide in place. Rotate the low-power objective lens over the hole in the stage.

Now you are ready to focus in on a world not visible to your unaided eyes. First turn the coarse adjustment until the lens is as close to the slide as it will go. Looking through the eyepiece, turn the coarse adjustment to raise the lens until the specimen is visible. Use the fine adjustment to bring the specimen into view.

When you want to use the higher-powered lenses, be careful when rotating them so that you don't bump your slide. After changing lenses, you may need to reposition the slide and to refocus.

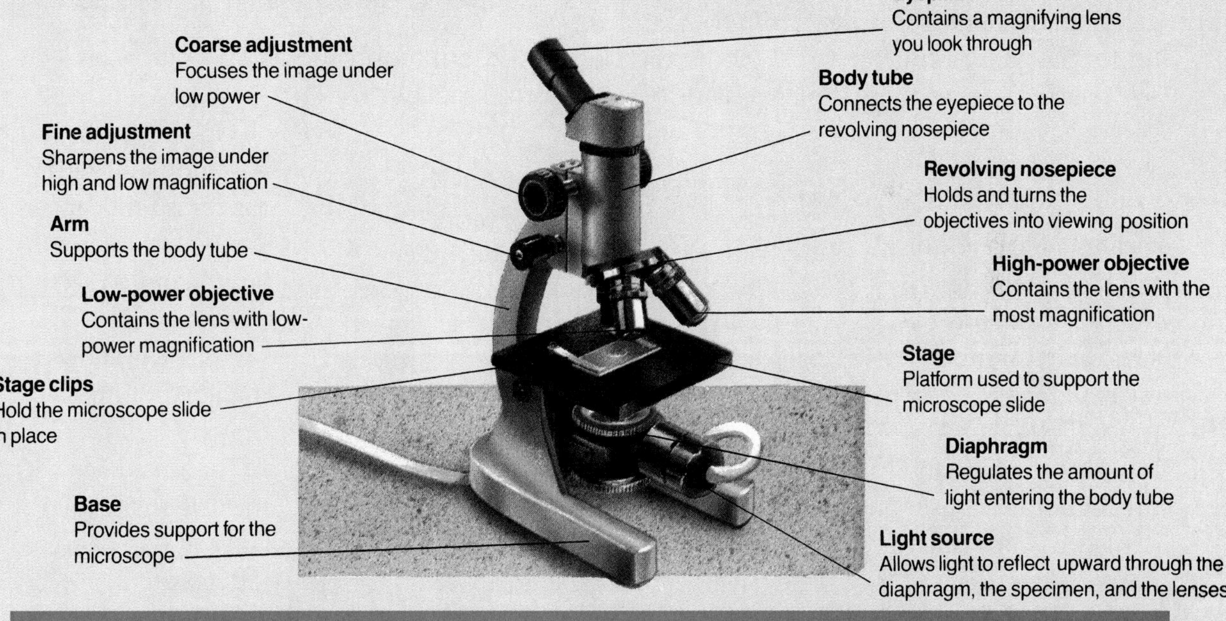

YOU TRY IT!

Prepare a wet mount slide.

1. Hold a glass slide that is free of dust and smudges by the outside edges.
2. Place a very small drop of milk at one end of the slide. Use the edge of another slide to smear the milk in a thin film down the length of the first slide.
3. Gently lower a cover slip in the center of the smear.
4. Place your wet mount slide in your microscope and focus. You will see large, dark-rimmed air bubbles and small round globules of fat floating in clear liquid.

*H*ealth CONNECTION

SKIN CELL MITOSIS AND CANCER

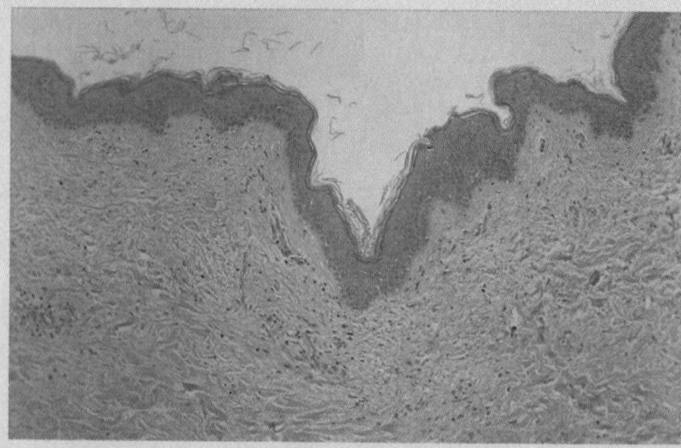

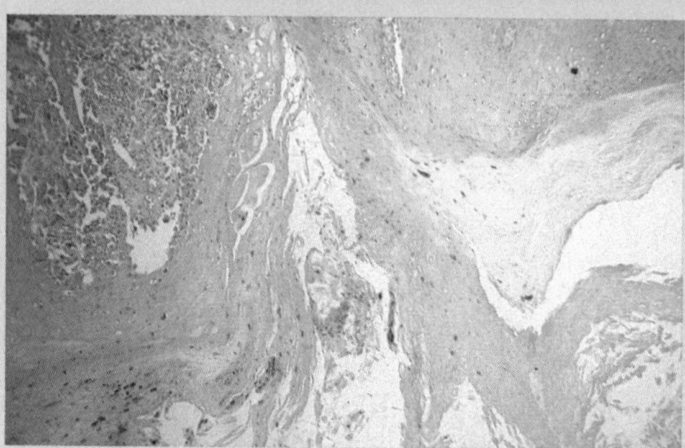

Each kind of cell in our bodies that reproduces undergoes mitosis at its own particular rate. The rate at which a cell reproduces is part of the information stored in the nucleus of that kind of cell. Sometimes a cell is damaged, however, and some of the information stored in its nucleus becomes permanently changed. This change often affects how the cell grows and reproduces.

The original damaged cell and the damaged cells it produces through mitosis form a growing mass of tissue called a tumor. A tumor that is 1 centimeter across (about the size of a pea) can contain as many as one billion damaged cells!

Some tumors are benign (buh NINE), meaning the cells do not have the ability to invade other body tissues. Other tumors are malignant (muh LIHG nant), meaning the cells are much more seriously damaged. They can invade other tissue and spread to other parts of the body. This is called cancer. Cancerous cells undergo mitosis in less than half the time of normal cells. Both kinds of tumors may grow very rapidly or very slowly, but most cancer tumors grow and spread quickly.

YOU TRY IT!

Your skin cells normally reproduce themselves by mitosis every 14 days. If that's the case, how many of your skin cells are undergoing mitosis each day? Here are some facts to help you calculate the answer.

- Your skin measures 1,900,000 square mm.
- One skin cell measures 0.02 mm in diameter, so the area of one cell is 0.0004 square mm. Now make the following calculations.

1. How many skin cells are present on your body? (Need help? Divide the area of one cell into the area of your entire skin.)
2. How many skin cells undergo mitosis each day? Need help? Divide the number of days needed to reproduce by mitosis into the number of skin cells.

One of the most common kinds of cancer is skin cancer. The top photograph is a magnified section of normal skin. The bottom one shows a malignant tumor of the skin called a melanoma. Each year, more than 500,000 cases of skin cancer are reported!

The major cause of skin cancer is ultraviolet radiation from the sun. However, people can use proper sunscreen to prevent ultraviolet rays from damaging their skin cells.

SCIENCE AND SOCIETY

OUR AGING POPULATION

How long can human beings live? There is a great deal of evidence that our bodies age and die according to a "biological clock."

Most gerontologists (scientists who study old age) think that the human body is designed to live no longer than 120 years. Of course, very few people have managed to live that long. Gerontologists say that 110 years is probably the longest that anyone could hope to live—if he or she is extremely healthy and extremely lucky. However, research in molecular biology has given some scientists reason to think we can extend the natural human life span to as long as 130 years! Nevertheless, our cells simply cannot continue to reproduce indefinitely. They wear out, and as a result, we get old and eventually die.

But even though we can't live forever, human beings in America are living longer than they ever have before. In 1900, the average American life expectancy was only 47 years. Today, life expectancy for the average American is 75 years. So, in less than one century, our life expectancy has increased by 28 years (or 63 percent). That's pretty remarkable, considering that it took 20 centuries (2000 years) for the average human life expectancy to increase from 25 years (the life expectancy when Julius Caesar was born in 100 B.C.E.) to 50 years.

The main reason that people in America are living longer is that more people survive childhood. Before modern medicine changed the laws of nature with vaccines and antibiotics, many youngsters died of common childhood diseases such as measles and whooping cough. Now that the chances of dying young are much lower, the chances of living long are much higher. Also, better diets and health care are helping people past 65 to live even more years.

Because fewer Americans are having children and more of them are living longer, America is turning into a "gray" society. Overall, our population is getting older. Since 1950, the number of Americans who are 65 and older has more than doubled to reach 28 million (more than the entire population of Canada). Of that 28 million older Americans, 2.6 million are over the age of 85—four times as many as in 1950.

Twenty-eight million people 65 years of age or older translates into 12 out of every 100 Americans. The United States Census Bureau

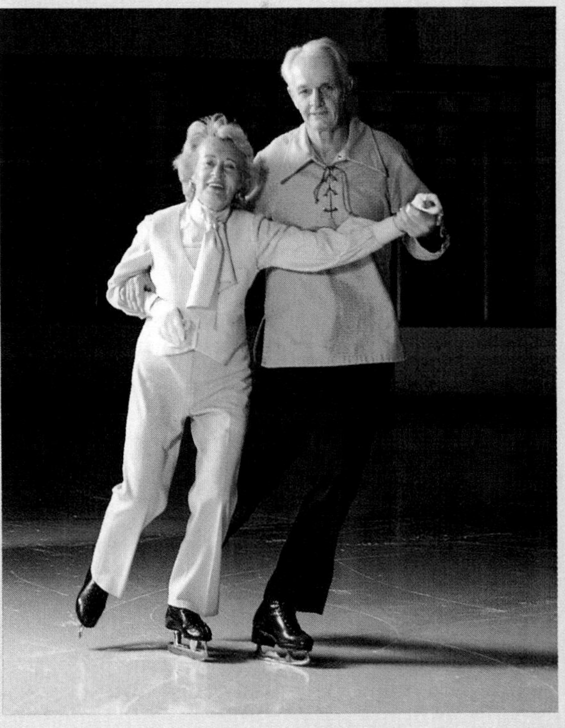

predicts that percentage will reach as high as 25 out of every 100 by the year 2035. Some scientists predict that by the year 2050, more than one-third of our population will be over 65, and only about one-fifth will be under 20!

One reason for the graying of America is the baby boom that followed World War II. Between the mid-1940s and the mid-1960s, 76 million children were born in the United States—increasing our population by one-third. That's as many people as the entire American population in 1900! Starting in 2010, the first of the baby boom generation will reach 65, and by 2030, all of the surviving baby boomers will be 65 to 85 years old. By 2050, there will be only five people of traditional working age (from 20 to 64 years old) for every four people who are past 65, the age of retirement.

Sixty-five may already be out-of-date as the dividing line between middle age and old age. After all, many older people don't begin to experience physical and mental decline until after age 75.

As American society continues to age, the shift in our population will have far-reaching effects on our economy and our way of life. Families, schools, jobs, and health care—all will be changed. Some people fear the changes will be for the worse. For example, money that should be used to provide an education for the young will be used instead to provide expensive medical care for the elderly. Also, working age people will have to pay incredibly high taxes so the government can afford to pay Social Security benefits to the retired.

On the other hand, some people see opportunity, not disaster, in the changes caused by our aging population. Today, many men and women in their "golden years" are healthy and alert, still active, and young in outlook if not in years.

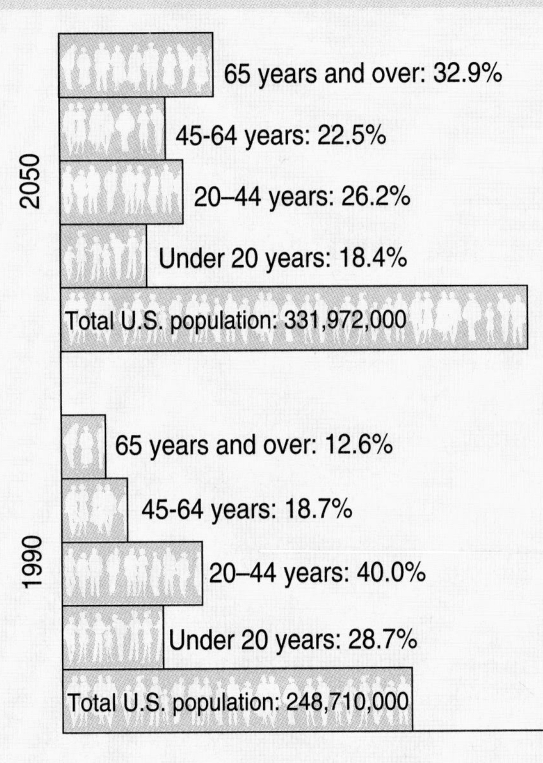

As our society ages, we will need the contributions of our millions of older citizens. And with long lives ahead of them, they will need to stay active and involved.

WHAT DO YOU THINK?

What changes might come about in American society as a result of the graying population? For example, do you think more people will work past the age of 65? What kinds of jobs might they have? What kinds of living arrangements will they have? Will they live with their adult children or perhaps with roommates or in senior citizen facilities? How will they get the medical care they need? Who will pay for it? As you look ahead, what effects do you think the aging of America will have on your life?

Chapter 18

Reviewing Main Ideas

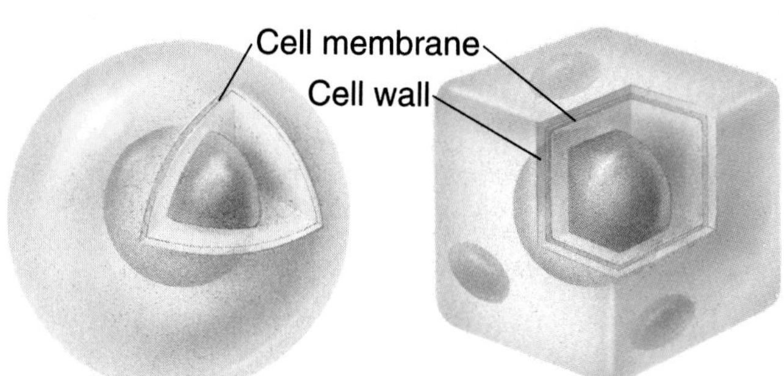

1. The cell is the basic unit of life for all living things. Most cells have a covering called a cell membrane. In addition, plant cells have a rigid outer structure called a cell wall.

2. A cell contains many structures that sustain its life. The nucleus directs the activities of the cell and contains information that controls the traits of an organism. Mitochondria release energy for the cell. In plant cells, light energy is converted into chemical energy in the form of food in choloroplasts.

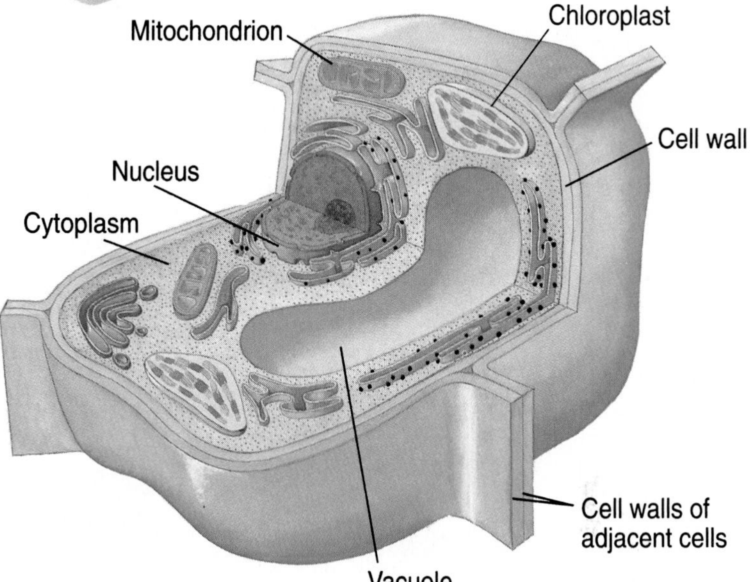

3. Cells reproduce themselves through a process called mitosis. In mitosis, the nucleus of a cell divides so that each new cell has the same number of chromosomes as the parent cell. Growth and healing in the body are evidence that mitosis is occurring.

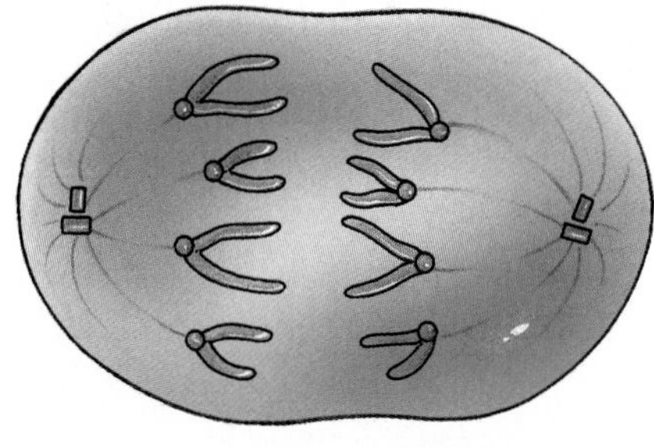

Chapter Review

USING KEY SCIENCE TERMS

cell
cell membrane
cell wall
chloroplast
chromosome
cytoplasm
mitochondria
mitosis
nucleus

For each set of terms below, explain the relationship that exists.

1. cell wall, cell membrane
2. chloroplast, cell wall
3. mitochondria, cytoplasm
4. chromosomes, mitosis
5. cytoplasm, mitochondria, chloroplast

UNDERSTANDING IDEAS

Answer the following questions.

1. How did the development of the microscope aid the understanding of cell structures?
2. How does the shape of a nerve cell provide clues as to the job of the cell?
3. Explain the relationship between the size of a cell and the movement of materials through it.
4. Suppose you want to classify a particular cell as being either a plant or an animal cell. The cell is green in color. What cell parts would you look for in it? Explain your answer.
5. What might large numbers of mitochondria in a cell probably tell you about that cell's amount of activity?
6. What is the relationship between a nucleus and chromosomes?
7. How can you conclude that some of your body cells are reproducing?
8. How does the final product of mitosis differ from the original cell that started the process?
9. Has the total number of cells in your body changed since your birth? Has the structure of your individual cells changed during your lifetime? Explain.
10. How is mitosis important to living things?

CRITICAL THINKING

Use your understanding of the concepts developed in the chapter to answer each of the following questions.

1. Why is it important that each new cell produced by mitosis has the same number of chromosomes as the parent?
2. Algae are protists that contain chlorophyll. While some algae are green in color, other forms of this plant may be red, brown, or even gold. What might cause this range of colors in organisms that contain chlorophyll?
3. How are mitochondria and chloroplasts similar?

4. Cancer is a disease in which there is abnormal rapid growth in body cells. What is happening with mitosis in cancer cells?
5. Cells that exist by themselves tend to be spherical in shape. Cells in many-celled organisms are often shaped like cubes or other regular shapes. How might you explain this difference?
6. The figure shows a cell that is reproducing by mitosis. Carefully examine what is occurring in the cell. Explain what will happen next in the cell as the mitosis process continues.

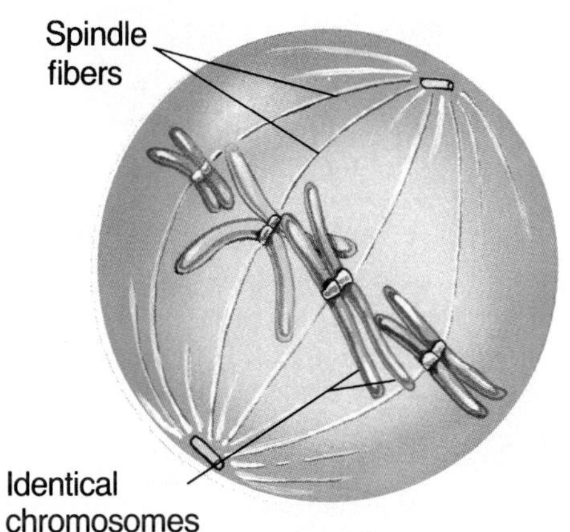

PROBLEM SOLVING

Read the following problem and discuss your answers in a brief paragraph.

Carla is investigating the growth rate of various types of cells. One of the organisms she is studying is *E.coli*, a one-celled bacterium. Carla observes that this bacterium can double its size in about 30 minutes if the environmental conditions are suitable. She also observes that once the cell has grown to twice its original size, it divides to form two new cells.

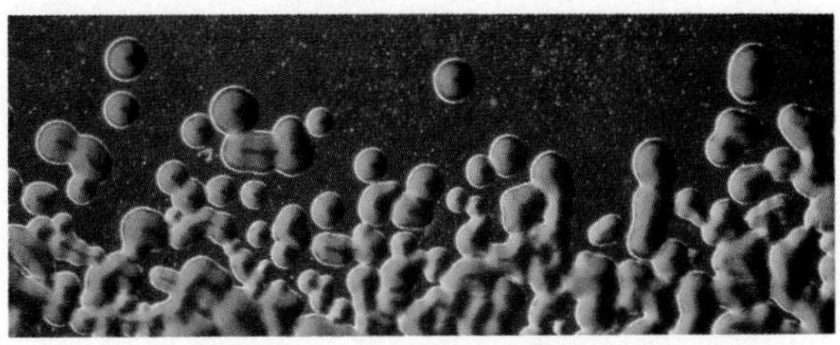

1. Why does *E.coli* divide when it grows to twice its size rather than continue to grow as a single cell?
2. If *E.coli* can divide at such a rapid rate, why doesn't the population of this bacterium outnumber all other kinds of organisms?

CONNECTING IDEAS

Discuss each of the following in a brief paragraph.

1. How is the nucleus of a cell similar to the brain?
2. How is a cell wall similar to a human skeleton?
3. What role do you think the development and improvement of the microscope played in scientists' understanding of cells?
4. **PHYSICS CONNECTION** What is the magnification power of a microscope equipped with a 10x eyepiece and a 100x objective lens?
5. **HOW IT WORKS.** Which knob is more useful for bringing objects into clear focus, the coarse adjustment knob, or the fine adjustment knob?

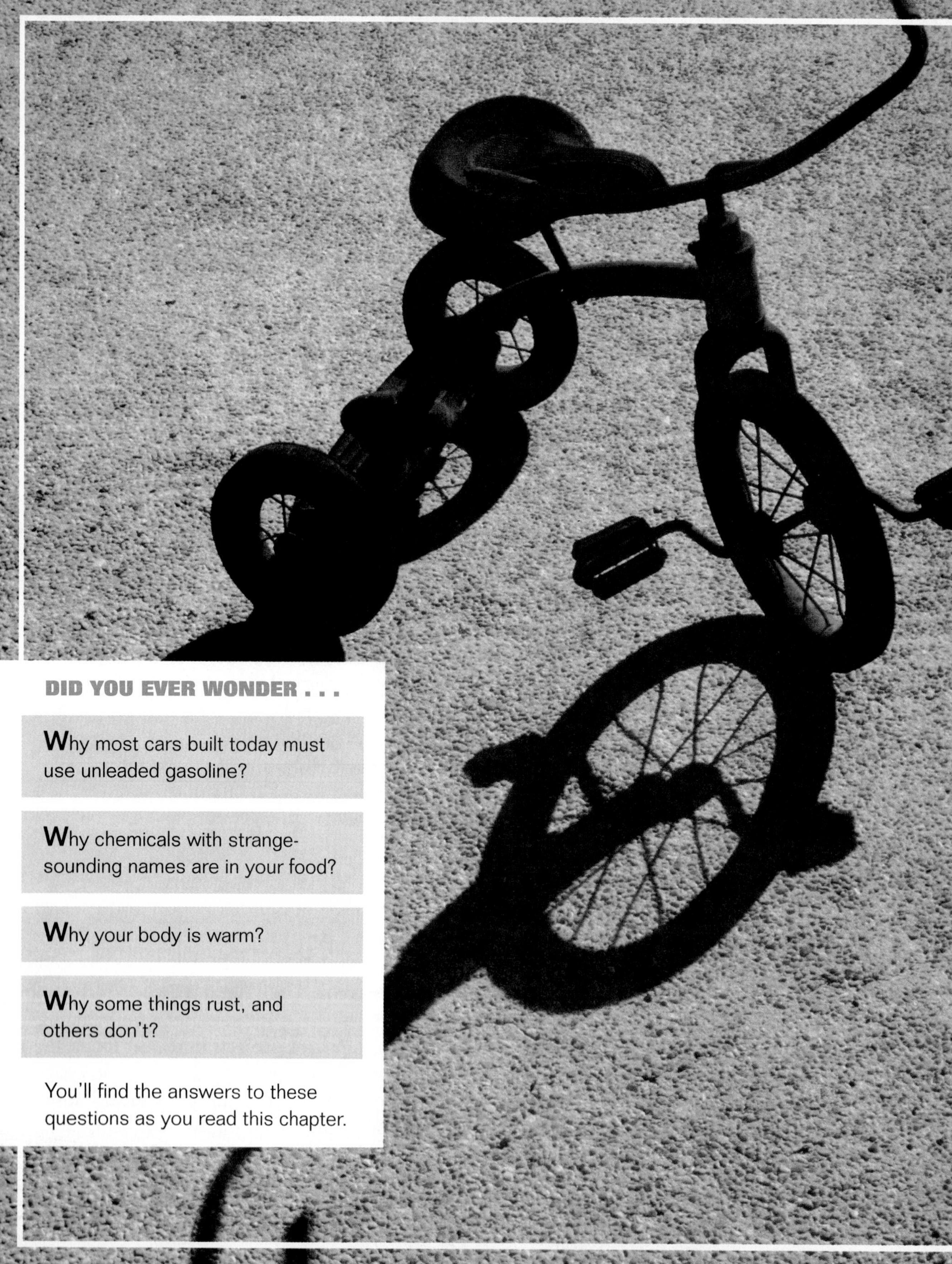

DID YOU EVER WONDER . . .

Why most cars built today must use unleaded gasoline?

Why chemicals with strange-sounding names are in your food?

Why your body is warm?

Why some things rust, and others don't?

You'll find the answers to these questions as you read this chapter.

Chapter 19

Chemical Reactions

Imagine what that tricycle once looked like and how it felt to ride it. Perhaps it belonged to someone like you. Not long ago, the wheels probably glistened in the sun. Surely, its owner had great fun riding it from place to place. Now much of the trike is coated with reddish-brown rust. It almost seems as if some of the metal would crumble if you touched it. In some places, the edges look sharp and dangerous.

Rusting is just one of many kinds of chemical changes that go on around you. A hamburger cooking, flowers growing and blooming, and the burning of gasoline in your automobile are all actions during which the properties of substances change. Chemical changes that take place in your body affect your health and well-being. In this chapter, you will find out how chemical changes take place.

EXPLORE!

What kinds of things rust?
Look for rust on objects at home, in school, and on your way to school. Do things that rust have anything in common? Where does rust form? Do you notice more rust on objects that are indoors or outdoors? Why do you think this is so?

19-1 How Does Matter Change Chemically?

OBJECTIVES

In this section, you will

- describe materials before and after chemical changes;
- recognize when chemical reactions have taken place;
- identify and describe several chemical reactions.

KEY SCIENCE TERMS

chemical reaction

OBSERVING CHEMICAL CHANGES

You're already familiar with many chemical changes. Burning wood turns to ashes. A newspaper left lying in the sun turns yellow. Rust forms on tools left out in the rain, and the paint on buildings begins to fade. Plants and animals grow. How are these chemical changes similar? How are they different?

FIND OUT!

Are all chemical changes alike? 

Observe what happens when a piece of paper burns. List the changes that you and your classmates observe. Watch what happens as a marshmallow burns. Again, list the changes you observe. Which changes are alike for the paper and the marshmallow? Which are different? Next, observe how a banana changes over a period of a few days. Describe any changes in the color, odor, and texture of the skin or the fruit inside.

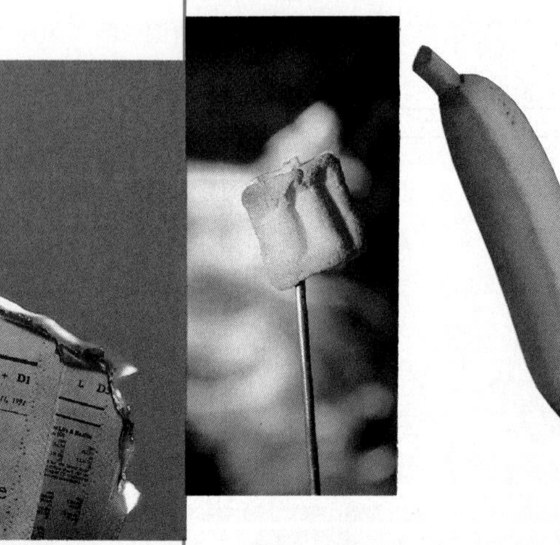

Conclude and Apply

1. Compare and contrast the changes in the banana, the paper, and the marshmallow.
2. How do these changes differ from what you observe when you boil a pot of water?

FIGURE 19-1. Chemical reactions are involved in many everyday events.

CHEMICAL REACTIONS AROUND YOU

When a piece of paper burns, a banana ripens, or a bike rusts, the chemical and physical properties of the substance change. These changes may happen quickly, or they may take place over a period of months or years. In each case, however, new substances are formed. A chemical reaction has taken place. A **chemical reaction** is a process that results in the formation of new substances having properties that are different from those of the original substances.

Whenever you see a cut apple turn brown, exhaust gases come out of a car's tailpipe, or a caterpillar change into a butterfly, you know that chemical reactions are taking place. Some of these chemical reactions can destroy precious historical objects such as books and paintings.

Have you ever tried to turn a page in a very old book only to have bits of the yellowed paper crumble in your fingertips? These changes are caused by the reaction between substances in the air and in the paper. Paper and other materials that resist such changes are now being used. However, older books, papers, and paintings must be stored under carefully controlled conditions. Study Figure 19-2 to see how the Constitution of the United States is protected from chemical reactions. The case is filled with nitrogen gas, and the document is protected from strong light that could cause further damage.

FIGURE 19-2. The Constitution is preserved in a specially designed case.

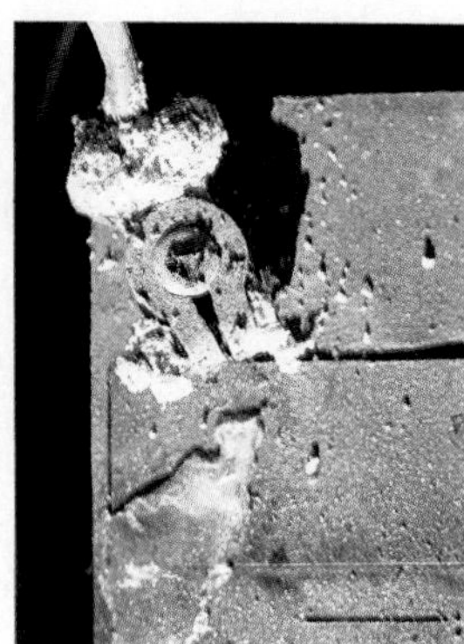

FIGURE 19-3. What chemical reactions are taking place in these pictures?

DESCRIBING CHEMICAL REACTIONS

Remember how you described what happened to the marshmallow and the banana? You probably used words that told about changes in physical properties, such as color, shape, texture, and smell. How could you describe a rusting bicycle or a burning paper? When you say that paper burns and iron rusts, you are describing the chemical properties that change during chemical reactions. How would you describe the chemical reactions pictured in Figure 19-3? It might appear that the substances haven't changed as the building collapses. You have brick or stone before and after the explosion. But what was the reaction that caused the building to collapse? While descriptive words are useful in telling someone what happened, they don't tell us much about the reaction itself. Why is it useful to be able to describe the chemical reactions that take place around you?

Check Your Understanding

1. List several ways that you can tell that a chemical change has taken place.
2. Name three chemical reactions that you read about in this section.
3. List two chemical changes not mentioned in this section. How did you decide that they were chemical rather than physical changes?
4. **APPLY:** When you dissolve sugar in water, does a chemical reaction take place? How do you know?

19-2 Word Equations

CHEMICAL REACTIONS INSIDE YOU

In the last section, you saw that chemical reactions take place around you all the time. Would you be surprised to find out that chemical reactions take place inside your body every moment of your life? You know you breathe in oxygen from the air around you. But what happens to that oxygen?

OBJECTIVES

In this section, you will

- distinguish between reactants and products;
- write word equations;
- differentiate between synthesis and decomposition reactions;
- recognize single displacement reactions.

KEY SCIENCE TERMS

reactants
products
synthesis reaction
decomposition reaction
single displacement reaction

FIND OUT!

Is oxygen changed inside your body?

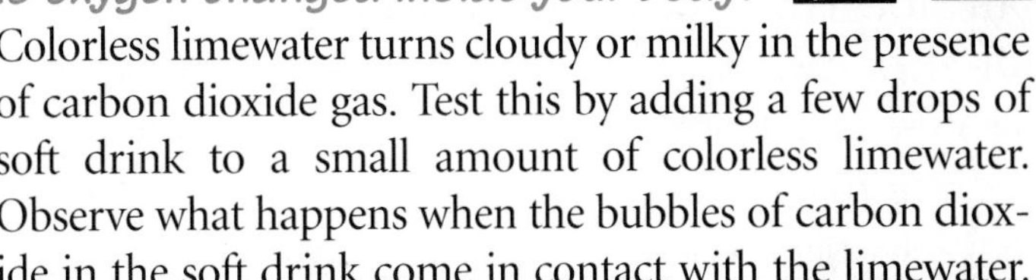

Colorless limewater turns cloudy or milky in the presence of carbon dioxide gas. Test this by adding a few drops of soft drink to a small amount of colorless limewater. Observe what happens when the bubbles of carbon dioxide in the soft drink come in contact with the limewater. Now gently blow out through a straw into a glass half-filled with colorless limewater. **CAUTION**: *Be sure not to take in or swallow any limewater.* Describe the changes you observe in the limewater as you continue to blow out through the straw.

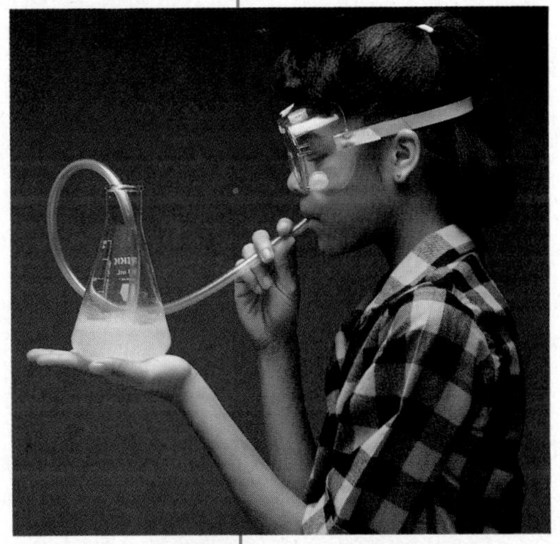

Conclude and Apply

1. How could you be sure that limewater does not turn cloudy when oxygen is present?
2. What can you infer from your observations?
3. Has a chemical reaction taken place?

You inhale oxygen gas into your lungs. The oxygen combines with the food you have taken in. Through a series of chemical reactions called respiration, carbon

FIGURE 19-4. It may look like just a pizza to you. But to your body, it's an energy-rich fuel.

dioxide and energy are produced. It is this carbon dioxide you exhaled into the lime-water in the glass. The energy sustains life and keeps your body running.

At the same time, another series of chemical reactions called digestion takes place in your stomach and intestines. During digestion, food is broken down by chemical reactions into small molecules that are carried by the blood to the many parts of your body. These molecules are the fuel that is combined with oxygen during respiration.

WRITING WORD EQUATIONS

How might you describe the chemical reactions in respiration? You could describe changes in the physical and chemical properties of the substances in words. Another way is to write a word equation. For example, you could use a + sign to mean *and* and an arrow (→) to mean *produces.* Then the word equation for respiration would look like this:

$$\text{oxygen} + \text{food} \rightarrow \text{carbon dioxide} + \text{water} + \text{energy}$$

Think about what happens when charcoal burns in a barbecue. The carbon in the charcoal combines with oxygen in air to produce carbon dioxide. Your experience tells you that light and thermal energy are also produced. The word equation for this reaction is:

$$\text{carbon} + \text{oxygen} \xrightarrow{\text{heat}} \text{carbon dioxide} + (\text{light} + \text{thermal energy})$$

FIGURE 19-5. Heat is necessary to start this chemical reaction.

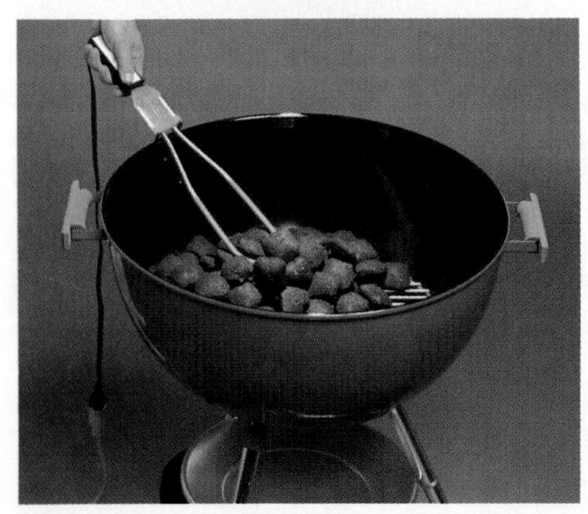

The word *heat* over the arrow means that heat is necessary to start this reaction. You would read this equation, "In the presence of heat, carbon and oxygen produce carbon dioxide. Light and thermal energy are given off."

In any chemical reaction, the substances that you start with are the **reactants**. The new substances formed by the reaction are the **products**. When charcoal burns, carbon and oxygen are the reactants. Carbon dioxide is the product. What are the reactants and products of respiration?

Photosynthesis is one of the most important chemical reactions on Earth. Without it, life as we know it could not exist. In photosynthesis, green plants take in carbon dioxide, produced during respiration, and water. They produce oxygen, needed for respiration, and sugar, which supplies food for the plants and for animals that eat plants. This reaction takes place only in the presence of sunlight or other strong light. What word equation could you write to describe photosynthesis?

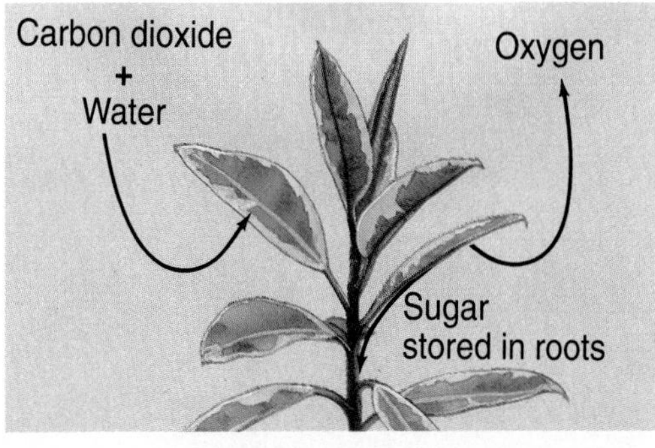

FIGURE 19-6. In photosynthesis, two reactants form two products in the presence of sunlight.

Notice that chemical reactions involve one or more reactants and one or more products. In general, any word equation can be written in the form:

reactant(s) → product(s)

SYNTHESIS REACTIONS

How is the word equation for the burning of charcoal different from the equations for respiration and photosynthesis? It describes a chemical reaction in which two or more substances (reactants) have combined to form one new substance (product).

The chemical reactions you have studied so far are synthesis reactions. A **synthesis reaction** takes place when two or more substances combine to form one new substance. How do you know this word equation describes a synthesis reaction?

$$\text{hydrogen} + \text{oxygen} \xrightarrow{\text{energy}} \text{water (hydrogen oxide)}$$

FIGURE 19-7. When aluminum combines with oxygen, a coating of aluminum oxide is formed.

Look at this close up of a lawn chaise lounge in Figure 19-7. The gray, powdery substance on the aluminum is aluminum oxide. Write a word equation for the synthesis reaction that produces aluminum oxide.

Rust is also the product of a synthesis reaction. When iron or steel rusts, iron combines with oxygen to form iron oxide, the chemical name for rust.

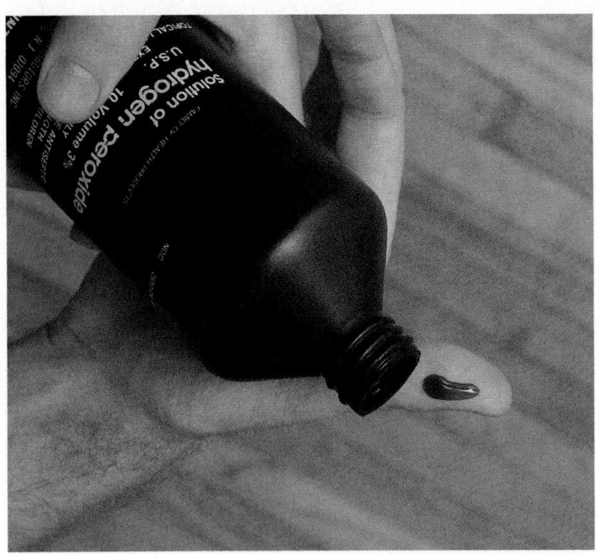

FIGURE 19-8. Why is hydrogen peroxide stored in brown bottles such as this?

The word equation that follows,

$$\text{iron} + \text{oxygen} \xrightarrow{\text{water}} \text{iron oxide (rust)}$$

describes what happens when your bike or other iron objects get the reddish-orange coating we call rust.

DECOMPOSITION REACTIONS

Perhaps you are wondering whether some reactions go the other way. Have you ever cleaned a wound with hydrogen peroxide? What makes the foaming you see? When hydrogen peroxide comes into contact with a non-smooth surface, it breaks down into oxygen and water. Hydrogen peroxide also is broken down by light, but this reaction occurs more slowly. Consider the word equation that describes what happens.

$$\text{hydrogen peroxide} \xrightarrow{\text{light}} \text{oxygen} + \text{water}$$

In the presence of light, hydrogen peroxide is broken down into two substances, namely oxygen and water.

Consider the word equation, which describes breaking down water. With the help of added energy, water can be broken down into hydrogen and oxygen. Water is the reactant. What are the products?

$$\text{water} \xrightarrow{\text{electricity}} \text{hydrogen} + \text{oxygen}$$

The breaking down of hydrogen peroxide and the breaking down of water are decomposition reactions. A **decomposition reaction** takes place when one substance is broken down into two or more new substances. Use paper clips to model a decomposition reaction. What letters can you use to represent the reaction? How does a decomposition reaction compare with a synthesis reaction?

Describe some properties of the substance that covers the pretzel in Figure 19-9. Clearly it is white, and the crystals are cube-shaped. And yes, it does taste salty. With

SKILLBUILDER

FORMULATING MODELS

On a piece of paper, write a word equation for a synthesis reaction. Place a red paper clip below the first reactant. Place a blue paper clip below the second reactant. Hook the clips together for the product. Write letters to represent what happens. You can use paper clips to model other reactions in this section. If you need help, refer to the **Skill Handbook** on page 690.

FIGURE. 19-9. The chemical name for table salt is sodium chloride.

the help of an electrical current, table salt can be decomposed into sodium and chlorine.

$$\text{sodium chloride} \xrightarrow{\text{electricity}} \text{sodium} + \text{chlorine}$$

While table salt, sodium chloride, is a necessary part of your diet, both sodium and chlorine are unpleasant elements. Sodium is a silvery white metal that reacts violently with water, and chlorine is a greenish, poisonous gas with a burning odor. In the synthesis reaction, these properties disappear, and the familiar white, crystalline solid is formed.

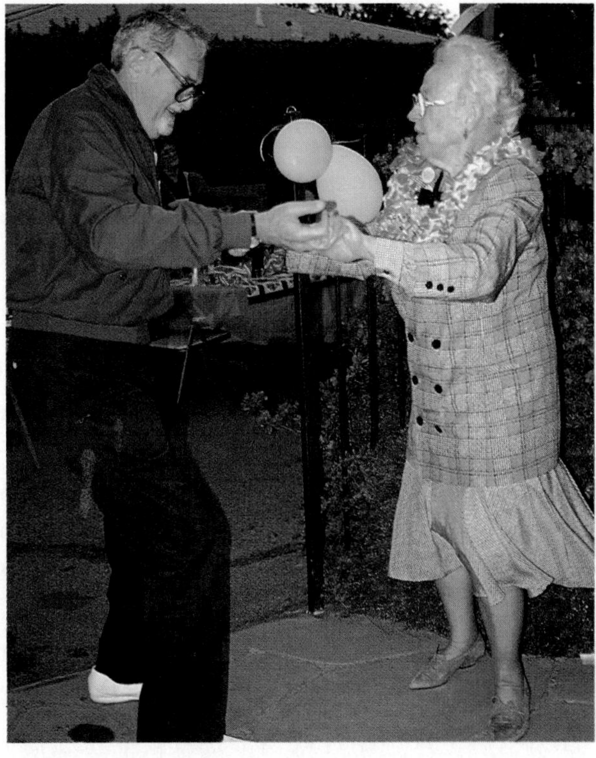

FIGURE. 19-10. How is the joining and separating of dance partners related to chemical reactions?

SINGLE DISPLACEMENT REACTIONS

Imagine that two people are dancing together. The first song ends, and they begin to dance to the next song together, when someone else cuts in. The first partner no longer has anyone to dance with.

Perhaps the joining and separating of dancing partners remind you of synthesis and decomposition reactions. But what does changing dance partners have to do with chemical reactions? The following activity will help you find out.

EXPLORE!

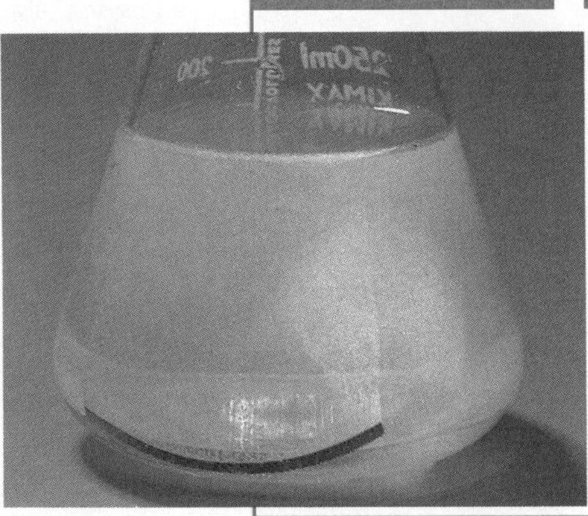

Do substances change partners in chemical reactions?

Drop a piece of magnesium ribbon into a small amount of white (distilled) vinegar. Observe carefully for several minutes. How do you know a reaction is taking place? How can you keep the reaction going?

The reaction that took place in the Explore activity is a bit more complicated than other reactions you've studied. Let's take it step by step to see what happened. Because vinegar is an acid, it contains hydrogen. In fact, vinegar contains acetic acid, also called hydrogen acetate. When the magnesium was placed in the vinegar, it reacted with the acetic acid. Bubbles of hydrogen gas were released. This is the word equation for the reaction:

magnesium + acetic acid (hydrogen acetate) →
magnesium acetate + hydrogen

Study the reactants and the products. Notice that at the start of the reaction, hydrogen and acetate were partners. Then magnesium joined with acetate, leaving hydrogen without a partner. The magnesium seems to have taken the place of hydrogen, just as your second dancing partner took the place of your first.

The switching of partners in the reaction between magnesium and vinegar is a single displacement reaction. In a **single displacement reaction**, one substance takes the place of another substance to form new substances. Make a model of this single displacement reaction. Use a combination of red and blue paper clips for vinegar and use a green clip for magnesium. With three more clips, show the products. What letters represent this reaction?

You've seen that magnesium displaces the hydrogen in vinegar, a dilute acid. In the activity that follows, you will test several metals to see how they react with a different dilute acid.

SKILLBUILDER

CLASSIFYING

Write word equations for each of the following reactions and classify each as a synthesis reaction, a decomposition reaction, or a single displacement reaction. If you need help, refer to the **Skill Handbook** on page 678.

1. Silver reacts with sulfur to form tarnish.
2. When iron reacts with hydrogen sulfate contained in sulfuric acid, hydrogen gas is released.

INVESTIGATE!

19-1 SINGLE DISPLACEMENT

In this activity, you will compare the reaction of several metals with an acid to see whether a single displacement reaction takes place.

PROBLEM

Which metals displace hydrogen from an acid?

MATERIALS  

3 test tubes
test-tube rack
small pieces of copper, zinc, and magnesium
graduated cylinder
wooden splint
15 mL dilute hydrochloric acid
goggles
apron

PROCEDURE

1. Copy the data table.
2. Put on goggles and an apron.
3. Set the three test tubes in a rack. Pour 5 mL of dilute hydrochloric acid, which contains hydrogen chloride, into each tube.
   CAUTION: *Handle acid with care. Immediately rinse away any spilled acid with plenty of water.*
4. Place a small piece of copper in the first tube, zinc in the second tube, and magnesium in the third tube.
5. **Observe** what happens in each tube and record your observations in the data table.
6. Have your teacher collect some of the gas from the third test tube and bring a lighted splint near the gas. Record what you observe.

DATA AND OBSERVATIONS

TUBE	SUBSTANCES MIXED	OBSERVATIONS
1	Hydrochloric Acid + Copper	
2	Hydrochloric Acid + Zinc	
3	Hydrochloric Acid + Magnesium	

ANALYZE

1. What evidence of chemical reaction did you **observe**? Which metals reacted with the acid?
2. Write a word equation for the reaction in the second test tube.

CONCLUDE AND APPLY

3. When ignited, hydrogen explodes with a "pop." What can you **infer** about the identity of the gas in test tube 3? Why?
4. **Predict** which metal would be least affected by acid rain if it were used to build statues.
5. **Going Further:** The method of displacement in this Investigate is the most common way to prepare large amounts of hydrogen for use in the laboratory. Which of the metals you tested would be best for this purpose? Why?

FIGURE 19-11. The effects of displacement reactions can be harmful or helpful.

Displacement reactions, like those that you just investigated, can be useful or destructive. The corrosion of metals by acid rain, the greenish film that coats and protects the Statue of Liberty, and the designs on an artist's metal plate all result from displacement reactions.

Being able to determine what products will be formed from certain reactions is useful. With such information we can predict the effects of some industrial process on the environment or the effects of a new medicine on the body.

Review the word equations you studied in this section. Can you suggest some other factors that play a part in determining whether some chemical reactions will take place? In the next section, we'll take a closer look at the role played by energy in chemical reactions.

Check Your Understanding

1. Write a word equation to describe this chemical reaction: In the presence of heat, iron and sulfur form iron sulfide.
2. Identify the kind of chemical reaction shown in the following equation.

$$\text{mercury oxide} \xrightarrow{\text{heat}} \text{mercury} + \text{oxygen}$$

3. Mercury oxide is a red, powdery substance. All substances that contain mercury, including mercury itself, are poisonous. Use this information to compare the properties of the reactants and products from question 2.
4. What type of reaction is represented by the equation?

$$\text{chlorine} + \text{sodium oxide} \rightarrow \text{sodium chloride} + \text{oxygen}$$

Explain how you know.

5. **APPLY:** Many foods, such as tomato sauce, contain acids. What factors would you consider when choosing a container to cook or store such foods?

19-3 Chemical Reactions and Energy

ENERGY IN REACTIONS

Have you ever seen a fireworks display on the Fourth of July? Brilliant colors and the sounds of exploding rockets fill the night sky. Did you know that these sights and sounds are caused by a series of chemical reactions? Although you can't actually see these reactions taking place, you can certainly observe the results! You've seen that chemical reactions produce new substances. But colored light and sound are forms of energy, not substances. Where did this energy come from?

OBJECTIVES

In this section, you will

- relate how energy is involved in chemical reactions;
- differentiate between endothermic and exothermic reactions.

KEY SCIENCE TERMS

endothermic reaction
exothermic reaction

EXPLORE!

Does a rubber band have energy?

Slip one end of a rubber band over a pencil. Push the other end of the rubber band through a small hole in the center of an index card, as shown. Hold the pencil flat against the back of the card. Pull on the rubber band to stretch it a bit. Then let it go and listen to the sound it makes. Pull on the rubber band several more times. Each time, stretch the rubber band a little bit more. What happens to the sound? How do you know that a stretched rubber band has energy? Where does the energy come from?

CHEMICAL ENERGY

The stretched rubber band in the Explore has potential energy. The rubber band absorbs (takes in) the energy you put in when you pull on the rubber band. When you let go, the potential energy of the rubber band is released

FIGURE 19-12. Chemical reactions can produce spectacular results.

(given off) and transformed into the energy of sound. There is a similar energy change in chemical reactions.

Like the stretched rubber band, the substances inside fireworks rockets contain chemical potential energy that was stored when the substances were formed. When the rockets are ignited, a series of chemical reactions begins to take place. During these reactions, the chemical potential energy in the substances is released and changed into the light you see and the sound you hear. If you were close enough to the rockets, you'd also feel the thermal energy that is given off.

Look back at the chemical reactions you studied in the last section. Notice how many of the word equations for these reactions use words such as heat, electricity, and light. All are forms of energy. In some cases energy was absorbed. In other cases energy was released.

CHEMICAL REACTIONS THAT ABSORB ENERGY

Exploding fireworks give off a lot of energy. However, some reactions require a lot of energy to get them started and keep them going. Does the following equation look familiar?

$$\text{carbon dioxide} + \text{water} \xrightarrow{\text{light}} \text{sugar} + \text{oxygen}$$

Recall that this photosynthesis reaction takes place only in the light. Green plants absorb energy from sunlight. This energy is changed into the chemical energy in sugar and in oxygen. Light is also needed to keep the reaction going. If you keep a green plant in the dark for too long, it will eventually die.

FIGURE 19-13. Plants use energy from sunlight to make food. Without this energy, they will die.

The photosynthesis reaction involves the absorbing of energy. A chemical reaction in which energy is absorbed is called an **endothermic reaction**. The decomposition of water into hydrogen and oxygen is also an endothermic reaction. What kind of energy is absorbed in this reaction? In an endothermic reaction, you must keep supplying energy for the reaction to continue.

CHEMICAL REACTIONS THAT RELEASE ENERGY

Imagine that you've worked very hard for several hours. Soon, your stomach begins to complain. When you eat, the chemical reactions of digestion release some of the chemical energy in food. This energy can then be used by the body for movement or other internal processes of the cells. The heat of your body is an example of chemical energy that has been changed to thermal energy.

Some of the chemical energy in the food is stored in the body to be released when needed. One of these materials is fat. When fat drips from a hamburger onto hot charcoal, the burning fat flares up into a big flame. That is the chemical energy in the fat that is being released and changed into thermal energy. The reaction inside your body does not take place as rapidly. In your body, the fat is burned slowly. The chemical energy in fat is released when the fat reacts with oxygen during respiration. This reaction provides the energy you need to play, work, and live.

FIGURE 19-14. Potassium is a very active metal. In contact with water, it reacts vigorously, producing hydrogen gas and releasing energy.

FIGURE 19-15. A hamburger contains chemical energy.

Both the burning of fat and the digestion of food release chemical energy and produce thermal energy. A chemical reaction in which energy is released is called an **exothermic reaction**. The explosion of fireworks is an exothermic reaction that produces light, sound, and thermal energy. Think back to the word equation for the burning of charcoal. How do you know this is also an exothermic reaction? Although you have to supply energy to start this reaction, you don't have to keep supplying energy for it to continue. The releasing of the chemical energy in the charcoal keeps the reaction going.

Consider what happens when dynamite is exploded. Although the dynamite must be ignited, this reaction not only produces thermal energy, light, and sound, but also moves large amounts of other matter. Clearly, exothermic reactions produce more energy than you have to put in.

Rusting is also an exothermic reaction, but you would never guess it. This reaction proceeds so slowly that it is difficult to measure the temperature change caused by the release of energy.

In the activity that follows, you will determine whether a reaction is endothermic or exothermic by measuring changes in temperature.

FIGURE 19-16. Only a small amount of energy is needed to start this exothermic reaction.

I N V E S T I G A T E !

19-2 ENERGY CHANGES

In this activity, you will observe a chemical reaction and **measure** and record any change in energy that takes place.

PROBLEM

How can you tell if a reaction is exothermic or endothermic?

MATERIALS   

clock or watch with second hand
3% hydrogen peroxide solution
thermometer
25 mL graduated cylinder
8 test tubes and rack
goggles
apron
raw liver
raw potato

PROCEDURE

Part A

1. Copy the data table.
2. Put on goggles and an apron. Add 5 mL of hydrogen peroxide to one test tube. **CAUTION**: *Hydrogen peroxide can irritate skin and eyes.*
3. Insert the thermometer and record the starting temperature of the hydrogen peroxide. **CAUTION**: *If using a mercury thermometer, handle carefully.*
4. Remove the thermometer. Add a small piece of liver.
5. Record the temperature of the liver and hydrogen peroxide every 30 seconds for 6 minutes.
6. Repeat the procedure three more times. Use clean equipment and new materials each time.
7. Average the four trials in each column to complete your data table.

Part B

1. Make a new data table.
2. Repeat Part A using small pieces of potato. Record your observations.
3. Again, average your results.

ANALYZE

1. What evidence indicates that a chemical reaction took place?
2. Were the reactions exothermic or endothermic? How do you know?

CONCLUDE AND APPLY

3. **Identify** the **variables** in this experiment.
4. **Predict** the effect of using smaller pieces of liver or potato.
5. **Going Further:** Where did the energy to start this reaction come from?

DATA AND OBSERVATIONS

		TEMPERATURE AFTER ADDING LIVER/POTATO											
TRIAL	STARTING TEMPERATURE	MINUTES											
1													
2													
3													
4													
Total													
Average													

SKILLBUILDER

MAKING GRAPHS

Make a graph of the data you collected in the Investigate. Plot the average temperature against time, beginning with the starting temperature. Plot the points for the liver in one color and the potato in a different color. For each set of data, connect the dots using straight lines. What do these lines show? If you need help, refer to the **Skill Handbook** on page 680.

TRACING ENERGY CHANGES

In the reactions you just observed, the chemical energy in hydrogen peroxide was released when the liver and the potato were added to it. The chemical energy was changed to thermal energy, as evidenced by the increase in the temperature over time.

Using information from this chapter, let's trace the energy changes and identify the endothermic and exothermic reactions in the following situation. You strike a match to light a camp stove to cook an egg that you eat for breakfast before taking a long hike in the woods. When you strike the match, the thermal energy produced by the friction starts an exothermic reaction. The chemical energy of the match is changed to light and thermal energy. You use the thermal energy to light the gas in your camp stove. The gas in the stove reacts with oxygen in the air in an exothermic reaction, releasing its chemical energy as thermal energy. You use the thermal energy released to start the chemical reaction that cooks the egg. If you don't keep the stove on, the egg will stop cooking. So the cooking of an egg is an endothermic process.

After you digest the egg, some of the chemical energy from the egg remains stored in your body. Later, as you are hiking in the woods, some of this stored energy is changed into the mechanical energy needed to move your muscles.

Make a list of things that you do and things around you that involve chemical reactions. Try to trace the changes in chemical energy for each one on your list.

Check Your Understanding

1. Describe the role of energy in the chemical reaction of baking a cake. Is the reaction endothermic or exothermic?
2. In writing a word equation for the burning of wood, where would you place thermal energy?
3. **APPLY:** Sometimes during thunderstorms, lightning may strike a tree and set it on fire. As you know, burning is a chemical reaction. Tell where the energy comes from to begin this reaction.

19-4 Speeding Up and Slowing Down Reactions

SPEEDING UP REACTIONS

You've just come home from school. The walk from the bus stop has made you hungry. You decide to make an omelet. You don't want to burn your eggs, so you keep the flame low. The omelet seems to take forever to cook. You know it would cook faster if you turned up the heat a little.

Above is a reaction that requires energy in order to take place. Some reactions, such as the decomposition of table salt, would never take place without a great deal of energy. Is there a way to speed up a reaction without using lots of energy?

OBJECTIVES

In this section, you will

- describe how a catalyst affects a chemical reaction;
- explain how to control a chemical reaction with an inhibitor.

KEY SCIENCE TERMS

catalyst

inhibitor

FIND OUT!

Can a chemical reaction be made to go faster without adding energy?

Remember that hydrogen peroxide decomposes very slowly when exposed to light. Wearing goggles and an apron, pour about 5 mL (2.5 cm) of hydrogen peroxide into each of two test tubes. Very carefully, watch for any signs that a chemical reaction is taking place. Use a small plastic spoon or a spatula to add a small amount of manganese dioxide into one of the test tubes. What do you observe? Light a wooden splint and blow it out. Place the glowing splint just inside the mouth of the tube without the manganese dioxide. What happens? Repeat with the other test tube. What happens? Heat this tube in a beaker of boiling water until no liquid is left. What do you see?

Conclude and Apply

1. Although oxygen doesn't burn, it must be present for burning to take place. How do you know oxygen was produced in this reaction?
2. What can you infer about the role of manganese dioxide in this reaction?

The manganese dioxide in the Find Out helped the reaction take place and made the reaction go faster. However, the manganese dioxide was not chemically changed as a result of the reaction. The word equation for this decomposition reaction is:

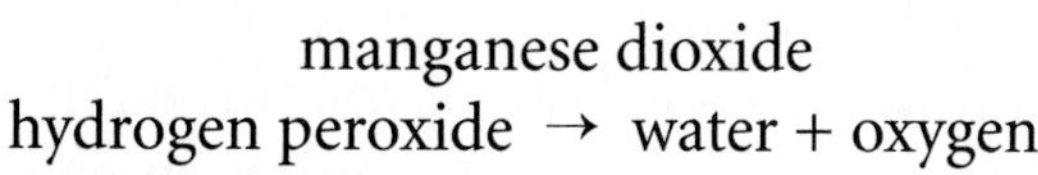

$$\text{hydrogen peroxide} \xrightarrow{\text{manganese dioxide}} \text{water} + \text{oxygen}$$

FIGURE 19-17. Chlorophyll in green plants is a catalyst in the photosynthesis reaction.

Any substance that speeds up a chemical reaction without being used up is called a **catalyst.** Manganese dioxide is a catalyst in the decomposition of hydrogen peroxide. How do you know? Salt is a catalyst in the formation of rust.

Some synthesis reactions are also helped or speeded up by catalysts. For example, the photosynthesis reaction would not take place, even in sunlight, without the help of chlorophyll. This substance that makes green plants green acts as a catalyst to bring about the reaction between CO_2 and water. Sunlight provides the energy that is needed for photosynthesis to take place. To be more complete, the word equation for photosynthesis should also include chlorophyll.

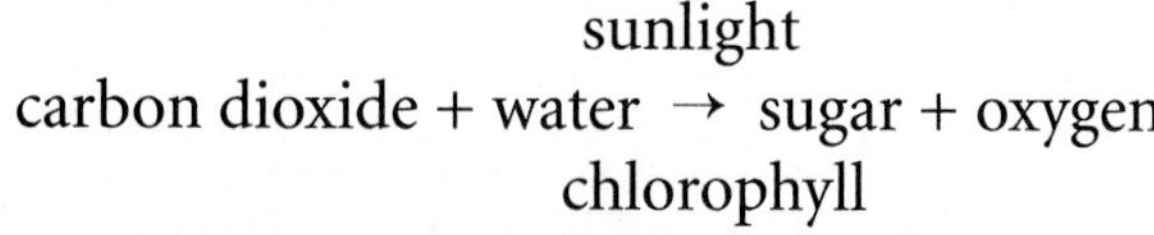

$$\text{carbon dioxide} + \text{water} \xrightarrow[\text{chlorophyll}]{\text{sunlight}} \text{sugar} + \text{oxygen}$$

Catalysts are also involved in many of the chemical reactions that take place in organisms. These catalysts are protein substances called enzymes. The digestion of food, for example, depends on enzymes. The enzyme amylase, found in saliva, helps break down starch into sugar. In the presence of the acid in your stomach, another enzyme,

How do we know?

The Role of Chlorophyll

One of the ways we know that chlorophyll is necessary for photosynthesis is by studying organisms that lack chlorophyll. Nongreen plants and fungi get their nourishment by living on food produced by other organisms. When separated from their host organisms, nongreen plants soon die.

From experimental evidence, we know that chlorophyll alone cannot produce the photosynthesis reaction. When chlorophyll is extracted from green plants mixed with water and carbon dioxide, and exposed to light, photosynthesis does not take place. The process is quite complex and not completely understood.

called pepsin, starts the digestion of protein. This chemical reaction is continued in your small intestine with the help of the enzyme trypsin. In this way, enzyme catalysts make possible the many chemical reactions that keep you alive.

DID YOU KNOW?

Because of enzyme catalysts, the chemical reactions in your body take place more than a million times faster than they would otherwise.

CATALYTIC CONVERTERS

In many cities, air pollution caused by automotive exhaust gases is a problem. Some of this pollution is reduced by using catalysts to speed up the chemical reaction between oxygen and the harmful substances produced by cars. The reaction takes place inside a device called a catalytic converter.

In one type of converter, air and exhaust gases are passed through a bed of small beads that are coated with the catalysts platinum and palladium. The harmful gases stick to the catalysts until the gases combine with oxygen to form harmless carbon dioxide and water. An automobile with a catalytic converter must use only lead-free gasoline because lead would coat the catalysts, making them ineffective.

FIGURE 19-18. Catalytic converters help reduce air pollution.

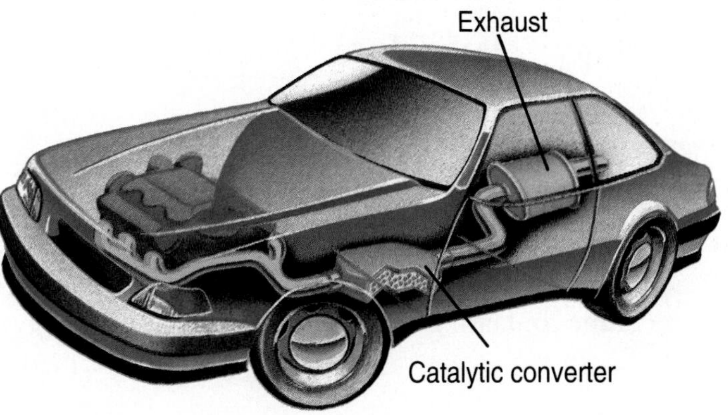

SLOWING DOWN REACTIONS

Look at the portion of a label from a box of cereal shown in Figure 19-19. You probably recognize most of the ingredients. One of the ingredients that may

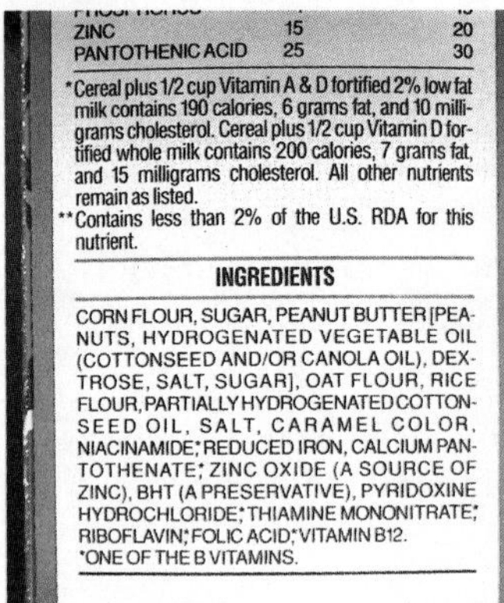

ZINC 15 20
PANTOTHENIC ACID 25 30
*Cereal plus 1/2 cup Vitamin A & D fortified 2% low fat milk contains 190 calories, 6 grams fat, and 10 milligrams cholesterol. Cereal plus 1/2 cup Vitamin D fortified whole milk contains 200 calories, 7 grams fat, and 15 milligrams cholesterol. All other nutrients remain as listed.
**Contains less than 2% of the U.S. RDA for this nutrient.
INGREDIENTS
CORN FLOUR, SUGAR, PEANUT BUTTER [PEANUTS, HYDROGENATED VEGETABLE OIL (COTTONSEED AND/OR CANOLA OIL), DEXTROSE, SALT, SUGAR], OAT FLOUR, RICE FLOUR, PARTIALLY HYDROGENATED COTTONSEED OIL, SALT, CARAMEL COLOR, NIACINAMIDE;* REDUCED IRON, CALCIUM PANTOTHENATE;* ZINC OXIDE (A SOURCE OF ZINC), BHT (A PRESERVATIVE), PYRIDOXINE HYDROCHLORIDE;* THIAMINE MONONITRATE;* RIBOFLAVIN;* FOLIC ACID;* VITAMIN B12.
*ONE OF THE B VITAMINS.

FIGURE 19-19. The BHT in this cereal helps keep it fresh longer.

not be familiar to you is BHT. BHT stands for butylated hydroxytoluene (BYEW til ate ed hydroxy–TOL u ene), which is more of a mouthful than the food itself! BHT is added to the packaging to slow down the rate at which breads and cereals combine with oxygen. Oxidation is a major cause of spoilage in foods.

Any substance that slows down a chemical reaction is called an **inhibitor**. BHT is an inhibitor, as are most other preservatives added to foods. Foods containing inhibitors will spoil eventually but inhibitors greatly decrease the rate at which this occurs. Inhibitors are also used as medicines. Some antibiotics inhibit the action of those enzymes in the body that tend to help bacteria grow. This, in turn, slows the growth rate of the bacteria. Then your body's natural defense system can more easily destroy the bacteria so that you get well faster.

Can you think of a destructive chemical reaction where an inhibitor might be useful? Some paints are advertised as being rust inhibitors. How do you think these paints work?

Catalysts and inhibitors help us control the rate of chemical reactions. By now you have seen many ways in which chemical reactions affect you. Some chemical reactions are helpful, and some are harmful. Some reactions can be speeded up, and some can be slowed down. You may be beginning to understand that every change creates other changes, and every action has an effect on your world. By understanding how chemical reactions take place and how to control them, you can make wiser decisions about the world you live in.

Check Your Understanding

1. You want to slow down the following reaction:

   iron + oxygen → iron oxide

   Which would act as an inhibitor, oil or water?
2. When a rusty iron nail is added to a test tube containing hydrogen peroxide, bubbles quickly form. The nail undergoes no obvious change. What conclusion can you draw about iron oxide (rust)?
3. **APPLY:** Enzymes are sometimes used in detergents to boost their cleaning power. What do you think that means?

EXPANDING YOUR VIEW

CONTENTS

A Closer Look
Steely Recipes 587

Life Science Connection
Edible Fuel 588

Science and Society
What's in Your Food Besides Food? 589

Health Connection
Are You Too Awake? 590

Technology Connection
What We Breathe Can Eat Bridges! 591

Teens in Science
Cellular Fun 592

A CLOSER LOOK

STEELY RECIPES

You've seen rust on steel bicycles and cars. You know rust forms when iron combines with oxygen. What is the relationship between iron and steel?

Pig iron is made from two parts iron ore (iron oxide and sand), one part carbon in coke form, a "pinch" of limestone (calcium carbonate), and four parts hot air.

When heated with a limited amount of air, carbon (coke) combines with oxygen in the air to produce carbon monoxide. The carbon monoxide reacts with the iron oxide in the ore to eventually produce carbon dioxide and pig iron. The sand from the ore has combined with calcium oxide formed by the heated limestone and is easily removed as slag. Pig iron, however, is not very strong—and it's not steel.

Removing the carbon from iron produces a metal that is malleable, strong, and durable. Molten pig iron is placed in an egg-shaped converter, and forced through a large quantity of hot air that combines with the carbon in the iron to form carbon monoxide. This produces a very vigorous reaction. A product of this reaction is iron with less than 1 percent carbon—called steel.

Stainless steel and other special steels are made with molten pig iron, scrap iron, and powdered limestone. These are all placed in an oven lined with calcium oxide. Oxygen is added, but heat is not. A series of rapid exothermic reactions takes place that keep the contents mixed and molten.

Corrosion as well as the strength of the steel can be varied by adding nickel, chrome, or tungsten at the beginning of the process. Stainless steel contains from 12 to 30 percent chrome.

YOU TRY IT!

Look through newspaper ads and clip those that mention stainless, nickel, chrome, or tungsten steels. List the use of each type of steel.

LIFE SCIENCE CONNECTION

EDIBLE FUEL

Like automobiles, our bodies have efficient engines. If they get the fuel they need, they have a better chance of running at peak performance. One essential food that provides energy is the carbohydrate.

Carbohydrates come in many shapes and sizes. They're in foods such as apples, pears, grapes, oatmeal, spaghetti, bread, corn, potatoes, and rice. All carbohydrates are made of carbon, oxygen, and hydrogen.

When you eat foods with sugar, such as refined white sugar, your body can quickly use the sugar as fuel. Inside your body's cells, the sugar combines with oxygen. This chemical reaction, called respiration, provides quick energy.

What can you eat if you need energy over a longer period of time? You may have heard of runners or athletes "carbohydrate loading" before a big race or game. Strenuous activities, such as marathon running, require a lot of energy. If an athlete's muscles are to get the energy they need for a long race, runners must consume large amounts of carbohydrates. Athletes are counting on the starch in these foods to provide the fuel for the respiration reactions throughout the event.

The starches in carbohydrates cannot provide quick energy because the starch molecule is, itself, composed of several sugar molecules joined together. First, there must be a chemical reaction to break apart the starch molecule. Then, the resulting sugar can be used by the cell for energy.

YOU TRY IT!

Test for starch in bread. Put on goggles and a lab apron. Add a few drops of iodine to two teaspoons of water and stir with a wooden splint.

CAUTION: *Iodine is poisonous and stains. Do not taste food you have tested.*

Put a few drops of solution on a small piece of bread and observe what happens. Starch turns blue when tested with iodine.

Test some other foods, including spaghetti and apples, to see which contain starch.

SCIENCE AND SOCIETY

WHAT'S IN YOUR FOOD BESIDES FOOD?

When George Washington Carver first made peanut butter, he probably gathered the nuts, roasted them, mashed them, and spread them on bread—all within a day or two. Now the peanut butter may spend weeks on a grocer's shelf and months in your cupboard.

The peanut butter can readily be changed by reactions with oxygen in the air. Some reactions cause the solid mashed peanuts to separate from the nut oil. The color might change. The oil might combine with oxygen and other elements in the air and spoil. To prevent chemical changes, food manufacturers add chemicals, called food additives, to food.

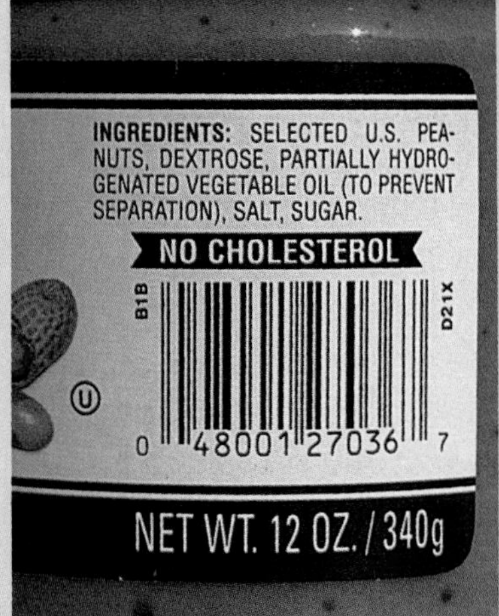

INGREDIENTS: SELECTED U.S. PEANUTS, DEXTROSE, PARTIALLY HYDROGENATED VEGETABLE OIL (TO PREVENT SEPARATION), SALT, SUGAR.
NO CHOLESTEROL
0 48001 27036 7
NET WT. 12 OZ. / 340g

Salt was one of the first additives and was used to preserve meats and fish. It was also a natural additive. Natural additives, such as salt and ascorbic acid (vitamin C), are still used today. The food industry, however, depends on hundreds of different chemicals to keep your food edible for a longer time.

Some additives are used for purposes other than preservation. There are additives to make foods taste better or replace the color lost in processing. Some additives make foods creamy, while others make foods thick. Still others keep ingredients from separating. Iodine in salt and vitamin D in milk are added to prevent diseases.

All these chemicals are regulated by the Food and Drug Administration (FDA). One of the many roles of the FDA is to regulate the use of any chemical that may cause cancer. Yet, there are questions about the need for, and safety of, many food additives. Occasionally, the FDA has approved additives that were later banned because they were shown to cause cancer. An example is red dye No. 2.

There are additives that cause reactions ranging from mild to life-threatening for certain individuals. One is the flavor enhancer monosodium glutamate, known as MSG. Most people show no allergic reaction to MSG at all. However about five percent of the population experiences dizziness, blurred vision, and sweating after eating foods with MSG. Sulfites, an additive often used to keep certain vegetables green and salad ingredients crisp without refrigeration, can bring an asthma patient to the brink of death.

CAREER CONNECTION

A food chemist or food technologist works with food manufacturers to develop additives. Food chemists study chemistry, biology, and biochemistry.

WHAT DO YOU THINK?

Make a list of your favorite foods and the food additives in them. Are any of these same foods available without additives? How much more would you be willing to pay for the additive-free item?

Health CONNECTION

ARE YOU TOO AWAKE?

The story goes that a monk in an Arabian monastery centuries ago observed goats in the field nibbling the berries from a coffee plant. After their evening snack, the goats ran and played all night long without ever seeming to be tired. The monk, thinking of all the things he had to do, decided to try the berries himself. He gathered some, added them to boiling water, and found that the resultant brew did indeed make him more alert and kept him from falling asleep.

Whether that story is true or not, caffeine has been used for centuries as a stimulant. Caffeine, which is never found alone in nature, is a combination of carbon, hydrogen, nitrogen, and oxygen. Pure caffeine is bitter-tasting white powder. When caffeine is taken into the body, chemical changes take place that turn caffeine into other chemicals. The chemicals that come from the caffeine interfere with your body's natural substances and stimulate the nerves. The result is that you get a jolt of nervous energy and feel more awake.

The problems come when there is too much caffeine in the body and the nerves are too stimulated. The results can be inability to sleep, irregular heartbeat, nervousness, high cholesterol, and difficulties in pregnancy.

Many products besides coffee contain caffeine. Tea, soft drinks, chocolate, cocoa, and several over-the-counter drugs contain fairly large amounts of caffeine. It is also hard to know exactly how much caffeine you are taking into your body. For example, a cup of coffee can contain 29 milligrams of caffeine or 176 milligrams of caffeine, or any amount in between. Tea can contain between 8 milligrams and 91 milligrams of caffeine in one cup. The amount of caffeine depends in part on the way the coffee or tea was prepared. Some researchers say that people can take up to 600 milligrams of caffeine per day without any harm being done. Others say that even smaller amounts can do damage.

Average Amounts of Caffeine	
Coffee	80mg-120mg
Hot cocoa	1-8mg
Tea	40mg
Soft drinks	40mg

WHAT DO YOU THINK?

The chart shows the average amounts of caffeine in milligrams in a cup of four drinks. Keep a record of how much caffeine you take a day from these sources. Would you be better off with less?

TECHNOLOGY CONNECTION

WHAT WE BREATHE CAN EAT BRIDGES!

Of all the chemical reactions possible in today's world, one probably receives more attention and costs more money than any other. Rust and corrosion take their toll on bridges, overpasses, and ships. Corrosion occurs when metals such as iron or steel are affected by ordinary water and oxygen in the environment. If rain is a bit acidic or if there are dissolved salts in the atmosphere, corrosion occurs even faster.

There are ways to protect metal from corrosion. Perhaps you've seen the overpasses along the expressway being painted. You may have coated your ice-skate blades or your bicycle chain with oil before you stored them for next season. On your way to school, you may pass a fence that has a plastic coating on it. Each of these methods of protection prevents oxygen and water in the air from reaching the metal and causing corrosion.

You already know that the reaction of some metals with oxygen can produce an oxide. For instance, if aluminum is exposed to air, a thin coating of aluminum oxide is formed. Unlike iron oxide, which is loose and dusty, aluminum oxide consists of very tightly packed molecules. These molecules are so tightly packed that the aluminum oxide actually protects the metal beneath from further reactions.

There is an alternate method for protecting metals from corrosion that relies on electricity. Perhaps you've heard of galvanized steel. It's often used for garbage cans, plumbing, and gutters. Galvanized steel is steel coated with zinc by means of an electrical process. The zinc slowly forms a zinc oxide coating that protects the iron or steel beneath it. Magnesium sheets bolted to bridge pillars and ship hulls protect in the same way. In each case, the applied metal is allowed to corrode in order to protect the structural metal beneath.

YOU TRY IT!

Design a sculpture of iron or steel using discarded items you might have at home or might find in an alley or vacant lot. Make a detailed drawing of your sculpture, showing clearly the items you might use. Then tell how you might protect it from corrosion.

TEENS *in* SCIENCE

CELLULAR FUN

Have you ever wondered exactly why your doctor or dentist uses certain types of equipment?

Edie Shin, a 17-year-old high school senior in Orland Park, Florida, did more than wonder. "I noticed that my dentist always covered me with a lead apron before she took X rays of my mouth. During my sophomore year, I decided to find out why she takes such great precautions with X rays. In my chemistry class, we'd been talking about the effects of radiation on human cells. I wanted to find out just how harmful X rays can be."

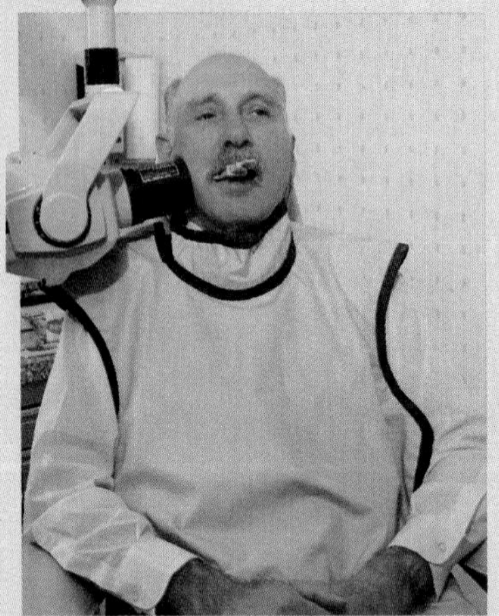

A local hospital assisted Edie in her experiment. They gave her a supply of human cells which had come from the throat culture of a healthy 50-year-old man. In addition, Edie got special permission to conduct her experiment in the radiology section of the hospital. Edie used the hospital's equipment to expose the throat cells to a minimum of 50 RADS of radiation every week for nearly a year. Each exposure equaled nearly 250 times the amount of radiation that you are exposed to during regular dental X rays.

Normally, human cells are small and rounded. Healthy cells contain only one nucleus. However, Edie soon discovered that the cells she had irradiated looked very different.

"Many cells died over the course of the experiment. But the cells that survived grew as much as ten times their normal size. Some had as many as six nuclei."

In examining the peculiar cells, Edie came to the conclusion that when precautions such as using the lead apron are taken, normal dental X rays do not harm human cells. However, when human cells are exposed to high levels of radiation over a long period of time, a series of chemical reactions occur in the cellular water of normal cells. This can result in mutations.

"At first, I wasn't sure what was going to happen. That's the best thing about science. It doesn't matter what you're getting. It's how much fun you have along the way."

YOU TRY IT!

Edie Shin's experiment helped her to better understand why her dentist uses a lead apron during X rays. Make a list of any medical or dental equipment that you would like to understand better.

Choose one item from your list. Telephone your doctor's or dentist's office and ask him or her to explain why this equipment is used.

Chapter 19

Reviewing Main Ideas

Synthesis:

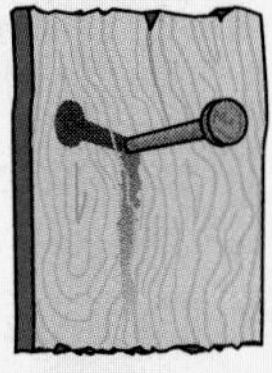

Iron + Oxygen → Iron oxide (Rust)

Decomposition:

Carbonic acid → Carbon dioxide + water

1. A chemical reaction involves the changing of substances into other substances. Synthesis, decomposition, and single displacement reactions are types of chemical reactions that affect you and the world around you.

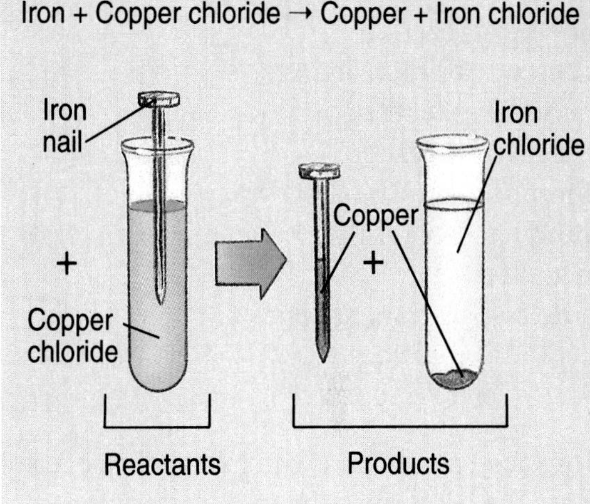

2. A word equation is a way to describe what happens in a chemical reaction.

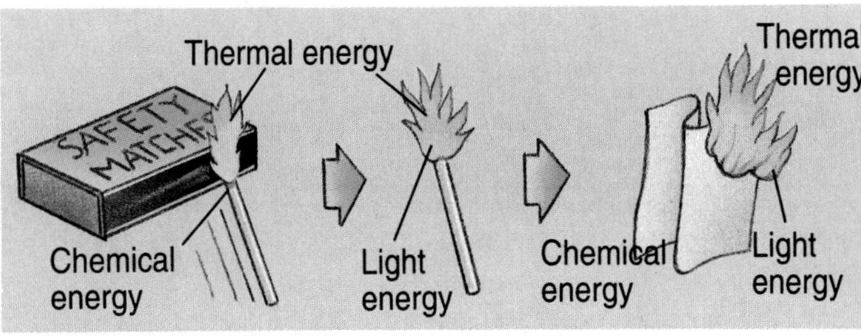

3. Every chemical reaction involves changes in energy. Energy may be absorbed, as in an endothermic reaction. Or energy may be released, as in an exothermic reaction.

4. Catalysts and inhibitors help control the rate at which chemical reactions take place. Substances themselves remain chemically unchanged at the end of the reaction.

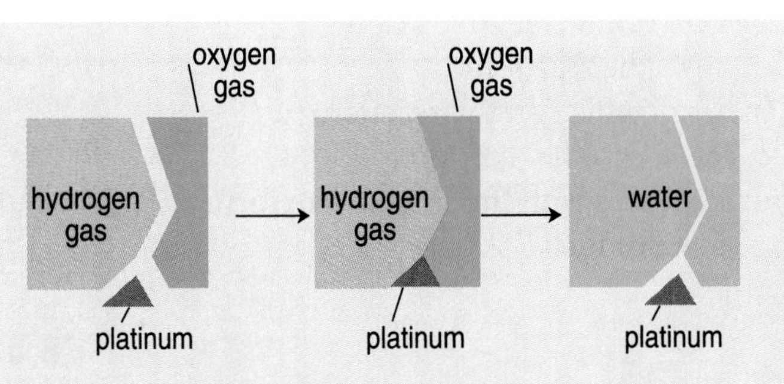

Chapter Review

USING KEY SCIENCE TERMS

catalyst
chemical reaction
decomposition reaction
endothermic reaction
exothermic reaction
inhibitor
products
reactants
single displacement reaction
synthesis reaction

For each term below, which key science term from the list is opposite in meaning? If a term has no opposite, say so.

1. reactants
2. chemical reaction
3. exothermic reaction
4. synthesis reaction
5. single displacement reaction
6. catalyst

UNDERSTANDING IDEAS

Choose the best answer to complete each sentence.

1. In a chemical reaction, a catalyst ____.
   a. slows the reaction
   b. has no effect on the reaction
   c. speeds up the reaction
   d. combines with the reactants to form a new product
2. The rusting of a bicycle is described best by ____.
   a. synthesis reaction
   b. oxygen + iron → iron oxide
   c. a solid metal combines with a colorless gas to produce a reddish-brown substance
   d. all of the above
3. A chemical reaction that results in a substance being broken into two or more simpler substances is a ____.
   a. composition reaction
   b. single displacement reaction
   c. synthesis reaction
   d. decomposition reaction

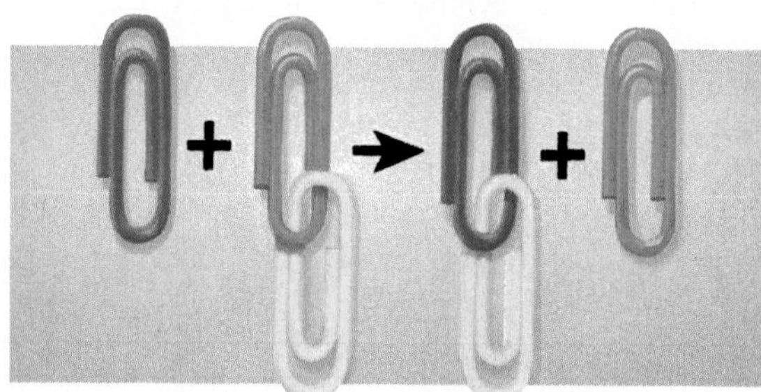

4. The paper clip model represents a ____.
   a. synthesis reaction
   b. decomposition reaction
   c. single displacement reaction
   d. catalytic reaction
5. A substance that slows down a reaction but remains unchanged is ____.
   a. a catalyst   c. an inhibitor
   b. a product   d. all of the above
6. $\text{starch} \xrightarrow{\text{amylase}} \text{sugars}$

   In the word equation, amylase is ____.
   a. a catalyst   c. an inhibitor
   b. a reactant   d. a product

7. When fat is burned by your body, ____.
   a. chemical energy is changed to light
   b. chemical energy is changed to thermal energy
   c. thermal energy is changed to chemical energy
   d. thermal energy is changed to light

CRITICAL THINKING

Use your understanding of the concepts developed in the chapter to answer each of the following questions.

1. In the decomposition of water, how do the products differ from the reactants?
2. Differentiate between an exothermic and an endothermic reaction. What evidence do you have that respiration is an exothermic reaction?
3. You know that burning is an exothermic reaction. If this is true, why doesn't toast continue to get darker after it is removed from the toaster?
4. Two identical pieces of apple were left out in the air. One piece was first dipped in lemon juice. Based on the results in the table, do you think lemon juice is a catalyst or an inhibitor? Explain your reasoning.

Time	With Lemon Juice	Without Lemon Juice
10	no browning	edges brown
20	no browning	more browning
30	no browning	surface brown

PROBLEM SOLVING

Read the following problem and discuss your answers in a brief paragraph.

You are a highway engineer assigned to maintain your company's equipment in good condition.

1. How can you use your knowledge of chemical reactions to design a maintenance program that will protect the equipment from rust?
2. Your work site is near the sea. What other factors in the environment might you need to consider?

CONNECTING IDEAS

Discuss each of the following in a brief paragraph.

1. What two factors might be responsible for bananas ripening more slowly if they are kept in the refrigerator?

2. In photosynthesis, is sunlight a catalyst or a reactant? Explain.

3. If your doctor prescribed an inhibitor, how would it affect how your nerves transmit impulses across the synapse?

4. **A CLOSER LOOK** Write a word equation for the burning of propane to form water and carbon dioxide. Be sure you indicate whether heat is needed for the reaction to proceed, or if the reaction gives off heat.

5. **LIFE SCIENCE CONNECTION** What is the word equation for the chemical reaction that changes sugar to energy in the cell? Is the reaction exothermic or endothermic? Explain.

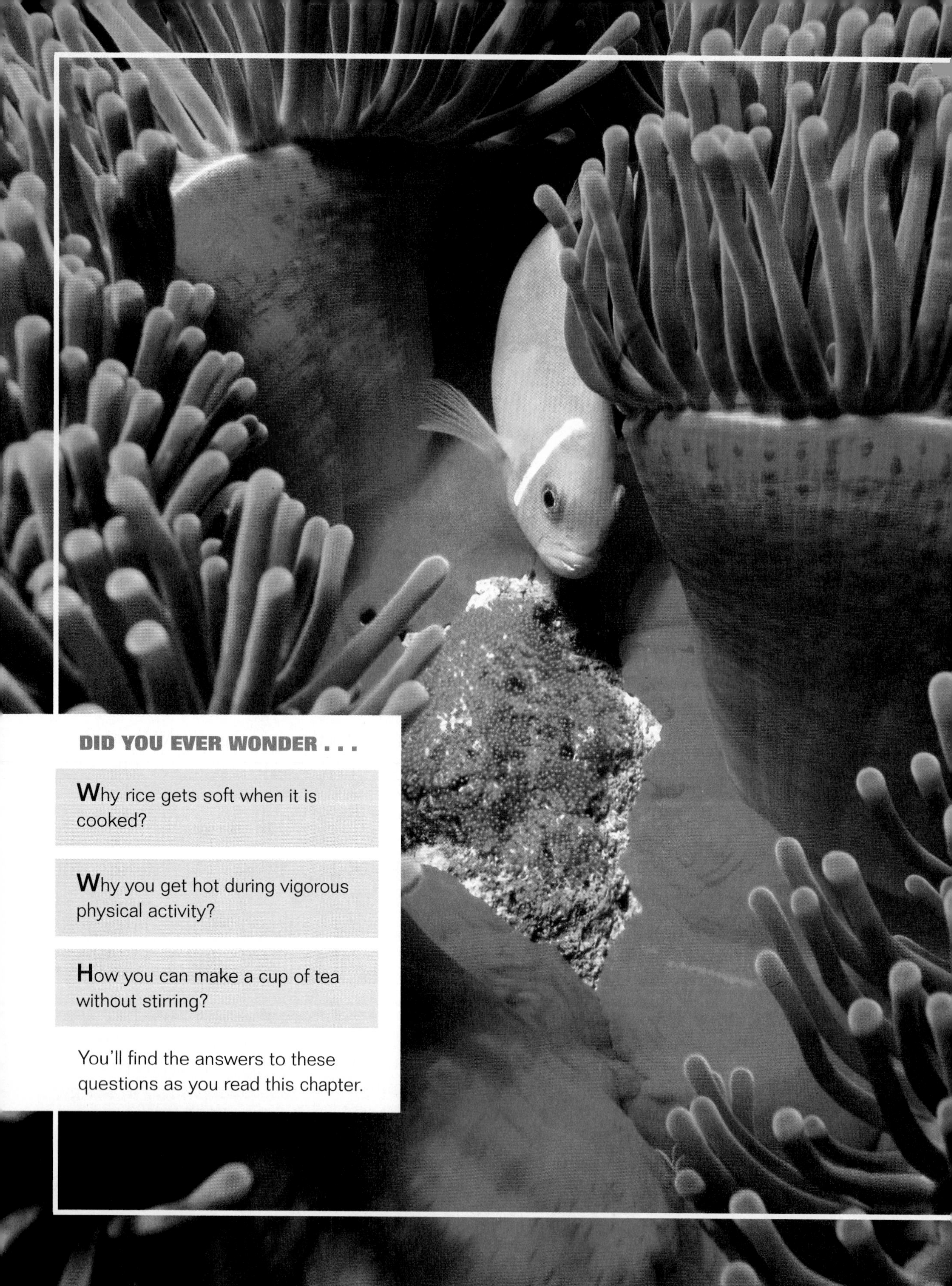

DID YOU EVER WONDER . . .

Why rice gets soft when it is cooked?

Why you get hot during vigorous physical activity?

How you can make a cup of tea without stirring?

You'll find the answers to these questions as you read this chapter.

Chapter 20

How Cells Do Their Jobs

Have you ever been swimming in the ocean? If so, you know that ocean water is quite different from water found in a lake or river. It's salty! As a matter of fact, ocean water is about 3.5 percent salt. Freshwater bodies such as lakes contain less than 0.005 percent salt. Many beautiful-colored fish like those seen in the photograph live in the ocean in tropical areas. You may know, if you have an aquarium, that it is deadly to place saltwater fish in a freshwater tank and freshwater fish in a saltwater tank.

Why can some organisms only live in salt water? Could you live in salt water for very long? What happens to cells in different environments? To understand these questions, you need to understand how cells work.

In Chapter 18, you learned that organisms are made of cells. Cells are "on duty" 24 hours a day, every day, taking in nutrients and giving off waste products. How can cells do all the things they do? This chapter will help you find out.

EXPLORE!

How does salt affect living things?

Use a pair of scissors to cut a 6-cm piece from the green end of a green onion. Cut one end of the section into thin strands. Dip the cut end of the onion into a container of distilled water. Wait about four minutes and watch what happens. Then take the onion and put it in a container of salt water. What happened to the strands of green onion? Do they look like the ones in the photograph?

20-1 Traffic in and out of Cells

OBJECTIVES

In this section, you will

- describe the function of the cell membrane;
- explain how materials move in and out of cells;
- compare and contrast osmosis and diffusion.

KEY SCIENCE TERMS

diffusion
osmosis

THE CELL MEMBRANE

In the Explore you just completed, you observed that onion strands soaked in salt water appear different from those soaked in distilled water. Somehow the salt in the salt water affected the cells. Did the salt coat the cells? Did it enter the cells? Did the water enter the cells? What caused the onion strands to change as they did in the presence of salt? To answer that question, you'll need to think back to Chapter 18, where you learned that all cells are covered by a thin cell membrane. The cell membrane gives the cell its shape. In order to live, a cell must obtain certain materials from its environment. Cells also release waste materials into the environment. If a cell has a membrane, how is it possible for these materials to enter and leave the cell?

FIND OUT!

What substances can pass through a barrier?

Obtain a double layer of cheesecloth, a small amount of sand or gravel, a funnel, a stirring rod, and two glass jars. Put the sand or gravel in one jar and add enough water to cover them by about 1 cm. Stir the mixture thoroughly. Place the layers of cheesecloth inside the funnel. While holding the funnel over an empty jar, pour your mixture through. What do you see happening? Wait several minutes and remove the cheesecloth from the funnel. Inspect the cheesecloth's contents. What do you find?

Conclude and Apply

Describe what happened. What was the job of the cheesecloth?

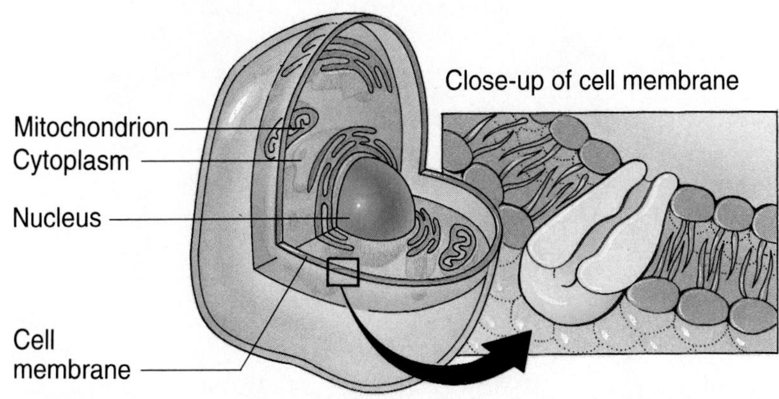

FIGURE 20-1. All cells have cell membranes made of many molecules.

You have just seen that all of the sand and maybe some of the gravel passed through the cheesecloth. Most of the gravel was held back by the cheesecloth. Something similar takes place in a cell. Figure 20-1 is a diagram of a cell and the cell membrane. In order for any material to enter or leave a cell, it must first pass through the cell membrane.

In the Find Out, you made a model of how a cell membrane works. The thin cell membrane that covers every cell works in a similar way to the cheesecloth. It allows some things to pass through and not others. It is said to be semipermeable. If a cell membrane had human characteristics, you might say it was fussy or particular about what and how things moved through it.

The microscope in your classroom uses glass lenses to bend light rays. An electron microscope uses a magnetic

How do we know?

The Cell Membrane

Even if you use a simple light microscope, such as the one in your classroom, you will not be able to see the details of a cell membrane's structure. How then do we know about the structure of the cell membrane?

One time or another, you've probably experienced the thrill of pulling and pushing metal objects with the invisible force supplied by a magnet. In the 1920s, scientists discovered that beams of tiny particles called electrons could be pushed or pulled with a very powerful magnet. Years later, researchers put this knowledge to use by building a new type of microscope called the electron microscope.

This microscope is much more powerful than a light microscope and can magnify an object over 200,000 times its normal size. Using it, we are able to see the microscopic structures of a cell membrane.

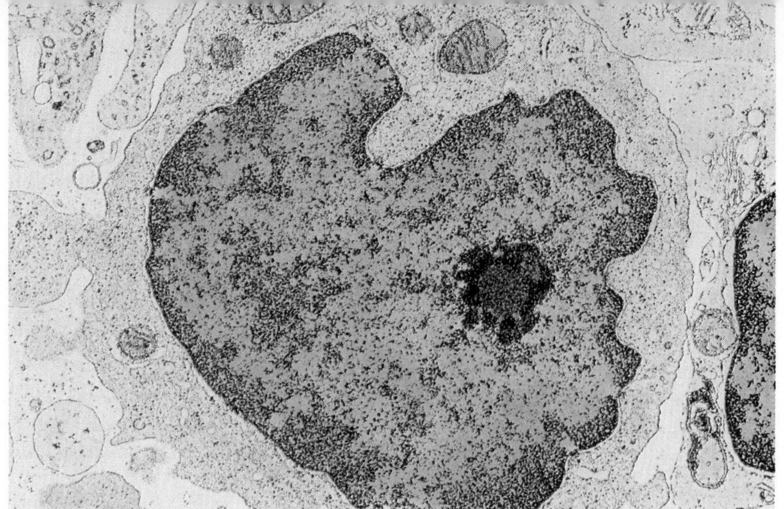

FIGURE 20-2. An electron microscope can show details of the cell's structures.

lens to bend a beam of electrons. The beam of particles is bounced off the object under study and reflected onto a screen. The result is an image of an object magnified over 200,000 times its normal size.

With an electron microscope, researchers have seen cell structures in great detail, as seen in Figure 20-2. The electron microscope has also helped researchers observe what happens when a cell is placed in different environments, such as distilled water or salt water. They have been able to observe that some substances with small-sized molecules pass through the cell membrane, whereas other materials with larger sized molecules do not.

DID YOU KNOW?

The word cell comes from the Latin word *cella*, which means small room.

CELLS: LIVING FACTORIES

In Chapter 18, a cell was described as being like a factory or a business. How is a cell like a factory? Automobile factories require many parts to build their finished products. In order to survive and make products needed by the organism, cells take in substances like water, food, and oxygen. They also release waste products, such as carbon dioxide.

The Find Out provided a model of how the cell membrane can act as a barrier between the cell and its environment. Like the front gate at a factory, the cell membrane permits certain molecules to pass in or out, depending on the type and size of the molecules. Molecules such as water, oxygen, and carbon dioxide pass through the cell membrane easily, just as the people who regularly work at a factory. They just pass right through the front door. Visitors have to stop at a reception desk to get permission to enter the factory. Usually, visitors are escorted through the factory by a person who has been assigned that particular job. In a cell membrane, some substances, such as sugar or sodium, are stopped or slowed down like the visitors. Entry of these kinds of substances may require work on the part of the cell membrane to get them in or out of the cell, or make use of special molecules in the cell membrane itself.

Whether or not the substances go in or out easily, or with the help of energy, there is always some movement taking place. What causes the movement of these molecules?

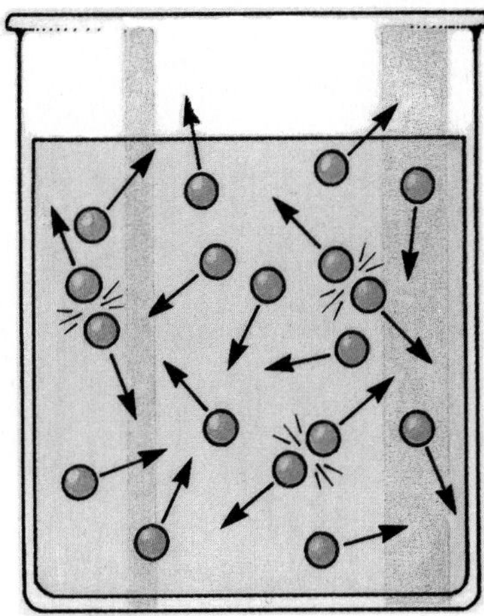

FIGURE 20-3. Molecules of matter constantly move and bump into one another.

To answer this question, you need to think about the nature of matter. If you have studied about atoms and gases, you have learned that all matter is made up of molecules that are constantly moving. As molecules move, they bump into one another. The collisions cause the molecules to move out away from each other. A diagram of molecular motion is shown in Figure 20-3. By bumping into each other and bouncing off, molecules move from an area where they are crowded together to places where there are fewer of them. It's easy to understand how molecular motion like this occurs in the air all around, but it also takes place in the cytoplasm of your cells.

EXPLORE!

How do tea bags work?

Would you believe that a cup of tea can help you understand something about molecular motion? Try this activity. Place a wet tea bag in a clear glass of hot water. Without stirring, carefully watch where the tea color first appears. Wait two minutes, then describe the glass. Make an observation every two minutes for ten minutes. What change in water color do you notice? How do you think the tea color got into the water?

In the Explore activity, you made a model that demonstrated molecular movement. In your model, the bag containing tea represented a cell membrane. When you placed the tea bag in the hot water, molecules that make up tea moved from inside the bag out into the water. Likewise, the water moved through the bag to the tea leaves. Why did these molecules move? As you learned in Chapter 6, the process of convection helped the tea move from the tea bag and throughout the glass because the hot water was in motion. But convection alone didn't mix the tea and hot water. The movement of molecules was also involved.

MOVEMENT OF MOLECULES

Molecules are in constant motion, causing many substances to move in and out of cells. This constant movement plays a role in changing the concentration of materials inside and outside the cells. If, for instance, a higher concentration of one type of food molecule exists outside the cell than inside, food molecules will pass through the cell membrane and enter the cell. This will continue until the concentration of the food molecules inside and outside the cell are equal.

When the concentrations are equal, a state called equilibrium (ee kwi LIB ree um) exists. But molecules don't stop moving through the membrane once equilibrium is reached. They continue to move back and forth through the membrane at an equal rate in each direction, maintaining equilibrium.

FIGURE 20-4. Molecules diffuse from an area of high concentration—the bottle—carrying the scent to an area of low concentration—the room.

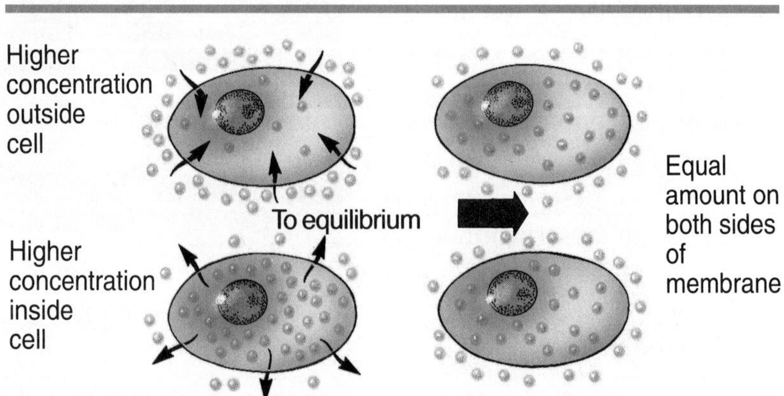

The process by which the constant motion of molecules causes movement from an area of high concentration to an area of low concentration is called **diffusion**. In Chapter 14, you learned about the behavior of gas molecules, and in Chapter 16 you learned how carbon dioxide and oxygen molecules are exchanged in the lungs by the process of diffusion. Whether or not diffusion involves gas molecules through air, or water through a cell membrane, it occurs without the use of energy on the part of the cell.

FIND OUT!

How does diffusion occur?

You can observe diffusion in the following activity. With your teacher's help, prepare a dialysis membrane bag according to your teacher's directions. Place about 1/4 cup of cooked rice in the bag. Place the bag into a beaker of iodine solution. Wait five minutes and look at the rice in the bag.

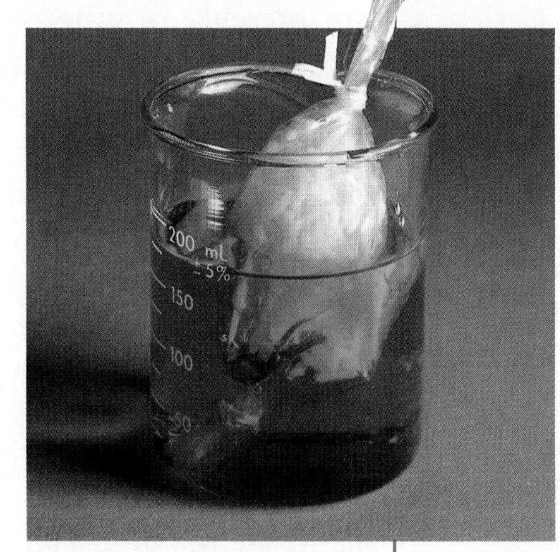

Conclude and Apply

1. Describe any changes you see in the rice.
2. What evidence do you have that iodine molecules diffused into the bag?

In the Find Out, you observed the diffusion of iodine molecules through the bag into the rice. A change in the color of the rice gives you evidence that diffusion had occurred. What would happen if you soaked uncooked rice in a pot of water overnight? Diffusion would also occur. When the dry rice grains, containing no water molecules, are placed in a container filled with water, water molecules will pass from the area of high concentration to the area of low concentration. The fact that the rice grains plump up and get soft gives you evidence that water had diffused into the grains. How does the amount of water in the pot before and after indicate diffusion has occurred?

SKILLBUILDER

OBSERVING AND INFERRING

Make a chart of the observations you made during the last Find Out. Head one column *Before* and head a second column *After*. Make a third column headed *Inference*. Explain how the three columns are related. If you need help, refer to the **Skill Handbook** on page 682.

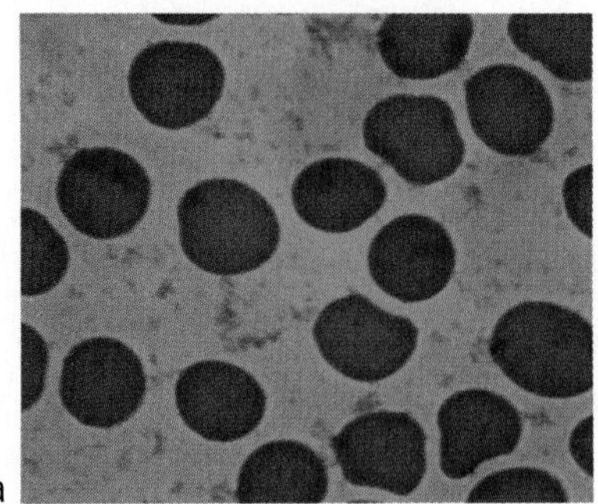

a

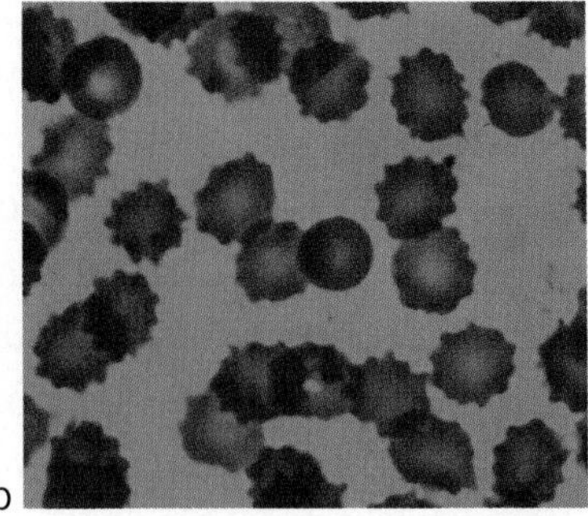

b

FIGURE 20-5. Blood cells gained water and bulged (a). The blood cells lost water and shriveled (b).

DID YOU KNOW?

Contact lens solution must contain the same amount of dissolved salt in water as that found in your tears that bathe your eyes. Unequal concentrations would cause diffusion of water into or out of the cells on the surface of your eye.

DIFFUSION OF WATER: A SPECIAL CASE

Cells live in an aqueous environment. In other words, they are bathed by fluids that are mostly water. This constant presence of water must be important. All life processes in cells take place in water. If a cell does not receive an adequate supply of water, it will die because it cannot carry out its life processes.

Recall the Explore activity at the beginning of this chapter. You observed the onion section spread out like a fan in the distilled water. The change in the onion section was due to diffusion of water into the onion cells. When the onion was in the distilled water, there was a higher concentration of water molecules outside the onion cells than inside. As a result, water molecules diffused into the onion cells. A similar experiment was performed on the blood cells in Figure 20-5. Did your onion cells, bulge like the blood cells in Figure 20-5 (a)? When you placed the onion in salt water, the cells lost water. This time, water molecules moved out of the onion cells and into the surrounding water. Did the onion cells shrivel up like the blood cells in Figure 20-5 (b)?

The diffusion of water through a cell membrane is called **osmosis**. In osmosis, water molecules diffuse from an area of high concentration to an area of low concentration through a membrane. This is illustrated in Figure 20-6. Eventually equilibrium is reached, and then the number of water molecules moving in each direction becomes equal. Osmosis requires no energy use by the cell. In the following Investigate, you will observe and measure osmosis.

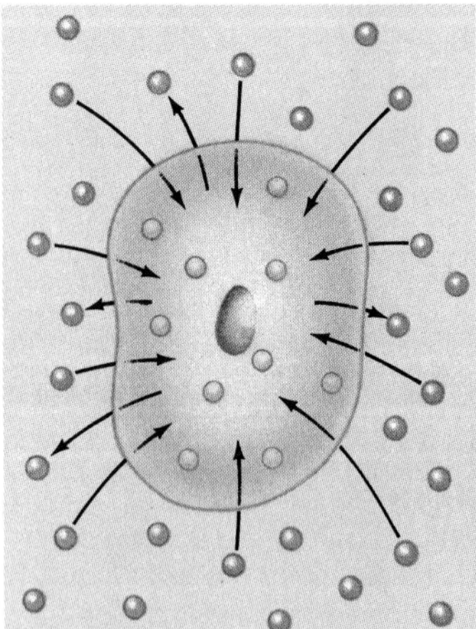

FIGURE 20-6. In osmosis, water molecules pass through the cell membrane until equilibrium is reached.

INVESTIGATE!

20-1 EGGS AS MODEL CELLS

A chicken egg can be used as a model cell because the yolk is actually a single large cell. Placing the egg into syrup or into distilled water allows you to **observe** and **measure** the amount of water that is lost or gained by the egg through osmosis.

PROBLEM

How can osmosis be measured?

MATERIALS 

2 raw eggs
2 250-mL beakers with lids
400 mL of white vinegar
200 mL of distilled water
200 mL of syrup
1 graduated cylinder
balance
paper towels
wax pencil

PROCEDURE

1. Copy the data table.
2. Use the wax pencil to label the beakers A and B.

3. Place one egg in each of the beakers.
4. Add enough vinegar to each beaker to cover the eggs.
5. After 24 hours, pour off the vinegar. **Observe** what has happened. Record your observations. Carefully remove the eggs from the beakers and dry with a paper towel.
6. Find the mass of each dry egg. Record your findings in the table. Rinse the beakers and dry them thoroughly. Return each egg to its original beaker.
7. Add exactly 200 mL of distilled water to Beaker A. Add exactly 200 mL of syrup to Beaker B.
8. Allow each egg to remain in its beaker for 24 hours.
9. After 24 hours, do the following for each egg:
   a. Carefully remove the egg and dry it.
   b. Record the mass of the egg.
   c. **Measure** and record the remaining liquid.

DATA AND OBSERVATIONS

EGG IN SOLUTION	MASS OF EGG		VOLUME OF LIQUID	
	Original	Final	Original	Final
Distilled Water (A)				
Syrup (B)				

ANALYZE

1. **Compare** what happened to the mass of the egg in distilled water to what happened to the mass of the egg placed in syrup.
2. What happened to the volume of the distilled water in Beaker A? Of syrup in Beaker B?

CONCLUDE AND APPLY

3. Can you **infer** that the egg membrane permitted any substances to pass through it? What evidence do you have that supports your conclusion?
4. **Going Further:** If you put a freshwater fish in salt water or a saltwater fish in fresh water, the fish will die. Use your knowledge of osmosis to explain how this happens.

FIGURE 20-7. Desalination plants, like this one, remove the salt from ocean water, producing fresh water for drinking and other uses.

As you observed in the last activity, osmosis occurred in the eggs. For the same reason that the eggs gained or lost water, and the blood cells bulged or shriveled, you can now explain why people who get their water from the ocean remove the salt before drinking it. If you were stranded on a deserted island, why wouldn't you drink seawater? As you guessed, drinking seawater would actually cause you to lose water.

While water can diffuse through a cell membrane, certain materials require energy to pass through it. Think back to the activity with the cheesecloth. Some of the larger pieces of gravel were too large to pass through the holes in the cheesecloth. You would have to use energy from your body to force the large pieces through the small holes.

In the same way, the cell membrane uses energy to move large molecules, such as protein molecules, through it. If materials require energy to move through the cell membrane, active transport occurs. You will learn more about how the cell membrane uses energy to move substances at the end of the chapter.

In this section, you have examined diffusion and osmosis, two important processes that depend on the movement of molecules. Through these processes, living cells obtain the substances they need as well as eliminate any waste materials they produce. In the next section, you will learn about other life processes that occur in living cells.

Check Your Understanding

1. Name two functions of the cell membrane.
2. How are osmosis and diffusion alike? How are they different?
3. A bottle of ammonia is left open in the back of a classroom. What causes the odor of ammonia to be detected in the front of the room after only several minutes?
4. **APPLY:** A cell is surrounded by a particular substance. If the cell itself contains a larger concentration of this substance than is outside the cell, in which direction would you expect diffusion of the substance to occur? Explain your answer.

20-2 Why Cells Need Food

CELLS AND ENERGY

You may recall that energy can be found in many forms. Figure 20-8 shows some examples. If you have ever been to the ocean or a large lake on a windy day, you may have seen the motion of waves. This is an example of kinetic energy. Wet clothes hanging on a clothesline eventually dry due to thermal energy. Televisions and video games run on electrical energy.

When you think about the production of energy, you usually think of power plants. Power plants use energy containing materials, such as oil, coal, water, or trash to produce the electrical energy that people use in their everyday activities.

Your cells, and the cells of other living organisms, also run on energy. Cells use this energy to carry out their life activities. At this very moment, your brain cells are using energy to allow you to read the words on this page. Muscle cells in your fingers are using energy to enable your fingers to turn the pages! Where does this energy come

OBJECTIVES

In this section, you will

- explain the importance of energy to cells;
- describe the process of respiration in terms of their products and reactants;
- relate the number of mitochondria in different types of cells to their levels of activity.

KEY SCIENCE TERMS

respiration
fermentation

FIGURE 20-8. Energy comes in many forms.

from? The original source of energy for the activities of living things is the sun. Think back to your earlier studies of plants and animals. You may recall that green plants convert light energy from the sun into a sugar through the process of photosynthesis. The sugar produced is a form of chemical energy. This same chemical energy is passed on to you through the food chain. Remember that a food chain is the feeding relationship that transfers energy through a community of producers, herbivores, and carnivores.

FIGURE 20-9. A simple food chain illustrates the transfer of energy.

Each of your cells changes chemical energy to other forms of energy through a process known as respiration. **Respiration** is a chemical process in which high energy molecules are rearranged to release stored energy. Oxygen must be available for this to occur. In many ways, a cell can be compared to a power plant. Each requires fuel to convert energy. One fuel human cells use is glucose. Glucose molecules are broken apart. The pieces combine with oxygen molecules to form new substances. During the rearrangement, energy is released. In this chemical reaction, oxygen and glucose are the reactants, and energy, carbon dioxide, and water are the products. A summary of this chemical process is given in Figure 20-10.

FIGURE 20-10. In respiration, glucose and oxygen molecules are rearranged to release energy.

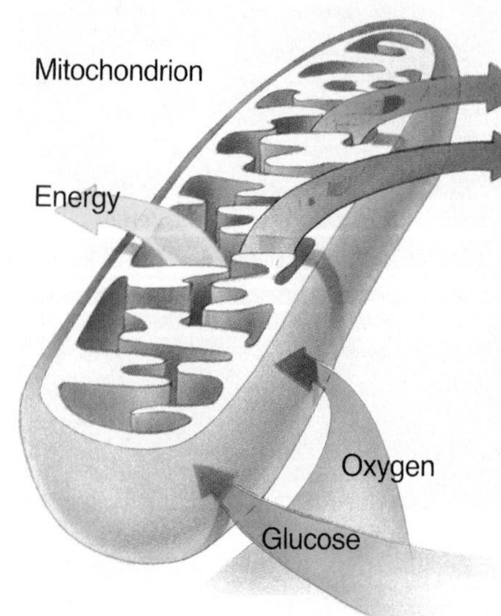

Living organisms that depend on oxygen carry out respiration. Your brain cells, kidney cells, and skin cells all carry out respiration. At this moment, the cells in your big toe are using energy released during respiration, and so are the leaves on the trees in the local park.

Do you think the racing dogs in Figure 20-11 are using energy? How can you tell? It is just as easy to tell that your body cells are producing energy. Feel your own forehead. It feels warm, doesn't it? What you are feeling is the heat produced as a waste product of the thousands of respiration reactions occurring in your body.

But what about plants? Plants don't feel warm. Do plants carry out respiration? In the following activity, you can prove to yourself that plants carry out respiration, and that this process converts one form of energy to another.

FIGURE 20-11. It's easy to tell that these dogs are using energy.

FIND OUT!

Does respiration release energy?

Thermal energy is a form of energy produced as a by-product of respiration. Plant seeds are living organisms, even though they may not look very lively. In this activity you will actually measure some of the energy released by the respiration of beans! Obtain the following materials: one large beaker, two clear glass jars, two thermometers, two corks to fit glass jars or a large ball of cotton, 50 dry kidney bean seeds, and 50 kidney beans that have soaked overnight.

Carefully place the soaked beans in one glass jar and label it. Place 50 dry beans in the other glass jar. Put a thermometer in each jar and a large wad of cotton. Take a temperature reading in each jar every half hour for three hours and record your observations.

Conclude and Apply

1. Did the two different bottles have the same temperatures each time you took a reading?
2. What conclusions can you draw between your observations and your knowledge of respiration?

DID YOU KNOW?

Each heart muscle cell contains more than 3000 mitochondria.

You saw evidence that respiration of the two bean treatments releases energy. You were able to measure the release of stored energy in the soaked beans by changes in the temperatures of the two treatments. Cells use the energy released by respiration in a variety of ways. Nerve cells need energy to transmit messages through the body. Plant cells need energy to form beautiful and complex flowers.

Although every living cell uses energy, the amount of energy one cell needs may differ from the amount of energy needed by a different cell. The amount and type of work a cell has to do determines how much energy it uses. Because it does a lot of work, a muscle cell requires an enormous amount of energy. A brain cell requires more energy than a skin cell. But how does a brain cell have more energy available to it than a skin cell? The answer lies in the number of mitochondria found within the cell.

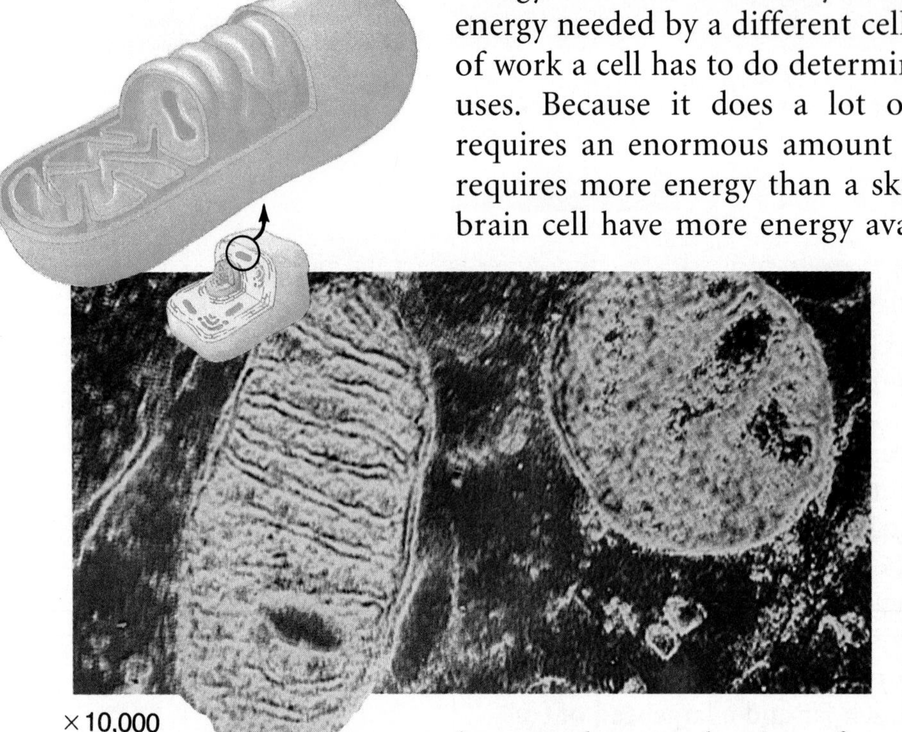

FIGURE 20-12. Respiration occurs in the mitochondria, or "powerhouses" of the cell.

As you recall, mitochondria, shown in Figure 20-12, are structures found within the cytoplasm of most cells. Mitochondria are often called the "powerhouses" of the cell because they are the sites of respiration. The greater the activity and energy use of a cell, the greater the number of mitochondria it contains. Do you think that brain cells contain many mitochondria?

You have learned that energy is one product of respiration. Cells, like most factories, produce waste. The waste products of respiration are water and carbon dioxide. They are released from your body when you are exhaling. Nearly all living organisms give off carbon dioxide as a result of respiration. However, the rate at which carbon dioxide is given off differs from organism to organism. In the activity that follows, you will investigate how temperature affects the rate at which respiration occurs.

I N V E S T I G A T E !

20-2 RESPIRATION AND TEMPERATURE

In this activity, you will observe evidence of respiration in yeast cells. You will also relate temperature to the rate of a reaction.

PROBLEM

How is respiration influenced by temperature?

MATERIALS  

two rubber stoppers with plastic tubing attached
two test tubes
20 mL 25% sucrose solution
metric ruler
two flasks
yeast cubes
glass-marking pencil
watch or clock
tap water

PROCEDURE

1. Copy the data table.
2. Fill each test tube with the sucrose solution.
3. Place the yeast into the test tubes, and mix well.

4. Insert a rubber stopper into each test tube. The end of the plastic tube should be below the surface of the liquid. Use the figure as a guide.
5. Add enough cold water to a flask to reach a height of 3 cm. Label this flask "cold."
6. Label the second flask "warm" and repeat Step 5 using warm water.
7. Carefully place one test tube in each flask.
8. **Measure** the height of the liquid in each plastic tube to the nearest millimeter. Position the ruler so that the 0.0 mm mark lines up with the bottom of the flask, as in the figure. Record your measurements in the table under "Starting Height."
9. Take measurements every 5 minutes for 20 minutes.
10. Calculate and record the total distance the yeast-water mixture moved. If the last reading was lower than the starting height, subtract this from your total.

DATA AND OBSERVATIONS

	STARTING HEIGHT	5 MINS	10 MINS	15 MINS	20 MINS	TOTAL DISTANCE
COLD						
WARM						

ANALYZE

1. What gas is released by yeast cells as they carry out respiration?
2. Which tube showed the greater rise in the height of the liquid? In which tube was more gas produced?

CONCLUDE AND APPLY

3. Do you think that temperature has an **effect** on the rate of respiration? What evidence do you have to support your statement?
4. **Going Further:** What can you **infer** about the rate of respiration in a fish swimming in cold water compared to the same fish swimming in warm water?

FIGURE 20-13. Your muscles get energy when your body temperature increases and speeds up the rate of respiration.

As you saw in the Investigate, a relationship exists between temperature and the rate at which respiration occurs. As temperature increases, so does the amount of respiration that occurs in an organism. This is true for your body as well as yeast cells. Think about the last time you exercised. Strenuous physical activities such as running or swimming require a lot of energy. If your arm and leg muscles are to get the energy they need, fast and numerous respiration reactions must occur. These reactions, as well as the muscle activity, release heat, which raises your body temperature. Your increased body temperature maintains the rate of respiration to continually supply your muscles with energy. Due to this cycle, your body gets the energy it needs so you can reach the finish line!

But do all cells undergo respiration? Some cells, such as bacteria, lack mitochondria and cannot obtain their energy through respiration. Instead, they use fermentation to get energy. **Fermentation** is a process that releases energy by breaking down glucose into alcohol and carbon dioxide, without the use of oxygen.

In this section, you learned that living organisms have mechanisms for supplying themselves with the energy they require. Organisms that make use of oxygen release energy by the process of respiration. This reaction takes place in the mitochondria of cells. Organisms such as bacteria release energy through the process of fermentation. Different types of cells have different energy needs. In the next section, you will see how these cells are organized in the body so that they can complete their jobs.

Check Your Understanding

1. Why do cells need energy?
2. Name three products of respiration.
3. What two reactants are needed for cell respiration?
4. How does fermentation differ from respiration?
5. **APPLY:** After examining a muscle cell from your lower jaw and a skin cell under a microscope, you find that the jaw muscle cell contains more mitochondria than the skin cell. What can you infer about the energy requirements of the jaw muscle cell?

20-3 Special Cells with Special Jobs

A VARIETY OF CELLS

If you've ever used a tool kit, you know that there is nothing better than having the right tool for the right job. Some tools have flat and heavy parts for banging things, like a hammer. Others, such as screwdrivers, have long and thin parts for fitting into thin, tight places. Still others, such as a saw, have specially shaped teeth for cutting things. There is a definite relationship between the size and shape of a tool and its job, isn't there? The same is true of cells. Like the tools in a tool kit, there is a relationship between the structure of a cell and its parts, and how it functions in the body.

OBJECTIVES

In this section, you will

- explain differences between types of cells and how their differences are related to cell functions;
- identify the levels of organization in life forms from cell to tissue, to organ, to organ system, to organism.

KEY SCIENCE TERMS

tissue
organ
organ system
organism

FIND OUT!

How do cells vary in size and shape?

Look at the following prepared slides of cells under your microscope: human cheek cells, leaf cells, red blood cells, and muscle cells. Diagram each type of cell and label the cell parts you have studied. Review your diagrams and compare the different types of cells.

Conclude and Apply

1. How are the cells similar? How are the cells different?
2. Explain why you think the size and shape of each cell might tell you something about its job.

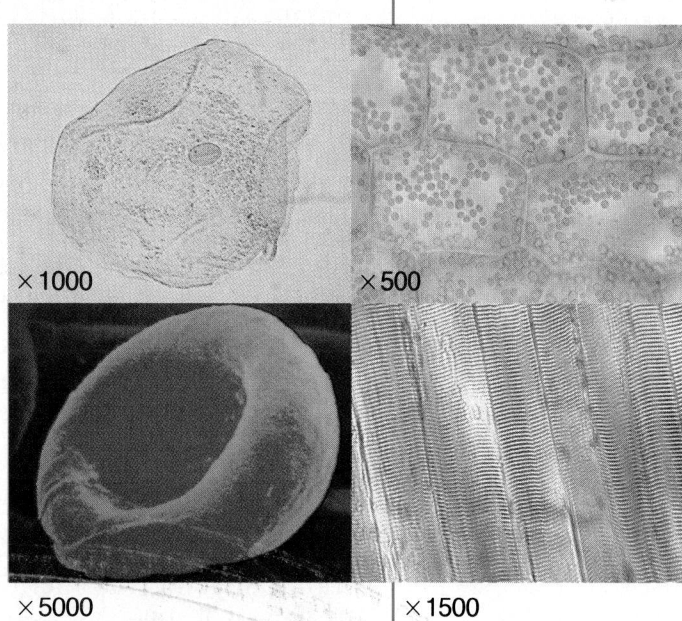

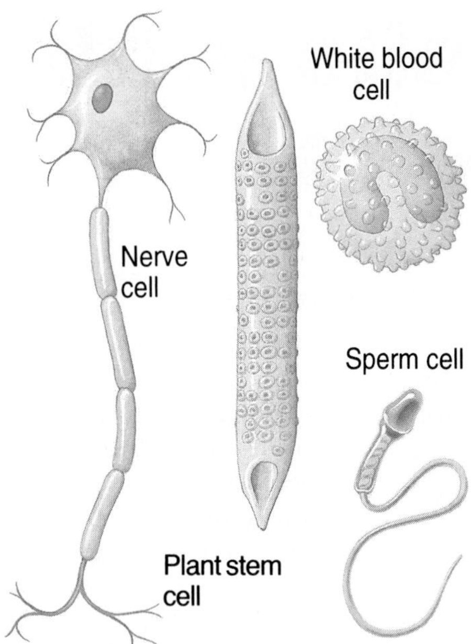

FIGURE 20-14. Cells differ in shape and size according to function.

As you saw in Find Out, cells come in a variety of shapes and sizes. Your body contains many different kinds of cells, each with its own unique shape and job. Nerve cells, like the one shown in Figure 20-14, are often long. The shape is useful for carrying messages long distances through the body. The cells in some plant stems can be long and hollow, like drinking straws. Sperm cells have an arrowlike head and a long, thin tail to help them swim through body fluids. White blood cells, which surround and destroy harmful bacteria in your body, change into many different shapes while performing their job. How do you think these traits help a white blood cell do its job?

LEVELS OF ORGANIZATION

The amoeba is a one-celled organism. The entire organism is composed of just one cell! The animal, plant, and fungus organisms that you are familiar with, are all many-celled organisms. They contain more than one cell. One-celled organisms, however, still carry out the same life processes that occur in many-celled organisms such as your dog, your cat, and you.

Unlike one-celled organisms, the cells of many-celled organisms usually cannot function by themselves. Like parts in a machine, cells in your body work together to function effectively. They are arranged in levels of organization. Each level is more organized than the one before.

What is meant by the phrase "levels of organization?" Figure 20-15 shows the levels of organization in this textbook. Letters of the alphabet are grouped together to form words. Words are grouped together in sentences. Many sentences arranged together are called paragraphs, and a group of paragraphs are organized on a page.

Cells in your body, like letters of the alphabet, are the most basic level of organization. Similar types of cells, working together to perform the same function, are called **tissues**, like the words that make up a sentence. Look at your hand. You are looking at skin tissue. All of

SKILLBUILDER

COMPARING AND CONTRASTING

Carefully observe the characteristics, such as size and shape, of each cell in Figure 20-14. Record the features of each type of cell under a separate heading. Think about where each cell comes from and about how the size and shape of each cell might be useful for its function. If you need help, refer to the **Skill Handbook** on page 683.

the skin cells on your hand are working together to form this tissue. Inside your body, you can also find nerve tissue and heart and muscle tissue.

Individual types of tissues usually are found with other types of tissue. An **organ** is a structure in the body made up of several different types of tissue that all work together to do a particular job, much like sentences that make up a paragraph. Figure 20-16 shows the organization from cell to tissue to organ in a plant. You have also studied some of the organs in your body already. The heart, for example, is an organ composed mostly of muscle and blood. Its job is to circulate blood throughout the body. Lungs are organs that remove oxygen from air so your cells can release energy. They are composed of air sacs, blood vessels, and cartilage. Plants have organs, too. Leaves are organs composed of mainly different types of leaf tissues. Some of them convert energy from the sun into food so the plant can use it. What other plant organs can you think of?

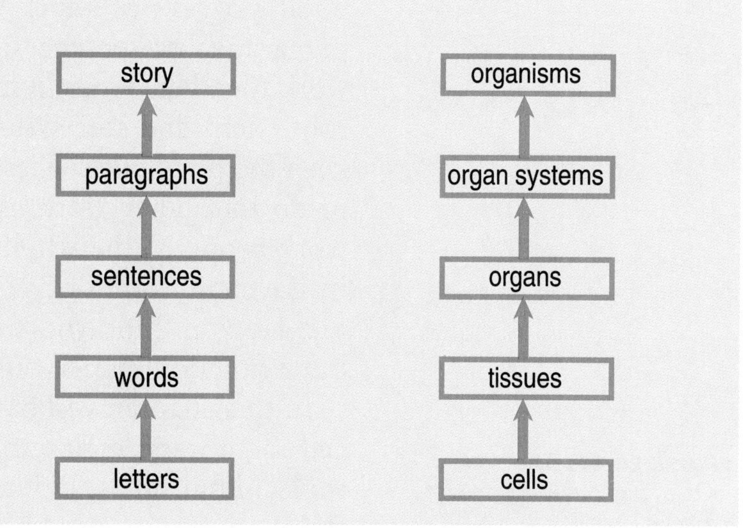

FIGURE 20-15. In books, letters of the alphabet are arranged in levels of organization.

The next level of organization in many-celled organisms like yourself is the organ system. **Organ systems** are simply groups of organs working together to perform a particular job, like the paragraphs organized to make a story. You already know many of the systems of many-celled organisms. Your heart, blood, and all of the blood vessels in your body work together in the form of the circulatory system. What are some of the other systems you learned about?

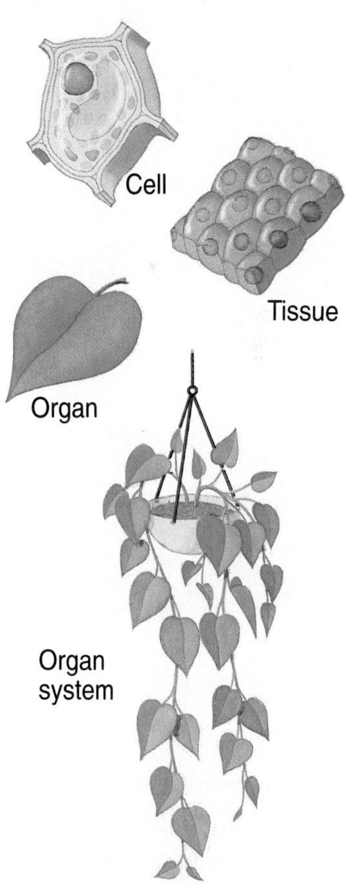

FIGURE 20-16. Levels of organization in a plant

The highest level of organization is an organism. An **organism** may be made up of several organ systems that work together, like the many chapters in a book, or may be a single cell, much like a poem. Each organism, whether one-celled or many-celled, functions normally. Figure 20-17 illustrates some very common organisms. Think back to the organization of this book. Would the book provide as much information if there were no paragraphs or sentences? Just as a book needs parts to work together, so do living, many-celled organisms. The root, stem and leaf systems of plants work together to keep the plant alive. These systems depend on each other to do this. They work as a team. If one system doesn't work properly, the whole plant will suffer. If the vessels in the stem don't deliver water, the tissues in the leaves die. Do you think you could be reading this book without a functioning nervous system?

In this chapter, you have seen that the structure of the cell membrane maintains the proper concentrations of molecules inside and outside the cell, so the cell can perform an important task: to provide usable forms of energy for life! You also observed that even though all cells in the body use energy, there are different types of cells for different jobs, and that similar cells work together as a team to complete these jobs. Finally, you learned that all of the cells, tissues, organs, and organ systems in your body work together to form a whole, living organism.

FIGURE 20-17. The highest level of organization is the organism itself.

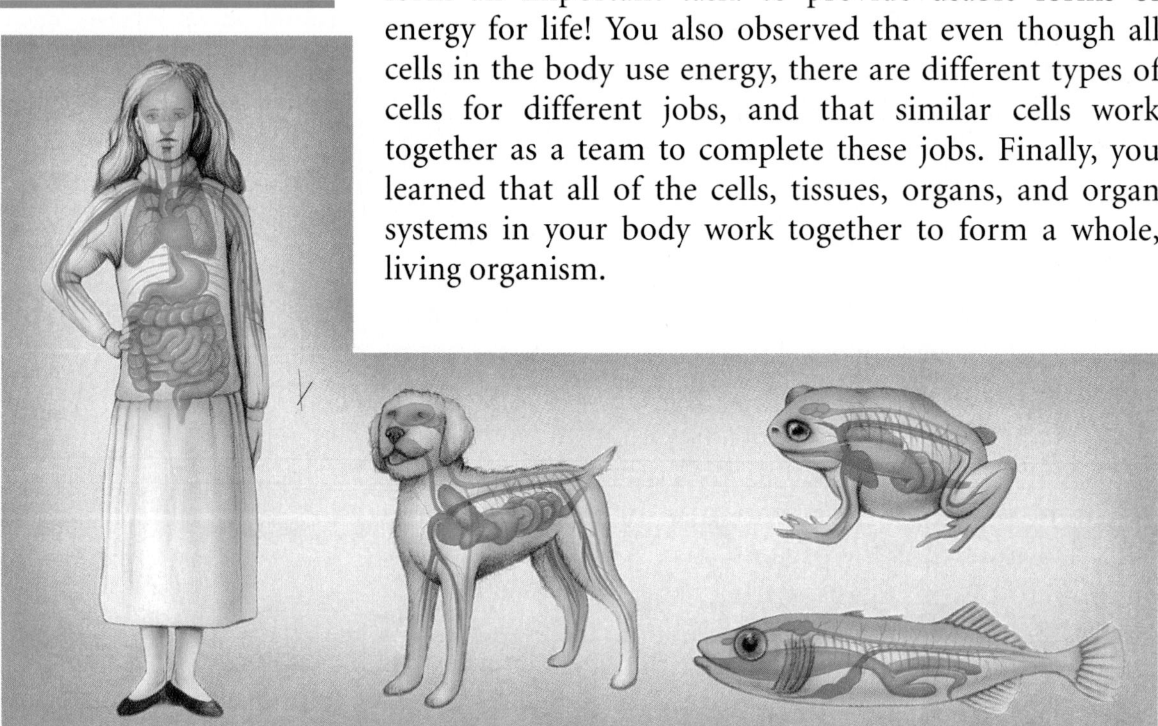

Check Your Understanding

1. Give an example of two cells that differ in size and shape. Explain how their differences are related to cell function.
2. Explain why levels of organization are not found in an amoeba.
3. **APPLY:** What four levels of organization do you think can be found in an earthworm?

EXPANDING YOUR VIEW

CONTENTS

A Closer Look
The Cell Membrane 617

Chemistry Connection
Does Mother Nature's Math Add Up? 618

Science and Society
End Stage Renal Disease: Costly in Different Ways 619

Health Connection
Shaping Up: You Can't Do It Overnight 620

How It Works
The Artificial Kidney Machine 622

A CLOSER LOOK

THE CELL MEMBRANE

As you recall, the cell membrane controls the movement of substances in and out of a cell. The key to understanding how the cell membrane works lies in its structure.

Scientists now know that the cell membrane not only acts as a passive filter, but that it is also a very active structure as well.

As you can see from the figure, the cell membrane looks somewhat like a double-layered cake. Each layer is made up of a sheet of fatlike molecules, with much larger protein molecules embedded in the layers. These protein molecules play a key role in the working of the membrane.

This depiction of the cell membrane is known as the fluid mosaic model. How does the fluid mosaic model work?

You've learned how small molecules pass through the cell membrane by the process of diffusion. Simple diffusion of some substances, such as glucose, is not possible. Glucose moves across the membrane by passing through channels made by protein molecules. These proteins are shaped like tubes to allow the glucose molecule to pass through.

Sometimes, however, cells require nutrients that are scarce in the environment. If the concentration of a substance outside a cell were lower than inside, the cell would lose that substance to the outside by diffusion. Cell membranes allow certain molecules to move in the reverse direction—from areas of low concentration to areas of high concentration. This type of movement requires energy and is known as active transport.

Protein molecules are directly involved in active transport. In active transport, molecules called carrier proteins attach to the molecules of the substance to be transported. When this occurs, energy released by the cell is transferred to the carrier protein. The carrier protein then changes shape, and a tunnel opens so the molecules can move into the cell.

WHAT DO YOU THINK?

Based on what you now know about the fluid mosaic model of a cell membrane, find out what is different about the cell membrane of a diabetic.

Chemistry Connection

DOES MOTHER NATURE'S MATH ADD UP?

When a cow eats grass, the cells in its body obtain energy from the grass through the process of respiration.

During this process, glucose molecules in the grass combine with oxygen that has been delivered by the circulatory system. Energy is released that the cow will use to grow, produce a calf, and make milk. In addition to energy, carbon dioxide and water are also produced during the process of respiration.

Respiration is a chemical reaction. In all chemical reactions, atoms are neither created nor destroyed. How can we be sure that Mother Nature's math adds up?

The chemical reaction of respiration can be written as the following equation:

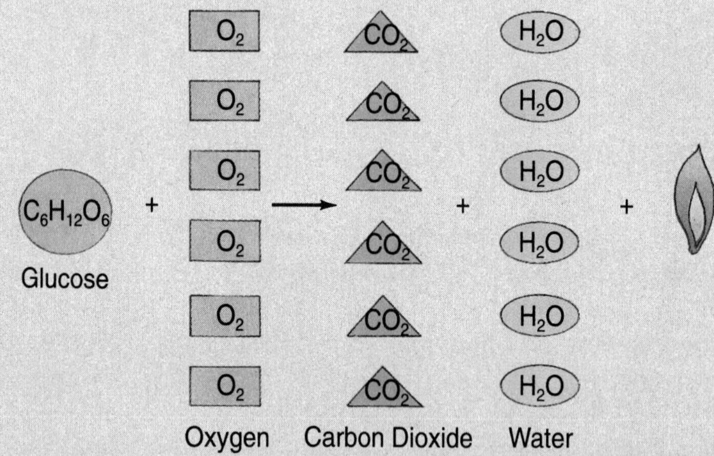

The equation can also be written in such a way that we can count up the atoms.

To find out if the math adds up, you only need to count up the atoms on both sides of the arrow.

Let's start on the left side of the arrow. Each carbon atom is represented by the letter C.

How many carbon atoms are there?

How many hydrogen atoms do you see?

How many oxygen atoms?

How many atoms total on the left side of the arrow?

Now let's look at the right side of the arrow. How many carbon atoms? How many hydrogen atoms? How many oxygen atoms? How many atoms total?

WHAT DO YOU THINK?

1. Is the sum of each kind of atom (C,H,O) on the left side of the arrow equal to the sum on the right side?
2. Does the total sum of atoms on the left side of the arrow equal the total sum of the atoms on the right side?
3. Were any atoms created or destroyed during respiration?

SCIENCE AND SOCIETY

END STAGE RENAL DISEASE: COSTLY IN DIFFERENT WAYS

As you learned in the chapter, cell processes such as respiration, in addition to releasing energy, also produce waste products. One of the waste products of respiration is carbon dioxide, which is removed from the body through the lungs.

Besides respiration, there are other processes that occur in cells. As you know, cells reproduce, grow, and repair themselves. For these processes, cells release energy from nutrients that they get from the food you eat. Some of the waste products made when nutrients break down contain nitrogen. These nitrogen-containing substances are sent to an organ called the liver, where they are changed into a substance called urea. Urea is toxic, and it must be removed from the body. How is urea removed from the body?

Besides your lungs, your body has another organ that functions to remove wastes from the body—the kidney. You have two kidneys, and they are major organs of the urinary system, the body system that removes waste from blood to produce urine.

As you can see, the kidneys are located on either side of the spine in the back, at about the level of the waist. Without kidneys, toxic substances, such as urea, can build up in the blood.

People who have permanent kidney failure, called End Stage Renal Disease, must depend on hemodialysis for survival. Hemodialysis (HEE moh di AL ih sis) is a medical procedure designed to filter wastes, such as urea, from the blood. Social workers at dialysis centers describe the patient's dependence on this procedure as very traumatic. The patient loses not only an organ, but a lifestyle.

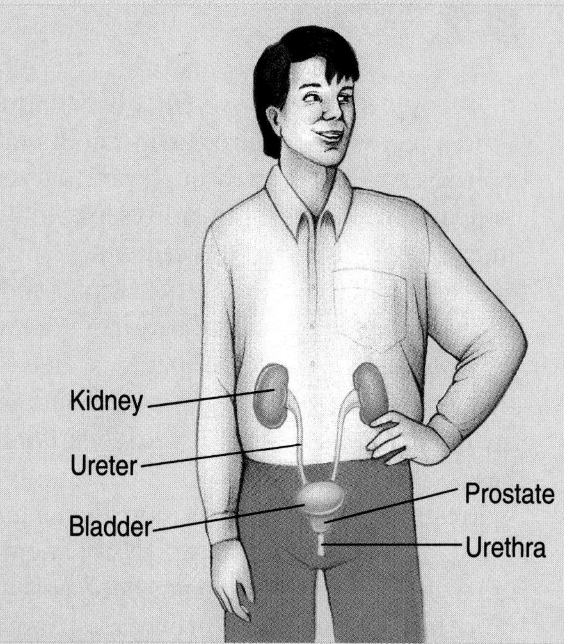

Of the estimated 20 million Americans who have kidney-related disease, more than 92,000 undergo dialysis every year. Patients

YOU TRY IT!

Contact your local Kidney Foundation to find out more about dialysis and the costs of treatment. Ask your teacher if you can bring in a guest speaker.

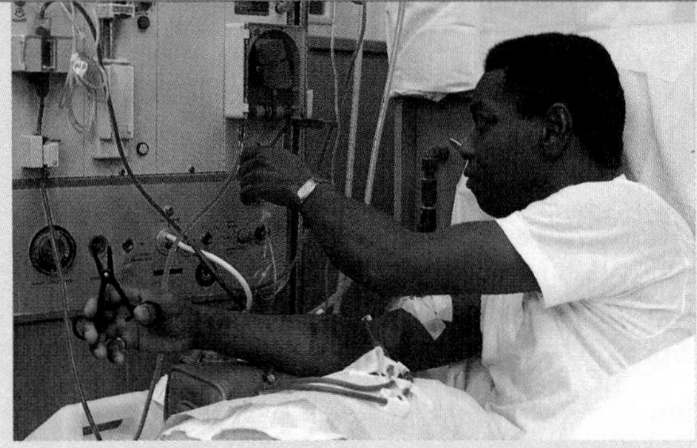

must come to the dialysis center two to three times every week for three to four hours each visit. Every week, even through vacations and holidays, for the rest of their lives, patients must plan to visit a dialysis center.

A team of professionals at the center cooperates in the individualized treatment of every patient. Dietitians monitor patients' diets and, at many dialysis centers, social workers are on hand to help patients and their families.

Treatment typically costs more than a hundred dollars per visit. Many dialysis patients are unable to work, so patients need assistance to meet their medical expenses. Some patients have private medical insurance, which pays most of the cost of dialysis. For patients who cannot pay for the treatment, government paid insurance plans may pay for part of the cost.

There is an alternative to hemodialysis—kidney transplantation. In this treatment, the kidney of a healthy individual is surgically implanted inside the body of the patient. Not every dialysis patient is a candidate for a kidney transplant. Patients over the age of 50 or patients with other medical problems have a higher risk of rejecting the new kidney. Transplant patients need antirejection medication for the rest of their lives. Many times these medications can cause other problems such as cancer and diabetes. Even if a patient were a candidate for a transplant and was willing to risk the operation and its consequences, there are relatively few donor kidneys available.

In the end, the choice of one treatment over another should be based on factors such as age and overall medical condition.

Health CONNECTION

SHAPING UP: YOU CAN'T DO IT OVERNIGHT

Your life is full of activity—running for a bus, climbing a flight of stairs, riding a bike, dancing, playing sports. You couldn't do any of these activities if the cells of your body didn't release energy.

As you learned in the chapter, your cells release energy through a process known as respiration. In this process, glucose from the foods you eat is combined with oxygen from the air you breathe, and energy is released. This type of respiration is known as aerobic respiration because it occurs in the presence of oxygen.

Energy for just about every activity you engage in during a single day, whether it's climbing stairs or playing sports, is supplied by the process of aerobic respiration. During these activities, your cells receive plenty of oxygen through the working of your respiratory and circulatory systems.

During some activities, however, your heart and lungs cannot work fast enough to provide your muscle cells with enough oxygen. Strenuous activities, such as sprinting or lifting weights, require so much energy that the supply of oxygen is rapidly used up. When this occurs, your muscle cells release energy from glucose without oxygen through a process known as anaerobic respiration.

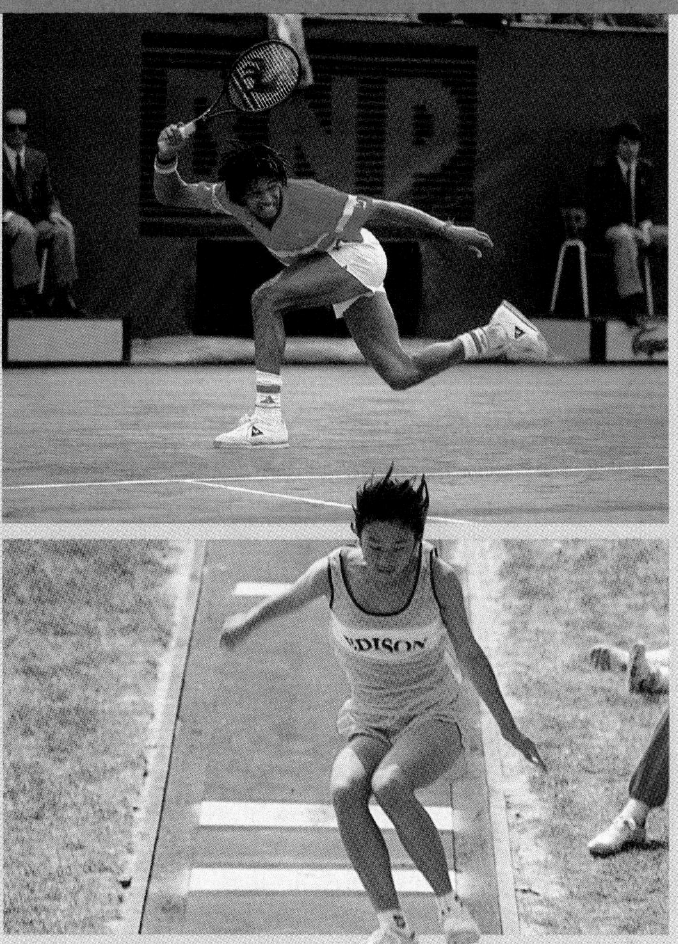

At some time or another, you have experienced the effects of your muscle cells generating energy anaerobically. Your muscles begin to burn and sting because of the buildup of toxic substance in your muscles called lactic acid. It takes time for the circulatory system to carry away this product. Even the next day, you may feel as if your muscles can barely move. In addition, anaerobic respiration doesn't produce as much energy as aerobic respiration, and your body quickly tires out.

In people who are out of shape, strenuous activities don't have to last for very long before anaerobic respiration takes over in muscle cells.

By keeping in shape through exercise, you can improve the efficiency of your circulatory and respiratory systems so your muscles will not run low on oxygen as rapidly.

Exercise can strengthen the muscle in the left ventricle of the heart so more blood can be pumped to your cells per heartbeat. Regular exercise can also improve your breathing by strengthening the muscles of respiration so more air can be moved through the lungs per breath.

In addition, exercise can also improve the oxygen-carrying properties of blood cells and increase blood volume in the body.

YOU TRY IT!

Getting into shape does not happen overnight. It is generally agreed by scientists and health professionals that, to maintain fitness, exercise must be performed on a regular basis. Your physician, physical education teacher, or a fitness professional can help you design the right fitness program for you.

HOW IT WORKS

THE ARTIFICIAL KIDNEY MACHINE

Every two minutes your entire blood supply circulates through your kidneys. The kidneys cleanse about 200 liters of blood every 24 hours, filtering waste products and water from your blood. As they do this, your kidneys produce about 2 liters of urine a day. When kidneys are diseased or damaged, water and nitrogen waste products can collect in the blood and cause a variety of unhealthy or even life-threatening conditions.

An artificial kidney machine duplicates some of the kidney's functions by removing nitrogen waste products and excess water. During the process, called hemodialysis, a patient's blood circulates through a filter outside the body.

The actual filtering device is a hemodialyzer. A hemodialyzer resembles a tube, like the tube inside a roll of paper towel. The tube is clear, with a thick bundle of white, hairy-looking material inside. This material is the filtering membrane, and it acts very much like the cell membranes of kidney cells.

The filtering membrane separates the hemodialyzer into two compartments. Blood from the patient's artery flows through one compartment, while a cleansing fluid flows through the second compartment.

As blood circulates through the tubing, the blood with a high concentration of waste molecules diffuses through the membrane into the cleaning fluid. Here the concentration of waste molecules is very low. Fresh cleansing fluid is constantly added to the second compartment so that waste molecules continue to diffuse. The freshly cleansed blood is then returned to the patient.

A single treatment may take from two to four hours and usually needs to be repeated every two to three days. Hemodialysis is not a cure for diseased or damaged kidneys. However, it is a treatment that allows patients to live longer.

WHAT DO YOU THINK?

The dialyzer and the cell membrane have much in common.

1. What characteristics do they have in common?
2. What processes occur in both the dialyzer and the cell membrane?

Reviewing Main Ideas

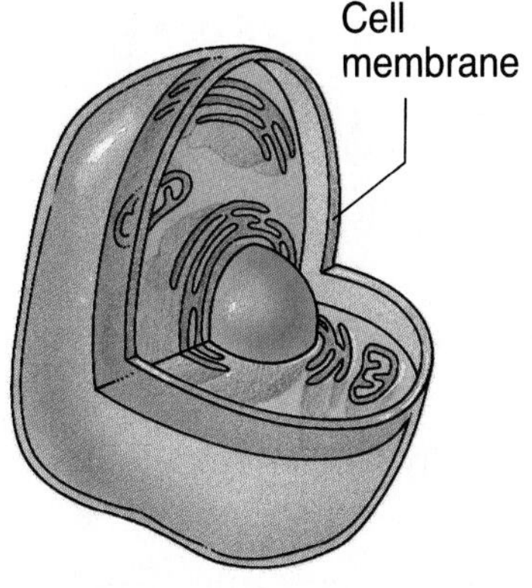

1. Cells carry out life processes with the help of the cell membrane, a specialized structure that controls what enters and leaves a cell.

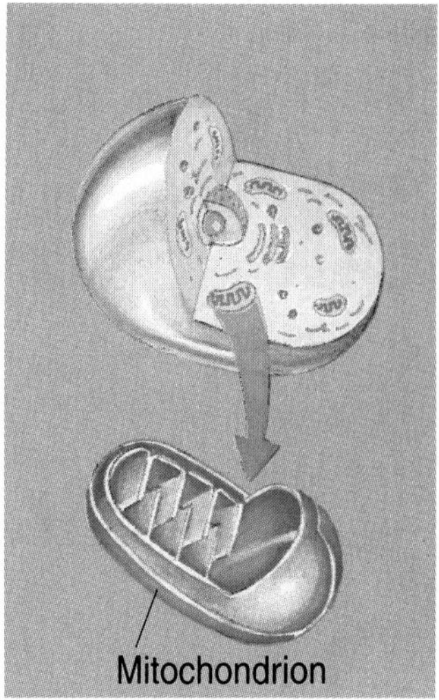

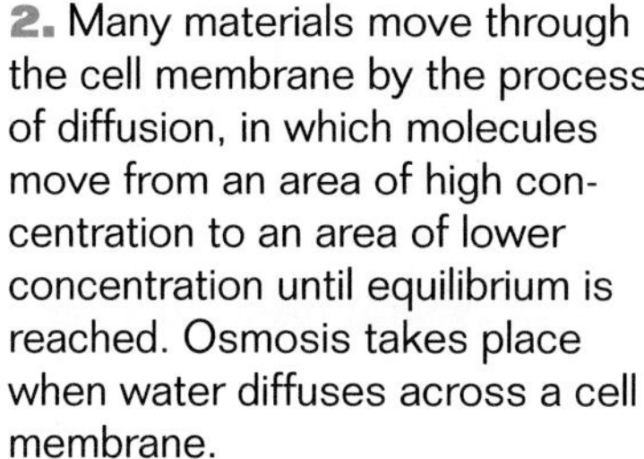

2. Many materials move through the cell membrane by the process of diffusion, in which molecules move from an area of high concentration to an area of lower concentration until equilibrium is reached. Osmosis takes place when water diffuses across a cell membrane.

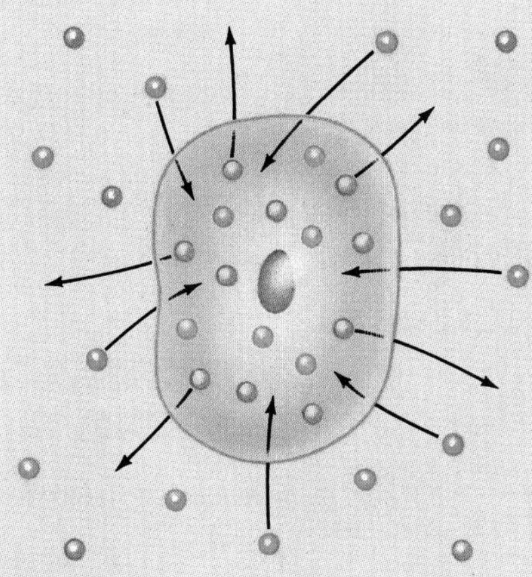

3. In the cells of most organisms, energy is released from food in the presence of oxygen by the process of respiration. Organisms that cannot utilize oxygen release energy through fermentation.

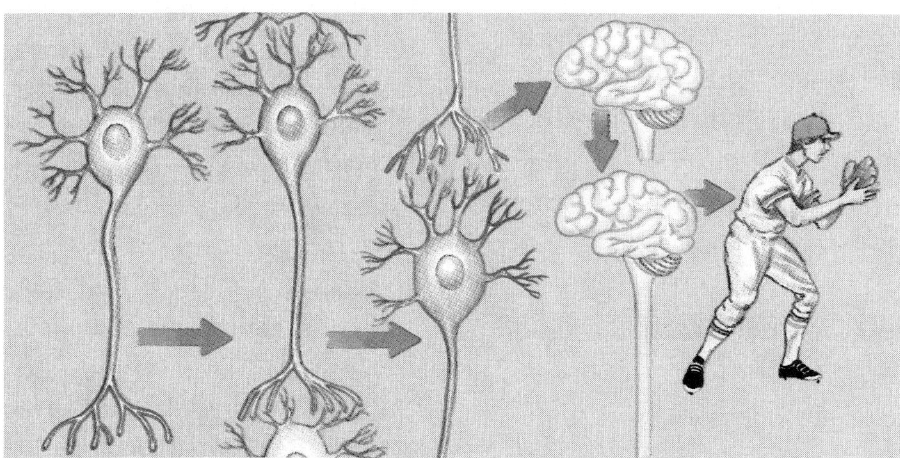

4. Most many-celled organisms are not just a collection of individual cells working by themselves, but are made up of tissues, organs, and systems.

Chapter 20

Chapter Review

USING KEY SCIENCE TERMS

fermentation
organ
organ system
organism
osmosis
respiration
tissue

Using the list above, replace the underlined words with the correct key science term.

1. Most cells release energy through the process of burning oxygen and glucose.
2. A group of similar cells working together is only one level of organization in an organism.
3. The diffusion of water through a cell membrane supplies a cell with its needed water.
4. Some organisms, such as bacteria, release energy by burning glucose without oxygen.
5. The circulatory system is a good example of a group of organs working together.
6. The heart is a good example of different tissues working together.
7. Dogs, plants, and flies are actually groups of organ systems working together.

UNDERSTANDING IDEAS

Answer the following questions.

1. How does respiration help an organism survive?
2. Would you expect to find more mitochondria in a more active cell or a less active cell? Why?
3. Do molecules stop moving through a cell membrane once equilibrium is reached? Explain your answer.
4. Name three types of tissue that are found in your body.
5. Why does your body get warm as you exercise?
6. In which direction do molecules flow during diffusion?
7. Why is a cell membrane called semipermeable?

CRITICAL THINKING

Use your understanding of the concepts developed in the chapter to answer each of the following questions.

1. In the first Investigate activity, you observed osmosis through an egg membrane. Do you think you would have obtained the same results if the shells had not been dissolved by the vinegar? Explain your answer.
2. Applying your knowledge of osmosis, explain how plant roots obtain water from the soil.
3. In snowy states, salt is used to melt ice on the roads. Explain what happens to many roadside plants as a result.
4. What do you think happens to substances that are not allowed to pass into your cells?

5. Under normal conditions, human red blood cells are circular and rounded as in the cells on the left. The cells on the right have lost water and changed shape. What conditions and processes caused this to happen?

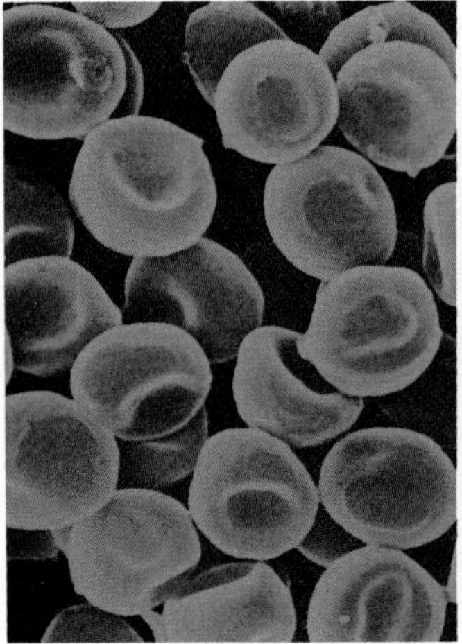

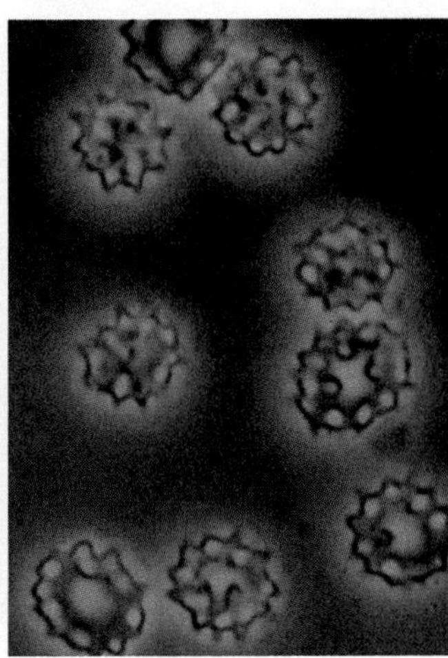

6. Why might a person feel very tired and weak after skipping several meals?

PROBLEM SOLVING

Read the following problem and discuss your answers in a brief paragraph.

Carla made a salad of lettuce, tomatoes, carrots, and cucumbers. She seasoned the damp salad with herbs, salt, and pepper. Then she placed it in the refrigerator for a couple of hours.

When Carla returned, she took the salad from the refrigerator. The lettuce had wilted and the other vegetables were limp. She noticed that there was liquid in the bottom of the bowl. Where did the liquid come from? Why did the lettuce wilt?

CONNECTING IDEAS

Discuss each of the following in a brief paragraph.

1. Why don't some cells obtain their energy through respiration? What other process do they use to get energy?

2. How do you think the energy requirements of a muscle cell compare to that of a skin cell? Explain your answer.

3. Describe how cells get the materials they need. Where do the nutrients, water, and oxygen come from?

4. **HEALTH CONNECTION** Sometimes when you exercise, your body is not able to provide enough oxygen to your muscle cells. What do you think happens then?

5. **SCIENCE AND SOCIETY** How would your life change if you had to depend on hemodialysis?

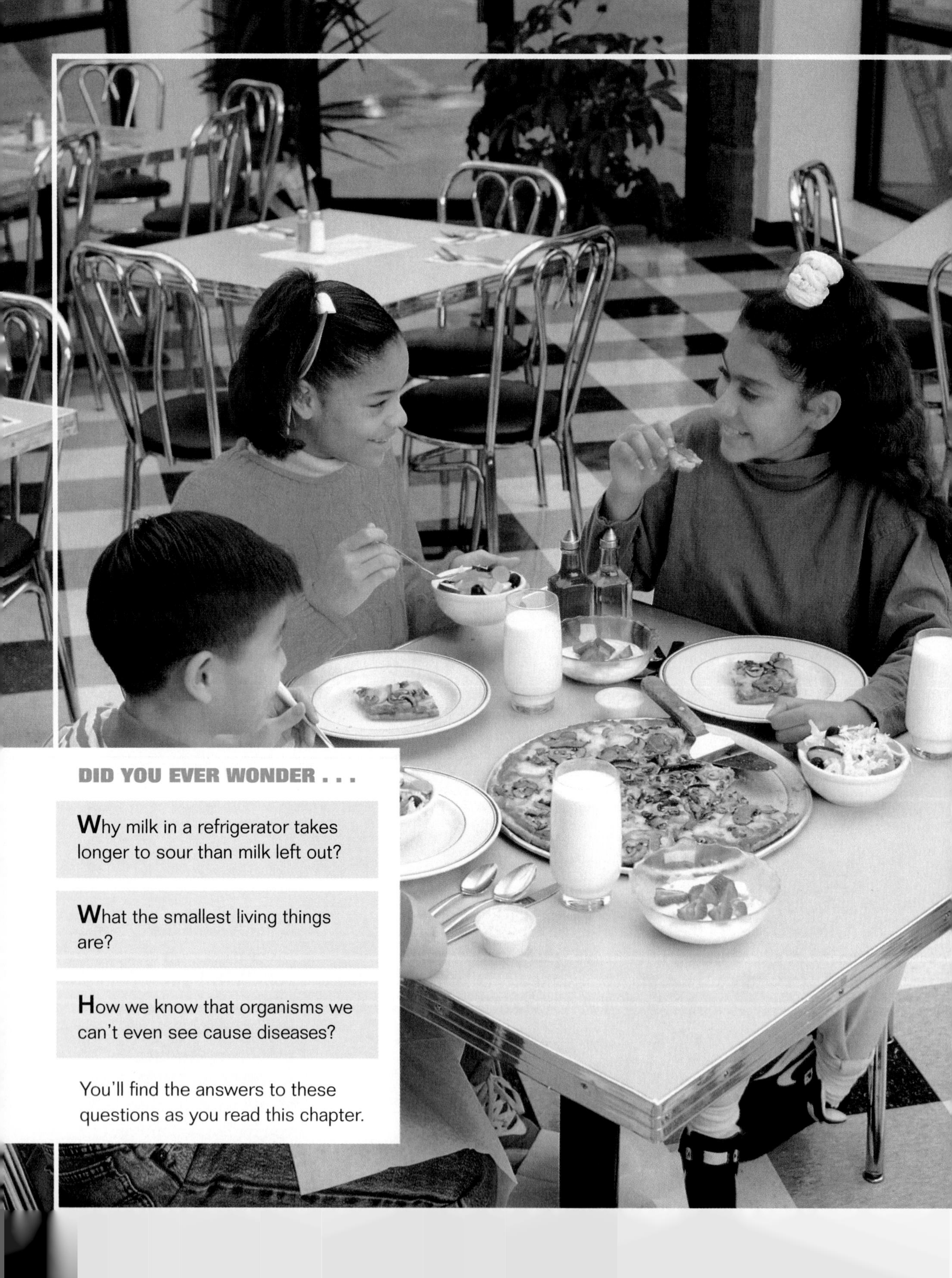

DID YOU EVER WONDER . . .

Why milk in a refrigerator takes longer to sour than milk left out?

What the smallest living things are?

How we know that organisms we can't even see cause diseases?

You'll find the answers to these questions as you read this chapter.

Chapter 21

Simple Organisms

Imagine yourself eating with two friends. One is biting into a cheese pizza. The other pours a vinegar dressing on a salad with chunks of blue cheese. You're eating strawberry yogurt.

Your pizza-eating friend makes up a puzzler: "What do our three meals have in common?" (HINT: What foods are made with the help of small organisms?)

One of your pals who is known for being smart in science says, "Small organisms you can't see give yogurt its flavor, so maybe other small organisms help make cheese and give vinegar in salad dressing its flavor." Pizza crust rises because of yeast. These foods were given their characteristics by small organisms!

The world around you is filled with many different types of small organisms. Some of these organisms can be found around your home. Some can be seen only with a microscope. In this chapter, you will explore these different types of organisms and how some of them are important to your life.

EXPLORE!

What does yeast look like?
Examine dry yeast, and then mix a small amount with warm tap water. Place a few drops of the mixture on a microscope slide. Examine it first with low power, then with high power. Wait five to ten minutes and observe the yeast again. Is yeast one-celled or many-celled?

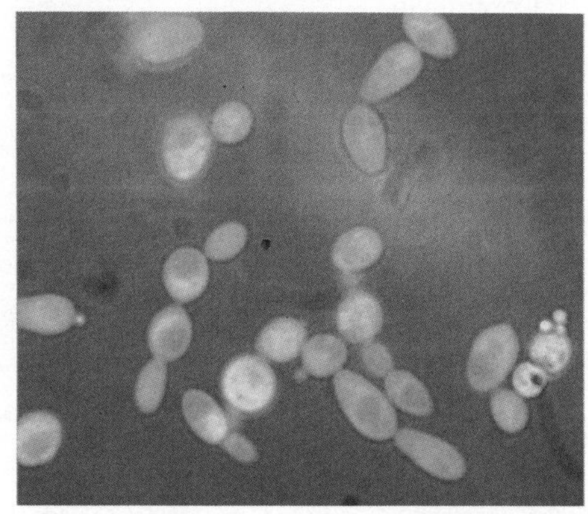

21-1 Living Organisms

OBJECTIVES

In this section, you will

- classify an organism as being one-celled or many-celled;
- recognize the difficulty of determining whether or not viruses are living;
- conclude that a one-celled organism is capable of carrying out the same life functions as a many-celled organism.

KEY SCIENCE TERMS

microorganism
virus

VARIETY AMONG LIVING THINGS

As you know, many of the foods you eat, such as hamburgers and salad, come from complex organisms, but were you surprised to find that some of the foods you eat are produced with the help of "simple" organisms? Keep in mind that simple does not refer to what these organisms do. The yeast you looked at in the activity use the sugar in pizza dough to make food for themselves. As they do this, they produce a gas that makes the dough light and good to eat. The process is anything but simple. The same is true of other small organisms. These organisms are called simple only because they are small and do not appear to be quite so complex in structure or appearance as some other organisms, such as a dog, an earthworm, and you.

However, despite the differences in size, complex organisms and simple organisms share many things in common. In the following activity, you will find out about some of these similarities.

FIND OUT!

How do two organisms compare to each other?

Your teacher will provide you with a wet-mount slide of an organism called *Ulva* and a slide of another organism known as a paramecium. Compare the size of the cells of the organisms. Do the organisms resemble each other? How many cells make up each organism? Carefully observe the activities of each organism. Pointing a flashlight or some other small light at the slide, quickly flash the light on and off. Do the organisms respond in any way to the light?

Contractile vacuole
Cell membrane
Macronucleus
Micronucleus
Oral groove
Food vacuole
Cilia

Conclude and Apply

1. How many cells make up each organism? Is the paramecium limited in what it can do because it consists of only one cell?
2. How might having many cells help *Ulva*?

ONE-CELLED ORGANISMS

In the activity you just completed, you could see that being one-celled did not slow the paramecium down! It is a very active organism. Since it is an organism—a living thing—the paramecium carries out all life functions. It is able to grow, obtain and consume food, carry out cellular respiration, and reproduce. As you may have seen, the paramecium, like other living things, can also respond to stimuli such as light, heat, or chemicals in its environment. It may move toward or away from a stimulus, depending on how the stimulus affects it.

Besides the paramecium, there are many other one-celled organisms. The bloblike organism in Figure 21-1 might not look like a living thing, but it is. Like the paramecium, the amoeba is a tiny organism made up of a single cell. It looks very different from the paramecium, but it can carry out all the same life functions.

As hard as you might try, it would be difficult to find a place where one-celled organisms do not live. To find them, check the air, the soil, plants and animals, and yes, even inside you or on your skin. One-celled organisms may also be found in fresh water and salt water.

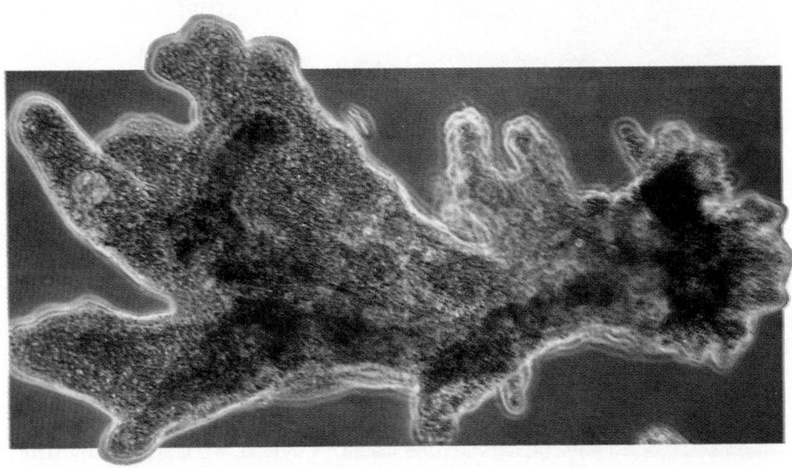

FIGURE 21-1. The amoeba is a one-celled organism.

MANY-CELLED ORGANISMS

When you looked at *Ulva* in the activity, you discovered that it is a many-celled organism. Many-celled organisms are the ones that you're probably more familiar with. Can you name a many-celled organism that is reading this book at this moment?

Does a many-celled organism have an advantage over a one-celled organism? As you recall, many-celled organisms have different types of cells that are specialized to carry out different life functions. If one part of a many-celled organism is injured, the organism may still be able to survive. You may wonder what advantage, if any, a one-celled organism might have. If you think about it, unlike many complex organisms, all the parts of a one-celled organism are in contact with the environment. In this way, one-celled organisms have an abundant supply of food and oxygen if and when they need it.

To see the one-celled and simple, many-celled organisms mentioned in this chapter, you may have to look through a microscope. Organisms that are too small to be seen with the naked eye are called **microorganisms**. Scientists use microscopes to see the microorganisms in Figure 21-2. You will be learning more about these microorganisms in the next section.

FIGURE 21-2. Most of these organisms can only be seen with the aid of a microscope.

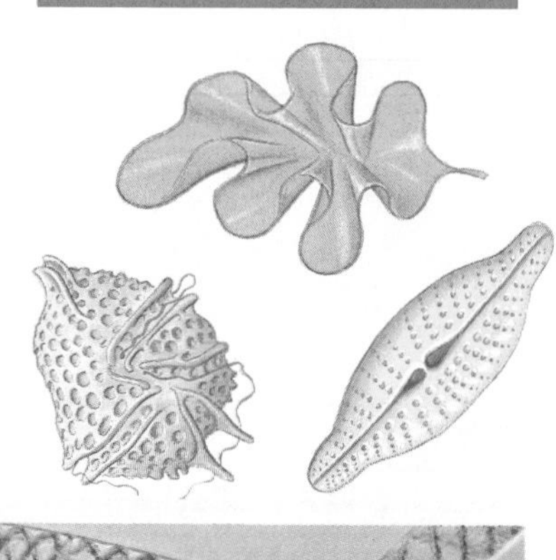

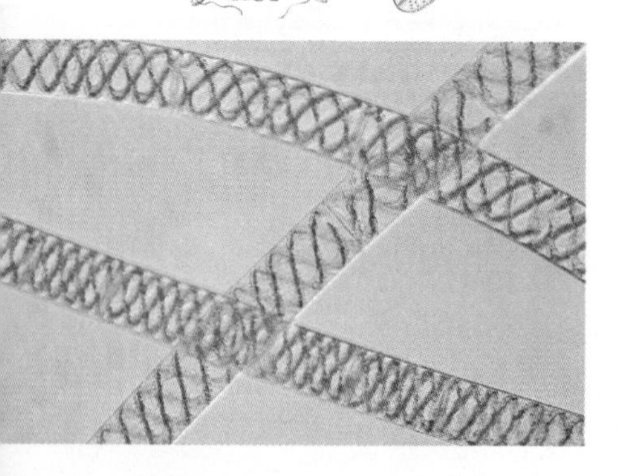

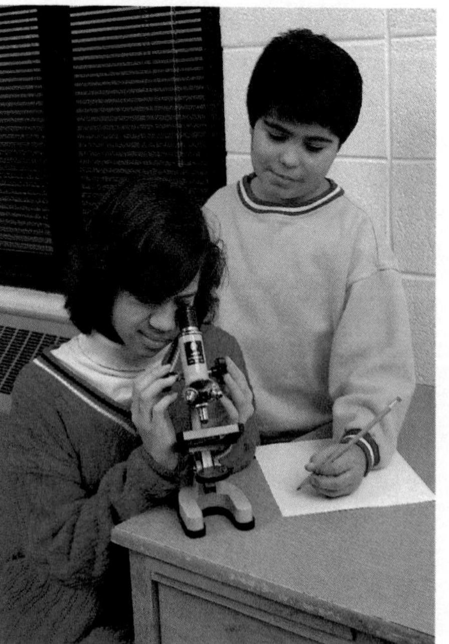

Think about the last time you had a cold. Those pesky viruses that caused it are structures that are too small to be seen except with an electron microscope. They do not appear in the photographs in Figure 21-2 because they are not microorganisms. Viruses are not made up of cells. The following activity will help you find out what viruses look like.

I N V E S T I G A T E !

21-1 SHAPES OF VIRUSES

Viruses all have a similar structure, yet they differ greatly in shape. In this activity, you can **observe** and make models of some viruses.

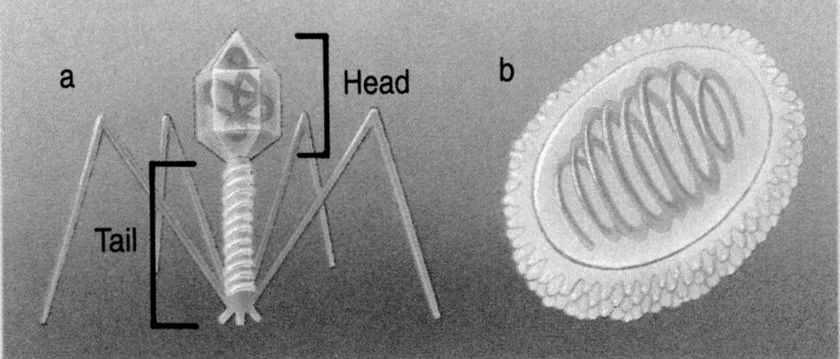

PROBLEM

How can you make a model of a virus?

MATERIALS

3.7 cm × 0.7 cm bolt
2 nuts to fit bolt
2 pieces #22-gauge wire, 14 cm long
polystyrene ball, 4.5 cm in diameter
pipe cleaners, cut in 2-cm lengths

PROCEDURE

1. Look at the photographs of the viruses taken with an electron microscope. Then study the drawings of the same viruses. The drawing in Figure a represents a virus enlarged 260,000 times. The drawing in Figure b represents a flu virus enlarged 300,000 times.
2. Notice the parts in Figure a that are labeled. To make a model of the virus, attach two nuts onto the bolt and screw them on as far as you can.
3. Twist the wires around the bolt near the bottom. Make the wire as tight as you can. Fold the wire ends and bend them so that they look like the drawing.
4. Use the polystyrene ball and pipe cleaners to **make a model** of the flu virus in Figure B.

ANALYZE

1. **Compare** your models with Figures a and b. How are they alike?
2. **Contrast** the two viruses. How are they different from each other?

CONCLUDE AND APPLY

3. How does the structure of a virus differ from that of a cell?
4. **Going Further:** What kinds of illnesses have you heard of that are caused by viruses? How do you think the structure of a virus might help it get inside your cells?

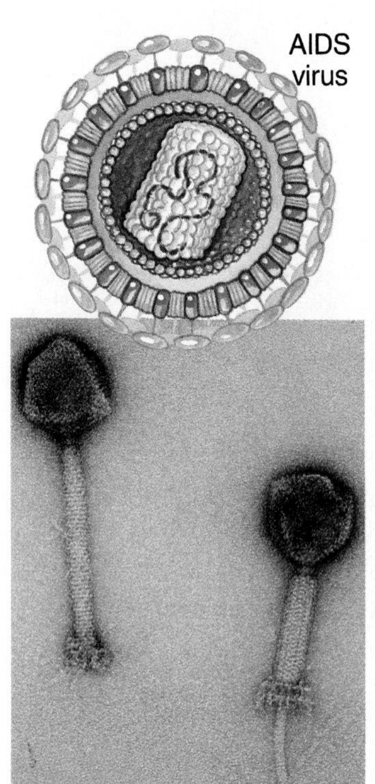

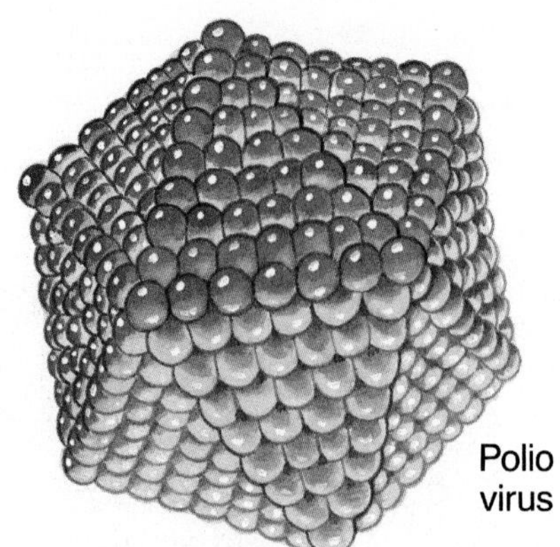

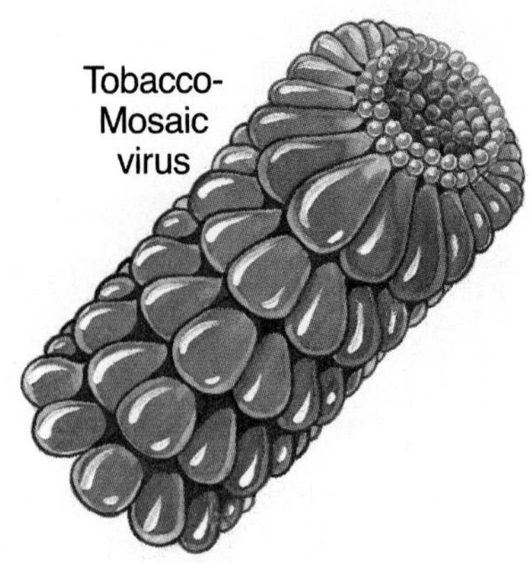

FIGURE 21-3. Viruses come in a variety of shapes and sizes.

ARE VIRUSES LIVING THINGS?

As you learned in the last activity, viruses do not resemble cells. As you can see in Figure 21-3, viruses do not possess the typical cell characteristics you have learned about, such as a cell membrane or a nucleus. **Viruses** are microscopic particles made up of a DNA or RNA core surrounded by a protein coat. DNA, as you recall, is the substance found in cell chromosomes that determines how organisms will look and behave. Viruses come in a variety of shapes and sizes. As you can see, the tobacco-mosaic virus is shaped somewhat like a tube. Some are shaped like a soccer ball with twenty sides. In fact, scientists classify viruses according to their shapes.

Viruses cannot grow, respond to a stimulus, or carry out respiration. For these reasons, viruses cannot be considered living things. However, when a virus enters a living cell, such as one of yours, it can reproduce. The ability to reproduce is among the few things viruses share in common with living organisms. How does a virus reproduce?

How do we know?

How do new viruses form?

How new viruses form was a mystery until 1969, when Nobel Prize winner Max Delbrük began his experiment.

In his experiment, Delbrük injected two different types of viruses into one bacterium. The viruses reproduced rapidly and new viruses erupted from the bacterium. Delbrük examined the offspring and found viruses similar to the two he injected. He also found a new type of virus that had traits that were a combination of the two. Delbrük concluded that when two types of viruses enter a cell, DNA is exchanged, and new viruses form.

Figure 21-4 shows that, once inside a cell, a virus can turn the cell into a virus factory. Virus DNA takes control of cell activities, and uses the cell's energy and other materials for reproduction. Eventually, the cell is destroyed and bursts open, releasing newly produced viruses. Other types of viruses can combine with cell chromosomes. When this happens, virus DNA is replicated right along with the cell's DNA. Exchange of DNA can occur and new types of viruses are produced. Viruses cause disease in plants and animals. Some of the viral diseases you are familiar with are the flu, measles, chicken pox, mumps, polio, rabies, and AIDS.

How do viruses get from one place to another? Influenza, or flu, viruses are commonly spread through coughing and sneezing. Some viruses are spread by contact with objects, such as water faucets or doorknobs.

Currently, there are no medications available to cure viral diseases. But some viral diseases, such as measles, the flu, and polio, can be prevented by vaccines.

In this section, you learned that all organisms—whether they are one-celled or many-celled—carry out the same basic life functions. Viruses, while they carry out the life process of reproduction, are not considered living organisms because they don't grow, eat, or respond to stimuli. Viruses can, however, reproduce when inside a living cell. As you learned, viruses can come in a variety of shapes. Viruses are classified into groups according to their shapes. In the next section, you will investigate how scientists classify simple organisms.

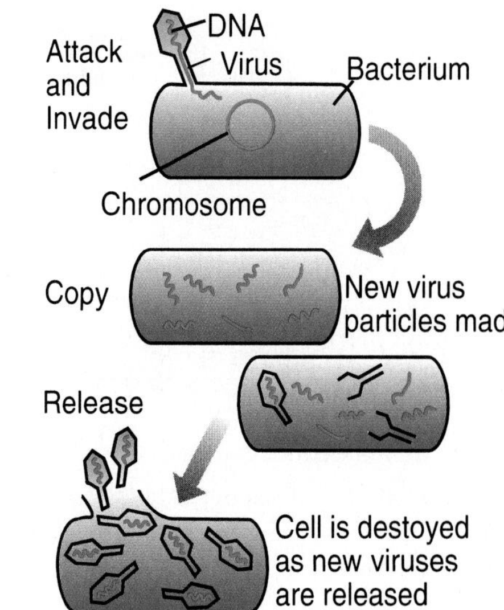

FIGURE 21-4. To reproduce, a virus attacks and invades a cell, eventually destroying it.

Check Your Understanding

1. Describe *Ulva,* a paramecium, an amoeba, yeast, and yourself as being one-celled or many-celled.
2. Which of the organisms named in Question 1 are microorganisms? Give evidence to support your answer.
3. Suppose you have a paramecium as a pet. What might this one-celled organism need from you?
4. **APPLY:** If you found an unknown but inactive structure in a test tube, what steps would you take to determine whether or not it is a virus?

21-2 Classifying Simple Organisms

OBJECTIVES

In this section, you will

- identify the general traits of three kingdoms—Monera, Protista, and Fungi;
- learn how scientists classify simple organisms.

KEY SCIENCE TERMS

Monera
Protista
Fungi

CLASSIFYING—MAKING THINGS EASIER

Going to the supermarket could be quite a challenge! Hundreds of different items are found on the shelves. What if you had to wander from aisle to aisle in search of what you want? Fortunately, the items in a supermarket are classified into groups. For example, you may find apples, oranges, and celery in aisle 1. Sugar and spices may be in aisle 4. By classifying the items into related groups, the people at the supermarket make it easy for you to find what you want.

Classifying makes it easier to study related groups of living things, too. In the last section, you were introduced to several different kinds of simple organisms. By classifying these organisms, you will get to know them even better. Try your skill at classifying with this next activity.

FIGURE 21-5. Foods in a supermarket are classified into groups.

EXPLORE!

In what ways can you classify organisms?

Look at the different kinds of organisms in Figure 21-6. Carefully observe their physical characteristics and keep in mind their size. How would you classify these organisms in groups? What characteristics would you use to separate the groups? Make a list of the characteristics of each group and explain your reasons for classifying them the way you did.

HOW SCIENTISTS CLASSIFY ORGANISMS

As you can see, there are many different ways to group, or classify, organisms. What do scientists use as their basis for classifying? They use characteristics such as the structure of an organism, the way the organism reproduces, and its method of obtaining food. You know that living things that produce or make food are called producers. These organisms use light energy to make food from water and carbon dioxide in the process of photosynthesis. Producers can be very small organisms, such as one-celled green algae, or tall trees. All green plants are producers. Other organisms are consumers, which feed on producers or other consumers. Consumers, too, can be as small as a paramecium or as large as a whale. Some of the organisms you will read about in this chapter are producers, and others are consumers.

FIGURE 21-6. Examples of simple organisms are: amoeba (a); mushroom (b); *Euglena* (c); bacteria (d); virus (e); blue-green bacteria (f), and bread mold (g).

Both you and a paramecium are consumers, but do you think you should be placed in the same category as paramecium? How an organism gets its food is just one of many characteristics that scientists look at to classify an organism. Today, most scientists use a system in which organisms are placed into one of five large groups called kingdoms, based on characteristics they have in common. The five kingdoms are Monera, Protista, Fungi, Plants, and Animals. In this chapter, we will only study monerans, protists, and fungi.

FIGURE 21-7. *Ulva* (a) and the sequoia tree (b) are both producers. The paramecium (c) is an example of a consumer.

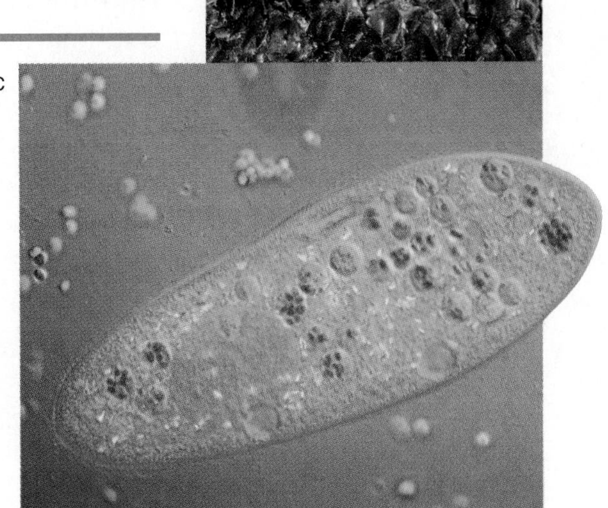

TABLE 21-1. Classifying Organisms by Kingdom

Characteristics	Monera	Protista	Fungi
One-celled?	all	most	some
Many-celled?	no	some	most
Has a nucleus?	no	yes	yes
Producers?	some	some	no
Consumers?	some	some	all
Examples	bacteria, blue-green bacteria	amoeba, *Euglena,* algae	mushroom, bread mold, yeast

Look at Table 21-1 to see what a scientist might ask to decide how to classify organisms by kingdom.

Kingdom Monera includes the bacteria and blue-green bacteria shown in Figure 21-6(d) and (f). Organisms in the Kingdom **Monera** have no nucleus and all are one-celled. Monerans are either producers or consumers.

Kingdom Protista includes many organisms, including the amoeba and *Euglena* shown in Figure 21-6(a) and (c). Organisms in Kingdom **Protista** have cells with a nucleus, and many are one-celled. Some protists are producers, whereas others are consumers.

Kingdom Fungi includes mushrooms and bread mold seen in Figure 21-6(b) and (g). **Fungi** have cells with a nucleus, and most are many-celled. Fungi are consumers that obtain food by absorbing it from dead or living organisms.

You may have noticed that none of the kingdoms includes the virus, as seen in Figure 21-6(e). Why do you think viruses are not included in any kingdom?

You have seen that classifying helps you to study and understand organisms better. In the next section, you will learn more about simple organisms and how they carry out their life functions.

Check Your Understanding

1. What is the main difference between monerans and protists?
2. Place each of the following organisms into one of the three kingdoms discussed in this section:
   Organism A: many-celled; has no chlorophyll
   Organism B: one-celled; has no nucleus
   Organism C: one-celled; has a nucleus
3. **APPLY:** If you were to create a sixth kingdom for viruses, describe the most important trait you would use for classifying organisms in this new kingdom.

21-3 Simple Organisms Doing Their Jobs

MONERANS

Have you ever accidentally tasted milk that was left in the refrigerator too long? What makes milk spoil?

Milk kept at room temperature "spoils," but milk kept in a refrigerator doesn't spoil as quickly. Why? Are there any differences between room temperature milk and milk that is refrigerated? The next activity will help you answer these questions.

OBJECTIVES

In this section, you will

- describe the major characteristics and activities of monerans, protists, and fungi;
- describe the way monerans, protists, and fungi affect other living things.

KEY SCIENCE TERMS

fission
cilia
flagella

FIND OUT!

What causes milk to spoil?

Place a drop of spoiled milk on a microscope slide. Add a drop of methylene blue stain to the milk. Then place a coverslip on the sample. Label this slide A. Prepare a slide for the unspoiled milk in the same way and label it B.

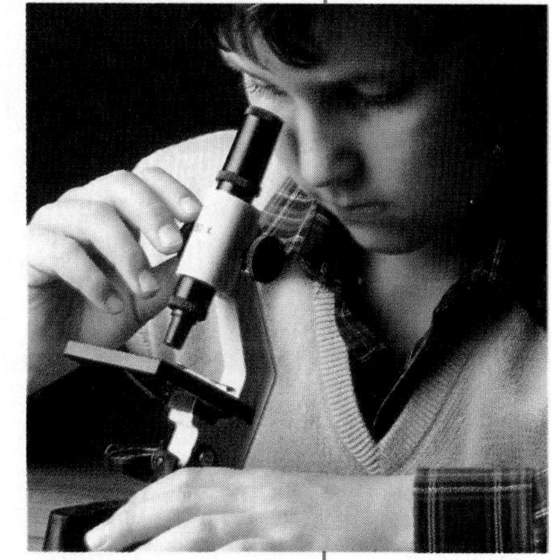

Conclude and Apply

1. Observe both slides under high power of a microscope. What do you observe in the spoiled milk that is not present or is present in very low numbers in the unspoiled milk?
2. What condition was needed for the growth of these organisms?

After observing and comparing the two samples of milk, do you think the organisms you saw caused the milk to spoil? Where did these organisms come from? What other needs might bacteria have besides the condition you found that was needed for growth? These bacteria are normally present in small numbers in any carton of milk you might take off a supermarket shelf; even though the milk has been pasteurized. But pasteurization

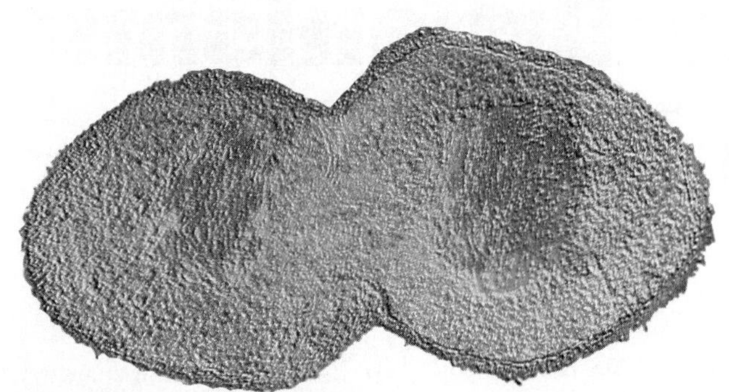

FIGURE 21-8. Many monerans, such as this bacterium, reproduce by fission.

doesn't kill all the bacteria in milk. Cooling milk slows down the rate of reproduction in these bacteria.

Most bacteria reproduce by fission. **Fission** is a process that produces two cells with genetic material exactly like that in the parent cell. During fission, the single chromosome in the moneran cell shown in Figure 21-8 makes a copy of itself. Eventually, the two chromosomes separate so that each new cell has an exact copy of the chromosome.

Monerans reproduce very rapidly. If ideal growing conditions are present, fission may take place every 20 minutes.

CHARACTERISTICS OF MONERANS

Monerans are the smallest living things on Earth. Although they are one-celled, some monerans form large groups of cells called colonies. You may have seen colonies of bacteria in the spoiled milk.

There are two main groups of monerans—bacteria and blue-green bacteria, also called cyanobacteria (SY-an-oh-bak-TIR-ee-uh). Figure 21-9 shows two cells: a typical bacterium and a cyanobacterium.

How do cyanobacteria differ from bacteria that caused the milk to spoil or give you a sore throat?

Cyanobacteria contain chlorophyll, which is a green pigment, and another pigment that is blue. That's why cyanobacteria are also called blue-green bacteria. Unlike most bacteria, cyanobacteria are producers, and they undergo photosynthesis.

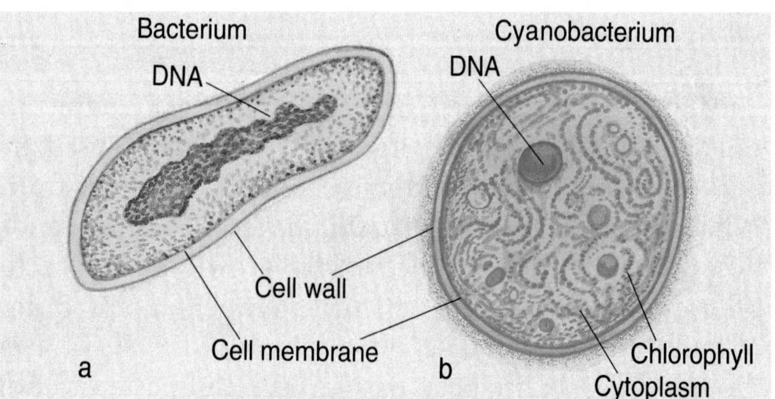

FIGURE 21-9. The two main groups of monerans are: bacteria (a) and cyanobacteria (b).

All cyanobacteria are one-celled organisms. However, some of these organisms live together in long chains. Others live together in globular groups.

HOW DO MONERANS AFFECT OTHER LIVING THINGS?

Though monerans are microscopic, they can be both helpful and harmful to other organisms much larger than themselves. The word *bacteria* may make you remember a sore throat or illness that was caused by these microorganisms. But only certain kinds of bacteria cause illness. Most bacteria are important for their helpful qualities. For example, one type of helpful bacteria that lives in the intestines of some plant-eating animals helps them digest cellulose, a substance found in the cell walls of plant cells.

Besides protecting your body from some diseases, certain bacteria digest and recycle the materials in dead organisms. With the help of these bacteria, these materials become available for use by other living things.

Have you ever had bacteria for lunch? As you learned at the beginning of the chapter, many foods are made with the help of bacteria. Bacteria break down substances in milk to produce the cheese being made in Figure 21-10. They also help give flavor to butter, yogurt, and sauerkraut.

Industries other than the food industry also rely on bacteria. Microbiologists have found ways to put bacteria to use in manufacturing medicines, cleansers, adhesives,

SKILLBUILDER

COMPARING AND CONTRASTING

For a closer look at the similarities and differences in the two groups of monerans, observe prepared slides of bacteria and cyanobacteria under high power with a microscope. How do the size, color, and shape of the cells compare? Make a chart comparing and contrasting these characteristics. If you need help, refer to the **Skill Handbook** on page 683.

FIGURE 21-10. Helpful monerans are used in the cheese and other food-making industries.

SKILLBUILDER

HYPOTHESIZING

You are a researcher in a laboratory. The bacteria in an experiment you have been working on have reproduced in large numbers. Then, all of a sudden, most of the bacteria begin to die. You need to find out what caused the deaths of the bacteria. What hypothesis can you make about what is happening to the bacteria? If you need help, refer to the **Skill Handbook** on page 687.

and other products. Bacteria that can digest oil are used in cleaning up oil spills around the world.

Although many bacteria are helpful rather than harmful, you have probably had firsthand experience with bacteria that cause disease. Strep throat, for example, is caused by bacteria. Other bacteria cause diphtheria and whooping cough in humans. If you have ever had a pimple or other skin infection, it was caused by bacteria using your cells as a source of food.

Cyanobacteria provide food and oxygen to living things in lakes and ponds. However, too many cyanobacteria in a pond can be harmful. Have you ever seen a pond covered with smelly green slime like the one in Figure 21-11?

Sometimes fertilizers get washed into a pond from nearby fields. This serves as food for the cyanobacteria. They reproduce rapidly. Once the food is used up, large numbers of the cyanobacteria die and other bacteria in the pond feed on their remains. The other bacteria, as they consume the dead cyanobacteria, use up the oxygen in the water. Less oxygen can cause fish and other organisms in the pond to die.

PROTISTS

Monerans can live in almost any environment where there is moisture. Protists need moist surroundings as well. Some live in damp soil, rotting logs, or the bodies of other organisms. Most, however, live in oceans, ponds, swamps, or other bodies of water.

FIGURE 21-11. Cyanobacteria are covering the surface of this pond.

EXPLORE!

What organisms live in pond water?

Make a wet mount of a drop of pond water. Observe the slide under both low and high power of the microscope. Compare this slide with a wet mount of tap water. Describe what you see. Is there a difference in what can be seen on the two slides?

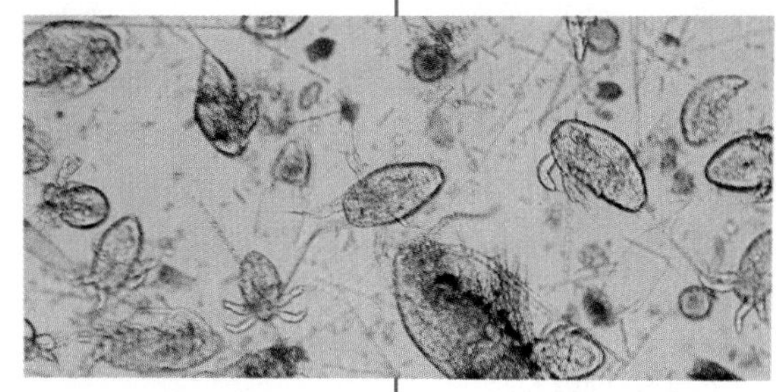

Most of the organisms that you see in pond water are protists. The protists are a large group of organisms with several different shapes. Look at Figure 21-12. All these organisms are protists.

Kingdom Protista contains a wide variety of organisms. They share more characteristics with one another than with members of any other kingdom. All protists have cells with one or more nuclei. Some protists, such as the amoeba, are one-celled. Others, such as the green algae, are many-celled. Some protists, such as *Euglena,* contain chlorophyll and make their own food, whereas others, such as the paramecium, feed on other organisms. As a result, protists are plantlike or animal-like. The life cycles of protists vary greatly. However, even protists with the simplest life cycles reproduce by mitosis and not by fission, as do monerans.

We will now discuss examples from two groups, plantlike and animal-like protists.

Plantlike Protists

Plantlike protists are known as algae. All algae can make their own food because they contain chlorophyll.

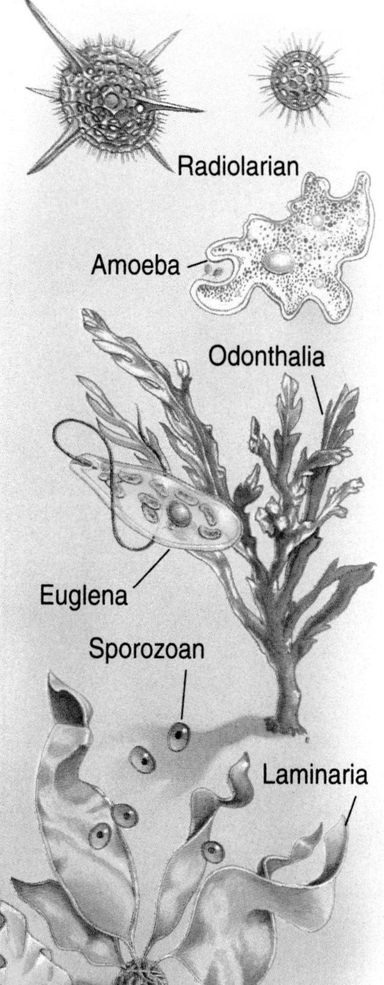

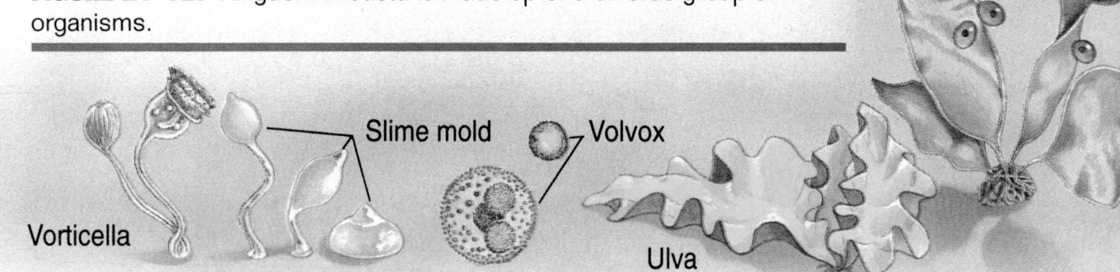

FIGURE 21-12. Kingdom Protista is made up of a diverse group of organisms.

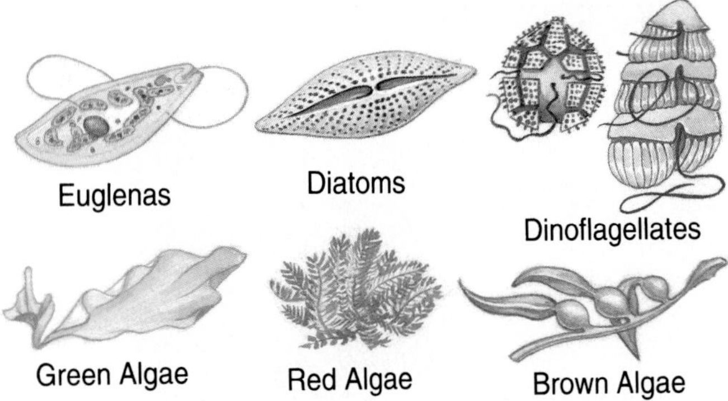

FIGURE 21-13. Plantlike protists, or algae, come in a variety of shapes and colors.

Does that mean that all algae are green? Figure 21-13 shows you the answer. Not all algae are green because some have other pigments that cover up the green color of their chlorophyll.

There are six main groups of algae. Each group has its own characteristics. You can observe the characteristics of one group—diatoms—in the following activity.

EXPLORE!

What can you learn from a diatom?

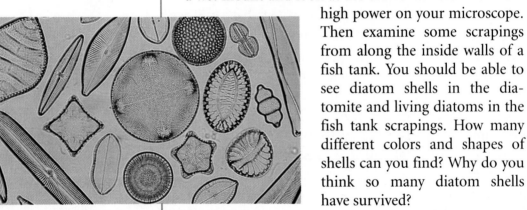

Diatomite is a sandy soil made up of shells left by diatoms that died about 20 million years ago. Prepare a wet mount and look at the diatomite under low and high power on your microscope. Then examine some scrapings from along the inside walls of a fish tank. You should be able to see diatom shells in the diatomite and living diatoms in the fish tank scrapings. How many different colors and shapes of shells can you find? Why do you think so many diatom shells have survived?

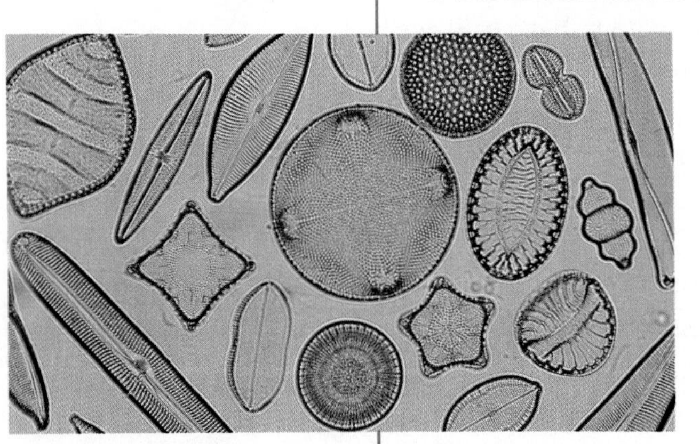

The diatoms and shells you observed in the activity were from two different habitats—salt water and fresh water. They form an important part of the plankton that feeds whales and many types of fish. The shells of the diatoms help to preserve them. Diatom shells contain silica, which is the main ingredient in glass.

DID YOU KNOW?

Your favorite ice cream contains a product made from brown algae! Algin is a substance made from the cell walls of certain brown algae. It is used to thicken ice cream.

Animal-like Protists

Some protists are animal-like in that they feed on other organisms. Animal-like protists are called protozoans.

They are classified into groups, according to the way they move. In the following activity, you will compare and contrast different groups of protozoans.

FIND OUT!

What characteristics do different protozoans have?

Label two slides as: *Amoeba* and *Paramecium*. Your teacher will provide material for you to prepare two wet mounts. Make certain that the material matches the label on your slide. Observe each slide under low power and high power. Notice the characteristics that distinguish one protozoan from the other.

Conclude and Apply

Describe how each protozoan moves about. Also try to see how it feeds and avoids obstacles. Each of these protozoans belongs to a different group. What characteristics would you use to classify them into separate groups?

One thing you probably noticed was how the amoeba and paramecium moved. Movement is the characteristic scientists use to classify protozoans. How do protozoans move about?

One group of protozoans, such as *Trypanosoma* that causes sleeping sickness, has whiplike structures called **flagella** to move through watery surroundings. Amoebas use protrusions of their cytoplasm, called pseudopods or "false feet," to move and to feed. In feeding, an amoeba extends pseudopods on either side of food such as a bacterium. The two ends of the pseudopods then join together to trap the food in a vacuole.

The paramecium belongs to the most complex group of protozoans. All organisms in this group have short, hairlike structures called **cilia** that extend from the cell membrane. They use the cilia like oars to move in any direction. The cilia also help sweep food into a mouthlike structure called

FIGURE 21-14. Protozoans such as these are classified according to the way they move around.

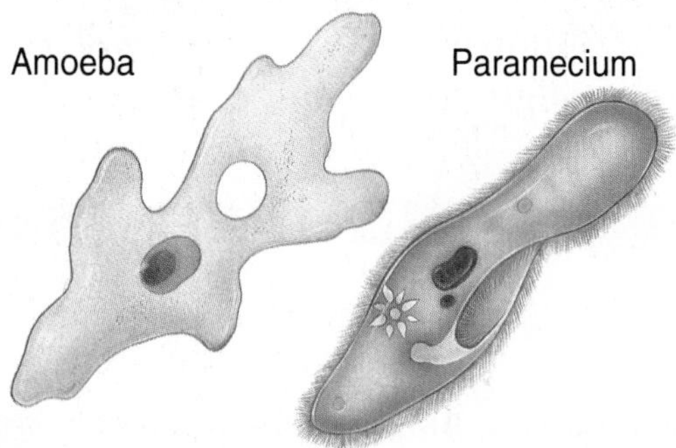

the oral groove. You can see the cilia of the paramecium in Figure 21-14. A fourth group of protozoans have no structures for movement. They live inside other organisms and feed on their tissues. One example of this group is *Plasmodium*, a protozoan found in tropical climates. This protozoan causes the disease malaria in humans.

HOW DO PROTISTS AFFECT OTHER LIVING THINGS?

Many protists are useful to other organisms. For example, those protists that carry on photosynthesis are helpful to just about everyone, including you. Not only does photosynthesis produce food, but at the same time, it also produces oxygen that is given off into the air. In fact, the oxygen used by organisms for respiration today was produced by diatoms 300 million years ago. Some scientists worry that if certain types of pollution in the ocean continue to exist, many plantlike protists will die.

Besides producing food and oxygen, diatoms are used for insulation, filters, and the paint used to make lines on roads. The diatom shells reflect light and produce the sparkle that makes the road lines visible at night.

Not all protists are helpful to other organisms. You know that one type, *Plasmodium*, causes malaria, which kills more people on Earth than any disease. There are other harmful protists as well. Figure 21-15 shows the protist *Trypanosoma*, another disease-causing protist. This protist is spread by the bloodsucking tsetse fly in Africa. When a trypanosome enters the bloodstream of animals and humans, it causes African sleeping sickness. The symptoms of this disease are fever, swollen glands, and extreme sleepiness.

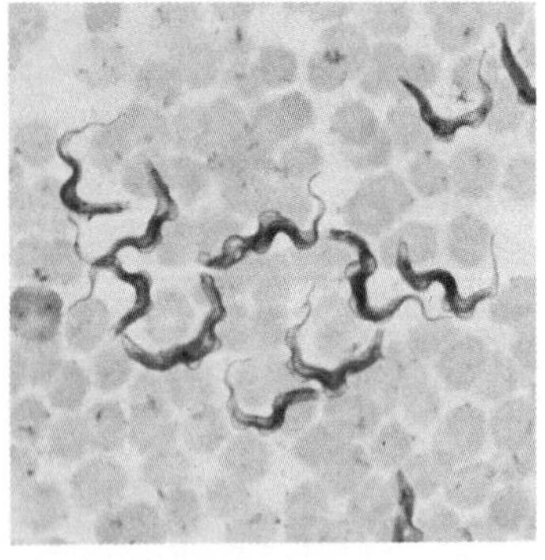

FIGURE 21-15. Trypanosoma, a harmful protist, is known to cause disease in humans.

FUNGI

The mushrooms you see in a grocery store or eat on your pizza make up only a small part of Kingdom Fungi. Mushrooms are fungi that are large enough to be seen easily. Other fungi are so tiny that they can only be seen with a microscope. You can become acquainted with one member of the Kingdom Fungi by doing the following activity.

DID YOU KNOW?

The word amoeba comes from the Greek word amoibe, which means *change*. This refers to the amoeba's ability to change shape.

EXPLORE!

What can you learn about fungi by observing them? Examine the kind of mushroom you buy in a grocery store. Observe its size. Would you say it is one-celled or many-celled? Carefully pull the cap off the stalk and lay it aside. Use your fingers to pull the stalk apart lengthwise. Continue to pull the stalk apart until the pieces are as thin as you can get them. Describe what you see. Look at the underside of the cap. Observe the many thin membranes. Look at one of the membranes under a hand lens. What do you see?

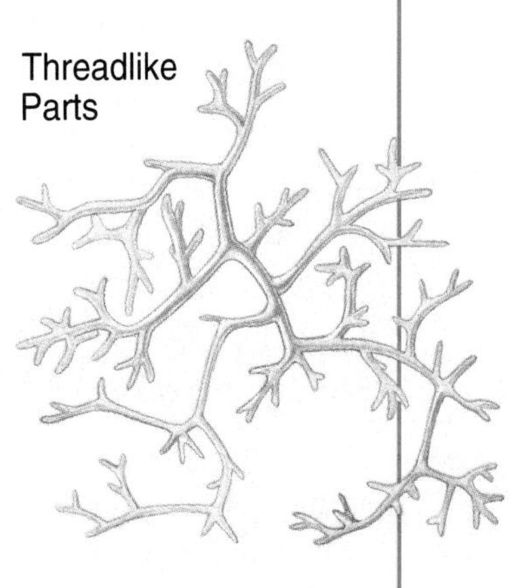

Fungi were once classified as plants. Based on your observations, would you accept this classification? In what ways do fungi differ from plants?

Unlike plants, fungi do not contain chlorophyll. Therefore, they cannot make their own food—they are consumers. Fungi do not have the specialized tissues and organs of plants. Instead, as you have seen, the body of a fungus is usually a mass of many-celled, threadlike tubes.

SKILLBUILDER

CLASSIFYING
Classify the monerans, protists, and fungi you have learned about into the categories of those that "Affect the Food Industry" and "Do Not Affect the Food Industry." If you need help, refer to the **Skill Handbook** on page 678.

Each cell of a tube has a nucleus. Like most other living things, fungi also need oxygen to carry out respiration. During the process, they give off carbon dioxide gas.

HOW DO FUNGI AFFECT OTHER LIVING THINGS?

People find fungi useful in many ways. The fungi called yeast make bread and pizza crust rise by producing gases. Other fungi give some cheeses, such as blue cheese, very different flavors that people like. Many people enjoy mushrooms on pizza and in salads and other dishes. One kind of fungus, called *Penicillium*, produces penicillin that doctors prescribe for patients with diseases caused by certain kinds of bacteria. If you've ever seen the green fungus growing on rotten oranges and old bread, then you're already familiar with what *Penicillium* looks like.

You may have seen fungi like those in Figure 21-16 growing on an old tree lying on a forest floor. If so, you've seen an example of fungi filling their most important role. Fungi are able to break down, or decompose, organic material. Food scraps, clothing, dead plants, and animals are all made of organic material. You know that fungi cannot make their own food and are consumers. They are a kind of consumer known as a decomposer because fungi decompose organic material and recycle the materials they are made of to the soil. These materials are then used by plants to grow. Like some bacteria, fungi help rid the land of mountains of waste.

FIGURE 21-16. Fungi break down and decompose dead organisms.

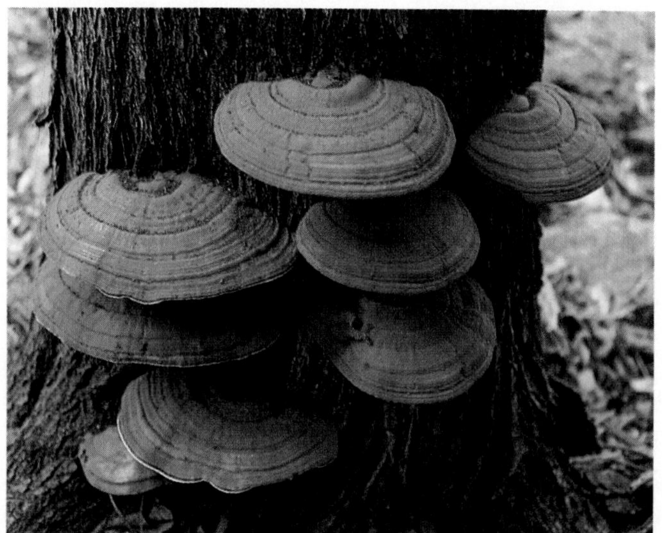

Some fungi, such as the ones that cause athlete's foot and ringworm, are parasites. Parasites are organisms that live on or in other living things and feed on them. Fungi that are parasites cause some of the most damaging diseases in plants. Wheat rust and corn smut are two fungi that can destroy food crops.

Where do fungi grow best? The following activity will help you find the answer.

I N V E S T I G A T E !

21-2 WHAT IS NEEDED FOR MOLDS TO GROW?

Molds are fungi that can feed on just about anything. Have you ever had to throw away an orange or cheese because of mold growing on it?

PROBLEM

What do molds need in order to grow?

MATERIALS 

8 small paper cups
sugarless dry cereal, dry macaroni, dry potato flakes, dry crackers without salt
water
hand lens
plastic wrap
labels
cotton swabs
mold source (from teacher)

DATA AND OBSERVATIONS

CUP CONTENTS	DAY 1	DAY 2	DAY 3	DAY 4
Dry cereal				
Wet cereal				
Dry potato				
Wet potato				
Dry macaroni				
Wet macaroni				
Dry cracker				
Wet cracker				

Water Water
A DRY CEREAL B DRY CEREAL C MACARONI D MACARONI
Cereal Macaroni
Water Water
E POTATO F POTATO G CRACKER H CRACKER
Potato flakes Cracker crumbs

PROCEDURE

1. Copy the data table.
2. Label the paper cups with your name and the letters A through H.
3. Add enough of the following to cover the bottom of each cup:
   A and B—dry cereal;
   C and D—dry macaroni;
   E and F—dry potato flakes;
   G and H—dry cracker crumbs.
4. Add just enough water to cups B, D, F, and H to moisten the food.
5. Rub a moist cotton swab across the dish of growing mold provided by your teacher.
6. Rub the cotton swab across the surface of the foods in all eight cups.
7. Cover each cup with plastic wrap and give the cups to your teacher to store.
8. **Observe** the cups for the next 4 days. Look for any evidence of mold growth. Try to estimate the amount of mold growth based on the diameter of the cup. Record your observations.

ANALYZE

1. In which cups did you **observe** evidence of mold growth?
2. Which cups showed no mold growth?
3. Would you **infer** that molds grow better in any particular kind of food?

CONCLUDE AND APPLY

4. **Compare and contrast** what was in the cups that showed mold growth and what was in the cups that did not. Explain.
5. Make a statement about what molds need to grow.
6. **Going Further:** If you wanted to prevent mold from growing in a food that you were packaging to sell, what is one way to prevent mold from spoiling your product?

HOW DO FUNGI MEET THEIR LIFE NEEDS?

As you saw in the activity, a damp or wet environment is needed for fungi to grow. Under the right conditions, you could find fungi growing on fabric, leather, fur, wood, paint, and even some plastics. You also saw that only a tiny bit of fungi on a cotton swab was needed to produce an entire colony on the various foods. How do fungi reproduce?

You can take a look at the reproductive parts of a fungus in the following activity.

EXPLORE!

How do fungi reproduce?

Examine some bread mold using a hand lens. Describe what you see. Then remove a small bit of mold and make a wet mount of the fungus. Observe the mold under low power with a microscope. What do you see all over the slide? What do you think they are?

A fungus begins life as a spore. In the activity, you observed spore cases containing millions of these reproductive cells.

You may now be thinking that even the simplest organism is very complex. The organisms you have studied so far are very different from one another in some ways. And yet they are all alike in the kinds of activities they must carry out to stay alive!

Check Your Understanding

1. Monerans are a mixed group of organisms. How are they all alike? How are they different?
2. Describe the ways animal-like protists are similar to plantlike protists. How do they differ?
3. Why does a mushroom farmer not have to worry about how much sunlight his or her crop gets?
4. **APPLY:** Make a list of the characteristics of protists and explain why they are grouped the way they are.

EXPANDING YOUR VIEW

CONTENTS

A Closer Look
The Versatile Molds 649

Earth Science Connection
Bacteria That Solve Pollution Problems 650

Science and Society
Using Viruses to Fight Disease 651

History Connection
The Countess's Powder 653

Teens In Science
When Are Gibberellins Too Much of a Good Thing? 654

A CLOSER LOOK

THE VERSATILE MOLDS

Have you seen any good fungi lately? One-fifth of all the different kinds of organisms on Earth are fungi. Hundreds of these fungi—most of them molds—live in the soil around your home, and even in your home!

As you learned in the chapter, fungi are important to humans and other organisms. Fungi, such as the mold *Penicillium*, are used to make antibiotic drugs. In addition, fungi are consumers. The organic materials they eat are broken down and returned to the soil. This process replenishes soil with essential nutrients plants need to grow.

The eating habits of fungi cause many problems for humans, however. Molds cause most of the spoiled food in your kitchen. How do they do this?

Molds grow very quickly under the right conditions. Most molds grow best between 23°C and 35°C, but their growth slows as the temperature gets lower. If the temperature falls below 6°C, molds become dormant.

Molds grow on and consume organic materials, such as fruits.When conditions are right, an average mold grows hundreds of thousands of tiny threadlike branches, called hyphae, that expand out to cover a fruit. The cells of hyphae release enzymes to break down the organic substances in the fruit, causing spoilage.

YOU TRY IT!

Design your own experiment to test one of the following hypotheses:

1. Peeled fruit will mold, but unpeeled fruit is better protected against mold growth.
2. Mold will grow faster on moist potatoes if left in the dark than if left in the light.

When you conduct an experiment, remember to test both parts of the hypothesis. For Hypothesis 1, test for mold growth on both a peeled and an unpeeled fruit. Also, you must maintain the same conditions for both fruits, so that nothing else (temperature, moisture, or light) affects the results. For Hypothesis 2, all conditions *except* the presence of light must be the same for both potatoes. Allow several days for your experiment to produce results, then estimate the mold growth on both items.

EARTH SCIENCE CONNECTION

BACTERIA THAT SOLVE POLLUTION PROBLEMS

In 1989, the *Exxon Valdez* spilled millions of gallons of oil on the Alaskan coastline. The oil soaked as much as two feet deep into the beaches. When nothing else cleaned up the spill, some scientists enlisted the help of bacteria. These microbes, living in the soil and water, like to eat hydrocarbons, the principle ingredient in oil. The scientists sprayed a fertilizer on the beaches to stimulate the bacteria to grow. Within two weeks, the oily beaches that had been sprayed were much cleaner than those that had not. The number of bacteria had tripled, and they were gobbling up the oil.

Many types of bacteria help solve our pollution problems. For example, some species of bacteria can metabolize sulfur, which occurs in large amounts in some kinds of coal. When this high-sulfur coal burns, it releases sulfur into the atmosphere, causing acid rain. However, when sulfur-eating bacteria are mixed into piles of high-sulfur coal, they change it into a much cleaner fuel.

Bacteria also help clean up toxic wastes. For example, scientists have identified several kinds of bacteria that eat the water-polluting chemical called polychlorinated biphenyl (PCB). PCBs are chemicals that were once used regularly in the electrical equipment industry. Like the bacteria that eat hydrocarbons, these microbes already live in the water and soil.

Medical wastes with radioactive ingredients are usually buried in toxic dumps. When these wastes decay, they produce radioactive methane gas. This gas can seep out and pollute the air. Research scientists have begun studying bacteria that change methane into water. When fertilized with nitrogen and phosphorus, these bacteria work two or three times faster to digest the dangerous methane gas.

Some researchers are creating new kinds of bacteria to solve pollution problems. For example, they have identified certain organisms that turn poisonous phenols into harmless salts. Phenols are by-products from wood-pulp processing plants. Scientists are putting genes from these organisms into the bacteria *Escherichia coli*, which reproduces quickly. In this way, they create many phenol-eating bacteria to solve this pollution problem.

WHAT DO YOU THINK?

If scientists can develop bacteria to metabolize pollution and waste, chemical companies might be able to eliminate waste treatment plants. Dump sites might be able to speed up the degradation of nontoxic waste, so that it converts to soil more quickly. Toxic waste might be changed into less harmful compounds.

Solutions to problems sometimes can cause new problems. Can you think of any new problems that might result from using bacteria to fight pollution?

SCIENCE AND SOCIETY

USING VIRUSES TO FIGHT DISEASE

One of the most amazing processes in the human body is the immune response. Immunity is our body's built-in defense against disease.

When a disease-causing bacterium or virus enters your body through breaks in your skin or other passageways, your immune system mobilizes a series of defenses against these foreign particles. White blood cells traveling through the circulatory system surround and engulf many of the intruding microorganisms. Other white blood cells produce antibodies in response to proteins called antigens located on the surfaces of bacteria and viruses. Antibodies are proteins that deactivate and destroy particular microorganisms. When your body produces antibodies to a particular bacterium or virus, you are said to be immune to those microorganisms. Your immunity can last a few months or years, as with the flu virus, or it can last an entire lifetime, as with the polio virus. Unfortunately, immunity against one type of bacterium or virus does not protect you against others, even though they may be similar. This is one reason why you catch a cold more than once. Your colds may seem like the same disease, but each is caused by a different virus.

When your body produces antibodies in response to a particular microorganism, it is called active immunity. Active immunity can either be natural or artificial. When your body produces antibodies as a result of contact with a disease-causing microorganism, this is a natural process. But your body can also produce antibodies after injection with a vaccine as shown here. A vaccine is a solution of dead or weakened bacteria or viruses that, when injected into the body, cause an immune response. Vaccination is an artificial process.

Recently, researchers have been experimenting with new ways to make vaccines safer and more effective. By studying the DNA and RNA of particular bacteria and viruses, scientists have found that they can change the characteristics of these microorganisms using genetic engineering techniques. RNA, like DNA, is a protein found in cells that determines the characteristics of an organism.These altered microorganisms,

when packaged in vaccines, are incapable of causing disease. But they do trigger immune responses against unaltered forms of the same microorganisms. The flu vaccine is an example of a vaccine made with an altered form of the virus.

But scientists have also found that it is not so easy to develop vaccines against other viruses. The AIDS virus, pictured here attacking a white blood cell, is a good example of this. Recently, Flossie Wong-Staal of the University of California at San Diego has been working on a vaccine that contains just the outer protein coat of the AIDS virus and not the virus's DNA. She is hoping that these modified viruses will act as decoys to stimulate an immune response.

This technique may not necessarily work with the AIDS virus. Scientists know that the AIDS virus mutates, or changes form, very often. One type of vaccine would not necessarily be effective against other forms of the virus. The AIDS virus is an example of a retrovirus. Retroviruses have different characteristics than normal viruses, and scientists have never produced a human vaccine against a retrovirus.

Scientists are hoping that new vaccine research using genetic engineering techniques may help produce an AIDS vaccine. In one study, scientists removed a piece of DNA that controls the production of antigens from an AIDS virus. The piece of DNA was then injected into an insect's cell, and the cell began to produce large amounts of AIDS antigen. Scientists hope the artificial antigens will stimulate an immune response to the AIDS virus.

WHAT DO YOU THINK?

The problem with newly developed vaccines, as with any new medicine, is how to test that it is safe to use in humans. New drugs are often tested first on animals, such as mice. The best test, though, is to inject a healthy person with the virus to observe if later the body protects itself with an immune response.

People who have a disease often volunteer to test a new drug or vaccine in hope that the treatment will work. Would you ever volunteer to test a new vaccine or drug? Tell why or why not.

*H*istory CONNECTION

THE COUNTESS'S POWDER

Malaria is a serious disease that is a worldwide concern for humans, particularly in the tropics. A one-celled organism called *Plasmodium* enters the body through a mosquito bite and attacks red blood cells. Fever, anemia, and other problems result—and it can be fatal. Even if one survives the attack, the disease is chronic. This means that symptoms can recur throughout the life of the person.

Malaria is one of the oldest diseases known. There are references to it as far back as the fifth century B.C. in Greece. Some groups in Africa, Asia, and the Mediterranean area show genetic adaptions that offer some protection. Malaria is relatively new to the Americas — probably around 500 years old. This is too short a time to develop any genetic response. The Indians of South America did find an effective treatment in the powdered bark of certain "quina quina" trees.

In the early 1600s, Lady Ana de Osorio, a Spanish noblewoman, married Don Luis Geronimo de Cabrera, Count of Chinchon, who became the viceroy of Peru in 1629. During this time the Countess became ill with a disease thought to be malaria. She was treated with the powdered Peruvian bark used by the Indians and recovered. Sometime later, Lady Ana left Peru to return to Spain. Reportedly, a supply of the bark was with her. The Countess did not survive the journey home, but the powder did and was used in Europe as a treatment for malaria. The trees and shrubs producing the bark were given the name "cinchon," and the drug, quinine, become known as pulvis comitessa, or the "countess's powder."

Quinine does not cure malaria, but relieves the symptoms, and may be used as a preventive measure. Quinine was the major treatment used for malaria until synthetic forms of the drug became available. In some places, such as Viet Nam, doctors have returned to the use of quinine where the malaria is resistant to the newer synthetic forms.

Today malaria is still a constant concern in the tropics. Over one million cases are estimated worldwide. South American cinchona trees began to die out during the 1800s, but trees were planted in other countries. Most of the quinine used today comes from Java in Indonesia.

WHAT DO YOU THINK?

People frequently use traditional treatments for medical problems. Should scientists and physicians encourage the use of "home cures" as well as "modern medicines"? Why or why not?

TEENS *in* SCIENCE

WHEN ARE GIBBERELLINS TOO MUCH OF A GOOD THING?

Scientists know that gibberellic acid, produced by a fungus, is just one of more than four dozen hormones called gibberellins that can dramatically affect plant growth. For example, researchers have observed that some citrus trees treated with gibberellins grow six times faster than normal. These plants have "foolish seedling disease." They were damaged by gibberellic acid. But scientists have learned to treat plants with smaller amounts of gibberellins to cause faster growth without damage.

When Audrey Cruz, a Filipino student in the accelerated studies program at Whitney Young High School in Chicago, learned about gibberellins, she knew there must be some way to determine how much gibberellic acid would best benefit plants.

First she planted beans in small containers, which she placed in a warm location. Then she obtained gibberellins from a local plant store.

When the bean plants were about 5 inches tall, she sprayed most of them with the gibberellins. To learn the effects of different amounts of the hormones, she used different concentrations of gibberellins. Her "controls" received no gibberellins.

From the experiment, Audrey learned that the lowest concentration of gibberellic acid (5 parts per million) caused some growth, but not as much as caused by more concentrated acid (10 parts per million). Yet, plants died soon after they were treated with the highest concentration (20 parts per million).

Audrey says she learned some interesting lessons from her project. She showed that too much gibberellic acid can be bad for the plant, as she had suspected. But she learned some unexpected lessons.

For example, after careful analysis of her results, she believed that the gibberellins in higher concentrations probably killed some of the bean plants. But she wondered if other factors could also have been involved. Had she given the plants too much water? Had something else affected the plants' growth?

Audrey learned something important about doing scientific experiments—to use caution in interpreting her results.

WHAT DO YOU THINK?

By questioning her own experimental technique, Audrey demonstrated the need for scientific objectivity. If you were to do Audrey's experiment, what would you do the same? What would you do differently?

Chapter 21

Reviewing Main Ideas

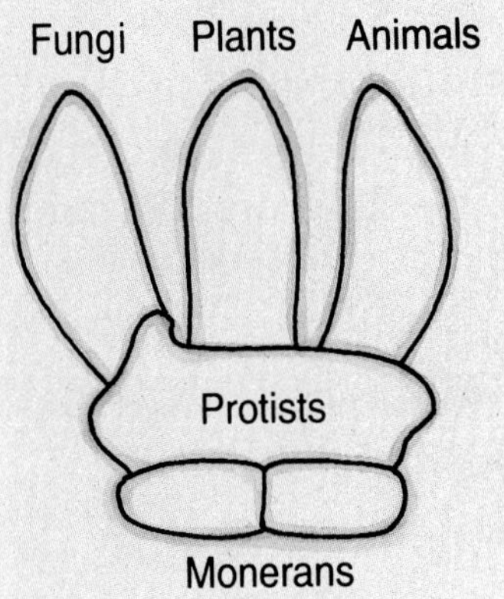

1. Scientists classify all living organisms into five kingdoms. Monera, Protista, and Fungi are the kingdoms of microscopic and simple organisms.

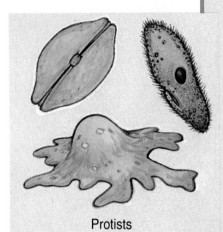

Protists

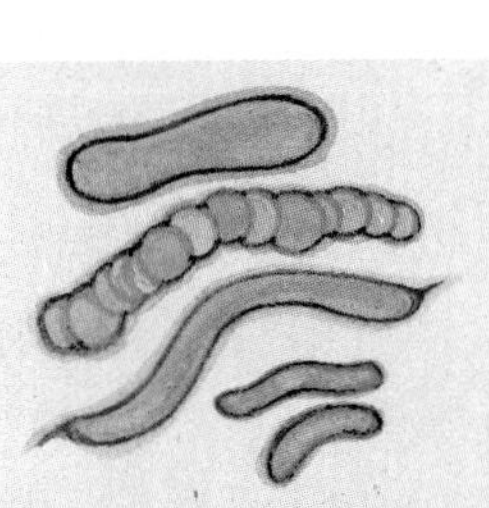

2. Monerans—the bacteria and blue-green bacteria—are the simplest and tiniest organisms on Earth. They live almost everywhere. Monerans are all one-celled and lack nuclei. Some are producers; others are consumers.

3. Protists are organisms with complex cells. Some are one-celled; others are many-celled. Some are plantlike; others are animal-like. All have nuclei, and all live in wet environments.

4. Fungi help decompose dead organisms and recycle the materials of which they are made. They feed mostly on dead matter; others are parasites that live in or on living things on which they feed.

Virus

Cell

5. Viruses are nonliving, noncellular structures. A virus consists of strands of DNA surrounded by a protein coat.

Chapter 21

Chapter Review

USING KEY SCIENCE TERMS

cilia
fission
flagella
Fungi
microorganism
Monera
Protista
virus

Each phrase below describes a science term from the list. Write the term that matches the phrase describing it.

1. Which term describes an organism too small to be seen with the unaided eye?
2. Which term names a nonliving thing?
3. Which terms are structures that help protists move around?
4. Which term is the kingdom containing cyanobacteria and bacteria?

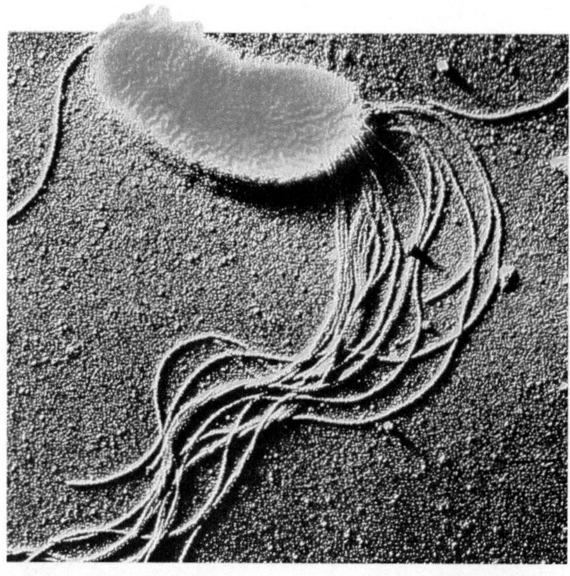

5. Which term is the kingdom that contains organisms you might find on a pizza or in a salad?
6. Which term is the kingdom containing algae?

UNDERSTANDING IDEAS

Answer the following questions.

1. Why are viruses not considered to be living organisms?
2. How do many-celled organisms differ from one-celled organisms?
3. Why are some members of Kingdom Protista described as microorganisms while others are not?
4. What is the main difference in cell structure between a moneran and a protist?
5. In what way are all the organisms studied in this chapter alike?
6. What would you look for in order to classify protists in a sample of pond water?
7. Why are some monerans considered to be producers while others are not?
8. How are fungi similar to plants? How are they similar to animals?
9. Why do you suppose fungi are more often found in wet or damp environments?
10. Describe the plantlike and animal-like characteristics of the protist *Euglena.*

CRITICAL THINKING

Use your understanding of the concepts developed in the chapter to answer each of the following questions.

1. Study this diagram of a protist cell. Even though this is a one-celled organism, why is such a protist considered to be one of the most complex of all cells?

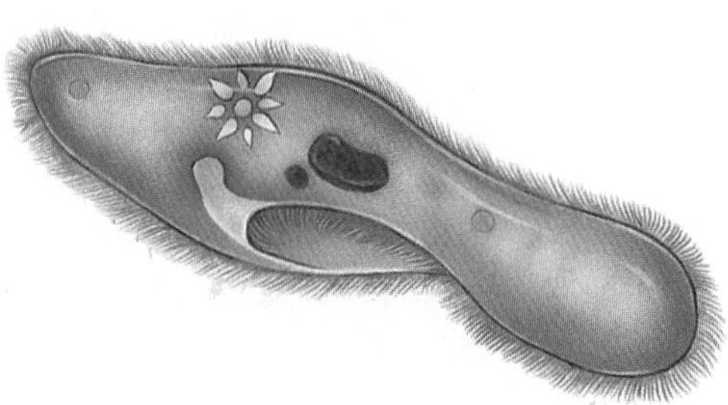

2. How is it an advantage to monerans, protists, and fungi to be able to respond to changes in their environment?
3. How can cyanobacteria be both beneficial and harmful to a lake?
4. A scientist discovered a new kind of organism growing on a rotting log. The organism was using the log as a food source and, at the same time, helping to decompose it. How would the scientist determine in which kingdom the new organism should be placed?
5. Use your knowledge of virus reproduction to explain why it is difficult to get rid of viruses.

PROBLEM SOLVING

Read the following problem and discuss your answers in a brief paragraph.

Imagine that a new kind of virus wipes out all bacteria on Earth.

1. What disadvantages for humans would there be in a world without bacteria? What advantages?
2. Would there be any way humans could live in a world without bacteria? Explain your reasons.

CONNECTING IDEAS

Discuss each of the following in a brief paragraph.

1. Using your knowledge of cells, compare and contrast the structures in cells to those in an animal-like protist such as a paramecium.
2. Compare and contrast fission in bacteria to the way your own cells reproduce.
3. How does a one-celled organism differ from a single cell that is part of a many-celled organism?
4. **HISTORY CONNECTION** Do you think quinine could be used to treat diseases other than malaria? Why or why not?
5. **SCIENCE AND SOCIETY** Some scientists are trying to find a vaccine effective against AIDS. Why is this difficult? (Hint: Think of the common cold.)

LOOKING BACK

UNIT 5 LIFE AT THE CELLULAR LEVEL

CONTENTS

Chapter 17 Mirrors and Lenses
Chapter 18 Basic Units of Life
Chapter 19 Chemical Reactions
Chapter 20 How Cells Do Their Jobs
Chapter 21 Simple Organisms

UNIT FOCUS

In this unit, you investigated how mirrors and lenses magnify, and that a microscope can be used to observe very small things such as cells. You learned that chemical reactions occur in living and nonliving matter.

In one such reaction, oxygen plus food produces carbon dioxide and releases chemical energy. This reaction explains how living organisms obtain energy through the process of respiration.

Try the exercises and activity that follow—they will challenge you to use and apply some of the ideas you learned in this unit.

CONNECTING IDEAS

1. Find a way to calculate the magnification of a hand lens and a bifocal lens. Use the magnifying power you calculate to determine how much larger a single cell would appear using both of these tools.
2. Remember the biosphere experiment you set up at the beginning of this book? What were some of the important factors you took into consideration when deciding what to place into your biosphere? How would you explain the outcome of your experiment using what you have learned about respiration and photosynthesis?

EXPLORING FURTHER

Test if air given off by your lungs shows the presence of carbon dioxide gas. Exhale at least 30 times through a straw into a test tube containing a limewater solution. The solution will turn cloudy if carbon dioxide is present. **CAUTION:** *Do not inhale through the straw.* Explain why or why not carbon dioxide is present. Could you test gases released by plants or other animals for carbon dioxide? How would you have to modify this experimental procedure?

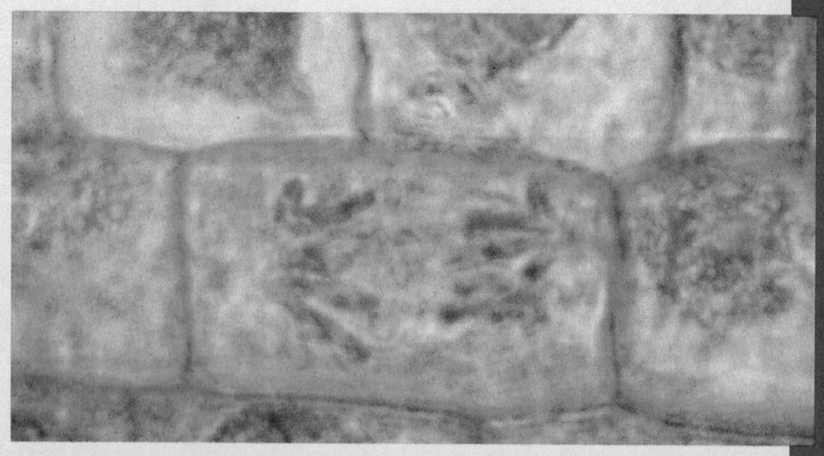

Appendices
Table of Contents

APPENDIX A
International System of Units 660

APPENDIX B
SI/Metric to English Conversions 661

APPENDIX C
Safety in the Science Classroom 662

APPENDIX D
Safety Symbols 663

APPENDIX E
Care and Use of a Microscope 664

APPENDIX F
The Cell 665

APPENDIX G
Classification of Monera, Protista, and Fungi 666

APPENDIX H
United States Map 668

APPENDIX I
World Map 670

APPENDIX J
Periodic Table 672

APPENDIX K
Minerals with Nonmetallic Luster 674

APPENDIX L
Minerals with Metallic Luster 676

Appendix A

INTERNATIONAL SYSTEM OF UNITS

The International System (SI) of Measurement is accepted as the standard for measurement throughout most of the world. Three base units in SI are the meter, kilogram, and second. Frequently used SI units are listed below.

TABLE A-1

FREQUENTLY USED SI UNITS	
LENGTH	1 millimeter (mm) = 1000 micrometers (μm)
	1 centimeter (cm) = 10 millimeters (mm)
	1 meter (m) = 100 centimeters (cm)
	1 kilometer (km) = 1000 meters (m)
	1 light-year = 9,460,000,000,000 kilometers (km)
AREA	1 square meter (m^2) = 10,000 square centimeters (cm^2)
	1 square kilometer (km^2) = 1,000,000 square meters (m^2)
VOLUME	1 milliliter (mL) = 1 cubic centimeter (cm^3)
	1 liter (L) = 1000 milliliters (mL)
MASS	1 gram (g) = 1000 milligrams (mg)
	1 kilogram (kg) = 1000 grams (g)
	1 metric ton = 1000 kilograms (kg)
TIME	1 s = 1 second

Temperature measurements in SI are often made in degrees Celsius. Celsius temperature is a supplementary unit derived from the base unit kelvin. The Celsius scale (°C) has 100 equal graduations between the freezing temperature (0°C) and the boiling temperature of water (100°C). The following relationship exists between the Celsius and kelvin temperature scales:

$$K = °C + 273$$

Several other supplementary SI units are listed below.

TABLE A-2

SUPPLEMENTARY SI UNITS			
MEASUREMENT	**UNIT**	**SYMBOL**	**EXPRESSED IN BASE UNITS**
Energy	Joule	J	$kg \bullet m^2/s^2$ or $N \bullet m$
Force	Newton	N	$kg \bullet m/s^2$
Power	Watt	W	$kg \bullet m^2/s^3$ or J/s
Pressure	Pascal	Pa	$kg/(m \bullet s^2)$ or N/m^2

Appendix B

TABLE B-1

SI/METRIC TO ENGLISH CONVERSIONS			
	WHEN YOU WANT TO CONVERT:	**MULTIPLY BY:**	**TO FIND:**
LENGTH	inches	2.54	centimeters
	centimeters	0.39	inches
	feet	0.30	meters
	meters	3.28	feet
	yards	0.91	meters
	meters	1.09	yards
	miles	1.61	kilometers
	kilometers	0.62	miles
MASS AND WEIGHT*	ounces	28.41	grams
	grams	0.04	ounces
	pounds	0.45	kilograms
	kilograms	2.2	pounds
	tons	0.91	tonnes (metric tons)
	tonnes (metric tons)	1.10	tons
	pounds	4.45	newtons
	newtons	0.23	pounds
VOLUME	cubic inches	16.39	cubic centimeters
	cubic centimeters	0.06	cubic inches
	cubic feet	0.02	cubic meters
	cubic meters	35.3	cubic feet
	liters	1.06	quarts
	liters	0.26	gallons
	gallons	3.78	liters
AREA	square inches	6.45	square centimeters
	square centimeters	0.16	square inches
	square feet	0.09	square meters
	square meters	10.76	square feet
	square miles	2.59	square kilometers
	square kilometers	0.39	square miles
	hectares	2.47	acres
	acres	0.40	hectares
TEMPERATURE	Fahrenheit	5/9 (°F – 32)	Celsius
	Celsius	9/5 °C + 32	Fahrenheit

*Weight as measured in standard Earth gravity

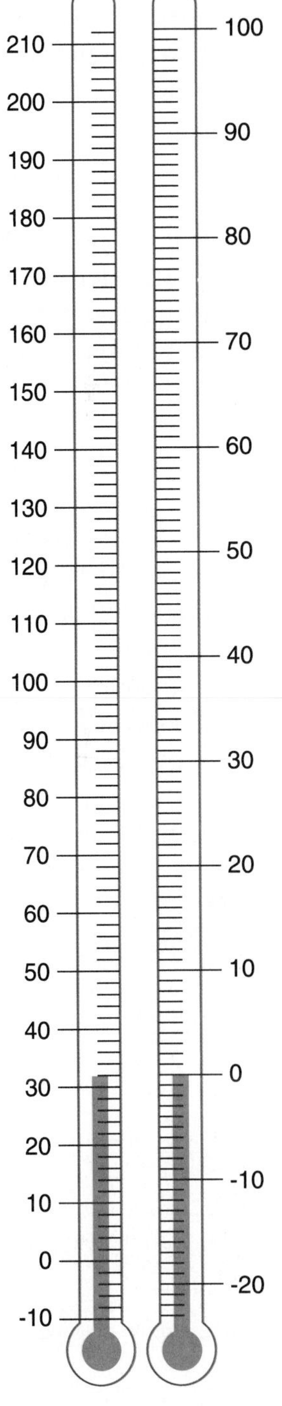

Appendix C

SAFETY IN THE SCIENCE CLASSROOM

1. Always obtain your teacher's permission to begin an investigation.
2. Study the procedure. If you have questions, ask your teacher. Understand any safety symbols shown on the page.
3. Use the safety equipment provided for you. Goggles and a safety apron should be worn when any investigation calls for using chemicals.
4. Always slant test tubes away from yourself and others when heating them.
5. Never eat or drink in the lab, and never use lab glassware as food or drink containers. Never inhale chemicals. Do not taste any substances or draw any material into a tube with your mouth.
6. If you spill any chemical, wash it off immediately with water. Report the spill immediately to your teacher.
7. Know the location and proper use of the fire extinguisher, safety shower, fire blanket, first aid kit, and fire alarm.
8. Keep materials away from flames. Tie back hair and loose clothing.
9. If a fire should break out in the classroom, or if your clothing should catch fire, smother it with the fire blanket or a coat, or get under a safety shower. **NEVER RUN.**
10. Report any accident or injury, no matter how small, to your teacher.

Follow these procedures as you clean up your work area.

1. Turn off the water and gas. Disconnect electrical devices.
2. Return all materials to their proper places.
3. Dispose of chemicals and other materials as directed by your teacher. Place broken glass and solid substances in the proper containers. Never discard materials in the sink.
4. Clean your work area.
5. Wash your hands thoroughly after working in the laboratory.

TABLE C-1

FIRST AID	
INJURY	**SAFE RESPONSE**
Burns	Apply cold water. Call your teacher immediately.
Cuts and bruises	Stop any bleeding by applying direct pressure. Cover cuts with a clean dressing. Apply cold compresses to bruises. Call your teacher immediately.
Fainting	Leave the person lying down. Loosen any tight clothing and keep crowds away. Call your teacher immediately.
Foreign matter in eye	Flush with plenty of water. Use eyewash bottle or fountain.
Poisoning	Note the suspected poisoning agent and call your teacher immediately.
Any spills on skin	Flush with large amounts of water or use safety shower. Call your teacher immediately.

Appendix D

SAFETY SYMBOLS

TABLE D-1

	**DISPOSAL ALERT** This symbol appears when care must be taken to dispose of materials properly.		**ANIMAL SAFETY** This symbol appears whenever live animals are studied and the safety of the animals and the students must be ensured.
	**BIOLOGICAL HAZARD** This symbol appears when there is danger involving bacteria, fungi, or protists.		**RADIOACTIVE SAFETY** This symbol appears when radioactive materials are used.
	**OPEN FLAME ALERT** This symbol appears when use of an open flame could cause a fire or an explosion.		**CLOTHING PROTECTION SAFETY** This symbol appears when substances used could stain or burn clothing.
	**THERMAL SAFETY** This symbol appears as a reminder to use caution when handling hot objects.		**FIRE SAFETY** This symbol appears when care should be taken around open flames.
	**SHARP OBJECT SAFETY** This symbol appears when a danger of cuts or punctures caused by the use of sharp objects exists.		**EXPLOSION SAFETY** This symbol appears when the misuse of chemicals could cause an explosion.
	**FUME SAFETY** This symbol appears when chemicals or chemical reactions could cause dangerous fumes.		**EYE SAFETY** This symbol appears when a danger to the eyes exists. Safety goggles should be worn when this symbol appears.
	**ELECTRICAL SAFETY** This symbol appears when care should be taken when using electrical equipment.		**POISON SAFETY** This symbol appears when poisonous substances are used.
	**PLANT SAFETY** This symbol appears when poisonous plants or plants with thorns are handled.		**CHEMICAL SAFETY** This symbol appears when chemicals used can cause burns or are poisonous if absorbed through the skin.

Appendix E

CARE AND USE OF A MICROSCOPE

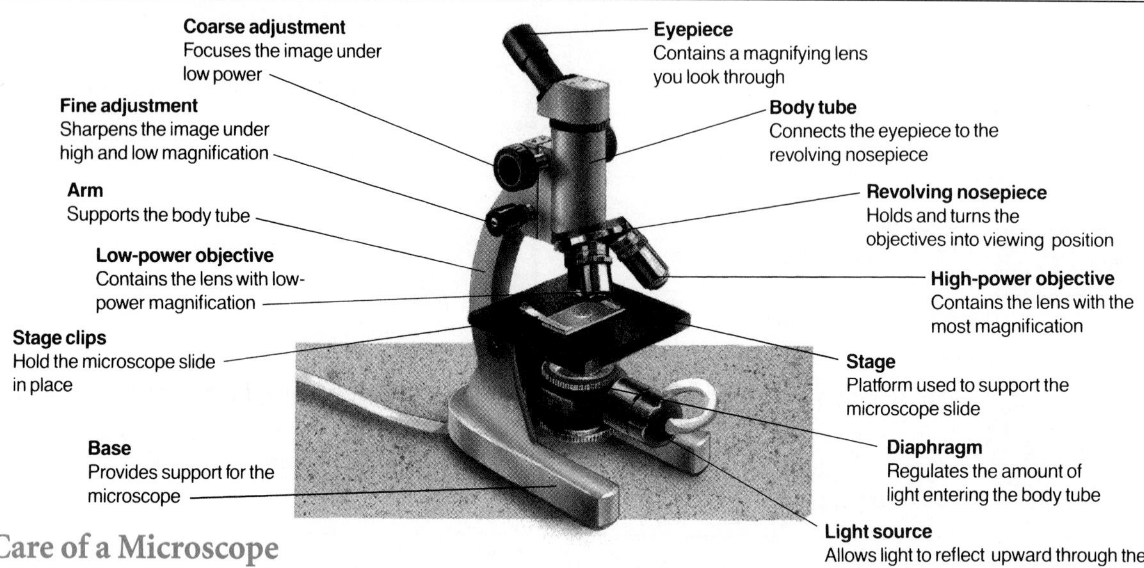

Care of a Microscope

1. Always carry the microscope holding the arm with one hand and supporting the base with the other hand.
2. Don't touch the lenses with your finger.
3. Never lower the coarse adjustment knob when looking through the eyepiece lens.
4. Always focus first with the low-power objective.
5. Don't use the coarse adjustment knob when the high-power objective is in place.
6. Store the microscope covered.

Using a Microscope

1. Place the microscope on a flat surface that is clear of objects. The arm should be toward you.
2. Look through the eyepiece. Adjust the diaphragm so that light comes through the opening in the stage.
3. Place a slide on the stage so that the specimen is in the field of view. Hold it firmly in place by using the stage clips.
4. Always focus first with the coarse adjustment and the low-power objective lens. Once the object is in focus on low power, turn the nosepiece until the high-power objective is in place. Use ONLY the fine adjustment to focus with this lens.

Making a Wet Mount Slide

1. Carefully place the item you want to look at in the center of a clean glass slide. Make sure the sample is thin enough for light to pass through.
2. Use a dropper to place one or two drops of water on the sample.
3. Hold a clean coverslip by the edges and place it at one edge of the drop of water. Slowly lower the coverslip onto the drop of water until it lies flat.
   If you have too much water or a lot of air bubbles, touch the edge of a paper towel to the edge of the coverslip to draw off extra water and force air out.

Appendix F

THE CELL

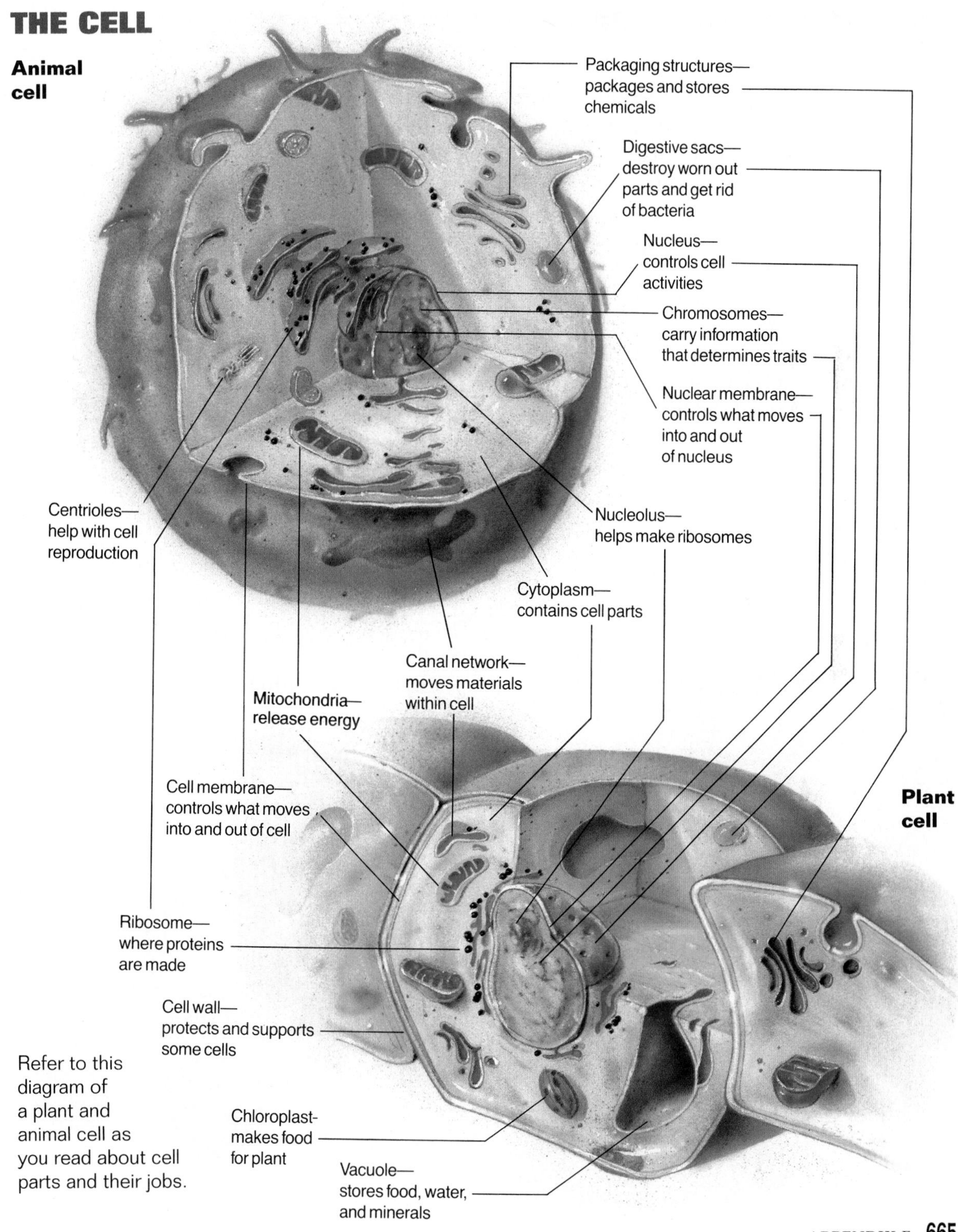

Refer to this diagram of a plant and animal cell as you read about cell parts and their jobs.

Appendix G

CLASSIFICATION OF MONERA, PROTISTA, AND FUNGI

The five kingdoms are Kingdom Monera, Kingdom Protista, Kingdom Fungi, the Plant Kingdom, and the Animal Kingdom. In this book, you have studied three kingdoms. The first, Kingdom Monera, contains organisms that lack a true nucleus and lack specialized structures in the cytoplasm of their cells. The members of Kingdom Protista have cells that contain a nucleus and structures in the cytoplasm that are surrounded by membranes. The members of the Kingdom Fungi absorb food from their surroundings. They are consumers.

KINGDOM MONERA

Phylum Cyanobacteria: one-celled; make their own food; contain chlorophyll, some species form colonies; most are blue-green

Bacteria: one-celled; lack a nucleus; most absorb food from their surroundings, some are photosynthetic; many are parasites; round, spiral, or rod shaped

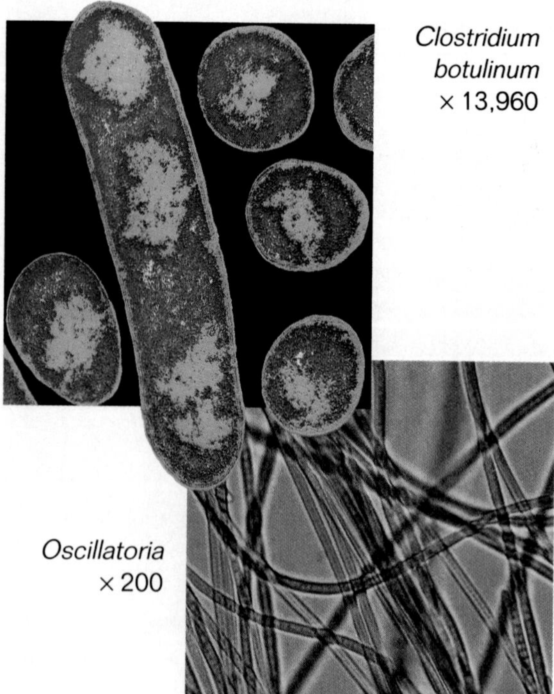

Clostridium botulinum × 13,960

Oscillatoria × 200

KINGDOM PROTISTA

Phylum Euglenophyta: one-celled; can photosynthesize or take in food; most have one flagellum

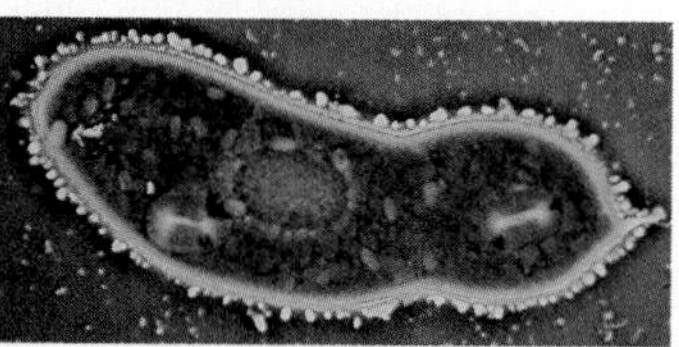

Euglena oxyuris × 2000

Phylum Crysophyta: most are one-celled; make their own food through photosynthesis; golden-brown pigments mask chlorophyll; diatoms

Phylum Pyrrophyta: one-celled; make their own food through photosynthesis; contain red pigments and have two flagella; dinoflagellates

Phylum Chlorophyta: one-celled, many-celled, or colonies; contain chlorophyll and make their own food; live on land, in fresh water or salt water; green algae

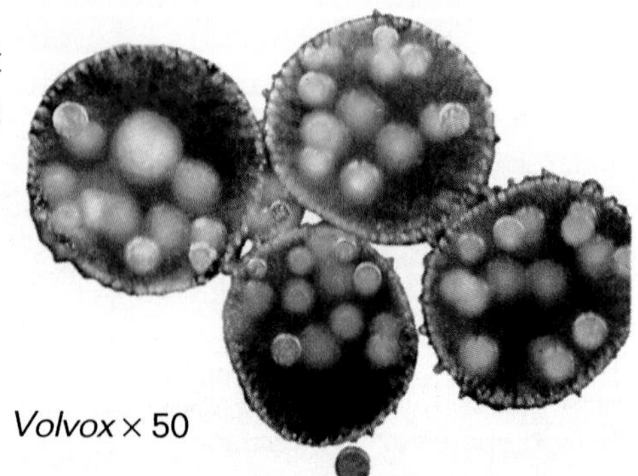

Volvox × 50

Phylum Rhodophyta: most are many-celled and photosynthetic; contain red pigments; most live in deep saltwater environments; red algae

Phylum Phaephyta: most are many-celled and photosynthetic; contain brown pigments; most live in saltwater environments; brown algae

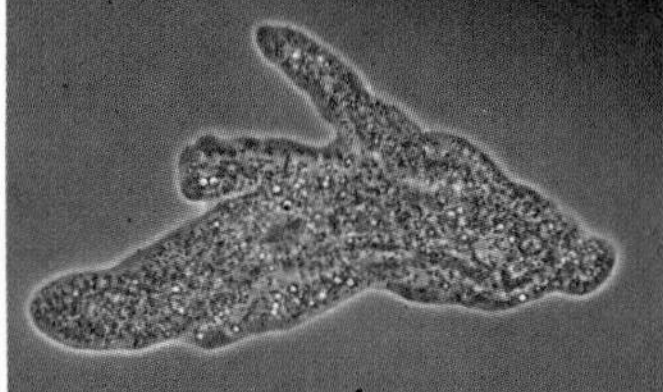

Amoeba discoides × 1000

Phylum Sarcodina: one-celled; take in food; move by means of pseudopods; free livng or parasitic; sarcodines

Phylum Mastigophora: one-celled; take in food; have two or more flagella; free living or parasitic; flagellates

Phylum Ciliophora: one-celled; take in food; have large numbers of cilia; ciliates

Phylum Sporozoa: one-celled; take in food; no means of movement; parasites in animals; sporozoans

Phylum Myxomycetes, Phylum Acrasiomycota: one- or many-celled; absorb food; change form during life cycle; cellular and plasmodial slime molds

Phylum Oomycota: live in water or on land; one- or many-celled parasites; absorb dead organic matter; cause diseases in plants and animals; water molds and mildews

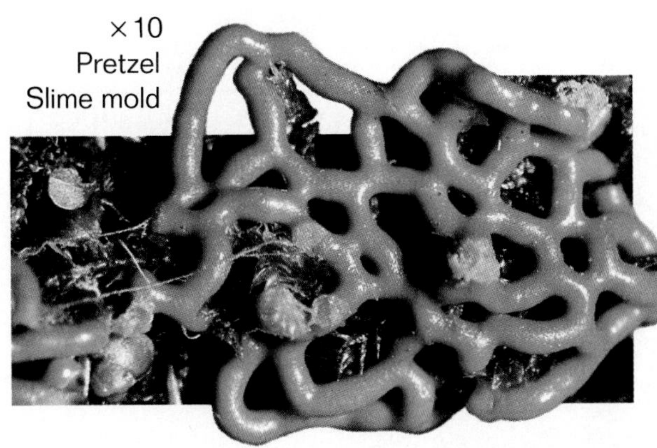

× 10 Pretzel Slime mold

KINGDOM FUNGI

Division Zygomycota: many-celled; absorb food; spores are produced in sporangia; zygote fungi

Division Ascomycota: one- and many-celled; absorb food; spores produced in asci; sac fungi

Yeast × 7800

Division Basidiomycota: many-celled; absorb food; spores produced in basidia; club fungi

Division Deuteromycota: members with unknown reproductive structures; imperfect fungi

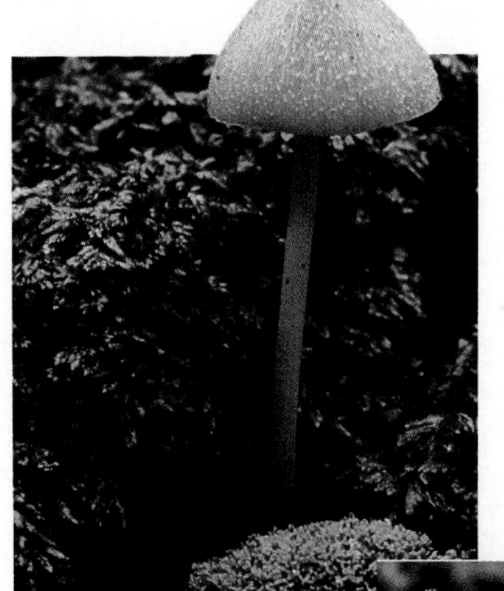

Mushroom

Lichens: organism formed by symbiotic relationship between an ascomycote or a basidiomycote and a green alga or a cyanobacterium; fungus provides protection and the alga or cyanobacterium provides food

Old Man's Beard lichen

WASHINGTON
OREGON
IDAHO
MONTANA
NORTH DAKOTA
SOUTH DAKOTA
WYOMING
NEBRASKA
GREAT BASIN
NEVADA
UTAH
COLORADO
KANSAS
CALIFORNIA
ARIZONA
NEW MEXICO
OKLAHOMA
TEXAS
MEXICO
PACIFIC OCEAN
GREAT PLAINS
ROCKY MOUNTAINS
COAST RANGES
CASCADE RANGE
SIERRA NEVADA
BITTERROOT RANGE
WASATCH RANGE
BIGHORN MTNS.
BLACK HILLS
COLUMBIA PLATEAU
COLORADO PLATEAU
MOJAVE DESERT
GREAT SALT LAKE DESERT
PAINTED DESERT
LLANO ESTACADO
EDWARDS PLATEAU
SANGRE DE CRISTO MTS.
Continental Divide
Mt. Rainier 14,410 ft. (4,392 m.)
Mt. Hood 11,235 ft. (3,424 m.)
Mt. Shasta 14,162 ft. (4,316 m.)
Mt. Whitney 14,494 ft. (4,418 m.)
Death Valley −282 ft. (−89 m.)
Borah Peak 12,662 ft. (3,859 m.)
Grand Teton Peak 13,770 ft. (4,197 m.)
Mt. Elbert 14,433 ft. (4,399 m.)
Cape Flattery
Bellingham
Juan de Fuca Strait
Puget Sound
Seattle
Tacoma
Olympia
F.D. Roosevelt Lake
Spokane
Pend Oreille Lake
Flathead Lake
Portland
Columbia River
Salem
Corvallis
Eugene
Medford
Lewiston
Helena
Butte
Missouri River
Great Falls
Fort Peck Lake
Yellowstone R.
Billings
Powder River
Minot
Lake Sakakawea
Grand Forks
Bismarck
Fargo
Lake Oahe
Aberdeen
Pierre
Rapid City
Sioux Falls
Boise
Idaho Falls
Snake River
Twin Falls
Pocatello
Goose Lake
Eureka
Cape Mendocino
Sacramento
Pyramid Lake
Reno
Lake Tahoe
Carson City
San Francisco
Oakland
Stockton
San Jose
San Joaquin
Mono Lake
Fresno
Bakersfield
Point Conception
Las Vegas
Great Salt Lake
Ogden
Salt Lake City
Orem
Provo
Utah Lake
Green River
Rock Springs
Casper
North Platte River
Laramie
Cheyenne
Fort Collins
Greeley
Boulder
Denver
Colorado Springs
Pueblo
North Platte
Grand Island
Lincoln
Platte River
South Platte River
Republican River
Salina
Hutchinson
Wichita
Arkansas River
Lake Powell
Lake Mead
Colorado River
Grand Canyon
Flagstaff
Los Angeles
San Bernardino
Riverside
Long Beach
Salton Sea
San Diego
Glendale
Phoenix
Mesa
Gila River
Yuma
Tucson
Santa Fe
Albuquerque
Rio Grande
Roswell
Las Cruces
El Paso
Enid
Canadian River
Amarillo
Oklahoma City
Norman
Lawton
Red River
Lake Texoma
Lubbock
Brazos River
Dallas
Fort Worth
Pecos River
Austin
San Antonio
Corpus Christi
Brownsville
GULF OF CALIFORNIA
HAWAII
Kauai Channel
Kailua
Honolulu
PACIFIC OCEAN
Alenuihaha Channel
Mauna Kea 13,796 ft. (4,205 m.)
Hilo
100 Miles
100 Kilometers
ALASKA
U.S.S.R.
Arctic Circle
Bering Strait
SEWARD PEN.
Pt. Barrow
BROOKS RANGE
Yukon River
Fairbanks
Tanana River
Denali (Mt. McKinley) 20,320 ft. (6,193 m)
ALASKA RANGE
Bethel
Anchorage
Iliamna Lake
BERING SEA
BRISTOL BAY
ALASKA PENINSULA
Shelikof Str.
Kodiak
GULF OF ALASKA
Juneau
Sitka
CANADA
ALEUTIAN ISLANDS
0 250 500 Miles
0 250 500 Kilometers

Appendix H

UNITED STATES
National capital
State capital
Major city
Other city
International boundary
State boundary
0 100 200 Miles
0 100 200 Kilometers
Projection: Albers Equal Area
ATLANTIC OCEAN
GULF OF MEXICO
THE BAHAMAS
Strait of Florida
MINNESOTA
WISCONSIN
MICHIGAN
IOWA
ILLINOIS
INDIANA
OHIO
PENNSYLVANIA
NEW YORK
MAINE
VT.
N.H.
MASS.
R.I.
CONN.
N.J.
MD.
DEL.
D.C.
WEST VIRGINIA
VIRGINIA
KENTUCKY
MISSOURI
TENNESSEE
NORTH CAROLINA
SOUTH CAROLINA
GEORGIA
ALABAMA
MISSISSIPPI
ARKANSAS
LOUISIANA
FLORIDA
CENTRAL LOWLAND
APPALACHIAN MOUNTAINS
COASTAL PLAIN
OZARK PLATEAU
CUMBERLAND PLATEAU
ADIRONDACK MTNS.
Lake Superior
Lake Michigan
Lake Huron
Lake Erie
Lake Ontario
Lake of the Woods
Red Lake
Lake Champlain
Moosehead Lake
Lake Okeechobee
St. Lawrence River
Mississippi River
Ohio River
Wabash R.
Tennessee R.
Cumberland River
Susquehanna River
Hudson R.
Roanoke River
Chattahoochee R.
Alabama R.
Harry S. Truman Res.
R.S. Kerr Res.
Lake Eufaula
Toledo Bend Res.
Sam Rayburn Reservoir
Lake Pontchartrain
CHESAPEAKE BAY
DELAWARE BAY
Cape Cod
Cape Hatteras
Cape Canaveral
Cape Sable
Mt. Washington 6,288 ft. (1,905 m.)
Mt. Mitchell 6,684 ft. (2,037 m.)
Washington
Duluth
Minneapolis
St. Paul
Rochester
Green Bay
Appleton
Madison
Milwaukee
Racine
Dubuque
Cedar Rapids
Davenport
Des Moines
Sioux City
Omaha
Council Bluffs
Rockford
Aurora
Joliet
Chicago
Gary
Hammond
South Bend
Peoria
Springfield
Decatur
Grand Rapids
Lansing
Flint
Detroit
Ann Arbor
Toledo
Fort Wayne
Muncie
Indianapolis
Dayton
Columbus
Cincinnati
Cleveland
Akron
Canton
Youngstown
Erie
Buffalo
Niagara Falls
Rochester
Syracuse
Utica
Albany
Binghamton
Pittsburgh
Harrisburg
Allentown
Philadelphia
Wheeling
Parkersburg
Charleston
Huntington
Topeka
Kansas City
Independence
Lawrence
Jefferson City
St. Louis
East St. Louis
Evansville
Louisville
Frankfort
Lexington
Owensboro
Roanoke
Richmond
Newport News
Norfolk
Baltimore
Annapolis
Arlington
Dover
Wilmington
Camden
Trenton
Newark
Yonkers
New York
Hartford
New Haven
Providence
Springfield
Worcester
Boston
Manchester
Concord
Portland
Lewiston
Augusta
Bangor
Burlington
Montpelier
Winston-Salem
Greensboro
Durham
Raleigh
Charlotte
Knoxville
Nashville
Chattanooga
Greenville
Spartanburg
Columbia
Charleston
Savannah
Augusta
Atlanta
Macon
Columbus
Albany
Huntsville
Birmingham
Tuscaloosa
Montgomery
Memphis
Tulsa
Fort Smith
North Little Rock
Little Rock
Hot Springs
Pine Bluff
Greenville
Meridian
Jackson
Hattiesburg
Shreveport
Mobile
Biloxi
Pensacola
Tallahassee
Jacksonville
Baton Rouge
Lafayette
Lake Charles
New Orleans
Houston
Orlando
Tampa
St. Petersburg
Palm Beach
Miami Beach
Miami
Key West
Copyright © by Glencoe Division of Macmillan/McGraw-Hill Publishing Company. All rights reserved.
N
95°
90°
85°
80°
75°
70°
45°
40°
35°
30°
25°

Appendix I

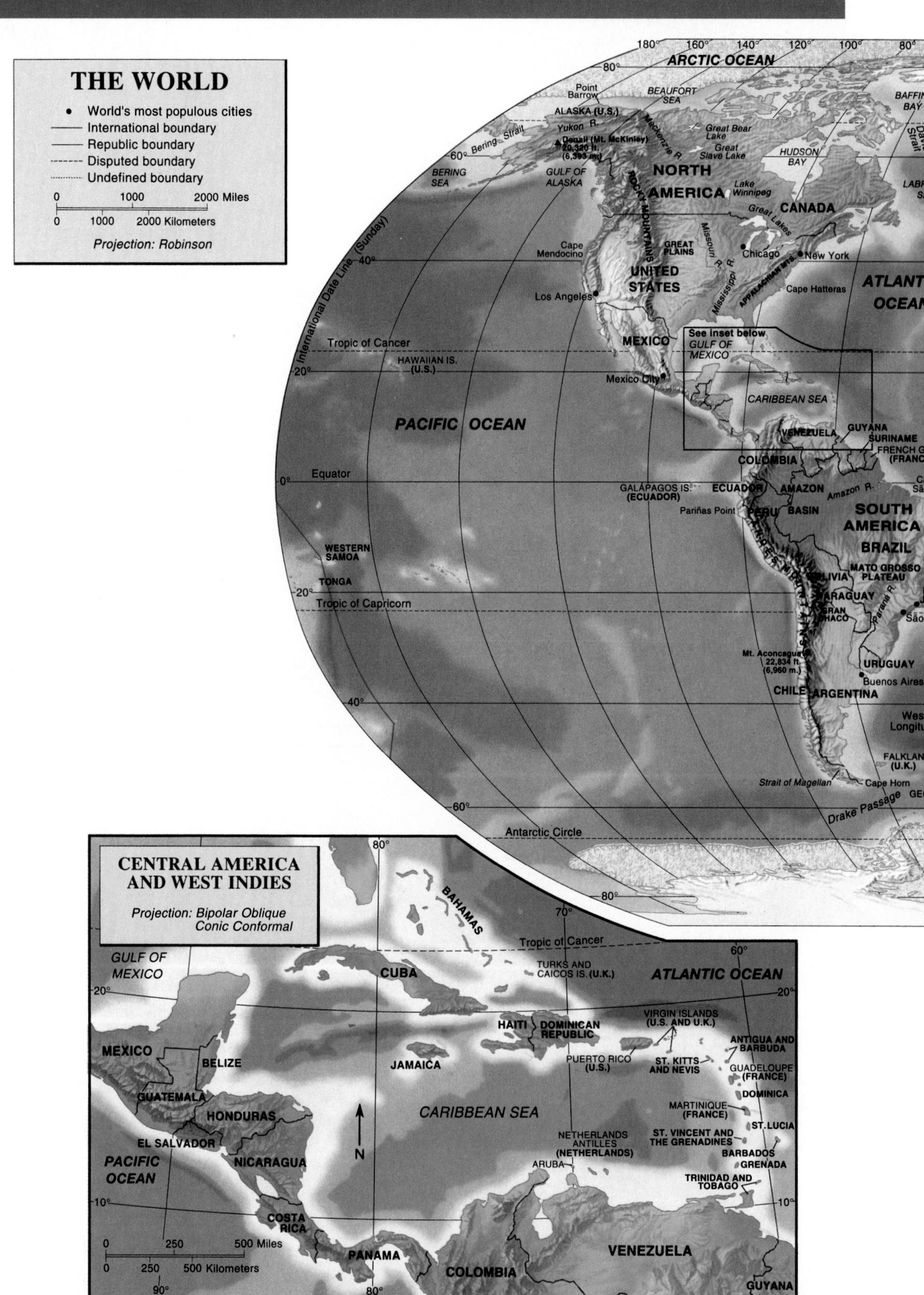
THE WORLD
World's most populous cities
International boundary
Republic boundary
Disputed boundary
Undefined boundary
0 1000 2000 Miles
0 1000 2000 Kilometers
Projection: Robinson
ARCTIC OCEAN
BEAUFORT SEA
Point Barrow
ALASKA (U.S.)
Bering Strait
BERING SEA
GULF OF ALASKA
NORTH AMERICA
CANADA
HUDSON BAY
BAFFIN BAY
UNITED STATES
GREAT PLAINS
Chicago
New York
Los Angeles
Cape Hatteras
ATLANTIC OCEAN
MEXICO
Mexico City
International Date Line (Sunday)
Tropic of Cancer
HAWAIIAN IS. (U.S.)
PACIFIC OCEAN
See inset below
GULF OF MEXICO
CARIBBEAN SEA
VENEZUELA
GUYANA
SURINAME
COLOMBIA
Equator
GALAPAGOS IS. (ECUADOR)
ECUADOR
AMAZON BASIN
PERU
SOUTH AMERICA
BRAZIL
MATO GROSSO PLATEAU
WESTERN SAMOA
TONGA
Tropic of Capricorn
BOLIVIA
PARAGUAY
URUGUAY
Buenos Aires
CHILE
ARGENTINA
West Longitude
FALKLAND IS. (U.K.)
Strait of Magellan
Cape Horn
Drake Passage
Antarctic Circle
CENTRAL AMERICA AND WEST INDIES
Projection: Bipolar Oblique Conic Conformal
GULF OF MEXICO
BAHAMAS
Tropic of Cancer
TURKS AND CAICOS IS. (U.K.)
CUBA
ATLANTIC OCEAN
HAITI
DOMINICAN REPUBLIC
VIRGIN ISLANDS (U.S. AND U.K.)
MEXICO
BELIZE
JAMAICA
PUERTO RICO (U.S.)
ST. KITTS AND NEVIS
ANTIGUA AND BARBUDA
GUADELOUPE (FRANCE)
DOMINICA
GUATEMALA
HONDURAS
CARIBBEAN SEA
MARTINIQUE (FRANCE)
ST. LUCIA
EL SALVADOR
NICARAGUA
NETHERLANDS ANTILLES (NETHERLANDS)
ST. VINCENT AND THE GRENADINES
BARBADOS
GRENADA
PACIFIC OCEAN
ARUBA
TRINIDAD AND TOBAGO
COSTA RICA
PANAMA
COLOMBIA
VENEZUELA
GUYANA
0 250 500 Miles
0 250 500 Kilometers

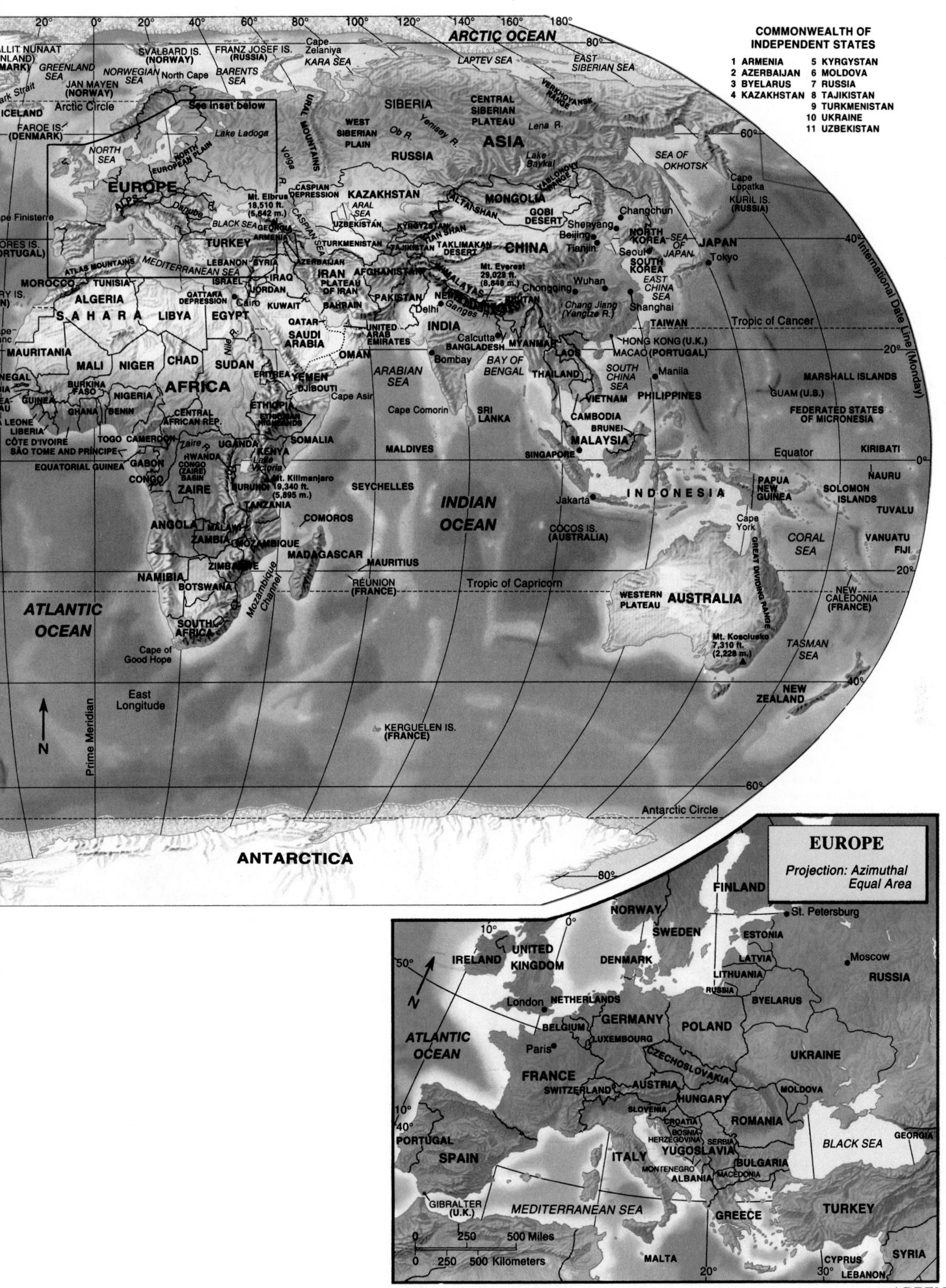
COMMONWEALTH OF INDEPENDENT STATES
1 ARMENIA
2 AZERBAIJAN
3 BYELARUS
4 KAZAKHSTAN
5 KYRGYSTAN
6 MOLDOVA
7 RUSSIA
8 TAJIKISTAN
9 TURKMENISTAN
10 UKRAINE
11 UZBEKISTAN
ARCTIC OCEAN
SVALBARD IS. (NORWAY)
FRANZ JOSEF IS. (RUSSIA)
Cape Zelaniya
KARA SEA
LAPTEV SEA
EAST SIBERIAN SEA
GREENLAND SEA
NORWEGIAN SEA
North Cape
BARENTS SEA
JAN MAYEN (NORWAY)
Arctic Circle
ICELAND
FAROE IS. (DENMARK)
See inset below
Lake Ladoga
NORTH SEA
NORTH EUROPEAN PLAIN
EUROPE
ALPS
Danube R.
URAL MOUNTAINS
Volga R.
WEST SIBERIAN PLAIN
Ob R.
SIBERIA
Yenisey R.
CENTRAL SIBERIAN PLATEAU
Lena R.
VERKHOYANSK RANGE
ASIA
RUSSIA
Lake Baykal
YABLONOVY RANGE
SEA OF OKHOTSK
Cape Lopatka
KURIL IS. (RUSSIA)
Mt. Elbrus 18,510 ft. (5,642 m.)
CASPIAN DEPRESSION
KAZAKHSTAN
ARAL SEA
CASPIAN SEA
MONGOLIA
ALTAI SHAN
GOBI DESERT
Changchun
Shenyang
Beijing
Tianjin
NORTH KOREA
SEA OF JAPAN
JAPAN
Tokyo
Seoul
SOUTH KOREA
BLACK SEA
GEORGIA
ARMENIA
UZBEKISTAN
KYRGYZSTAN
TIAN SHAN
TURKMENISTAN
TAJIKISTAN
TAKLIMAKAN DESERT
CHINA
TURKEY
LEBANON
SYRIA
AZERBAIJAN
ATLAS MOUNTAINS
MEDITERRANEAN SEA
IRAN
AFGHANISTAN
PLATEAU OF IRAN
Mt. Everest 29,028 ft. (8,848 m.)
HIMALAYAS
NEPAL
BHUTAN
Chongqing
Wuhan
EAST CHINA SEA
Chang Jiang (Yangtze R.)
Shanghai
MOROCCO
TUNISIA
ISRAEL
IRAQ
JORDAN
QATTARA DEPRESSION
Cairo
KUWAIT
BAHRAIN
PAKISTAN
Delhi
Ganges R.
ALGERIA
SAHARA
LIBYA
EGYPT
QATAR
SAUDI ARABIA
UNITED ARAB EMIRATES
INDIA
Calcutta
BANGLADESH
MYANMAR
LAOS
TAIWAN
HONG KONG (U.K.)
MACAO (PORTUGAL)
Tropic of Cancer
Nile R.
MAURITANIA
MALI
NIGER
CHAD
SUDAN
OMAN
ARABIAN SEA
Bombay
BAY OF BENGAL
THAILAND
SOUTH CHINA SEA
Manila
PHILIPPINES
MARSHALL ISLANDS
GUAM (U.S.)
International Date Line (Monday)
BURKINA FASO
AFRICA
ERITREA
YEMEN
DJIBOUTI
Cape Asir
GUINEA
NIGERIA
GHANA
BENIN
CENTRAL AFRICAN REP.
ETHIOPIA
ETHIOPIAN HIGHLANDS
Cape Comorin
SRI LANKA
VIETNAM
CAMBODIA
BRUNEI
FEDERATED STATES OF MICRONESIA
LIBERIA
CÔTE D'IVOIRE
TOGO
CAMEROON
SÃO TOME AND PRINCIPE
Zaire R.
UGANDA
KENYA
SOMALIA
MALDIVES
MALAYSIA
SINGAPORE
Equator
KIRIBATI
EQUATORIAL GUINEA
GABON
RWANDA
CONGO
CONGO (ZAIRE) BASIN
Lake Victoria
ZAIRE
BURUNDI
Mt. Kilimanjaro 19,340 ft. (5,895 m.)
TANZANIA
SEYCHELLES
INDIAN OCEAN
Jakarta
INDONESIA
PAPUA NEW GUINEA
NAURU
SOLOMON ISLANDS
TUVALU
ANGOLA
MALAWI
ZAMBIA
MOZAMBIQUE
COMOROS
COCOS IS. (AUSTRALIA)
Cape York
CORAL SEA
VANUATU
FIJI
MADAGASCAR
MAURITIUS
ZIMBABWE
NAMIBIA
BOTSWANA
Mozambique Channel
RÉUNION (FRANCE)
Tropic of Capricorn
GREAT DIVIDING RANGE
WESTERN PLATEAU
AUSTRALIA
NEW CALEDONIA (FRANCE)
ATLANTIC OCEAN
SOUTH AFRICA
Cape of Good Hope
Mt. Kosciusko 7,310 ft. (2,228 m.)
TASMAN SEA
NEW ZEALAND
East Longitude
Prime Meridian
N
KERGUELEN IS. (FRANCE)
Antarctic Circle
ANTARCTICA
EUROPE
Projection: Azimuthal Equal Area
FINLAND
NORWAY
St. Petersburg
SWEDEN
ESTONIA
IRELAND
UNITED KINGDOM
DENMARK
LATVIA
Moscow
LITHUANIA
RUSSIA
London
NETHERLANDS
BYELARUS
GERMANY
POLAND
BELGIUM
LUXEMBOURG
Paris
CZECHOSLOVAKIA
UKRAINE
FRANCE
SWITZERLAND
AUSTRIA
HUNGARY
MOLDOVA
SLOVENIA
ROMANIA
CROATIA
BOSNIA-HERZEGOVINA
SERBIA
PORTUGAL
SPAIN
ITALY
YUGOSLAVIA
BLACK SEA
GEORGIA
MONTENEGRO
BULGARIA
ALBANIA
MACEDONIA
GIBRALTER (U.K.)
MEDITERRANEAN SEA
GREECE
TURKEY
0 250 500 Miles
0 250 500 Kilometers
MALTA
CYPRUS
LEBANON
SYRIA

Appendix J

PERIODIC TABLE

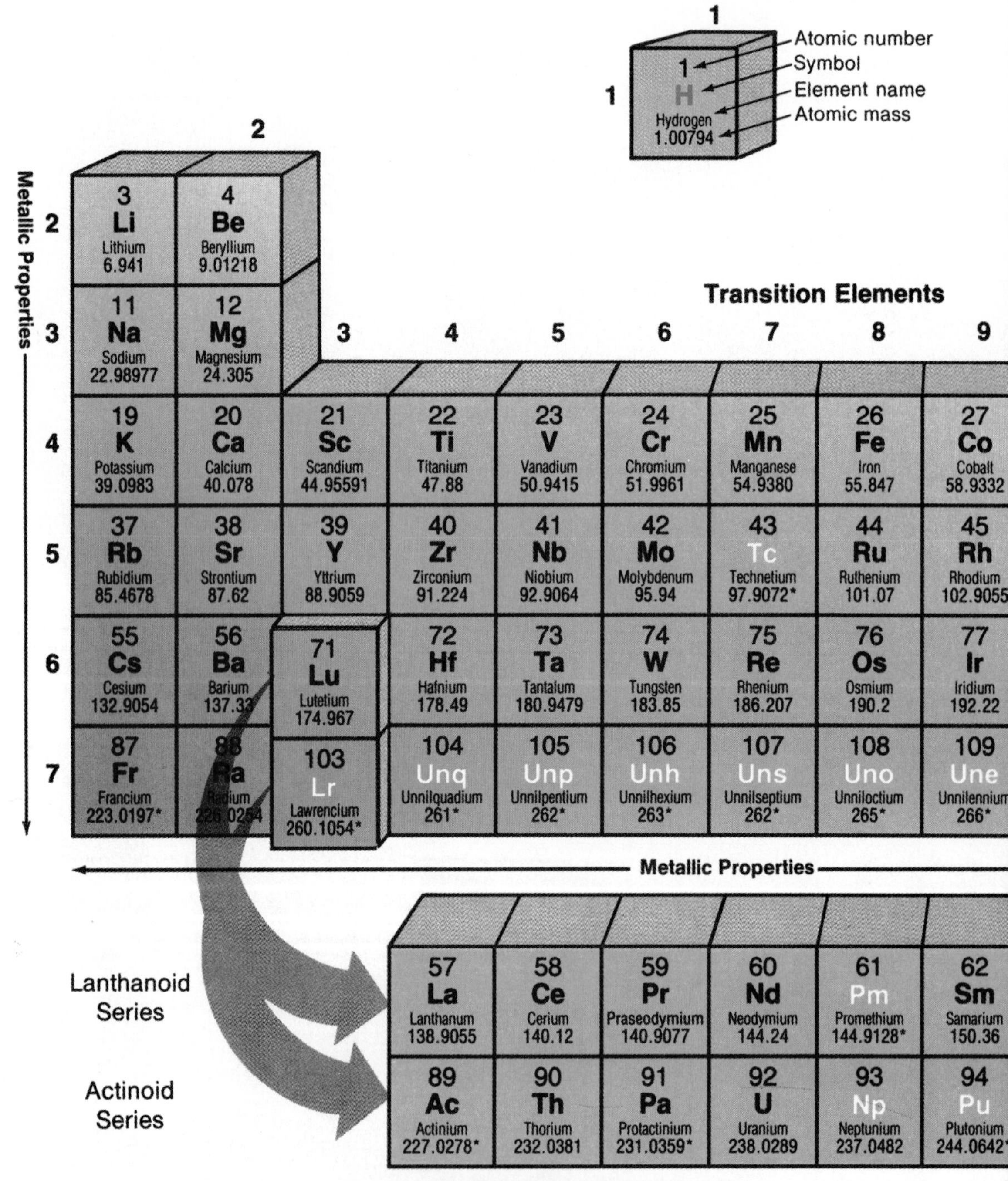

1
1
1
H
Hydrogen
1.00794
Atomic number
Symbol
Element name
Atomic mass
2
Metallic Properties
2
3
4
5
6
7
3 Li Lithium 6.941
4 Be Beryllium 9.01218
11 Na Sodium 22.98977
12 Mg Magnesium 24.305
Transition Elements
3
4
5
6
7
8
9
19 K Potassium 39.0983
20 Ca Calcium 40.078
21 Sc Scandium 44.95591
22 Ti Titanium 47.88
23 V Vanadium 50.9415
24 Cr Chromium 51.9961
25 Mn Manganese 54.9380
26 Fe Iron 55.847
27 Co Cobalt 58.9332
37 Rb Rubidium 85.4678
38 Sr Strontium 87.62
39 Y Yttrium 88.9059
40 Zr Zirconium 91.224
41 Nb Niobium 92.9064
42 Mo Molybdenum 95.94
43 Tc Technetium 97.9072*
44 Ru Ruthenium 101.07
45 Rh Rhodium 102.9055
55 Cs Cesium 132.9054
56 Ba Barium 137.33
71 Lu Lutetium 174.967
72 Hf Hafnium 178.49
73 Ta Tantalum 180.9479
74 W Tungsten 183.85
75 Re Rhenium 186.207
76 Os Osmium 190.2
77 Ir Iridium 192.22
87 Fr Francium 223.0197*
88 Ra Radium 226.0254
103 Lr Lawrencium 260.1054*
104 Unq Unnilquadium 261*
105 Unp Unnilpentium 262*
106 Unh Unnilhexium 263*
107 Uns Unnilseptium 262*
108 Uno Unniloctium 265*
109 Une Unnilennium 266*
Metallic Properties
Lanthanoid Series
Actinoid Series
57 La Lanthanum 138.9055
58 Ce Cerium 140.12
59 Pr Praseodymium 140.9077
60 Nd Neodymium 144.24
61 Pm Promethium 144.9128*
62 Sm Samarium 150.36
89 Ac Actinium 227.0278*
90 Th Thorium 232.0381
91 Pa Protactinium 231.0359*
92 U Uranium 238.0289
93 Np Neptunium 237.0482
94 Pu Plutonium 244.0642*

*Mass of isotope with longest half-life, that is, the most stable isotope of the element

Noble Gases

10	11	12	13	14	15	16	17	18
								2 **He** Helium 4.002602
			5 **B** Boron 10.811	6 **C** Carbon 12.011	7 **N** Nitrogen 14.0067	8 **O** Oxygen 15.9994	9 **F** Fluorine 18.998403	10 **Ne** Neon 20.179
			13 **Al** Aluminum 26.98154	14 **Si** Silicon 28.0855	15 **P** Phosphorus 30.97376	16 **S** Sulfur 32.06	17 **Cl** Chlorine 35.453	18 **Ar** Argon 39.948
28 **Ni** Nickel 58.69	29 **Cu** Copper 63.546	30 **Zn** Zinc 65.39	31 **Ga** Gallium 69.723	32 **Ge** Germanium 72.59	33 **As** Arsenic 74.9216	34 **Se** Selenium 78.96	35 **Br** Bromine 79.904	36 **Kr** Krypton 83.80
46 **Pd** Palladium 106.42	47 **Ag** Silver 107.8682	48 **Cd** Cadmium 112.41	49 **In** Indium 114.82	50 **Sn** Tin 118.710	51 **Sb** Antimony 121.75	52 **Te** Tellurium 127.60	53 **I** Iodine 126.9045	54 **Xe** Xenon 131.29
78 **Pt** Platinum 195.08	79 **Au** Gold 196.9665	80 **Hg** Mercury 200.59	81 **Tl** Thallium 204.383	82 **Pb** Lead 207.2	83 **Bi** Bismuth 208.9804	84 **Po** Polonium 208.9824*	85 **At** Astatine 209.98712*	86 **Rn** Radon 222.017*

Nonmetallic Properties →

Metallic Properties
Nonmetallic Properties
Metalloids
Synthetic Elements

State at Room Temperature: ■ and □ Solid ▢ Liquid ▢ Gas

63 **Eu** Europium 151.96	64 **Gd** Gadolinium 157.25	65 **Tb** Terbium 158.9254	66 **Dy** Dysprosium 162.50	67 **Ho** Holmium 164.9304	68 **Er** Erbium 167.26	69 **Tm** Thulium 168.9342	70 **Yb** Ytterbium 173.04
95 **Am** Americium 243.0614*	96 **Cm** Curium 247.0703*	97 **Bk** Berkelium 247.0703*	98 **Cf** Californium 251.0796*	99 **Es** Einsteinium 252.0828*	100 **Fm** Fermium 257.0951*	101 **Md** Mendelevium 258.986*	102 **No** Nobelium 259.1009*

Appendix K

MINERALS WITH NONMETALLIC LUSTER

Mineral (formula)	Color	Streak	Hardness	Specific gravity	Crystal system	Breakage pattern	Uses and other properties
talc ($Mg_3(OH)_2$ Si_4O_{10})	white, greenish	white	1	2.8	monoclinic	cleavage in one direction	easily cut with fingernail; used for taculm powder; soapstone; is used in paper and for table tops
bauxite (hydrous aluminum compound)	gray, red, white, brown	gray	1-3	2.0-2.5	—	—	source of aluminum; used in paints, aluminum foil, and airplane parts
kaolinite ($Al_4Si_2O_5$ $(OH)_4$)	white, red, reddish brown, black	white	2	2.6	triclinic	basal cleavage	clays; used in ceramics and in china dishes; common in most soils; often microscopic-sized particles
gypsum ($CaSO_4$ $\bullet$ $2H_2O$)	colorless, gray, white, brown	white	2	2.3	monoclinic	basal cleavage	used extensively in the preparation of plaster of paris, alabaster, and dry wall for building construction
sphalerite (ZnS)	brown	pale yellow	3.5-4	4	cubic	cleavage in six directions	main ore of zinc; used in paints, dyes, and medicine
sulfur (S)	yellow	yellow to white	2	2.0	ortho-rhombic	conchoidal fracture	used in medicine, fungicides for plants, vulcanization of rubber, production of sulfuric acid
muscovite ($KAl_3Si_3O_{10}$ $(OH)_2$)	white, light gray, yellow, rose, green	colorless	2.5	2.8	monoclinic	basal cleavage	occurs in large flexible plates; used as an insulator in electrical equipment, lubricant
biotite ($K(Mg, Fe)_3$ $AlSi_3O_{10}$ $(OH)_2$)	black to dark brown	colorless	2.5	2.8-3.4	monoclinic	basal cleavage	occurs in large fexible plates
halite (NaCl)	colorless, red, white, blue	colorless	2.5	2.1	cubic	cubic cleavage	salt; very soluble in water; a preservative
calcite ($CaCO_3$)	colorless, white, pale, blue	colorless, white	3	2.7	hexagonal	cleavage in three directions	fizzes when HCl is added; used in cements and other building materials
dolomite ($CaMg$ $(CO_3)_2$)	colorless, white, pink, green, gray, black	white	3.5-4	2.8	hexagonal	cleavage in three directions	concrete and cement, used as an ornamental building stone

Mineral (formula)	Color	Streak	Hardness	Specific gravity	Crystal system	Breakage pattern	Uses and other properties
fluorite (CaF_2)	colorless, white, blue, green, red, yellow, purple	colorless	4	3-3.2	cubic	cleavage	used in the manufacture of optical equipment; glows under ultraviolet light
limonite (hydrous iron oxides)	yellow, brown, black	yellow, brown	5.5	2.7-4.3	—	conchoidal fracture	source of iron; weathers easily, coloring matter of soils
hornblende ($CaNa(Mg, Al, Fe)_5Al,Si)_2 Si_6O_{22}(OH)_2$)	green to black	gray to white	5-6	3.4	monoclinic	cleavage in two directions	will transmit light on thin edges; 6-sided cross section
feldspar (orthoclase) ($KAlSi_3O_8$)	colorless, white to gray, green and yellow	colorless	6	2.5	monoclinic	two cleavage planes meet at 90° angle	insoluble in acids; used in the manufacture of porcelain
feldspar (plagioclase) ($NaAlSi_3O_8$) ($CaAl_2Si_2O_8$)	gray, green, white	colorless	6	2.5	triclinic	two cleavage planes meet at 86° angle	used in ceramics; striations present on some faces
augite ($(Ca, Na)(Mg, Fe, Al)(Al, Si)_2 O_6$)	black	colorless	6	3.3	monoclinic	2-directional cleavage	square or 8-sided cross section
olivine ($(Mg, Fe)_2SiO_4$)	olive green	colorless	6.5	3.5	ortho-rhombic	conchoidal fracture	gemstones, refractory sand
quartz (SiO_2)	colorless, various colors	colorless	7	2.6	hexagonal	conchoidal fracture	used in glass manufacture, electronic equipment, radios, computers, watches, gemstones
garnet ($(Mg, Fe, Ca)_3 (Al_2Si_3O_{12})$)	deep yellow-red green, black	colorless	7.5	3.5	cubic	conchoidal fracture	used in jewelry, also used as an abrasive
topaz ($(Al_2SiO_4)(F, OH)_2$)	white, pink yellow, pale blue, colorless	colorless	8	3.5	ortho-rhombic	basal cleavage	valuable gemstone
corundum (Al_2O_3)	colorless, blue, brown, green, white, pink, red	colorless	9	4.0	hexagonal	fracture	gemstones: ruby is red, sapphire is blue; industrial abrasive

Appendix L

MINERALS WITH METALLIC LUSTER

Mineral (formula)	Color	Streak	Hardness	Specific gravity	Crystal system	Breakage pattern	Uses and other properties
graphite (C)	black to gray	black to gray	1-2	2.3	hexagonal	basal cleavage (scales)	pencil lead, lubricants for locks, rods to control some small nuclear reactions, battery poles
silver (Ag)	silvery white, tarnishes to black	light gray to silver	2.5	10-12	cubic	hackly	coins, fillings for teeth, jewelry, silverplate, wires; malleable and ductile
galena (Pbs)	gray	gray to black	2.5	7.5	cubic	cubic cleavage perfect	source of lead, used in pipes, shields for X rays, fishing equipment sinkers
gold (Au)	pale to golden yellow	yellow	2.5-3	19.3	cubic	hackly	jewelry, money, gold leaf, fillings for teeth, medicines; does not tarnish
bornite (Cu_5FeS_4)	bronze, tarnishes to dark blue, purple	gray-black	3	4.9-5.4	tetragonal	uneven fracture	source of copper; called "peacock ore" because of the purple shine when it tarnishes
copper (Cu)	copper red	copper red	3	8.5-9	cubic	hackly	coins, pipes, gutters, wire, cooking utensils, jewelry, decorative plaques; malleable and ductile
chalcopyrite ($CuFeS_2$)	brassy to golden yellow	greenish black	3.5-4	4.2	tetragonal	uneven fracture	main ore of copper
chromite ($FeCr_2O_4$)	black or brown	brown to black	5.5	4.6	cubic	irregular fracture	ore of chromium, stainless steel, metallurgical bricks
pyrrhotite (FeS)	bronze	gray-black	4	4.6	hexagonal	uneven fracture	often found with pentlandite, an ore of nickel; may be magnetic
hematite (specular) (Fe_2O_3)	black or reddish brown	red or reddish brown	6	5.3	hexagonal	irregular fracture	source of iron; roasted in a blast furnace, converted to "pig" iron, made into steel
magnetite (Fe_3O_4)	black	black	6	5.2	cubic	conchoidal fracture	source of iron, naturally magnetic, called lodestone
pyrite (FeS_2)	light, brassy, yellow	greenish black	6.5	5.0	cubic	uneven fracture	source of iron, "fool's gold," alters to limonite

Skill Handbook
Table of Contents

ORGANIZING INFORMATION

CLASSIFYING 678
SEQUENCING 678
MAKING AND USING TABLES 679
MAKING AND USING GRAPHS 680

THINKING CRITICALLY

OBSERVING AND INFERRING 682
COMPARING AND CONTRASTING 683
RECOGNIZING CAUSE AND EFFECT 683
MEASURING IN SI 684

PRACTICING SCIENTIFIC METHODS

OBSERVING 687
FORMING A HYPOTHESIS 687
DESIGNING AN EXPERIMENT TO TEST A HYPOTHESIS 687
SEPARATING AND CONTROLLING VARIABLES 688
INTERPRETING DATA 689

REPRESENTING AND APPLYING DATA

INTERPRETING SCIENTIFIC ILLUSTRATION 689
MAKING MODELS 690
PREDICTING 691

Skill Handbook

ORGANIZING INFORMATION

CLASSIFYING

You may not realize it, but you make things orderly in the world around you. If your shirts hang in the closet together, your socks take up a particular corner of a dresser drawer, or your favorite cassette tapes are stacked together, you have used the skill of classifying.

Classifying is the process of sorting objects or events into groups based on their common features. When classifying, you first make observations of the objects or events to be classified. Then, you select one feature that is shared by some members in the group but not by others. Those members that share the feature are placed in a subgroup. You can classify members into smaller and smaller subgroups based on characteristics.

How would you classify a collection of cassette tapes? You might classify cassettes you like to dance to in one subgroup and cassettes you like to listen to in another. The cassettes you like to dance to could be subdivided into a rap subgroup and a rock subgroup. Note that for each feature selected, each cassette only fits into one subgroup. Keep selecting features until all the cassettes are classified. The concept map in the next column shows one possible classification.

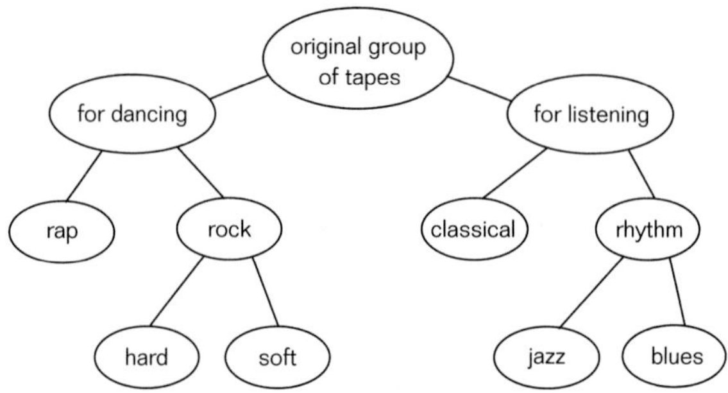

Remember when you classify, you are grouping objects or events for a purpose. Select common features to form groups and subgroups with your purpose in mind.

SEQUENCING

A sequence is an arrangement of things or events in a particular order. A sequence with which you are familiar is sitting in alphabetical order in a class. Another example of sequence would be the steps in a recipe. Think about baking chocolate chip cookies. The steps in the recipe have to be followed in order for the cookies to turn out right.

When you are asked to sequence objects or events, identify what comes first, then what should come second. Continue to choose objects or events until they are all in order. Then, go back over the sequence to make sure each thing or event in your sequence logically leads to the next.

Suppose you wanted to watch a movie that just came out on videotape. What sequence of events would you have to follow to watch the movie? You would first turn the television set to Channel 3 or 4. Then you would turn the videotape player on and insert the tape. Once the tape started playing, you would adjust the sound and picture. When the movie was over, you would rewind the tape and return it to the store.

MAKING AND USING TABLES

Browse through your textbook, and you will notice many tables both in the text and in the activities. Tables arrange data or information in such a way that makes it easier for you to understand. Activity tables help organize the data you collect during an activity so that results can be interpreted more easily.

Most tables have a title that tells what the table is about. The table then is divided into columns and rows. The first column lists items to be compared. In the table in the next column, different magnitudes of force are being compared. The rows across the top list the specific characteristics being compared. Within the grid of the table, the collected data is recorded. Look at the features in the following table.

EARTHQUAKE MAGNITUDE

MAGNITUDE AT FOCUS	DISTANCE FROM EPICENTERS THAT TREMORS ARE FELT	AVERAGE NUMBER EXPECTED PER YEAR
1.0 to 3.9	24 km	> 100 000
4.0 to 4.9	48 km	6 200
5.0 to 5.9	112 km	800
6.0 to 6.9	200 km	120
7.0 to 7.9	400 km	20
8.0 to 8.9	720 km	< 1

What is the title of this table? The title is "Earthquake Magnitude." What is being compared? The distance away from the epicenter that tremors are felt and the average number of earthquakes expected per year are being compared for different magnitudes on the Richter scale.

What is the average number of earthquakes expected per year for an earthquake with a magnitude of 5.5 at the focus? Locate the column labeled "Average number expected per year" and the row "5.0 to 5.9." The data in the box where the column and row intersect is the answer. Did you answer "800"? What is the distance away from the epicenter for an earthquake with a magnitude of 8.1? If you answered "720 km," you understand how to use the table.

To make a table, you simply list the items compared in columns and the characteristics compared in rows. Make a table and record the data comparing the mass of recycled materials collected by a class. On Monday, students turned in 4 kg of paper, 2 kg of aluminum, and 0.5 kg of plastic. Wednesday, they turned in 3.5 kg of paper, 1.5 kg of aluminum, and 0.5 kg of plastic. On Friday, the totals were 3 kg of paper, 1 kg of aluminum, and 1.5 kg of plastic. If your table looks like the one shown, you should be able to make tables to organize data.

RECYCLED MATERIALS			
DAY OF WEEK	PAPER (KG)	ALUMINUM (KG)	PLASTIC (KG)
Mon.	4	2	0.5
Wed.	3.5	1.5	0.5
Fri.	3	1	1.5

MAKING AND USING GRAPHS

After scientists organize data in tables, they may display the data in a graph. A graph is a diagram that shows how variables compare. A graph makes interpretation and analysis of data easier. There are three basic types of graphs used in science, the line graph, bar graph, and pie graph.

A line graph is used to show the relationship between two variables. The variables being compared go on two axes of the graph. The independent variable always goes on the horizontal axis, called the *x*-axis. The dependent variable always goes on the vertical axis or *y*-axis.

Suppose a school started a peer study program with a class of students to see how science grades were affected.

AVERAGE GRADES OF STUDENTS IN STUDY PROGRAM	
GRADING PERIOD	AVERAGE SCIENCE GRADE
First	81
Second	85
Third	86
Fourth	89

You could make a graph of the grades of students in the program over the four grading periods of the school year. The grading period is the independent variable and is placed on the *x*-axis of your graph. The average grade of the students in the program is the dependent variable and would go on the *y*-axis.

After drawing your axes, you would label each axis with a scale. The *x*-axis simply lists the four grading periods. To make a scale of grades on the *y*-axis, you must look at the data values. Since the lowest grade was 81 and the highest was 89, you know that you will have to start numbering at least at 81 and go through 89. You decide to start numbering at 80 and number by twos through 90.

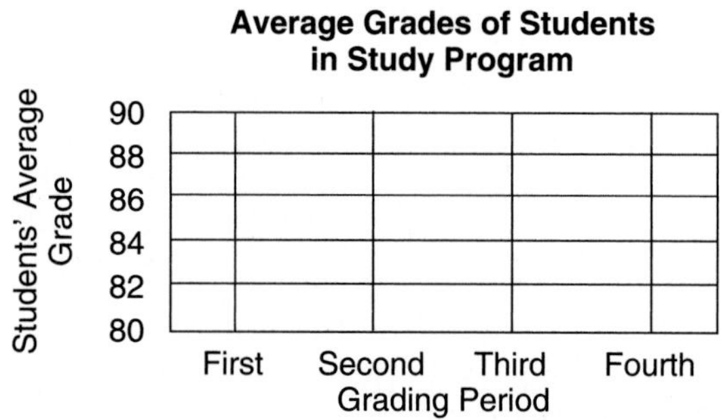

Next, you must plot the data points. The first pair of data you want to plot is the first grading period and 81. Locate "First" on the *x*-axis and locate "81" on the *y*-axis. Where an imaginary vertical line from the *x*-axis and an imaginary horizontal line from the *y*-axis would meet, place the first data point. Place the other data points the same way. After all the points are plotted, connect them with straight lines.

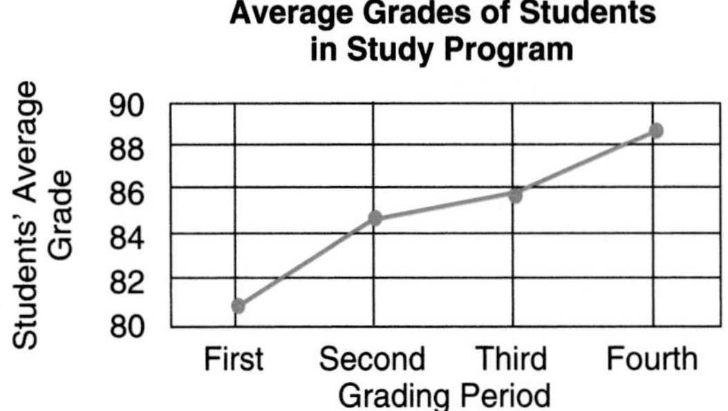

Bar graphs are similar to line graphs, except they compare or display data that do not continuously change. In a bar graph, thick bars show the relationships among data rather than data points.

To make a bar graph, set up the *x*-axis and *y*-axis as you did for the line graph. The data is plotted by drawing thick bars from the *x*-axis up to a point where the *y*-axis would intersect the bar if it was extended.

Look at the bar graph comparing the masses lifted by an electromagnet with different numbers of dry cell batteries. The *x*-axis is the number of dry cell batteries, and the *y*-axis is the mass lifted. The lifting power of the electromagnet as it changed with different numbers of dry cell batteries is being compared.

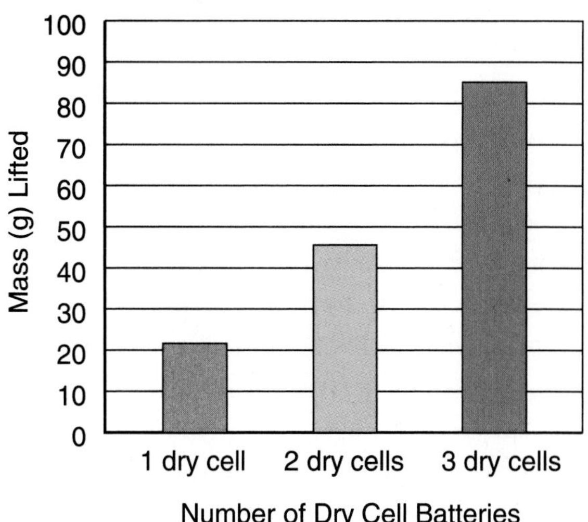

A pie graph uses a circle divided into sections to display data. Each section represents part of the whole. All the sections together equal 100 percent.

Suppose you wanted to make a pie graph to show the number of seeds that germinated in a package. You would have to count the total number of seeds and the number of seeds that germinated out of the total. You find that there are 143 seeds in the package. This represents 100 percent, the whole pie.

You plant the seeds, and 129 seeds germinate. The seeds that germinated will make up one section of the pie graph, and the seeds that did not germinate will make up the remaining section.

To find out how much of the pie each section should take, divide the number of seeds in each section by the total number of seeds. Then multiply your answer by 360, the number of degrees in a circle, and round to the nearest whole number. The number of seeds germinated as a measure of degrees is shown on the following page.

$$\frac{143}{129} \times 360 = 324.75 \text{ or } 325 \text{ degrees}$$

Plot this group on the pie graph, with a compass and a protractor. Use the compass to draw a circle. Then, draw a straight line from the center to the edge of the circle. Place your protractor on this line and use it to mark a point on the edge of the circle at 325 degrees. Connect this point with a straight line to the center of the circle. This is the section for the group of seeds that germinated. The other section represents the group of seeds that did not germinate. Label the sections of your graph and give the graph a title.

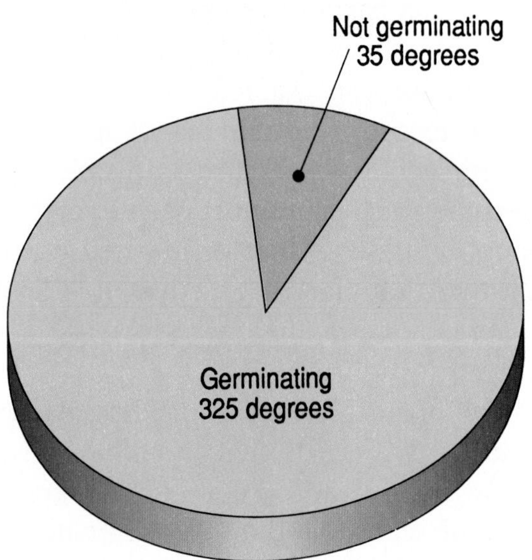

THINKING CRITICALLY

OBSERVING AND INFERRING

Imagine that you have just finished a volleyball game. At home, you open the refrigerator and see a jug of orange juice on the back of the top shelf. The jug feels cold as you grasp it. "Ah, just what I need," you think. When you drink the juice, you smell the oranges and enjoy the tart taste in your mouth.

As you imagined yourself in the story, you used your senses to make observations. You used your sense of sight to find the jug in the refrigerator, your sense of touch to feel the coldness of the jug, your sense of hearing to listen as the liquid filled the glass, and your senses of smell and taste to enjoy the odor and tartness of the juice. The basis of all scientific investigation is observation.

Scientists try to make careful and accurate observations. When possible, they use instruments, like microscopes, to extend their senses. Other instruments, such as a thermometer or a pan balance, measure observations. Measurements provide numerical data, a concrete means of comparing collected data that can be checked and repeated.

When you make observations in science, you may find it helpful first to examine the entire object or situation. Then, look carefully for details. Write down everything you see before using other senses to make additional observations.

Scientists often make inferences based on their observations. An inference is an attempt to explain or interpret observations or to say what caused what you observed. For example, if you observed a CLOSED sign in a store window around noon, you might infer the owner is taking a lunch break. But, it's possible that the owner has a doctor's appointment or has taken the day off to go fishing. The only way to be sure your inference is correct is to investigate further.

When making an inference, be certain to make use of accurate data and observations. Analyze all of the data that you've collected. Then, based on everything you know, try to explain or interpret what you've observed. If possible, investigate further to determine if your inference is correct. What is there in the photo that you could use to check your inference?

COMPARING AND CONTRASTING

Observations can be analyzed by noting the similarities and differences between two or more objects or events that you observed. When you examine objects or events to see how they are similar, you are comparing them. Contrasting is looking for differences in similar objects or events.

Suppose you were asked to compare and contrast the planets Venus and Earth. You would start by looking at what is known about these planets. Then make two columns on a piece of paper. List ways the planets are similar in one column and ways they are different in the other. Then, report your findings in a table or in a paragraph.

COMPARISON OF VENUS AND EARTH

PROPERTIES	EARTH	VENUS
Diameter (km)	12 742	12 112
Average density (g/cm^3)	5.5	5.3
Percentage of sunlight reflected	39	76
Daytime surface temperature	300	750
Number of satellites	1	0

Similarities you might point out are that both are similar in size, shape, and mass. Differences include Venus having hotter surface temperatures, a dense cloudy atmosphere, and an intense greenhouse effect.

RECOGNIZING CAUSE AND EFFECT

Have you ever watched something happen and then tried to figure out why

or how it happened? If so, you have observed an event and inferred a reason for its occurrence. The event is an effect, and the reason for the event is the cause.

Suppose that every time your teacher fed fish in a classroom aquarium, she or he tapped the food container on the edge of the aquarium. Then, one day your teacher just happened to tap the edge of the aquarium with a pencil while making a point about an ecology lesson. You observed the fish swim to the surface of the aquarium to feed. What is the effect, and what would you infer to be the cause? The effect is the fish swimming to the surface of the aquarium. You might infer the cause to be the teacher tapping on the edge of the aquarium. In determining cause and effect, you have made a logical inference based on your observations.

Perhaps the fish swam to the surface because they reacted to the teacher's waving hand or for some other reason. When scientists are unsure of the cause for a certain event, they design controlled experiments to determine what caused the event. Although you have made a logical conclusion about the fish's behavior, you would have to perform an experiment to be certain that it was the tapping that caused the effect you observed.

MEASURING IN SI

You're probably somewhat familiar with the metric system of measurement. The metric system is a system of measurement developed by a group of scientists in 1795. The development of the metric system helped scientists avoid problems by providing an international standard of comparison for measurements that all scientists around the world could understand. A modern form of the metric system called the International System, or SI, was adopted for worldwide use in 1960.

Your text uses metric units in many measurements. In the activities and experiments you will be doing, you will frequently use the metric system of measurement.

The metric system is convenient because it has a systematic way of naming units and a decimal base. For example, meter is a unit for measuring length, gram for measuring mass, and liter for measuring volume. Unit sizes vary by multiples of ten. When changing from smaller units to larger, you divide by ten. When changing from larger units to smaller, you multiply by ten. Prefixes are used to name units. Look at the following table for some common metric prefixes and their meanings.

METRIC PREFIXES			
PREFIX	**SYMBOL**	**MEANING**	
kilo-	k	1000	thousand
hecto-	h	100	hundred
deka-	da	10	ten
deci-	d	0.1	tenth
centi-	c	0.01	hundreth
milli-	m	0.001	thousandth

Do you see how the prefix kilo- attached to the unit gram is kilogram, or 1000 grams? The prefix deci- attached to the unit meter is decimeter, or one-tenth (0.1) of a meter.

You have probably measured distance many times. The meter is the SI unit used to measure distance. To visualize the length of a meter, think of a baseball bat. A baseball bat is about one meter long. When measuring smaller distances, the meter is divided into smaller units called centimeters and millimeters. A centimeter is one-hundredth (0.01) of a meter, which is about the size of the width of the fingernail on your ring finger. A millimeter is one-thousandth of a meter (0.001), about the thickness of a dime.

Most metric rulers have lines indicating centimeters and millimeters. The centimeter lines are the longer numbered lines, and the shorter lines are millimeter lines.

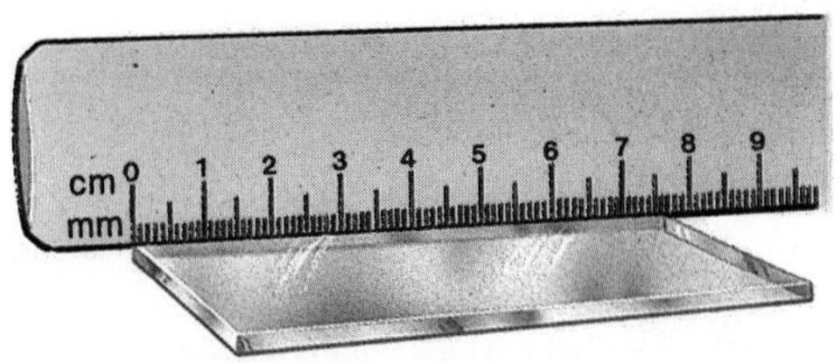

When using a metric ruler, first decide on a unit of measurement. You then line up the zero centimeter mark with the end of the object being measured and read the number where the object ends.

Units of length are also used to measure surface area. The standard unit of area is the square meter (m^2). A square that's one meter long on each side has a surface area of one square meter. Similarly, a square centimeter (cm^2) is a square one centimeter long on each side. The surface area of an object is determined by multiplying the number of units in length times the number of units in width.

The volume of rectangular solids is also calculated using units of length. The cubic meter (m^3) is the standard SI unit of volume. A cubic meter is a cube one meter on a side. You can determine the volume of rectangular solids by multiplying length times width times height.

Liquid volume is measured using a unit called a liter. A liter has the volume of 1000 cubic centimeters. Since the prefix milli- means thousandth (0.001), a milliliter equals one cubic centimeter. One milliliter of liquid would completely fill a cube measuring one centimeter on each side.

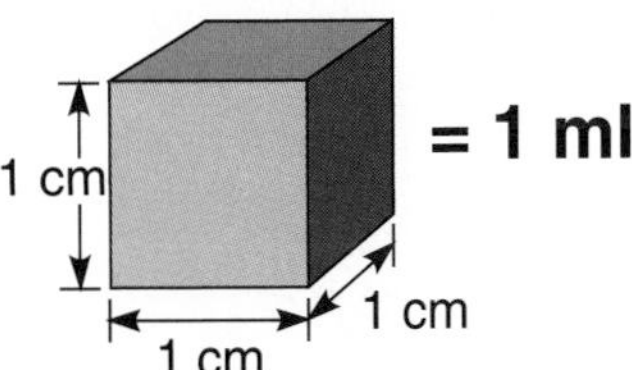

During science activities, you will measure liquids using beakers and graduated cylinders marked in milliliters. A graduated cylinder is a tall cylindrical container marked with lines from bottom to top.

Scientists use a balance to find the mass of an object in grams. You will likely use a beam balance similar to the one illustrated. Notice that on one side of the beam balance is a pan and on the other side is a set of beams. Each beam has an object of a known mass called a rider that slides on the beam.

Before you find the mass of an object, set the balance to zero by sliding all the riders back to zero point. Check the pointer on the right to make sure it swings an equal distance above and below the zero point on the scale. If the swing is unequal, find and turn the adjusting screw until you have an equal swing.

You are now ready to use the balance to find the mass of the object. Place the object on the pan. Slide the rider with the largest mass along its beam until the pointer drops below the zero point. Then move it back one notch. Repeat the process on each beam until the pointer swings an equal distance above and below the zero point. Read the masses indicated on each beam. The sum of these masses is the mass of the object.

You should never place a hot object or pour chemicals directly on the pan. Instead, find the mass of a clean container, such as a beaker or a glass jar. Place into the container the dry or liquid chemicals you want to measure. Next, you need to find the combined mass of the container and the chemicals. Calculate the mass of the chemicals by subtracting the mass of the empty container from the combined mass.

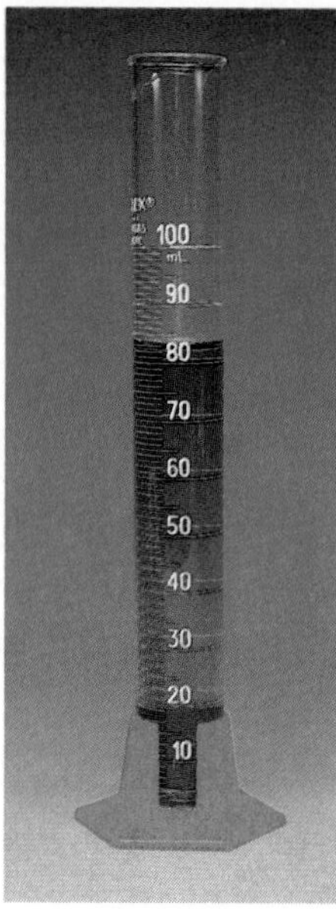

PRACTICING SCIENTIFIC METHODS

You might say that the work of a scientist is to solve problems. But when you decide how to dress on a particular day, you are doing problem solving, too. You may observe what the weather looks like through a window. You may go outside and see if what you are wearing is warm or cool enough.

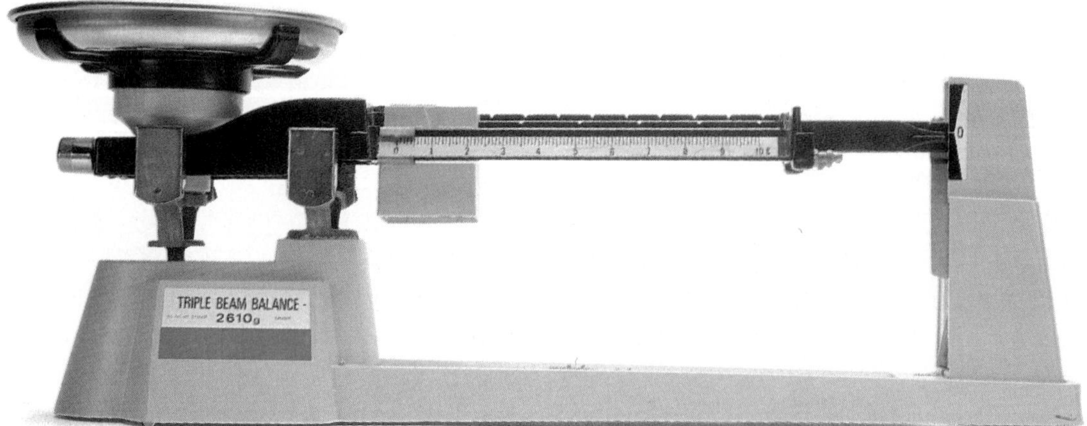

Scientists use an orderly approach to learn new information and to solve problems. The methods scientists use include observing, forming a hypothesis, testing a hypothesis, separating and controlling variables, and interpreting data.

OBSERVING

You observe all the time. Anytime you smell wood burning, touch a pet, see lightning, taste food, or hear your favorite music, you are observing. Observation gives you information about events or things. Scientists must try to observe as much as possible about the things and events they study.

Some observations describe something using only words. These observations are called qualitative observations. If you were making qualitative observations of a dog, you might use words such as cute, furry, brown, short-haired, or short-eared.

Other observations describe how much of something there is. These are quantitative observations and use numbers as well as words in the description. Tools or equipment are used to measure the characteristic being described. Quantitative observations of a dog might include a mass of 459 g, a height of 27 cm, ear length of 14 mm, and an age of 283 days.

FORMING A HYPOTHESIS

Suppose you wanted to make a perfect score on a spelling test. You think of several ways to accomplish a perfect score. You base these possibilities on past observations. If you put these possibilities into a sentence using the words *if* and *then*, you have formed a hypothesis. All of the following are hypotheses you might consider to explain how you could score 100% on your test:

If the test is easy, then I will get a good grade.

If I am intelligent, then I will get a good grade.

If I study hard, then I will get a good grade.

Scientists use hypotheses that they can test to explain the observations they have made. Perhaps a scientist has observed that plants that receive fertilizer grow taller than plants that do not. A scientist may form a hypothesis that says: If you fertilize plants, their growth will increase.

DESIGNING AN EXPERIMENT TO TEST A HYPOTHESIS

Once you have stated a hypothesis, you probably want to find out if it explains an event or an observation or not. This requires a test. A hypothesis *must* be something you can test. To test a hypothesis, you have to design and carry out an experiment. An experiment involves planning and materials. Let's figure out how you would conduct an experiment to test the hypothesis stated before about the effects of fertilizer on plants.

First, you need to lay out a procedure. A procedure is the plan that you will follow in your experiment. A procedure tells you what materials to use and how you will use them. In this experiment, your plan may involve using ten bean plants that are 15-cm tall in two groups, Groups A and B. You will water the five bean plants in Group A with 200 mL of plain water and no fertilizer once a week for three weeks. You will treat the five bean plants in Group B with 200 mL of fertilizer solution once a week for three weeks.

You will need to measure all the plants in both groups at the beginning of the experiment and again at the end of the three-week test period. These measurements will be the data that you record in a table. For instance, look at the data in the table for this experiment. From the data you recorded, you will draw a conclusion and make a statement about your results. If your conclusion supports your hypothesis, then you can say that your hypothesis is reliable. If it did not support your hypothesis, then you would have to make new observations and state a new hypothesis, one that you could also test.

GROWING BEAN PLANTS

PLANTS	TREATMENT	HEIGHT 3 WEEKS LATER
Group A	no fertilizer added to soil	17 cm
Group B	3 g fertilizer added to soil	31 cm

SEPARATING AND CONTROLLING VARIABLES

In the experiment above with the bean plants, you made everything the same except for treating one group (Group B) with fertilizer. By doing so, you've controlled as many things as possible. The type of plants, their beginning heights, the soil, the frequency with which you watered them—all these things were kept the same, or constant. By doing this, you made sure that at the end of three weeks any change you saw depended on whether or not the plants had been fertilized. The only thing that you changed, or varied, was the use of fertilizer. The one factor that you change in an experiment—in this case, the fertilizer—is called the *independent* variable. The factor that changes as a result of the independent variable is called the *dependent* variable—in this case, growth. Always make sure that there is only one independent variable. If you allow more than one, you will not know what causes any change you observe in the dependent variable.

Experiments also need a control, a treatment that you can compare with the results of your experiment. In this case, Group A was the control because it was not treated with fertilizer. Group B was the test group. At the end of three weeks, you were able to compare Group A with Group B and draw a conclusion.

INTERPRETING DATA

The word *interpret* means to explain the meaning of something. Information, or data, needs to mean something. Look at the problem originally being explored and find out what the data is trying to show. Perhaps you are looking at a table from an experiment designed to answer the question: does fertilizer affect plant growth and leaf color? Look back to the table showing the results of the bean plant experiment.

Identify the control group and the experimental group so you can see whether or not the variable has had an effect. In this example, Group A was the control and Group B was the experimental group. Now you need to check differences between the control and experimental groups. These differences may be qualitative or quantitative. A qualitative difference would be if the leaf colors of plants in Groups A and B were different. A quantitative difference would be the difference in number of centimeters of height among the plants in each group. Group B was in fact taller than Group A after three weeks.

If there are differences, the variable being tested may have had an effect. If there is no difference between the control and the experimental groups, the variable being tested probably had no effect. From the data table in this experiment, it appears that fertilizer does have an effect on plant growth.

REPRESENTING AND APPLYING DATA

INTERPRETING SCIENTIFIC ILLUSTRATIONS

Most of the textbooks you use in school have illustrations. Illustrations help you to understand what you read. As you read this textbook, you will see many drawings, diagrams, and photographs. Some are included to help you understand an idea that you can't see by yourself. For instance, we can't see atoms, but we can look at a diagram of an atom and that helps us to understand what atoms are and how they work. Seeing something often helps you remember more easily. The text may describe the surface of Jupiter in detail, but seeing a photograph of it may help you to remember that it has cloud bands. Illustrations also provide examples that clarify something you have read or give additional information about the topic you are

studying. Maps, for example, help you to locate places that may be described in the text.

Most illustrations have captions. A caption is a brief comment that identifies or explains the illustration. Diagrams often have labels to identify parts of the item shown or the order of steps in a process.

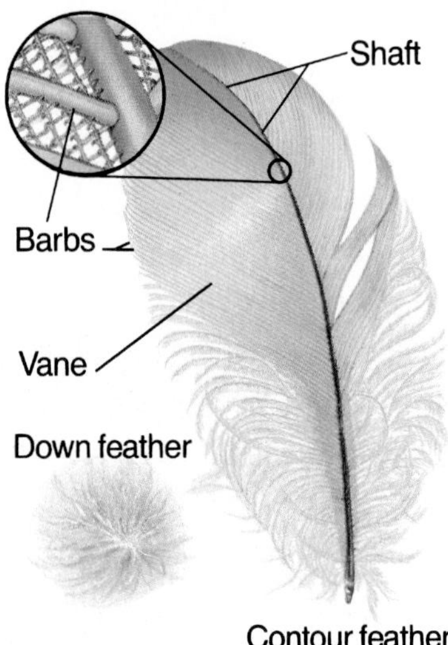

An illustration of an organism shows that organism from a particular view or orientation. In order to understand the illustration, you need to identify the front (anterior) end, tail (posterior) end, the underside (ventral), and the back (dorsal) side of the organism shown.

You might also check for symmetry so you know how many sides the organism has. A shark has bilateral symmetry. This means that drawing an imaginary line through the center of the animal from the anterior to posterior end forms two mirror images. If you can draw a second imaginary line at right angles to the first and divide the organism into four equal parts, the organism has radial symmetry.

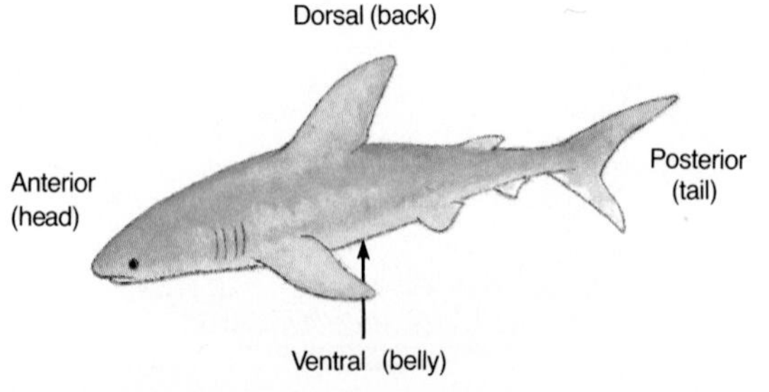

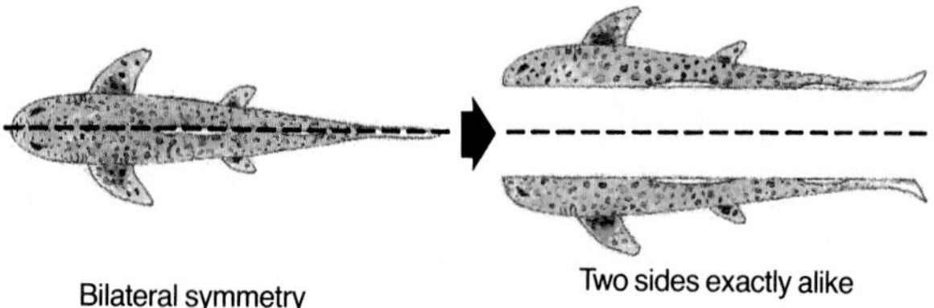

Some illustrations give an internal view of an organism or object. These illustrations are called sections.

Look at all illustrations carefully and read captions and labels so that you understand exactly what the illustration is showing you.

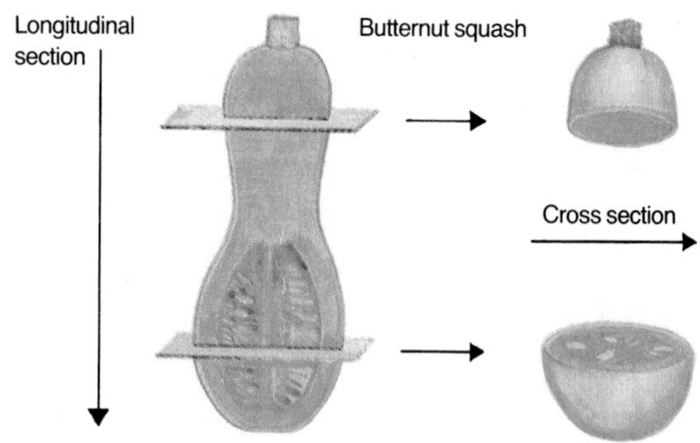

MAKING MODELS

You or your friends may have worked on a model car or plane or rocket. These models look, and sometimes work, just like the real thing, but they are usually much smaller than the real thing. In science, models are used to help simplify processes or structures that may be difficult to understand.

Often, everyday objects are used to make scientific principles and ideas simpler.

In order to make a model, you first have to learn about the structure or process involved. You decide to make a model showing the differences in size of arteries, veins, and capillaries. First, you must read about these structures. All three are hollow tubes. Arteries are round and thick. Veins are flat and thinner than arteries. Capillaries are very small.

Now you will need to decide what you can use for your model. Different kinds and sizes of pasta might work. Different sizes of rubber tubing might do just as well. Cut and glue the different noodles or tubing onto thick paper so the openings can be seen. Then label each. Now you have a model showing the differences in size of arteries, veins, and capillaries.

What other scientific ideas might a model help you to understand? A model of a compound can be made from gumdrops (using different colors for the different elements present) and toothpicks (to show different chemical bonds). A working model of a volcano can be made from clay, a small amount of baking soda, vinegar, and a bottle cap.

PREDICTING

When you apply a hypothesis, or general explanation, to a specific situation, you predict something about that situation. First, you must identify which hypothesis fits the situation you are considering. Maybe you want to predict whether or not eating a chocolate candy bar will increase your pulse rate. You've read that chocolate contains caffeine. So you could hypothesize that: if you consume caffeine in some form, then your pulse rate will increase. Next, you must figure out how the hypothesis affects the question you are asking. Since chocolate candy bars have caffeine and you think caffeine increases your pulse rate, you would predict that eating a chocolate candy bar would make your pulse rate faster.

We use predicting to make everyday decisions. Based on your previous observations and experiences, you may form a hypothesis that if it is wintertime, then temperatures will be lower. You may then use this hypothesis to predict specific temperatures and weather for four or five days in advance. You may use these predictions to plan what your activities will be for that time period.

Glossary

This glossary defines each key term that appears in **bold type** in the text. It also shows the page number where you can find the word used.

A

abyssal plain : flat seafloor in the deepest part of the ocean basin created by deposits filling in valleys (363)
action force: one force of an action-reaction pair (17)
alveoli: tiny thin-walled sacs in the lungs where exchange of oxygen and carbon dioxide occurs (474)
arteries: blood vessels that carry blood away from the heart (70)
asthma: disorder of the lungs in which there may be shortness of breath, wheezing, or coughing (484)
atherosclerosis: condition in which coronary arteries are clogged by a buildup of fatty deposits (83)
atmosphere: layer of gases hundreds of kilometers thick around Earth (442)
atom: smallest particle of an element (426)
atomic theory of matter: theory that matter is composed of small particles called atoms (423)

B

balanced forces: forces acting on an object that cancel one another (15)
blood pressure: pressure exerted by blood against the inner walls of blood vessels (76)
bone marrow: red or yellow fatty tissue inside bones where red blood cells are produced (198)
Boyle's law: the volume of a certain amount of gas is inversely proportional to the pressure, at a constant temperature (416)
brainstem: part of the brain that controls involuntary body activities (231)
buoyant force: upward force a fluid exerts on an object (24)

C

capillaries: thin-walled vessels through which nutrients, oxygen, and wastes pass to and from cells (71)
cardiac muscle: specialized muscle found only in the heart (206)
cartilage: soft, flexible material found in joints and other parts of the skeletal system (200)
catalyst: any substance that speeds up a chemical reaction without being used up (584)
cell: basic unit of life in all living things (533)
cell membrane: flexible outer boundary of the cell; controls movement of substances into and out of cell(542)
cell wall: rigid structure surrounding the cell membrane of plant and some bacterial cells (547)
cerebellum: part of the brain that coordinates muscle movement (229)
cerebrum: largest part of the brain that controls thought, interprets impulses from the senses, and controls voluntary movement (228)
Charles' law: the change in volume of a gas is directly proportional to the change in temperature, provided pressure and amount of gas are constant (418)
chemical reaction: process that results in the formation of new substances having properties that are different from those of the original substances (567)
chloroplast: cell structure containing chlorophyll, a green pigment that allows plants and some microorganisms to make their own food (548)
chromosomes: threadlike structures in cells made up of proteins and DNA, the molecule that controls the activities of cells (545)
cilia: short, hairlike structures that extend from the cell membrane in some protozoans to help them move (643); in respiratory passages (483)
cleavage: the physical property of a mineral that allows it to break along smooth flat surfaces (296)
coinage metals: three metals, copper, silver, and gold, that have been widely used as coins (261)
compact bone: thick, hard outer layer of bone (197)
compound machines: combinations of simple machines that make it possible to do something one simple machine alone cannot do (148)
concave lens: piece of transparent material that is thicker at the edges than in the middle (516)
concave mirror: mirror surface that curves inward (506)
conduction: heat moving through a material or from one material to another (173)
continental shelf: flat part of a continent that extends out under the ocean (363)
convection: heat transfer by motion of a heat-carrying medium (174)

convex lens: piece of transparent material that is thicker in the middle than at the edges (513)
convex mirror: mirror surface that curves outward (509)
cytoplasm: gel-like material inside cells containing structures that carry out life processes (543)

D

decomposition reaction: chemical reaction that takes place when one substance is broken down into two or more new substances (572)
diaphragm: thin sheet of muscle under your lungs that helps move air in and out of your lungs (475)
diffusion: process by which the constant motion of molecules causes movement from an area of high concentration to an area of low concentration (603)
ductile: characteristic of a metal that can be pulled into a wire without breaking (256)

E

effort force: force you exert on a machine (132)
emphysema: disease that occurs when air passageways or alveoli lose their ability to expand and contract (484)
endothermic reaction: chemical reaction in which energy is absorbed (579)
epicenter: point on Earth's surface directly above the focus of an earthquake (44)
exothermic reaction: chemical reaction in which energy is released (580)
extrusive: describing igneous rocks formed by lava cooling on Earth's surface (319)

F

fault: fracture within Earth where rock movement occurs (38)
fermentation: process that releases energy by breaking down glucose into alcohol and carbon dioxide, without the use of oxygen (612)
fission: reproductive process in microorganisms that produces two cells with genetic material exactly like that in the parent cell (638)
flagella: whiplike structures of some protozoans that help them move through watery surroundings (643)
focal point: point where parallel rays from a convex lens or concave mirror converge (506)
focus: point in Earth's interior where seismic waves originate (43)
foliated: describing metamorphic rocks formed when mineral grains flatten under pressure and line up in parallel bands (326)
force: mass times acceleration; a push or pull (14)
fossil fuel: remains of ancient plants or animals that can be burned to produce thermal energy (384)
fracture: the physical property of a mineral that causes it to break along rough or jagged surfaces (296)
Fungi: kingdom of organisms, most of which are many-celled, having cells with a nucleus; consumers(636)

G

gem: highly prized mineral because it is rare, durable, and beautiful (289)
generator: any machine that converts mechanical energy into electrical energy (381)
geothermal: describing energy extracted from Earth's internal heat (398)
gills: respiratory structures of some aquatic animals that remove oxygen from water (471)
greenhouse effect: trapping of heat by the atmosphere (454)

H

hardness: measure of how easily a mineral can be scratched (292)
heat: energy transferred because of a difference in temperature (170)
heat engine: engine that uses fuel to make thermal energy do work (179)
hemoglobin: oxygen-binding substance contained in red blood cells (478)
hydroelectric: describing power plants that use waterpower to generate electricity (393)
hypertension: disorder of the circulatory system in which blood pressure is higher than normal (84)

I

igneous rock: rock that formed as molten material cooled (318)
inclined plane: ramp or slope that reduces the force you need to exert to lift something (137)
inertia: tendency to resist changes in motion (5)
inertial balance: device used to measure an object's mass by measuring its resistance to a change in motion (9)
inhibitor: any substance that slows down a chemical reaction (586)
intrusive: describing igneous rocks formed by magma cooling beneath Earth's surface (319)

J

joints: places in the skeleton where two or more bones meet or are joined together (201)

K

kinetic energy: energy of an object due to its motion (107)

L

Law of Conservation of Energy: law that states energy can change form, but cannot be created or destroyed under ordinary conditions (119)
lever: bar that turns or pivots on a fixed point called a fulcrum (134)
ligaments: strong bands of tissue that hold bones together at joints (202)
longshore current: flow of ocean water that runs close and parallel to the shore (350)
lung: main organ of the respiratory system where the exchange of oxygen and carbon dioxide takes place (474)
lung cancer: disease of the lungs, typically linked to smoking (485)

M

malleable: characteristic of an element that can be hammered or pressed into various shapes without breaking (255)
mechanical advantage: formula that tells the ratio of the resistance force to the effort force (143)
metalloids: elements that have properties of both metals and nonmetals (272)
metals: elements, usually shiny, malleable, and ductile, that are good conductors of heat and electricity (255)
metamorphic rock: rock changed by heat or pressure or both (325)
microorganisms: organisms invisible to the naked eye (630)
mid-ocean ridges: chains of underwater mountains alongside rift zones (365)
mineral: naturally occurring, nonliving solid, with a definite structure and composition (286)
mitochondria: cell structures that release the energy needed for cell processes (545)
mitosis: reproductive process in which a cell divides to produce two cells, each with the same type and number of chromosomes as the parent cell (552)
Monera: kingdom of one-celled organisms having no nucleus (636)

N

neuron: working unit of the nervous system (224)
newton: unit used to measure force (14)
nonfoliated: a texture of metamorphic rocks in which mineral grains change, combine, and rearrange, but do not form visible bands (327)
nonmetals: elements that are mostly dull and brittle, as well as poor conductors of heat and electricity (264)
nonrenewable resources: resources used up faster than nature can replace them (389)
normal fault: fracture within Earth along which rocks above the fault surface move downward in relation to rocks below the fault surface (38)
nucleus: structure in cell that directs all the activities of the cell (545)

O

organ: structure in the body made up of several different types of tissue that all work together to do a particular job (615)
organism: living body made up of several organ systems working together (615)
organ system: group of organs working together to perform a particular job (615)
osmosis: diffusion of water through a cell membrane (604)
ozone: gas in a layer of the atmosphere that absorbs some of the harmful radiation from the sun (446)

P

plane mirror: flat piece of glass with a metallic coating on one side (500)
pollution: unwanted or harmful materials or effects in the environment (355)
potential energy: stored energy (109)
power: work done divided by the time interval (150)
pressure: weight or force acting on each unit of area (19)
prevailing westerlies: winds between 30° and 60° latitude (457)
products: new substances formed by the reactants in a chemical reaction (570)
Protista: kingdom of organisms, many of which are one-celled, having cells with a nucleus (636)
pulley: wheel that has a rope or chain passing over it (135)
pulse: rhythmic expanding and contracting of an artery (74)

R

radiation: transfer of thermal energy across space (176)
reactants: the starting substances used in any chemical reaction (570)
reaction force: second force in an action-reaction pair of forces (17)
real image: image that occurs where light rays from an object converge and pass through; can be captured on a screen (506)
reflex: automatic body response to a stimulus (239)
refraction: bending of light as it passes from one material to another (512)
renewable resource: natural resource that can be replaced (388)
resistance force: force exerted by a machine (132)
respiration: chemical process in which oxygen combines with food molecules to release energy and give off carbon dioxide and water as wastes (480, 608)
reverse fault: fracture within Earth along which rocks above the fault surface are forced up and over rocks below the fault surface (39)
rift zone: region where the seafloor is spreading apart (365)
rock: a mixture of one or more minerals (317)
rock cycle: processes by which Earth materials change to form different kinds of rocks (335)

S

screw: inclined plane wound around a post (140)
sedimentary rock: solid rock that forms when sediments become pressed or cemented together (328)
seismic waves: waves generated by earthquakes (43)
single displacement reaction: one substance takes the place of another substance to form new substances in a chemical reaction (574)
skeletal muscles: muscles that move bones (206)
smog: type of air pollution made up of sulfur, nitrogen, and oxygen that is visible as a smokelike haze (444)
smooth muscle: muscle in many internal organs, such as the stomach and intestines (206).
solar cell: device that turns solar energy into electricity (396)
spinal cord: bundle of neurons that carry impulses from all parts of the body to the brain (231)
spongy bone: light but strong type of bone found inside the ends of bones; not compact; with many openings (197)
streak: color of a mineral when it is broken up and powdered (295)
strike-slip fault: fracture within Earth along which rocks move past one another without much upward or downward movement (40)
synapse: space between neurons (225)
synthesis reaction: chemical reaction that takes place when two or more substances combine to form one new substance (571)

T

tendons: strong elastic bands of tissue that connect muscles to bones (206)
thermal equilibrium: state when two items are in contact and the temperature of one is the same as the temperature of the other (167)
tissue: similar types of cells working together to perform the same function (614)
trachea: passageway through which air passes into and out of the body (471)
trade winds: steady winds about 15° north and south of the equator, caused by cool, descending air (456)
troposphere: layer of atmosphere closest to the ground (446)
turbine: machine with fanlike blades arranged around a central axle that spin when air or water pushes on them; it turns a generator to produce electricity (380)

V

veins: blood vessels that carry blood back to the heart (71)
vents: openings in Earth's surface from which magma flows (49)
virtual image: image that light does not actually pass through; cannot be captured on a screen (510)
viruses: nonliving, microscopic particles; DNA or RNA core surrounded by a protein coat (632)

W

watt: a measure of power equal to one joule per second (150)
wedge: inclined plane that uses the sharp, narrow end to cut through material (141)
weight: gravitational force on an object (16)
wheel and axle: device in which a small wheel is attached to the center of a larger wheel (135)
work: energy transferred through motion (104)

Index

The Index for *Science Interactions* will help you locate major topics in the book quickly and easily. Each entry in the Index is followed by the numbers of the pages on which the entry is discussed. A page number given in **boldface type** indicates the page on which that entry is defined. A page number given in *italic type* indicates a page on which the entry is used in an illustration or photograph. The abbreviation *act.* indicates a page on which the entry is used in an activity.

A

Abyssal plain, **363**
Acceleration, 4-5, *4*
  factors affecting, *act.* 6-7
  and gravity, 11, *11*
  and mass, *act.* 13
Acetylcholine, 243
Acid rain, 392
Acromegaly, 215
Action force, 17-18, **17,** *18*
Active transport, 606, 617
Aerobic exercises, 85
Aerobic respiration, 620-621
Aerostat, 432, *432*
Aging population, 559-560
Air mass, *act.* 441
Air pollution, 442, *442,* 444-445, 585
  and burning fossil fuels, 391-392, *391*
Algae, 641-642, *642*
Alum, *act.* 318
Aluminum, 263, *263,* 424
  recycling, 277, *277*
Aluminum oxide, 571, *571*
Alveoli, **474,** *474*
Alzheimer's disease, 243-244, *243, 244*
Amethyst, 289
Ammonia, 267
Amoeba, 66, 67, 614, 629, *629, 635, 641,* 643, *644*
Amphibians, 470
Amylase, 584
Anabolic steroids, 215, *215*
Anaerobic respiration, 621
Anemia, 260
Animal cells, comparison to plant cells, *act.* 546
Animal-like protists, 642-644
Animals, rock in diet of, 338, *338*
Appliances, labor saving, 125, *125*
Aquamarine, 304
Archimedes, 23, 29
  principle of, 23, 48
Area, and force, *19-20*
Argon, 270
Arteries, **70**
Artificial kidney machine, 622, *622*
Artificial respiration, 489, *489*
Asbestos, 307-308, *307, 308*
Asbestos Hazardous Emergency Response Act, 308
Ascorbic acid (vitamin C), 589
Asthma, **484**
Atherosclerosis, **83,** *83*
Athletes
  and carbohydrate loading, 588
  and use of anabolic steroids, 215, *215*
Athlete's foot, 646
Atmosphere, **442**
  composition of, 442, *443, act.*443, 444-445
  and global winds, 455-458,*456, 457, 458*
  layers of, 446-447, *446, 447*
  of Mars, 451-452, *451*
  and ozone layer, 461, *461*
  pollution in, 442, *442,* 444-445
  and smog, 460, *460*
  solids in, *act.* 445
  of Venus, 451-452, *451*
Atmospheric pressure, 448, *act.* 448
Atom, **426,** *426*
Atomic theory of matter, 422-423, **423,** 424-427, *act.* 428, 429 430
Atrium, 69
Axons, 224

B

Backbone, *204*
Bacteria, *635,* 638, *638*
  in oil spill cleanup, 650, *650*
  uses of, 639-640
Balance, *act.* 222
Balanced forces, **15,** 17
Ball and cage valve, 90
Balloons, in research, 432, *432*
Barometer, *act.* 449, 448
Basalt, 320, *320,* 323, 354
Beach erosion, 369-370, *370*
Beach sand, characteristics of, *act.* 353, 354, *354*
Beetles, respiration in, 487
Beryl, 304
Biceps, 207, *210*
Blimps, 432
Blood pressure, **76,** *76, act.* 77, 78-79
  in closed circulatory systems, 79-81, *80, 81*
  measurement of, 88
  taking, *84*
Blood pressure chart, 78, *78*
Blood pressure transducer, 30, *30*
Blood vessels, types of, 70-71, *71*
Blue-green bacteria, *635,* 638
Bone, *196*
  density of, 211, *211*
  development of, 200, *200*

growth of, *act.* 550
hardness of, *act.* 196
parts of, *act.* 199, 196-198, *197*
relationship between muscles and, *act.* 208, *210*
strength of, 212, *212*
Bone marrow, **198**
Borax, 272-273
Boron, 272-273, *272*
Boyle, Robert, 436, 492
Boyle's law, **416,** *416,* 434, 475
Brain, 227-228, *228. See also* Nervous system
brainstem, 231
centers in, *233*
cerebellum, *228,* 229
cerebrum, 228, *228*
size of, 228, *228*
use of PET in studying, 245,*245*
Brainstem, **231**
Brakes, 153
Bread mold, *635*
Breathing, *act.* 469
Bronchial tubes, 474
Bronze, 290
Buoyancy, 26
Archimedes on, 29
and pressure, 19-24, *act.* 23
Buoyant force, **24,** 432
Butylated hydroxytoluene (BHT), 586, *586*

C

Calcite, 293, 297, 327, 332, 333
in body, 306
Calcium, 259, *259*
in body, 306
Calcium carbonate, 259
Calories, using, 184, *184*
Cameras, 521, *521*
Cancer, 558, *558*
Capillaries, **71,** 72
Carbohydrate loading, 588
Carbohydrates, 588
Carbon, 265, 267
Carbon dioxide, 71, 72
in atmosphere, 445
in circulation system, 71-72
density of, 431, *431*
Carbon monoxide, 587
effect of on body, 460
and lung disease, 486
Cardiac muscle, **206**
Cardiopulmonary resuscitation (CPR), 489
Careers
chemical oceanographers, 371
economic geologists, 307
engineers, 158
food chemists, 589
water quality engineers, 186
Cartilage, **200,** *200*
Carver, George Washington, 589
Catalyst, 584-585, **584,** *584,* 586
Catalytic converter, 392, 585, *585*
Cave exploration, 342, *342*
Cell membrane, **542,** *542,* 598-600, *act.* 598, *599,* 617, *617*
Cell walls, **547,** *547*
Cells, 531, **533**
comparison of different, 533-534, *act.* 533-534
comparison of plant and animal, *act.* 546
definition of, 532-533
discovery of, 533
division of, 536
effect of temperature on, 555, *555*
eggs as model of, *act.* 605
and energy, 607-608, 610
as living factories, 600-602
number of, in body, 535
parts of, *540, act.* 540, 541, 542-548, *543, 545, 546, act.* 546, *547*
reproduction of, *550,* 551-552, *552, act.* 553, 554
shape of, 534, *534*
size of, 534-536, *act.* 535, *act.* 538
variety in, 613-614, *act.* 613
Celsius, Anders, 168
Celsius scale, 169
Cementation, *329,* 330
Central nervous system, 226-227, *227, 231*
Cerebellum, *228,* **229**
Cerebrum, **228,** *228,* 233
Change and growth, 549-551
Charles, Jacques, 436
Charles' law, 418-419, **418,** *419*
Chemical changes
observing, 566, *act.* 566
tracing, 582
Chemical energy, 577-578, *578*
Chemical reactions, **567,** *567*
that absorb energy, 578-579, *579, act.* 581
describing, 568, *568*
energy in, 577-578, *act.* 577, *578*
inside human body, 569-570, *act.* 569
protecting objects from, 567, *567*
that release energy, 579-580, *580, act.* 581
slowing down, 585-586, *586*
speeding up, 583-585, *584*
tracing energy changes in, 582
writing word equations for, 570-571
Chemical sedimentary rocks, 331-332, *332*
Chlorine, 265, 270
Chlorofluorocarbons (CFCs), 461
Chlorophyll, 260, *260,* 585, 638
Chloroplasts, 547-548, **548,** *act.* 548
Cholesterol level, lowering of, 89
Chromosomes, **545,** *545*
visibility of, *act.* 551
Cilia, *483,* 643, **643**
Cinder cone, 51, *51*
Circulatory system, 65-68, *act.* 65
closed, 68, *68,* 72
disorders in, 82-86, *82, 83, act.* 83, *84, 85, 86*
function of, 65, 66
and importance of exercise, 85, *85*

open, 67-68, *67,* 72
and optical fiber technology, 87
pumping action of heart in, 73-74, *act.* 73, 76
role of heart and blood vessels in, 68-72
Clam, circulation in, 67-68, *67*
Cleavage, **296**
Closed circulatory system, 68, *68*
Coal
as fossil fuels, *act.* 382, 382-384, *383*
as nonrenewable resource, 389
Cobalt, *262*
Coinage metals, 261-263, **261,** *261*
Color, of minerals, 294
Colorado River, 315
Compact bone, **197,** *197,* 198
Compaction, 329
Composite cone volcano, 51-52, *52*
Compost, 306
Compound, 425-426, *425,* 427
Compound machines, 148-149, **148,** *149*
Compression, and reverse faults, 39-40, *39*
Compression wave, *act.* 43
Computers
and quartz, 309, *309*
voice-activated, 242, *242*
Concave lens, 516-517, **516,** *517*
Concave mirror, 506-507, **506,** *507,* 508-509, *508, act.* 508, *509,* 518
uses of, 507, *507*
Condenser, 556
Conduction, 173-174, **173,** *173, 174*
Conduction transfer, 454, *act.* 454
Cones, 236
Conservation, of energy, 116-117, *117, act.* 118, 119-120, *119, 120*
Construction, earthquake-proof, 57-58, *57, 58*
Consumers, 635
Continental shelf, **363**
Convection, **174,** 176
Convection current, 458
Convection transfer, 455, *455*
Convex lens, 513-516, **513,** *513, 514, 515, 516*
Convex mirror, 509-510, **509,** *510*
Copper, 263, 290, *290*
Copper sulfide, 427
Coquina, 333
Corn smut, 646
Corrosion, 576, 587, 591
Corundum, 304
Cough, 474
Cousteau, Jacques, 28, 434
Crop rotation, 306
Crystals, 300, *300, act.* 301
structure of, 287-288, *287, act.* 288
Cyanobacteria, 638-639, 640, *act.* 641
Cytoplasm, 542-544, **543,** *543*

D

Dalton, John, 423, 429
da Vinci, Leonardo, 207
Decomposition reactions, 572-573, **572,** *572*
Decompression chamber, 435, *435*
Decompression sickness, 435
Deep-sea submersible, 27
Democritus, 423
Dendrites, 224
Desalination plants, *606*
Detrital sedimentary rocks, 330-331, *330, 331*
Dialysis, *act.* 603
Diamond, 276, *276*
Diaphragm, **475**
Diastolic pressure, 88
Diatom, 642, *act.* 642
Diffusion, **603,** *act.* 603, 606
of water, 604, *604*
Digestion, 570, 579
Dirigibles, 432
Disease
role of bacteria in, 640
role of monerans in, 639, 640
role of protists in, 644
DNA, 545, *545,* 632
Dolomite, in body, 306
Ductile, **256**
Dynamite, 580

E

Earth, interior forces of, *act.* 35
Earthquake
destruction of, 47, *47*
locating epicenter, 44, *act.* 45
preparing buildings for, 57-58, *57, 58*
seismic waves in, 42-44, *act.* 43
Earthworm, 470
Efficiency, 153
Effort force, **132,** 143
Eggs, as model cells, *act.* 605
Elasticity, 56
Electricity
generation of, *act.* 379, 380-381, *380*
importance of, *act.* 377
source of, 378-379, *378, 379*
Electron microscope, 599, *600*
Elements, *act.* 253, 425
symbols for, *act.* 254, 254
Emeralds, 304
Emphysema, 484-485, **484**
End stage renal disease, 619-620, *619, 620*
Endothermic reaction, 579, **579,** *579, act.* 581, 582
Energy, 99
and cells, 607-608, 610
conservation of, 116-117, *117, act.* 118, 119-120, *119, 120*
and fuel, 100-102, *100, 101, 102*
kinetic, 106-108, *106, act.* 107, *act.* 111, 112
potential, 108-110, *108, act.* 111

solar, 188, *188*
and thermal equilibrium, 167
use of, 113-115
from work, 115
Energy resource, 393
geothermal, as alternative, 397-398, *398*
hydroelectric, as alternative, 393-395, *act.* 393
renewable, 388
solar, as alternative, 395-396, *395, 396*
wind, as alternative, 397, *397*
English system, 14
Environment
and beach erosion, 369-370, *370*
and burning of fossil fuels, 391-392, *391*
and debate over asbestos, 307-308, *307, 308*
and greenhouse effect, 459, *459*
and ocean pollution, 355-359, *355, 356, 357, 358, 359*
and ozone, 269, 446-447, 461, *461*
and recycling, *263*
and smog, 460, *460*
Environmental Protection Agency (EPA), 307
Enzymes, 584-585
Epicenter, **44**
locating an, *act.* 45, 44, *44*
Epiglottis, 473
Equilibrium, 602, 604
Euglena, *636*, 641
Eutrophication, 186
Evaporation, formation of minerals from, 302, *302, 303*
Everest, Mount, 60
Exercise
effect of, on respiration, *act.* 481
importance of, to circulatory system, 85
Exothermic reaction, 579-580, **580,** *580, act.* 581, 582, 587
Extrusive, 319-321, **319,** *320*

F

Fahrenheit, 169
Fahrenheit, G. D., 165
Fainting, 85
Fault, **38**
normal, 38-39, *38*
reverse, 39-40, *39*
strike-slip, 40-41, *40*
Fermentation, **612,** 653
Fish, use of swim bladder by, 26, *26*
Fission, **638**
Fixed ratios, in chemical reactions, 427, *427, act.* 428, 429-430, *430*
Flagella, **643**
Flat shore zones, 352, *352*
Floating, reasons for, 22-24, *22, 24*
Fluid
depth of, and pressure, *act.* 21, 20-22
displacement of, *act.* 23
Fluorine, 265, 270
Focal point, **506,** 507, *507, 508*
Focus, **43**
Foliated, **326**
Food additives, 589-590
Food and Drug Administration (FDA), 589
Food chain, 608, *608*
in the ocean, 28
Force, **14,** 25
and area, 19-20
and motion, 4-7, *act.* 6-7, 9-11
balanced and unbalanced, 14-15
centripetal, 25
effort, 132, 143
measurement of, *act.* 15
resistance, 132, 143
types of, 55
weight as, 16, *16*
Force transducer, 30
Fossil fuels, **384**
availability of, 388
coal as, 382-384, *act.* 382, *383*
costs in burning of, 391-392, *391*
natural gas as, 384-385, *385,* 387
as nonrenewable, 389
oil as, *act.* 386, 384-385, *384, 385,* 387, *387*
Fracture, **296**
Freon, 187
Friction, as force, *act.* 10
Fulcrum, 205
Fungi, **636,** 645-646, *645*
characteristics of, *act.* 645
effect of, on living things, 646, *646*
life needs of, 648
reproduction of, *act.* 648

G

Gabbro, *321,* 323
Gagnan, Emile, 434
Galapagos Rift, 28
Galilei, Galileo, 165
Galvanized steel, 591
Gas
density of, 431, *431*
description of, *act.* 420, 420-421
effect of temperature on pressure and volume of, 417-419
movement by, *act.* 413
particle movement in, *act.* 421
properties of, 412-413, *412*
relating pressure and volume, 414, *414, act.* 415, 416
relationship between pressure and temperature, 421-422, *act.* 421
Gas laws, 436
Gas mask, 490
Gay-Lussac, Joseph, 436
Gem, 288-289, **289,** *289*
Generator, **381,** *381*
Geothermal energy, 397-398, **398,** *398*

Gerontologists, 559
Gill filaments, 472, *472*
Gills, **471**
Global warming, 392
Global winds, 455-456
  local winds, 457-458, *458*
  prevailing westerlies, 456-457,*457*
  trade winds, 456, *456*
Glucose, 207
Gneiss, 325, 326, 330
Gold, 262, 290, 294, *294,* 295
  value of, 278
Goldfish, *471*
Gold rush, 310, *310*
Gorrie, John, 187
Grand Canyon, *314,* 315, 323
Granite, *act.* 316-317, *317,* 323, 330
Graphite, 276, 290
Grasshopper, respiration in, 487
Gravitational potential energy, 109-110, *109*
Gravity, *14*
  and acceleration, 11, *11*
  force of, 109
  pull of, 15
Green algae, 641
Greenhouse effect, 391-392, *act.* 453, **454,** *454*
Gypsum, 290

H

Habitat destruction, in shore zones, 359-360
Hales, Stephen, 74
Halite, 290, 300
Hardness, of minerals, 292-293, **292,** *292, 293*
Harvey, William, 71, *71*
Health
  metals dangerous to, 261
Heart
  parts of, *act.* 68, 69-70, *69*
  pumping action of, 73-74, *act.* 73, 76
  sounds of, *act.* 70
Heart disease, 82-83
Heart valves, problems of, 90
Heat, **170**
  latent, 183
  as a transfer of energy, 170, *170*
  use of work to transfer, 181-182
  work from, 179-180, *act.* 179
Heat engine, **179**
  inefficiency in, *act.* 179, 180
Heat transfer
  and conduction, 454, *act.* 454
  and convection, 455, *455*
  minimizing, 177-178, *177, 178*
  through radiation, 453-454, *act.* 453
Heimlich maneuver, 489, *act.* 489
Helium, 270
Hemodialysis, 619-620, 622, *622*
Hemodialyzer, 622
Hemoglobin, **478,** 486
Herbicides, 358-359, *358*
High blood pressure, 84
Himalaya Mountains, 39, *39*
  climates of, 60, *60*
Hooke, Robert, 533
Hornblende, *317,* 327
Hualalai, 50
Hubble space telescope, 523-524, *523, 524*
Human body
  chemical reactions inside, *act.* 569, 569-570
  effect of carbon dioxide on, 460
  as machine, 154, *154*
  metals in your, 259-260, *259*
  minerals in the, 306, *306*
Human-powered vehicles (HPVs), 155-156, *155, 156,* 158, *158*
Hurricane, destruction in, 56, *56*
Hydroelectric, **393**
Hydroelectric energy, as alternative energy resource, 393-395, *act.* 393
Hydrogen, 265, 266, *266*
Hypertension, **84,** *84*

I

Ice, melting of, *act.* 175
Igneous rock, **318**
  classifying, 321, *321, act.* 322, 323, *323*
  formation of, 336
Impulse, 223-224
  speed of, 225
Inclined plane, 137-138, *137,* **137,** *138,* 157, *157*
Industry, diamonds in, 276
Inertia, *act.* 3, **5,** *6*
  and mass, 6-7, 9
Inertial balance, **9**
Inertial mass, measuring, *act.* 8, 8
Infant, learning by, 246, *246*
Inhibitor, **586,** *586*
Insecticides, 358-359, *358*
Interactions, that push or pull, 9-10, *9*
Intrusive rocks, **319,** *319*
Involuntary activities, 231
Iron, 258, 259-260, *262,* 306
  in body, 306
  evolution of, 305
Iron oxide, 571-572

J

Jansky, Karl, 522
Jewelry, metalworking in, 279, *279*
Jewels, value of, *act.* 285
Jirsa, James D., 58
Joints, **201,** *201*
  movements allowed by, *act.* 202, 203-204, *203*
  need for, *act.* 201
Jones, Frederick McKinley, 187

Joule, 105
Joule, James Prescott, 105, 126, *126*

K

Kidney transplantation, 620
Kilauea, 49, *49*, 50, *54*
Kinetic energy, 106-108, *106*, **107**, *act.* 107, 112, 121
Kohala, 50

L

Labradorite, 321
Larynx, 473, 488, *488*
Latent heat, 183
Lava, 303
  rhyolitic, 337
Law of capture, 339
Law of Conservation of Energy, 117, 119-120, **119**
Law of definite proportions, 427, *act.* 428
Lead, 261
Lens
  concave, 516-517, *517*
  effect of light on, *act.* 511
  objectives, 518
  and vision, 525, *525*
Lever, 132-134, *act.* 133, **134**, *134*
  in body, *act.* 205
  length of and force needed, *act.* 143-144
  measuring mass with, *act.* 146
Life expectancy, 559-560
Lifestyle, moderation of, 89-90
Ligaments, **202**, *202*
Light
  angles of reflection, *act.* 503
  behavior of, *act.* 501-502
  effect of lenses on, *act.* 511
  reflection of, 500-502, *501*, 504, *504*
  refraction of, 511-513, *512*, *act.* 514
Light microscope, 556, *556*
Limestone, 330, 332
Liver, 619
Living things, composition of, *act.* 531
Local winds, 457-458, *458*
Longshore current, **350**, *351*
Lung cancer, 307, 485-486, **485**, *485*
Lung capacity, measurement of, 476
Lung disease, 483-486, *483*, *485*
  and asbestos, 307, 308, *307*, *308*
Lungs, 72, *72*, **474**, *474*
Luster, of minerals, 293-294, *293*

M

Machine
  compound, 148-149, *149*
  human body as, 154, *154*
  inclined plane as, 137-138, *137*, *138*
  lever as, *act.* 133, 132-134, *134*, *142*
  in making jobs easier, *act.* 131, 132, *152*
  mechanical advantage of, 142-145, *142*, *143*, *144*, *145*, *act.* 146, 147, *147*
  and power, 149-150, *act.* 151
  pulley as, 135-137, *136*, *act.* 136, 137
  screws as, 138-140, *140*
  using, 148-150, 152
  wedges as, 140-141, *141*
  wheel and axle as, 134-135, *134*, *135*
Magma, 48, 50-51, 300
  formation of minerals from, 303-304, *304*
  movement of, *act.* 48
Magnesium, 260, *260*
Magnetite, 297
  in body, 306
Malleable, **255**
Manometer, 88
Many-celled organisms, 614, 630, *630*
Marble, 327, *327*
Marianas Trench, 366, *366*
Marine life
  adaptation of, in rift zones, 368
  and habitat destruction, 359-360
  and rescue of whales, 372, *372*
Marionettes, *act.* 193
Mars, atmosphere of, 451-452, *451*
Mass, 6-7
  and acceleration, *act.* 13
  and inertia, 6-7, 9
  measuring with levers, *act.* 146
Matter, composition of, 426
Mauna Kea, 50
Mauna Loa, 50
Mechanical advantage, **143**
  of machines, 142-145, *142*, *143*, *act.* 143-144, *144*, *145*, *act.*, 146, 147, *147*
Mechanical energy, conversion to thermal energy, *act.* 379, 380-381, *380*
Mercury, 261
Mesosphere, 447, *447*
Metallic luster, 294
Metalloids, **272**
  boron, 272-273, *272*
  properties of, 272
  silicon, 273-274
Metals, **255**
  health dangers of, 261
  identifying, *act.* 255, *act.* 257
  prices of precious, *278*
  properties of, 255-256, *255*, *256*, 258, *258*
  in your body, 259-260, *259*
Metalworking, in jewelry, 279, *279*
Metamorphic rock, **325**
  classifying, 326-327
  comparison of nonmetamorphic rocks and, *act.* 325-326

exposure to pressure, *act.* 324-325
formation of, 324-326, *326,* 335, 336
Meters, 105
Mica, *317*
Microchips, 309
Microorganisms, **630,** *630*
Microscope, 520, 532
electron, 599, *600*
light, 556, *556*
scanning electron, 539
transmission electron, 539
using, *act.* 532, 557, *557*
Mid-ocean ridges, **365**
Milk, spoilage of, *act.* 637
Mineral supplements, elements in, *act.* 274
Minerals, 285, **286,** *286*
in the body, 306, *306*
characteristics of, 291
clear, *act.* 296, *297*
cleavage of, 296
color of, 294
cooling of, *act.* 318
crystals of, 300, *300, act.* 301
formation of, from cooling magma, 303-304, *304*
formation of, from evaporation, 302, *302, 303*
fracture of, 296
gems as, 288-289, *289*
hardness of, 292-293, *292, 293*
identifying, *act.* 291, *act.* 293
interior crystal structure of, *act.* 303
luster of, 293-294, *293*
metal and nonmetal, 290
mining, in rift zones, 367, *367*
nonmetallic, 290
properties of, 287-288, *287, act.* 288, 296-297
recycling, 306
streak of, 295-296
using physical properties to identify, 297, *act.* 298, 299
Mirrors
concave, 506-507, *507, 509,* 510, 518
convex, 509-510, *510*
curved, 505-510, *act.* 505, *act.* 508
reflection in, *act.* 499, 500-502, *act.* 500, *501*
Mitochondria, 545-546, **545,** *546,* 610, *610,* 612
Mitosis, *act.* 553, 551, **552,** *552,* 554
Mohs, Friedrich, 292
Mohs scale, 292
Mold
experimenting with, 649, *649*
growing conditions for, *act.* 647
Molecule, 425-426, *425, 426*
movement of, 602-603, *602*
Monera, **636,** 637-638, *act.* 637, *638*
characteristics of, 638-639
effect of, on other living things, 639-640, *639*
Monosodium glutamate (MSG), 589
Morgan, Garrett, 490
Mosquito larvae, respiration in, 487
Motion, 193
definition of, 7
and force, 4-7, 9-11, *act.* 10
Newton's first law of, 7
Newton's second law of, 12, *12,* 14-16
Newton's third law of, 17-18
Motor nerves, 232, 233
Multiple proportions, law of, 430
Muscle cells, 540
Muscle tone
increasing, 210
maintaining, 216, *216*
Muscles, 209
action in, 206-207, 209
number of, in body, 207
relationship between bones and, *act.* 208, 209-210, *210*
and skeletal motion, 205-206, *act.* 205
types of, 206, *206*
Mushroom, *635*

N

National Aeronautics and Space Administration (NASA), 491
National Center for Earthquake Engineering Research (NCEER), 57
Natural gas
as fossil fuel, 384-385, *385,* 387
predicting reserves of, *act.* 390
Natural resource, 388
Neon, 270, 271
Neon lights, 280, *280*
Nerve cells, *534,* 540
Nerves, 224
motor, 232, 233
sensory, *232,* 233
Nervous system. *See also* Brain
central, 226-227, *227*
movement of information through, *act.* 224
neurons in, 223-225, *225*
peripheral, 231-233, *232*
response of, to stimulus, *act.* 226-227
role of, 222-223, *223*
Neurons, 223-225, **224,** 225
Nevado del Ruiz, 54
Newton, Isaac, 12, *14,* 24
first law of motion of, 7
second law of motion of, 12, *12,* 14-16
third law of motion of, 17-18
Newtonmeter, 105
Newtons, **14,** 105
Nickel, 262-263, *262*
Nitrogen, 265, 266-267, *267*
Noble gases, 270-271
Nonfoliated, **327**
Nonmetallic luster, 294
Nonmetallic minerals, 290

Nonmetals, **264**
identifying, *act.* 264
properties of, *act.* 265, 264-267, 269
Nonmetamorphic rocks, comparison of metamorphic rocks and, *act.* 325-326
Nonrenewable resources, **389**
Normal fault, 38, **38,** *38*
Northover, William, 87
Nostrils, 473
Nucleus, 544-545, *act.* 544, **545**

O

Objective lens, 518
Obsidian, 320-321, *320,* 337, *337*
Ocean currents, 363
Ocean floor
adaptation of marine life in rift zones, 368, *368*
exploring, 361-362, 434-435
features of, 362-363, *363,* 365-366, *365, 366*
mining minerals in rift zones, 367, *367*
profile, *act.* 364
Offshore oil, 371, *371*
Oil
as fossil fuel, 384-385, *384, 385, act.* 386, 387, *387*
reaction with water, *act.* 385
seismic waves in searching for, 59, *59*
Oil spills, 356-357, *357*
cleanup of, *act.* 357-358, 640, 650, *650*
One-celled organism, 614, 629, *629*
Opal, 273, *273*
Open circulatory system, 67, *67*
Optic nerve, 236
Optical fiber technology, 87
Organ, **615**
Organ systems, **615**
Organic sedimentary rocks, 332
Organism, 615-616, **615,** 634
classification of, 634-636, *act.* 634
comparison of, *act.* 628-629
levels of organization, 614-616, *615*
many-celled, 614, 630, *630*
one-celled, 614, 629, *629*
Ortiz, Simon, 463
Osmosis, **604,** *604,* 606
Osteoporosis, 197
Oxygen, 265, 267, 269
in atmosphere, *act.* 443
in circulatory system, 72
discovery of, 492
preparing and observing, *act.* 268
Ozone, 269, 446-447, **446**
in atmosphere, 446, 461, *461*

P

Palladium, 585
Paramecium, 470, *470, 635,* 643
comparison of *Ulva* with, *act.* 628
Parasites, 646
Pascal, Blaise, 22
Pascal's Principle, 22, 76
Pasteur, Louis, 653
Pasteurization, 637-638, 653
Peña, Sylvia C., 372
Pencil, 276
Pendulum, motion of, *act.* 118, 119, *119*
Penicillium, 646
Pepsin, 585
Percussing, *act.* 484
Periosteum, 196
Peripheral nervous system, 231-233, *232*
Periscope, 526, *526*
Perpetual motion, search for, 123-124, *123*
PET (positron emission tomography), 233, 245, *245*
Pets, teaching tricks to, 241
Pharynx, 473
Photography, 521
Photosynthesis, 306, 571, *571,* 578-579, *579,* 584, *584*
Physical fitness, 212-213, *213*
Physical properties, in identifying minerals, *act.* 298, 297, 299
Pig iron, 305, 587
Pinatubo, Mount, 49, 54
Plane mirror, 500-501, **500**
Plant cells
chloroplasts in, *act.* 548, 547-548
comparison to animal cells, *act.* 546
Plant stem cells, *534*
Plants, role of, in air purification, 491
Plasmodium, 644
Platinum, 585
Pollution, **355**
air, 391-392, *391,* 442, *442,* 444-445, 585
in shore zones, 355-359, *355, 356, 357, 358, 359*
thermal, 185-186, *185, 186*
Positron emission tomography (PET), 233, 245, *245*
Potential energy, 108-110, *108,* **109,** *act.* 111, 121
conversion of, to kinetic energy, 122
elastic, 112-113
Pound, 14
Powell, John Wesley, 315
Power, 149-150, **150,** 151
calculating, *act.* 151
measuring, *act.* 152
Pressure, **19**
and buoyancy, 19-24, *act.* 19
cooking under, 435, *435*
and weight, *act.* 19
Prevailing westerlies, 456-457, **457,** *457*
Priestley, Joseph, 471
Producers, 635
Products, **570**
Protista, **636**

Protists, 66, 640-641
animal-like, 642-644
effect of, on living things, 644
plantlike, 641-642, *642*
Protozoans, characteristics of, *act.* 643
Pseudopods, 643
Pulley, **135,** 135-137, *136, act.* 136, *137*
Pulse, 74, **74**
taking, 73, *act.* 73
Pulse rate, 74, *act.* 75
Pumice, 320-321, *320*
Pyrite, 294, *294,* 295
in body, 306
Pyroxene, 321

Q

Quartz, 293, *317*
and computers, 309, *309*
Quicksilver, 261

R

Radiation, **176,** *176*
heat transfer through, 453-454, *act.* 453
Radio telescope, 522, *522*
Radiographs, *486*
Reactants, **570**
Reaction force, 17-18, **17,** *18*
Reaction time, *act.* 230
Real image, **506**
Receptors, 240
Recycling, *263*
of aluminum, 277, *277*
of minerals, 306
Reflection
angles of, *act.* 503
in mirror, *act.* 499, 500-502, *act.* 500
Reflex, 238-240, *act.* 238, **239,** *239, 240*
Reflex arcs, 239-240
Refracting telescope, 518, *act.* 519
Refraction, **512,** *act.* 514
Refrigerators, 181-182, *act.* 181, *182,* 187, *187*
Renal disease, end stage, 619-620, *619, 620*
Renewable resource, **388**
Research, balloons in, 432, *432*
Resistance force, **132,** 143
Resources
nonrenewable, 389
renewable, 388
Respiration, **480,** 482, 569-570, **608,** *act.* 609
aerobic, 620-621
anaerobic, 621
chemical reaction of, 618, *618*
effect of exercise on, *act.* 481
and temperature, *act.* 611, 612
Respiratory system
air pathway in, 472-474
breathing process in, *act.* 469, 470-472
comparing inhaled with exhaled air, 479-480
delivery of oxygen to body, 478-479
disorders of, 483-486, *485*
exhalation in, 477, *477, act.* 479
in humans, 472-475, 477
inhalation in, 475, *477*
in lesser organisms, 470-472, *470*
and lifesaving techniques, 489, *489*
lung capacity in, *act.* 476
Responses, 223
Retina, 556
Reverse fault, 39-40, **39,** *39*
Rhyolite, *321,* 323
Rhyolitic lava, 337
Rickets, 197, *197*
Rift zone, **365**
adaptation of marine life in, 368, *368*
mining minerals at, 367, *367*
Ringworm, 646
Robot arms, 214, *214*
Rock cycle, 335-336, **335,** *336*
Rock salt, 332, *332*
Rockies, history of, 323
Rocks, **317**
in animal diet, 338, *338*
characteristics of, *act.* 315, *act.* 316-317
collecting, 341, *341*
igneous, 316-318, *317*
classifying, 321, *321, act.* 322, 323, *323*
extrusive, 319-321, *320*
intrusive, 319, *319*
metamorphic, 324-326, *act.* 325
classifying, 326-327, *327*
ownership of, 339-340
sedimentary, 328-330, *329, act.* 334
classifying, 330-333, 335
Rods, 236
Rubies, 304
Rust, *act.* 565, 571-572, 580, 591

S

Saint Helens, Mount, 49, *49*
Salt, 589
impact of, on living things, *act.* 597
Salt water, 597
San Andreas fault, 34, 35, *40,* 41
Sand, 273, *act.* 347
beach, *act.* 353, 354, *354*
Sandstone, 331, *331, act.* 347
Sapphires, 304
Scanning electron microscopes, 539
Schleiden, Matthias, 533
Schwann, Theodor, 533
Scoria, 320-321, *320*
Scorpions, respiration in, 487
Screw, 138-140, **140,** *140*
Screwdriver, 139, *139, act.* 139

SCUBA (Self-Contained Underwater Breathing Apparatus), 434
Sedimentary rock, **328,** *328*
  chemical, 331-332, *332*
  classifying, 330, *act.* 334
  detrital, 330-331, *330, 331*
  formation of, *act.* 329, 328-330, *329,* 335-336
  organic, 332
Sediments, 328
Seismic waves, 42-44, **43,** *act.* 43, *44*
  and search for oil, 59, *59*
Seismograph, 44, 45
Semiconductors, *273*
Senses, 234-236, *235,* 238
  importance of, *act.* 234
Sensory nerves, *232,* 233
Sequoia tree, *635*
Serpentine, 327
Shale, 331
Shasta Dam, 394, *394*
Shearing, 40-41
Shield volcano, 51-52, *51*
Shock, 85-86, *85*
Shore zones
  and beach erosion, 369-370, *370*
  changes in, 348-350, *348, 349, act.* 349, *350, 351*
  flat, 352, *352*
  habitat destruction in, 359-360
  pollution in, 355-359, *355, 356, 357, act.* 357-358, *358, 359*
  steep, 351-352, *352*
Shoreline, impact of waves on, *act.* 349, 350
Sight, sense of, 236
Silica, 337
Silicon, 273-274
Silicon chips, 309
Silver, 262, 290
Single displacement reactions, 573-574, **574,** *act.* 575, *576*
Skeletal motion, 205-206, *act.* 205
Skeletal muscles, **206,** *act.* 208
Skeletal system, 194-196, *act.* 194, *195*
Skin, senses in, *236*
Skin cancer, 558, *558*
Skin sensitivity, testing for, *act.* 237
Skull, *204*
Slate, 326, *327*
Slingslot effect, 122, *122*
Smell, sense of, 235, *235*
Smog, **444,** 460, *460*
Smoking
  as health hazard, 483,485
  and lung diseases, 484-486, *485*
Smooth muscle, **206**
Sodium chloride, 573, *573*
Solar cell, **396,** *396*
Solar energy, 188, *188,* 395-396, *395, 396*
Sonar, 27-28, 362
Soong, T. T., 58
Spectroscopy, 266
Spelunking, 342, *342*
Sphygmomanometer, 88
Spiders, respiration in, 487
Spinal cord, **231,** *231*
Sponges, 67
  circulation in, 67, *67*
Spongy bone, *197,* **197**
Steel, 587
  galvanized, 591
Steep shore zones, 351-352, *352*
Stethoscope, *act.* 70, 70, 82, *82*
Stimulus, 223
  in infant, 246, *246*
  nervous system response to, *act.* 226-227
Streak, **295**, 295-296
Streak test, *act.* 295, 296
Streaming, 67
Strike-slip fault, 40-41, **40,** *40*
Stroke, *84*
Substance
  relationship between size of and distance to center, 536-537, *act.* 536
Sulfur, 265, *270*
Surgery, open heart, *90,* 91
Swim bladder, in fish, 26, *26*
Synapse, **225**
Synthesis reactions, 571-572, **571,** *571*
Systolic pressure, 88

T

Table salt, 573, *573*
Taste, sense of, 235, *235*
Tea bags, *act.* 601
Telescope, radio, 522, *522*
Temperature
  changing, *act.* 166
  effect of, on cells, 555
  effect of, on gas pressure and volume, 417-419
  and respiration, *act.* 611, 612
Temperature inversion, 460
Temperature scales, 168-169, *act.* 168
Tendons, **206**
Tension, and normal faults, 38-39, *38*
THA, 244
Thermal energy, 163, *act.* 163. *See also* Heat
  conversion to mechanical energy, *act.* 379, 380-381, *380*
  definition of, 171
  in muscles, 207
  and temperature scales, 168-169, *act.* 168, 169
  and thermal equilibrium, 164-167
  transfer of, 172-173, *act.* 172
Thermal equilibrium, 164-167, *act.* 166, **167**
Thermal pollution, 185-186, *185, 186*
Thermogram, *177*
Thermometer, work of heat in, 171, *act.* 171
Thermoscope, 165, *165*
Thermosphere, 447, *447*
Thermostats, 275, *275*
Tissues, 614-615, **614**
Topaz, 304

Touch, sense of, 164-165, *act.* 164, 236
Trachea, **471,** *act.* 473
Trade winds, 456, **456,** *456*
Transducer, 30
Transmission electron microscope (TEM), 539
Transplantation, kidney, 620
Transverse wave, 42, *act.* 43
Triceps, 210
Troposphere, **446**
Trypanosoma, 644, *644*
Trypsin, 585
Turbine, 380-381, **380**

U

Ulva, 635
  comparison of paramecium with, *act.* 628
Unbalanced forces, 17
Universe, composition of, *act.* 266
Unzen, Mount, 54
Urban living, and lung disease, 486
Urea, 619

V

Vaccines, 651-652, *651, 652*
Vacuole, 544
Vacuum, 433, *433*
Valves, 70
Veins, **71,** 302
Velocity, 4-5
Ventricles, 68, 69
Vents, **49**
Venus, atmosphere of, 451-452, *451*
Virtual image, **510,** *510*
Virus DNA, 632
Viruses, 630, 632-633, **632,** *632, 635*
  reproduction of, 632
  shapes of, *act.* 631
Vision, and lenses, 525, *525*
Voice-activated computers, 242, *242*
Volcanoes
  analyzing, *act.* 53
  causes of eruptions, 48-49
  impact of, on people, 54
  movement of magma, *act.* 48
  selected eruptions, *52*
  types of eruptions, 49-51, *49, 50*
Voluntary activities, 231
von Linde, Karl, 187

W

Water
  composition of, *act.* 424-425
  reaction with oil, *act.* 385
Watt, **150**
Waves, impact of, on shoreline, *act.* 349, 350
Wedge, 140-141, **141,** *141*
Weight, **16**
  as force, 16, *16*
  and pressure, *act.* 19
Whales, rescue of, *372*
Wheat rust, 646
Wheel and axle, 134-135, *134,* **135,** *135*
Williams, Daniel Hale, 91
Wind energy, 397, *397*
Wong-Staal, Flossie, 652
Word equations, writing, 570-571
Work, 100, *100,* 103-105, *act.* 103, **104,** *104, 105*
  definition of, 99, *act.* 99
  energy from, 115
  from heat, 179-180, *act.* 179
  storage of, *act.* 112, 113, *113*
  use of work to transfer heat, 181-182
Wrigglers, respiration in, 487

X

Xenon, 270

Y

Yeast, 627, *act.* 627
Yeast cell, 535

Photo Credits

xx, AP/Wide World Photos, (inset, l), Space Biosphere Ventures, (inset, r), Peter Menzell/Space Biosphere Ventures; **xxi** (t), NASA/Science Source/Photo Researchers, (b), NASA; **xxii** (t), Robert Fridenstine, (lb), Frank Balthis; **xxiii,** Mak 1; **xxiv,** Stock Imagery; **1,** H. Armstrong Roberts; **2,** Brian Parker/Tom Stack & Associates; **3,** Studiohio; **4,** Doug Martin; **6,** (t) Kenji Kerins, (b) Ralph Brunke; **7,** ©Bill Sanderson/SPL/Photo Researchers; **8,** Ken Ferguson; **9,** (t) Ralph Brunke, (b) Focus on Sports; **10,** (t) David R. Frazier Photolibrary, (b) Kenji Kerins; **14,** Kenji Kerins; **15,** Ken Ferguson; **16,** Studiohio; **17,** National Rifle Association of America; **19,** Ken Ferguson; **20,** (l) Maria Teghenti/The Image Bank, (r) H. Armstrong Roberts; **21,** Ralph Brunke; **22,** Doug Martin; **24,** (l) Tony Freeman/PhotoEdit, (r) George Mars Cassidy/Tony Stone Worldwide; **25,** David Madison/Duomo Photography; **27,** (t) ©Norbert Way/Peter Arnold, Inc., (b) Emory Kristof/National Geographic Society; **28,** UPI/Bettmann Newsphotos; **30,** Tim Courlas; **31,** (t) National Highway Administration, (b) NASA; **32,** Holt Confer/Grant Heilman; **33,** H. Armstrong Roberts; **34,** H. Armstrong Roberts/E.R. Degginger; **35,** Studiohio; **36,** Kenji Kerins; **37,** G.R. Roberts; **38,** Greg Vaughn/Tom Stack & Associates; **39,** Earth Scenes/Mike Andrews; **40,** Kevin Schafer/Tom Stack & Associates; **41, 42,** Kenji Kerins; **48,** Ken Ferguson; **49,** (t) Keith Ronnholm, (b) ©James Summerhays/Photo Researchers; **50,** Ken Frick; **51,** Earth Scenes/Breck P. Kent; **52,** ©David Weintraub/Photo Researchers; **53,** Doug Martin; **54,** ©K & M Krefft/Photo Researchers; **55,** Kenji Kerins; **56,** (t) Christopher Harris/SuperStock, (b) David Young-Wolff/PhotoEdit; **57,** Burri Hartman/Magnum; **58,** ©David Parker/Photo Researchers;**59,** (l) Comstock/Boyd Norton, (r) David R. Frazier Photolibrary; **61,** (l) Manfred Gottschalk/Tom Stack & Associates, (c) ©Otto Hahn/Peter Arnold, Inc., (r) Anna E. Zuckerman/Tom Stack & Associates; **64,** Kenji Kerins; **65,** Ralph Brunke; **66,** ©Biophoto Associates/Photo Researchers; **67,** ©Fred Bavendam/Peter Arnold, Inc.; **69,** Yoav Levy PhotoTake; **70,** Kenji Kerins; **71,** Bettmann Archives; **73,** Kenji Kerins; **74,** Michael Newman/PhotoEdit; **76,** (t) Kenji Kerins, (b) Ralph Brunke; **77,** Ralph Brunke; **81,** H. Armstrong Roberts; **82,** Steven Burr Williams/The Image Bank; **83,** (t) Ken Ferguson, (bl,bc) Custom Medical Stock Photo, (br) ©Biophoto Associates/Photo Researchers; **84,** Studiohio; **85,** (t) ©Warren Morgan/Westlight, (b) Robert Brenner/PhotoEdit; **86,** Kenji Kerins; **87,** M. English/Custom Medical Stock Photo; **88,** (t) L. Steinmark/Custom Medical Stock Photo, (b) David R. Frazier Photolibrary; **89,** (l) Barry L. Runk/Grant Heilman, (tr) Tony Freeman/PhotoEdit, (br) David Young-Wolff/PhotoEdit; **90,** Marka/Custom Medical Stock Photo; **91,** Historical Pictures Service; **92,** Courtesy of Tamika Walker; **93,** Bob Daemmrich/Tony Stone Worldwide; **96,** Kevin Schafer/Tom Stack & Associates; **97,** H. Armstrong Roberts/Mick Roessler; **98,** BLT Productions; **99,** Kenji Kerins; **100,** (l) Comstock/Ed Pieratt, (c) Comstock, (r) Focus on Sports; **101,** David Dennis; **102,** Ron Grishaber/PhotoEdit; **103,** Ralph Brunke; **104,** (t) Kenji Kerins, (b) Studiohio; **106,** Comstock/Denver Bryan; **107,** Tony Freeman/PhotoEdit; **108,** (t) Kenji Kerins, (b) E.R. Degginger/Color-Pic; **109,** (l) David Young-Wolff/PhotoEdit, (r) John Gerlach/Tom Stack & Associates; **112,** Ralph Brunke; **113,** (l) Focus on Sports, (c) Joe Strunk, (r) Studiohio; **114,** Runk/Schoenberger/Grant Heilman; **115,** Tim Courlas; **116,** Ken Ferguson; **117,** (t) Peter Marlon/Magnum, (b) Dan Helms/Duomo Photography; **118,** Ralph Brunke; **120,** Focus on Sports; **121,** Aaron Haupt; **122,** NASA; **124, 126,** (l) Bettmann Archives, (r) Paul Zitzewitz; **127,** (tl) NASA, (tr) First Image, (bl) Doug Martin, (br) ©Porterfield/Chickering/Photo Researchers; **128,** Studiohio; **129,** Focus on Sports; **130,** H. Armstrong Roberts/J. Moss; **131,** Ken Frick; **132, 133,** Kenji Kerins; **134,** (l) Steve Lissau, (c) Ken Frick, (r) Studiohio; **136,** Doug Martin; **137,** Edward Lee/Tony Stone Worldwide; **138,** ©Helmut Gritscher/Peter Arnold, Inc.; **139,** Ken Ferguson; **141,** Tony Freeman/PhotoEdit; **142,** David R. Frazier Photolibrary; **143,** Lefever/Grus-how/Grant Heilman; **144,** (t) Ken Ferguson, (b) Kenji Kerins; **145,** Hickson & Associates; **146, 148,** Kenji Kerins; **150,** Ralph Brunke; **151,** Ken Ferguson; **152,** Aron Haupt; **153,** Kenji Kerins; **154,** (t) SIU/Custom Medical Stock Photo, (b) SPL/Custom Medical Stock Photo; **155,** C. Michael Lewis; **156,** (b) C. Michael Lewis, (t) Ken Ferguson; **157,** (t) Tony Freeman/PhotoEdit, (b) ©Ron & Kris Liss/Peter Arnold, Inc.; **158,** Courtesy of Stephanie Ostler; **162,** John Warde/SuperStock; **163,** Ken Ferguson; **164,** Kenji Kerins; **165,** (l) Tony Freeman/PhotoEdit, (r) Alan Oddie/PhotoEdit; **167,** Kenji Kerins; **169,** David R. Frazier Photolibrary; **170,** Kenji Kerins; **172, 173, 174,** Ralph Brunke; **177,** ©NASA/Science Source/Photo Researchers; **178,** H. Armstrong Roberts/E.R. Degginger; **181,** Comstock/M. & C. Werner; **183,** Ralph Brunke; **184,** Tony Freeman/PhotoEdit; **185,** Courtesy of Dr. Otis Brown/Rosentiel School of Marine & Atmospheric Science, University of Miami; **186,** (t) Susan Van Etten/PhotoEdit, (b) Bob Winslow/Tom Stack & Associates; **187,** Bettmann Archives; **188,** Ulrike Welsch/PhotoEdit; **189,** Kenji Kerins; **190,** ©Chuck O'Rear/Westlight; **191,** First Image; **192,** SuperStock; **193,** From *Make and Do*, Volume II of *Childcraft-The How and Why Library.* ©1987 World Book, Inc. By permission of the publisher; **194,** Ken Ferguson; **195,** Hedrich-Blessing, Inc.; **196,** (t) ©Franke Keating/Photo Researchers, (b) Kenji Kerins; **197,** ©Biophoto Associates/Photo Researchers; **198,** Tony Freeman/PhotoEdit; **200,** ©Biophoto Associates/Photo Researchers; **201,** Kenji Kerins; **202,** David R. Frazier Photolibrary; **203,** Hickson & Associates; **205,** Kenji Kerins; **206,** (l,r) Runk/Schoenberger/Grant Heilman, (c) ©Michael Abbey/Science Source/Photo Researchers; **207,** Bettmann Archives; **208,** Kenji Kerins; **209,** Ralph Brunke; **211,** Ken Ferguson; **212,** Ralph Brunke; **213,** (t) Michael Newman/PhotoEdit, (c) ©Martha Cooper/Peter Arnold, Inc., (b) Tony Freeman/PhotoEdit; **214,** Hank Morgan/Rainbow; **215,** Custom Medical Stock Photo; **216,** Courtesy of Jennifer November; **220,** Doug Martin; **221,** Myrleen Ferguson/PhotoEdit; **222,** ©Jerry Wachter/Photo Researchers; **223,** (t) Doug Martin, (b) Comstock/D. MacTavish; **224,** (t) Leestima/Custom Medical Stock Photo, (b) F. Stuart Westmorland/Tom Stack & Associates; **226,** ©Photo Researchers; **227,** Kenji Kerins; **229,** Doug Martin; **232,** Kenji Kerins; **233,** ©M. Raichle/Peter Arnold, Inc.; **234,** Kenji Kerins; **235,** (t) ©Martha Cooper/Peter Arnold, Inc., (bl) Lennart Nilsson/*Behold Man*/Little, Brown & Co., (br) ©Cecil Fox/Science Source/Photo Researchers; **237, 238,** Kenji Kerins; **239,** (tl,tr) Runk/Schoenberger/Grant Heilman, (b) Kenji Kerins; **241,** David DeLossy/The Image Bank; **242,** IBM/PhotoEdit; **243,** SIU/Custom Medical Stock Photo; **244,** Alvis Uppitus/The Image Bank; **245,** Peter Arnold, Inc; **246,** Myrleen Ferguson/PhotoEdit; **249,** Richard Hutchings/PhotoEdit; **250,** Doug Martin; **251,** Kenji Kerins; **252,** H. Armstrong Roberts/G. Keller; **253,** Ralph Brunke; **255,** Kenji Kerins, **255,** (t) Matt Meadows; **256,** (t) Phil Degginger, (b) Chip Clark; **257,** Kenji Kerins; **258,** Toyofumi Mori/The Image Bank; **259,** Ken Ferguson; **260,** (t) Ken Ferguson, (c,br) Michael Newman /PhotoEdit, (bl) Alan Oddie/PhotoEdit; **261,** Doug Martin; **262,** Ralph Brunke; **263,** Aluminum Company of America; **264, 265,** Kenji Kerins; **266,** UPI/Bettmann Archives; **267,** (t) ©Hugh Spencer/Photo Researchers, (b) General Electric Research and Development Center; **268,** Doug Martin; **269,** NASA; **270,** (t) Doug Martin, (bl) NASA, (br) Steve Vidler/SuperStock; **271,** ©Carl Purcell/Photo Researchers; **272,** (l) NASA, (r) Ken Ferguson; **273,** (t) Comstock/Russ Kinne, (b) Comstock/M. & C. Werner; **274,** Matt Meadows; **276,** ©Spencer Grant/Photo Researchers; **277,** (t) Erik Leigh Simmons/The Image Bank, (b) Tony Freeman/PhotoEdit; **278,** ©Dieter Blum/Peter Arnold, Inc.; **279,** PhotoEdit; **280,** (t) Paul Conklin/PhotoEdit, (b) Stanley Schoenberger /Grant Heilman; **281,** (tr) Ann Duncan/Tom Stack & Associates, (c) Robert Brenner/PhotoEdit, (bl) ©Astrid & Hans Frieder Michler/Photo Researchers, (br) Pictures Unlimited; **282,** Doug Martin; **283,** Kenji Kerins; **284,** Elena Rooraid/PhotoEdit; **285,** Kenji Kerins; **286,** (t) File Photo, (c,b) Studiohio; **287,** (t,b) Doug Martin; **289,** (tl) ©M. Clayel Jacana/ Photo Researchers, (tr) Comstock/Russ Kinne, (b) Kris Coppieters/SuperStock; **290,** ©Tom McHugh /Photo Researchers; **292,** (tl) Smithsonian Institute, (tr,bc,br) Craig Kramer, (bl) Roger K. Burnard; **293,** (t,c,b) Doug Martin; **294,** (t) Allen B. Smith/Tom Stack & Associates, (b) Runk/ Schoenberger/Grant Heilman; **295, 296,** Doug Martin; **297,** Tim Courlas; **298,** Ken Ferguson; **299,** (l) Earth Scenes/Helen Thompson, (r) H. Armstrong Roberts/W. Janoud; **300, 301,** Doug Martin; **302,** Runk/Schoenberger/Grant Heilman; **303,** (t) Barry L. Runk/ Grant Heilman, (b) William Felger/Grant Heilman; **304,** Tim Courlas; **305,** ©David Goyon, The BOC Picture Group/Photo Researchers; **307,** John Chiasson/Laison International; **308,** (t) Robertson/Custom Medical Stock Photo, (b) Gold Information Center; **309,** David R. Frazier Photolibrary; **310,** The Granger Collection; **311,** (tl) ©Kevin Schafer/Peter Arnold, Inc.; (tr) Runk/Schoenberger/Grant Heilman, (b) Doug Martin; **314,** Spencer Swanger/Tom Stack & Associates; **315, 316,** Kenji Kerins; **317,** (lc) Linda Young, (l,rc,r,b) Doug Martin; **318,** (c,b) Doug Martin, (t) Kenji Kerins; **319, 320,** (tl,bl,bc,br) Doug Martin, (tr) Earth Scenes/Breck P. Kent; **321,** (t,bl) Grant Heilman, (br) Earth Scenes/Michael P. Gadomsky; **322,** Studiohio; **323,** ©Galen Rowell/Peter Arnold, Inc.; **325,** Doug Martin; **326,** (tl) Barry L. Runk/Grant Heilman, (tc) ©George Whiteley/Photo Researchers, (tr) ©A.W. Ambler/Photo Researchers, (b) William Felger/Grant Heilman; **327,** (tl) E.R. Degginger/ Color-Pic, (tr) Earth Scenes/E.R. Degginger, (b) FPG International; **328,** Doug Martin; **330,** (t) Tim Cairns, (b) Craig Kramer; **331,** Tom Bean; **332,** Elaine Comer-Shay; **333,** Kevin Schafer/Tom Stack & Associates; **334,** Doug Martin; **335,** H. Armstrong Roberts; **336,** Doug Martin; **337,** Doug

Sokell/Tom Stack & Associates; **338,** Comstock/Russ Kinne; **339,** Comstock/M. Thompson; **340,** Comstock/Ernst Braun; **341,** (l) ©D. Zirinsky/Photo Researchers, (r) Ken Ferguson; **342,** Courtesy of Mike Bittinger; **343,** (tl) Barry L. Runk /Grant Heilman, (bl) Tom Till/Tony Stone Worldwide, (br) ©Mary M. Thacher/Photo Researchers; **344,** (l) Runk/Schoenberger/Grant Heilman, (r) Grant Heilman; **345,** (tl) Comstock/Russ Kinne, (tr) North Museum/Franklin & Marshall College/Grant Heilman, (b) H. Armstrong Roberts/D. Degnan; **346,** Ken W. Davis/Tom Stack & Associates; **347,** Ralph Brunke; **348,** M. Timothy O'Keefe/Tom Stack & Associates; **349,** ©Jack Dermid/Photo Researchers; **352,** (t) Bruce F. Molnia/Terraphotographics/BPS; (b) Runk/Schoenberger/Grant Heilman; **354,** (t) George Glod/SuperStock, (b) Index Stock Photography; **355,** Alan Pitcairn/Grant Heilman; **356,** ©Jim Olive/Peter Arnold, Inc.; **357,** (t) ©Randy Brandon/Peter Arnold, Inc., (b) Kenji Kerins; **358,** Tony Freeman/PhotoEdit; **365,** Bruce C. Heezen/Marie Tharp/"The Floor of the Oceans;" **367,** Wood's Hole Oceanographic Institute; **368,** (t) Dr. Robert Hessler/Scripps Institute of Oceanography; (b) Wood's Hole Oceanographic Institute; **369,** ©Bill Ross/Westlight; **370,** Earth Scenes/Michael Habicht; **371,** ©Robert Evans/Peter Arnold, Inc; **372,** Courtesy of Marc D'Anto; **373,** (l) Scott Blackman/Tom Stack & Associates, (r) Al Satterwhite/The Image Bank, (bl) Wood's Hole Oceanographic Institute; **376,** Comstock/Marvin Koner; **377,** Tony Freeman/PhotoEdit; **378,** David W. Hamilton/The Image Bank; **379,** ©Helga Lade/Peter Arnold, Inc.; **381,** E. Paul Cone/SuperStock; **382,** Barry L. Runk/Grant Heilman; **384,** ©Jack Fields/Photo Researchers; **385,** Ken Ferguson; **386, 387,** Kenji Kerins; **388,** H. Armstrong Roberts/Ed Cooper; **389,** Conoco; **391,** Graham Finlayson/Tony Stone Worldwide; **393,** Kenji Kerins; **394,** ©Bill W. Marsh/Photo Researchers; **396,** (t) ©Peter Arnold, Inc., (b) David R. Frazier Photolibrary; **397,** Comstock/Bruce Hands; **398,** Comstock/Jack K. Clark; **400,** Greg Vaughn/Tom Stack & Associates; **401,** Byron Augustin/Tom Stack & Associates; **402,** Greg Vaughn/Tom Stack & Associates; **403,** Comstock/George Lepp; **404,** (t) David R. Frazier Photolibrary, (b) David Young-Wolff/PhotoEdit; **405,** Tony Craddock/Tony Stone Worldwide; **406,** H. Armstrong Roberts/F. Sieb; **408,** Grant Heilman; **409,** ©Bruno J. Zehnder/Peter Arnold, Inc.; **410,** Lawrence Migdale; **411,** Ralph Brunke; **413,** Kenji Kerins; **414,** Roderick Chen/SuperStock; **416,** Michael Newman/PhotoEdit; **417,** (t) Chris Jones/The Stock Market, (b) Kenji Kerins; **420,** Ken Ferguson; **421, 424, 425,** Kenji Kerins; **427,** Chip Clark; **428,** Ken Ferguson; **431,** Ralph Brunke; **432,** (l) Susan Van Etten/PhotoEdit, (r) David R. Frazier Photolibrary; **433,** Ralph Brunke; **434,** ©Fred Bavendam/Peter Arnold, Inc.; **435,** Tony Freeman/PhotoEdit; **436,** Leonard Nolt; **437,** Robert E. Daemmrich/Tony Stone Worldwide; **438,** Doug Martin; **439,** (l) Felicia Martinez/PhotoEdit, (r) Barry L. Runk/Grant Heilman; **440,** H. Armstrong Roberts; **441, 443,** Kenji Kerins; **444,** Glencoe & Morgan Photos; **445, 448,** Kenji Kerins; **450,** Tony Freeman/PhotoEdit; **454,** ©Susan Cuklin/Photo Researchers; **459,** ©Michael J. Balick/Peter Arnold, Inc.; **460,** ©Martha Cooper/Peter Arnold, Inc.; **462,** (t) The Image Bank, (b) Tony Freeman/PhotoEdit; **463,** Robert Brenner/PhotoEdit; **464,** Courtesy of David Bair; **466,** (l) NASA, (r) Runk/Schoenberger/Grant Heilman; **468,** Lawrence Migdale; **469,** Kenji Kerins; **471,** John Dean/SuperStock; **473, 475, 479,** Kenji Kerins; **480,** H. Armstrong Roberts; **481,** (Inset), Matt Meadows; **482,** H. Armstrong Roberts/R. Walker; **483,** ©SPL/CNRI/Photo Researchers; **484,** ©Blair Seitz/Photo Researchers; **485,** (tl) Martin/Custom Medical Stock Photo, (tr) C. Childs/Custom Medical Stock Photo, (bl) SPL/Custom Medical Stock Photo, (br) Lennart Nilsson/*The Incredible Machine*/Boehringer Ingelheim International/National Geographic Society; **486,** (l) SPL/Custom Medical Stock Photo, (r) ©Susan Leavines/Photo Researchers; **487,** ©Robert Noonan/Photo Researchers; **488,** (t) ©Martha Cooper/Peter Arnold, Inc., (b) Ralph Brunke; **489,** Richard Hutchings/PhotoEdit; **491,** (l) Comstock/Russ Kinne, (r) Comstock/T. P. Dickinson; **492,** Bettmann Archives; **493,** (tl) Bill Apton/SuperStock, (tr) Don & Esther Phillips/Tom Stack & Associates, (c) ©K. G. Vock/OKAPIA/Photo Researchers, (b) Sylvia Miller/Custom Medical Stock Photo; **494,** David Young-Wolff/PhotoEdit; **495,** Kenji Kerins; **496,** M. Richards/PhotoEdit; **497,** Runk/Schoenberger/Grant Heilman; **498,** Tony Freeman/PhotoEdit; **499, 500,** Kenji Kerins; **501,** Jim Pickerell/Tony Stone Worldwide; **505,** Kenji Kerins; **507,** Comstock/Georg Gerster, (r) ©Paolo Koch/Photo Researchers; **508,** Latent Image; **511,** Kenji Kerins; **512,** Pictures Unlimited; **513,** ©David Parker/Photo Researchers; **517,** ©Peter Arnold, Inc.; **521,** (l) The George Eastman House, (r) Don Mason/The Stock Market; **522,** Springer/Bettmann Film Archives; **523, 524,** NASA; **526,** ©Yogi/Peter Arnold, Inc.; **527,** (tl) Allen Zak, (cr) Riviera Collection/Superstock, (tr) Carol Lee/Tony Stone Worldwide, (br) NASA, (cl) Henry Leap & Jim Lehman, (tc,bl) Runk/Schoenberger/Grant Heilman; **529,** Tony Freeman/PhotoEdit; **530,** ©CNRI/SPL/Photo Researchers; **531,** H. Armstrong Roberts; **532,** Kenji Kerins; **534,** (tl) ©Andrew Syred/Photo Researchers, (tr) SPL/Custom Medical Stock Photo, (c) ©Petit Format/Photo Researchers, (b) ©Biophoto Associates/Photo Researchers; **536,** (t) ©Dr. Tony Brian & David Parker/Photo Researchers, (b) Kenji Kerins; **537,** (tl) SIU/Custom Medical Stock Photo, (cl) Becker/Custom Medical Stock Photo, (cr) Runk/Schoenberger/Grant Heilman, (tr) ©Jim Zuckerman/Westlight, (b) Studiohio; **538,** ©Leonard Lessin/Peter Arnold, Inc.; **539,** (t) ©Dr. Jeremy Burgess/SPL/Photo Researchers, (b) ©Photo Researchers; **540,** Ken Ferguson; **543,** (t) ©Leonard Lessin/Peter Arnold, Inc., (b) Eric Grave/PhotoTake; **544,** ©Ed Reschke/Peter Arnold, Inc.; **545,** P. Birn/Custom Medical Stock Photo; **546,** (t) ©Peter Arnold, Inc., (b) Ken Ferguson; **547,** ©Manfred Kage/Peter Arnold, Inc.; **549,** (tl,tc) Barry L. Runk/Grant Heilman, (tr,l) Larry Lefever/Grant Heilman, (bl) ©D. Cavagnaro/Peter Arnold, Inc., (br) Runk/Schoenberger/Grant Heilman; **550,** (t) ©Manfred Kage/Peter Arnold, Inc., (b) ©James Stevenson/Photo Researchers; **551,** ©Robert Knauft/Photo Researchers; **553,** Barry L. Runk/Grant Heilman; **554,** Comstock/Michael Stuckey; **555,** Comstock/George Lepp; **556,** (l) Kenji Kerins, (r) ©Manfred Kage/Peter Arnold, Inc.; **558,** Custom Medical Stock Photo; **559,** Richard Hutchings/PhotoEdit; **561,** L. Steinmark/Custom Medical Stock Photo; **563,** ©Manfred Kage/Peter Arnold, Inc.; **564,** Roy King/SuperStock; **565,** Grant Heilman; **566,** (l,r) ©Leonard Lessin/Peter Arnold, Inc., (c) Tony Freeman/PhotoEdit; **567,** (tl) ©Ray Pfortner/Peter Arnold, Inc., (tr) Comstock/Gwen Fidler, (b) David M. Doody/Tom Stack & Associates; **568,** (l) Laurence Hughs/The Image Bank, (c) ©James L. Amos/Photo Researchers, (r) Tom Stack & Associates; **569,** Ken Ferguson; **570,** (t) ©Lois Ellen Frank/Westlight, (b) Ken Ferguson; **571,** Tony Freeman/PhotoEdit; **572,** Yoav Levy/PhotoTake; **573,** (t) Tony Freeman/PhotoEdit, (b) Leslye Borden/PhotoEdit; **574,** Matt Meadows; **575,** Matt Meadows; **576,** Guido Alberto Rossi/The Image Bank; **576,** Comstock/M. Thompson; **577,** Ralph Brunke; **578,** ©Joseph Nettis/Photo Researchers; **579,** (t) Runk/Schoenberger/Grant Heilman, (b) Doug Martin; **580,** (t) Barry L. Runk/Grant Heilman, (b) ©James Foote/Photo Researchers; **583,** Kenji Kerins; **584,** John Shaw/Tom Stack & Associates; **586,** Ken Ferguson; **587,** ©Peter Arnold, Inc.; **588,** (t) Holt Confer/Grant Heilman, (b) Ken Ferguson; **589,** Michael Newman/PhotoEdit; **590,** Ken Ferguson; **591,** Steve Elmore/Tom Stack & Associates; **592,** Custom Medical Stock Photo; **596,** H. Armstrong Roberts/Zefa/H.; **597, 598,** Kenji Kerins; **600,** ©CNRI/Photo Researchers; **601,** Ken Ferguson; **602,** Chris Collins/The Stock Market; **603,** Kenji Kerins; **604,** ©Ed Reschke/Peter Arnold, Inc.; **605,** Doug Martin; **606,** Comstock/Russ Kinne; **607,** (l) Alan Oddie/PhotoEdit, (c) David R. Frazier Photolibrary, (r) Paul Berger/Tony Stone Worldwide; **609,** (t) H. Armstrong Roberts/A. Riccio, (b) Ken Ferguson; **610,** ©CNRI/SPL/Photo Researchers; **612,** Robert E. Daemmrich/Tony Stone Worldwide; **613,** (tl) ©Ed Reschke/Peter Arnold, Inc., (tr) Runk/Schoenberger/Grant Heilman, (bl) ©Bill Longcore/Photo Researchers, (br) Tom Stack & Associates; **620,** Reidlinger/Custom Medical Stock Photo; **621,** (t) ©Peter Arnold, Inc., (b) Tony Freeman/PhotoEdit; **625,** (tl) Grant Heilm Photography, Inc, (tr) Biophoto Assoc/Photo Researchers; **626,** Kenji Kerins; **627,** Eric V. Grave/PhotoTake; **629,** ©Eric V. Grave/Photo Researchers; **630,** (l) Runk/Schoenberger/Grant Heilman, (r) Kenji Kerins; **631,** (l) ©M. Wurtz/Photo Researchers, (r) ©Alfred Pasieka/Peter Arnold, Inc.; **632,** ©B. Heggeler/Biozentrum, U of Basel/SPL/Photo Researchers; **634,** ©Spencer Grant/Photo Researchers; **635,** (tl,bc) Brian Parker/Tom Stack & Associates, (tcl) ©David Scharf/Peter Arnold, Inc., (tc) Rod Planck/Tom Stack & Associates, (tcr) ©J. Broek/Photo Researchers, (tr,cl) ©Biophoto Associates/Photo Researchers, (cr) ©Ralph Eagle/Photo Researchers, (bl) Comstock/M. & C. Werner, (br) ©Eric V. Grave/Photo Researchers; **637,** The Image Bank, **638,** ©CNRI/SPL/Photo Researchers; **639,** (l) Richard Gross, (r) John Colwell/Grant Heilman; **640,** Brian Parker/Tom Stack & Associates; **641,** Runk/Schoenberger/Grant Heilman; **642,** ©Jim Zuckerman/Westlight; **643,** Comstock/Russ Kinne; **644,** ©John Dorham/SPL/Photo Researchers; **645,** William D. Popejoy; **646,** Ulrike Welsch/PhotoEdit; **648,** Tom Stack & Associates; **649,** Ken Ferguson; **650,** Reuters/Bettmann Archives; **651,** ©Joe Munroe/Photo Researchers; **652,** (l) Lennart Nilsson/Ingelheim International, (r) James Aronovsky, Illustration by James Crymble /©1991 *Discover Magazine*; **653,** Bettmann Archives; **654,** Courtesy of Audrey Cruz; **655,** Custom Medical Stock Photo; **656,** ©Dr. Tony Brian/SPL/Photo Researchers; **657,** ©Keith Kent/SPL/Photo Researchers; **658,** Runk/Schoenberger/Grant Heilman; **661,** (r) ©Bill Bachman/Photo Researchers; **666,** (tr) ©Biophoto Associates/Photo Researchers, (cl) ©A. B. Dowsett/Photo Researchers, (bl,br) Runk/Schoenberger/Grant Heilman; **667,** (tl) Ham's Biological Supplies, (tr) ©David Scharf/Peter Arnold, Inc., (c) Gustan Verderber, (bl) David Dennis/Tom Stack & Associates, (br) Lynn Stone; **678, 680, 682,** Ken Frick; **683,** Lloyd Lemmermann; **684,** Janet L. Adams; **686,** Doug Martin; **689,** NASA; **691,** (l) Ken Ferguson, (r) ©Bill Bachman/Photo Researchers